nature

The Living Record of Science

《自然》百年科学经典

英汉对照版　套装共十卷

第四卷

1946-1965

总顾问：李政道（Tsung-Dao Lee）

英方主编：Sir John Maddox
Sir Philip Campbell
中方主编：路甬祥

外语教学与研究出版社 · 麦克米伦教育 · 自然科研

FOREIGN LANGUAGE TEACHING AND RESEARCH PRESS · MACMILLAN EDUCATION · NATURE RESEARCH

北京 BEIJING

图书在版编目（CIP）数据

《自然》百年科学经典 ：套装共十卷. 第四卷 ：英汉对照 /（英）约翰 · 马多克斯（John Maddox），（英）菲利普 · 坎贝尔（Philip Campbell），路甬祥主编. -- 北京 ：外语教学与研究出版社，2020.9

ISBN 978-7-5213-2021-3

Ⅰ. ①自… Ⅱ. ①约… ②菲… ③路… Ⅲ. ①自然科学－文集－英、汉 Ⅳ. ①N53

中国版本图书馆 CIP 数据核字（2020）第 154888 号

地图审图号：GS（2020）5244 号

出 版 人　徐建忠
项目统筹　章思英
项目负责　刘晓楠　黄小斌
责任编辑　王丽霞
责任校对　黄小斌
封面设计　高　蕾
版式设计　孙莉明
插图设计　麦克米伦提供原图扫描版
出版发行　外语教学与研究出版社
社　　址　北京市西三环北路 19 号（100089）
网　　址　http://www.fltrp.com
印　　刷　北京华联印刷有限公司
开　　本　787×1092　1/16
印　　张　78.5
版　　次　2021 年 1 月第 1 版　2021 年 1 月第 1 次印刷
书　　号　ISBN 978-7-5213-2021-3
定　　价　8000.00 元

购书咨询：（010）88819926　电子邮箱：club@fltrp.com
外研书店：https://waiyants.tmall.com
凡印刷、装订质量问题，请联系我社印制部
联系电话：（010）61207896　电子邮箱：zhijian@fltrp.com
凡侵权、盗版书籍线索，请联系我社法律事务部
举报电话：（010）88817519　电子邮箱：banquan@fltrp.com
物料号：320210001

《自然》百年科学经典（英汉对照版）

总 顾 问：李政道（Tsung-Dao Lee）

英方主编：Sir John Maddox
Sir Philip Campbell

中方主编：路甬祥

编审委员会

英方编委

Philip Ball
Vikram Savkar
David Swinbanks

中方编委（以姓氏笔画为序）

许智宏
赵忠贤
滕吉文

本卷审稿专家（以姓氏笔画为序）

于　涌	王有刚	王秀娥	王晓晨	邓祖淦	厉光烈	冯兴无
邢　松	同号文	吕　扬	朱永生	刘　武	刘京国	江丕栋
李三忠	李芝芬	李素霞	杨茂君	肖伟科	吴秀杰	吴新智
沈志侠	张　旭	张元仲	张忠杰	陈继征	陈新文	林圣龙
尚仁成	昌增益	金　侠	周筠梅	孟庆任	赵见高	赵凌霞
胡　荣	袁　峥	顾孝诚	高守亭	崔　巍	董　为	蒋世仰
熊秉衡						

编译委员会

本卷翻译工作组稿人（以姓氏笔画为序）

王耀杨	刘　明	刘晓楠	关秀清	李　琦	何　铭	沈乃澂
张　健	郭红锋	黄小斌	蔡　迪	蔡则怡		

本卷翻译人员（以姓氏笔画为序）

王耀杨	毛晨晖	尹　金	田晓阳	冯　翀	刘振明	刘皓芳
齐红艳	孙玉诚	孙惠南	苏　慧	杜　丽	李　响	李任伟
吴　彦	沈乃澂	张玉光	张立召	张锦彬	金世超	周志华
郑建全	荆玉祥	胡雪兰	钱　磊	高如丽	郭　娟	崔娅铭
彭丽霞	曾菊平	蔡则怡	樊　彬			

本卷校对人员（以姓氏笔画为序）

王帅帅	王阳兰	王丽霞	王晓萌	王晓蕾	王赛儿	甘秋玲
丛　岚	乔萌萌	刘　明	刘丛丛	许向科	孙　娟	孙瑞静
杜赛赛	李　四	李　梅	李　琦	李　景	李红菊	肖　莉
吴　茜	张　帆	张世馥	张亦卓	张梦璇	张媛媛	周玉凤
周平博	郑期彤	赵凤轩	姜　薇	顾海成	郭　琴	唐　颖
黄小斌	崔天明	葛云霄	韩少卿	潮兴娟	潘卫东	

Contents
目录

Volume IV
(1946-1965)

Significance of the Australopithecinae

W. E. L. G. Clark

Editor's Note

The Second World War inevitably put a stop to the previously avid search for evidence for the antiquity of human beings. As if to display the eagerness of palaeontologists to resume their previous work, Sir Wilfred Le Gros Clark, by then the doyen of British palaeontology, wrote the following article for *Nature* in which he expressed enthusiasm for the work of Raymond Dart and in particular for Dart's identification of the Taungs skull as a representative of the genus *Australopithecus*. He also urged further research in southern Africa for additional specimens.

IN 1924, the immature skull of a large ape-like primate was discovered in some lime workings at Taungs in the valley of the Harts River, South Africa. It was briefly described by Prof. R. A. Dart, who regarded it as representing an extinct race of apes intermediate between living anthropoid apes and man. To this extinct race he gave the name *Australopithecus africanus*. There followed a mild controversy on the interpretation of this fossil, but many anatomists quite properly preferred to wait before committing themselves to definite statements until a full and systematic report on the original remains should appear. Twelve years later, Dr. Robert Broom, who had decided to search for more remains of *Australopithecus*, paid a visit to a cave at Sterkfontein, near Krugersdorf. Here he found portions of skulls and jaws of a fossil primate similar to *Australopithecus* but (in his opinion) sufficiently distinct in some of its characters to be referred to a separate genus. He called it *Plesianthropus transvaalensis*. Then, in 1938, the remains of what were taken to represent still another type, called by Broom *Paranthropus robustus*, were brought to light at Kromdraai, two miles east of Sterkfontein. Thus there are now available for consideration three series of extinct ape-like primates from South Africa, which are believed to be representatives of one sub-family, the Australopithecinae. Excellent casts of the skull of *Australopithecus* have been available in Britain for many years now, and during the course of his excavations since 1936 Dr. Broom has been extremely generous in distributing casts of most of the valuable material which he has collected. Thus anatomists in Britain have for some time had this sort of evidence before them. Now there has appeared the long-awaited report on the Australopithecinae by Dr. Broom and Dr. Schepers[1]. In this monograph, which is abundantly illustrated and incorporates numerous comparative studies, Broom deals in considerable detail with the osteological material, while Schepers discusses the endocranial casts. Apart from the obvious fact that access to the original material is really necessary to complete the evidence on which to base a considered opinion, it is now possible, at least in general terms, to assess independently the significance of these remarkable fossils.

南方古猿亚科发现的意义

克拉克

编者按

第二次世界大战无疑使先前急切寻找古人类证据的工作停滞下来。似乎是为了表示古生物学家们对他们以前的工作又恢复了热情，时为英国首席古生物学家的威尔弗雷德·勒格罗·克拉克爵士在《自然》上发表了这篇文章，文中他对雷蒙德·达特的研究工作，尤其是对达特把汤恩头骨鉴定为南方古猿属的代表表现出极大的兴趣。为得到更多的标本他还强烈主张在南非进行更进一步的研究。

1924 年，在位于南非哈茨河流域的汤恩，人们在一些石灰岩矿区内发现了一种类似猿类的大型灵长类动物的幼年个体头骨。达特教授对其进行了简要描述，他认为这代表了一种已经灭绝的介于现存类人猿与人类之间的猿类。他将这种已经灭绝的猿类命名为南方古猿非洲种。随后产生了少许争论，但许多解剖学家在做出他们最终判断之前明智地选择了等待，等待一份关于这类化石详尽而系统的研究报告的发表。12 年后，致力于搜寻更多南方古猿化石的罗伯特·布鲁姆博士考察了克鲁格斯多普附近的斯泰克方丹的一个洞穴。在这里他发现了类似于南方古猿的灵长类动物的部分头骨和颌骨化石，但是（他认为）这些化石所具有的一些非常独特的特征使之能被划分为一个独立的属。他把这些化石命名为德兰士瓦迩人。随后在 1938 年，在斯泰克方丹以东 2 英里的克罗姆德拉伊发掘出的化石又被用来代表另一个种类，布鲁姆将其命名为粗壮傍人。因此现在可以对来自于南非的 3 组已经灭绝的类似猿类的灵长类动物化石进行研究，这些化石被认为属于同一个亚科，即南方古猿亚科。多年以来，在英国就可以得到极好的南方古猿头骨模型，而且自从 1936 年布鲁姆博士开始他的发掘工作以来，他一直都极为慷慨地分发出大部分他所收集到的极其珍贵的化石的模型。因此一段时间以来，英国的解剖学家们已经在使用这一类证据了。现在期盼已久的由布鲁姆博士和舍佩尔斯博士合著的关于南方古猿亚科的研究报告终于公之于世[1]。这份专题论著图片丰富，并且结合图片进行了大量对比研究。在报告中，布鲁姆对骨骼材料做了非常详尽的论述，舍佩尔斯则主要对颅内模进行了论述。显而易见的事实是确实需要通过原始的化石标本来获取证据以便在此基础上建立一个成熟的学术观点，除此之外，至少现在有可能在大体上对这些著名化石的意义独立地做出评价。

Dr. Broom has demonstrated beyond any doubt at all that the Australopithecinae are extremely important for the study of human evolution, since they present an astonishing assemblage of simian and human characters. Such an assemblage, indeed, might well be postulated, entirely on indirect evidence, for hypothetical ancestors of the Hominidae. Thus it should be said at the outset of this review that Dart's original interpretation of the *Australopithecus* material has in several respects been completely vindicated. Some of the most outstandingly human features of the Australopithecinae are undoubtedly those of the teeth and jaws. In both the deciduous and permanent dentitions, the incisors and canines are of human rather than simian proportions and pattern. The deciduous premolars are quite similar to those of the human child, while the permanent premolars, though very large, have the distinctive human pattern. The permanent molar teeth, in spite of their size (which is exceeded only by male gorillas and certain large extinct apes such as *Sivapithecus giganteus*), also show some approach to man in the disposition of their cusps. The dental arcade forms a rounded curve as in man and not an elongated U-shape such as is characteristic of modern large apes. The nature of the wear of the teeth and the anatomy of the temporo-mandibular region show, also, that the teeth and jaws were used in human fashion. In contrast with the remarkably human features of the teeth, the skull as a whole resembles in its general proportions those of anthropoid apes; and in a number of details, for example, the great facial extension of the premaxilla, the contour of the mandibular symphysis, and the apparent absence of a foramen spinosum, it is entirely simian and departs widely from the human condition.

So far, then, the Australopithecinae might perhaps be regarded as a group of extinct apes, somewhat similar to the gorilla and chimpanzee, in which the characters of the dentition had developed (possibly independently) along lines almost identical with those of human evolution. But Dr. Broom has also, in his indefatigable search, brought to light some most important fragments of limb bones, which allow, and even make probable, a much more startling interpretation of these fossil remains. For example, of *Paranthropus* there are available the lower end of the humerus, the upper end of the ulna, and the talus. Judging from casts and Dr. Broom's illustrations, the humeral and ulnar fragments are entirely similar to those of *Homo sapiens*. Indeed, anatomists without the full evidence before them might well be excused if they expressed scepticism at their association with the skull of *Paranthropus*. But Dr. Broom states explicitly that the skull, jaw, humeral and ulnar fragments and the talus were all obtained from one mass of bone breccia less than a cubic foot in size, and that nowhere in any of the same deposits have remains of *Homo* come to light. Thus there seems no reason to doubt that this extinct ape-like creature had upper limbs of human proportions (at least so far as the elbow region is concerned), and which were evidently not used for brachiation. On the other hand, the talus is a remarkably small bone—in its dimensions, so far as these can be measured on a cast, it falls well short of the minimum recorded for modern races of mankind (cf. the data for Japanese women reported by B. Adachi[2]). Compared with the humeral fragment (which presumably belongs to the same individual) the size of the talus indicates a disproportionately small tarsus—more so, indeed, than would be expected if *Paranthropus* used its hind-limbs for the bipedal mode of progression characteristic of man. Further, the unusual medial extent of the

布鲁姆博士证明了南方古猿亚科对人类进化的研究是极为重要的，他的论证根本毋庸置疑，因为南方古猿亚科惊人地呈现出猿和人类的特征组合。事实上，完全依靠间接的证据很有可能去假定这样一种组合是假想的人科祖先所具有的。因此应该说在本文开头提到的达特关于南方古猿化石最初的解释有几个方面是完全正确的。毫无疑问，南方古猿亚科具有的那些最突出的人类特征为牙齿和颌骨的特征。在乳齿期和恒齿期，其门齿与犬齿的大小和形态与人类一致，而与猿的不同。其乳齿期的前臼齿与人类儿童的前臼齿非常相似，而其恒齿期的前臼齿尽管很大但却具有人类所特有的形态。恒齿期的臼齿，不管其尺寸大小（仅有雄性猩猩以及诸如巨型西瓦古猿之类的某些已灭绝的大型猿类的尺寸才比它大），其齿尖的排列同样与人类有些相似。它的齿弓形成了一个圆形曲线，这与人类相似，而与现代大型猿类所特有的一个拉长的 U 形不同。牙齿磨损的特征以及颞–下颌区的解剖学特征也表明，它的牙齿和颌骨的使用方式与人类一样。与其牙齿具有的显著人类特征形成鲜明对比的是，整体看来其头骨的比例大体上与类人猿的头骨相似；而且在很多细节上也是如此，例如，其面部前颌骨延伸很大，下颌联合部的外形以及棘孔的明显缺失，这完全是猿的特征，而与人类的特征相去甚远。

到目前为止，人们认为南方古猿亚科可能是一群已经灭绝的猿类，在某种程度上与大猩猩和黑猩猩相似，其齿系特征的演变（可能是独立地）与人类齿系的演化方式几乎相同。但是布鲁姆博士经过坚持不懈的搜寻，也发现了一些十分重要的肢骨破片，例如，傍人的肱骨下端、尺骨上端以及距骨，利用这些破片可对上述化石做出更加令人吃惊的解释。从模型以及布鲁姆博士的插图来判断，傍人的肱骨与尺骨破片与智人的非常相似。的确，在获得这些充分证据之前，如果解剖学家对其与傍人头骨存在联系表示怀疑，那是可以理解的。但是布鲁姆博士明确声明头骨、颌骨、肱骨破片与尺骨破片以及距骨都是从一堆小于一立方英尺的骨头角砾岩中获得的，而其他任何地方的相同堆积物中都没有发现人属的化石。因此似乎可以确定，该灭绝的类似猿类的动物的上肢与人类的上肢大小一致（至少就肘部而言），并且很明显它不是用来在树枝间游荡的。另一方面，距骨是一块尺寸非常小的骨，就对模型进行测量所得的尺寸而言，其远未达到现代人种的最小记录（参考安达报告的日本女性的数据[2]）。与肱骨破片（它与距骨大概属于同一个体）相比，距骨的尺寸表明跗骨的尺寸过小而不合比例——的确，尤其是加之此前推测傍人的后肢是用于人类所特有的两足行走，因此就更显得跗骨过小。而且，骨端关节面独特的中间部位似乎表明在距骨下关节处的灵活性非常好，而缩短的颈部显示其身体的大部分重量转移

articular surface of the head of the bone seems to indicate a very considerable mobility at the sub-talar joint, while the truncated neck suggests the transference of the major component of the weight of the body to the fore-part of the foot, a feature which Morton[3] has shown to be characteristic of the type of foot found in the great apes and therefore different from the trend shown in human evolution.

Of *Plesianthropus* there have been found the capitate bone of the carpus and the lower end of the femur. The former confirms the evidence of the arm bones of *Paranthropus*, that the Australopithecine upper limb closely corresponded to the modern human type, for the capitate bone seems to come well within the range of variation shown in the Bushman[4]. The lower end of the femur is perhaps the most important of all these limb-bone fragments, and Dr. Broom infers from it that *Plesianthropus* "walked, as does man, entirely or almost entirely on its hind feet". From the appearance of the femur as depicted in Dr. Broom's drawing of it, we are inclined to agree with his interpretation. But his description of this most important evidence is tantalizingly brief (it is confined to 34 lines!). Indeed, we could have wished that the author had dealt with all this limb material in much more detail. The illustrations, too, while they give a good general impression of the appearance of the bones, are not sufficiently accurate for comparative studies. For example, the text-figure of the *Paranthropus* talus, although stated to be natural size, actually represents the bone as somewhat larger than the cast. So much depends on this limb material for a proper assessment of the Australopithecinae. Thus, when Broom states at the conclusion of his section that "at Sterkfontein there are deposits of breccia probably as extensive as those of Choukoutien, and we may confidently assert that these are likely to yield dozens of skulls and probably fairly complete skeletons of the Sterkfontein ape-man", we can only implore all those concerned to see that facilities are provided forthwith in order that systematic excavations can be continued without interruption.

In addition to the skeletal material of the Australopithecinae, there were available for study the natural endocranial cast of *Australopithecus*, portions of endocranial casts (partly distorted) of *Plesianthropus*, and an endocranial cast of the left temporal region of *Paranthropus*. The study of endocranial casts of fossil man and apes always raises afresh the oft-debated question as to how far the sulcal pattern of the brain itself can really be inferred from them. Studies of endocranial casts of modern man and apes, and their direct comparison with the actual brains, have shown that in these forms attempts to delineate the sulcal pattern may be grossly misleading[5]. Dr. Schepers regards the conclusions drawn from such careful and objective studies as "pessimistic", and, of course, it may be true that, for some reason or other (and very conveniently for the palaeontologist!), the convolutions of the brain were more faithfully impressed on the bony walls of the cranial cavity in fossil than in living species. Nevertheless, neurological anatomists will be surprised to find that Dr. Schepers has apparently been able not only to map out with confidence the sulcal pattern over the whole cerebral hemisphere of *Australopithecus* and *Plesianthropus*, but also to delineate no less than twenty-six separate cyto-architectural areas and to compare them in their relative extent with those of modern apes and man. Cortical physiologists may likewise feel inclined to demur at some of the

到了足前部，这个特征与莫顿[3]发现的大型猿类的足部特征相同，因此也有别于人类足部进化的趋势。

迩人腕骨的头状骨与股骨的下端已被发现。前者进一步确认了傍人臂骨的证据，即南方古猿亚科的上肢与现代人类的类型几乎相同，因为头状骨似乎刚好在布须曼人[4]表现出的变化范围之内。股骨的下端可能是所有这些肢骨破片中最为重要的，并且布鲁姆博士据此推断迩人“像人一样完全或几乎完全依靠后足行走”。依据布鲁姆博士为其绘制的图中所示的股骨外观，我们愿意接受他的解释。但是他对于这个最为重要的证据的记述却简短到令人着急的程度（仅有34行！）。确实，我们希望作者更加详细地论述所有这些肢骨材料。尽管从整体上来看骨的外观画得还不错，但是对于比较研究来说这些插图也是不够精确的。例如，正文图中傍人距骨标明为实际大小，但实际上图中描绘的骨比模型稍微大一点。为了正确评价南方古猿亚科，要在很大程度上依赖于这些肢骨资料。因而，当布鲁姆在他这一部分的结论里说“在斯泰克方丹地区有角砾岩沉积，其分布范围可能像周口店的角砾岩沉积分布一样广泛，并且我们可以有把握地断定在这些角砾岩沉积中可能会出土许多头骨，还可能出土相当完整的斯泰克方丹猿人骨架”，我们仅能做的就是恳求所有相关方面都明白，要使系统发掘能够持续不间断地进行，他们需要立刻为此提供便利条件。

除南方古猿亚科的骨架材料之外，还可以利用天然的南方古猿颅内模、迩人的部分颅内模（有点变形）和傍人左颞骨区颅内模进行研究。关于化石人类和化石猿类的颅内模的研究总能再度引发那个一直存在争议的问题，即通过对这些内模的研究到底能够在多大程度上推断出大脑沟回的形态。对现代人类和现代猿类的颅内模进行的研究以及将它们与真实的大脑进行直接比较的研究表明，这些试图描绘颅内模沟回的研究方法可能引起很大的误导[5]。如此谨慎而客观的研究所得出的结论在舍佩尔斯博士看来却是“悲观的”。并且，由于某种原因，在化石中大脑结构在颅腔内壁上留下的印模比在现存的种类中更为真实准确当然也可能是真的（这种解释给古生物学家的研究提供了便利！）。不过，如果神经解剖学家知道舍佩尔斯博士不仅有把握绘制出南方古猿与迩人的整个脑半球的沟回形态，而且还能描绘出26个以上单个的细胞结构区，并将其与现代猿类和现代人类的相应区域进行比较，他们一定会感到惊讶。有人认为仅仅通过对颅内模的考查便可推知大脑的功能（例如语言、抽象思维和运动技能），大脑皮层生理学家可能也会对此推论表示反对。但是在这部

inferences regarding functions such as speech, abstract thought and motor skill which, it is suggested, can be drawn simply from the examination of a cast of the inside of the skull. But Dr. Schepers, in the introduction to this section, makes his attitude perfectly plain, for he says: "In all attempts at representing these fossils in a reconstructed form, the method employed was that of claiming the maximum dimensions considered likely for the type. It is … much less satisfactory to hear that a new find of fossil material does *not* suggest any new hypothesis or does not corroborate evidence already at hand about a cognate theory, than to discover that at least someone is prepared to claim the maximum importance for his discovery. Such enthusiasm encourages criticism and comment, and is therefore to be recommended."

There may be some who doubt the propriety of preparing a scientific report with a bias of this kind, but at least it makes for lively reading. At the same time it does make it somewhat difficult for the reviewer not to appear in the role of the carping critic; and any appearance of carping criticism in the present instance is certainly to be avoided, if only because it might seem (unintentionally) to belittle the importance of this fossil material of which, in fact, the importance can scarcely be exaggerated. Also, the thoroughness with which Dr. Schepers has pursued his studies, and his evident eagerness to squeeze every drop of information from his material (even when this is defective) must evoke the greatest admiration for his assiduity. The cranial capacity of *Australopithecus* is estimated at 500 c.c., and of *Plesianthropus* at 435 c.c. The cranial capacity of *Paranthropus* is judged to be as high as 650 c.c.; but since this estimate is based on little more than the left temporal region of the skull, it is not easy to accept it without qualification. For the same reason, the contours of the reconstructed endocranial cast of *Paranthropus*, which are used for graphic comparison with casts of other primates, should probably be discounted as being too conjectural. Thus, so far as the absolute volume of the brain is concerned, the Australopithecinae appear to fall well within the limits of the anthropoid apes. On the other hand, if, as Dr. Schepers surmises might be the case, the endocranial casts hitherto obtained happen by chance to represent the lower limits of variation, the cranial capacity of the Australopithecinae may in its upper limits have transcended the range of variation found in modern large apes. Only the accession of further material can decide this point. But it remains a matter of very considerable interest that the volume of the Australopithecine brain *relative to the body size* (so far as this can be inferred in a very general way from fragments of the limb skeleton) does appear to have exceeded somewhat that of modern large apes.

Enough has been said in this review to indicate the intermediate position which many of the anatomical characters of the Australopithecinae in their combination occupy in relation to apes and men. Whether on the basis of this morphological evidence the South African representatives of this sub-family, which have so far been found, may be assumed to bear any direct relation to the line of human evolution, depends partly on the geological age of their remains. The evidence for this hitherto rests almost entirely on faunistic data. Dr. Broom is now of the opinion that the presence of a primitive hyaena, *Lycyaena*, and of two species of sabre-tooth tigers, in the deposits at Sterkfontein signifies a date not later than Upper Pliocene, and that the Taungs site is probably still older, perhaps

分的导言中，舍佩尔斯博士十分清晰地表明了自己的态度，他说："复原这些化石所能采取的所有方法中，这个方法声称最大限度地利用了颅内模提供的信息。……相对于得知新发现的化石材料**不能**支持任何新的假说，或者不能确证相关理论的已有证据，人们更乐于看到至少有人准备去声称他有了重大的发现。这种热情能够激发批评和评论，因此也受到欢迎。"

抱着这种偏见来准备科学报告至少是有助于活跃学术气氛的，尽管有人怀疑这种做法是否妥当。同时这也使那些吹毛求疵的评论家们想不挑剔都难；如果没有这么（无意地）强调化石的重要性，一定可以避免那些吹毛求疵的批评，但事实上，其重要性根本没有被夸大。此外，舍佩尔斯博士对研究的彻底投入，以及对从材料（即使有时候不完备）中尽量获取证据的强烈渴望，这些使人对他的敬意油然而生。据估计，南方古猿的颅容量为500毫升，而迩人的颅容量为435毫升，傍人的颅容量被认为高达650毫升；但这个估测主要依据头骨左颞骨区及其周边头骨的小部分信息，因此不宜无条件地接受。出于同样的原因，用来与其他灵长类动物颅内模作图样比较的复原傍人颅内模轮廓也因过于依赖推测而使其可信度大打折扣。因此，就脑的绝对容量而言，南方古猿亚科似乎正好在类人猿的范围之内。另一方面，因为舍佩尔斯博士的猜测可能就是事实，如果迄今获得的颅内模刚好代表了变化值的下限，那么南方古猿亚科颅容量的上限值就很可能超出了已发现的现代大型猿类的颅容量变化范围。只有获取更进一步的化石材料后才能确定这一点。但是还有一点相当重要，**相应于体型大小**（其体型大小大体上能从肢骨破片中推断出来），南方古猿亚科的脑量似乎确实比现代大型猿类的脑量大一些。

这篇评述充分论证了南方古猿亚科介于猿类和人类之间，其许多解剖学特征混合了猿类和人类的特点。以形态学证据为基础，迄今发现的南非该亚科的代表是否与人类进化有直接联系，这在一定程度上取决于其化石的地质年代。目前为止此类证据几乎完全依据动物群的资料。现在布鲁姆博士认为，斯泰克方丹堆积中发现的原始鬣狗（狼鬣狗属）及两种剑齿虎的化石表明其年代不晚于上新世晚期，而汤恩化石产地的年代可能还要早一些，可能是上新世中期。但是他明确指出，如同克罗姆德拉伊堆积一样，目前要测定此处确切的地质年代是不可能的。然而，南方古猿

Middle Pliocene. But he specifically states that, as with the deposits at Kromdraai, it is quite impossible at present to determine the geological age with certainty. However, the importance of the Australopithecinae is so great for the study of primate palaeontology, and particularly human palaeontology, that it becomes imperative to obtain more information about their antiquity. Even the skeletal remains, in spite of the magnificent work of Dr. Broom, still remain too scanty for firm conclusions regarding their significance. For Dr. Broom and Dr. Schepers they provide evidence for an assumption that the modern apes, and even the fossil apes of the *Dryopithecus-Sivapithecus* group, have no close relation to man (they are the result of a prolonged period of parallel development), and that the line of human evolution diverged from that of other primates so far back as Eocene times. On the other hand, the distinguished palaeontologist, Dr. W. K. Gregory (who has also had the opportunity of examining the original Australopithecine material) concludes[6] that "the evidence afforded by the morphology of the braincast and skull structure can hardly leave a well-founded doubt that the Australopithecine group were derived from the *Dryopithecus-Sivapithecus* stock", and that "although it is too much to expect that the close structural approach of *Plesianthropus* towards *Sinanthropus* will discourage those who cling hopefully to the myth of Eocene man, all the facts ... tend to confirm the conclusions of [those] who regard man as the result of a morphological revolution which took place during the later Tertiary period".

Such a divergence of opinion among recognized experts only serves to emphasize the need for still more fossil material. In this connexion we would quote a remarkable statement by Dr. Broom: "When some wealthy man or corporation undertakes the systematic exploration of our deposits ... I think one can safely affirm that within three or four years we will discover more of the origin of man than has been revealed during the past hundred. Practically all the discoveries described in the present work, except the Taungs skull, were made by me in about two years working almost single-handed. Not only had I to find all the specimens, I had to develop them out of the matrix, give all the descriptions and make all the drawings."

Dr. Broom is a veteran palaeontologist unequalled today in experience and reputation. This monograph on the Australopithecinae is a fitting climax to a long life devoted to palaeontological research, and to a record of fossil-collecting which is quite unsurpassed for its rich discoveries. Moreover, with the preliminary work on *Australopithecus* contributed by Prof. Dart, he has very considerably enhanced the prestige of South African science in the eyes of the world generally. Surely one may express with some confidence the expectation that his magnificent contributions to the story of human evolution will be recognized by his fellow countrymen, to the extent that they will provide the funds and the facilities for the realization of his hopes for further discoveries at Sterkfontein and elsewhere. No greater service could be done to the study of human origins, and no more appropriate expression of gratitude could be made to Dr. Broom.

(**157**, 863-865; 1946)

亚科对于灵长类动物古生物学研究，特别是对人类古生物学研究，是非常重要的，因此迫切需要获得更多有关它们古代遗迹的资料。尽管布鲁姆博士做了大量的工作，但是考虑到结论的重要性，即便是骨化石也不足以证实这一结论。布鲁姆博士和舍佩尔斯博士对以下设想提供了证据：现代猿类，甚至是森林古猿–西瓦古猿群的化石猿类与人类都没有紧密联系（它们是长期平行进化的结果），人类进化路线早在始新世之后就已从其他灵长类动物的进化路线中分离出来了。另一方面，著名古生物学家格雷戈里博士（他也有机会观察到南方古猿亚科的化石原件）推断[6]："依据脑模形态和头骨结构提供的证据，还不足以对南方古猿亚科群的祖先来自于森林古猿–西瓦古猿支干这个结论提出质疑"，而且"尽管难以期待迩人与中国猿人在结构上的相似会给信奉虚构出的始新世人的人泼冷水，但是所有的事实……却趋向于肯定那些人的结论，他们认为在第三纪晚期完成形态的进化后，人类诞生了"。

知名专家们在此观点上的分歧显示出他们仍然需要更多的化石材料。在此我们将引用布鲁姆博士的一段著名论述："当一些富有的人或者企业帮助我们对堆积物进行系统发掘的时候……我想人们可以坚信，在3、4年之内对于人类起源会有更多的发现，而这些发现会比在过去100年内已经发现的还要多。因为除汤恩头骨外，目前研究中所有的发现几乎都是依赖我一个人的力量在大约2年内完成的。我不仅发现了所有这些标本，还要把它们从围岩中挖掘出来，并对它们进行描述和绘图。"

古生物学家布鲁姆博士经验丰富，其经历与声望目前无人能及。这部论述南方古猿亚科的专著代表他长期致力于古生物学研究生涯的顶峰；同时，因其丰富的发现很难被超越，这也是化石收集记录的顶峰。达特教授为南方古猿的前期研究做出了很大的贡献，布鲁姆在此基础上大幅提高了南非的科学在世界范围内总体上的声望。当然，也许有人会满怀信心地期待，他的同胞能够认可他对人类进化史研究所做出的巨大贡献，甚至给他提供资金与便利使他得以实现自己的愿望：在斯泰克方丹及其他地方有进一步的发现。为人类起源研究做再多的工作也不为多，对布鲁姆博士表示再多感谢都不为过。

（田晓阳 翻译；董为 审稿）

References:

1. The South African Fossil Ape-Men: The Australopithecinae. By Dr. R. Broom and G. W. H. Schepers. (Transvaal Museum Memoir No. 2.) Pp. 272+18 plates. (Pretoria: Transvaal Museum, 1946.)

2. *Mitt. med. Fac. Kais.-Jap. Univ.*, 6, 307 (1905).

3. Morton, D. J., *Amer. J. Phys. Anthrop.*, 7, 1 (1924).

4. See Kaufmann, H., and Sauter, M., *Arch. Suisses d'Anthrop. gén.*, **8**, 161 (1939).

5. See, for example, the most recent monograph on the subject, "Anthropoid and Human Endocranial Casts". By Pierre Hirschler. Pp. ix+150+11 plates. (Amsterdam: N. V. Noord-Hollandsche Uitgeversmij., 1942.) n.p.

6. *Ann. Transvaal Mus.*, **19**, 339 (1939).

Australopithecinae or Dartians

A. Keith

Editor's Note

Of all the anthropologists who objected to Raymond Dart's assertion that his *Australopithecus*, discovered at Taungs in Southern Africa in 1924, was an intermediate between apes and humans, Arthur Keith was perhaps the most vehement. This short note, published 23 years and many fossil discoveries later, was a plain and public admission of error: "I am now convinced that Prof. Dart was right and I was wrong". Keith suggested that australopithecines should be called "Dartians" by way of compensation. Keith's apology did not save his reputation. Less than five years later, the Piltdown Man remains, by which Keith had set such store in his own conception of human evolution, were exposed as forgeries.

WHEN Prof. Raymond Dart, of the University of the Witwatersrand, Johannesburg, announced in *Nature*[1] the discovery of a juvenile *Australopithecus* and claimed for it a human kinship, I was one of those who took the point of view that when the adult form was discovered it would prove to be near akin to the living African anthropoids—the gorilla and chimpanzee[2]. Like Prof. Le Gros Clark[3], I am now convinced, on the evidence submitted by Dr. Robert Broom[4], that Prof. Dart was right and that I was wrong; the Australopithecinae are in or near the line which culminated in the human form. My only complaint now is the length of the name which the extinct anthropoid of South Africa must for ever bear. Seeing that Prof. Dart not only discovered them but also rightly perceived their true nature, I have ventured, when writing of the Australopithecinae, to give them the colloquial name of "Dartians", thereby saving much expenditure of ink and of print. The Dartians are ground-living anthropoids, human in posture, gait and dentition, but still anthropoid in facial physiognomy and in size of brain. It is much easier to say there was a "Dartian" phase in man's evolution than to speak of one which was "australopithecine".

(**159**, 337; 1947)

Arthur Keith: Downe, Kent, Feb. 15.

References:

1. *Nature*, **115**, 195 (1925).
2. *Nature*, **115**, 234 (1925).
3. *Nature*, **159**, 216 (1947).
4. "The South African Fossil Ape-Men: The Australopithecinae" (1946).

南方古猿亚科或达特猿

基思

编者按

雷蒙德·达特教授宣称他于 1924 年在南非汤恩发现的南方古猿是介于猿类和人类之间的中间类型，在所有反对他的这一结论的人类学家中，阿瑟·基思可能是反对最强烈的一个。23 年后，又有许多化石被发现，不久之后基思在这篇短文中公开坦率地承认错误："现在我深信达特教授是正确的，而我是错误的。"基思建议应该将南方古猿亚科称作"达特猿"作为对达特教授的补偿。但基思的道歉并没有挽回他的声誉。接下来不到 5 年的时间里，基思提出的作为人类进化理论重要证据的皮尔当人遗骸被曝光是伪造物。

南非约翰内斯堡威特沃特斯兰德大学的雷蒙德·达特教授在《自然》[1] 上宣布他发现了幼年南方古猿，并声称它同人类具有亲缘关系。当时我和其他一些人持有以下观点，即如若人们发现的是成年个体时，也许将能够证实它拥有和现存非洲类人猿——大猩猩和黑猩猩有更加接近的亲缘关系 [2]。和克拉克教授 [3] 一样，依据罗伯特·布鲁姆博士 [4] 提出的证据，现在我深信达特教授是正确的，而我是错误的；南方古猿亚科位于或者靠近这条最终进化为人类的线。现在我唯一不满的是这个已经灭绝的南非类人猿命名的长度。鉴于达特教授不仅发现了它们，而且正确地认识到了它们真正的本质，我冒险地提议在写南方古猿亚科时使用通俗的名字"达特猿"，这样能节省大量的油墨和印刷费用。达特猿是在地面生活的类人猿，在姿势、步态和齿系上与人类一致，但是在面部相貌和脑的大小上仍属类人猿。在人类进化过程中说存在一个"达特猿"时期比说一个"南方古猿亚科"时期要更容易。

（张玉光 张立召 翻译；赵凌霞 审稿）

Discovery of a New Skull of the South African Ape-Man, Plesianthropus

R. Broom

Editor's Note

World War II had halted the search for fossil man in South Africa from 1941 until 1946, when General Smuts himself asked palaeontologist Robert Broom to continue his hunt for fossils of ape-men. Starting at the beginning of 1947, Broom searched the fruitful site at Kromdraai for three months, but found only one possible hominid bone. The hunt moved to Sterkfontein on 1 April and met success within a week: on 8 April the search was rewarded with remains of the ape-man *Plesianthropus* (now *Australopithecus*), including a partial skull of what Broom believed was an elderly female. In time, this fossil, named "Mrs Ples", became an iconic image of the South African ape-men.

BETWEEN 1924, when the Taungs ape-man was discovered, and 1941, when the jaws of the baby Kromdraai ape-man were found, remains of many individuals of this wonderful family, which some of us consider to be nearly related to man, were discovered; sufficient to show that in South Africa we may have the key which will solve the problem of the origin of man. But from 1941 until a few months ago, no further research was undertaken.

In 1946, a book was published on all we know of the South African ape-man; and the world awoke to the possibilities of the wonderful results that might be achieved by the further study of our caves. The United States has come to realize that South Africa is a more promising centre for the solution of the problem than even Java or China; and she seems determined to see that the problem must be solved, and solved soon.

At the beginning of this year, at the special request of General Smuts, I again started to hunt for more "missing links". My assistants and I commenced work at Kromdraai and continued there for three months. We found many interesting remains, including a very fine skull of a sabre-tooth tiger (*Megantthereon*) and the skull of a large type of "baboon", which belongs to a new genus; but only one bone that had possibly belonged to an ape-man.

一件新的南非猿人——迩人头骨的发现

布鲁姆

编者按

由于第二次世界大战，从1941年到1946年，在南非搜索人类化石的工作暂停了下来，后来斯穆茨将军亲自邀请古生物学家罗伯特·布鲁姆继续寻找猿人化石。从1947年年初开始，布鲁姆在曾有丰富收获的克罗姆德拉伊地区搜索了3个月，但仅发现了一件可能属于人科的骨。4月1日起，搜索工作转移到了斯泰克方丹，并在1周内取得了重要发现：4月8日发现了迩人（现称南方古猿）的化石，包括布鲁姆认为的属于老年女性的部分头骨。后来，这件化石被命名为“普莱斯夫人”，成为南非猿人的标志性形象。

1924年，汤恩猿人的头骨化石被发现，接着在1941年，在克罗姆德拉伊地区发现了婴儿猿人的颌骨。在这一期间，发现了许多属于这个令人惊奇的猿人科的个体化石，有些人认为其与人类的关系较近；这些证据足以说明在南非我们可能找到解决人类起源问题的钥匙。但从1941年直到几个月前，再没有人进行过进一步的研究。

1946年，一本关于所有已知南非猿人的书籍问世了；全世界都意识到通过对洞穴进行深入研究也许会取得非凡的成果。美国逐渐认识到南非是一个比爪哇或中国更能揭示人类起源问题的地方；她似乎坚信人类起源问题肯定能被解决，而且会很快得到解决。

今年年初，在斯穆茨将军的专程邀请下，我再次开始搜寻更多的“缺失环节”。我与助手们在克罗姆德拉伊开始工作，并在那里持续工作了3个月。我们发现了许多有趣的化石，包括一件保存完好的剑齿虎（巨颏虎）的头骨和一件属于一个新属的大型“狒狒”的头骨；但只发现了一件可能属于猿人的骨。

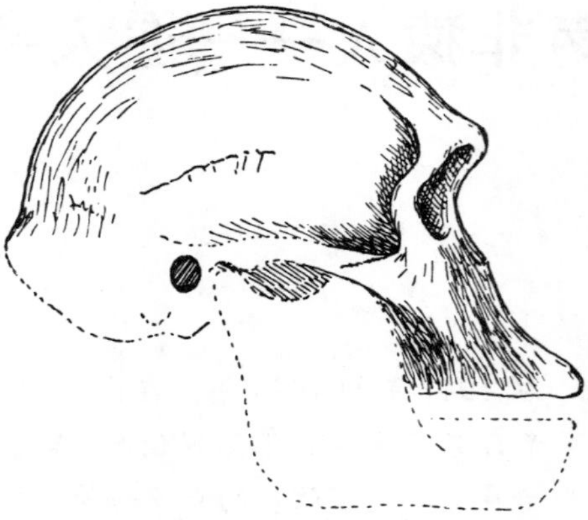

Fig. 1. Side view of skull of old female Sterkfontein ape-man *Plesianthropus transvaalensis* (Broom). $\frac{1}{3}$ natural size. The lower part of the occiput and part of the jugal arch are still embedded in matrix, and the lower jaw is not present

Then on April 1 we started work at Sterkfontein, and almost immediately our labours were rewarded by sensational discoveries. On April 8 we found an isolated crushed snout of an adolescent *Plesianthropus* with some beautiful teeth; and a fragment of a snout of a child of possibly three years. This showed the perfect upper milk molars, and a note on the discovery was sent to *Nature* [see issue of May 3, p.602. Editors]. On April 11 two quite isolated teeth of Sterkfontein apes were found—one the beautiful upper canine of a male of perhaps thirty years, and a lower molar probably of a female of forty years.

But on April 18 a small blast cracked open a block of breccia, and there in the middle lay a perfect skull without the mandible of an adult *Plesianthropus*, with the brain case broken across. In ten days we had found the remains of five—possibly six—individuals of the Sterkfontein ape-man, *Plesianthropus*, and one of them represented by a complete skull.

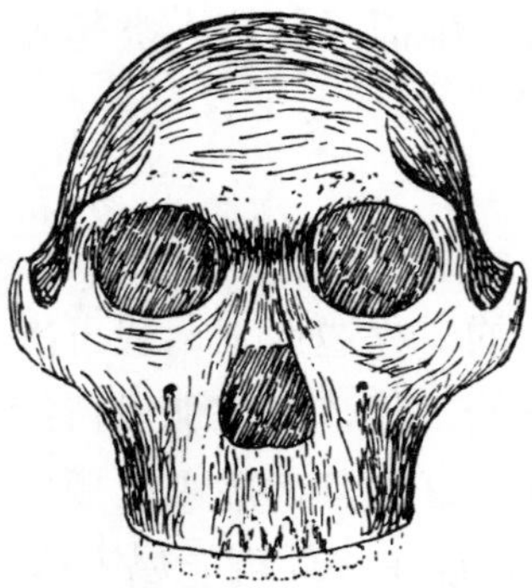

Fig. 2. Front view of skull of old female Sterkfontein ape-man, *Plesianthropus transvaalensis* (Broom). $\frac{1}{3}$ natural size

The bones are very friable and the matrix not only rather hard lime, but also breccia

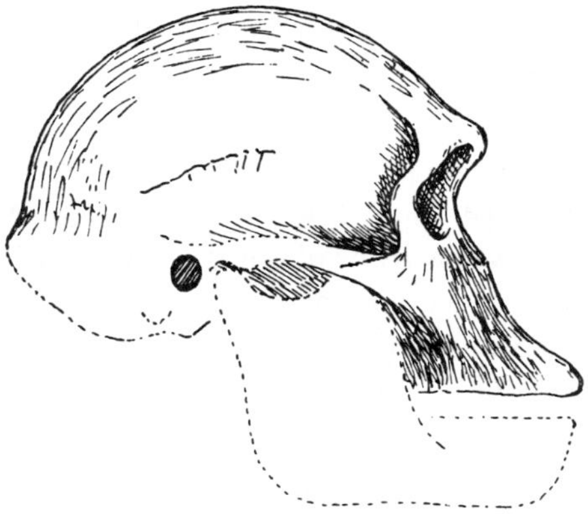

图 1. 老年女性斯泰克方丹猿人——德兰士瓦迩人头骨的侧面图（布鲁姆）。该图为真实尺寸的$\frac{1}{3}$。枕骨的下部以及部分颧弓仍埋在基质中，没有发现下颌骨。

然后，我们于 4 月 1 日开始在斯泰克方丹工作，并且几乎在工作一开始就取得了重大发现。4 月 8 日，我们发现了一件青少年迩人被压碎的口鼻部骨化石，其上带有一些漂亮的牙齿；还发现了一件大约 3 岁孩子的口鼻部骨破片。这上面有保存完好的上乳臼齿，关于此发现的说明已发给《自然》杂志［见 5 月 3 日那一期，第 602 页，编者注］。4 月 11 日，我们发现了两颗单个的斯泰克方丹猿类的牙齿——一颗是约 30 岁男性的漂亮的上犬齿，另一颗可能属于 40 岁女性的下臼齿。

但在 4 月 18 日，一次小爆破炸开了一块角砾岩，在其中间发现一件保存完好的成年迩人头骨，只是没有下颌骨，头盖骨裂开了。10 天中我们发现了 5 个（也可能是 6 个）斯泰克方丹猿人（即迩人）个体的残骸，其中有一件是完整的头骨。

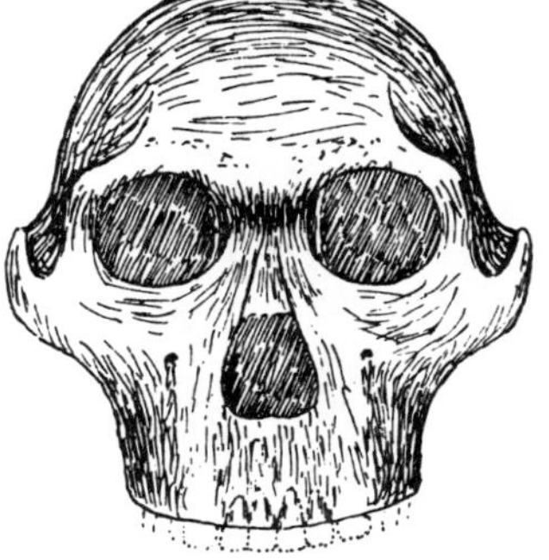

图 2. 老年女性斯泰克方丹猿人——德兰士瓦迩人头骨的正面图（布鲁姆）。该图为真实尺寸的$\frac{1}{3}$。

这些骨十分易碎，而埋藏它们的基质不仅有颇为坚硬的石灰，而且还有很多大

with many large broken pieces of chert; it will take many weeks before the skull can be completely developed from the matrix.

Enough, however, has now been done to reveal most of the more striking features of the skull. In the type skull the brain cavity was filled with matrix. In the newly discovered skull there is only a lining of lime crystals from about $\frac{1}{8}$ in. to nearly $\frac{1}{2}$ in. in thickness. When this layer is removed we will have every detail of the anatomy of the inner side of the base of the skull. The under surface of the base of the skull appears to be just as perfect; but it will take some further weeks of preparation to reveal it all.

So far, our labours have been concentrated on the details of the face, and in cleaning the cranial vault. The teeth are all lost, but many sockets remain, and we can say with much confidence that the skull is that of an elderly female.

The drawings I give will serve to show the general aspect of the face and the side view. I think there will be very general agreement that the being is not a chimpanzee or even closely allied to any of the living anthropoids, and that, though small, the skull has many resemblances to that of man.

The skull from glabella to opisthocranion is about 150 mm., and the greatest parietal width is about 100 mm. It is thus seen to have an index of about 66, and to be extremely dolichocephalic. As yet, we can only give a roughly approximate size for the brain cavity, but it seems probable that it will be about 500 c.c.

Of course, it will take many weeks before the skull is completely worked up and a full account can be published, but it seems well that the world should know that such a valuable skull has been discovered.

(**159**, 672; 1947)

R. Broom: Transvaal Museum, Pretoria, April 2.

块燧石的角砾岩，因此将头骨从这些基质中完好地取出需要几周时间。

不过现在这些发现完全可以揭示头骨中大部分比较显著的特征。在正型标本头骨的颅腔中充满了基质。在新发现的头骨中，仅内侧有一层厚度约 $\frac{1}{8}$ 英寸 ~ $\frac{1}{2}$ 英寸的石灰晶体。当移除这层后，我们会观察到头骨底内侧的所有解剖学细节。头骨底的下表面看起来很完美；但是要揭示全部信息的话，还需要再做几个星期的准备工作。

到目前为止，我们的精力主要集中在研究脸部细节和清理头骨穹隆。虽然牙齿已经全部没有了，但是许多牙槽还在。我们可以确信地说，这是一件老年女性的头骨。

我提供的图画可用以展示其面部的轮廓及侧面情况。我认为大家会赞同这样的观点：这种生物不是黑猩猩，甚至不与任何现存类人猿有密切的亲缘关系，尽管头骨很小，但与人类头骨有很多相似之处。

该头骨从眉间点到颅后点约 150 毫米，在顶骨的最大颅宽约 100 毫米。因此可以看到这个头骨的颅指数约为 66，属极端的长颅型。到目前为止，我们对脑颅大小只能给出一个粗略的估计，可能约为 500 毫升。

当然，将这个头骨完全整理出来并发表一份完整的报告，还需要花费几个星期的时间，但是世界应该知道这样一件有价值的头骨已经被发现了，这一点看起来很好。

（刘皓芳 田晓阳 张立召 翻译；赵凌霞 审稿）

Processes Involving Charged Mesons

C. M. G. Lattes *et al.*

Editor's Note

César Lattes and colleagues from the University of Bristol here report recent results from cosmic-ray experiments suggesting the existence of hitherto unknown particles. They had found that some particles having masses small compared to the proton could cause nuclear disintegrations involving the emission of several heavy particles. They referred to the particles as mesons, this being the accepted term for any particle of mass intermediate to the electron and proton. Lattes and colleagues detected the particles from their unusual tracks on photographic plates, showing occasional decays of these mesons into secondary mesons. The primary mesons were later identified as the positive and negative charged pi mesons (pions), which would be created in the laboratory in a few years.

IN recent investigations with the photographic method[1,2], it has been shown that slow charged particles of small mass, present as a component of the cosmic radiation at high altitudes, can enter nuclei and produce disintegrations with the emission of heavy particles. It is convenient to apply the term "meson" to any particle with a mass intermediate between that of a proton and an electron. In continuing our experiments we have found evidence of mesons which, at the end of their range, produce secondary mesons. We have also observed transmutations in which slow mesons are ejected from disintegrating nuclei. Several features of these processes remain to be elucidated, but we present the following account of the experiments because the results appear to bear closely on the important problem of developing a satisfactory meson theory of nuclear forces.

In identifying the tracks of mesons we employ the method of grain-counting. The method allows us, in principle[3], to determine the mass of a particle which comes to the end of its range in the emulsion, provided that we are correct in assuming that its charge is of magnitude $|e|$. We define the "grain-density" in a track as the number of grains per unit length of the trajectory. Knowing the range-energy curve for the emulsion[4], we can make observations on the tracks of fast protons to determine a calibration curve showing the relation between the grain-density in a track and the rate of loss of energy of the particle producing it. With this curve, the observed distribution of grains along the track of a meson allows us to deduce the total loss of energy of the particle in the emulsion. The energy taken in conjunction with the observed range of the particle then gives a measure of its mass.

We have found that the above method gives satisfactory results when, in test experiments, it is applied to the determination of the mass of protons by observations on plates

涉及带电介子的过程

拉特斯等

编者按

布里斯托尔大学的塞萨尔·拉特斯及其同事们在这篇文章中报告说，近期宇宙射线的实验结果表明存在迄今未知的粒子。他们发现一些质量比质子小的粒子可以引起核嬗变，并且在此过程中会发射出一些重粒子，他们称其为介子。介子这一专有名词是指任意一个质量介于电子和质子之间的粒子，这已得到公认。拉特斯及其同事们在照相底片上不寻常的粒子径迹中观测到了介子，同时这些照相底片还显示出这些介子有时会衰变为次级介子。随后人们将初级介子确定为正负 π 介子，几年后在实验室中生成了这些粒子。

近期，我们利用照相法进行的研究[1,2]显示，作为高纬度处宇宙辐射的组分，小质量的带电慢粒子可以进入核并引起核嬗变同时发射出重粒子。对于任何质量介于质子和电子之间的粒子，用“介子”一词来表示都是合适的。通过连续的实验我们发现了有关介子的实验证据，它们在射程末端产生了次级介子。与此同时，我们还观测到了嬗变的核发射出慢介子的嬗变过程。这些过程的某些特性虽然还有待阐明，但是由于其实验结果似乎与发展一套令人满意的核力介子理论这样的重大问题有密切关系，我们将介绍以下的实验内容。

在鉴别介子的径迹时我们应用了颗粒计数法。假设一种粒子的电荷量为 $|e|$，如果我们的假设是正确的，那么当该粒子的射程末端终止于乳胶内时，颗粒计数法从原理上[3]允许我们测定该粒子的质量。我们定义径迹的“颗粒密度”为单位径迹长度中的颗粒数。知道了对于乳胶的射程–能量曲线[4]，我们就可以观测快质子的径迹，以测定描述径迹的颗粒密度与粒子能量损失率间关系的标定曲线。利用这条曲线，所观测到的沿着介子径迹的颗粒分布能够使我们推导出乳胶中粒子的总能量损失。利用粒子被带走的能量以及观测到的粒子射程可以对粒子的质量进行测量。

在测试实验中，对受粒子辐射后立即显影的照片进行观测，并用上述方法对质子质量进行测定，我们发现上述方法给出了令人满意的结果。各条径迹颗粒计数观

developed immediately after exposure. The errors in the observed values, based on grain-counts along individual tracks, are only a little greater than those corresponding to the statistical fluctuations associated with the finite number of grains in a track. As we have previously emphasized, however, serious errors arise when the method is applied to the plates exposed for several weeks to the cosmic rays[2]. These errors are due mainly to the fading of the latent image in the time elapsing between the passage of the particle and the development of the plate.

We have attempted to allow for fading by determining a calibration curve for each individual plate by grain-counts on the tracks of a number of protons, chosen at random from those originating in "stars". Such a calibration curve corresponds to an average value of the fading of the tracks in the plate. While we thus obtain improved mean values for the mass of particles of the same type, as shown by test measurements on the tracks of protons other than those used in making the calibration, the individual values are subject to wide variations. In no case, however, have mass determinations by grain-counts of particles, judged to be protons from the frequency of the small-angle scattering, given values exceeding 2,400 m_e or less than 1,300 m_e.

In these circumstances it is not possible to place serious reliance on the masses of individual mesons determined by grain-counts; and we employ the method, in the present experiments, only to distinguish the track of a meson from that of a proton. In searching a plate, an experienced observer quickly learns to recognize the track of a meson by inspection, provided that its range in the emulsion exceeds 100μ. Nevertheless, we regard it as established that a particular track was produced by a meson only if both the grain-density and the frequency of the Coulomb scattering correspond to the values characteristic of a particle of small mass. We have considered the possibility that as a result of a rare combination of circumstances we might, in spite of the above precautions, wrongly attribute the track of a proton to a meson of mass less than 400 m_e. It is difficult to give a numerical estimate of the probability of making such an error, but we believe it to be very small.

Secondary Mesons

We have now made an analysis of the tracks of sixty-five mesons which come to the end of their range in the emulsion. Of these, forty show no evidence for the production of a secondary particle. The remaining twenty-five lead to the production of secondary particles. Fifteen of them produce disintegrations with the emission of two or more heavy particles, and from each of the remaining ten we observe a single secondary particle. Of these latter events, the secondary particle is in four cases a hydrogen or heavier nucleus; in four other cases the identification is uncertain, and in the last two cases it is a second meson.

Fig. 1 is a reproduction of a mosaic of photomicrographs which shows that a particle, m_1, has come to the end of its range in the emulsion. The frequent points of scattering and

测值的误差，只是略大于一条径迹中有限的颗粒数的统计波动对应的误差。然而，正如我们先前所强调的那样，在将这种方法用于被宇宙射线[2]辐射数周的照片时，会产生严重的误差。这些误差主要是由于在粒子穿过照片和照片显影之间的这段时间内发生的潜影衰退。

通过随机地选取来自“星”状的质子，对若干条质子径迹进行颗粒计数，来测定每张照片的标定曲线，我们试图以此顾及潜影衰退。这样一个标定曲线对应于照片中径迹衰退的一个平均值。于是，我们得到改进后同类粒子质量的平均值，对标定曲线的测定中没有用到的那些质子的径迹进行的测试性测量显示，单条径迹的颗粒计数测量值变化很大。不过，根据小角度散射的发生频率而判定其为质子的粒子，由其颗粒计数确定的粒子质量都不会超过 2,400 m_e 或小于 1,300 m_e。

在这些情况下，不可能太认真地相信由颗粒计数测定的单个介子质量；因为在目前的实验中我们采用这种方法，仅是为了把介子与质子的径迹区分开来。在观察一张照片时，如果乳胶中粒子的射程超过 100 微米，有经验的观测者通过观察很快就能学会识别出介子的径迹。然而，只有在颗粒密度和库仑散射的发生频率都与小质量粒子的特征值相对应的情形下，我们才确定这一特别的径迹是由介子产生的。尽管采取了上述的防范措施，我们仍然考虑了由于罕见的综合环境条件而将质子径迹误认为是质量小于 400 m_e 的介子径迹的可能性。虽然很难给出发生这类误差的概率估计值，但我们相信这个数值是很小的。

次级介子

现在，我们已经对 65 个介子（射程末端落在乳胶之内）的径迹做了分析，其中 40 个介子没有产生次级粒子的迹象。剩余的 25 个介子则产生了次级粒子，其中的 15 个介子发生嬗变并放射出两个或更多个重粒子，我们观测到剩余的 10 个介子中每个介子都产生一个单独的次级粒子。而在后面提到的 10 个事例当中，经我们研究发现其中有 4 个事例的次级粒子是氢或是更重的核；另 4 个事例产生的次级粒子的种类还不能确定，最后 2 个事例产生的则是次级介子。

图 1 是显微相片中的图像的再现，显示了粒子 m_1 在乳胶中到达了射程的末端。由靠近射程末端处散射点的频繁出现和颗粒密度的快速变化，我们推算出该径迹是

the rapid change of grain-density towards the end of the range show that the track was produced by a meson. It will be seen from the figure that the track of a second particle, m_2, starts from the point where the first one ends, and that the second track also has all the characteristics of that of a particle of small mass. A similar event is shown in Fig. 2. In each case the chance that the observation corresponds to a chance juxtaposition of two tracks from unrelated events is less than 1 in 10^9.

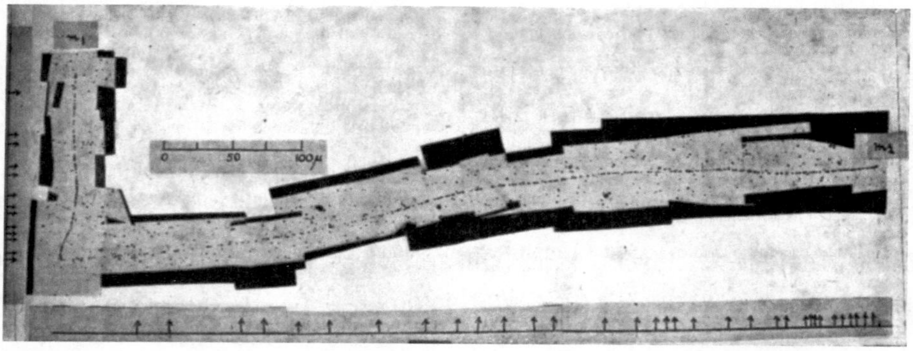

Fig. 1. Observation by Mrs. I. Roberts. Photomicrograph with Cooke × 45 "fluorite" objective. Ilford "Nuclear Research", boron-loaded *C*2 emulsion. m_1 is the primary and m_2 the secondary meson. The arrows, in this and the following photographs, indicate points where changes in direction greater than 2° occur, as observed under the microscope. All the photographs are completely unretouched

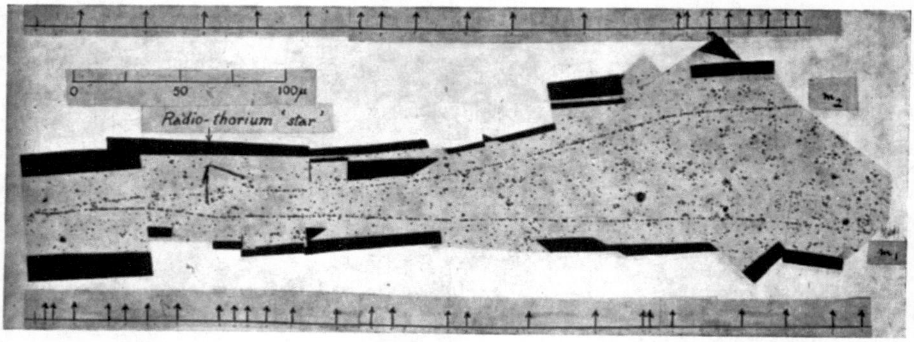

Fig. 2. Observation by Miss M. Kurz. Cooke × 45 "fluorite" objective. Ilford "Nuclear Research" emulsion, type *C*2, boron-loaded. The secondary meson, m_2, leaves the emulsion

Grain-counts indicate that the masses of the primary particles in Figs. 1 and 2 are 350±80 and 330±50 m_e, respectively; and of the secondary particle in Fig. 1, 330±50 m_e, the limits of error corresponding only to the standard deviations associated with the finite numbers of grains in the different tracks. All these values are deduced from calibration curves corresponding to an average value of the fading in the plate, and they will be too high if the track was produced late in the exposure, and too low if early. We may assume, however, that the two-component tracks in each event were produced in quick succession and were therefore subject to the same degree of fading. In these circumstances the measurements indicate that if there is a difference in mass between a primary and a secondary meson, it is unlikely that it is of magnitude greater than 100 m_e. The evidence provided by Fig. 2 is not so

由介子产生的。如图 1 所示，一个次级粒子 m_2 的径迹起始于第一个粒子 m_1 的终点，并且它的径迹也具有小质量粒子径迹的所有特征。图 2 显示了一个类似的事例。在这两张图的情形中，我们所观测到的图像是由两个不相关的事例产生的两条径迹造成的偶然毗邻的可能性不到十亿分之一。

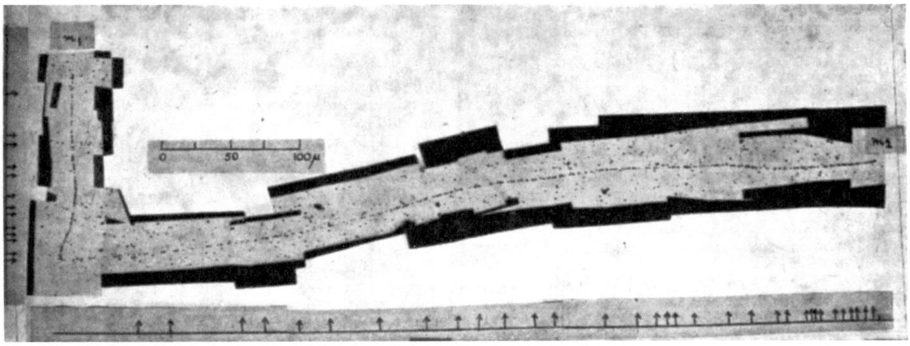

图 1. 由罗伯茨夫人观测。用库克 45 倍“萤石”物镜得到的显微照片。伊尔福载硼 $C2$“核”乳胶。m_1 是初级介子，m_2 是次级介子。这张和以下各张照片中的箭头，指示出显微镜观测下方向变化大于 2°的点，所有的相片全部未经修改。

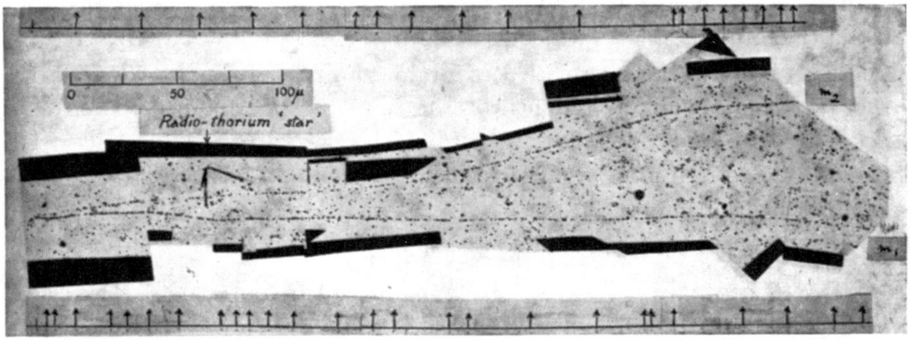

图 2. 由库尔茨小姐观测。库克 45 倍“萤石”物镜。伊尔福载硼 $C2$“核”乳胶。次级介子 m_2 射离了乳胶。

颗粒计数表明，图 1 和图 2 中初始粒子的质量分别为 $350\pm80\ m_e$ 和 $330\pm50\ m_e$；图 1 中次级粒子的质量为 $330\pm50\ m_e$，误差限仅相应于与不同径迹中有限数量的颗粒关联的标准偏差。所有这些值都是从照片中衰退的平均值所对应的标定曲线导出的，如果径迹在照射后期产生，该数值将偏高；而如果该径迹在照射早期产生，此数值就会太低。然而，我们可以假定，每个事例中的双组元径迹是迅速接连产生的，因此衰退程度相同。在这类情况下，测量表明，如果初级介子与次级介子之间存在质量差，其量级不可能大于 $100\ m_e$。图 2 提供的证据并不充分，因为次级粒子穿出了乳胶，但径迹颗粒密度的变化表明，它接近射程末端。由此我们得出结论，次级

complete because the secondary particle passes out of the emulsion, but the variation in the grain density in the track indicates that it was then near the end of its range. We conclude that the secondary mesons were ejected with nearly equal energy.

We have attempted to interpret these two events in terms of an interaction of the primary meson with a nucleus in the emulsion which leads to the ejection of a second meson of the same mass as the first. Any reaction of the type represented by the equations

$$A^N_Z+\mu^0_{-1} \rightarrow B^N_{Z-2}+\mu^0_{+1} \text{ or } A^N_Z+\mu^0_{+1} \rightarrow C^N_{Z+2}+\mu^0_{-1}, \tag{1}$$

in which A represents any stable nucleus known to be present in the emulsion, involves an absorption of energy, in contradiction with the fact that the secondary meson is observed to have an energy of about 2 MeV.

A second process, represented by the equation

$$\mathrm{Ag}_7+\mu^0_{-1} \rightarrow X_Z+Y_{45-Z}+\mu^0_{+1}, \tag{2}$$

in which X and Y represent two nuclei of approximately equal charge number, may be energetically possible, but the chance of it occurring in conditions where the total energy of the two recoiling nuclei is of the order of only a few million electron-volts is remote. It is therefore possible that our photographs indicate the existence of mesons of different mass[5,6,7]. The evidence provided by grain counts is not inconsistent with such an assumption. We have no direct evidence of the signs of the charges carried by the two mesons, except that the one secondary meson which comes to the end of its range in the emulsion does not lead to a disintegration with the emission of heavy particles. If, however, we assume that the transmutation corresponds to the interaction of the primary meson with a light nucleus, of a type represented by the equation

$$\mathrm{C}^{12}_6+\mu^0_{-1} \rightarrow \mathrm{Be}^{12}_4+\mu^0_{+1}, \tag{3}$$

the difference in mass of the two mesons must be of the order of 60 m_e, according to estimates of the mass of the beryllium nucleus.

The only meson theory, to our knowledge, which assumes the existence of mesons of different mass is that of Schwinger[8]. It is visualized[9] that a negative vector meson should have a very short life and should lead to the production of a pseudo-scalar meson of the same charge but lower mass, together with a quantum of radiation. It will therefore be of great interest to determine whether the secondary meson, in transmutations of the type we have observed, is always emitted with the same energy. If this is so, we must assume that we are dealing with a more fundamental type of process than one involving particular nuclei such as is represented in equation (3). If, as an example of such a process, we assume that the momentum of the secondary meson appearing in our experiments is equal and opposite to that of an emitted photon, the total release of energy in the transmutation is of the order of 25 MeV.

介子是以几乎相等的能量发射的。

我们试图用初级介子与乳胶中的核相互作用来解释这两个事例，由这种相互作用导致了一个与初级介子质量相同的次级介子的发射。方程（1）表示的任何类型的反应都涉及能量的吸收，

$$A_Z^N+\mu_{-1}^0 \rightarrow B_{Z-2}^N+\mu_{+1}^0 \text{ 或者 } A_Z^N+\mu_{+1}^0 \rightarrow C_{Z+2}^N+\mu_{-1}^0 \tag{1}$$

式中 A 表示乳胶中存在的已知的任何稳定核，但这与观测到的次级介子的能量约为 2 兆电子伏的事实相矛盾。

第二个过程用以下方程表示

$$\mathrm{Ag}_7+\mu_{-1}^0 \rightarrow X_Z+Y_{45-Z}+\mu_{+1}^0 \tag{2}$$

式中 X 和 Y 表示电荷数近似相等的两个核，这个反应按能量守恒可能发生，但在两个反冲核的总能量仅为几百万电子伏特量级的条件下发生的可能性很小。因此我们的照片显示的可能是不同质量的介子 [5,6,7] 的存在。由颗粒计数提供的证据与这个猜想不矛盾。除了知道在乳胶中到达射程末端的一个次级介子并不引发伴随重粒子发射的嬗变外，我们还没有两个介子带电荷符号的直接证据。然而，如果我们假设，嬗变对应于初级介子与轻核的相互作用用方程（3）表示，

$$\mathrm{C}_6^{12}+\mu_{-1}^0 \rightarrow \mathrm{Be}_4^{12}+\mu_{+1}^0 \tag{3}$$

那么，根据对铍核的质量估计，2 个介子的质量差一定是 60 m_e 的量级。

我们所知道的，认为存在不同质量介子的唯一介子理论是施温格模型 [8]。该模型设想 [9] 一个负矢量介子应具有很短的寿命，并应产生具有相同电荷但质量较小的赝标量介子，同时伴随量子辐射。因此，在我们已观测的嬗变类型中测定次级介子是否总释放相同的能量将具有很大意义。如果事实果真如此，我们必定认为，我们正在处理一个比公式（3）所表示的含有特殊核的过程更为基本的过程。作为这类过程的一个例子，如果我们假定在我们实验中出现的次级介子与发射的光子的动量大小相等而方向相反，则在嬗变中释放的总能量是 25 兆电子伏的量级。

In recent communications[10,11] very radical conclusions have been drawn from the results of observations on the delayed coincidences produced by positive and negative mesons in interactions with light and heavy nuclei[12,13]. It is assumed that a negative meson, at the end of its range, falls into a *K* orbit around a nucleus. In the case of a heavy nucleus, it is then captured, giving rise to a disintegration with the emission of heavy particles. With a light nucleus, on the other hand, it is regarded as suffering β-decay before being captured, so that, like a positive meson, it can produce a delayed coincidence. The conclusion is drawn that the nuclear forces are smaller by several orders of magnitude than has been assumed hitherto. Since our observations indicate a new mode of decay of mesons, it is possible that they may contribute to the solution of these difficulties.

Emission of Mesons from Nuclei

Fig. 3 shows a mosaic of photomicrographs of a disintegration in which six tracks can be distinguished radiating from a common centre. The letters at the edge of the mosaic indicate whether a particular track passes out of the surface of the emulsion, *s*, into the glass, *g*, or ends in the emulsion, *e*. The grain-density in tracks *a* and *c* indicate that the time between the occurrence of the disintegration and the development of the plate was sufficiently short to avoid serious fading of the latent image.

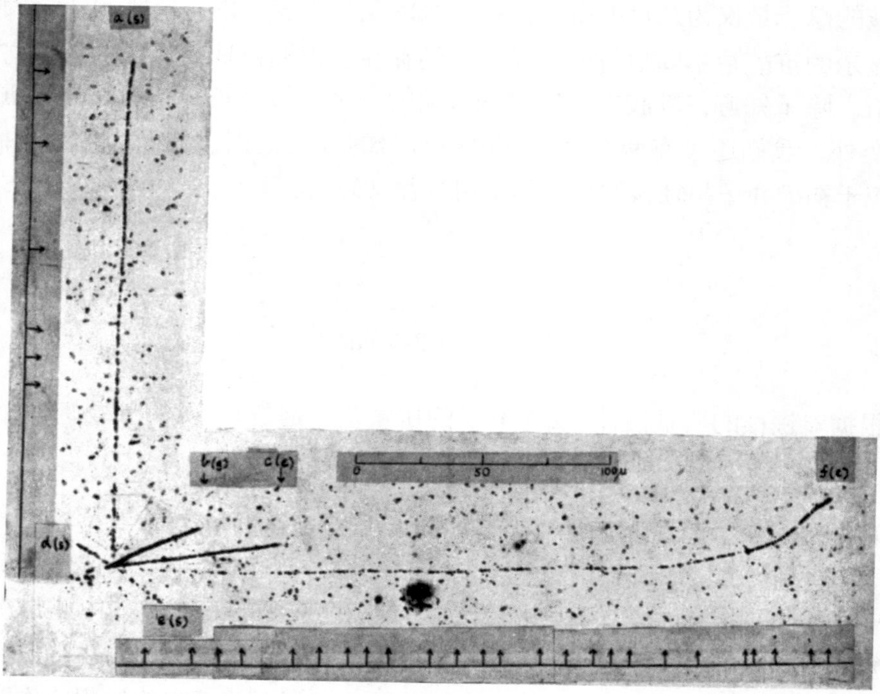

Fig. 3. Observation by Mrs. I. Roberts. Photomicrograph with Cooke × 45 "fluorite" objective. Ilford "Nuclear Research", boron-loaded *C*2 emulsion. The track (*b*) dips steeply and its apparent grain density is greater than the true value through foreshortening. Both (*b*) and (*c*) were probably produced by α-particles

在最近的报道中[10,11]，从对正负介子与轻核和重核的相互作用[12,13]产生的延迟符合的观测结果中已得出基本性结论。该结论认为，一个负介子在其射程终端落入了核的 K 轨道中。在重核情况下，负介子会被俘获而导致嬗变及发射重粒子。另一方面，在轻核情况下，负介子被认为在被俘获前先发生 β 衰变，因此像一个正介子一样，可以产生一个延迟符合。由此得出的结论如下，核力要比到目前为止认为的数值小几个数量级。鉴于我们的观测表明了介子衰变的一种新模式，其可能有助于解决这些困难。

由核发射的介子

图 3 显示了一次嬗变的显微照相图像，其中可以分辨出从同一中心辐射出的 6 条径迹。图像边缘的字母表示特定的径迹是否穿透乳胶表面 *s*，进入玻璃 *g*，或终止于乳胶 *e* 中。径迹 *a* 和 *c* 的颗粒密度表明，嬗变的发生与照片显影之间的时间间隔足够短，可以避免严重的潜影衰退。

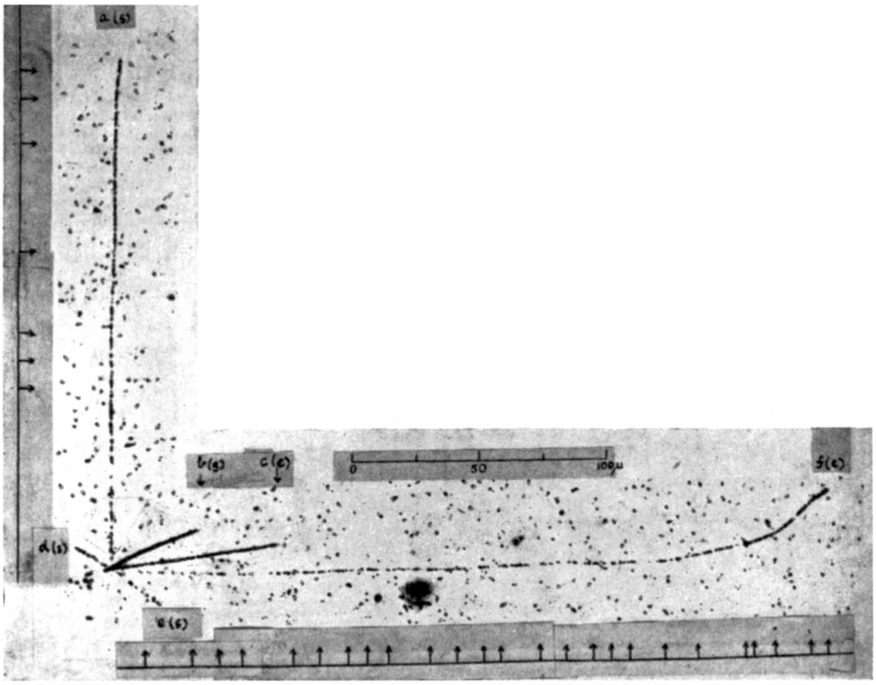

图 3. 由罗伯茨夫人观测。库克 45 倍的“萤石”物镜下的显微相片。伊尔福载硼 *C*2“核”乳胶。径迹 (*b*) 陡峭地下沉，其表观颗粒密度大于用透视缩小法得到的真值。(*b*) 和 (*c*) 可能都是由 α 粒子产生的。

The track marked *f* suffers frequent changes in direction due to scattering, and there is a very rapid change in the grain-density in moving along the trajectory. These two features, taken together, make it certain that the track was produced by a light particle, and grain counts give an estimate for the mass of 375±70 m_e[14].

We have now observed a total of 1,600 disintegration "stars", in each of which three or more charged particles are ejected from a nucleus. Of these, 170 correspond to the liberation of an amount of energy equal to, or greater than, that in the "star" represented in Fig. 4, but only in two cases can we identify an emitted particle as a meson. We cannot conclude, however, that the emission of mesons in such disintegrations is so rare as these figures suggest. If a meson is emitted with an energy greater than 5 MeV., it is likely to escape detection in the conditions of our experiments. Mr. D. H. Perkins, of the Imperial College of Science and Technology, has shown that, in the B_1 emulsion, the grain-density in the track of a meson becomes very small at energies greater than 2 MeV., and we must anticipate a similar result in the C_2 emulsion at higher energies. Our observations are therefore not inconsistent with the view that the ejection of mesons is a common feature of the disintegration of nuclei by primary particles of great energy, and that the present instance, in which the velocity of ejection has been exceptionally low so that an identification of the particle has been possible, is a rare example. It is possible that the example of meson production recently described[15] is due to a similar process, produced by a primary particle of higher energy, in which some of the heavier fragments emitted on the disintegration have escaped detection because of the depth inside the lead plate at which the event occurred.

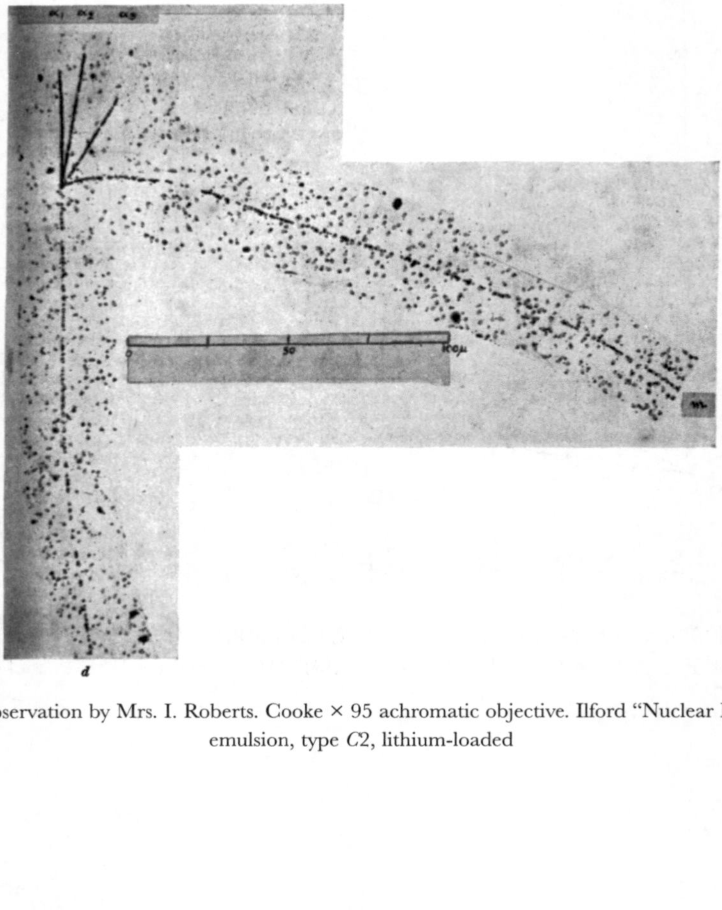

Fig. 4. Observation by Mrs. I. Roberts. Cooke × 95 achromatic objective. Ilford "Nuclear Research" emulsion, type $C2$, lithium-loaded

标记 f 的径迹由于散射而频繁地改变方向，并且在沿着径迹的运动中，颗粒密度也快速变化。这两个特性一起确定了径迹是由轻粒子产生的，颗粒计数给出的质量估计值是 $375 \pm 70\ m_e$[14]。

我们现在已观测到总共 1,600 个“星”状嬗变，每一个都会从一个核中发射出 3 个或更多个的带电粒子。其中的 170 个能量释放大于或等于图 4 表示的“星”状嬗变中的能量释放，但仅在两个嬗变事例中我们可以判定发射粒子是介子。然而，我们并不能认为，这类嬗变中的介子发射是如这些图中所示的如此罕见。如果发射介子的能量大于 5 兆电子伏，在我们的实验条件下似乎很难观测到它。帝国理工学院的珀金斯先生已指出，在 B_1 乳胶中，当能量大于 2 兆电子伏时介子径迹的颗粒密度变得很小，在 C_2 乳胶中更高的能量下我们可以预测到类似的结果。因此，我们的观测与以下观点不矛盾：介子的发射是高能初级粒子核嬗变的共同特性；而目前的事例即粒子的发射速度特别低以至于能够鉴别粒子的种类，是一个罕有的例子。最近描述的介子产生的例子 [15] 是高能初级粒子由类似过程产生的，其中，由于事例发生时铅片的深度，没有观测到嬗变中发射的一些重质量碎片。

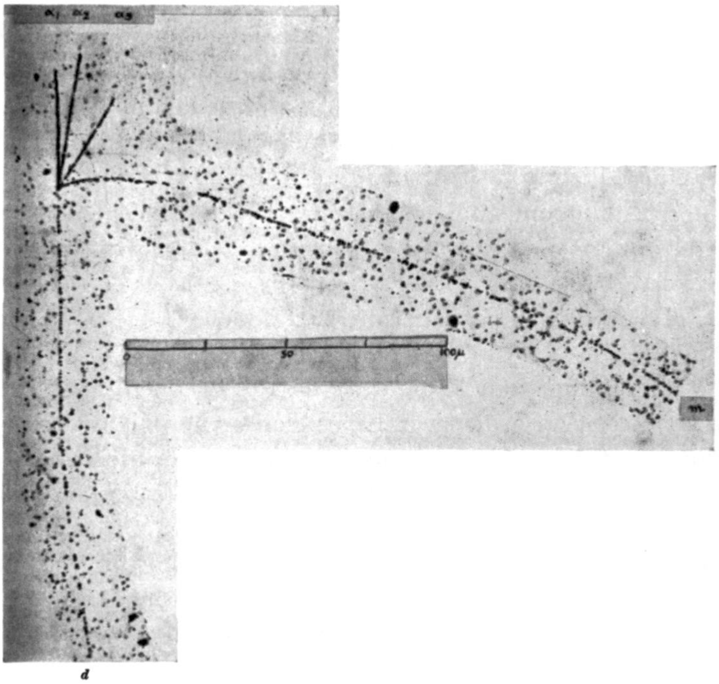

图 4. 由罗伯茨夫人观测。库克 95 倍消色差物镜。伊尔福载锂 C2“核”乳胶。

The disintegration shown in Fig. 3 may be the representative of a type, common in the high atmosphere with particles of great energy. In the present instance the energy of the primary particle must have been of at least 200 MeV., and, if its mass was equal to or less than that of a proton, it would not have been recorded by the emulsion.

Disintegrations Produced by Mesons

The observation of the transmutations of nuclei by charged mesons has led to the suggestion of a method for determining the mass of these particles based on observations of the total energy released in the disintegration[1,2]. In attempting to apply the method, we meet the difficulty of identifying the particular type of nucleus undergoing disintegration and of taking account of any ejected neutrons which will not be recorded by the emulsion. A photograph of such a disintegration which, at first sight, appears to allow us to draw definite conclusions, is shown in Fig. 4. In the photograph, the tracks of four heavy particles can be distinguished, of which the short tracks α_1, α_2 and α_3 end in the emulsion; α_1 and α_2 were certainly produced by α-particles, and grain-counts show that α_3 is due to a proton. The observations are therefore consistent with the equation

$$N_7^{14}+\mu_{-1}^{0} \rightarrow 2He_2^4+H_1^1+H_1^1+4n_0^1; \qquad (4)$$

or, less probably, to a similar equation involving the emission of a deuteron or a triton in addition to the particles of short range.

Grain-counts on the track of the particle of long range, *d*, which passes out of the emulsion, indicate that if it was produced by a proton, the initial energy of the particle was about 15 MeV. Alternatively, if the particle was a deuteron, its energy was 30 MeV.; or, if a triton, 45 MeV. In any case, we can determine the minimum energy which must be attributed to the emitted neutrons if momentum is to be conserved in the disintegration. As a result, we find a minimum value for the mass of the primary meson of 240 m_e. The value determined by grain-counts is also 240±50 m_e.

In view of the recent results of experiments on delayed coincidences, referred to previously[12,13], such results must, for the present, be accepted with great reserve. We must expect the liberation of an amount of energy of magnitude 100 MeV. in any nucleus to lead to the ejection of several particles, some of which may be neutrons. There is therefore no firm basis for assuming that the disintegration represented in Fig. 4 corresponds to the disintegration of a nucleus of nitrogen rather than one of silver or bromine. Indeed, the delayed coincidence experiments suggest that the second assumption is the more probable. When a sufficient number of observations with loaded plates has been accumulated, it may be possible to draw more definite conclusions from observed regularities in the modes of disintegration of particular types of nuclei.

图 3 所示的衰变可能是高能粒子在高层大气中一类具有代表性的常见过程。在当前的例子中，初级粒子的能量至少已达到 200 兆电子伏，如果其质量小于或等于质子的质量，将不会在乳胶中被记录到。

介子导致的嬗变

基于对嬗变中释放的总能量的观测，通过对带电介子导致的核嬗变的观测，我们提出了测定这些粒子质量的方法[1,2]。尝试采用这个方法时，在鉴别嬗变核的种类和考虑不能被乳胶记录的发射中子问题上我们遇到了困难。图 4 所示的这类嬗变的一张照片初看起来似乎允许我们做出确定的结论。在照片中，我们可以分辨出四个重粒子的径迹，其中的短径迹 α_1、α_2 和 α_3 终止于乳胶中；α_1 和 α_2 无疑是由 α 粒子产生的，颗粒计数表明，α_3 是由质子产生的。因此，观测与以下方程一致

$$N_7^{14}+\mu_{-1}^0 \rightarrow 2He_2^4+H_1^1+H_1^1+4n_0^1 \tag{4}$$

或者与发射若干短程粒子加上一个氘核或氚核的类似方程一致，但是后者的可能性较小。

穿透乳胶的长程粒子径迹 d 的颗粒计数表明，如果它是由质子产生的，那么粒子的初始能量约为 15 兆电子伏。如果粒子是氘，那么其能量为 30 兆电子伏；或者，如果是氚核，则能量为 45 兆电子伏。无论如何，在嬗变中如果动量守恒，我们可以确定来自发射的中子的最小能量。结果，我们发现初级介子质量的最小值为 240 m_e。颗粒计数测定的值也是 240±50 m_e。

鉴于最近的关于延迟符合的实验结果，并参考以前的结果[12,13]，目前而言，必须以相当保留的态度采纳上述结论。我们可以预测，在任何核中释放出 100 兆电子伏量级的能量将导致若干个粒子的发射，其中有些可能是中子。因此，认为图 4 中所示的衰变是氮核嬗变而不是银或溴的嬗变的假设并没有牢固的依据。实际上，延迟符合的实验表明第二种假设具有更大的可能性。当用乳胶片积累足够数量的观测时，可能会从各类核嬗变中观测到的规律中得出更明确的结论。

A detailed account of the experiments will be published elsewhere.

(**159**, 694-697; 1947)

C. M. G. Lattes, H. Muirhead, G. P. S. Occhialini and C. F. Powell: H. H. Wills Physical Laboratory, University of Bristol.

References:

1. Perkins, D. H., *Nature*, **159**, 126 (1947).
2. Occhialini and Powell, *Nature*, **159**, 186 (1947).
3. Bose and Choudhuri, *Nature*, **148**, 259 (1941); **149**, 302 (1942).
4. Lattes, Fowler and Cuer, *Nature*, **159**, 301 (1947).
5. Hughes, *Phys. Rev.*, **69**, 371 (1946).
6. Leprince-Ringuet and L'Héritier, *J. Phys. et Rad.*, 7, 65 (1946).
7. Bethe, *Phys. Rev.*, **70**, 821 (1947).
8. Schwinger, *Phys. Rev.*, **61**, 387 (1942).
9. Wentzel, *Rev. Mod. Phys.*, **19**, 4 (1947).
10. Fermi, Teller and Weisskopf, *Phys. Rev.*, **71**, 314 (1947).
11. Wheeler, *Phys. Rev.*, **71**, 320 (1947).
12. Conversi, Pancini and Piccioni, *Phys. Rev.*, **71**, 209 (1947).
13. Sigurgeirsson and Yamakawa, *Phys. Rev.*, **71**, 319 (1947).
14. Zhdanov, *Akad. Nauk. Odtel. Bull. Ser. Phys.*, **3**, 734 (1938); **4**, 272 (1939). *C.R.* (*U.S.S.R.*), **28**, 110 (1940).
15. Rochester, Butler and Runcorn, *Nature*, **159**, 227 (1947).

实验的详细情况即将在别处发表。

（沈乃澂 翻译；朱永生 审稿）

Jaw of the Male Sterkfontein Ape-Man

R. Broom and J. T. Robinson

Editor's Note

Our extinct australopithecine cousins are known to have shown marked sexual dimorphism, with the males larger than the females. This was first shown with the discovery of a mandible (lower jaw) of a male *Plesianthropus* (now *Australopithecus*) at Sterkfontein in the Transvaal, to supplement the jaw of a female discovered earlier at the same site. The authors were impressed by how human the jaw looked, with signs of a chin, and few of the ape-like features they had expected. Their natural comparison was the Mauer mandible, the type specimen of the near-human Heidelberg Man (now *Homo heidelbergensis*). We now believe that all such signs of humanity were convergent, and probably not signs of direct descent from these australopithecines.

ON June 24, we blasted out at Sterkfontein, at a spot only about 8 ft. away from where we discovered the old female skull of *Plesianthropus*, the almost perfect lower jaw of a large male. The left mandible is complete except for the loss of the condyle and a little part of the margin of the angle. The whole symphysial region appears to be complete, while the right ramus is much broken and crushed. All the teeth of the left side are present, though worn.

The horizontal ramus is considerably larger than that of man but essentially similar. The ascending ramus is higher than in man, but otherwise not unlike that of the human jaw.

The front of the jaw is remarkably interesting. It does not slope rapidly backwards as in the living anthropoids but more downwards than backwards, giving an appearance not unlike that of the Heidelberg jaw. The front of the Sterkfontein jaw is narrower owing to the incisors being smaller. The symphysis, so far as can yet be seen, seems to agree fairly well with that of the Heidelberg jaw, and there appears to be no simian shelf.

The molars and premolars are much larger than in the Heidelberg jaw, and the canine very much larger. The molars and premolars are much worn. In the case of the lst and 2nd molars, the whole outer sides of the crowns are worn off; but on the inner side parts of the enamel cusps still remain.

The canine is the most interesting tooth of the jaw. We know the unworn lower canine crown in the male *Plesianthropus*. It is much larger than in man and has a well-developed

斯泰克方丹男性猿人的颌骨

布鲁姆，鲁滨逊

编者按

已经灭绝的人类近亲南方古猿亚科具有明显的两性异形，即男性个体大于女性。这一现象最早发现于南非德兰士瓦的斯泰克方丹，在此发现了一件男性迩人（现称南方古猿）的下颌骨，与先前在同一地点发现的女性颌骨的形态特征明显不同。通过与最接近现代人的海德堡人（人属海德堡种）的典型标本——毛尔下颌骨的比较，作者惊奇地发现，这件下颌骨的形态与人类的非常类似，已有下巴雏形的迹象，几乎没有类似猿类颌骨的特征。我们现在相信，人类的这些特征具有趋同性，现代人类所具有的特征可能并不是从南方古猿亚科直接演化而来的。

6 月 24 日，我们炸开了位于斯泰克方丹的一处地点，这里距离我们先前发现那具老年女性迩人头骨的地方只有大概 8 英尺远，在这里我们发现了一件近乎完美的男性的下颌骨。此下颌骨的左侧基本完整，只缺失了髁突和下颌角边缘的一小部分。左右颌骨联合部看起来很完整，而右侧下颌支大部分已断裂并被压碎了。左侧的牙齿虽然有些磨损，但是全部保存了下来。

颌骨的水平支比人类的大很多，但是基本上与人类相似。上升支比人类的要高，但也与人类颌骨有着相似之处。

该颌骨的前部非常有趣，它并不像现存的类人猿的颌骨前部那样迅速向后倾斜，相比之下其向下倾斜的角度更大，这与海德堡下颌骨的外观有些类似。斯泰克方丹颌骨由于门齿比较小，前部显得比较窄。就我们目前所能看到的，其联合部与海德堡下颌骨颇有几分相似，已经看不出猿的框架了。

臼齿和前臼齿比海德堡下颌骨的大得多，犬齿也更大一些。臼齿和前臼齿磨损严重。虽然第一臼齿和第二臼齿的整个齿冠的表面都被磨损掉了，但是内侧齿尖的部分珐琅质还可见。

整个颌骨中最有趣的牙齿就是犬齿了。我们都知道男性迩人未被磨损的下犬齿齿冠比现代人类的大很多，并且具有一个发达、尖锐的主齿尖，以及一个小的后齿

and pointed main cusp and a small posterior cusp. In the female the upper canine we knew was worn down as in man, but in the male it was suspected that the lower canine passed in front of the upper as in the anthropoid apes. Now we find that the lower canine, while it may in the young animal pass up in front of the upper, is ground down, as age advances, by attrition with the upper, exactly as in man. The whole jaw is thus practically a human jaw.

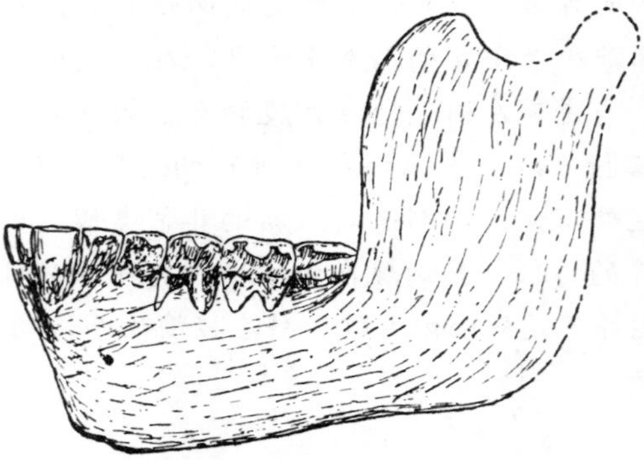

True side view of mandible of male *Plesianthropus transvaalensis* (Broom). $\frac{1}{2}$ natural size. The molars are badly worn along their outer sides. The canine has its crown ground down quite flat and in line with the other teeth. Parts of the outer sides of the premolars are in the counter slab and will later be replaced

This jaw is much too large to have fitted the elderly female skull recently discovered; and the skull that belonged to this jaw must have been remarkably large. If a restoration of the skull is made from the known female skull, but large enough to have fitted this jaw, it is seen that we have a skull that is nearly human.

The brain of the female skull was only about 450 c.c., but the male skull that belonged to this jaw must have had a brain of 600 c.c., or perhaps even 700 c.c.

Another interesting point is that on the lower part of the front of the jaw there is a little bony thickening which might be regarded as an incipient chin.

This jaw seems to us to be of considerable importance on the question of man's origin.

(**160**, 153; 1947)

R. Broom and J. T. Robinson: Transvaal Museum, Pretoria, South Africa, July 3.

尖。而女性的上犬齿和男性的一样受到了磨损，但是有人怀疑男性的下犬齿像类人猿的一样长到上犬齿的前方。现在我们发现，正如人类一样，年轻动物随着年龄的增长，下犬齿可能向上生长至上犬齿的前方，由于上犬齿的磨擦，下犬齿便被碾磨掉了。因此整个颌骨实际上就是一个人类的颌骨。

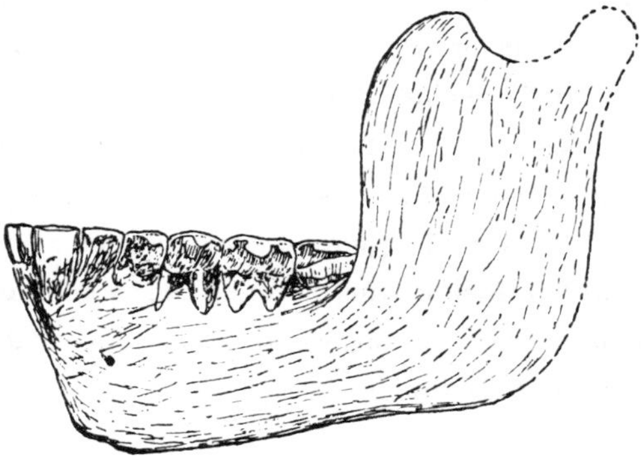

德兰士瓦迩人男性下颌骨侧面观（布鲁姆）。该图是真实尺寸的 $\frac{1}{2}$。臼齿颊侧面磨损严重。犬齿的齿冠被碾磨得很平整，与其他牙齿相平。前臼齿颊侧面部分位于相对面上，并且不久将会被替换。

由于这件颌骨太大，因此与最近发现的老年女性头骨无法匹配在一起；这一颌骨所属的头骨一定很大。如果根据已知的女性头骨的尺寸对该头骨进行复原，并使其足够大以匹配这个颌骨的话，那么我们就会得到一个接近现代人的头骨。

女性头骨的脑量只有 450 毫升左右，估计这具颌骨所属的男性头骨的脑量可达到 600 毫升，甚至 700 毫升。

另一个有趣的发现是，颌骨前方的下部有一点骨质增厚，被认为可能是下巴的雏形。

这个颌骨对我们研究人类起源问题可能具有相当重要的意义。

（刘皓芳 田晓阳 翻译；吴秀杰 审稿）

A Floating Magnet

V. Arkadiev

Editor's Note

Russian physicist V. Arkadiev here reports his observation of a levitation phenomenon achieved with the aid of a superconductor. He notes that a diamagnetic substance (in essence, a conventionally "non-magnetic" one) pulled toward a magnetic surface by gravity can hover over it. For example, a linear magnet one centimetre long could hover about one centimetre above a copper sphere some 20 metres in diameter. To prevent a magnet falling onto a diamagnetic sphere the size of the Earth, however, requires a superconductor beneath the magnet. Arkadiev demonstrates the effect with a small magnet hovering over a concave lead disk held over liquid helium. Today, with liquid nitrogen and high-temperature superconductors, Arkadiev's levitation is a common trick in the physics classroom.

BY assuming that diamagnetic bodies are pushed out of a magnetic field, it may be shown that a diamagnetic particle attracted to a magnet by gravitational forces will take up a position in space in the equatorial plane of the straight magnet at a certain distance from the latter. The "satellite" can vibrate elastically about the point of equilibrium, describing a certain curve. The period of vibration in the radial and meridional directions is close to the period of the Kepler rotation of a magnetically indifferent satellite about a body of the same mass. Several identical particles arrange themselves around the magnet. Such a combination of bodies is in the nature of a static planetary system as distinct from the Kepler dynamic planetary system.

However, systems thus formed can only be of small dimensions. The orbit of the outermost bodies can be no larger than several metres, and in the case of small magnetized iron meteorites amounts to several millimetres.

Computation shows that in space a straight magnet keeps at a certain distance from a large diamagnetic body. Thus a magnet 1 cm. long will take up a position at a distance of 1 cm. from the surface of a copper sphere about 20 m. in diameter. Diameters of 300 m. and 3,000 m. respectively would be necessary for bismuth and carbon spheres. To prevent a magnet falling on to a diamagnetic sphere the size of the Earth, the sphere must consist of the strongest diamagnetic substance, or be a superconductor. In this case, however, it is sufficient that the superconductor is placed only under the magnet itself.

The approach of a magnet to the surface of a superconductive semispace is accompanied by the appearance of the magnetic image of this magnet within the superconductor. In the case of a common steel magnet, this may lead to demagnetization, while a ferro-nickel-

悬浮的磁体

阿卡迪耶夫

编者按

俄罗斯物理学家阿卡迪耶夫在本文中报道了他借助超导体对悬浮现象所做的观察。他注意到，在重力的作用下被拉向磁体表面的抗磁物质（其实就是传统的“非磁性”物质）可以停留在其上方。譬如说，一个1厘米长的条状磁体可以飘浮在直径约为20米的铜球上方约1厘米处。然而，为了避免磁体落到具有地球尺寸大小的抗磁性球体上，需要在磁体下方放置一个超导体。阿卡迪耶夫通过一个在置于液氦中的凹面铅盘上方悬浮的小磁体来演示上述效应。如今，利用液氮和高温超导体技术，阿卡迪耶夫悬浮已成为物理课堂中一个常用的演示。

假设磁场排斥抗磁体，我们也许可以看到，当抗磁粒子因为重力作用而落向磁体时，其将会处于条形磁体中心面所在空间的某个位置上，与条形磁体相距一定距离。通常这个“卫星”可以围绕平衡点作弹性振动，得到某一曲线轨迹。而径向和经向的振动周期接近于与磁性无关的卫星围绕具有相同质量的物体作开普勒转动的周期。若有几个这样的粒子则会围绕磁体取一定的排列。这种物体的组合在性质上是静态行星系，与开普勒动力学的行星系有所不同。

然而，由此形成的系统只能是小尺寸的。最远物体的轨道可能不会大于几米，对于小块磁化了的铁陨石，其量级仅为几毫米。

计算表明，条形磁体与大块抗磁体间可在空间中保持一定的距离。因此1厘米长的磁体将与直径约为20米的铜球表面保持1厘米的距离。而对铋球和碳球而言，则其直径分别需要达到300米和3,000米才能实现上述距离。为了防止磁体落到具有地球尺寸大小的抗磁球体上，该球体必须由最强的抗磁物质组成，或是一个超导体。然而，在这种情况下，只要在磁体下方放置一个超导体就能实现上述情况。

磁体靠近超导半空间表面时在超导体内部产生该磁体的映像。对一个普通的钢磁体而言，这将导致退磁；而对一个含有铁–镍–铝的钢磁体，在这种力的作用下将被排斥在超导半空间的水平面以外，即使没有支撑物也能悬浮（“漂浮”）在该水平

aluminium steel magnet will be repelled from the horizontal surface of the semispace with such force that it will hang suspended ("float") over the latter without any support. Thus one of the cases of a static planetary system may be reproduced in the laboratory. The Earth, screened by a superconductor in the neighbourhood of a magnet, repels the latter with the same force as it is attracted owing to universal gravitation. The accompanying photograph shows a magnet, 4 mm. × 4 mm. × 10 mm. in dimensions, floating above a concave lead disk 40 mm. in diameter in a Dewar vessel over liquid helium.

The experimental test of these views was possible through the kindness of Prof. P. L. Kapitza, in the Institute of Physical Problems, Moscow.

The lower the coercive force of the magnet, the smaller the magnet itself must be. Carbon steel magnets, for example, can "float" when they have the dimensions of 0.5 mm. × 9 mm. By scattering microscopically small magnets over the surface of a body, it is possible to reveal superconductive inclusions directly, since the magnetic particles will roll to the spots where there is no superconductivity.

(**160**, 330; 1947)

V. Arkadiev: Maxwell Laboratory, Physical Department, University, Moscow, March 25.

面上方。因此，一种静态行星系中的情况可能在实验室中重现。但被与磁体相邻的超导体所屏蔽的地球，将以与万有引力相同大小的力把磁体推开。附图的照片展示了尺寸为 4 毫米 × 4 毫米 × 10 毫米的磁体，悬浮在充有液氦的杜瓦瓶内直径为 40 毫米的凹面铅盘的上方。

在莫斯科物理问题研究所卡皮查教授的热心帮助下，检验这些观点的实验才得以顺利开展。

磁体的抗磁力越低，则磁体本身必然越小。例如，碳钢磁体在其尺寸小至 0.5 毫米 × 9 毫米时才可能“浮起”。将微观尺度中的小磁体散在物体表面上，就有可能直接揭示出超导杂质的存在，因为磁性粒子将会滚到没有超导电性的地方。

（沈乃澂 翻译；赵见高 审稿）

Observations on the Tracks of Slow Mesons in Photographic Emulsions*

C. M. G. Lattes *et al.*

Editor's Note

Physicists in the late 1940s had adopted the term "meson" to refer to any particle having mass between that of an electron and a proton. Here the Brazilian physicist Cesar Lattes and colleagues reported on their observations of several hundred meson-like particles detected in photographic plates exposed at high altitudes, and presumably having origins as cosmic rays. Their observations led them to suggest that some of the initial mesons, when striking the photographic emulsions, created secondary mesons of a new kind. It soon became clear that this new particle—the pion—takes part in nuclear interactions. It was initially predicted to mediate such interactions by Hideki Yukawa in 1935, a prediction for which he won the Nobel Prize in 1949.

INTRODUCTION. In recent experiments, it has been shown that charged mesons, brought to rest in photographic emulsions, sometimes lead to the production of secondary mesons. We have now extended these observations by examining plates exposed in the Bolivian Andes at a height of 5,500 m., and have found, in all, forty examples of the process leading to the production of secondary mesons. In eleven of these, the secondary particle is brought to rest in the emulsion so that its range can be determined. In Part 1 of this article, the measurements made on these tracks are described, and it is shown that they provide evidence for the existence of mesons of different mass; In Part 2, we present further evidence on the production of mesons, which allows us to show that many of the observed mesons are locally generated in the "explosive" disintegration of nuclei, and to discuss the relationship of the different types of mesons observed in photographic plates to the penetrating component of the cosmic radiation investigated in experiments with Wilson chambers and counters.

Part 1. Existence of Mesons of Different Mass

As in the previous communications[1], we refer to any particle with a mass intermediate between that of a proton and an electron as a meson. It may be emphasized that, in

* This article contains a summary of the main features of a number of lectures given, one at Manchester on June 18 and four at the Conference on Cosmic Rays and Nuclear Physics, organised by Prof. W. Heitler, at the Dublin Institute of Advanced Studies, July 5-12. A complete account of the observations, and of the conclusions which follow from them, will be published elsewhere.

感光乳胶中慢介子径迹的观测*

拉特斯等

编者按

20 世纪 40 年代后期，物理学家采用“介子”来称谓所有质量介于电子和质子间的粒子。在这篇论文中，巴西物理学家塞萨尔·拉特斯和他的同事们报道了在高海拔处受照射的照片中探测到几百个类介子粒子的观测结果，并推测其源自宇宙射线。根据上述观测结果，他们提出，初级介子进入感光乳胶时，有一部分产生了一种新的次级介子。不久他们就弄清楚了这种新粒子（即 π 介子）参与了核相互作用。早在 1935 年汤川秀树首先预言了 π 介子是核作用的媒介，由此他获得了 1949 年的诺贝尔奖。

引言　最近实验显示，终止于感光乳胶中的带电介子有时会导致次级介子的产生。我们现已通过检查置于玻利维亚安第斯山脉海拔 5,500 米处的受照射的底片来延伸这些观测，现已发现共计有 40 个导致次级介子产生的事例。其中 11 个事例的次级粒子终止于乳胶中，因此其射程是可以确定的。本文的第一部分描述了对这些粒子径迹的测量，同时也证明了不同质量介子的存在。第二部分中（编者注：本书未收录第二部分），我们进一步证明了介子的产生，这使得我们可以得出，许多可观测到的介子是以“爆炸”式的核嬗变在局部区域产生的，同时也使我们可以对威尔逊云室和计数器实验中研究的宇宙射线的穿透成分与受照的感光底片中观测到的不同类型介子之间的关系进行探讨。

第一部分. 不同质量介子的存在

如之前的报道 [1] 所述，我们把所有质量介于电子与质子之间的粒子称为介子。在这里需要强调的是，使用这个术语并不意味着我们认为相应的粒子必然与核子有

* 这篇论文包含一些已做的演讲主要内容的总结，其中一篇是 6 月 18 日在曼彻斯特发表的，还有 4 篇是于 7 月 5 日～12 日在都柏林高等研究所由海特勒教授组织的宇宙射线和核物理会议上发表的。关于这些观测及由此导出的结论的完整描述将在别处发表。

using this term, we do not imply that the corresponding particle necessarily has a strong interaction with nucleons, or that it is closely associated with the forces responsible for the cohesion of nuclei.

We have now observed a total of 644 meson tracks which end in the emulsion of our plates. 451 of these were found, in plates of various types, exposed at an altitude of 2,800 m. at the Observatory of the Pic du Midi, in the Pyrenees; and 193 in similar plates exposed at 5,500 m. at Chacaltaya in the Bolivian Andes. The 451 tracks in the plates exposed at an altitude of 2,800 m. were observed in the examination of 5 c.c. emulsion. This corresponds to the arrival of about 1.5 mesons per c.c. per day, a figure which represents a lower limit, for the tracks of some mesons may be lost through fading, and through failure to observe tracks of very short range. The true number will thus be somewhat higher. In any event, the value is of the same order of magnitude as that we should expect to observe in delayed coincidence experiments at a height of 2,800 m., basing our estimates on the observations obtained in similar experiments at sea-level, and making reasonable assumptions about the increase in the number of slow mesons with altitude. It is therefore certain that the mesons we observe are a common constituent of the cosmic radiation.

Photomicrographs of two of the new examples of secondary mesons, Nos. III and IV, are shown in Figs. 1 and 2. Table 1 gives details of the characteristics of all events of this type observed up to the time of writing, in which the secondary particle comes to the end of its range in the emulsion.

Table 1

Event No.	Range in emulsion in microns of Primary meson	Range in emulsion in microns of Secondary meson
I	133	613
II	84	565
III	1,040	621
IV	133	591
V	117	638
VI	49	595
VII	460	616
VIII	900	610
IX	239	666
X	256	637
XI	81	590

Mean range 614±8μ. Straggling coefficient $\sqrt{\Sigma \Delta i^2 / n}$ = 4.3 percent, where $\Delta_i = R_i - \overline{R}$, R_i being the range of a secondary meson, and $\overline{R}$ the mean value for n particles of this type.

强相互作用，或是与核的凝聚力密切相关。

我们现已观测到终止于底片乳胶中的介子径迹总共为 644 条，其中 451 条发现于比利牛斯山脉的米迪山峰海拔 2,800 米处天文台受照射的不同类型的底片中；另外 193 条发现于玻利维亚安第斯山脉恰卡尔塔亚山海拔 5,500 米处受照射的类似底片中。海拔 2,800 米处受照底片中的 451 条径迹是在 5 厘米^3 的乳胶检测中观测到的，这相当于每天每立方厘米乳胶中到达约 1.5 个介子。该数据是一个下限，因为某些介子的径迹可能由于潜影衰退和射程极短难以观测而丢失。因此，真正的数值将会比该数值要稍高一些。基于我们在海平面上类似实验观测的估计，以及慢介子数目随着海拔上升而增大的合理猜想，总是可以得出，这个数值与我们在 2,800 米高度延迟符合实验的观测中所预期的数值具有相同量级。因此可以确定，我们观测到的介子是宇宙射线的一般组分。

图 1 和图 2 分别是次级介子的两个新事例 III 和 IV 的显微照片。表 1 给出了直至本文执笔时观测到的所有这类事例的详细特性，其中次级粒子射程末端终止于乳胶中。

表 1

事例编号	初级介子在乳胶中的射程	次级介子在乳胶中的射程
I	133	613
II	84	565
III	1,040	621
IV	133	591
V	117	638
VI	49	595
VII	460	616
VIII	900	610
IX	239	666
X	256	637
XI	81	590

平均射程：614 ± 8 微米。离散系数：$\sqrt{\Sigma \Delta i^2 / n} = 4.3\%$，式中，$\Delta_i = R_i - \bar{R}$，$R_i$ 是次级介子的射程，$\bar{R}$ 是 n 个这类粒子的射程平均值。

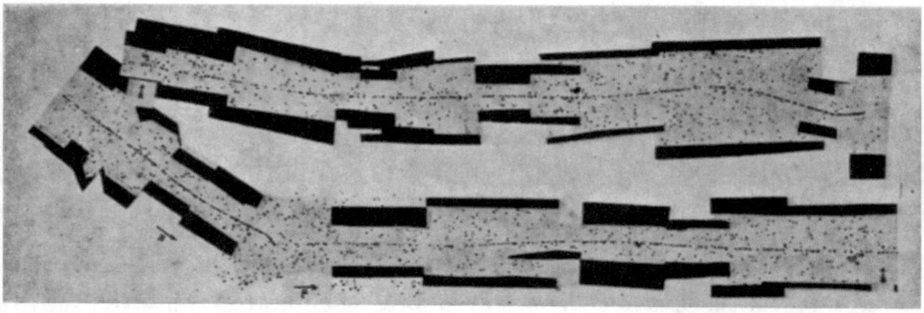

Fig. 1. Observation by Mrs. I. Powell. Cooke × 95 achromatic objective; *C*2 Ilford Nuclear Research emulsion loaded with boron. The track of the μ-meson is given in two parts, the point of junction being indicated by *a* and an arrow

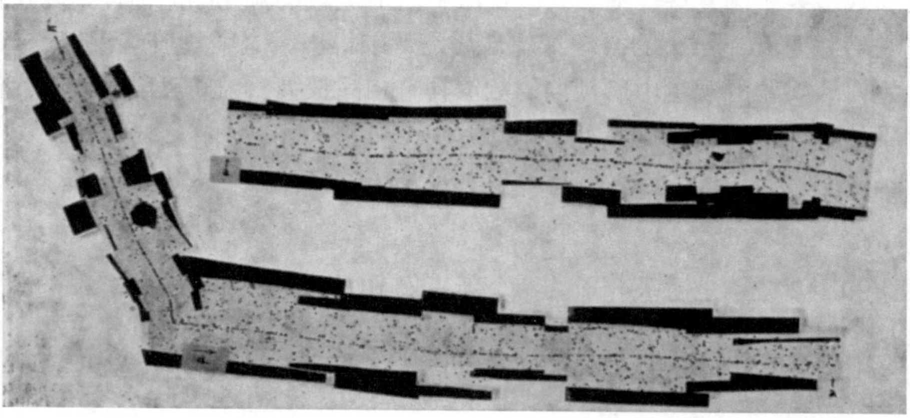

Fig. 2. Cooke × 95 achromatic objective. *C*2 Ilford Nuclear Research emulsion loaded with boron

The distribution in range of the secondary particles is shown in Fig. 3. The values refer to the lengths of the projections of the actual trajectories of the particles on a plane parallel to the surface of the emulsion. The true ranges cannot, however, be very different from the values given, for each track is inclined at only a small angle to the plane of the emulsion over the greater part of its length. In addition to the results for the secondary mesons which stop in the emulsion, and which are represented in Fig. 3 by black squares, the length of a number of tracks from the same process, which pass out of the emulsion when near the end of their range, are represented by open squares.

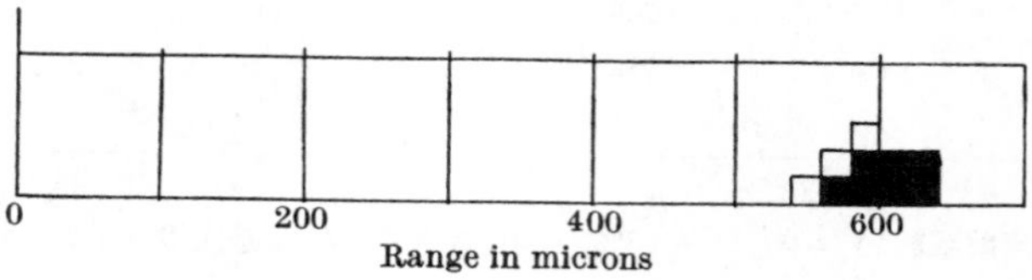

Fig. 3. Distribution in range of ten secondary mesons. Those marked ■ stop in the emulsion; the three marked □ leave the emulsion when near the end of their range. Mean range of secondary mesons, 606 microns. The results for events Nos. VIII to XI are not included in the figure

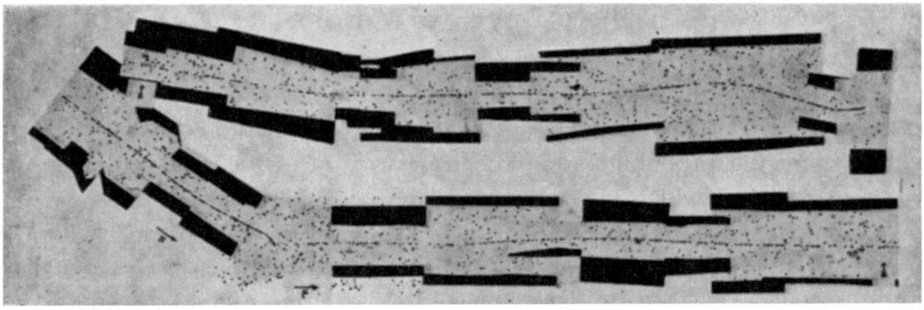

图 1. 由鲍威尔夫人观测。库克 95 倍消色差物镜；C2 伊尔福载硼核乳胶。μ 介子（编者注：现在粒子物理认为“μ 介子”不是介子，而是一种轻子，因此正确的称谓应为“μ 子”。考虑到历史原因，文中仍保留“μ 介子”的译法）的径迹由两部分给出，连接点用 *a* 和箭头表示。

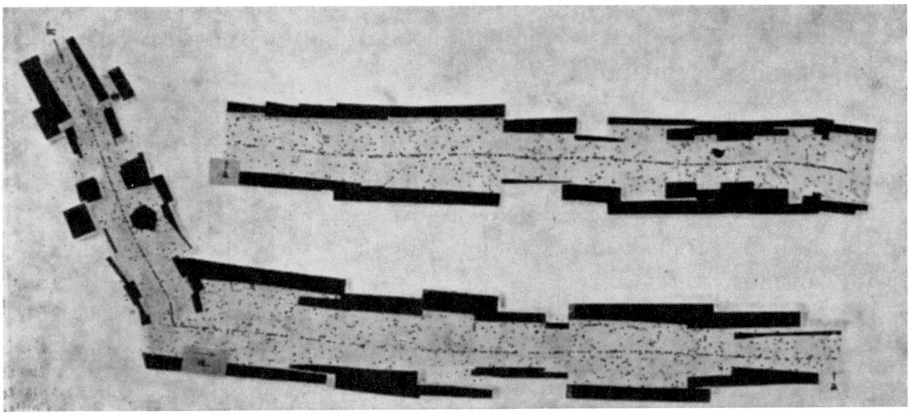

图 2. 库克 95 倍消色差物镜。C2 伊尔福载硼核乳胶。

图 3 是次级粒子射程的分布，这些值指的是粒子实际径迹在平行于乳胶表面的平面上的投影长度。不过真实的射程不会与给出的数值有很大的差异，因为每个径迹在大部分长度中相对于乳胶平面只倾斜很小的角度。图 3 中除了用黑方块表示出终止于乳胶中的次级粒子的结果之外，还用白方块表示出产生于相同过程的、于射程末端附近穿出乳胶的一些径迹的长度。

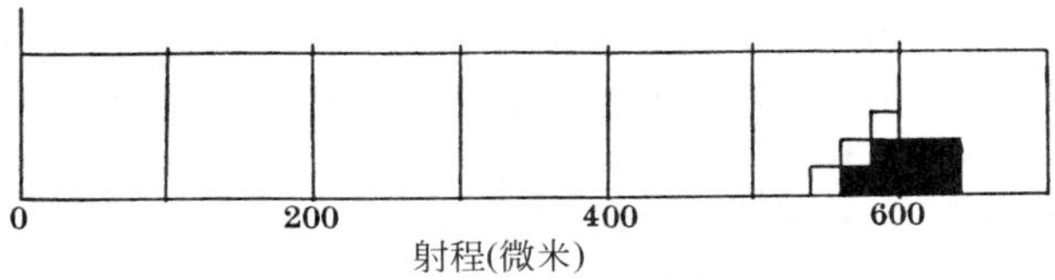

图 3. 10 个次级介子的射程分布。■表示 7 个次级介子在乳胶中停止；3 个□表示 3 个次级介子在接近射程末端时离开乳胶。次级介子的平均射程为 606 微米。事例 VIII~XI 的结果未包含在本图内。

The μ-Decay of Mesons

Two important conclusions follow from these measurements. Our observations show that the directions of ejection of the secondary mesons are orientated at random. We can therefore calculate the probability that the trajectory of a secondary meson, produced in a process of the type which we observe, will remain within the emulsion, of thickness 50 μ, for a distance greater than 500 μ. If we assume, as a first approximation, that the trajectories are rectilinear, we obtain a value for the probability of 1 in 20. The marked Coulomb scattering of mesons in the Nuclear Research emulsions will, in fact, increase the probability of "escape". The six events which we observe in plates exposed at 2,800 m., in which the secondary particle remains in the emulsion for a distance greater than 500 μ, therefore correspond to the occurrence in the emulsion of 120±50 events of this particular type. Our observations, therefore, prove that the production of a secondary meson is a common mode of decay of a considerable fraction of those mesons which come to the end of their range in the emulsion.

Second, there is remarkable consistency between the values of the range of the secondary mesons, the variation among the individual values being similar to that to be expected from "straggling", if the particles are always ejected with the same velocity. We can therefore conclude that the secondary mesons are all of the same mass and that they are emitted with constant kinetic energy.

If mesons of lower range are sometimes emitted in an alternative type of process, they must occur much less frequently than those which we have observed; for the geometrical conditions, and the greater average grain-density in the tracks, would provide much more favourable conditions for their detection. In fact, we have found no such mesons of shorter range. We cannot, however, be certain that mesons of greater range are not sometimes produced. Both the lower ionization in the beginning of the trajectory, and the even more unfavourable conditions of detection associated with the greater lengths of the tracks, would make such a group, or groups, difficult to observe. Because of the large fraction of the mesons which, as we have seen, can be attributed to the observed process, it is reasonable to assume that alternative modes of decay, if they exist, are much less frequent than that which we have observed. There is, therefore, good evidence for the production of a single homogeneous group of secondary mesons, constant in mass and kinetic energy. This strongly suggests a fundamental process, and not one involving an interaction of a primary meson with a particular type of nucleus in the emulsion. It is convenient to refer to this process in what follows as the μ-decay. We represent the primary mesons by the symbol π, and the secondary by μ. Up to the present, we have no evidence from which to deduce the sign of the electric charge of these particles. In every case in which they have been observed to come to the end of their range in the emulsion, the particles appear to stop without entering nuclei to produce disintegrations with the emission of heavy particles.

Knowing the range-energy relation for protons in the emulsion, the energy of ejection

介子的 μ 衰变

从以上测量中得到了两个重要的结论。我们的观测表明，次级介子的发射方向是随机的。因此，我们可以计算出我们所观测的那类过程中产生的次级介子径迹停留在厚度为 50 微米乳胶内且射程大于 500 微米的概率。作为一个初步近似，如果我们假定径迹是直线，则我们得出的概率为 1/20。实际上，核乳胶中介子的显著的库仑散射将增加“逃逸”的概率。我们在海拔 2,800 米处受照底片中观测到的 6 个事例中的次级粒子在乳胶中的射程大于 500 微米，因而这 6 个事例相当于乳胶中出现 120±50 个这类特殊形式的事例。因此我们的观测证明，对于射程终止于乳胶内的介子，相当大一部分的衰变模式通常是产生次级介子。

其次，次级介子射程值之间存在显著的一致性，如果粒子总以相同的速度发射，各个数值之间的变化类似于“离散”预期的值。因此我们可以得出，次级介子是质量相同的粒子，它们会以恒定的动能发射。

如果较短射程的介子偶尔以另一种类型的方式发射，它们出现的频率必定比我们观测到的要低得多；因为几何条件以及径迹中较大的平均颗粒密度将会为探测它们提供更为有利的条件。实际上，我们尚未发现这类较短程的介子。然而，我们不能肯定是否有时候会产生更长射程的介子。长程介子径迹开始处的电离能力较低，加之与长径迹相关的更不利的探测条件，这两个因素将使这一类或这些类长程介子难以观测。如我们所见，由于大部分介子产生于我们已观测到的过程，因此有理由假设，如果存在其他模式的衰变，其出现频率要远低于我们已观测到的过程。因此，有力的证据证明，只产生了质量和动能为常数的一类次级介子。这就强有力地提出了一个基本过程，但这个过程并不涉及初级粒子与乳胶中的特殊类型核的相互作用。为方便起见，这一过程在后面的陈述中被称为 μ 衰变。我们用 π 表示初级介子，μ 表示次级介子。至今，我们尚无可以推断出这些粒子的电荷符号的证据。在粒子射程末端终止于乳胶中的事例中，粒子停止时似乎并未进入核并产生发射重粒子的嬗变。

知道了乳胶中质子的射程–能量关系后，如果设定了粒子的某个质量值，次级介

of the secondary mesons can be deduced from their observed range, if a value of the mass of the particles is assumed. The values thus calculated for various masses are shown in Table 2.

Table 2

Mass in m_e	100	150	200	250	300
Energy in MeV.	3.0	3.6	4.1	4.5	4.85

No established range-energy relation is available for protons of energies above 13 MeV., and it has therefore been necessary to rely on an extrapolation of the relation established for low energies. We estimate that the energies given in Table 2 are correct to within 10 percent.

Evidence of a Difference in Mass of π- and μ-Mesons

It has been pointed out[1] that it is difficult to account for the μ-decay in terms of an interaction of the primary meson with the nucleus of an atom in the emulsion leading to the production of an energetic meson of the same mass as the first. It was therefore suggested that the observations indicate the existence of mesons of different mass. Since the argument in support of this view relied entirely on the principle of the conservation of energy, a search was made for processes which were capable of yielding the necessary release of energy, irrespective of their plausibility on other grounds. Dr. F. C. Frank has re-examined such possibilities in much more detail, and his conclusions are given in an article to follow. His analysis shows that it is very difficult to account for our observations, either in terms of a nuclear disintegration, or of a "building-up" process in which, through an assumed combination of a negative meson with a hydrogen nucleus, protons are enabled to enter stable nuclei of the light elements with the release of binding energy. We have now found it possible to reinforce this general argument for the existence of mesons of different mass with evidence based on grain-counts.

We have emphasized repeatedly[1] that it is necessary to observe great caution in drawing conclusions about the mass of particles from grain-counts. The main source of error in such determinations arises from the fugitive nature of the latent image produced in the silver halide granules by the passage of fast particles. In the case of the μ-decay process, however, an important simplification occurs. It is reasonable to assume that the two meson tracks are formed in quick succession, and are subject to the same degree of fading. Secondly, the complete double track in such an event is contained in a very small volume of the emulsion, and the processing conditions are therefore identical for both tracks, apart from the variation of the degree of development with depth. These features ensure that we are provided with very favourable conditions in which to determine the ratio of the masses of the π- and μ-mesons, in some of these events.

In determining the grain density in a track, we count the number of individual grains in successive intervals of length 50 μ along the trajectory, the observation being made with

子的发射能量便可以根据其观测到的射程导出。据此，表 2 列出了不同质量对应的介子能量的计算值。

表 2

质量 (m_e)	100	150	200	250	300
能量（兆电子伏）	3.0	3.6	4.1	4.5	4.85

对于能量大于 13 兆电子伏的质子尚未确立射程–能量关系，因此必须依靠已经确立的低能关系外推。我们估计，表 2 中给出的能量在 10% 以内是正确的。

π 介子和 μ 介子质量差的证据

我们已指出[1]，用初级介子与乳胶中原子核的相互作用导致一个与初级介子质量相同的高能介子的产生难以解释 μ 衰变。因此可以认为，已有的观测表明存在不同质量的介子。由于支持这个观点的论据完全依赖于能量守恒定律，因此无论它们在其他理论背景中的合理性如何，都对能够产生必要的能量释放的若干过程进行了探索。弗兰克博士更加仔细地重新检验了这种可能性，并在随后发表的一篇论文中给出了他的结论。他的分析指出，无论用核嬗变或用“聚集”过程都很难解释我们的观测，其中“聚集”过程是指，假设负介子能够与氢核结合，质子可以进入轻元素的稳定核内并释放结合能。我们现已发现，基于颗粒计数的证据，可能会巩固存在不同质量介子的总论点。

我们已反复强调[1]，由颗粒计数推出粒子质量的结论时，一定要十分地谨慎。这类测定中的误差主要来自于由快速粒子通过卤化银颗粒所产生的潜影的易变性。然而，在 μ 衰变过程的情况下，出现了重要的简化现象。我们可以合理地假设，两个介子的径迹是快速接连产生的，并遭到相同程度的潜像衰退。其次，在这类事例中完全的双径迹包含于很小的乳胶体积内，因此除了显影的程度在深度上的变化之外，两条径迹的处理条件是一样的。这些特点保证了我们是在非常有利的条件下，利用这一类事例来测定 π 介子和 μ 介子的质量比。

测定径迹的颗粒密度时，我们沿着径迹对每 50 微米长度间隔内的颗粒计数依次进行了统计，观测是用大放大倍数（×2,000）的光学装置，并达到了最高可能的分

optical equipment giving large magnification (×2,000), and the highest available resolving power. Typical results for protons and mesons are shown in Fig. 4. These results were obtained from observations on the tracks in a single plate, and it will be seen that there is satisfactory resolution between the curves for particles of different types. The "spread" in the results for different particles of the same type can be attributed to the different degrees of fading associated with the different times of passage of the particles through the emulsion during an exposure of six weeks.

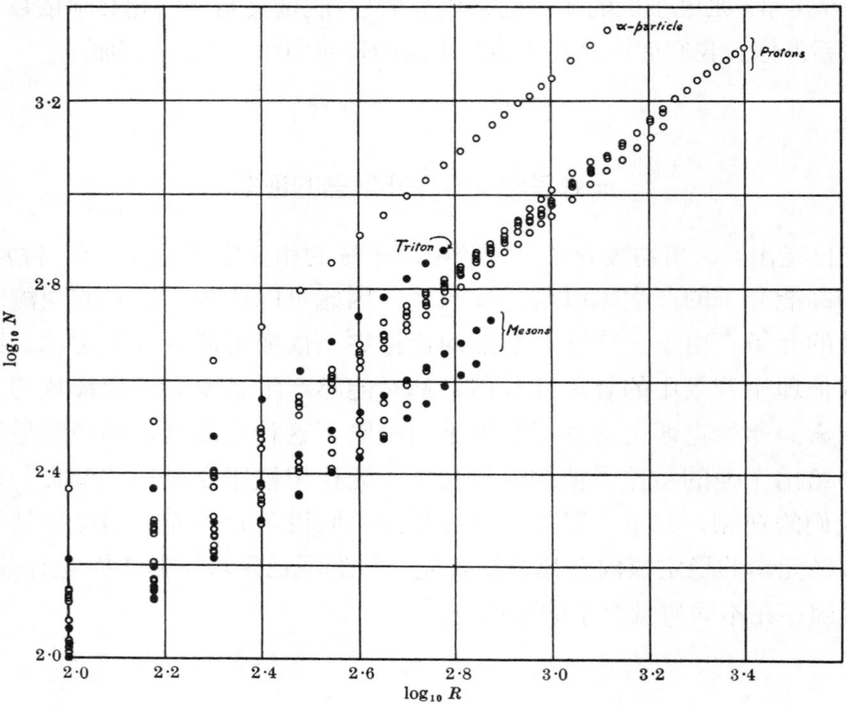

Fig. 4. N is total number of grains in track of residual range R (scale-divisions).
1 scale-division=0.85 microns

Applying these methods to the examples of the μ-decay process, in which the secondary mesons come to the end of their range in the emulsion, it is found that in every case the line representing the observations on the primary meson lies above that for the secondary particle. We can therefore conclude that there is a significant difference in the grain-density in the tracks of the primary and secondary mesons, and therefore a difference in the mass of the particles. This conclusion depends, of course, on the assumption that the π- and μ-particles carry equal charges. The grain-density at the ends of the tracks, of particles of both types, are consistent with the view that the charges are of magnitude $|e|$.

A more precise comparison of the masses of the π- and μ-mesons can only be made in those cases in which the length of the track of the primary meson in the emulsion is of the order of 600 μ. The probability of such a favourable event is rather small, and the

辨率。图 4 是质子和介子的典型结果。这些结果是从单张底片的径迹观测中获得的，我们看到在不同类型的粒子曲线间得到了满意的分辨率。结果中相同类型的不同粒子的“发散”可归因于，在 6 周的受照期间内，与粒子穿过乳胶的时间相关的不同程度的潜影衰退。

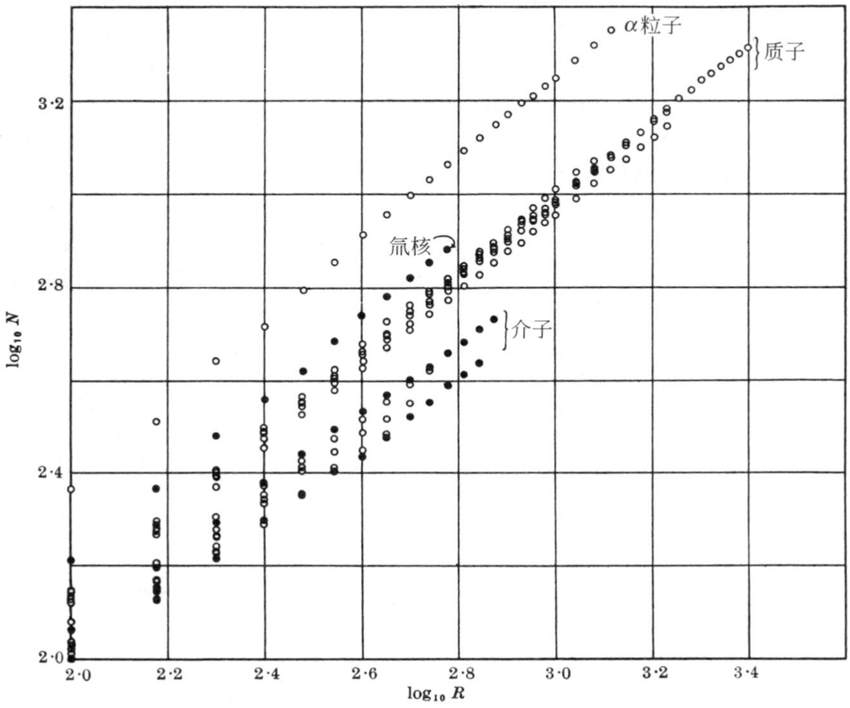

图 4. N 是剩余射程 R 径迹中的颗粒总数（标尺分度）。
1 标尺分度 = 0.85 微米

将这些方法应用于那些次级介子射程末端终止于乳胶内的 μ 衰变过程，我们发现，在所有这些事例中表示初级介子观测的线位于次级粒子之上。因此我们可以认为，初级介子与次级介子径迹中的颗粒密度存在显著差异，从而可知它们的质量也是不同的。当然，这个结论依赖于 π 介子和 μ 介子带有相等电荷的假定。两类粒子在径迹末端的颗粒密度与电荷量为 $|e|$ 的观点是一致的。

对 μ 介子和 π 介子质量更精密的比较只能在下述情况下进行，即乳胶中初级介子的径迹长度为 600 微米量级的情况。这样理想的事例的出现概率是很小的，表 1

only examples we have hitherto observed are those listed as Nos. III and VIII in Table 1. A mosaic of micrographs of a part only of the first of these events is reproduced in Fig. 1, for the length of the track of the μ-meson in the emulsion exceeds 1,000 μ. The logarithms of the numbers of grains in the tracks of the primary and secondary mesons in this event are plotted against the logarithm of the residual range in Fig. 5. By comparing the residual ranges at which the grain-densities in the two tracks have the same value, we can deduce the ratio of the masses. We thus obtain the result $m_\pi/m_\mu=2.0$. Similar measurements on event No. VIII give the value 1.8. In considering the significance which can be attached to this result, it must be noticed that in addition to the standard deviations in the number of grains counted, there are other possible sources of error. Difficulties arise, for example, from the fact that the emulsions do not consist of a completely uniform distribution of silver halide grains. "Islands" exist, in which the concentration of grains is significantly higher, or significantly lower, than the average values, the variations being much greater than those associated with random fluctuations. The measurements on the other examples of μ-decay are much less reliable on account of the restricted range of the π-mesons in the emulsion; but they give results lower than the above values. We think it unlikely, however, that the true ratio is as low as 1.5.

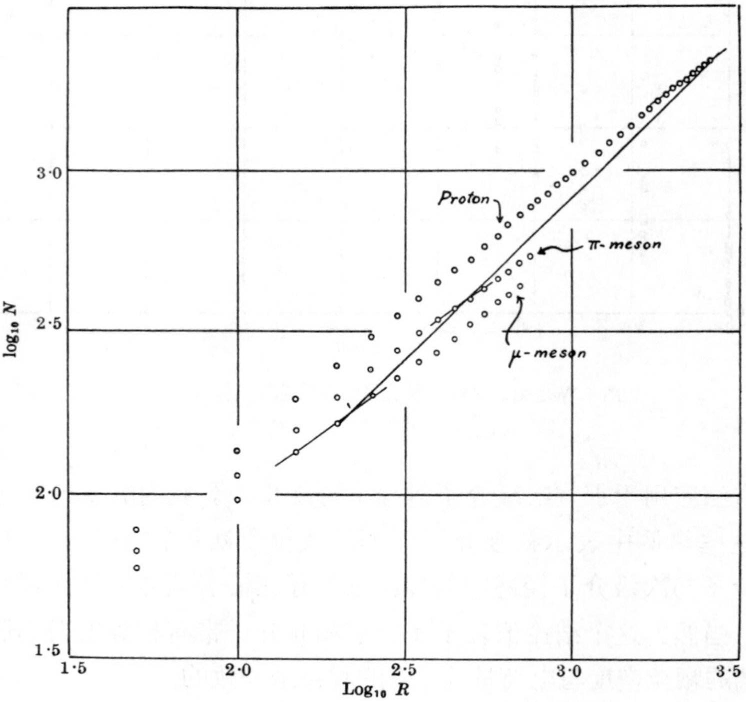

Fig. 5. N is total number of grains in track of residual range R (scale-divisions). 1 scale-division=0.85 microns
The 45°-line cuts the curves of the mesons and proton in the region of the same grain density

The above result has an important bearing on the interpretation of the μ-decay process. Let us assume that it corresponds to the spontaneous decay of the heavier π-meson, in which the momentum of the μ-meson is equal and opposite to that of an emitted photon.

中的 III 和 VIII 列出了我们迄今为止观测到的仅有的例子。第一个这样事例的部分显微照片的图像重现于图 1，其中乳胶中的 μ 介子径迹长度超过 1,000 微米。图 5 是这一事例中初级和次级介子径迹颗粒数的对数与剩余射程的对数的关系图。通过比较在两个径迹中具有相同颗粒密度的剩余射程，我们可以导出质量比。据此，我们获得的结果为 $m_\pi/m_\mu = 2.0$。对事例 VIII 的类似测量给出的值为 1.8。在考虑这项结果的意义时必须注意到，除颗粒计数的标准偏差外，还存在其他可能的误差来源。例如，由于乳胶不是由完全均匀分布的卤化银颗粒构成而导致的误差。其中存在一些“岛屿”，其颗粒密度明显高于或低于平均值，其变化量比随机涨落要大得多。考虑到乳胶中 π 介子的有限射程，μ 衰变的其他事例的测量不太可靠；不过它们给出的结果低于上述数值。尽管如此，我们认为真正的比值不可能低到 1.5。

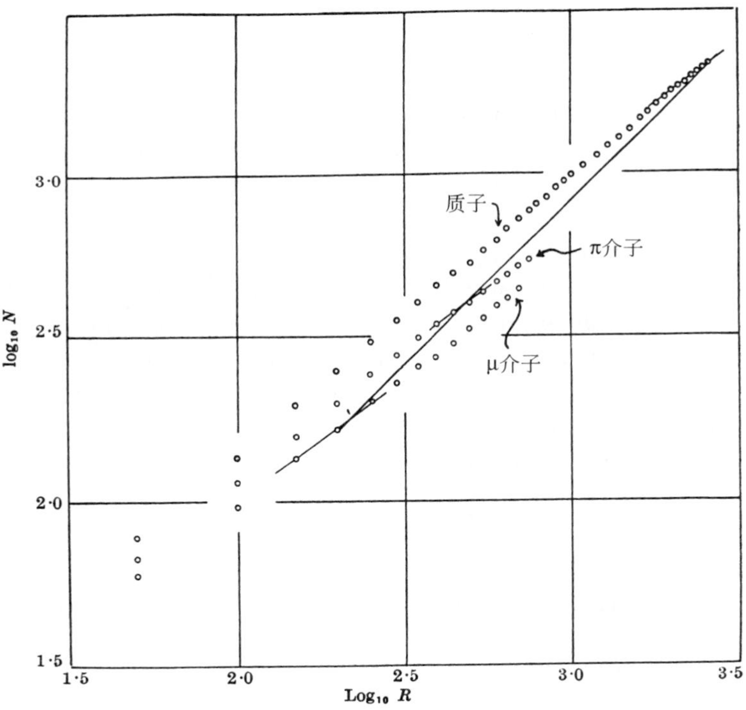

图 5. N 是剩余射程 R 的径迹中的颗粒总数（标尺分度）。1 标尺分度 = 0.85 微米。45° 线在相同的颗粒密度区域处与介子和质子曲线相交。

上述结果对 μ 衰变过程的解释具有重要的意义。我们假定，它相应于较重的 π 介子的自发衰变，其中 μ 介子的动量与发射光子的动量数值相等但方向相反。对

For any assumed value of the mass of the μ-meson, we can calculate the energy of ejection of the particle from its observed range, and thus determine its momentum. The momentum, and hence the energy of the emitted photon, is thus defined; the mass of the π-meson follows from the relation

$$c^2 m_\pi = c^2 m_\mu + E_\mu + h\nu.$$

It can thus be shown that the ratio m_π/m_μ is less than 1.45 for any assumed value of m_μ in the range from 100 to 300 m_e, m_e being the mass of the electron (see Table 3). A similar result is obtained if it is assumed that a particle of low mass, such as an electron or a neutrino, is ejected in the opposite direction to the μ-meson.

Table 3

Assumed mass m_μ	E(MeV.)	$h\nu$(MeV.)	m_π	m_π/m_μ±3 percent
100 m	3.0	17	140 m_e	1.40
150	3.6	23	203	1.35
200	4.1	29	264	1.32
250	4.5	34	325	1.30
300	4.85	39	387	1.29

On the other hand, if it is assumed that the momentum balance in the μ-decay is obtained by the emission of a neutral particle of mass equal to the μ-meson mass, the calculated ratio is about 2.1:1.

Our preliminary measurements appear to indicate, therefore, that the emission of the secondary meson cannot be regarded as due to a spontaneous decay of the primary particle, in which the momentum balance is provided by a photon, or by a particle of small rest-mass. On the other hand, the results are consistent with the view that a neutral particle of approximately the same rest-mass as the μ-meson is emitted. A final conclusion may become possible when further examples of the μ-decay, giving favourable conditions for grain-counts, have been discovered.

(**160**, 453-456; 1947)

C. M. G. Lattes, G. P. S. Occhialini and C. F. Powell: H. H. Wills Physical Laboratory, University of Bristol.

Reference:

1. *Nature*, 159, 93, 186, 694 (1947).

μ 介子质量的任何假定值，我们均能通过粒子的观测射程值计算其发射能量值，从而确定其动量。据此可以确定发射光子的动量和能量；π 介子的质量遵从以下关系：

$$c^2m_\pi = c^2m_\mu + E_\mu + h\nu$$

因此可以表明，对质量 m_μ 在 100 m_e~300 m_e 区间内的任意假定值，m_π/m_μ 比值都小于 1.45，其中 m_e 是电子质量（见表 3）。如果假定一个小质量粒子，例如电子或中微子，与 μ 介子以相反方向射出，亦会得到类似结果。

表 3

假定质量m_μ	E(兆电子伏)	$h\nu$（兆电子伏）	m_π	m_π/m_μ ±3%
100 m	3.0	17	140 m_e	1.40
150	3.6	23	203	1.35
200	4.1	29	264	1.32
250	4.5	34	325	1.30
300	4.85	39	387	1.29

另一方面，如果假定在 μ 衰变中的动量平衡是通过发射一个与 μ 介子质量相等的中性粒子而达到的，则计算出的比值约为 2.1 : 1。

因此，我们的初步测量表明，不能将次级介子的发射归因于初级粒子的自发衰变，其中一个光子或静止质量很小的粒子提供了动量平衡。另一方面，观测结果与发射了一个与 μ 介子质量近似相等的中性粒子的观点相一致。当发现了更多的能够为颗粒计数提供更有利条件的 μ 衰变事例时，才有可能做出最终的结论。

（沈乃澂 翻译；朱永生 审稿）

Evidence for the Existence of New Unstable Elementary Particles

G. D. Rochester and C. C. Butler

Editor's Note

By 1947, physicists knew of the positron and the neutrino, and had recently discovered the neutral pion. A tidy picture of the particle zoo seemed to be emerging, except for some minor confusion concerning the muon. But here physicists George Rochester and Clifford Butler reported shocking evidence for yet further heavy particles of an unknown kind. They analysed photographs of energetic particles penetrating a cloud chamber, and in two cases noted V-like patterns apparently showing one incident massive particle spontaneously disintegrating into two others. These processes would later be identified as involving two new particles, the theta and tau particles: just two of a host of new particles to be discovered over the coming decades.

AMONG some fifty counter-controlled cloud-chamber photographs of penetrating showers which we have obtained during the past year as part of an investigation of the nature of penetrating particles occurring in cosmic ray showers under lead, there are two photographs containing forked tracks of a very striking character. These photographs have been selected from five thousand photographs taken in an effective time of operation of 1,500 hours. On the basis of the analysis given below we believe that one of the forked tracks, shown in Fig. 1 (tracks *a* and *b*), represents the spontaneous transformation in the gas of the chamber of a new type of uncharged elementary particle into lighter charged particles, and that the other, shown in Fig. 2 (tracks *a* and *b*), represents similarly the transformation of a new type of charged particle into two light particles, one of which is charged and the other uncharged.

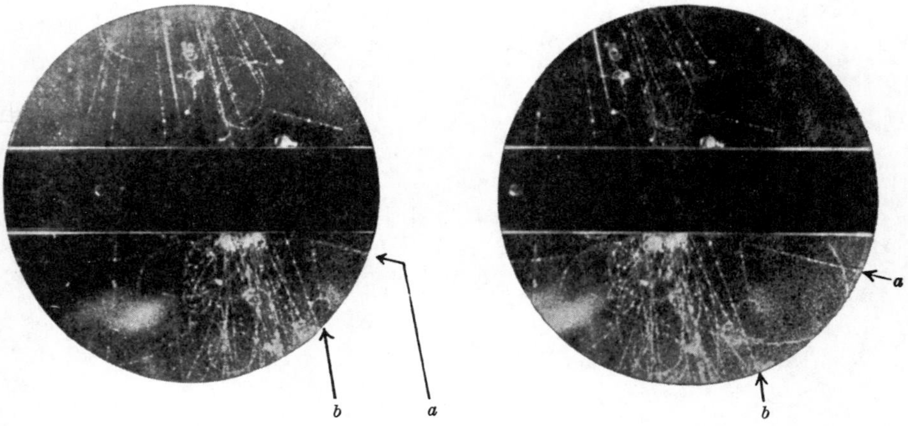

Fig. 1. Stereoscopic photographs showing an unusual fork (*a b*) in the gas. The direction of the magnetic field is such that a positive particle coming downwards is deviated in an anticlockwise direction

新的不稳定基本粒子存在的证据

罗切斯特，布特勒

编者按

到 1947 年，物理学家们已经知道正电子和中微子，并刚刚发现了中性介子。除了关于 μ 介子存在一些小争议外，一个关于粒子园的令人满意的图景似乎已经成形了；但是在本文中物理学家乔治·罗切斯特和克利福德·布特勒报道了一种未知重粒子存在的证据，令人震惊。他们分析了穿透云室的高能粒子的照片，并在其中两张照片中注意到 V 形径迹，这显然表明一个有质量的入射粒子自发衰变为另外两种粒子。后来证实这些衰变过程与两种新粒子有关，分别是 θ 粒子和 τ 粒子，而它们仅仅是后来几十年中发现的大量新粒子中的两种。

在过去的一年中，我们得到了约 50 张由计数器控制的贯穿簇射的云室照片，这些射线流是在对宇宙射线辐射铅板时，穿透铅板的粒子，照片是在研究穿透粒子的自然特征的实验中得到的，其中有两张具有显著的叉状特征。这些照片是从经过 1,500 个小时的有效工作时间中拍摄得到的 5,000 张照片中筛选出来的。在以下分析的基础上，我们相信其中图 1 中的一条叉状径迹（*a*、*b* 径迹）代表了云室气体中的自发转变过程：一种新的不带电的基本粒子转化为更轻的带电粒子。而图 2 中的另一条径迹（*a*、*b* 径迹）代表了相似的转变过程：一种新的带电粒子转化为两种轻粒子，其中一种粒子带电，另一种粒子不带电。

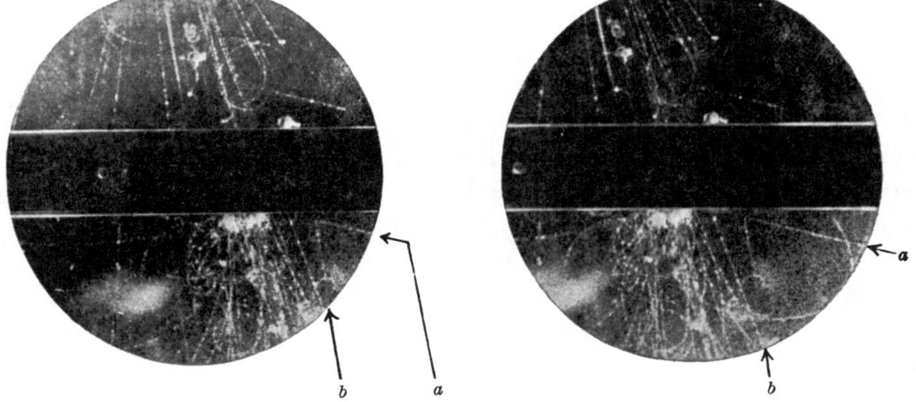

图 1. 立体照片显示了云室气体中一条不同寻常的叉状径迹 (*a b*)。磁场的方向使得向下运动带正电的粒子沿着逆时针方向发生偏转。

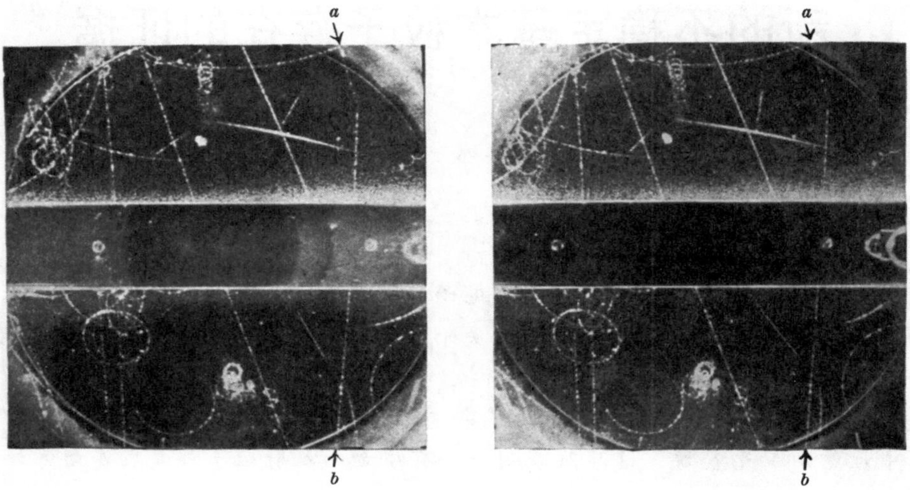

Fig. 2. Stereoscopic photographs showing an unusual fork (*a b*). The direction of the magnetic field is such that a positive particle coming downwards is deviated in a clockwise direction

The experimental data for the two forks are given in Table 1; H is the value of the magnetic field, α the angle between the tracks, p and Δp the measured momentum and the estimated error. The signs of the particles are given in the last column of the table, a plus sign indicating that the particle is positive if moving down in the chamber. Careful re-projection of the stereoscopic photographs has shown that each pair of tracks is copunctal. Moreover, both tracks occur in the middle of the chamber in a region of uniform illumination, the presence of background fog surrounding the tracks indicating good condensation conditions.

Table 1. Experimental data

Photograph	H (gauss)	α (deg.)	Track	p (eV./c.)	Δp (eV./c.)	Sign
1	3,500	66.6	*a*	3.4×10^8	1.0×10^8	+
			b	3.5×10^8	1.5×10^8	−
2	7,200	161.1	*a*	6.0×10^8	3.0×10^8	+
			b	7.7×10^8	1.0×10^8	+

Though the two forks differ in many important respects, they have at least two essential features in common: first, each consists of a two-pronged fork with the apex in the gas; and secondly, in neither case is there any sign of a track due to a third ionizing particle. Further, very few events at all similar to these forks have been observed in the 3 cm. lead plate, whereas if the forks were due to any type of collision process one would have expected several hundred times as many as in the gas. This argument indicates, therefore, that the tracks cannot be due to a collision process but must be due to some type of spontaneous process for which the probability depends on the distance travelled and not on the amount of matter traversed.

This conclusion can be supported by detailed arguments. For example, if either forked

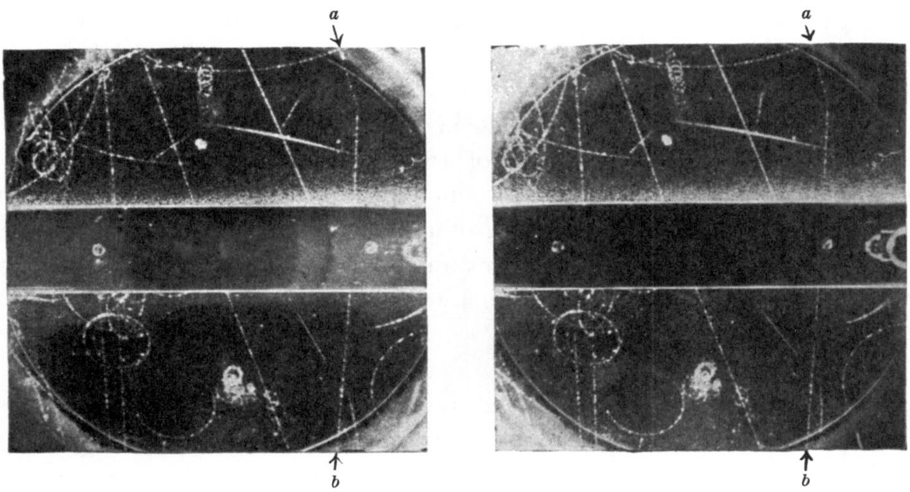

图 2. 立体照片显示了云室气体中一个不同寻常的叉状径迹 ($a\ b$)。磁场的方向使得向下运动带正电的粒子沿着顺时针方向发生偏转。

这两条叉状径迹的实验数据如表 1 所示。H 为磁场的强度值，α 为叉状径迹的夹角，p 和 Δp 为动量的测量值和估计的误差值。在表格的最后一列给出这些粒子的符号，其中正号表示如果粒子穿过云室向下运动，则粒子带正电。对立体照片进行细致的重新投影发现，每一对径迹都是共点的。而且，每对中的两条径迹均出现在具有相同亮度的云室的中间区域，径迹周围雾化背景的存在表示该情况具有良好的凝聚状态。

表 1. 实验数据

照片	H（高斯）	α（度）	径迹	p（电子伏 / 光速）	Δp（电子伏 / 光速）	符号
1	3,500	66.6	a	3.4×10^8	1.0×10^8	+
			b	3.5×10^8	1.5×10^8	−
2	7,200	161.1	a	6.0×10^8	3.0×10^8	+
			b	7.7×10^8	1.0×10^8	+

尽管这两条叉状径迹在很多重要的方面是不一样的，但它们具有至少两个相同的基本特征：第一，每一个都由两条叉状径迹组成，且尖端在气体中；第二，没有任何迹象表明任何一条径迹的符号是由第三个离子化的粒子引起的。另外，在 3 厘米厚的铅板的观测实验中几乎没有出现与这种叉状径迹相类似的情况。然而，如果叉状径迹是由任何一种类型的碰撞过程产生的，则预期在气体中能探测到的分叉应多几百倍。因此，以上讨论表明，这些径迹并不是由碰撞过程产生的，而是由某种自发过程引起的，而这种过程发生的概率依赖于粒子走过的路程而不是横向穿过粒子的数量。

下面更细节的讨论将支持以上的结论。例如，如果叉状径迹的任意一支是由于

track were due to the deflexion of a charged particle by collision with a nucleus, the transfer of momentum would be so large as to produce an easily visible recoil track. Then, again, the attempt to account for Fig. 2 by a collision process meets with the difficulty that the incident particle is deflected through 19° in a single collision in the gas and only 2.4° in traversing 3 cm. of lead—a most unlikely event. One specific collision process, that of electron pair production by a high-energy photon in the field of the nucleus, can be excluded on two grounds: the observed angle between the tracks would only be a fraction of a degree, for example, 0.1° for Fig. 1, and a large amount of electronic component should have accompanied the photon, as in each case a lead plate is close above the fork.

We conclude, therefore, that the two forked tracks do not represent collision processes, but do represent spontaneous transformations. They represent a type of process with which we are already familiar in the decay of the meson into an electron and an assumed neutrino, and the presumed decay of the heavy meson recently discovered by Lattes, Occhialini and Powell[1].

The Masses of the Incident Particles

Let us assume that a particle of mass M and initial momentum P is transformed spontaneously into two particles of masses m_1 and m_2, momenta p_1 and p_2 at angles of θ and φ with the direction of the incident particle. Then the following relations must hold:

$$\sqrt{M^2c^4 + P^2c^2} = \sqrt{m_1^2c^4 + P_1^2c^2} + \sqrt{m_2^2c^4 + P_2^2c^2} \tag{1}$$

$$P = p_1\cos\theta + p_2\cos\varphi \tag{2}$$

$$p_1\sin\theta = p_2\sin\varphi. \tag{3}$$

These general relations may be used to obtain the mass of the incident particle as a function of the assumed messes of the secondary particles.

The value of M must be greater than that obtained by taking the rest masses of the secondary particles as small compared with their momenta; thus the minimum value M_{min} is given by the following equation:

$$M_{min}c^2 = c\sqrt{(p_1 + p_2)^2 - P^2}. \tag{4}$$

Applying this equation to the forked track of Fig. 1, after calculating P from the observed values of p_1 and p_2, it is found that M_{min} is $(770\pm200)m$, where m is the mass of the electron. The application of equation (4) to the forked track of Fig. 2, however, after calculating p_2 from the observed values of P and p_1, shows that $M_{min}=(1{,}700\pm150)m$. This

带电粒子与核粒子碰撞发生偏转而产生的，动量的转移将足以产生一个清晰易辨的反冲径迹。这时，试图用碰撞过程来解释图 2 再次遇到了困难，即入射粒子在气体中的单个碰撞过程中偏离了 19°，而在穿透 3 厘米铅板的过程中仅偏离了 2.4°，这几乎是不可能的。基于以下两点考虑，我们可以排除在核子场中由高能光子产生电子对这种特有的碰撞过程：被观测到的叉状径迹之间的角度仅仅是 1 度的几分之一，例如图 1 中叉状径迹的角度只有 0.1°；而且，在每次实验中铅板紧挨着叉状径迹的上方都应该有大量的电子伴随着光子出现，但事实上却没有发现大量电子的出现。

因此，我们得出结论：这两条叉状径迹与碰撞过程无关，而是由自发转变过程产生的。它们代表了我们已经熟悉的介子衰变成电子和一种假定的中微子的过程，而且，最近拉特斯、奥恰利尼和鲍威尔[1]已经观测到这种假想的重介子的衰变过程。

入射粒子的质量

让我们假定质量为 M、初始动量为 P 的一个粒子自发转化为两个粒子，这两个粒子的质量分别为 m_1 和 m_2，动量分别为 p_1 和 p_2，与入射粒子的夹角分别为 θ 和 φ，则该过程应该满足以下关系式：

$$\sqrt{M^2c^4+P^2c^2}=\sqrt{m_1^2c^4+P_1^2c^2}+\sqrt{m_2^2c^4+P_2^2c^2} \tag{1}$$

$$P=p_1\cos\theta+p_2\cos\varphi \tag{2}$$

$$p_1\sin\theta=p_2\sin\varphi \tag{3}$$

这些普适的关系式可以用来求解入射粒子的质量，求得的解为假定的次级粒子质量的函数。

假设次级粒子的静止质量相对于其动量来说很小，则真实的 M 值大小应该比在该假设极限情况下得到的解要大，因此 M 的最小值 $M_{\min}$ 可由下面的公式给出：

$$M_{\min}c^2=c\sqrt{(p_1+p_2)^2}-P^2 \tag{4}$$

通过测得的 p_1 和 p_2 值计算得出 P 之后，将以上公式用于求解图 1 中的叉状径迹，计算得到 $M_{\min}$ 为 $(770\pm200)m$，其中 m 为电子的质量。然而由观测得到的 P 和 p_1 值得出 p_2 后，将等式（4）用于求解图 2 中的叉状径迹，计算得到 $M_{\min}=(1{,}700\pm150)m$。这一质量值将对应于质量为两倍质量最小值的入射粒子发生电离，这与观测到的电

value of the mass would require an ionization for the incident particle of twice minimum, which is inconsistent with the observed ionization. We are therefore justified in assuming that the real value of P is greater than the observed value which, as indicated in Table 1, has a large error. If larger values of P are assumed, then M_{min} is reduced in value. The lowest value of M_{min} is $(980\pm150)m$ if P is 14.5×10^8 eV./c. Beyond this value of P the mass increases slowly with increasing momentum. No choice of incident momentum will bring the mass of the incident particle below $980m$.

In the special case where the incident particle disintegrates transversely into two particles of equal mass m_0, giving a symmetrical fork, equation (1) reduces to the following expression,

$$\frac{M}{m} = \frac{2m_0}{m}\left(1 + \frac{p^2c^2}{m_0^2c^4}\cdot\sin^2\theta\right)^{1/2}, \tag{5}$$

where p is the momentum of each of the secondary particles. Some typical results for different assumed secondary particles, calculated from equation (5), are given in Table 2. On the reasonable assumption that the secondary particles are light or heavy mesons, that is, with masses of $200m$ or $400m$, we find that the incident particle in each photograph has a mass of the order of $1{,}000m$.

Table 2. Mass of incident particle as a function of mass of secondary particle

Photograph	Assumed secondary particle m_0/m	Momentum of observed secondary particle (eV./c.)	Incident particle M/m
1	0	$3.5\times10^8\pm1.0\times10^8$	770 ± 200
	200	”	870 ± 200
	400	”	1,110 ± 150
	1,837	”	3,750 ± 50
2	0	$7.7\times10^8\pm1.0\times10^8$	980 ± 150
	200	”	1,080 ± 100
	400	”	1,280 ± 100
	1,837	”	3,820 ± 50

Upper values of the masses of the incident particles may also be obtained from the values of the ionization and the momenta. Thus for each of the observed particles in Fig. 1, the ionization is indistinguishable from that of a very fast particle. We conclude, therefore, that $\beta=v/c \geqslant 0.7$. Since the momentum of the incident particle may be found from the observed momenta of the secondary particles, we can apply equation (1) to calculate M. In this way we find $M/m \leqslant 1{,}600$. Again, since the ionization of the incident particle in Fig. 2 is light, $\beta \geqslant 0.7$, from which it can be shown that $M/m \leqslant 1{,}200$. This last result, however, must be taken with caution because of the uncertainty in the measured value of the momentum of the incident particle.

One further general comment may be made. This is that the observation of two spontaneous disintegrations in such a small number of penetrating showers suggests that

离情况不一致。因此，我们有理由认为动量 P 的真实值大于测量值，正如表 1 中给出的那样，存在很大的误差。如果假定动量 P 的值更大，则 M_{min} 将会减小。如果 P 为 14.5×10^8 电子伏 / 光速，则 M_{min} 的最小值为 $(980 \pm 150)m$。当动量 P 超过这一值后，入射粒子的质量随着动量的增加而缓慢地增加。无论动量取何值，入射粒子的质量都不会低于 $980m$。

在一个入射粒子分解为两个质量均为 m_0 的粒子的特定过程中，产生了一个对称的叉状径迹，而等式（1）将简化成以下表达式：

$$\frac{M}{m} = \frac{2m_0}{m}\left(1 + \frac{p^2c^2}{m_0^2c^4} \cdot \sin^2\theta\right)^{1/2} \tag{5}$$

式中 p 为每个次级粒子的动量。对于不同的假定的次级粒子，由等式（5）计算得到的特定结果如表 2 所示。在次级粒子分别为质量 $200m$ 的轻介子或质量 $400m$ 的重介子的合理假定下，我们发现，每一张照片中入射粒子的质量都在 $1,000m$ 的量级上。

表 2. 入射粒子质量与次级粒子质量的函数关系

照片	假定的次级粒子 m_0/m	探测到的次级粒子动量（电子伏 / 光速）	入射粒子 M/m
1	0	$3.5 \times 10^8 \pm 1.0 \times 10^8$	770 ± 200
	200	”	870 ± 200
	400	”	$1,110 \pm 150$
	1,837	”	$3,750 \pm 50$
2	0	$7.7 \times 10^8 \pm 1.0 \times 10^8$	980 ± 150
	200	”	$1,080 \pm 100$
	400	”	$1,280 \pm 100$
	1,837	”	$3,820 \pm 50$

上表中入射粒子的质量值也可以通过电离值和动量值计算得到。因此对于图 1 中观测到的每一种粒子，其电离情况与快粒子的电离情况是难以辨别的。因此，我们得出结论 $\beta=v/c \geqslant 0.7$。既然入射粒子的动量可以由探测到的次级粒子的动量得出，我们就可以用公式（1）计算得出入射粒子的质量 M。按这种方法分析，我们得到 $M/m \leqslant 1,600$。此外，由于图 2 中入射粒子的电离结果是轻粒子，$\beta \geqslant 0.7$，由此得到 $M/m \leqslant 1,200$。然而，我们必须谨慎处理最后的结果，因为入射粒子动量的测量值具有不确定性。

下面进行更深一步的全面讨论。即在这种少量的贯穿簇射中观测到的两个自发

the life-time of the unstable particles is much less than the life-time of the ordinary meson. An approximate value of this life-time may be derived as follows. The probability of an unstable particle of life-time τ_0 decaying in a short distance D is given by

$$p = \frac{D(1-\beta^2)^{1/2}}{\tau_0 c\beta} . \tag{6}$$

Since the total number of penetrating particles in the penetrating showers so far observed is certainly less than 50, we must assume that the number of our new unstable particles is unlikely to have been greater than 50. Since one particle of each type has been observed to decay, we can therefore put $p \approx 0.02$. Setting $D \approx 30$ cm., and $\beta = 0.7$, we find from equation (6) that $\tau_0 = 5.0\times10^{-8}$ sec.

We shall now discuss possible alternative explanations of the two forks.

Photograph 1. We must examine the alternative possibility of Photograph 1 representing the spontaneous disintegration of a charged particle, coming up from below the chamber, into a charged and an uncharged particle. If we apply the argument which led to equation (4) to this process, it is readily seen that the incident particle would have a minimum mass of 1,280*m*. Thus the photograph cannot be explained by the decay of a back-scattered ordinary meson. Bearing in mind the general direction of the other particles in the shower, it is thought that assumption of the disintegration of a neutral particle moving downwards into a pair of particles of about equal mass is more probable. Further, it can be stated with some confidence that the observed ionizing particles are unlikely to be protons because the ionization of a proton of momentum 3.5×10^8 eV./c. would be more than four times the observed ionization.

Photograph 2. In this case we must examine the possibility of the photograph representing the spontaneous decay of a neutral particle coming from the right-hand side of the chamber into two charged particles. The result of applying equation (4) to this process is to show that the minimum mass of the neutral particle would be about 3,000*m*. In view of the fact that the direction of the neutral particle would have to very different from the direction of the main part of the shower, it is thought that the original assumption of the decay of a charged particle into a charged penetrating particle and an assumed neutral particle is the more probable.

We conclude from all the evidence that Photograph 1 represents the decay of a neutral particle, the mass of which is unlikely to be less than 770*m* or greater than 1,600*m*, into the two observed charged particles. Similarly, Photograph 2 represents the disintegration of a charged particle of mass greater than 980*m* and less than that of a proton into an observed penetrating particle and a neutral particle. It may be noted that no neutral particle of mass 1,000*m* has yet been observed; a charged particle of mass 990*m* ± 12 percent has, however, been observed by Leprince-Ringuet and L'héritier[2].

衰变表明，不稳定粒子的寿命要比普通介子的寿命短得多。下面的推导中将给出这个寿命的近似值。寿命为 τ_0 的不稳定粒子在短距离 D 范围内发生衰变的概率为：

$$p = \frac{D(1-\beta^2)^{1/2}}{\tau_0 c\beta} \tag{6}$$

目前为止探测到的贯穿簇射中贯穿粒子的总数量小于 50，我们必须假设这种新的不稳定粒子的数目不可能大于 50。由于观测发现每一种类型的粒子中都有一个粒子发生衰变，因此我们可以令 $p \approx 0.02$。取 $D \approx 30$ 厘米以及 $\beta = 0.7$，通过等式（6）我们可以得出 $\tau_0 = 5.0 \times 10^{-8}$ 秒。

下面我们将讨论这两种叉状径迹另一种可能的解释。

照片 1　我们必须研究照片 1 所代表的另一种可能性：从云室的下方向上运动的带电粒子发生自发衰变，成为一个带电粒子和一个不带电粒子。如果我们将导出等式（4）的讨论应用到这一过程中，将会很容易地发现，入射粒子质量的最小值为 1,280m。因此，不能用普通的背散射介子的衰变来解释这张照片。考虑到簇射中其他粒子的一般方向，我们认为一个中性粒子向下移动，转化为具有相同质量的一对粒子这种假定的可能性比较大。进一步讲，我们有理由认为探测到的电离粒子不可能是质子，因为动量为 3.5×10^8 电子伏 / 光速的质子发生电离的结果将是实际探测到的电离结果的四倍多。

照片 2　在这种情况中，我们必须研究照片所代表的一种可能性：来自云室右边的一个中性粒子自发衰变为两个带电粒子。在这一过程中应用等式（4）得到的结果表明，中性粒子质量的最小值大约为 3,000m。鉴于实际情况为中性粒子的方向应该不同于簇射中大部分粒子的方向，因此认为一个带电粒子衰变为一个带电的贯穿粒子和一个中性粒子这种最初的假设可能性更大。

通过所有的证据我们推断，照片 1 代表了一个质量介于 770m 和 1,600m 之间的中性粒子衰变为两个观测到的带电粒子的过程。类似的，照片 2 代表了质量大于 980m 但小于质子质量的带电粒子衰变为观测到的贯穿粒子和中性粒子的过程。这里还必须声明，目前我们还没有探测到质量为 1,000m 的中性粒子。然而，勒普兰斯–兰盖和莱里捷[2] 已经探测到一个质量为 990$m \pm 12\%$ 的带电粒子。

Peculiar cloud-chamber photographs taken by Jánossy, Rochester and Broadbent[3] and by Daudin[4] may be other examples of Photograph 2.

It is a pleasure to record our thanks to Prof. P. M. S. Blackett for the keen interest he has taken in this investigation and for the benefit of numerous stimulating discussions. We also wish to acknowledge the help given us by Prof. L. Rosenfeld, Mr. J. Hamilton and Mr. H. Y. Tzu of the Department of Theoretical Physics, University of Manchester. We are indebted to Mr. S. K. Runcorn for his assistance in running the cloud chamber in the early stages of the work.

(**160**, 855-857; 1947)

G. D. Rochester and C. C. Butler: Physical Laboratories, University, Manchester.

References:

1. Lattes, C. M. G., Occhialini, G. P. S., and Powell, C. F., *Nature*, **160**, 453, 486 (1947).
2. Leprince-Ringuet, L., and L'héritier, M., *J. Phys. Radium*.(Sér. 8), 7, 66, 69 (1946). Bethe, H. A., *Phys. Rev*., **70**, 821 (1946).
3. Jánossy, L., Rochester, G. D., and Broadbent, D., *Nature*, **155**, 1 42 (1945). (Fig. 2. Track at lower left-hand side of the photograph.)
4. Daudin, J., *Annales de Physique*, 11e Série, **19** (Avril-Juin), 1944 (Planche IV, Cliché 16).

由亚诺希、罗切斯特、布罗德本特[3]以及多丹[4]得到的特殊的云室照片可能是照片 2 中的其他情况。

在这里感谢布莱克特教授对本项研究的极大关注及许多受益匪浅的讨论，感谢曼彻斯特大学理论物理学院罗森菲尔德教授、哈密顿先生和滋先生为我们提供的帮助，最后我们还要感谢朗科恩先生在本项研究工作的初期帮助我们操控云室。

（胡雪兰 翻译；尚仁成 审稿）

A New Microscopic Principle

D. Gabor

Editor's Note

Dennis Gabor was an employee of a large electrical manufacturer when be produced this paper, ostensibly directed at the improvement of the electron microscope but which has now become the principle underlying the technique called holography, by means of which all the information needed to construct a three-dimensional view can be stored on a two-dimensional surface, and which is widely used in devices such as bank and credit cards. Gabor moved to Imperial College London in the 1950s and received a Nobel Prize in 1971.

IT is known that the spherical aberration of electron lenses sets a limit to the resolving power of electron microscopes at about 5 A. Suggestions for the correction of objectives have been made; but these are difficult in themselves, and the prospects of improvement are further aggravated by the fact that the resolution limit is proportional to the fourth root of the spherical aberration. Thus an improvement of the resolution by one decimal would require a correction of the objective to four decimals, a practically hopeless task.

The new microscopic principle described below offers a way around this difficulty, as it allows one to dispense altogether with electron objectives. Micrographs are obtained in a two-step process, by electronic analysis, followed by optical synthesis, as in Sir Lawrence Bragg's "X-ray microscope". But while the "X-ray microscope" is applicable only in very special cases, where the phases are known beforehand, the new principle provides a complete record of amplitudes *and* phases in one diagram, and is applicable to a very general class of objects.

Fig. 1 is a broad explanation of the principle. The object is illuminated by an electron beam brought to a fine focus, from which it diverges at a semi-angle α. Sufficient coherence is assured if the nominal or Gaussian diameter of the focus is less than the resolution limit, $\lambda/2 \sin \alpha$. The physical diameter, determined by diffraction and spherical aberration of the illuminating system, can be much larger. The object is a small distance behind (or in front of) the point focus, followed by a photographic plate at a large multiple of this distance. Thus the arrangement is similar to an electron shadow microscope; but it is used in a range in which the shadow microscope is useless, as it produces images very dissimilar to the original. The object is preferably smaller than the area which is illuminated in the object plane, and it must be mounted on a support which transmits an appreciable part of the primary wave. The photographic record is produced by the interference of the primary wave with the coherent part of the secondary wave emitted

一种新的显微原理

盖伯

编者按

丹尼斯·盖伯在完成这篇论文时还是一家大型电子制造企业的一名雇员，表面上这篇论文指导了电子显微镜的改进，而如今，这篇论文业已成为全息摄影技术的原理。这项技术可以将构造三维影像所需的全部信息储存于二维表面中，并已广泛应用于银行和信用卡等设备中。20 世纪 50 年代盖伯进入伦敦帝国学院，并于 1971 年获得诺贝尔奖。

我们已经知道，电子透镜的球差决定了电子显微镜的分辨率极限约为 5 埃。虽然人们已经提出建议对物镜进行校正，但是这些都很难实现，而分辨率极限正比于球差的四次方根这一事实使得改进分辨率的希望更为渺茫。也就是说，要将分辨率提高 10 倍，需要将物镜的校正提高一万倍，这几乎是一项不可能完成的任务。

下面所描述的新的显微原理提供的方法可绕过上述困境，因为它完全无需使用电子物镜。可通过两步处理获得显微图像，即电子分析和随后的光学合成，就像劳伦斯·布拉格爵士的"X 射线显微镜"那样。但是"X 射线显微镜"只适用于那些预先知道相位的非常特殊的情况，而新原理则在一张图像中提供了振幅**和**相位的完整记录，因而适用于极其一般的各类物体。

图 1 是对该原理的一个概括性解释。用一束向细微焦点聚焦后并以半角 α 发散的电子束照明物体。如果焦点的标称直径或高斯直径小于分辨率极限值 $\lambda/2\sin\alpha$，就能确保充分的相干性。由照明系统的衍射和球差所决定的物理直径可能还要大得多。物体位于焦点后方（或前方），与焦点相隔很小的一段距离，在其后面比这段距离大很多倍的位置放置照相干板。因而这样的排列方式与电子阴影显微镜类似；但是它可以在阴影显微镜力不能及的范围使用，因为它会产生与初始图像截然不同的图像。物体最好小于物平面中的照明面积，而且必须被固定在一个可透射相当一部分初级波的支架上。通过初级波与物体发出的次级波中的相干部分之间的干涉产生照相记录结果。可以看到，至少在图像靠外的区域中会出现干涉极大，其位置非常

by the object. It can be shown that, at least in the outer parts of the diagram, interference maxima will arise very nearly where the phases of the primary and of the secondary wave have coincided, as illustrated in Fig. 1.

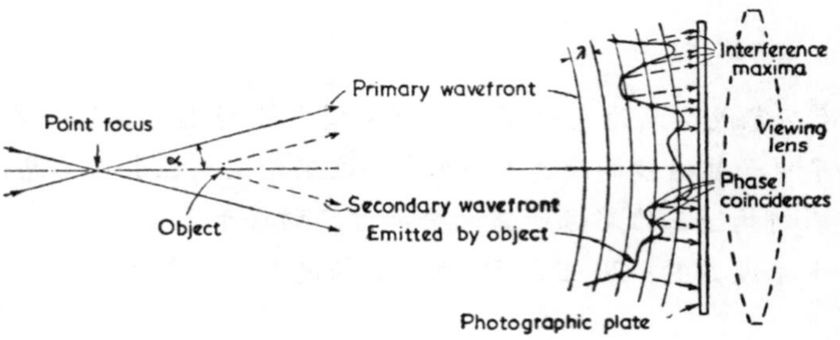

Fig. 1. Interference between homocentric illuminating wave and the secondary wave emitted by a small object

If this photograph is developed by reversal, or printed, the loci of maximum transmission will indicate the regions in which the primary wave had the same phase as the modified wave, and the variations of the transmission in these loci will be approximately proportional to the intensity of the modified wave. Thus, if one illuminates the photographic record with an optical imitation of the electronic wave, only that part of the primary wave will be strongly transmitted which imitates the modified wave both in phases and in amplitudes. It can be shown that the "masking" of the regions outside the loci of maximum transmission has only a small distorting effect. One must expect that looking through such a properly processed diagram one will see behind it the original object, as if it were in place.

The principle was tested in an optical model, in which the interference diagram was produced by monochromatic light instead of by electrons. The print was replaced in the apparatus, backed by a viewing lens which admitted about $\sin \alpha = 0.04$, and the image formed was observed and ultimately photographed through a microscope. It can be seen in Fig. 2 that the reconstruction, though imperfect, achieves the separation of some letters which could just be separated in direct observation of the object through the same optical system. The resolution is markedly imperfect only in the centre, where the circular frame creates a disturbance. Other imperfections of the reconstruction are chiefly due to defects in the microscope objectives used for the production of the point focus, and for observation.

It is a striking property of these diagrams that they constitute records of three-dimensional as well as of plane objects. One plane after another of extended objects can be observed in the microscope, just as if the object were really in position.

接近于图 1 所示的初级波相位和次级波相位达到一致的位置。

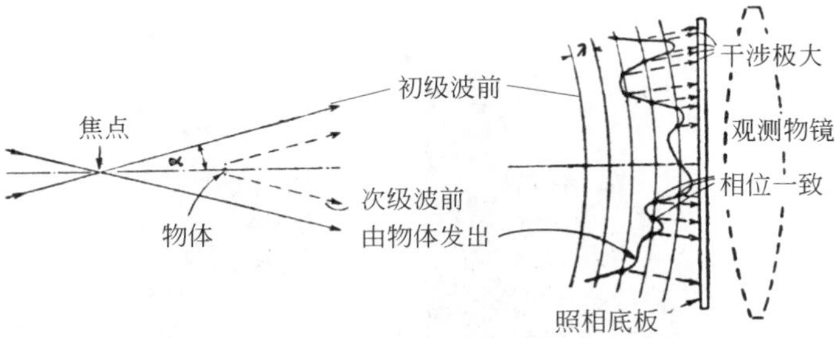

图 1. 共心照明波与微小物体发出的次级波之间的干涉

如果将照片进行反转处理或者翻印出来，最强的透射位点就代表了初级波（译者注:“初级波”的一部分被用作物体的照明光；另一部分，即其未被物体散射的部分被用作参考光）与修正波（译者注:“修正波”是“初级波”照射在物体上，被物体散射而发生改变的波，也就是“物波”）具有相同相位的区域，而这些位置上透射率的变化将近似正比于修正波的强度变化。因此，如果用电子波的光学模拟去照射照相记录，只有能够同时模拟修正波的相位和振幅的部分初级波才会被强烈透射。可以看出，对最强透射位置之外区域的“掩蔽”只会产生小的扭曲效应。应该可以预期，通过仔细查看这类经过适当处理的图像，我们将会看到它背后的原物体，好像它就在眼前一样。

可用一个光学模型来检验这一原理，即用单色光而不是电子产生干涉图像。将装置中的照片放回原处，背后加一面观测物镜，它允许的入射半角近似为 $\sin\alpha = 0.04$，通过一台显微镜观察所形成的图像并最终进行拍照。在图 2 中可以看到，虽然重现影像并不完美，但是利用相同的光学系统直接观察物体时刚好可以区分的那些字母，在重现影像中也能够被区分。只有中心部分的分辨率明显不足，那是圆框造成了干扰。重现影像的其他不足主要是由用以产生焦点和进行观测的显微镜物镜的瑕疵导致的。

这些图像具有一个引人注目的特性，即它们能像记录平面物体一样地记录三维物体。可以在显微镜中逐一地连续观察延伸物体的不同平面，就好像它们真的在那个位置一样。

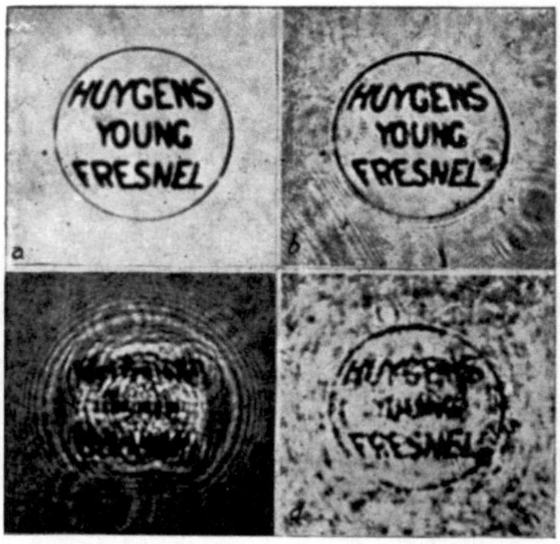

Fig. 2. (*a*) Original micrograph, 1.4 mm. diameter. (*b*) Micrograph, directly photographed through the same optical system which is used for the reconstruction (*d*). Ap. 0.04. (*c*) Interference diagram, obtained by projecting the micrograph on a photographic plate with a beam diverging from a point focus. The letters have become illegible by diffraction. (*d*) Reconstruction of the original by optical synthesis from the diagram at the left. To be compared with (*b*). The letters have again become legible

Racking the microscope through and beyond the point focus, one finds a second image of the original object, in central-symmetrical position with respect to the point focus. The explanation is, briefly, that the photographic diagram cannot distinguish positive and negative phase shifts with respect to the primary wave, and this second image corresponds to the same phase shifts as the original, but with reversed sign.

If the principle is applied to electron microscopy, the dimensions in the optical synthetizer ought to be scaled up in the ratio of light waves to electron waves, that is, about 100,000 times. One must provide an illuminating system which is an exact optical imitation of the electronic condenser lens, including its spherical aberration. To avoid scaling-up the diagram, one has to introduce a further lens, with a focal length equal to the distance of the object from the photographic plate in the electronic device, in such a position that the plate appears at infinity when viewed from the optical space of the point focus. Work on the new instrument, which may be called the "electron interference microscope", will now be taken in hand.

I wish to thank Mr. I. Williams for assistance in the experiments, and Mr. L. J. Davies, director of research of the British Thomson-Houston Company, for permission to publish this note.

(**161**, 777-778; 1948)

D. Gabor: Research Laboratory, British Thomson-Houston Co., Ltd., Rugby.

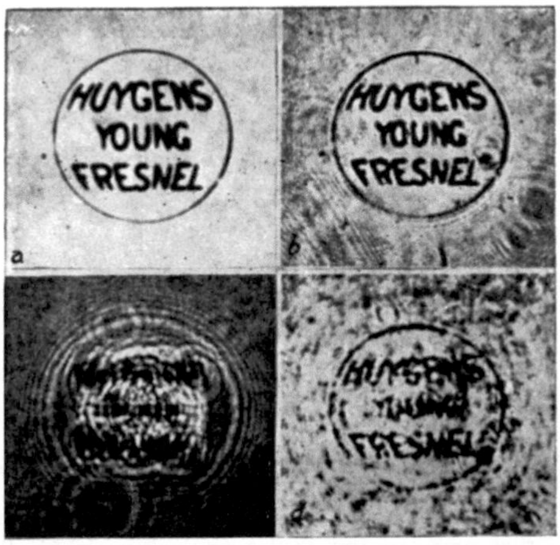

图 2.（*a*）原始显微图，直径为 1.4 毫米。（*b*）显微图，通过直接照相得到，与重现影像（*d*）使用相同的光学系统。Ap. 0.04。（*c*）干涉图，利用从一个焦点发散出来的射线束将显微图投影于照相干板上得到。字母由于衍射而变得模糊。（*d*）利用光学合成从左侧图像得到的重现影像。以（*b*）为参照，字母再度由模糊变得清晰。

编者注：图中所使用的三个人名 Huygens（惠更斯）、Young（杨）、Fresnel（菲涅耳）代表证明光的波动性的三位重要科学家。

将显微镜经过焦点向另一侧移动，我们会在相对于该焦点中心对称的位置发现原物体的第二个像。对此现象的简要解释是，照相图像无法区分初级波的正相移与负相移，这第二个像与原物体的相移相同，但是符号相反。

如果将该原理应用于电子显微镜，那么在光学合成仪器中的尺度应该按光波对电子波的比值（即大约 100,000 倍）同比例增加。同时必须提供一个照明系统，它是电子聚焦透镜及其球差的严格光学模拟。为避免图像按比例增大，还必须再引入一个透镜，其焦距等于从电子装置中的照相干板到物体之间的距离，其放置位置应使得从焦点的光学距离看来干板出现在无穷远处。对于这种我们不妨称为“电子干涉显微镜”的新型装置的研究即将展开。

我要感谢威廉姆斯先生在实验中给予的协助，感谢英国汤姆森–休斯敦电气公司研究主管戴维斯先生对这篇短文的公开发表给予允准。

（王耀杨 翻译；熊秉衡 审稿）

African Fossil Primates Discovered during 1947*

W. E. Le Gros Clark

Editor's Note

The 1930s and 1940s were a Golden Age for the discovery of fossil hominids, largely due to Robert Broom's work at Sterkfontein and Kromdraai in South Africa, and Louis Leakey's in Kenya. Here anatomist Le Gros Clark summarizes the work to date. He concentrated, naturally, on Broom's 1947 "ape-man" discoveries at Sterkfontein, showing how they put paid to any doubts arising after Dart's initial discovery of the Taung "baby" in 1924. But Le Gros Clark also looked at the much more ancient (and more apelike) *Proconsul*, remains of which had been emerging in Eastern Africa for some years, thanks to Louis Leakey and others. Leakey's own ventures into ape-man territory still lay more than a decade in the future.

THE elucidation of the fossil record of the group of mammals of which man himself is a member is clearly a matter of the most profound interest. But it is a study which in the past has progressed extremely slowly, for the reason that the remains of fossil Primates are usually found only at rare intervals. It is all the more remarkable, therefore, that the year 1947 was outstanding in the field of palaeontology for the great abundance of extinct representatives of the higher Primates, the Hominoidea, which have come to light. These discoveries were made in Africa, and it is particularly interesting to note that they followed so closely on the Pan-African Congress of Prehistory, held in Nairobi in January of that year, when the implications of earlier finds first gained a wide recognition. The discoveries are due primarily to two men of science, Dr. Robert Broom in South Africa and Dr. L. S. B. Leakey in Kenya.

The new discoveries made by Dr. Broom supplement those which he made between 1936 and 1941 at Sterkfontein and Kromdraai, and which he described in detail in a monograph published in 1946[1]. They are remarkable both in quantity and quality, for not only do they include considerable numbers of skulls, jaws, teeth and limb-bones of the Australopithecinae, but also some of this material is extraordinarily complete and well preserved.

It will be recalled that the first specimen of the Australopithecinae, an immature skull with an endocranial cast, was found at Taungs in 1924 and afterwards described by Prof. Raymond Dart[2]. Then in 1936 and later, Dr. Broom found portions of several adult skulls, jaws and teeth, as well as fragments of some limb-bones, at Sterkfontein

* Substance of a communication to the Linnean Society, April 22, 1948.

1947年间发现的非洲灵长类化石*

克拉克

编者按

20 世纪 30 和 40 年代是人科化石发现的黄金年代，这在很大程度上归功于罗伯特·布鲁姆在南非斯泰克方丹和克罗姆德拉伊的工作，以及路易斯·利基在肯尼亚的工作。本文中，解剖学家勒格罗·克拉克总结了迄今为止的工作。他自然地将注意力集中到 1947 年布鲁姆在斯泰克方丹发现的“猿人”，并展示了这些材料如何回应自 1924 年达特首次发现汤恩“小孩”头骨以来的各种质疑。然而，勒格罗·克拉克还将目光投向更为古老（以及更加类似猿类）的原康修尔猿，该物种的化石是数年前由路易斯·利基等人在东非发现的。而至少在未来十多年的时间内，利基仍将在猿人领域中进行他自己的冒险。

由于人类自身就是哺乳动物群体中的一员，所以对于这一群体化石记录的探究肯定是人类最感兴趣的事了。但是在过去，该方面的研究进展得极其缓慢，因为通常只偶尔才能发现灵长类的化石。因此 1947 年对古生物学领域来说是极不寻常的一年，因为发现了大量已灭绝高等灵长类的代表——人猿超科的化石，至此它们逐渐为人所知。这些发现是在非洲取得的，尤其有趣并要加以说明的是，这些发现恰巧发生在 1947 年 1 月在内罗毕举行的泛非史前学大会之前，而正是在这次会议上，该发现的意义首次得到广泛认可。这些发现主要归功于科学界的两个人，即南非的罗伯特·布鲁姆博士和肯尼亚的利基博士。

布鲁姆博士取得的新发现，是对他 1936 年 ~ 1941 年间在斯泰克方丹和克罗姆德拉伊发现的补充，他在 1946 年出版的一本专著中详细地描述了这些发现[1]。这些发现在数量和质量上都是引人注目的，不仅因为它们包含了相当大量的南方古猿亚科的头骨、颌骨、牙齿和肢骨，也因为这些材料中有不少特别完整，保存得也特别好。

人们不会忘记南方古猿亚科的第一份标本，即一件具有颅内模的未成年头骨，它于 1924 年发现于汤恩，后来雷蒙德·达特教授对其进行了描述[2]。1936 年及其后，布鲁姆博士在约翰内斯堡附近的斯泰克方丹和克罗姆德拉伊发现了几个成年个体的

* 向林奈学会所提交通讯的主要内容，1948 年 4 月 22 日。

and Kromdraai near Johannesburg. His report on this material made it clear that the Australopithecinae were ape-like creatures with brains of simian dimensions, but which at the same time showed such a remarkable assemblage of characters hitherto regarded as distinctive of the Hominidae that there could be little doubt of their importance for problems of human evolution. Among these hominid characters may be mentioned the morphology of the frontal region of the skull, the low level of the occipital torus, the construction of the tympanic region, the forward position of the foramen magnum, the palatal contour, the small canines, the bicuspid character of the anterior lower premolars, the morphology of the first deciduous molars, the flat wear of the molars, the details of the lower end of the femur, and certain features of the talus and the capitate bone. The evidence of the femur, combined with that of the foramen magnum, it should be noted, seemed to make it clear that the Australopithecinae were capable of assuming an erect posture closely approaching that of man.

This accumulation of evidence was sufficient to convince most anatomists that the importance of the Australopithecinae had not been exaggerated. A few critics, however, expressed scepticism, mainly, no doubt, because they had not had the opportunity of examining the original material for themselves. It is also a fact, however, that this material, although abundant, was in some respects fragmentary, and thus required a rather intimate acquaintance with the comparative osteology of the Hominoidea for a correct appreciation of its unusual characters. Early in 1947, Dr. Broom renewed his excavations at Sterkfontein, and in April announced the discovery of a practically complete adult Australopithecine skull, as well as the upper jaw of another adult, an upper jaw of an adolescent, and some isolated teeth[3]. The complete skull has been listed in the material from Sterkfontein as "Skull No. 5". Further excavations soon showed that many more remains of the Australopithecine fossils were embedded in the limestone matrix in the same area at Sterkfontein, and parts of at least five other skulls (some of which are fairly complete) have since come to hand. The preliminary notes on these discoveries so far published have now provided a remarkable vindication of the views previously expressed by those who had personally studied the earlier material described by Dart and Broom. For example, they appear to confirm the forward position of the foramen magnum and the human resemblances in the occipital and tympanic regions, while many other features such as the contour of the frontal region and the shape of the dental arcade conform closely with the evidence already supplied by less complete material. The discovery of a massive jaw in June 1947, with all the teeth in position, has also added further evidence that the canine was relatively small (compared with the premolars) and became worn down flat to the level of the adjacent teeth[4]. In all these skulls the endocranial capacity seems to vary about 500 c.c.

Dr. Broom, however, has not only found a number of skulls, but has also collected a considerable number of limb-bone fragments, including portions of a scapula, humerus and femur, a tibia, some ribs and vertebrae, and an almost complete os innominatum[5]. The last-named is without doubt the most remarkable find. In the shape of the ilium it corresponds very closely with that of man, and shows no resemblance at all to the os

头骨残块、颌骨和牙齿、以及一些肢骨破片。他对这些材料的报道表明，南方古猿亚科是一种脑量与猿相当的类似猿类的生物，但是该报道同时也展示了这些标本所具有的人科独有的一系列显著特征，以至于几乎无人怀疑其对解决人类进化问题所具有的重要性。在这些人科特征中，值得一提的包括头骨额区的形态、枕圆枕位置较低、鼓室区的构造、枕骨大孔位置前移、腭轮廓、犬齿较小、下前臼齿前部的双齿尖特征、第一乳臼齿的形态、臼齿平磨、股骨下端的细节以及距骨和头状骨的某些特征。需要说明的是，股骨以及枕骨大孔的证据似乎表明南方古猿亚科几乎和人类一样可以直立行走。

这些证据的积累足以使大多数解剖学家相信南方古猿亚科的重要性并未被夸大。然而，一些评论家表示了怀疑，毫无疑问，这主要是因为他们没有机会亲自查看原始材料。另一个事实是，尽管这些材料很丰富，但是从某些方面看，它们是破碎的，因此要想正确理解其不寻常的特征，就需要对人猿超科的比较骨骼学有相当缜密的认识。1947 年初，布鲁姆博士在斯泰克方丹重新开始了他的发掘工作，4 月他宣布发现了一件非常完整的成年南方古猿头骨、另一个成年南方古猿的上颌骨、一个未成年南方古猿的上颌骨以及一些单个的牙齿[3]。在斯泰克方丹化石材料中，该完整头骨被编为“5 号头骨”。随后进一步的发掘工作表明在斯泰克方丹同一区域的石灰岩基质中埋藏了更多的南方古猿亚科化石，而且在后续发掘中又获得了部分化石，包括至少代表 5 个其他头骨的化石（其中有些非常完整）。目前发表的关于这些发现的研究简报，为那些亲自研究过达特和布鲁姆以前描述的早期材料的那些人先前所持有的观点提供了非常有力的实证。例如，它们证实了枕骨大孔的前移、枕骨和鼓室区与人类的相像，而许多其他的特征，如额区的轮廓和齿弓的形状也与那些由不太完整的材料所提供的证据非常吻合。1947 年 6 月发现的粗大下颌骨，其所有牙齿原位保存，该标本进一步证明了犬齿（与前臼齿相比）相对较小，并且磨耗后与相邻牙齿处于相同水平[4]。所有这些头骨的颅容量好像都在 500 毫升左右变化。

然而，布鲁姆博士不仅发现了大量头骨，也搜集到了相当多的肢骨破片，包括肩胛骨、肱骨和股骨残块，一件胫骨、一些肋骨和椎骨以及一件几乎完整的髋骨[5]。最后一件无疑是最引人注目的发现。从髂骨的形状来看，它与人类的非常相符，而与类人猿的髋骨几乎没有任何相似之处。这的确为证明南方古猿亚科具有与人类一

innominatum of an anthropoid ape. Indeed, it provides the final proof (if further proof were needed) that the Australopithecinae stood and walked in approximately human fashion. So human in appearance is this fossil bone that the question may well be raised whether it really is part of an Australopithecine skeleton. But, apart from the fact that it is entirely consistent with the evidence previously provided by the femur and talus (and also the construction of the base of the skull), it was actually found by Dr. Broom embedded in a block of limestone matrix with portions of several other limb-bones, vertebrae and ribs and with a crushed Australopithecine skull. There can scarcely be any doubt, therefore, that all these bones are the remains of the skeleton of a single individual. It should be noted, also, that in certain features of the os innominatum, such as the details of the ischial tuberosity, it shows unusual characters which, it seems, are not paralleled either in the modern anthropoid apes or man.

It will naturally be some time before a detailed account of all this new material from Sterkfontein can be published, but private communications, together with unpublished photographs and drawings, make it clear that the information now available on the anatomy of the Australopithecinae is astonishingly complete. Stated briefly, they are ape-like creatures in respect of the general proportions of the braincase and jaws, but approach the Hominidae closely in the constructional details of the skull, in numerous features of the dentition, and particularly in the limb skeleton. There is no sign yet that the rich "lode"of Australopithecine material discovered by Dr. Broom is yet approaching exhaustion, and thus there is a reasonable possibility that further remains of the hand and foot skeleton may be found which will permit an even more precise definition of the status of these extinct hominoids. But, when all the evidence now available is published, systematists will inevitably be faced with the question whether the Australopithecinae should not be allocated to the Hominidae rather than the Pongidae.

Simultaneously with these remarkable discoveries of fossil hominoids in South Africa, discoveries of similar importance were being made in Early Miocene deposits of Kenya by Dr. L. S. B. Leakey and Dr. D. McInnes. In 1931, Dr. A. T. Hopwood described some fossil jaws and teeth recovered from Koru in Kenya and assigned them to three new genera of extinct anthropoid apes, *Proconsul*, *Xenopithecus* and *Limnopithecus*[6]. Afterwards, more Early Miocene material referable to these genera were obtained on Rusinga Island and adjacent areas by Leakey[7] and McInnes, and were described by the latter in 1943[8]. Following the Pan-African Congress on Prehistory, some of the delegates had the opportunity of visiting the sites of these discoveries and were impressed with the possibilities of further excavation. A British-Kenya Miocene Expedition was therefore organised with the aid of a grant from the Royal Society, with Dr. Leakey as field director. The expedition proved to be an outstanding success, for almost fifty specimens of fossil hominoids were collected[9]. This material is now being examined in the Department of Anatomy at Oxford, and the brief account which follows is entirely of a preliminary nature. Perhaps the most striking feature of the collection is the great variety of fossil apes which it represents. Before the first discoveries in Kenya, the only certain information available about fossil apes which existed earlier than the Middle Miocene was provided by two fragmentary jaws from the

样的直立行走方式提供了最终的证据（如果还需要进一步证据的话）。这件化石骨在形态上如此接近人类，以至于人们可能会怀疑其是否真的属于南方古猿亚科的部分骨。但是除了它与先前股骨和距骨（以及颅底的构造）提供的证据完全一致之外，实际上布鲁姆博士发现它时，它与其他的几块肢骨、椎骨和肋骨及一件压扁的南方古猿头骨一起埋在同一块石灰岩基质中。因此很难怀疑所有这些骨不是属于同一个个体的骨架残骸。另外应该说明的是，髋骨的某些特征，例如坐骨结节的细节，显示了它的确不同寻常，既不同于现代类人猿的，也不同于人类的。

对于在斯泰克方丹新发现的这批材料的详细研究成果，自然还需要一段时间才会发表，但是通过私人交流以及那些未发表的照片和绘图，我们可以确信现在获得的有关南方古猿亚科的解剖学信息已经达到了惊人的完整程度。简而言之，从脑颅和颌骨的总体比例来看，它们是类似猿类的生物；而从头骨的构造细节、齿系的诸多特征，尤其是从肢骨来看，它们又与人科很接近。然而还没有迹象表明布鲁姆博士发现的南方古猿亚科材料的丰富“矿脉”正在枯竭，因此仍然很有可能进一步发现手骨和脚骨的遗骸，这将有助于人们更准确地界定出这些已灭绝的人猿超科动物的身份。但是，当现在得到的所有证据得以发表时，分类学家们将不可避免地面对这样一个问题，即是否应该将南方古猿亚科归为猿科，而不是人科。

在南非发现这些引人注目的人猿超科动物化石的同时，利基博士和麦金尼斯博士在肯尼亚的中新世早期堆积物中也获得了类似的重要发现。1931 年，霍普伍德博士描述了从肯尼亚的科鲁挖掘的一些颌骨和牙齿化石，并将它们归入 3 个已灭绝的类人猿新属，即原康修尔猿、异猿和湖猿[6]。后来，利基[7]和麦金尼斯在鲁辛加岛及其相邻地区得到了更多属于这些属的中新世早期材料，1943 年麦金尼斯对它们进行了描述[8]。在泛非史前学大会之后，部分代表有幸参观了这些遗址，并对进一步发掘的可能性留下了深刻的印象。因此，在皇家学会资助下，一支以利基博士为野外领队的英国–肯尼亚中新世探险队组建起来了。事实证明这支探险队的组建是一项伟大的成功，因为他们收集了将近 50 件人猿超科动物化石标本[9]。现在牛津大学解剖学系正在对这批材料进行研究，即将完成的简要记述仅仅是个初步认识。这批标本最显著的特征大概是它代表了各种各样的化石猿类。在肯尼亚的第一个发现之前，关于存在于中新世中期之前的猿化石唯一确切信息是从埃及渐新世的傍猴和原上猿的两块颌骨破片上获得的。现在，在肯尼亚得到的所有新材料使我们对中新世早期

Oligocene of Egypt, *Parapithecus* and *Propliopithecus*. Now, with the accession of all the new material from Kenya, we are faced with such a bewildering variety of Early Miocene apes that it is by no means an easy matter to sort them all out. Much of the material consists of jaws and teeth of an ape considerably larger than *Proconsul africanus* (Hopwood), and in which the relative sizes of the premolars and molars, as well as the cusp pattern of the latter, also show differences. There is little doubt, therefore, that they should be assigned to a different species. To this group belongs the almost complete mandible found on Rusinga Island in 1942, as has now been established by the discovery during 1947 of a portion of the maxilla of the same individual, with the cheek teeth in position. A still larger species is represented by portions of a huge mandible found by the British-Kenya Miocene Expedition at Songhor. This jaw is in some respects more massive than that of many adult male gorillas.

In all these specimens (which provisionally are regarded as constituting several species of the genus *Proconsul*), there are certain characteristic features. The incisors are relatively small in comparison with modern apes, and the symphysial region of the jaw in narrow, the axis of the symphysis tending to be more vertical; the canines are large and there is little definite evidence of any marked sexual difference; the first lower molar is proportionately rather small, the upper molars have a well-developed internal cingulum which in some cases is elaborately beaded, and the lower molars have very evident traces of an external cingulum. Some immature jaws of *Proconsul* which have been found are particularly instructive for the information which they give on the dental succession in these primitive apes. Of similar dimensions to *Proconsul*, but with a very different cusp pattern, are a number of upper teeth found at Rusinga and the surrounding area. These show some resemblance to the teeth of the Middle Miocene Indian genus, *Sivapithecus*, and in the absence of a strongly developed internal cingulum presumably represent a type which is more generalized (or perhaps more advanced) than *Proconsul*. But more material of this type is needed before a definite diagnosis can be made.

Portions of upper and lower jaws of *Xenopithecus* with the teeth in position have now made it possible to make a fairly complete study of the dentition of this genus, and to demonstrate that it differs from *Proconsul* mainly in its smaller size and in the elongation of the last lower molar. Still smaller than *Xenopithecus* is the gibbon-like *Limnopithecus*, of which a number of jaw fragments are now available and also a maxilla and palate with the upper premolars and molars. It now appears probable, from this material, that at least two species of *Limnopithecus* existed in East Africa in the Early Miocene.

Only a few limb-bones of the Early Miocene hominoids have so far been found, but these have provided information of unusual interest. The femur provisionally referred to *Proconsul* is a long, slender and straight bone, very similar to the Eppelsheim femur, which is probably that of *Dryopithecus*. The humerus is likewise of somewhat delicate construction and, though of about the same length as that of an adult chimpanzee, lacks the powerful muscular ridges which are associated with brachiating habits. The talus and calcaneus of *Proconsul* have already been described by McInnes. It is a striking fact that, in many

就有如此多样的猿类感到困惑，因此要想将它们全部进行分类，绝不是件易事。许多标本属于一种比非洲原康修尔猿（霍普伍德）大得多的猿类，包括它的颌骨和牙齿，其中前臼齿和臼齿的相对大小以及臼齿的齿尖式样都有差异。因此，毫无疑问，它们应该被归入另一物种。1942 年在鲁辛加岛发现的几乎完整的下颌骨也属于这类猿，1947 年间发现的上颌骨残块以及原位的颊齿也属于同一个体。英国 – 肯尼亚中新世探险队在松戈尔发现一个巨大下颌骨的残块，它代表了一种更大的物种，在某些方面这件颌骨比许多成年雄性大猩猩的颌骨还要粗大。

在所有这些标本中（我们暂时把它们当作原康修尔猿属下的几个不同物种），都存在几个典型特征。与现代猿类相比门齿较小；颌骨联合部狭窄，联合部轴线更加垂直；犬齿巨大，几乎没有明显的性别差异；相应地第一下臼齿有些小，上臼齿具有发育良好的内齿带，内齿带有时候呈现为精细的串珠状，下臼齿具有非常明显的外齿带痕迹。已发现的一些原康修尔猿的未成年颌骨对于了解这些原始猿类的牙齿更替情况很有帮助。鲁辛加岛及其周边地区发现的一些上牙与原康修尔猿的上牙大小相似，但是齿尖样式差异很大。这些表明它们与中新世中期的印度的西瓦古猿属的牙齿具有某些相像之处，并且缺少发达的内齿带，这些大概代表了它们是一种比原康修尔猿更广适（或可能是更高等）的物种。但这需要更多此类材料才可以做出准确的判断。

异猿的上、下颌骨残块及其原位保存的牙齿，使得现在对该属的齿系进行非常完整的研究成为可能，也可以证明它与原康修尔猿之间的差异主要在于其牙齿较小以及最后一颗下臼齿较长。比异猿更小的是一种类似长臂猿的湖猿，现在已经获得了一些它的颌骨破片、以及带有上前臼齿和臼齿的上颌骨和腭骨。现在从这些材料似乎可以判断，在中新世早期的东非很可能曾经存在至少两种湖猿。

目前为止只发现了少量中新世早期人猿超科动物的肢骨，但它们却提供了异常有趣的信息。暂时被归入原康修尔猿的股骨为一根又长又细又直的骨，它与发现于埃珀尔斯海姆的股骨非常相似，后者可能属于森林古猿。肱骨的构造同样有些精致，并且，尽管长度与成年黑猩猩的大致相同，但是缺少供肌肉附着的强壮脊，这些脊与臂行生活习性有关。麦金尼斯已经描述了原康修尔猿的距骨和跟骨。一个惊人的

of their details, they conform much more closely to the corresponding tarsal bones of the cercopithecoid monkeys than those of the modern large apes. It is probable, indeed, that *Proconsul* was not a brachiating specialist, but led a more cursorial type of existence. Combined with certain features of the femur, the tarsal bones indicate that these Early Miocene apes were lightly built and active creatures, capable of running and leaping with considerable agility.

These observations will certainly have an important bearing on the problem of the evolution of the higher Primates, for they suggest that the adoption of the brachiating habits which are characteristic of the modern apes may have been a relatively late acquisition. More limb-bone material of the Early Miocene apes of East Africa is needed in order to follow up the very interesting implications of the specimens already available, and we require also to know more about the structure of the skull (which we have already learned was much shorter in the facial region than in the recent large apes). There is a reasonable prospect that, in continuing their excavations during the coming season, Dr. Leakey and Dr. McInnes may be able to secure this important evidence. Meanwhile, it is not a little remarkable to find, as the result of the excavations in Kenya, that already in Early Miocene times East Africa was populated with numerous species of primitive apes ranging in close gradations of size from small creatures no larger than *Hylobates* to great apes of gorilloid dimensions.

(**161**, 667-669; 1948)

W. E. Le Gros Clark: F.R.S., Department of Human Anatomy, Oxford.

References:

1. Broom, R., and Schepers, G. W. H., *Transvaal Mus. Mem.*, No. 2 (1946).
2. Dart, R., *Nature*, **155**, 195 (1925).
3. Broom, R., *Nature*, **159**, 672 (1947).
4. Broom, R., and Robinson, J. T., *Nature*, **160**, 153 (1947).
5. Broom, R., and Robinson, J. T., *Nature*, **160**, 430 (1947).
6. Hopwood, A. T., *J. Linn. Soc.*, **38**, 437 (1933).
7. Leakey, L. S. B., *Nature*, **152**, 319 (1943).
8. McInnes, D. G., *J. East Africa and Uganda Nat. Hist. Soc.*, 17 (1943).
9. Le Gros Clark, W. E., *Nature*, **160**, 891 (1947).

事实是，与现代大型猿类相比，在许多细节上它们的跗骨与猴超科的猴类更加一致。原康修尔猿可能确实不适于臂行生活，而是更适于灵巧型行走的生存方式。这些跗骨与股骨的某些特征共同暗示了这些中新世早期猿类是身体结构轻盈并且很活跃的物种，它们能够非常敏捷地奔跑和跳跃。

上述观察对研究高等灵长类的进化问题具有相当重要的意义，因为它们揭示了作为现代猿类所特有的臂行生活习性可能是在较晚时候才获得的。要想进一步探寻这些现有标本所具有的科学意义，还需要在东非发现更多中新世早期猿类的肢骨材料，我们也需要对头骨的结构（我们现在已知道这些面骨区都比近代的大型猿类的要短）了解得更多。我们希望在接下来的野外发掘工作中，利基博士和麦金尼斯博士能够保证这一重要证据的安全。同时从肯尼亚的发掘结果不难看出，早在中新世早期，在东非就生活着许多大大小小的原始猿类，其小者比长臂猿还小，而大者却类似大猩猩的体形。

（刘皓芳 翻译；同号文 审稿）

A (?) Promethean *Australopithecus* from Makapansgat Valley

R. A. Dart

Editor's Note

While investigating stone-age localities in the Makapansgat Valley, Raymond Dart and his students picked over spoil-heaps from nearby lime-works, discovering fossils of a similar age to those from Sterkfontein. Among them was the occiput (rear skull) of a "robust" australopithecine, similar to *Paranthropus* discovered at Kromdraai. In this brief report, Dart notes that whereas none of the australopithecine localities had yielded stone tools, the wide variety of animal bones seemed to have been subjected to great heat. From this evidence, Dart conceived that australopithecines used fire (hence "promethean") and perhaps exploited the bones and horns of their prey as tools and weapons, what Dart called the "osteodontokeratic" culture. These ideas have since fallen from favour for lack of evidence.

DURING 1947 the Bernard Price Foundation for Palaeontological Research in the University of the Witwatersrand maintained an archaeological party in the Makapansgat Valley, twelve miles north-east of Potgietersrust. Their principal objective was to excavate the Cave of Hearths, a site of human habitation containing palaeoliths of Chell-Acheul facies embedded in limestone breccia.

About a mile lower down the same valley is the Limeworks site where no implements have been found and from the dumps of which students and members of the staff of the Anatomy Department have been recovering primate and other mammalian fossils for several years past. The presence of *Parapapio broomi*, Jones, in the lowest stratum of the Limeworks cavern breccia shows that this earliest stratum belongs to the same geological horizon as that of Sterkfontein. Consequently it was a happy confirmation of our expectations when Mr. James Kitching came across an australopithecine occiput in this type of breccia during September 1947, while searching among the Limeworks dumps.

The new occiput (see photograph) exhibits an *Australopithecus* comparable in brain size to *Paranthropus robustus*, Broom, from Kromdraai. Owing to partial synostosis of the sagittal and lambdoid sutures the cranial fragment comprises the major portion of the occipital bone including most of the right margin of the foramen magnum and the posterior third of each parietal bone. It displays several significant humanoid anatomical features, namely, an expanded planum occipitale; an inferior situation of the inion relative to the opisthocranion and a consequent downward deflexion of the palnum nuchale

在马卡潘斯盖河谷发现的一种普罗米修斯南方古猿（尚未确定）

达特

编者按

雷蒙德·达特和他的学生们在马卡潘斯盖河谷调查石器时代的遗址，在仔细检查石灰厂附近的废石堆时，发现了一些化石，这些化石和在斯泰克方丹发现的化石年代相近。其中有一块“粗壮型”南方古猿亚科的枕骨（后颅骨），与在克罗姆德拉伊发现的傍人非常类似。在这份简要的研究报告中，达特认为没有一个南方古猿亚科遗址中有石器工具，许多野生动物的骨似乎都被大火灼烧过。根据这一证据，达特认为南方古猿亚科能够使用火（因此称为“普罗米修斯”），并且也许能将他们捕获的猎物的骨和角加以利用，做成工具和武器。达特将其称之为“骨牙角”文化。由于缺乏证据，这些观点到现在还未被完全认同。

1947 年间，威特沃特斯兰德大学的伯纳德普莱斯古生物学研究基金会在距离波特希特斯勒斯东北方向 12 英里的马卡潘斯盖河谷设立了一个考古队。他们的主要目的是发掘哈斯洞穴，这是一处被埋入石灰石角砾岩的人类居住地遗址，发现有阿舍利期的旧石器。

马卡潘斯盖河谷下游约 1 英里处有一个石灰厂，在那里没有发现任何器具。在过去的几年里，解剖学系的学生和工作人员一直都在废墟中出土灵长类和其他哺乳动物的化石。在石灰厂洞穴的角砾岩最下层保留着琼斯命名的布鲁姆副狒的化石，这表明这一早期的角砾岩与斯泰克方丹的属于同一地质年代。随后在 1947 年 9 月间，詹姆斯·基钦先生在石灰厂废墟中进行搜寻时，在这种类型的角砾岩中偶然发现了一件南方古猿亚科的枕骨，这很好地验证了我们的猜测。

这件新枕骨（见图）所展现的南方古猿与布鲁姆在克罗姆德拉伊农场发现的粗壮傍人的脑部大小相当。由于矢状缝和人字缝部分骨联合，可以认为这些颅骨破片构成了绝大部分枕骨，包括枕骨大孔的大部分右侧区域和每一顶骨的后 1/3 部分。这块枕骨显示出几个显著的人类解剖特征，即延展的枕平面，枕外隆凸点相对于颅后点较低，向下偏斜的项平面（这反映了人类直立行走的姿势），中度发育的枕横圆

(thus proving the upright posture); the existence, but moderate development, of a torus transversus occipitalis (thus indicating the lack of a gorilloid "bullneck" in the type) and the presence of a sutura transversa occipitalis (or sutura mendosa) with subsidiary sulci forming a complex "Inca" bone (which has never been found hitherto in anthropoids).

Australopithecine occiput from the Makapansgat Valley

In all these features the Makapansgat *Australopithecus* distinguishes itself from its smaller-brained contemporary *Plesianthropus* at Sterkfontein. Further, if *Paranthropus* is geologically more recent (as Broom believes), the Makapansgat type probably differed considerably from *Paranthropus*. The final answer to this question must await the discovery of further remains.

But the most potent reason for separating the new fossil from its relatives is the difference between the bone breccia of Makapansgat Limeworks on one hand and the bone breccias of all the other manape sites on the other. The breccia shows first that the Makapansgat *Australopithecus* had advanced hunting habits and secondly that it was acquainted with the use of fire. Both of these inferences from the breccia were announced nine months before the discovery of the occiput in a communication to the First Pan-African Congress of Prehistory at Nairobi in January, 1947. They are briefly recapitulated here to explain why the name, *Australopithecus prometheus*, has been given to this specimen.

In addition to the Sterkfontein types of baboons such as *Parapapio broomi*, Jones, and *Parapapio jonesi*, Broom, the Makapansgat breccia has yielded fourteen species of Bovidae, eight of which appear to be new; three carnivores (namely, lion, hyena and jackal); two extinct pigs; a rhinoceros; a hippopotamus; and two giraffes (including the extinct *Griquatherium*). Thus apart from the elephant we have concrete evidence that these creatures drew upon every family of big game found in Southern Africa for their food supply. The dentitions of the big game specimens, however, show that these Australopithecines were more frequently successful in slaying juvenile and aged representatives of these various mammalian families. But the profusion of the bone breccia shows that they were capable and successful in their hunting of very big game.

枕（提示缺乏类似大猩猩的“粗壮的颈部”）以及一个枕横缝（或称之为假缝）和一些附带的沟槽，它们共同构成一个复合“印加”骨（目前为止在类人猿中尚未发现这种结构）。

马卡潘斯盖河谷的南方古猿亚科枕骨

马卡潘斯盖南方古猿所具有的这些特征使之与其同时代的脑量稍小的斯泰克方丹迩人区别开来了。此外，布鲁姆认为，如果从地质学角度来说傍人更接近于现代的话，那么马卡潘斯盖类型就可能与傍人存在相当大的差异了。这一问题的最终答案有待更多化石的发现才能解答。

但是将新发现的化石与其相关物种区分开来的最强有力的依据是马卡潘斯盖的石灰厂的骨角砾岩与所有其他人猿遗址的骨角砾岩之间的差异。角砾岩表明马卡潘斯盖南方古猿不仅已经改进了狩猎习性，而且已经熟悉了火的使用。在 1947 年 1 月于内罗毕举行的第一届泛非史前学大会上，已经宣布了我们从角砾岩得到的这两个推论，这比发现该枕骨的时间早 9 个月。在这里简要地概括一下以解释为什么将这一标本命名为普罗米修斯南方古猿。

除了斯泰克方丹类型的狒狒（如琼斯命名的布鲁姆副狒和布鲁姆命名的琼斯副狒）外，已经从马卡潘斯盖角砾岩出土了 14 种牛科动物（其中有 8 个似乎是新种），3 种肉食动物（即狮子、鬣狗和胡狼），2 种已灭绝的猪，1 种犀牛，1 种河马和 2 种长颈鹿（包括已灭绝的长颈鹿科中的 *Griquatherium* 属）。因此除了大象，我们现在有确实的证据表明这些南方古猿亚科是依靠在南非发现的每个科的大型猎物来满足自己的食物需求的。然而，大型猎物标本的齿系显示，这些南方古猿亚科通常更善于猎杀各种哺乳动物科中的幼年和老年动物。而丰富的骨角砾岩表明它们有能力成功猎取到很大的猎物。

In 1925 the presence of *Australopithecus* was unsuspected because of the great size of these bones and their charred appearance—so the specimens of this Makapansgat Valley Limeworks bone breccia were submitted to two chemists (Drs. Moir and Fox) for analysis to discover whether the bones had been subjected to fire. From the great size of the beasts represented in the breccia, the intentional fracturing or splitting of the bones, and corroborative reports of the chemists relative to the presence of carbon, the deposit was claimed at that time as a primitive human kitchen midden. Today it appears that all this "human" activity at Makapansgat Limeworks site is the handiwork of man's australopithecine predecessors. No traces of stone implements have been found in the Makapansgat Limeworks strata nor have they been found at Taungs, Sterkfontein and Kromdraai. But we have found at Makapansgat a number of large ungulate humeri the epicondylar ridges of which were battered and broken and apparently as the result of deliberate use prior to their fossilization. Most of the bones are fresh and firm, and display clean clear lines of gross fracture before fossilization, but others crack and crumble easily. These exhibit so fine a state of macroscopic and microscopic cracking as to preclude explaining their pre-fossilization fragmentation by the crude impact of stone or bone. The most likely force to have been responsible for their crumbling and altered condition is heat. That fire was the splintering agent is corroborated by their discoloration, disintegration and the chemical reports of free carbon made more than twenty years ago, and by the vesicular character of the adjacent glassy collophanites and clays recently discovered in the breccia by Dr. V. L. Bosazza and the comparative analysis he has made of ashy deposit from the breccia with ash from local Transvaal wood.

(**162**, 375-376; 1948)

Raymond A. Dart: Medical School, Hospital Street, Johannesburg, June 15.

1925年，南方古猿的存在尚未被意料到，因为这些骨太大并且它们的外观都是烧焦的，因此在马卡潘斯盖河谷石灰厂发现的骨角砾岩标本被送到了两位化学家（莫伊尔博士和福克斯博士）的手中，以分析这些骨是否曾受到过大火的灼烧。从角砾岩中发现的野兽个头之大、这些曾被故意折断或者拆分的骨、以及化学家们给出的关于碳存在的确证报告都表明，该沉积物在那时是作为原始人类的厨房内堆积物。现在，马卡潘斯盖河谷石灰厂遗址的所有这些“人类”的活动可能都是这些南方古猿亚科祖先们的行为。在马卡潘斯盖河谷石灰厂地层没有发现任何石器的踪迹，在汤恩、斯泰克方丹和克罗姆德拉伊也没有发现石器。但是我们在马卡潘斯盖发现了许多大型有蹄类动物的肱骨，其上髁的脊很多被击打破损，表明这些肱骨在石化前曾被使用过。大部分骨是新而结实的，表明石化前就有清晰的骨折纹路，其他的骨则易碎裂。这些骨的宏观裂缝和微观裂缝保存得如此之好，足以排除在石化前它们被石器或骨强烈击打而破碎的可能。导致这些裂缝和状态改变最可能的因素就是火。另外，这些骨的脱色现象、瓦解特点和含有的自由碳，在二十多年前的化学报告中就报道了，这些现象都支持裂缝是由火造成的。最近博萨扎博士发现当地角砾岩中含有多孔易燃的胶磷矿和黏土，以及他对角砾岩中的灰烬沉积物和德兰士瓦当地木材燃烧而成的灰烬所进行的比较分析，都进一步支持裂缝是由火造成的。

（刘皓芳 翻译；刘武 邢松 审稿）

Another New Type of Fossil Ape-Man

R. Broom

Editor's Note

Robert Broom was perhaps the single most important figure in palaeoanthropology in South Africa in the early twentieth century. Without Broom's researches from the mid-1930s onwards, Dart's 1925 announcement of *Australopithecus africanus* from Taung would have remained a curiosity. By the late 1940s, Broom felt justified in saying that South Africa would yield most stages of human evolution: having unearthed slender australopithecines such as *Plesianthropus* from Sterkfontein and more robust forms such as *Paranthropus* from Kromdraai, he moved to a new site. Although only a mile from the main Sterkfontein quarry, Swartkrans quarry immediately yielded a very large form of robust australopithecine, which Broom called *Paranthropus crassidens* (now assigned to *P. robustus*, along with all other South African robust forms).

SOME years ago, I pointed out that in my opinion the cave deposits in the dolomite of the Transvaal when fully worked will give us the remains of most stages of early man and pre-man that have inhabited South Africa from probably Middle Pliocene to Recent. In the Sterkfontein area alone there are apparently in about ten square miles more than a hundred different cave deposits, and many of these are of quite different ages judging by the faunas. Almost all the animals at Kromdraai main deposit are quite different species from those at the main quarry at Sterkfontein. The jackals, the sabre-toothed tigers, the baboons, the dassies and the ape-men are quite different species.

At the beginning of November we started work at a new spot in association with the California University Expedition. Though the deposit is on the farm Swartkrans and only a mile from the main Sterkfontein quarry, the fauna so far as we have gone proves to be very different—whether older or younger we cannot yet say. Luckily we found teeth of a new type of ape-man within ten days, and a week later discovered much of a mandible with the complete lower premolars and molars.

The new mandible is not closely allied to that of the Sterkfontein ape-man *Plesianthropus*; the teeth are allied to those of the Kromdraai ape-man *Paranthropus*; but they are much larger and differ in a number of respects.

We have found two beautiful upper incisors and a perfect upper canine. These teeth are almost typically human, though a little larger than most human teeth. The canine has no deep infolding of the enamel on the lingual side as we have in the canines of *Plesianthropus*. It is also interesting to note that the canine and the 2nd incisor have been in contact, as each has been abraded by the other.

又一新型猿人化石

布鲁姆

编者按

20世纪上半叶，罗伯特·布鲁姆可能是南非古人类学界最重要的人物。如果没有布鲁姆在20世纪30年代中期之后的研究，达特于1925年在汤恩发现的南方古猿非洲种至今仍然是个谜。到20世纪40年代末，布鲁姆提出人类进化的绝大部分阶段产生于南非大陆：他挖掘出纤细型南方古猿如斯泰克方丹的迩人、粗壮型南方古猿如克罗姆德拉伊的傍人，之后他转战到新的地点。在距斯泰克方丹采石场仅一英里的斯瓦特克朗斯采石场，布鲁姆随后发现了粗壮型南方古猿的又一巨型种类，并称之为傍人粗齿种（目前已与南非所有其他粗壮型物种一起归入粗壮傍人）。

多年前我曾指出，如果充分挖掘德兰士瓦的白云石洞穴沉积物，我们会发现居住在南非的早期人类和猿人绝大部分进化阶段的化石，时间大约在上新世中期到全新世。仅在斯泰克方丹地区，大约十平方英里的区域内就有一百多个不同的洞穴沉积物，我们从动物群来判断，其中许多洞穴沉积物都代表着迥然不同的年代。从克罗姆德拉伊主要沉积物中出土的几乎所有的动物都与在斯泰克方丹主采石场发现的物种有相当大的差异，如胡狼、剑齿虎、狒狒、蹄兔和猿人之间的差异非常大。

11月初，我们和加利福尼亚大学探险队合作，在一新遗址处开始了发掘工作。尽管此处沉积物所在的斯瓦特克朗斯农场距离斯泰克方丹主采石场仅仅一英里，但是就我们发现的动物群而言，它们存在着很大差异，但是还不能断定二者谁的年代更久远。幸运的是，我们在10天之内就发现了一种新型猿人的牙齿，并在一星期后又发现了大半块下颌骨化石——具有完整的下前臼齿和臼齿。

这件新型下颌骨与斯泰克方丹猿人（迩人）的下颌骨并无紧密的亲缘关系；而牙齿与克罗姆德拉伊猿人（傍人）的牙齿具有亲缘关系，但它们的尺寸更大，并且在许多方面都有所不同。

我们发现了两颗完好的上门齿和一颗完美的上犬齿。这些牙齿几乎都是典型的人类牙齿，只不过比大多数人的牙齿稍大一点。犬齿并不像我们观察的迩人那样舌侧的珐琅质具有深层折叠现象。我们很感兴趣的一点是，其犬齿和第二门齿紧密接触，彼此间有相互磨损的痕迹。

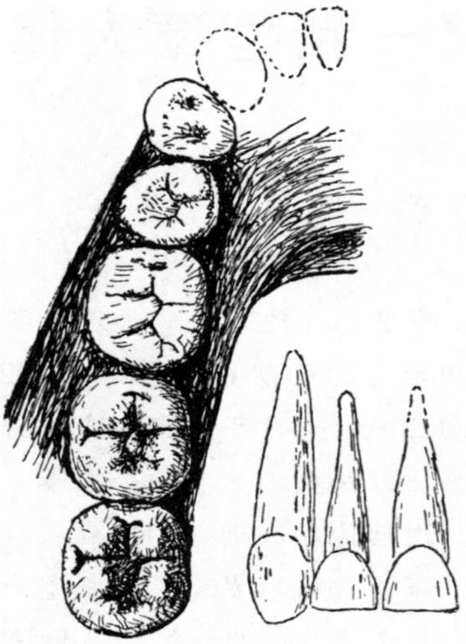

Teeth of *Paranthropus crassidens* Broom. $\frac{3}{4}$ Natural size. *A*. Left mandibular ramus. The 1st premolar is a little displaced in the specimen and has been restored to its natural position. The 3rd molar is drawn from the 3rd right molar reversed. *B*. Right upper incisors and canine

The mandible was found in the same deposit but at a spot about 10 ft. from the isolated upper teeth, and it cannot belong to the same individual though it is clearly of the same species.

The mandible is very massive. The horizontal ramus is preserved from the 2nd premolar to the 2nd molar; the 1st premolar is also preserved but a little displaced. Most of the inner side of the symphysis resembles more closely that of the Heidelberg jaw than any other specimen of man or ape-man I know.

But the teeth are relatively huge. The drawing is of the occlusal view with the 1st premolar in position, and the left 3rd molar drawn from the right tooth reversed.

This new type of ape-man is not closely allied to either *Australopithecus* or *Plesianthropus*, but is allied to *Paranthropus*. When a skull is discovered it may prove to belong to a new genus; but provisionally we may call it *Paranthropus crassidens*.

As further evidence of the richness of our deposits, attention may be directed to the wonderful finds being made in the northern Transvaal at the Makapan caves. For about a couple of years the Bernard Price Institute has been working there, and Prof. R. A. Dart has recently announced the discovery of a remarkable ape-man occiput, and a few weeks later of a very fine mandible. These he has referred to a species of *Australopithecus*, and has called the animal *A. prometheus*. Though I am not convinced that he made fire, I am of opinion that the being belongs not only to a new species but also to a new genus.

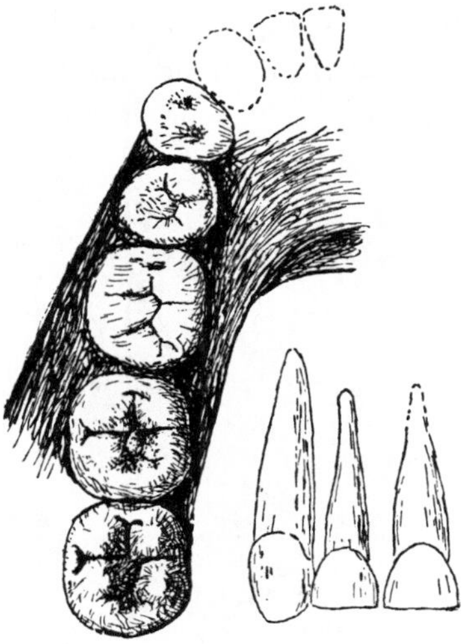

傍人粗齿种的牙齿（布鲁姆）。该图是真实尺寸的$\frac{3}{4}$。*A.* 左下颌支。第一前臼齿在本标本中有点移位了，图中将其复原到了自然位置上。第三臼齿是根据右侧第三右臼齿镜像画出来的。*B.* 右上门齿和犬齿。

下颌骨和单颗的上牙发现于同一沉积物中，但它们被发现的地点相距约10英尺，因此尽管它们明显属于同一物种，但并不能将其归属于同一个体。

该下颌骨非常大。水平支从第二前臼齿到第二臼齿都被保存下来了；第一前臼齿虽然也保存下来了，但是有些移位。与我所知的人类或者猿人任何其他的标本相比，该颌骨联合部内侧面的大部分与海德堡下颌骨更为相像。

牙齿则相对较大。图中给出的是原位上第一前臼齿的咬合面，第三左臼齿是根据右侧牙齿镜像画出来的。

这种新型的猿人与南方古猿或者迩人都没有密切的亲缘关系，而与傍人具有亲缘关系。如果再发现一件头骨，就能证明它是否属于新属，目前我们可以暂时称其为傍人粗齿种。

随着我们的沉积物中证据进一步丰富，人们可能会把注意力转移到德兰士瓦北部的马卡潘洞穴中所取得的令人惊奇的发现。伯纳德普莱斯研究所花了大约两年时间对那里进行挖掘，达特教授最近宣称发现了一件引人注目的猿人枕骨，并在几周后又发现了一具非常完好的下颌骨。他将这些定为南方古猿的一个物种，并称之为普罗米修斯南方古猿。尽管我不相信这种猿人会生火，但是我认为它们不仅是一种新的物种，而且是一新属。达特教授还有其他一些非常重要的化石，对于这些化石

Prof. Dart has some other most important remains which he is describing. But I feel at liberty only to refer to what has been already announced.

(**163**, 57; 1949)

R. Broom: Transvaal Museum, Pretoria, Dec. 7.

他还在描述当中。但是我只想冒昧地谈论一下那些已经发表了的材料。

（刘皓芳 翻译；吴秀杰 审稿）

Observations with Electron-Sensitive Plates Exposed to Cosmic Radiation

R. Brown *et al.*

Editor's Note

Inspired by recent evidence of new particles having a mass approximately 1,000 times that of the electron, physicist Cecil Powell and colleagues here report on high-altitude cloud-chamber experiments on cosmic rays: high-energy particles coming from space. They analyse one track from a particle having unit charge, called a "*k*-particle" (later a kaon), which entered the chamber and subsequently decayed into two other particles. Estimating the *k*-particle's mass by counting photographic grains, they found a value of roughly 1,080 times the electron mass. They interpret its decay as a process involving the creation of two particles called pions. These discoveries led towards the discovery, within a decade, that interactions involving the weak nuclear force do not respect mirror symmetry.

ONE of the first events found in the examination of electron-sensitive plates exposed at the Jungfraujoch is represented in the mosaic of photomicrographs shown in Fig. 8. There are two centres, *A* and *B*, from which the tracks of charged particles diverge, and these are joined by a common track, *t*. Because of the short duration of the exposure, and the small number of disintegrations occurring in the plate, the chance that the observation corresponds to a fortuitous juxtaposition of the tracks of unrelated events is very small—of the order 1 in 10^7. It is therefore reasonable to exclude it as a serious possibility. Further observations in support of this assumption are presented in a later paragraph.

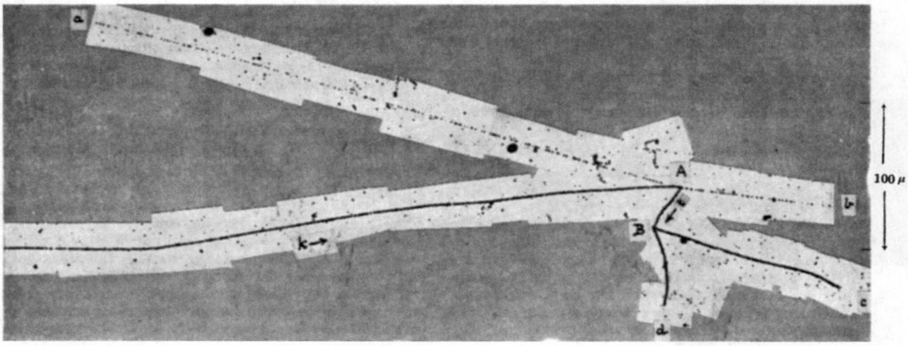

Observer: Mrs. W. J. van der Merwe

Fig. 8

在宇宙辐射下曝光的电子敏感底片的观测

布朗等

编者按

最近新发现了一种大约具有1,000倍电子质量的粒子，受到其实验证据的启发，物理学家塞西尔·鲍威尔和同事们在本文中报道了高海拔云室宇宙射线实验：来自太空的高能粒子。他们分析了一个具有单位电荷的“*k*粒子”（后来称为K介子）的径迹，这个粒子进入云室后衰变为另外两个粒子。通过计算照相颗粒他们估算了这个*k*粒子的质量，结果发现其质量大约是电子质量的1,080倍。他们把这种衰变解释为一个产生两个π介子的过程。这些结果促使人们在之后十年内有了新的发现，即包含弱核力相互作用并不遵守镜面对称。

在检查少女峰上曝光的电子敏感底片时，我们最初的重要发现之一就是如图8中显微照片的拼嵌图所表示的记录。图中存在两个中心A和B，带电粒子的径迹从这两点开始分裂，并且以常见的径迹t相连接。由于曝光的时间很短，并且仅有少量的蜕变反映在底片上，因此观测结果中对应于无关事件径迹偶然交叉重叠的可能性是非常小的，仅为1×10^{-7}量级，因此我们可以将这种重要的可能性合理地排除。后面我们将会给出进一步支持上述假设的观测结果。

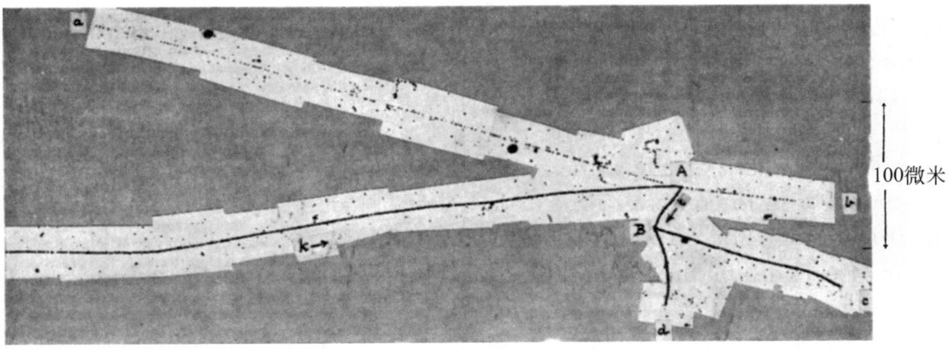

观测者：范德梅伟

图8

An inspection of the track *k* shows that the particle producing it approached the centre of disintegration *A*. The range of the particle in the emulsion exceeds 3,000 μ, and there is continuous increase in the grain-density along the track in approaching *A*. Near *A*, the grain-density is indistinguishable from that of particles of charge *e*, recorded in the same plate, near the end of their range.

The evidence for the direction of motion of the particle based on grain-counts is supported by observations on the small-angle deviations in the track due to Coulomb scattering. These deviations are most frequent near *A*, and the scattering is less marked at points remote from it.

From these observations, it is reasonable to conclude that the particle *k* approached the point *A*; that it carried the elementary electronic charge and that it had reached, or was near, the end of its range at the point *A*. We therefore assume that the particle *k* initiated the train of events represented by the tracks radiating from *A* and *B*. It follows that the particle producing track *t* originated in star *A*, and produced the disintegration *B*. In order to analyse the event, we first attempted to determine the mass of the particle *k*.

Mass Determinations by Grain-Counts

About a year ago, experiments were made in this Laboratory to determine the ratio, m_π/m_μ, of the masses of π- and μ-mesons, by the method of grain-counting[5], and by studying the small-angle scattering of the particles in their passage through the emulsion[4]. The values obtained by the two methods were $m_\pi/m_\mu = 1.65 \pm 0.11$, and $m_\pi/m_\mu = 1.35 \pm 0.10$*, respectively. Recent experiments at Berkeley[6] suggest that the true value is 1.33 ± 0.02, a result which throws serious doubt on the reliability of the method based on grain-counts. Because of the advantage of this method, and of the important conclusions which have been based on it, experiments were made to determine the conditions in which reliable results can be obtained.

In the first experiments[5], the two most serious experimental difficulties arose from the fading of the latent image and from the variation of the degree of development with depth. This made it necessary to work only with tracks formed contemporaneously; to compare the grain-density along the tracks of the π- and μ-mesons of the same pair. As a result, the tracks of the π-mesons available for measurement were, in most cases, shorter than 400 μ. In continuing the experiments, much more favourable conditions were obtained by using short exposures, so that the effects of fading were negligible; and by developing the plates by the method employed by Dilworth, Occhialini and Payne[7], which

* For the following reasons, the limits of error quoted above, in the determination of m_π/m_μ by observations on scattering, are less than those given in ref. 4. Previously, values for the mass of the different types of mesons, classified phenomenologically, were given separately. It is now known, however, that at least the majority of the σ-mesons are π^--particles; and the ρ-mesons, μ^+- and μ^--particles. The different results can therefore be combined to give a value for m_π/m_μ with a greater statistical weight.

对径迹 k 的检验表明，产生它的粒子到达蜕变中心 A 的附近。该粒子在乳胶中的射程超过 3,000 微米，在接近 A 的过程中，径迹的颗粒密度逐渐增加。在 A 附近，其颗粒密度与同在该底片上记录的电荷为 e 的粒子接近射程终端处的颗粒密度无法区分。

观测发现库仑散射造成了径迹的小角度偏离，这支持了基于颗粒计数得到的关于粒子运动方向的证据。这些偏离在靠近 A 时出现得最为频繁，而散射在远离 A 的各点处比较不明显。

根据这些观测我们有理由认为，粒子 k 向 A 点靠近；它携带着基本电子电荷，并在 A 点附近达到或接近其射程的终端。因此我们假设，粒子 k 引发了一连串由 A 和 B 的辐射径迹所代表的事件。由此可知，该粒子产生了源自于 A 点并在 B 点产生蜕变的径迹 t。为了分析该事件，我们首先尝试了对粒子 k 的质量进行确定。

根据颗粒计数所做的质量测定

约在一年前，本实验室采用颗粒计数的方法 [5] 以及研究粒子通过乳胶时小角度散射的方法 [4]，进行了测定 π 介子和 μ 介子（编者注：现在粒子物理认为“μ 介子”不是介子，而是一种轻子，因此正确的称谓应为“μ 子”。考虑到历史原因，文中仍保留“μ 介子”的译法。）的质量比 m_π/m_μ 的实验。用这两类方法得到的结果分别为 $m_\pi/m_\mu=1.65\pm0.11$ 和 $m_\pi/m_\mu=1.35\pm0.10$*。最近在伯克利进行的实验 [6] 表明，其真值为 1.33 ± 0.02，这个结果使人们对颗粒计数方法的可靠性产生了严重的怀疑。但是考虑到该方法的优点，以及据此得到的一些重要结论，我们进行了一些实验来确定在何种条件下才能获得可靠的结果。

在首次实验中 [5]，两个最为严重的实验难点来自于潜影的褪色和显像度随深度的变化。若要对同一对 π 介子和 μ 介子径迹的颗粒数密度进行对比，就必须研究同时形成的径迹。然而这样一来，可以用于测量的 π 介子的径迹大多小于 400 微米。在后续的实验中，通过运用短期曝光的方法获得了更多良好条件，这使得褪色效应可以被忽略；与此同时，还采用了迪尔沃思、奥恰利尼和佩恩 [7] 所使用的冲洗底片

---

* 基于以下理由，上文所引用的由散射观测给出的 m_π/m_μ 值的误差极限要比参考文献 4 中的小。以前，基于现象分类的不同介子的质量是分别给出的。然而现在已知，至少 σ 介子中大部分是 π^- 粒子，ρ 介子中大部分是 μ^+ 和 μ^- 粒子，将不同的结果综合起来可得一个更大统计权重下的 m_π/m_μ 数值。

gives a nearly uniform degree of development with depth.

In the plates obtained by these methods, it is legitimate to compare the grain-density in the tracks of unrelated particles. Further, it is now known that at least the majority, and possibly all, the mesons which produce "stars" are π^--particles[6,8]; and that most of the ρ-mesons are μ^+- and μ^--particles. In determining m_π and m_μ, we have therefore made measurements on the tracks of π^+- and π^--, μ^+- and μ^--particles, of length greater than 1,000 μ, comparing the results with those of similar measurements made on the tracks of protons. In these conditions, we have found $m_\pi/m_\mu = 1.33 \pm 0.05$. A detailed account of the observations will be published elsewhere; but, for the purpose of the present paper, it is sufficient to note that the results appear to be in good accord with those obtained by other methods. We conclude that, using the Ilford *C*2 emulsion in the new conditions, reliable information can be obtained.

We have seen that the conditions of uniform development and absence of fading have been achieved in the present experiments with the new Kodak emulsions, and we therefore attempted to measure the mass of particles by similar methods to those employed with the Ilford plates. The results obtained in observations on the tracks of four protons and four μ-particles, occurring in the same plate, are represented in Fig. 9. In this figure, the number of grains per unit length in the tracks is plotted for different values of the residual range; and the mean values, for tracks of the same type, are indicated by the full lines. The ratio of the masses of the two types of particles can be deduced by making a comparison of the values of the residual range at which the grain densities have the same value. The result thus obtained is $m_\mu = 220 \pm 20\ m_e$.

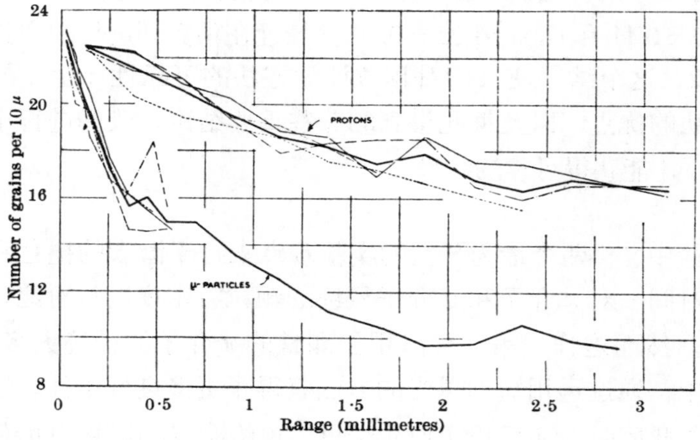

Fig. 9

Using similar methods, we have made estimates of the mass of the particle, *k*, and the measurements are represented in Fig. 10. This figure shows the mean values of the grain-density in the tracks of the four μ-mesons and four protons, together with the corresponding results for the particle *k*. All the tracks under consideration occurred in the same plate.

的方法，这种方法获得了与深度几乎一致的显像度。

用上述方法得到的底片来比较不相关粒子径迹的颗粒密度是合理的。此外，现在知道，产生“星”点的介子中至少多数甚至可能全部是 π^- 粒子 [6,8]；而大多数 ρ 介子是 μ^+ 粒子和 μ^- 粒子。因此在测定 m_π 和 m_μ 的实验中，我们对长度大于 1,000 微米的 π^+ 和 π^-、μ^+ 和 μ^- 粒子的径迹进行了测量，并将其与用类似方法对质子径迹的测量结果作了比较。在上述条件下，我们得出 $m_\pi/m_\mu=1.33\pm0.05$。观测的详细计算将另行发表；考虑到本文的目的，这里只需指出该结果与用其他方法获得的结果非常一致就足够了。由此我们认为，在新的条件下，用伊尔福 $C2$ 乳胶能够获得可靠的信息。

我们已经知道，目前实验中所用的新柯达乳胶已可以同时满足均匀显像和不变色的条件，因此我们试图用类似方法并使用伊尔福胶片对粒子的质量进行测量。图 9 显示了在同一胶片中四个质子和四个 μ 粒子的径迹的观测结果。在图中，用径迹中单位长度的颗粒数对不同残余射程值作图；同一类型径迹的平均值用粗线表示。两类粒子的质量比可通过比较颗粒密度相同时所对应的残余射程值导出。由此得到的结果为 $m_\mu = 220 \pm 20\ m_e$。

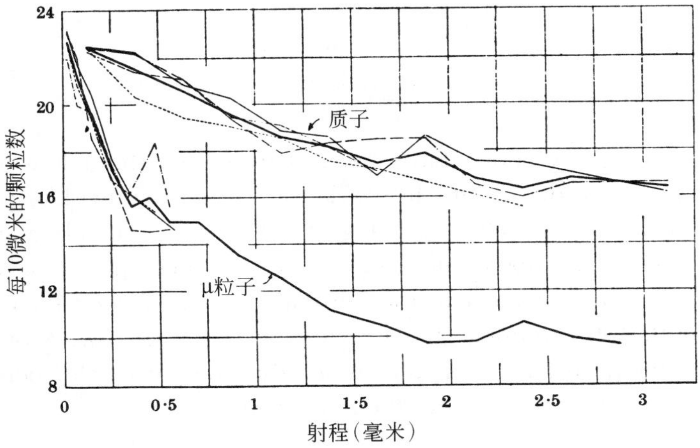

图 9

用类似的方法，我们已估算了粒子 k 的质量值，测量结果如图 10 所示。这个图给出了四个 μ 介子和四个质子的径迹中的颗粒密度的平均值，同时也给出了粒子 k 的颗粒密度。上述所有径迹均在同一张底片中获得。

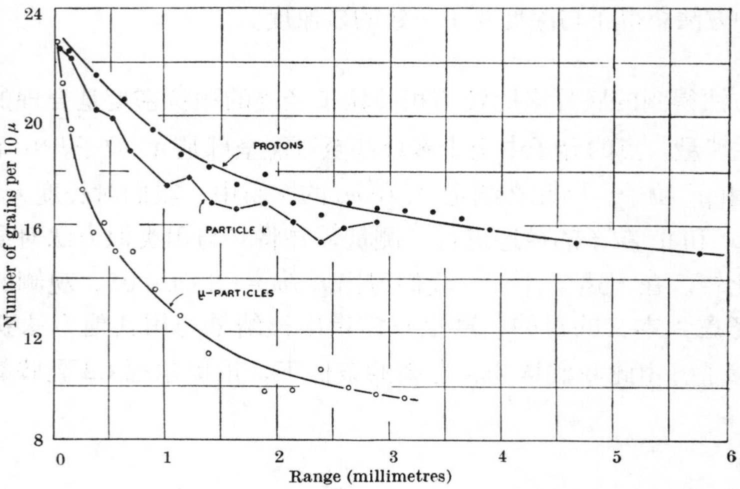

Fig. 10

Table 1 shows the values of the mass of the particle, *k*, as determined from these results, by making a comparison of the grain-density in the track of the particle with the mean curve for protons. The values thus obtained are all independent and the mean is m_k=1,080±160 m_e.

Table 1. Determination of the ratio, m_P/m_k, of the mass of a proton to that of particle, *k*, by grain-counting

	Individual independent values						
m_P/m_k	1.77	1.88	1.49	1.64	2.17	1.79	1.32
	1.71	1.66	1.27	1.69	2.13	1.55	
	Mean value: 1.70; m_k =1,080 ± 160 m_e						

The limits of error given above have been deduced in the following manner: We have compared the grain-density in the tracks of the four individual protons with the mean curve for the same particles—(see Fig. 9)—and have thus obtained a number of independent values for the apparent mass of each of these particles. The distribution in these values allows us to calculate the "probable error" associated with the mass as determined from the observations on any one track, expressed as a percentage of the apparent mass of the particle. It is then assumed that the "probable" percentage error in the calculated mass of the particle *k* has the same value.

We have also determined the mass m_k by studying the small-angle scattering of the particle, by the methods recently described[4], and the result thus obtained is m_k = 1,800 ± 400 m_e. If the true mass of the particle is 1,080 m_e, the chance that the value obtained by observations on scattering shall be equal to, or greater than, 1,800 m_e is one in four. Because of the large statistical fluctuations associated with the observations in the scattering experiments, we give more weight to the measurements by grain-counting.

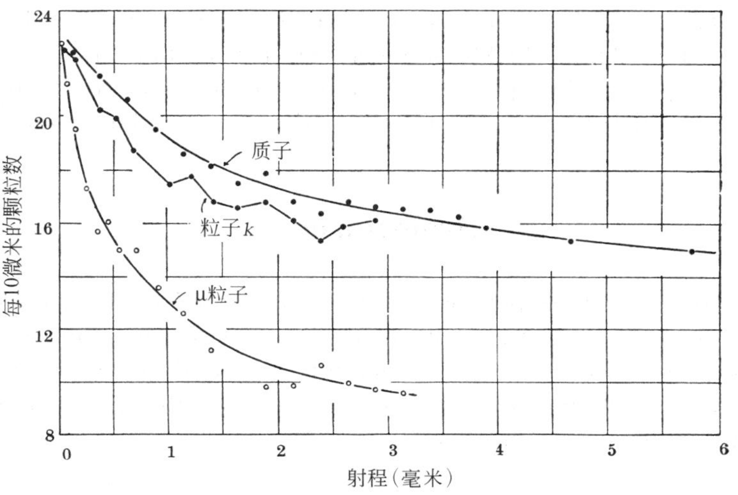

图 10

将粒子 k 径迹中的颗粒密度与质子平均曲线进行对比，表 1 给出了比较结果以及由此测定的 k 粒子的质量值。这些值都是独立的，平均值是 m_k =1,080 ±160 m_e。

表 1. 利用颗粒计数测得的质子质量与粒子 k 质量的比值 m_P/m_k

	各自独立的值						
m_P/m_k	1.77	1.88	1.49	1.64	2.17	1.79	1.32
	1.71	1.66	1.27	1.69	2.13	1.55	
	平均值：1.70; m_k =1,080 ± 160 m_e						

上述给出的误差极限由下述方式导出：我们已对四个单独质子的径迹中的颗粒密度与它们的径迹颗粒密度的平均曲线（见图 9）进行了比较，并由此得到了每个粒子表观质量的若干独立值。根据这些值的分布，我们可以计算出在依据每个单独径迹测定质量的过程中所产生的“或然误差”,并将其表示为粒子表观质量的百分比。然后我们假设计算出的粒子 k 的质量具有相同的“或然”百分比误差。

我们也用最近介绍的方法[4]，即通过研究粒子的小角度散射确定了质量 m_k，由此得到的结果是 m_k=1,800±400 m_e。如果粒子质量的真值是 1,080 m_e，通过散射观测得到的值等于或大于 1,800 m_e 的概率是 1/4。由于散射实验的观测有较大的统计涨落，因此我们给颗粒计数的测量以更大的权重。根据这些观测，似乎可以肯定，m_k 的真

It appears certain, from these observations, that the true value of m_k lies between 700 and 1,800 m_e, and we think it highly probable that it is substantially less than that of the proton. Thus every individual point representing the grain-density in the track k, at a particular value of the residual range, lies below the corresponding points for each of the four protons.

Disintegration "*B*"

The tracks, *c* and *d*, of the two particles emitted from point *B* are characteristic of protons or heavier particles, and we regard them as due to a disintegration produced by the particle *t*. This particle was frequently scattered in passing through the emulsion and was therefore of low velocity; and the evidence is consistent with the assumption that it had reached the end of its range at the point *B*.

The only known slow charged particle which is capable of producing a disintegration of the type represented by star *B* is a π^--particle[6,8]. We therefore assume that a negative meson of mass 286 m_e was created at the point *A*, and reached the end of its range to produce the disintegration *B*.

Transmutation "*A*"

In order to interpret the transmutation *A*, we first made a detailed examination of the tracks of the emitted particles. Of the two tracks *a* and *b*, the former has a length in the emulsion of more than 2,000 μ, and ends in the surface, whereas *b* ends in the glass and is 116 μ long. The grain-densities in the two tracks are equal to within the limits defined by the statistical fluctuations. The average grain-density in the long track *a* is 49.0 grains per 100 μ; that is, 2.17 times the value characteristic of minimum ionization for a particle of charge *e*. Unless we admit the existence of fractional values of the electronic charge, we must conclude that the particles producing the tracks *a* and *b* both carried charges of magnitude *e*.

In order to determine the possible values for the energy of the particles producing tracks *a* and *b*, we have calculated the variation with energy of the specific ionization of a particle of charge *e*, from the formula of Halpern and Hall[9], assuming the atomic composition of the emulsion to be identical with that of the Ilford *C*2 plates. This formula is a modification of that of Bloch[10]; it applies to particles moving in a solid medium and gives results in good agreement with experiment for particles of low energy. The results are shown in Fig. 11, where the specific ionization is plotted as a function of the quantity E/m, where E is the energy and m the mass of the particle, both quantities being measured in MeV. From Fig. 11, we have determined the possible values of the energy of the particles, *a*, *b*, corresponding to the observed grain-density in the tracks, assuming them to be protons, π-mesons, μ-mesons or electrons. The resulting values are tabulated in Table 2.

值位于 700 m_e 和 1,800 m_e 之间，我们认为它极可能远小于质子的质量。因此，在某一特定的残余射程值处，径迹 k 中每一个表示颗粒密度的点，都位于四个质子中相应的点之下。

"B" 蜕变

由点 B 发射的两个粒子的径迹 c 和 d 具有质子或较重粒子的特性，我们认为这源自于粒子 t 产生的蜕变。该粒子在通过乳胶时频繁地散射，因此速度很低；这个现象与其在 B 点达到射程终点的假设是一致的。

目前已知能够产生具有星点 B 特征的蜕变的慢带电粒子只有 π^- 粒子 [6,8]。因此我们假定，在点 A 产生了质量为 286 m_e 的负介子，在达到其射程终点时产生 B 蜕变。

"A" 嬗变

为了解释 A 嬗变，我们首先对发射粒子的径迹做了详细的检查。在径迹 a 和 b 中，前者的径迹在乳胶中的长度大于 2,000 微米，并在表面终止，而径迹 b 的长度是 116 微米且在玻璃中终止。两个径迹的颗粒密度在统计涨落所确定的极限之内相等。在长径迹 a 中，平均颗粒密度是每 100 微米 49.0 个颗粒，该密度是电荷为 e 的粒子最小电离特征值的 2.17 倍。除非我们允许存在电荷的分数值，否则我们必然会得出，产生径迹 a 和 b 的粒子的带电量均为 e 的量级。

为了测定产生径迹 a 和 b 的粒子能量的可能值，我们假定乳胶的原子组分与伊尔福 C2 胶片相同，根据哈尔彭和霍尔的公式 [9] 计算了电荷为 e 的粒子的比电离值随能量的变化。这个公式是布洛赫公式 [10] 的修正形式；该公式适用于在固体介质中运动的粒子，并给出了与低能粒子的实验非常符合的结果。结果示于图 11 中，将比电离值作为量 E/m 的函数绘图，E 和 m 分别为粒子的能量和质量，两个量均以兆电子伏为单位测量。根据图 11，假定粒子是质子、π 介子、μ 介子或电子，我们确定了对应于径迹中观测到的颗粒密度的粒子 a、b 能量的可能值。所得到的结果列于表 2 中。

Table 2. Values of the energy and momentum of the particle producing track *a*, as deduced from the observed grain-density and scattering, making various assumptions concerning the mass of the particle

Assumed particle			proton	π-meson	μ-meson	electron
Energy in MeV.	(*a*)	below minimum ionization	235±95	37±13	27±11	0.13±0.05
	(*b*)	above minimum ionization				>1,000
Momentum MeV./*c*	(*a*)	below minimum ionization	700±160	109±22	80±15	0.4±0.1
	(*b*)	above minimum ionization				>1,000
	(*c*)	from scattering observations	245±40	113±18	100±16	68±11
	(*d*)	from momentum balance	98±5	98±5	98±5	98±5

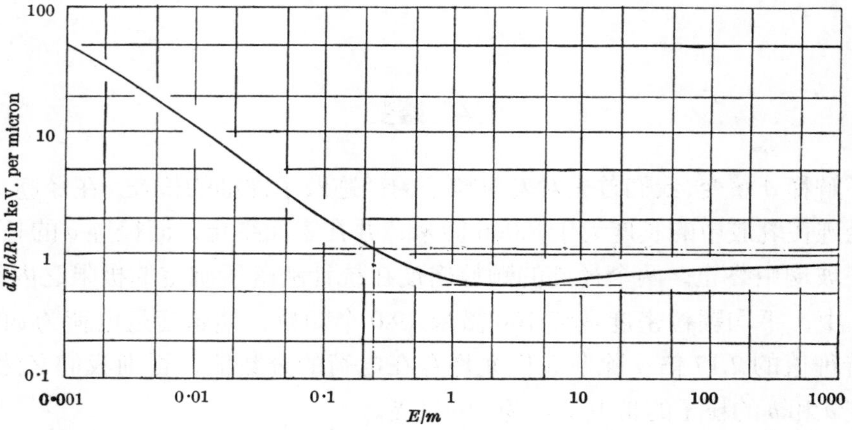

Fig. 11. Variation of the rate of loss of energy of a particle of charge $|e|$ as a function of the quantity E/m, where E is the kinetic energy and m the mass of the particle, both quantities being measured in MeV.

There are two possible interpretations of the transmutation produced at *A* by the particle *k*. We can assume, either that the particle was captured by a nucleus, or that it decayed spontaneously. From the measured values of the mass of the particle, it would be possible, from the point of view of the conservation of mass and energy, to admit that, at the end of its range in the emulsion, it was captured by a nucleus and led to the ejection of two energetic protons and a π^--particle. It appears almost certain, however, that the release in a nucleus of such a large amount of energy would lead to the "evaporation" of many nucleons, a process commonly observed in plates exposed to the cosmic radiation; and that two protons of great energy would be only two components of a "many-pronged" star. (It may be noticed that we cannot assume that the particle *k* was captured by one of the rare nuclei of heavy hydrogen, present in the gelatine. In such an interaction, the algebraic sum

表 2. 基于有关粒子质量的各类假设，根据观测颗粒密度和散射导出的产生径迹 a 的粒子的能量和动量值

假设的粒子		质子	π 介子	μ 介子	电子
能量（兆电子伏）	(*a*) 在最小电离作用之下	235±95	37±13	27±11	0.13±0.05
	(*b*) 在最小电离作用之上				＞1,000
动量（兆电子伏 / 光速）	(*a*) 在最小电离作用之下	700±160	109±22	80±15	0.4±0.1
	(*b*) 在最小电离作用之上				＞1,000
	(*c*) 根据散射观测	245±40	113±18	100±16	68±11
	(*d*) 根据动量平衡	98±5	98±5	98±5	98±5

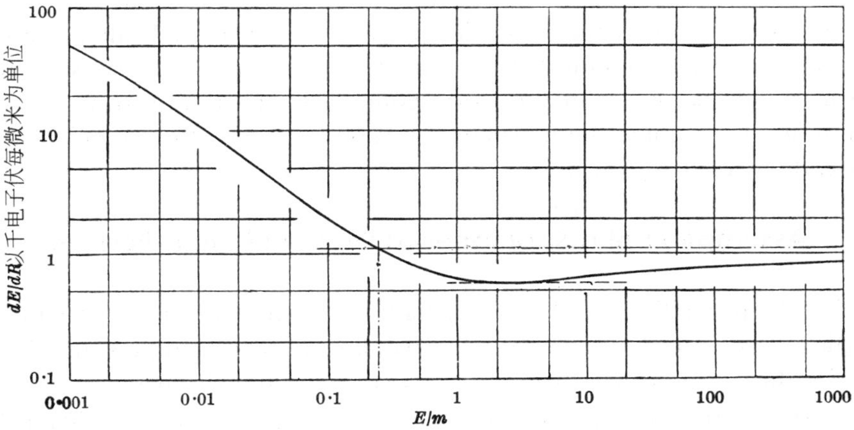

图11. 电荷为 $|e|$ 的粒子能量损失的速率随 E/m 变化的函数。其中 E 是动能，m 是粒子质量，两个量的测量单位都是兆电子伏。

粒子 k 在 A 点产生嬗变有两种可能的解释。我们可以假定，粒子或被核俘获，或产生自发衰变。从粒子质量的测量值来看，根据质量和能量守恒的观点，可能的情况是它在乳胶中射程的终点处被核俘获，并导致两个高能质子和一个 π^- 粒子的发射。然而几乎同样确定的是，如此大量的能量在核中释放将导致很多核子的“蒸发”，这个过程在对宇宙辐射曝光的底片中很常见；还可以基本确定的是两个高能质子将是“多股”星仅有的两个组分。（可以注意到，我们不可以假定粒子 k 是被存在于凝胶体中的某个稀有的重氢核所俘获。在这种相互作用中，两个初始粒子电荷的代数

of the charges on the two initial particles is 0 or $2e$, whereas that of the product particles is e or $3e$.) We shall see later that there are other objections to the hypothesis that the tracks a and b were produced by protons, or heavier nuclei of charge e.

It follows from the above considerations that if we are to describe the transmutation in terms of particles of which the existence is already established, we must attribute the tracks a and b either to electrons, to μ-mesons or to π-mesons. Considering the first of these possibilities, we must assume the electrons to have had an energy value greater than that corresponding to minimum ionization, namely, greater than 1,000 MeV.; for with the alternative lower value corresponding to the observed ionization, 300 keV., the particle would have had a range in the emulsion of only about 100 μ, and would have been frequently scattered. The assumption that the particles a and b were electrons is therefore inconsistent with the conservation of energy and can be rejected. We are left with the alternatives that the tracks were produced either by π- or by μ-mesons.

If the particles a and b were mesons, we must assume, in order to conserve mass-energy, that their kinetic energies were 27 MeV. or 37 MeV., respectively, in the case of μ- or π-mesons (see Fig. 11). In either case, it appears to be very difficult to reconcile the observations with the assumption that the particles were emitted as a consequence of the liberation in a nucleus of the energy corresponding to the rest-mass of particle k. We are therefore led to examine the possibility of explaining the observations in terms of a spontaneous decay of this particle.

Assumption of a Spontaneous Decay of the *k*-Particle

In examining the possibility that the transmutation A corresponds to a spontaneous decay of the particle k, we require to know the relative directions of motion of the three ejected particles. For this purpose it is necessary to determine the shrinkage of the emulsion; the ratio, S, of the thickness of the emulsion during exposure to that after it had been developed, fixed and dried. We have measured this quantity by examining the tracks of α-particles, produced in the emulsion by uncontrolled radioactive contamination. Among such "stars", it is possible to identify some, due to an original atom of radiothorium, from which an α-particle of thorium C′ was emitted. The shrinkage has been measured by determining the lengths of the projection of the corresponding tracks on the surface of the emulsion, and their apparent angles of "dip". The value of the "shrinkage" thus found is $S = 2.7 \pm 0.1$. Knowing the value of S, the original orientation of a track in the emulsion, before processing, can be determined, in favourable cases, with a precision of the order of 1°, by observing the apparent angle of "dip" of the particle, and the direction of its projection on the plane defined by the surface of the emulsion. Using these methods, the original directions of motion of the three particles a, b and t were found to be coplanar. The departure of the direction of motion of any one particle from the plane defined by the other two is less than 4°. The error in this determination is largely due to the fact that track t is of short range, and the particle producing it was of low velocity, and frequently scattered.

和是 0 或 $2e$，而产生的粒子的电荷代数和是 e 或 $3e$。）对于径迹 a 和 b 是由质子或带电荷 e 的较重核产生的这一假说，稍后我们将介绍其他一些反对意见。

根据上述考虑，如果我们要用已确定存在的粒子来描述嬗变，那么我们必须将径迹 a 和 b 认为是由电子、μ 介子或 π 介子这三者之一所产生的。如果是电子，则我们必须假设电子的能量大于相应的最小电离能，即大于 1,000 兆电子伏；对应于观测到的较低的电离入射能量 300 千电子伏，粒子在乳胶中仅有约 100 微米的射程，并且会被频繁地散射。因此认为粒子 a 和 b 是电子的假设与能量守恒不相符，可以被排除。我们只能在剩下的 π 介子或 μ 介子中择一作为产生径迹的粒子。

如果粒子 a 和 b 是介子，那么为了使质能守恒，我们必须假定在 μ 介子或 π 介子的情况下（见图 11），其动能分别为 27 兆电子伏和 37 兆电子伏。如果假设粒子的发射是由于核内释放了相应于粒子 k 静止质量的能量，那么无论是上述哪种介子，观测结果都很难与该假设相一致。因此，我们只能尝试用这个粒子的自发衰变来对观测结果进行解释了。

k 粒子自发衰变的假定

在确定 A 嬗变是否对应于粒子 k 的自发衰变时，我们需要知道三个射出粒子的相对运动方向。为此必须确定乳胶的收缩，即在曝光时乳胶的厚度与经过显影、定影和烘干后的乳胶的厚度比值 S。我们已经通过检验在不可控制的放射性沾染下乳胶中产生的 α 粒子的径迹测量了这个量。在这类“星”中，可以确定其中一些情况是由放射性钍的天然原子产生的，一个钍 C′ 发射一个 α 粒子。通过测定乳胶表面上相应径迹投影的长度以及其“下陷”的表观角度，已测得了乳胶的收缩。由此获得的“收缩”值为 $S=2.7\pm0.1$。知道了 S 的值，那么通过观测粒子“下陷”的表观角度以及由乳胶表面确定的平面投影方向，便可以测定乳胶被处理前其中的径迹的原始取向，在较好的情况下，精度可达 1°量级。采用这些方法，获得的三个粒子 a、b、t 运动的原始方向是共面的。任何一个粒子的运动方向与另两个粒子所确定的平面之间的偏离小于 4°。在这项测定中的误差主要来源于径迹 t 是短程的，产生它的粒子是低速的并被频繁地散射。

The values of the angles between the directions of motion of the particles in the common plane are shown in Fig. 12. The observed coplanarity makes it legitimate to assume that the three particles arise as a result of the spontaneous decay of the *k*-particle at the end of its range in the emulsion, and that they are the only product of its disintegration; that no neutral particles, which would escape observation, are emitted. It follows that the vector sum of the momenta of the three particles must be assumed to be equal to zero.

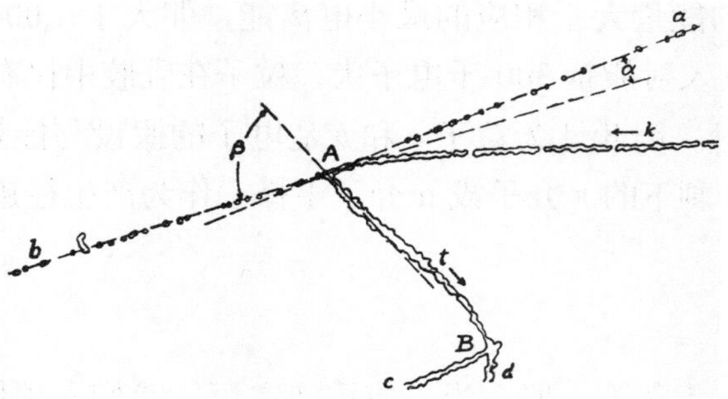

Fig. 12. Facsimile drawing of the event shown in Fig. 8, made with the projection microscope. The actual angles α and β, measured in the common plane of the three tracks, *a*, *b* and *t*, are: $\angle\ \alpha=9.8°$; $\angle\ \beta=76.6°$

If we are correct in attributing the track *t* to a π^--particle, it follows from the observed range, 45 μ, that the kinetic energy of ejection was 1.04 MeV. The corresponding value of the momentum of the particle is 17.5 MeV./*c*. From the observed directions of motion, the momenta of the particles giving tracks *a* and *b* are then found to be 98±5 and 104±5 MeV./*c*, respectively. These values are to be compared with those corresponding to electrons or mesons listed in Table 2, which have been deduced from the observed grain-density in the tracks. We have seen that the values given in Table 2 for the momenta of the two particles, if they are assumed to be electrons, are many times too large. It follows that there is a wide departure from a momentum balance if the tracks *a* and *b* are assumed to be due to either electrons or protons. Further, the values of the momenta, as deduced from observations on the scattering of the particles, are inconsistent with those obtained from grain-counts, if the particles are assumed to have been either electrons or protons (see Table 2).

The agreement between the sets of values for mesons, however, is most remarkable, and gives strong support for the assumption of a spontaneous decay of the *k*-particle. Only a very rare combination of unrelated features, including the co-planarity of the tracks and the directions of motion of the particles in the common plane, the range of the particle *t*, and the specific ionization of the particles producing tracks *a* and *b*, could produce such an agreement between the estimated values of the momenta, if the result is fortuitous.

The values of the momenta of the particles producing tracks *a* and *b*, as determined by the three different methods, are consistent, within the errors of measurements, with the assumption of a spontaneous decay of the *k*-particle whether the product particles are assumed to be μ-mesons or π-mesons. We can apply a further test by calculating the values of the rest-mass of the particle *k* which corresponds to the two different assumptions, and

共面的粒子运动方向之间的角度值示于图 12 中。根据观测到的共面性可以合理地得出以下假设：三个粒子来自于粒子 k 在乳胶的射程终端的自发衰变，并且它们是蜕变仅有的产物，整个过程没有中性粒子发射（中性粒子无法观测）。由此，必然会得出三个粒子动量的矢量和等于零的结论。

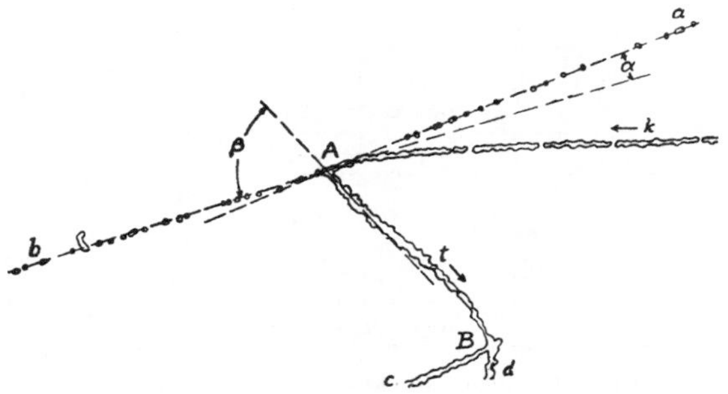

图 12. 用投影显微镜作的图 8 中示出的事件的复制图。在三个径迹 a、b、t 的共面中测得的实际角 α 和 β 分别是：$\angle\alpha = 9.8°$，$\angle\beta = 76.6°$。

如果我们将径迹 t 归因于 π^- 粒子是正确的，则根据观测到 45 微米的射程可得，发射的动能是 1.04 兆电子伏。该粒子相应的动量值是 17.5 兆电子伏 / 光速。根据观测到的运动方向，可得产生径迹 a 和 b 的粒子的动量分别为 98 ± 5 兆电子伏 / 光速和 104 ± 5 兆电子伏 / 光速。这些值将与表 2 中列出的根据观测的径迹中颗粒密度而导出的相应的电子或介子的数值相比较。我们已看到表 2 中列出的两个粒子的动量值，如果假定它们是电子，则这些值显然已大出很多倍。因此如果假定径迹 a 和 b 是由电子或质子产生的，则与动量平衡存在很大的偏差。而且无论粒子是电子还是质子（见表 2），根据粒子观测到的散射而导出的动量值与从颗粒密度得出的值也是不一致的。

然而，介子的数值之间的一致性是最为突出的，这有力地支持了粒子 k 的自发衰变的假设。如果结果是偶然的，那么须同时具备以下几个不相关的特征才能得到与估算的动量值吻合很好的情况，这些特征包括：在同一平面中粒子的径迹和运动方向的共面性、粒子 t 的射程以及产生径迹 a 和 b 的粒子电离比值，而这种情况是非常罕见的。

假设粒子 k 发生自发衰变，则无论产生的粒子是 μ 介子还是 π 介子，用三类不同方法测定的产生径迹 a 和 b 的粒子的动量值，在测量误差允许的范围内都是一致的。我们可以通过计算两种不同假设下的粒子 k 的静止质量来进行进一步的测试，结果

the results are tabulated in Table 3.

Table 3. Estimates of the mass of particle *k* based on total release of mass and energy, for two assumed modes of decay

	Track "*a*"	Track "*b*"	Track "*t*"
(i) $k \rightarrow \pi^- + \pi + \pi$			
Particle	π	π	π^-
Rest-mass (m_e)	286	286	286
Energy in m_e	61	64	2
Total = m_k = 985 m_e			
(ii) $k \rightarrow \pi^- + \mu + \mu$			
Particle	μ	μ	π^-
Rest-mass (m_e)	212	212	286
Energy in m_e	76	81	2
Total = m_k = 869 m_e			

In calculating the energy of the particles producing tracks *a* and *b*, it is assumed that the particle producing track *t* is a π^--particle, of momentum 17.5 MeV./*c*; knowing the relative directions of motion of the three ejected particles, the momenta of the other two particles are determined, and hence the energies corresponding to any assumed mass.

It will be seen from Table 3 that the assumption of two μ-mesons corresponds to a rest mass of the *k*-particle of 869 m_e; and for two π-mesons, 985 m_e. The assumption of different particles, one π- and one μ-meson, gives an intermediate value of approximately 925 m_e. In view of the error in the direct determination of m_k, the results are not decisive.

If the transmutation is to be interpreted in terms of particles of which the existence is already established, we are left with four possibilities for the nature of the particles producing tracks *a* and *b*. These are indicated schematically in Table 4.

Table 4. Comparison of the observed and calculated values of the grain-density in track *b*, for various assumptions regarding the nature of the particles producing the tracks *a* and *b*

	Length of track in microns	Number of grains	Grain-density	Assumed particles			
				1	2	3	4
Track *a*	2,100	1,025	49±1.5	π	μ	π	μ
Track *b*	116	59	51±6	π	μ	μ	π
Calculated grain-density in *b*				45	45	34	64

Values of the grain-density are given in grains per 100 μ.

For the following reasons, case 3, Table 4, is the most improbable. If track *a* is that of a π-meson, we can calculate the momentum and the grain-density to be expected in track *b*. We thus obtain the value of 34 grains per micron instead of 51.0±6.0 as observed. For case 4, on the other hand, if *a* is a μ-meson, the calculated grain-density for track *b* is 64, a value which differs from that observed by an amount only twice that corresponding to the standard deviations. The observed grain-densities agree best with the assumption that the two particles are of the same type.

列于表 3 中。

表 3. 对两类假定的衰变方式，基于总的质量和能量释放对粒子 k 的质量估算

(i) $k \to \pi^- + \pi + \pi$			
	径迹“a”	径迹“b”	径迹“t”
粒子	π	π	π^-
静止质量（m_e）	286	286	286
能量（m_e）	61	64	2
总质量 = m_k = 985 m_e			
(ii) $k \to \pi^- + \mu + \mu$			
粒子	μ	μ	π^-
静止质量（m_e）	212	212	286
能量（m_e）	76	81	2
总质量 = m_k = 869 m_e			

在计算产生径迹 a 和 b 的粒子的能量时，假设产生径迹 t 的是一个 π^- 粒子，动量为 17.5 兆电子伏 / 光速；已知三个出射粒子的相对运动方向，则另两个粒子的动量可确定，因此可以得出对应于任一假定质量的能量值。

由表 3 可见，两个 μ 介子的假设对应于粒子 k 的静止质量为 869 m_e；两个 π 介子对应 985 m_e。不同粒子，即一个 μ 介子和一个 π 介子的假设，给出的中间值近似为 925 m_e。考虑到直接测定 m_k 时产生的误差，上述结果无法给出决定性判据。

如果用已确定存在的粒子来解释嬗变，考虑到产生径迹 a 和 b 的粒子所具有的特征，那么就只剩下四种可能性，结果列于表 4 中。

表 4. 根据产生径迹 a 和 b 的粒子的特征而对粒子种类做出的各类假设，并对径迹 b 的颗粒密度的观测值与计算值进行了比较

	径迹的长度（微米）	颗粒数	颗粒密度	假设的粒子			
				1	2	3	4
径迹 a	2,100	1,025	49±1.5	π	μ	π	μ
径迹 b	116	59	51±6	π	μ	μ	π
径迹 b 的颗粒密度的计算值				45	45	34	64

颗粒密度的值指每 100 微米的颗粒数。

由于下述的理由，表 4 中第三种情况是最不可能的。因为如果径迹 a 是一个 π 介子形成的，我们可以计算出径迹 b 中预期的动量值和颗粒密度。由此我们获得的颗粒密度是每微米 34 个颗粒，而不是观测到的 51.0±6.0。反之，对于第四种情况，如果 a 是一个 μ 介子，计算的径迹 b 的颗粒密度为 64，这个值与观测量之间的差别仅为相应标准偏差的 2 倍。观测的颗粒密度与在假定两个粒子是同类型的情况下计算得到的颗粒密度值吻合得最好。

Observations on the scattering of the particle producing track *a* are in better accord with the assumption that it is a π-meson rather than a μ-meson (see Table 2); but the results are again indecisive. We may sum up this evidence, and that provided by the mass determinations by grain-counting, by saying that there is some support for the view that the three product-particles are π-mesons; but that the alternative possibilities of one π- and two μ-, or two π- and one μ-meson cannot be excluded.

Chance Juxtaposition of Unrelated Events

In the light of the analysis made in the preceding sections, we can now return to the original assumption that the event is not to be regarded as a fortuitous juxtaposition of tracks. The accuracy of the determination of the mass of the particle *k* does not allow us to exclude the possibility that it has a mass as great as that of a proton, although the observations by grain-counts render it very improbable. Suppose then that a proton, unrelated to the particles producing the other tracks, came to the end of its range at *A*. Even with this assumption, the event is still difficult to explain in conventional terms. Many examples of π^--particles ejected from stars have been observed in this Laboratory[8], but in the present instance the existence of a nuclear interaction in which two protons of great energy are emitted, unaccompanied by slow protons and α-particles, would remain to be explained. A similar difficulty is met if we assume that a particle producing one of the tracks, *a* or *b*, approached *A* and produced the transmutation.

If, alternatively, the tracks *c* and *d*, diverging from star *B*, represent an unrelated disintegration—produced, for example, by a γ-ray—we could then assume track *t* to be that of a proton. We are then left with the difficulties associated with the features peculiar to star *A*, which must now be assumed to have been produced by a slow, charged particle; difficulties which have already been discussed in a previous paragraph. These considerations give further support to the original assumption, that all the tracks shown in the mosaic represent a succession of associated processes.

Relation of the Present Results to Other Observations

If a particle with the elementary electronic charge suffers a spontaneous decay, the law of the conservation of charge demands that the number of emitted particles of charge *e* shall be odd. From this point of view, the sign of the charge of the original particle can have been either positive or negative. If the particles producing tracks *a* and *b* form a pair of opposite sign, then the original *k*-particle was negative. The only other alternative is that they were both positively charged, in which case the *k*-particle was also positive. It is therefore possible that our observations correspond to a mode of decay of positive particles of mass approximately 900 m_e, and that the observation by Leprince-Ringuet[2] demonstrates the fate of the corresponding negative particles—nuclear capture with the production of a "star" and the ejection of a π^--particle.

Rochester and Butler[2] have published an expansion-chamber photograph which appears

产生径迹 a 的粒子的散射观测更符合 π 介子的假设，而不是 μ 介子（见表 2）；但结果也是非决定性的。我们可以将这个证据与用颗粒密度的质量测定所提供的证据综合在一起，认为这是对产生的三个粒子都是 π 介子的观点的支持；但一个 π 介子和两个 μ 介子的组合或两个 π 介子和一个 μ 介子的组合的可能性也不能排除。

无关事件的机遇并置

按照前几节的分析，我们现在回到最初的假设，即事件并不是径迹偶然的交叉重叠。粒子 k 质量测定的准确度不允许我们排除其质量大如质子的可能性，虽然颗粒计数的观测结果证明这种情况不可能。假设质子与产生其他径迹的粒子无关，在 A 处到达射程终点。即使采用这个假设，事件仍然很难用传统观点来解释。本实验室[8]观测到许多从星发射出 π^- 粒子的例子，但在目前的例子中，发射两个高能质子，并且不伴随产生慢质子和 α 粒子，这种核相互作用的情况是否存在仍然需要进一步证实。而如果我们假设产生径迹 a 或 b 的粒子靠近 A，并产生嬗变，也会遇到类似的困难。

另一种可能性是，如果从星 B 散射的径迹 c 和 d 代表一个无关的蜕变（例如是由 γ 射线所导致的），那么我们可以假定径迹 t 是质子的径迹。我们可以将困难与星 A 独有的特点相联系，并必须假定它是由低速带电粒子产生的，而这样假设遇到的困难已在以前的段落中进行了讨论。这些分析给原始假设以进一步的支持，拼嵌图中所有的径迹代表了一个不断延续发生的相关过程。

目前结果与其他观测的关系

如果带有基本电子电荷的粒子发生自发衰变，根据电荷守恒定律可知，其发射的电荷为 e 的粒子的数量应为奇数。根据这个观点，原始粒子的电荷符号不是正号就是负号。如果产生径迹 a 和 b 的粒子的电荷符号相反，则原始的 k 粒子带负电。仅有的另一种可能是，它们两者都带正电荷，在这种情况下，k 粒子也是正的。因此可能的情况是，我们的观测对应于质量近似为 900 m_e 的带正电粒子的衰变模式，而由勒普兰斯·兰盖[2]的观测则表明了相应的负电粒子的情况，即核俘获产生“星”并发射 π^- 粒子。

罗切斯特和布特勒[2]已发表了一张膨胀室的照片，它记录的可能是一个质量近

to be due to the spontaneous decay of a neutral particle of mass approximately 900 m_e into a pair of oppositely charged particles of rest-mass approximately 300 m_e. We have therefore considered the possibility that the decay process suggested by the present results can be regarded as taking place in two stages: the emission of a π^--particle of low energy, followed by the spontaneous decay of the resulting neutral particle. On this view, however, it would be necessary to assume that the neutral particle has a life-time of the order of 10^{-14} sec. Otherwise, in recoiling from the π-particle, it would move away from the original point of decay, and the two charged particles into which it became transformed would originate from a point separated from the beginning of the track of the π^--particle. It follows that we cannot identify such a postulated unstable neutral particle with that for which evidence is provided in the experiments of Rochester and Butler.

Finally, we have considered the possible relations of the present results to the particles of mass approximately 800 m_e referred to as τ-mesons, evidence for which has been recently reported by Bradt and Peters[2]. It is a remarkable feature of their experiments that their τ-mesons give rise to no recorded secondary particles at the end of their range. It appears to be possible that these particles also decay with the emission of three fast mesons, but that the transmutation usually takes place with a more equal partition of kinetic energy than in the case we have observed. It would then follow that in the Ilford *C*2 emulsion the disintegration products would commonly escape observation. If this view is correct, we must regard the event we have observed as representing a rare example of a common mode of decay of these mesons; an example which, by chance, has allowed a detailed analysis to be carried out. If so, the τ-meson of Bradt and Peters, when recorded by electron-sensitive emulsions, should show the tracks of three particles, of low specific ionization, and of which the directions of motion are co-planar.

We have pleasure in thanking Prof. von Muralt and members of the staff of the Jungfraujoch Forschungsstation for hospitality and assistance in obtaining the exposures; Dr. E. R. Davies and Dr. W. E. Berriman, of Messrs. Kodak, Ltd., for special photographic plates; Miss C. Dilworth and Dr. G. P. S. Occhialini for advice on development; Mr. W. O. Lock and Mr. J. H. Davies for assistance in making observations on the scattering of particles in the emulsion; and to the team of microscope observers of this Laboratory. We are indebted to Prof. N. F. Mott and other colleagues for a number of discussions on the processes associated with the capture of negative mesons by nuclei.

Note added in proof. Since completing this article, we have been informed by Dr. Peters that, in Ilford *C*2 emulsions exposed at 90,000 feet, he and Dr. Bradt have observed three events with the following characteristics. A particle, which they judge to be similar in mass to their τ-mesons, appears to come to rest and to lead to the emission of a particle of smaller mass, which, at the end of its range, produces a nuclear disintegration. The ranges of the secondary particles, in the three cases, are 20, 25 and 45 μ, respectively. The authors were not aware of our results when they suggested to us that their observations may correspond to the spontaneous decay of heavy mesons. According to their description, these events are

似为 900 m_e 的中性粒子自发衰变形成了一对电荷相反的静止质量近似为 300 m_e 的粒子。因此我们认为，该结果反映的衰变过程可能分为两个步骤：一个低能 π^- 粒子的发射和随后产生的中性粒子的自发衰变。然而，根据这个观点，必须假设，中性粒子的寿命为 10^{-14} 秒的量级。否则中性粒子在 π 粒子的反冲中，可能会离开衰变的原点，因此嬗变产生的两个带电粒子将从与 π^- 粒子径迹的起点不同的点起源。因此，根据罗切斯特和布特勒的实验中提供的证据，我们并不能确认存在这类假定的不稳定的中性粒子。

最后，我们考虑了目前的结果与质量近似为 800 m_e 的 τ 介子（编者注：现在粒子物理认为"τ 介子"不是介子，而是一种轻子，因此正确的称谓是 τ 子。考虑到历史原因，文中仍保留"τ 介子"的译法。）的可能关系，关于 τ 介子的证据最近已由布拉特和彼得斯 [2] 作了报道。他们实验的一个显著特征就是，在 τ 介子的射程内没有记录到次级粒子。因此很可能是 τ 介子在衰变的过程中伴随三个快介子的发射，但是这种嬗变通常发生在比我们所观测到的动能更加均分的情况下。由此可知，在伊尔福 *C*2 乳胶中，蜕变产物通常会观测不到。如果这个观点是正确的，我们必须认为我们已观测到的事件是这些介子衰变的一般模式中的一个稀有例子，一个碰巧允许我们进行详细分析的例子。如果是这样，那么布拉特和彼得斯的 τ 介子在被用电子敏感的乳胶记录时，应该会显示低电离比值的三个粒子的径迹，且运动方向是共面的。

诚挚感谢冯·穆拉尔特教授和少女峰研究站的工作人员，感谢他们的热情和在曝光过程中对我们的帮助；感谢柯达公司的戴维斯博士和贝里曼博士提供的特殊的照相底片；感谢迪尔沃斯女士和奥恰利尼博士关于显影的建议；感谢洛克先生和戴维斯先生在观察感光乳液中的粒子散射时所给予的协助；感谢本实验室的显微镜观测小组。此外，我们还特别感谢莫脱教授和其他同事关于核子捕捉负电介子的过程而进行的大量讨论。

附加说明：本文完成以后，彼得斯博士又给我们提供了一些新的信息：将伊尔福 *C*2 乳胶置于海拔 90,000 英尺处曝光，他和布拉特博士观测到三个具有下述特性的事件。一个质量与他们的 τ 介子相当的粒子在其射程的终端趋于静止，并产生一个质量更小的粒子，该粒子在其射程的终端激发了一个核蜕变。在三类情况下，次级粒子的射程分别为 20 微米、25 微米和 45 微米。当他们向我们提出他们的观测可能与重介子的自发衰变相符合时，作者并不知道我们的结果。按照他们的描述，这

precisely similar to those we should expect to observe in *C*2 emulsions as a result of the spontaneous decay of heavy particles of the type we have postulated; for any particles of low specific ionization will not be recorded by the Ilford plates. The observations of Peters and Bradt appear, therefore, to give further support for the assumption that the present observations are not due to a chance juxtaposition of tracks; and they suggest that it will be possible, in the near future, to find similar examples suitable for making a detailed analysis.

(**163**, 82-87; 1949)

R. Brown, U. Camerini, P. H. Fowler, H. Muirhead and C. F. Powell: H. H. Wills Physical Laboratory, University of Bristol.

D. M. Ritson: Clarendon Laboratory, Oxford.

References:

1. Berriman, *Nature*, **162**, 992 (1948).
2. Leprince-Ringuet, *C.R.*, **226**, 1897 (1948). Rochester and Butler, *Nature*, **160**, 855 (1947). Bradt and Peters, Report to the Bristol Symposium, 1948 (in the press). Alichanian. Alichanov and Weissenberg, *J. Exp. and Theoret. Phys., U.S.S.R.*, **18**, 301 (1948); and other references.
3. Camerini, Muirhead, Powell and Ritson, *Nature*, **162**, 433 (1948).
4. Goldschmidt-Clermont, King, Muirhead and Ritson, *Proc. Phys. Soc.*, **61**, 138 (1948).
5. Lattes, Occhialini and Powell, *Proc. Phys. Soc.*, **61**, 173 (1948).
6. Serber, Report of Solvay Conference for 1948.
7. Dilworth, Occhialini and Payne, *Nature*, **162**, 102 (1948).
8. Occhialini and Powell, *Nature*, **162**, 168 (1948).
9. Halpern and Hall, *Phys. Rev.*, **73**, 477 (1948).
10. Livingston and Bethe, *Rev. Mod. Phys.*, **9**, 263 (1937).
11. Camerini and Lattes (private communication); see also Powell and Occhialini, "Nuclear Physics in Photographs", 112 (Oxford, 1947).

些事件非常类似于我们预期在 *C*2 乳胶中观测的我们所假设的这类重粒子的自发衰变结果；伊尔福 *C*2 胶片不能记录任何低电离比值的粒子。因此，彼得斯和布拉特的观测结果进一步支持了下述假设，即目前的观测并不是偶然的径迹交叉重叠；他们表示在不久的将来有可能发现适合作详细分析的类似实例。

（沈乃澂 翻译；尚仁成 审稿）

A New Type of Fossil Man

R. Broom and J. T. Robinson

Editor's Note

The cave site of Swartkrans, near Sterkfontein, yielded a very large form of robust australopithecine, which its discoverer, Robert Broom, named *Paranthropus crassidens*. But the same site also produced the jaw of another type of fossil man, unlike *Paranthropus* and more human. It was found in a lens of much more recent material than that which had yielded the australopithecines. Broom and Robinson compared the jaw with the famous Mauer mandible, exemplar of "Heidelberg Man" (now called *Homo heidelbergensis*), calling it *Telanthropus capensis*. This form was later reclassified as *Homo erectus*.

IN the cave at Swartkrans which has now yielded the jaws and skulls of the huge ape-man *Paranthropus crassidens*, there was found by Mr. J. T. Robinson, on April 29, 1949, the lower jaw of what is fairly manifestly a new type of man. Though this was discovered in the same cave as the large ape-man, it is clearly of considerably later date. In the main bone breccia of the cave deposit there has been a pocket excavated and refilled by a darker type of matrix. The pocket was of very limited extent, being only about 4 ft. by 3 ft. and about 2 ft. in thickness. The deposit was remarkably barren, there being no other bones in it except the human jaw and a few remains of very small mammals. We are thus at present unable to give the age of the deposit except to say that it must be considerably younger than the main deposit. If the main deposit is Upper Pliocene, not improbably the pocket may be Lower Pleistocene.

The jaw is smaller than many human jaws, though the 3rd molar is larger than in any known man. On the left ramus the three molars are preserved in good condition though a little worn, and the last two molars are well preserved in the right ramus. No other teeth are preserved, though we have sockets of all of them.

The jaw has been a little broken during fossilization, and slightly crushed; but otherwise it is nearly perfect except for the loss of most of the left condyle and the whole of the right. A very small part of the lower symphyseal region is lost. The symphysis runs downwards and slightly backwards, making an angle with the base of the ramus of about 75°.The depth of the symphysis is about 33 mm. The horizontal ramus is remarkably shallow. At the 1st molar it is only 29 mm. The base of the ramus is nearly level, and the angle is rounded and scarcely at all below the general level.

The ascending ramus has apparently been fairly broad, but very shallow. Fortunately the cast of the side of the one condyle is preserved, and the height of the back of the jaw is

一种新型人类化石

布鲁姆，鲁滨逊

编者按

邻近斯泰克方丹，在斯瓦特克朗斯的洞穴出土了一种大型的粗壮型南方古猿亚科化石，它的发现者罗伯特·布鲁姆将其命名为傍人粗齿种。虽然在同一个洞穴中还发现了另一种类型的古人类颌骨化石，但是这个颌骨与傍人的不同而更像人类。它所在的沉积物的年代比发现南方古猿亚科所在的沉积物的年代晚很多。布鲁姆和鲁滨逊将此颌骨与作为"海德堡人"（现在称为人属海德堡种）标本的著名的毛尔下颌骨化石进行比较，并将其命名为开普远人。这种类型后来被归为直立人。

在斯瓦特克朗斯一处洞穴中，已出土过一个巨型猿人傍人粗齿种的颌骨和头骨，1949年4月29日，鲁滨逊先生在其中发现了一个下颌骨，很明显，它是一个新型古人类的下颌骨。尽管这个下颌骨与早先发现的大型猿人是在同一个洞穴里发现的，但是很明显这种新型古人类所处的年代要晚得多。在洞穴主要骨角砾岩的沉积物中有一个被挖掘过的凹坑的痕迹，凹坑曾被一种较暗类型的基质回填过。这个凹坑的大小约为4英尺×3英尺，厚度约为2英尺。该处沉积物非常贫瘠，除了这一人类颌骨和少量小型哺乳动物的残骸外就没有其他骨了。因此我们现在除了能确定这些沉积物一定比主沉积物的年代晚很多外，并不能指出这些沉积物的年代。如果主沉积物是上新世晚期的，那么这处凹坑为下更新世的也并非不可能。

该颌骨比许多人类的颌骨小，但第三臼齿比现在任何已知人类的都要大。左下颌支的三颗臼齿除有一点磨损外都保存得很好，右下颌支最后两颗臼齿保存良好。其他牙齿都没有保存下来，但其牙槽都在。

由于石化作用，颌骨有一点破损和轻微的变形；但是除了缺少左侧大部分髁突和右侧全部髁突以外，其余部分的保存状况近乎完好。联合部的下面丢失了很小的一部分。联合部向下及稍向后方向进行，与下颌支基部形成约75°角。联合部厚约33毫米。水平支非常浅，距第一臼齿处仅有29毫米。下颌支基部接近水平，角为圆形，几乎不低于总体水平线。

很明显，上升支相当宽阔但是很浅。幸运的是，一个髁突的侧面模型被保存下来了，而且颌骨背面的高度仅在颌骨水平线上方约55毫米处。最后一颗臼齿的外面

only about 55 mm. above the horizontal base of the jaw. Outside the last molar is a wide hollow as in the Heidelberg jaw, and the jaws of the ape-men. There is no simian shelf and the whole symphysis is not unlike that of Heidelberg man, but smaller. The mylohyoid groove runs up to the foramen as in typical human skulls. In *Paranthropus crassidens* the groove is, as in *Eoanthropus*, lower down.

The incisors and canines, so far as can be judged from the sockets, are human. The premolars have been a little larger than typically human premolars. The 1st molar is almost typically human in size and structure. It has five cusps and a trace of a sixth. The 2nd molar is also nearly human. It is larger than in *Homo*, and has a small sixth cusp. The 3rd molar is the largest of the three molars. It has five well-developed cusps and a small sixth.

The jaw in general structure comes nearest to that of Heidelberg man, but is smaller and has a lower horizontal ramus. The teeth differ markedly in the 3rd molar, being the largest of the series.

In the large size of the molars there is some resemblance to the condition seen in *Plesianthropus* and *Paranthropus*; but in this human jaw the molars are much smaller. In *Plesianthropus transvaalensis* the three molars measure in the male about 43 mm.; in *Paranthropus robustus* they measure 45 mm. In *Paranthropus crassidens* the three measure in the male about 51 mm., while in this new human jaw they only measure 38.4 mm. In the South African native the molars measure about 35 mm.

The new type of man represented by this fossil jaw we propose to call *Telanthropus capensis*. We regard him as somewhat allied to Heidelberg man, and intermediate between one of the ape-men and true man.

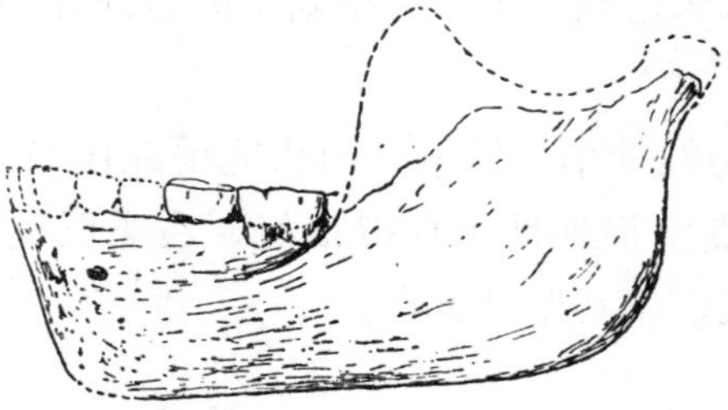

Fig. 1. Side view of lower jaw of *Telanthropus capensis* B. and R. (half-size)

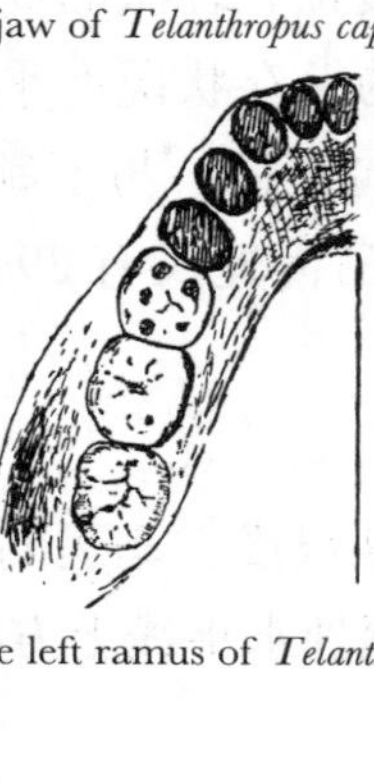

Fig. 2. Occlusal view of teeth of the left ramus of *Telanthropus capensis* B. and R. (half-size)

是一个大的空洞，这与海德堡下颌骨以及猿人颌骨的情况一样。它没有猿的框架，整个联合部与海德堡人的不同，但相对较小。下颌舌骨沟向上延伸至孔处，这与典型的人类头骨一样。傍人粗齿种的沟与曙人一样都是降低的。

目前根据牙槽可以判定其门齿和犬齿是属于人类的。前臼齿比典型的人类前臼齿大一点。第一臼齿在大小和结构方面都几乎与典型的人类牙齿一样。第一臼齿具有五个齿尖，并有第六齿尖的痕迹。第二臼齿也接近于人类的第二臼齿，但比人属的要大，并且具有一个小的第六齿尖。第三臼齿是三颗臼齿中最大的。该臼齿具有五个发育完全的齿尖和一个小的第六齿尖。

在整体结构上，该颌骨与海德堡人的最接近，只是稍小并且水平支较低。第三臼齿明显不同，是所有臼齿系列中最大的。

这种大尺寸的臼齿与在迩人和傍人中观察到的情况有些相似；但是在这具人类颌骨中，臼齿要小得多。德兰士瓦迩人男性的三颗臼齿的尺寸约为 43 毫米；粗壮傍人的尺寸为 45 毫米。傍人粗齿种男性的三颗臼齿的尺寸约为 51 毫米，而在这具新型人类颌骨中，只有 38.4 毫米。南非本土人的臼齿尺寸约为 35 毫米。

我们建议将这具颌骨化石代表的新型古人类命名为开普远人。我们认为它与海德堡人有些亲缘关系，介于猿人和真正的人类之间。

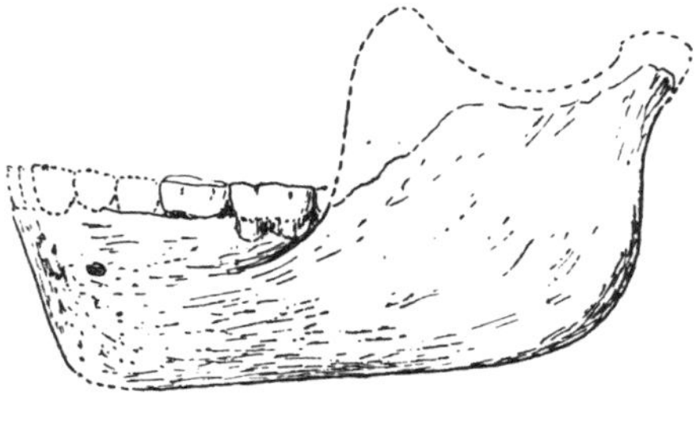

图 1. 开普远人下颌骨的侧面观（布鲁姆和鲁滨逊）（原尺寸的一半）

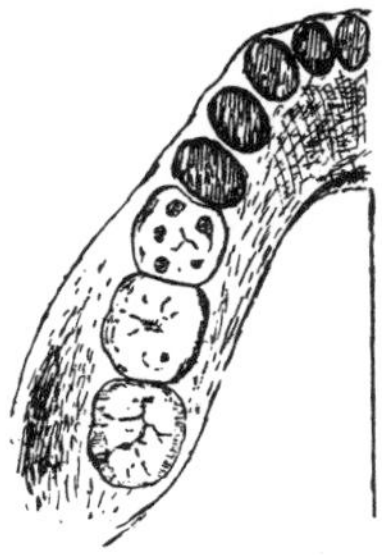

图 2. 开普远人的左侧下颌支牙齿咬合图（布鲁姆和鲁滨逊）（原尺寸的一半）

It might be thought that as *Plesianthropus transvaalensis*, of which we now know about a dozen skulls and about a hundred and fifty teeth, shows considerable variation, this supposed human jaw might be an extreme variant of *Paranthropus crassidens*. In man there are no doubt great variations, and the difference in size between the jaw of a small Bushman woman and the Wadjak and Heidelberg jaws is nearly as great as between our supposed human jaw and the huge *Paranthropus crassidens* jaw. We now have three good lower jaws and a number of isolated teeth of *P. crassidens*, and there is not much variation in either size or structure. It may be held that all these large jaws are male jaws, and the small jaw that of a female; but not only the size of the teeth but also the structure seems to rule out such a view. The 1st molar in the type of *P. crassidens* is about 16 mm. by 14.6 mm. In the supposed human jaw it is only 12 mm. by 11.5 mm. Further, the structure of the two teeth differ considerably. The typically human mylohyoid groove in our supposed man, and the certainly not typically human groove in *Paranthropus*, seem to make it certain that the two jaws belong to different genera. If we are right in believing that our new jaw is in structure intermediate between *P. crassidens* and *Homo*, it is but natural that there should be numerous resemblances to both.

(**164**, 322-323; 1949)

R. Broom and J. T. Robinson: Transvaal Museum, Pretoria, July 2.

从目前我们拥有的十多件头骨和150颗左右的牙齿来看，德兰士瓦迩人的变异相当大，我们可以推测人类的颌骨可能是傍人粗齿种的一种极端变异形式。人类的颌骨无疑也存在很大的变异，矮小的布须曼妇女颌骨、瓦贾克人颌骨以及海德堡下颌骨在大小上存在着较大的差异，这个差异相当于我们现在假定的人类颌骨与巨大的傍人粗齿种的颌骨之间的差异。我们现在有三件完好的下颌骨和傍人粗齿种的一些单个的牙齿，它们在大小或结构上都没有太大变异。也许有人认为所有这些大的颌骨都是男性的，小的颌骨则是女性的；但是，不论从牙齿的大小还是从结构上看，似乎都可以排除这种观点。傍人粗齿种类型的第一臼齿大约为16毫米 ×14.6毫米。假定的人类颌骨只有12毫米 ×11.5毫米。另外，两颗牙齿的结构差异很大。根据我们假定的人类的典型人类下颌舌骨沟以及傍人的显然非典型人类下颌舌骨沟，似乎可以确定这两件颌骨属于不同的属。我们认为这个新型颌骨在结构上介于傍人粗齿种和人属之间，如果我们的这一想法是正确的，那么二者之间具有很多的相像之处也就不足为奇了。

（刘皓芳 翻译；吴秀杰 审稿）

New Evidence on the Antiquity of Piltdown Man

K. P. Oakley and C. R. Hoskins

Editor's Note

The famous skull and jawbone of a fossil human excavated near Piltdown in southern England in 1912 had been the focus of much attention by anthropologists. By the 1940s, the combination of modern-looking skull and ape-like jaw seemed out of tune with discoveries from Asia and Africa, showing fossil humans with small brains and human-like jaws. Here Kenneth Oakley and Randall Hoskins used a new method of dating bones mixed up in the same deposit (such as found at Piltdown), by measuring the amount of fluorine that had seeped into the bone. The Piltdown bones showed relatively little fluorine, suggesting a relatively recent date. At this stage, however, nobody was prepared to admit that the Piltdown remains were fraudulent.

FEW, if any, fossils have given rise to more controversy than the remains discovered by Charles Dawson in gravel at Piltdown, near Fletching, Sussex, and described in 1913 by Sir Arthur Smith Woodward as representing a new genus and species of man, *Eoanthropus dawsoni*. The geological age of "Piltdown man" was a matter of dispute from the first, moreover, this problem has latterly become linked with the question as to whether the thick but essentially human cranial bones and the remarkably ape-like lower jaw (and canine tooth) might be a chance association and represent two creatures of different geological ages. The present investigation, using the fluorine method for determination of the relative antiquity of fossil bones, has shown that the cranial bones and jaw-bone are of the same age, at the earliest Middle, more probably early Upper, Pleistocene.

Earlier Evidence

The Piltdown gravel is a thin remanié deposit in a terrace about 50 ft. above the River Ouse, containing fossil mammals of two distinct ages: a derived Villafranchian series ("Upper Pliocene" of earlier authors, now classed as Lower Pleistocene), and a later Pleistocence group, in part at least contemporary with the gravel. The "contemporary" group was classed by Dawson and Woodward[1] as "early Pleistocene", but according to more recent authorities it is not earlier than Middle Pleistocene.

To which of these two groups does *Eoanthropus* belong? This might be thought a simple question to decide by comparison of the states of preservation of the various remains. Yet examination of the specimens from this very point of view has led different authorities to diametrically opposed conclusions. In fact, anatomists regarding

皮尔当人年代的新证据

奥克利，霍斯金斯

编者按

这件著名的化石人类的头骨和颌骨，是于1912年在英格兰南部皮尔当附近发掘得到的，一直以来都得到了古人类学家的广泛关注。它具有类似现代人类的头骨和类似猿类的颌骨。到20世纪40年代，人们发现它与在亚洲和非洲发现的化石人类不同，这些化石人类的脑较小，而颌骨更像人类。本文中肯尼思·奥克利和兰德尔·霍斯金斯使用一种全新的方法，即通过测量渗透入骨的氟含量，对同一沉积物（例如在皮尔当发现的沉积物）中掺杂在一起的骨进行年代测定。皮尔当人骨的含氟量相对较低，表明其处于相对较近的年代。然而直到此时，还没有人会想到皮尔当化石是个骗局。

几乎没有化石比查尔斯·道森在萨塞克斯的弗莱彻附近的皮尔当砾石层中发现的化石引发过更多的争议，1913年阿瑟·史密斯·伍德沃德爵士将这些化石描述成一种人类新属和新种的代表——道森曙人。皮尔当人的地质年代从一开始就存在争议，此外，最近这个难题已经开始变得与另一个问题相关，即这些厚的但本质上属于人类的颅骨和明显类似猿类的下颌骨（和犬齿）是否只是偶然共生在一起，并代表了两种不同地质年代的生物？目前使用氟年代测定法对骨化石的相对年代进行了测定，结果表明颅骨和颌骨属于同一年代，即中更新世的最早期，更可能是上更新世早期。

早期证据

皮尔当砾石层是位于乌斯河之上大约50英尺的一处阶地上的经过再沉积的薄层沉积物，含有两个不同年代的哺乳动物化石：维拉方期的一个次生系列（早期作者将其命名为“上新世晚期”，现在被列入下更新世）和更新世晚期群，其至少部分与砾石层属于同一年代。道森和伍德沃德[1]将这“同年代”的群划为“更新世早期”，但是根据更为新近的主流观点，它们所处的时代并不早于中更新世。

那么曙人属于这两个群中的哪一个呢？人们认为这是一个简单的问题，可以通过比较不同化石的保存状况而确定。然而仅仅从这一点来检验标本，不同的专家就得到了完全相反的结论。事实上，认为该下颌骨和犬齿属于类人猿的解剖学家表示

the mandible and canine tooth as anthropoid have felt free to place these with the Villafranchian group, and to dismiss the cranium as later Pleistocene and referable to *Homo sapiens* (cf. Marston[2]). This hypothesis is permissible in so far as mammalian remains of two ages (for example, "*Stegodon*", Villafranchian; and *Castor fiber*, post-Villafranchian) occurred with *Eoanthropus* at the base of the dark gravel (ref. 3, pp. 83-85), but it would be erroneous to claim that none of the cranial fragments was closely associated with the mandible. Although the fragments of skullcap were for the most part recovered loose on spoil heaps, Dawson states (ref. 1, p. 121) that Smith Woodward dug out a small portion of the occipital bone "from within a yard of the point where the jaw was discovered, and at precisely the same level".

In reading their first paper, Dawson and Woodward (ref. 1, pp. 123, 143) stated their view that the human skull and mandible, being practically unrolled, were contemporary with the gravel and therefore probably "Pleistocene". However, in the discussion which followed, Sir Arthur Keith[4] argued that the skull should be assigned to the "Pliocene" group. He was influenced, he said, by the fact that in the Heidelberg jaw, of early Pleistocene date, the region of the chin was essentially human, whereas the Piltdown mandible showed simian characters. E. T. Newton[5] said that the mineralized condition of the skull bones pointed to their being of "Pliocene" age. In replying to the discussion, Dawson admitted this possibility, for he said (ref. 1, p. 151): "... the occurrence of certain Pliocene specimens in a considerably rolled condition, suggested a difference as to age, but not to the extent of excluding the possibility of their being coeval. The rolled specimens may have entered the stream further up the river than the human remains. ... Then again the skull might have been surrounded by some colloid material [that is, clay] which preserved it in its passage from some earlier deposit." But in the second paper (ref. 3, p. 86) Dawson wrote: "Putting aside the human remains and those of the beaver, the remains all point to a characteristic land fauna of the Pliocene age; and though all are portions of hard teeth, they are rolled and broken. The human remains on the other hand, although of much softer material, are not rolled, and the remains of beaver are in a similar condition. It would therefore seem that the occurrence of these two individuals belongs to one of the periods of reconstruction of this gravel."

In 1935, Dr. A. T. Hopwood[6] reconsidered the evidence, and, largely on the basis of the state of preservation of the specimens, concluded that *Eoanthropus* belonged to the Villafranchian or Lower Pleistocene faunal assemblage. He pointed out that the absence of indications of rolling was unreliable as a criterion, for one of the teeth of "*Stegodon*" (*Elephas* cf. *planifrons*), undoubtedly a member of the derived group, was practically unrolled. The evidence then available, he said, justified the statement that "Piltdown Man is the oldest human fossil yet discovered" (ref. 6, p. 57).

In recent years many anthropologists have held the view that, so long as its date remained uncertain, this material was better placed in a suspense account, for the anatomical features of *Eoanthropus* (assuming the material to represent one creature) are wholly

可以把这些样本归入维拉方群中去，并且排除了其颅骨所处年代为更新世晚期而将其列为智人的可能性（参见马斯顿[2]）。如果仅就目前为止与曙人一起出现于暗色砾石层底部（参考文献 3，第 83~85 页）的两个不同年代的哺乳动物化石（例如，维拉方期的“剑齿象”以及后维拉方期的欧亚河狸）而言，这一假说是可以成立的，但是如果声称没有一个颅骨破片与下颌骨存在密切关系的话，那么这一假说就是错误的。尽管后来修复的大部分颅骨顶部破片都曾散布在废石堆上，但是道森仍强调(参考文献 1，第 121 页)，史密斯·伍德沃德从“距离发现颌骨的地点一码之内，并且正是在同一高度上”挖出了小部分枕骨。

在读到道森和伍德沃德的第一篇论文（参考文献 1，第 123 页和第 143 页）时，他们在文中陈述了自己的观点，即实际上未被滚磨过的人类头骨和下颌骨与砾石层是同一时代的，因此可能是“更新世”时期的。然而在接下来的讨论中，阿瑟·基思[4]爵士认为，头骨应该属于“上新世”时期，这是由于更新世早期的海德堡下颌骨的颏部本质上是人类的颏，而皮尔当人的下颌骨却显示出了猿的特征。牛顿[5]认为头骨的矿化情况表明它们是“上新世”时期的生物。在对这一讨论进行回复时，道森承认了这一可能性，因为他指出（参考文献 1，第 151 页）：“……处于被显著滚磨过的状态的某些上新世时期标本的出现，提示了年代的差异，但是并不排除它们属于同时代生物的可能性。这些被滚磨过的标本可能在比人类化石更上游的位置进入溪流之中……然后头骨可能又被一些胶体材料 [即黏土] 包围，这种材料将标本从较早沉积物的搬运过程中保留下来。”但是第二篇论文中（参考文献 3，第 86 页），道森写道：“先撇开人类化石和河狸化石不谈，其他所有的化石都指向一种特征性的上新世时期的陆地动物群；尽管所有的化石都是坚硬牙齿的一部分，但它们都被滚磨过并且是破碎的。另一方面，尽管人类化石都是些硬度小得多的材料，但是它们都没有被滚磨过，河狸化石的保存状况也与之相似。因此这两个个体的出现时期似乎属于该砾石层的一个再堆积时期。”

1935 年，主要基于这些样本的保存状况，霍普伍德[6]博士重新考虑了这一证据，他推断曙人属于维拉方期或下更新世期的动物群组合。他指出将缺乏滚磨迹象作为一个标准是不可靠的，因为“剑齿象”（平额象相似种）的一枚牙齿完全没有被滚磨过，而它毫无疑问是次生组群的成员之一。他认为现有的证据可用于证明“皮尔当人是至今发现的最古老的人类化石”的论述（参考文献 6，第 57 页）。

最近几年许多人类学家所持有的观点是，只要没有确定标本所属的年代，那么最好将其暂且搁置，因为曙人（假设这些材料代表一种生物）的解剖特征与在远东

contrary to what discoveries in the Far East and in Africa have led us to expect in an early Pleistocene hominid. However, if one could at least be certain of the contemporaneity of the parts associated under the name *Eoanthropus*, and of their precise geological age, the number of possible interpretations would be much reduced.

The Fluorine-Dating Method

It has long been known that fossil bones accumulate fluorine in course of time. The major constituent of bones and teeth is hydroxyapatite, which acts as a natural trap for wandering fluorine ions. Bones absorb fluorine from the ground-water, and it becomes fixed in their substance as fluorapatite by a process of ionic interchange. Owing to the porous texture of bones (and teeth), this progressive alteration is not confined to the surface, but usually proceeds more or less uniformly throughout the body of the material. It was suggested at the British Association meeting in 1947[7] that the percentage distribution of this element in the various bones and teeth from the Piltdown gravel might reflect their relative ages sufficiently clearly to throw some light on the major problem. Later, in response to a request from the Keeper of Geology at the British Museum, the Government Chemist agreed to undertake experimental work on the fluorine analysis of fossil bones.

After preliminary trials, Mr. R. H. Settle and one of us (C. R. H.), assisted by Mr. E. C. W. Maycock, adapted published methods of analysis to the exact determination of fluorine in very small samples of bone. A description of the analytical technique and a discussion on the limits of accuracy will be presented in a report on "fluorine-dating" to be published later in the *Bulletin of the British Museum* (*Nat. Hist.*), and it is not necessary in this article to refer other than briefly to these matters.

The method was based on that originally devised by Willard and Winter[8] and afterwards modified by various authors. The fluorine in the bone was separated as hydrofluosilicic acid by distillation with perchloric acid in presence of a few beads of soft glass to serve as a source of silica. Suitable aliquots of concentrated distillate were titrated with dilute thorium nitrate solution, using Alizarin S as indicator. The solution of thorium nitrate was standardized against solutions of known fluorine content under identical conditions, particularly with regard to titrating to the same stage in the colour change of the indicator. In the majority of cases, the amount of fluorine in the distillate was sufficient for at least three aliquots to be titrated, and the average fluorine content, after making a small correction for a blank determination, was adopted. There was generally close agreement between the fluorine contents calculated from titrations of different aliquots from a given distillation.

Where possible, at least 20 mgm. of bone was used for fluorine determination; but in several cases it was necessary to rely on samples of the order of 5 mgm. The errors of analysis naturally increase as the weight of sample decreases, but it is believed that with

和非洲的发现完全相反，而那些发现让我们对更新世早期的人科有所期待。然而，如果有人能够至少确定与曙人相关的同时代部分以及它们确切的地质年代的话，那么就会大大减少可能性的解释的数量了。

氟年代测定法

很久以前人们就知道，随着时间的推移，氟会在骨化石中累积。骨和牙齿的主要成分是羟磷灰石，它是游离氟离子的天然收集器。骨从地下水中吸收氟，然后氟通过离子交换过程在骨中以氟磷灰石的形态固定下来。由于骨（和牙齿）的多孔结构，这一渐进性的变化并不局限于表面，而是通常在整个材料体大致均匀地发生。1947 年的英国科学促进会会议[7]上提出，这一元素在皮尔当砾石层中发现的各种骨和牙齿中的百分比分布情况可能反映了它们所处的相对年代，这对阐明主要问题会有帮助。后来，应大英博物馆的地质学管理人的请求，政府部门的化验师同意承担对骨化石进行氟分析的实验工作。

初步尝试之后，在梅科克先生的协助下，塞特尔先生和我们中的成员之一霍斯金斯将已发表的分析方法进行调整，以适用于准确测定非常小的骨样本中的氟。对这种分析技术的描述及对其在准确性方面的局限性的讨论将在关于“氟年代测定法”的报道中进行陈述，这篇报道不久将发表在《大英博物馆公报》（自然探究）上，因此在这篇文章里只简单地介绍一下这种方法。

这一方法建立在威拉德和温特[8]最初的设计基础之上，后来经过了不同研究者的修改。通过几粒软质玻璃珠作为硅的来源，将骨骼中的氟通过高氯酸的蒸馏作用分离为氟硅酸。使用茜素 S 作为指示剂，将浓缩的蒸馏液适当地分为几等份，用稀释的硝酸钍溶液进行滴定。在相同条件下，用已知的含氟溶液对硝酸钍溶液进行标准化，尤其是在指示剂颜色变化的指导下滴定到相同阶段。大多数情况下，蒸馏物中的氟含量足以滴定至少三等份，在对空白测定进行微小的矫正后，就可以采用平均氟含量了。根据不同等份蒸馏物得到的滴定溶液计算出的氟含量之间，通常具有良好的一致性。

如果可能的话，进行氟测定至少需要用 20 毫克的骨；但是有些情况下，依样本情况该值可能以 5 毫克为单位向下浮动。分析误差随样本重量的减少而自然增加，

sample weights of 5 mgm. and upwards the error in the adopted values is not greater than ±0.1 percent of fluorine. For sample weights less than 5 mgm. the error may be ±0.2 percent of fluorine.

Approximate estimations of the iron and phosphate contents of the bones were made on residues of the samples remaining after the fluorine determinations. Colorimetric methods were used in each case (thioglycollic acid for iron, and ammonium molybdate followed by reduction of phosphomolybdate with stannous chloride for phosphate).

The fluorine-dating method was first applied to the Galley Hill skeleton[9]. Briefly, it was shown that indigenous fossil bones in the Middle Pleistocene terrace gravels at Swanscombe contain around 2 percent fluorine, those from Upper Pleistocene deposits in the same region around 1 percent, and post-Pleistocene bones not more than 0.3 percent; while the Galley Hill skeleton, although found *in* the Middle Pleistocene gravels, proved to contain only about 0.3 percent fluorine, and was therefore clearly an intrusive burial, at earliest end-Pleistocene. The Swanscombe skull bones, on the other hand, discovered in these gravels by Mr. A. T. Marston in 1935-36, showed the expected 2 percent fluorine.

Series of bones from other sites have been analysed, and the results show that the method, although limited in scope, is useful for differentiating fossil bones of diverse antiquity when they occur mixed together, provided that the specimens compared have similar matrices. It cannot be used to determine the relative antiquity of bones from widely separated localities. The method was ideally suited to the Galley Hill problem. There seemed reasonable hope that it would help to resolve the Piltdown enigma. Accordingly, in October 1948, Mr. W. N. Edwards, Keeper of Geology in the British Museum, authorized the sampling of *Eoanthropus* and associated mammalian bones and teeth. For the most part the samples were obtained by applying a dental drill to broken or worn edges of the specimens until a small but sufficient quantity of bone powder had been cored out. Where possible, powder from several drill holes in each specimen was mixed in order to ensure a representative sample. In view of the ferruginous nature of the deposits, it was thought advisable to determine the iron content of all the samples, but we found that there is no appreciable correlation in the Piltdown material between fluorine content and iron impregnation.

In the case of coarsely porous bone, it is sometimes difficult to obtain a sample which is completely free from silt contamination. The fluorine content of a contaminated portion of a bone will obviously be misleadingly low. It was therefore decided to determine the phosphate content of all samples, and to express the fluorine value of each sample as the percentage ratio of fluorine to phosphate (as P_2O_5). This procedure facilitates comparison of the fluorine contents of bones in which there has been variable contamination.

但是如果使用 5 毫克或更多量样本的话，就认为采用的氟含量测定值误差不大于 ±0.1%。而对于样本重量少于 5 毫克的检测，氟含量的误差可能达到 ±0.2%。

在测定完氟含量之后，根据剩余的样本残渣近似估算骨中铁和磷酸盐含量。每个样本的铁和磷酸盐含量估算都使用比色法（铁通过巯基乙酸进行比色，磷酸盐通过钼酸铵以及随后的氯化亚锡对磷钼酸盐的还原作用进行比色）完成。

氟年代测定法首先应用于伽力山骨架[9]。简单地说，斯旺斯孔布的中更新世阶地砾石层中的本地的骨化石含有约 2% 的氟，而同一地区的上更新世沉积物化石骨的氟含量约为 1%，晚更新世骨的氟含量则不高于 0.3%。尽管伽力山骨架发现于中更新世时期的砾石层**之中**，但是事实证明这些样本的氟含量只有约 0.3%，因此很明显这是发生在更新世末的早期阶段的一处侵入型埋藏。另一方面，1935 年 ~ 1936 年间，马斯顿在这些砾石层发现的斯旺斯孔布头骨氟含量为 2%，这与预期的结果一致。

对其他遗址的一系列骨也进行了分析，结果表明尽管使用范围有局限性，但是当许多样本混合在一起同时出现、并且假如用来进行比较的样本具有相似的基质的话，那么用这种方法来区分不同年代的骨化石还是很有效的。这种方法不能用来确定出土地点相差很远的骨的相对年代关系，而对于解决伽力山问题则是非常理想的，因此人们希望这种方法有助于解决皮尔当之谜的想法也是合理的。相应地，大英博物馆的地质学管理人爱德华兹先生于 1948 年 10 月批准了对曙人以及共生的哺乳动物骨和牙齿进行采样。采样方法为使用牙钻来钻取样本破碎的或磨损的边缘，直到获取少量但足以用来进行分析的骨粉为止。如果有可能，对从每份样本的不同钻孔得到的骨粉进行混合以保证采样具有代表性。鉴于沉积物含铁的这一性质，有人认为确定所有样本的含铁量是可取的，但我们发现皮尔当材料的氟含量和铁浸渍之间并没有明显的相关性。

对于粗糙多孔的骨，有时很难得到完全没有受土壤污染的样本。显然，骨的污染部分的低含氟量会产生误导。因此我们决定测定所有样本的磷酸盐含量，然后将每个样本的氟值表达为氟与磷酸盐（以 P_2O_5 的形式）的百分比。这一步骤使得比较存在不同程度污染的骨的含氟量容易很多。

Application to the Piltdown Material

Every available bone and tooth from the Piltdown gravel and from neighbouring deposits was analysed, including seventeen samples of the *Eoanthropus* material. The results are shown in the accompanying table. For comparative purposes the mammalian remains have been grouped according to known or probable age. Their colour, degree of rolling or other physical states have been ignored in making this age classification, except in the case of some of the subfossil or recent specimens. The teeth of *Mastodon arvernensis*, *Elephas* cf. *planifrons* (= "*Stegodon*" auctt.) and "*Rhinoceros*" cf. *etruscus* cannot be younger than Lower Pleistocene. All the rest of the Pleistocene material from the gravel is either certainly later (*Cervus elaphus*, *Castor fiber*), or possibly later (*Hippopotamus* sp., *Equus* sp., *Cervus* sp.), than Villafranchian. Any such post-Villafranchian elements might theoretically be of first interglacial age (when according to Hopwood's terminology the "Middle Pleistocene" fauna began to appear); of great interglacial age (that is, Middle Pleistocene of all authors), or of last interglacial age (that is, early Upper Pleistocene of some authors, late Middle Pleistocene of others). Since distinctively Cromerian forms are absent and as there are indications that the deposit has been repeatedly re-worked, the post-Villafranchian material is probably partly Middle and partly Upper Pleistocene. A problem of classification typical of this site is presented by the so-called bone implement from Piltdown (*P.* 18). It is part of the femur of an elephant, judged on the basis of size to be that of a member of the *Elephas meridionalis-antiquus* group. It is conceivably Cromerian (first interglacial), more probably later, but can safely be classed as "possibly Middle or Upper Pleistocene".

Analyses of fossil materials from Piltdown

	Fluorine %	P_2O_5 %	$\frac{\%F}{\%P_2O_5} \times 100$	Iron %
Eoanthropus I				
*P.*1 L. parieto-frontal (*E.* 590)†	0.1 (2)*	21	0.5	7
*P.*2 L. temporal (*E.* 591)	0.4	18	2.2	7
*P.*3 R. parietal (*E.* 592)	0.3	17	1.8	6
*P.*4 Occipital (*E.* 593)	0.2	28	0.7	5
*P.*5 R. mandibular ramus (*E.* 594)	0.2 (5)	20	1.0	6
*P.*17 Canine (*E.* 611)	<0.1	27	0.4	Trace
*P.*42 Molar (rm_1) (*E.* 594)	<0.1	23	0.4	Trace
Eoanthropus II				
*P.*30 R. frontal (*E.* 646)	0.1	13	0.8	12
*P.*31 Occipital (*E.* 647)	0.1 (2)	17	0.6	17
*P.*32 Molar (lm_1) (*E.* 648)	0.4 (2)	30	1.3	Trace
Other Mammalian Remains Lower Pleistocene				
*P.*6 Molar, *Mastodon* cf. *arvernensis* (*E.* 595)	1.9	23	8.3	5
*P.*7 Molar, *Elephas* cf. *planifrons* (*E.* 596)	2.7 (2)	33	8.2	3
*P.*8 Molar, *Elephas* cf. *planifrons* (*E.* 597)	2.5	34	7.4	1
*P.*23 Molar, *Elephas* cf. *planifrons* (*E.* 620)	3.1	39	7.9	4
*P.*25 Molar, *Mastodon arvernensis* (*E.* 622)	2.3	36	6.4	4
*P.*26 Premolar, "*Rhinoceros*" cf. *etruscus* (*E.* 623)	2.0	24	8.3	6

应用到皮尔当材料

我们对每件从皮尔当砾石层及附近沉积物中得到的骨和牙齿都进行了分析，包括 17 件曙人材料样本。分析结果见附表。为了进行比较，根据已知或者可能的年代对哺乳动物化石进行了分组。除了亚化石样本或近世的样本外，在进行年代分类时，都忽略了样本的颜色、滚磨程度或其他物理状态。阿维尔乳齿象、平额象相似种（一般作者所认为的“剑齿象”）和艾特鲁斯克“古犀”相似种的牙齿都不会晚于下更新世时期。源自砾石层的所有其余的更新世材料，其年代或者可以肯定比维拉方期更晚（马鹿、欧亚河狸），或者可能比维拉方期晚（河马未定种、马未定种、鹿未定种）。理论上，任何这种后维拉方期的成员都可能生存于第一间冰期（根据霍普伍德的说法，当时正是“中更新世”动物群开始出现的时候），大间冰期（即所有作者所说的中更新世）或者末次间冰期（即有些作者所谓的上更新世早期，而另一些作者认为应该说是中更新世晚期）的。由于具有特征性的克劳默间冰期动物种类并不存在，并且有迹象表明此处堆积物曾经多次再沉积，所以后维拉方期的材料可能一部分是中更新世时期的，另一部分则是上更新世时期的。这一遗址典型的分类问题可以由所谓的皮尔当骨制品来说明（*P*. 18）。该样本是一头大象的股骨的一部分，根据大小来判断，应该是南方象–古象群的成员之一的股骨。它可能属于克劳默间冰期（第一间冰期）或者更晚的时期，但将其分类到“可能为中更新世或上更新世”时期是没有问题的。

皮尔当人化石材料分析

	含氟量 %	P_2O_5%	$\frac{\%F}{\%P_2O_5}\times 100$	铁含量 %
曙人 I				
P.1 左顶骨–额骨 (*E*. 590) †	0.1 (2)*	21	0.5	7
P.2 左颞骨 (*E*. 591)	0.4	18	2.2	7
P.3 右顶骨 (*E*. 592)	0.3	17	1.8	6
P.4 枕骨 (*E*. 593)	0.2	28	0.7	5
P.5 右下颌支 (*E*. 594)	0.2 (5)	20	1.0	6
P.17 犬齿 (*E*. 611)	<0.1	27	0.4	痕量
P.42 臼齿 (第一右下臼齿) (*E*. 594)	<0.1	23	0.4	痕量
曙人 II				
P.30 右额骨 (*E*. 646)	0.1	13	0.8	12
P.31 枕骨 (*E*. 647)	0.1 (2)	17	0.6	17
P.32 臼齿 (第一左下臼齿) (*E*. 648)	0.4 (2)	30	1.3	痕量
其他哺乳动物化石 下更新世				
P.6 臼齿，阿维尔乳齿象相似种 (*E*. 595)	1.9	23	8.3	5
P.7 臼齿，平额象相似种 (*E*. 596)	2.7 (2)	33	8.2	3
P.8 臼齿，平额象相似种 (*E*. 597)	2.5	34	7.4	1
P.23 臼齿，平额象相似种 (*E*. 620)	3.1	39	7.9	4
P.25 臼齿，阿维尔乳齿象 (*E*. 622)	2.3	36	6.4	4
P.26 前臼齿，艾特鲁斯克“古犀”相似种 (*E*. 623)	2.0	24	8.3	6

Continued

	Fluorine %	P_2O_5 %	$\frac{\%F}{\%P_2O_5} \times 100$	Iron %
Possibly Middle and Upper Pleistocene				
P.9 Molar, *Hippopotamus* sp. (*E*. 598)	0.1 (3)	37	0.3	3
P.10 Premolar, *Hippopotamus* sp. (*E*. 599)	1.1 (3)	29	3.8	5
P.11 Antler, *Cervus elaphus* (*E*. 600)	1.5 (3)	28	5.4	3
P.12 Metatarsal, *Cervus* sp. (*E*. 601)	0.1	27	0.4	4
P.13 Molar, *Equus* sp. (*E*. 602)	0.4 (3)	25	1.6	2
P.14 Molar, *Castor fiber* (*E*. 603)	0.4	30	1.3	3
P.18 Femur, *Elephas* cf. *antiquus* (*E*. 615)	1.3 (3)	30	4.3	2
P.19 Indet. bone from basal clay (*E*. 616)	1.4	33	4.2	1
P.21 Incisor, *Castor fiber* (*E*. 618)	0.1	27	0.4	10
P.22 Mandible, *Castor fiber* (*E*. 619)	0.3	18	1.7	6
P.24 Fragment of enamel, *Elephas* sp. indet. (*E*. 621)	0.8 (3)	36	2.2	1
Holocene or Pleistocene				
P.36 Tibia, *Cervus* sp. (*E*. 1383)	<0.1	35	0.3	1
P.37 Caprine molar (*E*. 1384)	0.3 (3)	22	1.4	2
P.39 Bovine long-bone (*E*. 1385)	0.1 (3)	30	0.3	9
P.40 Indet. bone (sub-fossil) (*E*. 1386)	0.1	30	0.3	Trace
P.41 Indet. bone (sub-fossil) (*E*. 1387)	0.3	42	0.7	2
Holocene (Recent)				
P.33 Fragment of fresh bone from soil	<0.1	33	0.3	Trace
P.34 Pelvis, *Bos taurus*	<0.1	24	0.4	4
P.35 Metatarsal, *Bos taurus* (*E*. 1388)	<0.1	27	0.4	2
P.38 Ungual phalange, *Bos taurus* (*E*. 1389)	0.3	32	0.9	5

* Where more than one determination of fluorine content has been made indicated by the number in brackets, the value recorded is the average.

† The register numbers of specimens in the Department of Geology, British Museum (Nat. Hist.), are given in brackets after the description.

In attempting to interpret the analytical results, it is important to note that there is no significant difference in the rate of absorption of fluorine by bone and by dentine. The fluorine content of the mandibular ramus of *Eoanthropus*, for example, ranged from less than 0.1 to 0.3 percent, while that of a molar embedded in this jaw-bone was less than 0.1 percent. If there is differential absorption, the slight advantage is with bone. There are indications that enamel is more resistant to absorption of fluorine than dentine. The analyses of teeth, with two exceptions, were based on samples which were either wholly dentine, or which included a substantial proportion of dentine. The two exceptions were samples of enamel (*P.* 6, *P.* 24).

On the evidence of their state of preservation, the molar and premolar of *Hippopotamus* were placed by Hopwood (ref. 6, p. 49) with *Eoanthropus* in the Lower Pleistocene group. He noted, however, that *Hippopotamus* had never been recorded in a Red Crag association; so that on general grounds it would appear that these teeth more probably belong to the later group[10]. The molar, the fluorine content of which is closely comparable with that of *Eoanthropus*, shows unique preservation (*P.* 9). Whereas its enamel (0.1 percent fluorine) is practically unaltered, its dentine is stained blackish-brown throughout and contains 0.05 percent fluorine. An X-ray powder diffraction photograph showed that this blackened

续表

	含氟量%	P_2O_5%	$\frac{\%F}{\%P_2O_5}\times 100$	铁含量%
可能为中更新世和上更新世				
*P.*9 臼齿，河马未定种 (*E.* 598)	0.1 (3)	37	0.3	3
*P.*10 前臼齿，河马未定种 (*E.* 599)	1.1 (3)	29	3.8	5
*P.*11 鹿角，马鹿 (*E.* 600)	1.5 (3)	28	5.4	3
*P.*12 跖骨，鹿未定种 (*E.* 601)	0.1	27	0.4	4
*P.*13 臼齿，马未定种 (*E.* 602)	0.4 (3)	25	1.6	2
*P.*14 臼齿，欧亚河狸 (*E.* 603)	0.4	30	1.3	3
*P.*18 股骨，古象相似种 (*E.* 615)	1.3 (3)	30	4.3	2
*P.*19 底部黏土中的未确定的骨 (*E.* 616)	1.4	33	4.2	1
*P.*21 门齿，欧亚河狸 (*E.* 618)	0.1	27	0.4	10
*P.*22 下颌骨，欧亚河狸 (*E.* 619)	0.3	18	1.7	6
*P.*24 珐琅质破片，象不能鉴定种 (*E.* 621)	0.8 (3)	36	2.2	1
全新世或更新世				
*P.*36 胫骨，鹿未定种 (*E.* 1383)	<0.1	35	0.3	1
*P.*37 山羊臼齿 (*E.* 1384)	0.3 (3)	22	1.4	2
*P.*39 牛亚科长骨 (*E.* 1385)	0.1 (3)	30	0.3	9
*P.*40 未确定的骨（亚化石）(*E.* 1386)	0.1	30	0.3	痕量
*P.*41 未确定的骨（亚化石）(*E.* 1387)	0.3	42	0.7	2
全新世（近世）				
*P.*33 土壤中的新鲜骨破片	<0.1	33	0.3	痕量
*P.*34 骨盆，家牛	<0.1	24	0.4	4
*P.*35 跖骨，家牛 (*E.* 1388)	<0.1	27	0.4	2
*P.*38 有蹄类指骨，家牛 (*E.* 1389)	0.3	32	0.9	5

* 这里对氟含量进行了不止一次的测定，括号中的数字表明测定次数，记录的数值是平均值。

† 描述后在括号中给出的是大英博物馆（自然分馆）地质学系登记的样本编号。

在解释分析结果的过程中，有一点很重要，那就是要注意到骨和牙本质对氟的吸收率并无显著差异。例如，曙人的下颌支的含氟量从不足 0.1% 到 0.3% 不等，而附着在这具下颌骨中的臼齿的含氟量却小于 0.1%。如果说吸收情况有差异的话，那么骨应该稍具优势。有迹象表明珐琅质比牙本质对氟吸收的抗性更强。除了两次例外，牙齿的分析都是基于具有完整牙本质的样本，或者包含牙本质重要部分的样本，两次例外情况是指分析的珐琅质样本（*P.* 6，*P.* 24）。

根据样本的保存状况提供的证据，霍普伍德（参考文献 6，第 49 页）将河马的臼齿、前臼齿与曙人一起放到了下更新世群中。但是他认为，河马从来没有在与红岩共生的记录中出现过，因此一般情况下这些牙齿更可能属于较晚的群[10]。该臼齿样本的含氟量与曙人的非常接近，表明其独特的保存情况（*P.* 9）。然而其珐琅质（含氟量为 0.1%）实际上并没有遭受蚀变，而其牙本质全部被染成了黑褐色，含氟量为 0.05%。X 射线粉晶衍射照片显示，这一变黑的牙本质由羟磷灰石构成，还可

dentine consists of hydroxyapatite with slight admixture, possibly, of calcium sulphate. Analysis indicated 7 percent iron. A probable interpretation of the specimen is that at some stage of fossilization the hydroxyapatite prisms in the dentine became coated by iron sulphide which inhibited fluorine absorption. The teeth of *Eoanthropus* are in striking contrast to this *Hippopotamus* tooth, and indeed to all the associated fossil animal teeth. Drill holes in the canine and in the molars of *Eoathropus* revealed—most unexpectedly—that below an extremely thin ferruginous surface stain their dentine was pure white, apparently no more altered than the dentine of recent teeth from the soil.

Comparison of the fluorine values of the specimens attributed to *Eoanthropus* and of the bones and teeth the geological ages of which are certain leaves little doubt that: (1) all the specimens of *Eoanthropus*, including the remains of the second skull found two miles away, are contemporaneous; (2) *Eoanthropus* is, at the earliest, Middle Pleistocene.

There can no longer be any question of *Eoanthropus* belonging to the Villafranchian group; but whether it is Middle Pleistocene or later is arguable. That the figures scarcely provide any differentiation between *Eoanthropus* and recent bones requires some explanation; but at least it serves to emphasize the probably enormous time-gap separating the former from the Lower Pleistocene material.

The wide range of fluorine content in the post-Villafranchian material (0.1-1.5 percent) is consistent with the suggestion that this age group is composite. Although none of these specimens is markedly water-worn, the gravels could have been reconstructed at several dates without the component materials travelling far. It is interesting to recall that Dawson (ref. 3, p. 86) considered that the remains of beaver (*Castor*) were the only fossils from the Piltdown pit which could be counted as contemporary with *Eoanthropus*. This is precisely the conclusion which one would draw from the fluorine results.

The eroded (and afterwards worked) fragment of elephant femur (*P.* 18, with 1.3 percent fluorine was not found *in situ*, but appears to have come from clay below the gravel, where it would surely have been a derivative from an older deposit. The red-deer antler (*P.* 11, with 1.5 percent fluorine) was found some distance from the skull site, and may have been preserved in a patch of gravel also representing an earlier phase of the Pleistocene. The fluorine results are, in fact, so consistent with the known or probable relative ages of the mammalian fossils in the Piltdown mélange, that it now appears justifiable to regard *Eoanthropus* and *Castor fiber* as the latest elements in the mixture, and to ascribe them to the period immediately preceding the final re-arrangement of the gravel, since which time free fluorine ions have apparently been remarkably deficient in the ground-water.

Geological Evidence: Conclusion

From the palaeontological data alone, it is not possible to decide whether the final settlement of the Piltdown gravel took place during Middle or early Upper Pleistocene

能混合了少许的硫酸钙。分析表明其铁含量为 7%。对该样本可能的解释是，石化作用的某一阶段，牙本质中的羟磷灰石棱晶表面覆盖上了一层硫化铁，这就阻止了牙本质对氟的吸收。曙人的牙齿与该河马牙齿形成了鲜明的对比，实际上它与所有相关的动物牙齿化石都截然不同。非常出乎意料地是，曙人犬齿和臼齿上的钻孔揭示出，在非常薄的一层铁锈斑点表面之下，它们的牙本质是洁白的，这显然与从土壤中发现的近代牙齿的牙本质完全一样。

对归于曙人的样本的氟值与地质学年代已确定的骨和牙齿的氟值进行的比较几乎可以确信：(1) 包括两英里外发现的第二件头骨化石在内的所有曙人标本都是同一时代的；(2) 曙人所处的年代最早是中更新世。

任何关于曙人是否属于维拉方群的疑问都不复存在了，但是它属于中更新世还是更晚年代则还在争论之中。那些无法提供曙人和最近骨之间存在任何差异的数值尚需解释，但它至少强调了把曙人与下更新世材料分开的可能是巨大的时间差。

后维拉方期材料中的氟含量变化范围很广（0.1%~1.5%），这与这一年代的群体是混合体的推测是一致的。尽管这些样本没有明显出现被水冲磨过的现象，但是这一砾石层可能在几个时期、在组成的材料并未搬运很远的情况下重新堆积的。有趣的是，道森（参考文献 3，第 86 页）认为河狸化石是皮尔当坑发现的唯一可以视为与曙人同时期的化石，而这也正是我们可以从氟含量的计算结果推导出来的结论。

被侵蚀的（后来被加工过的）大象股骨破片（*P.* 18，氟含量为 1.3%）并不是在原位发现的，而似乎是从砾石层之下的黏土中发现的，由此可以推断出，它肯定是一处更古老的堆积物的衍生物。马鹿鹿角（*P.* 11，氟含量为 1.5%）是在距离发现头骨的地点的不远处发现的，它可能在代表更新世较早阶段的一片砾石层中保存过。事实上，得到的氟含量的结果与皮尔当记录中的哺乳动物化石已知的或可能的相对年代如此一致，因此现在将混合物中的曙人和欧亚河狸当作年代最晚的成分并且将它们归于砾石层发生最后一次沉积之前的那个时期是合理的，因为很明显，该时期地下水非常缺乏自由氟离子。

地质学证据：结论

单单依据古生物学资料就决定皮尔当砾石层的最终沉积是否发生在中更新世时

times.

It was pointed out by Clement Reid[11] that these gravels rest on a low plateau surface (100-120 ft. above O.D.) which was extensively developed in the Weald, but which was nowhere covered by marine deposits of the period of the submergence represented by the Goodwood raised beach (135 ft. above O.D.). In any event, it seems unlikely that this surface existed before the base levelling associated with the close of the great interglacial period. Furthermore, if the Piltdown gravel is viewed as a river terrace deposit, its position about fifty feet above the River Ouse[12] places it in a group grading with the Main Monastirian sea-level. From the temperate character of even the latest faunal elements in the Piltdown faunal mélange, it is probable that *Eoanthropus* lived under interglacial conditions, although the final resorting of the gravels may have been brought about by periglacial soil-flow (solifluxion). The question of the precise geological age of the Piltdown gravel is open to further inquiry, but taking the balance of available evidence, *Eoanthropus* may be provisionally referred to the last warm interglacial period (Riss-Würm interglacial; that is, early Upper Pleistocene, although here it should be noted that some authorities count Riss-Würm as Middle Pleistocene).

We wish to record our thanks to the Government Chemist, Dr. G. M. Bennett, and to the Keeper of Geology, British Museum, Mr. W. N. Edwards, for their co-operation, and for permission to publish the relevant portions of this communication.

(**165**, 379-382; 1950)

Kenneth P. Oakley: Department of Geology, British Museum (Natural History).
C. Randall Hoskins: Department of the Government Chemist.

References:

1. Dawson, C., and Woodward, A. S., *Quart. J. Geol. Soc. London*, **69**, 117 (1913).
2. Marston, A. T., *Geol. Assoc. London, Circular*, No. 483, 1 (1946).
3. Dawson, C., and Woodward, A. S., *Quart. J. Geol. Soc. London*, **70**, 82 (1914).
4. Keith, A., *Quart. J. Geol. Soc. London*, **69**, 148 (1913).
5. Newton, E. T., *Quart, J. Geol. Soc. London*, **69**, 151 (1913).
6. Hopwood, A. T., *Proc. Geol. Assoc. London*, **46**, 46 (1935).
7. Oakley, K. P., *Advancement of Science*, **4**, 336 (1948).
8. Willard, H. H., and Winter, O. B., *Indust. Eng. Chem.* (*Anal. Edit.*), **5**, 7 (1933).
9. Oakley, K. P., and Montagu, M. F. A., *Bull. Brit. Mus.* (*Nat. Hist.*), *Geol.*, **1**, 2 (1949).
10. Curwen, E. C., "Archaeology of Sussex", 38 (London: Methuen, 1937).
11. Reid, C., *Quart. J. Geol. Soc. London*, **69**, 149 (1913).
12. Edmunds, F. H., *Abs. Proc. Geol. Soc. London*, No. 1457, 39 (1950).

期或者上更新世早期是不可能的。

克莱门特·里德[11]指出这个砾石场覆盖在一片低的高原表面上（海拔100英尺～120英尺），这一表面在威尔德是广泛形成的，但是该表面并没有被以古德伍德上升的海滩为代表的淹没时期的海洋性沉积物（海拔135英尺）所覆盖。无论如何，这一表面似乎都不可能存在于与大间冰期结束相关的基准面夷平之前。此外，如果皮尔当砾石层被视为一片河流阶地堆积物，那么它位于乌斯河[12]之上50英尺处的位置就会将其放置于一个依最终间冰期极相期海平面逐级变化的群体了。即使从皮尔当混杂动物群中最年轻动物成员的生活温度特征来看，曙人都是可能生活在间冰期环境下的，尽管砾石层的最终形成可能是借助于冰川边缘的泥流（泥流作用）完成的。皮尔当砾石层的准确地质学年代问题还需要进一步的研究，但是考虑到已得到的证据，我们认为可以暂时将曙人归于最后的温暖间冰期（里斯–玉木间冰期，即上更新世初期，但是这里需要说明的一点是，有些专家将里斯–玉木间冰期当作中更新世）。

我们对政府化验师贝内特博士和大英博物馆地质学管理人爱德华兹先生表示感谢，感谢他们提供的合作以及允许我们将这部分信息的相关内容进行发表。

（刘皓芳 翻译；林圣龙 审稿）

Ape or Man?

R. Broom and J. T. Robinson

Editor's Note

The validation of Dart's Taung skull, *Australopithecus*, as representative of an intermediate stage between ape and human, rather than an ape, was largely due to Robert Broom and his fossil hominid discoveries starting in 1936. Here he and colleague Robinson summarize their work to date, on *Pleisanthropus* (now *Australopithecus*) and the more robust form *Paranthropus*. They admit that controversy still raged between those who saw the fossils as almost human, and those who regarded them more as apes, with the intermediate "ape-man" designation being seen by some as a kind of compromise. Broom and Robinson say that all those who had actually seen the fossils came away with the feeling that they had seen something intermediate between ape and man.

IN 1925, Prof. Dart announced the discovery of a new type of higher primate that seemed to be somewhat intermediate between ape and man. This was the skull of the Taungs child which he called *Australopithecus africanus*. For some years there was considerable dispute between those of us who regarded the little skull as that of a being closely allied to the ancestor of man, and those who considered it only a variety of ape, allied to the chimpanzee, which by parallelism had come to resemble man in many characters.

Since 1936 we have made a large number of new discoveries, and this group of higher primates is now known by many skulls and skeletal remains of adults of a considerable variety of forms which we think should be placed in different genera and species.

In the past two years we have discovered a number of nearly complete skulls which give us a new picture of the origin of man. When the only known skulls of our so-called "ape-men" had brains of between 450 and 650 c.c., those who said they were only apes and had no close relationship to man seemed to have some case. But now that we have skulls with brains of 750, 800 and possibly 1,000 c.c., we seem to be dealing with beings that have some claim to be called human.

Recently we have found five skulls with fair-sized brains. One is a child skull with a brain of perhaps 600 c.c., and one that of a child with a brain of about 700 or 750 c.c. Then we have two nearly complete female skulls with brain cases which we estimate at about 800 or 850 c.c. Each skull lacks the occiput, but is otherwise nearly complete although somewhat crushed. It will take some time to reconstruct an uncrushed skull; but we seem very safe in considering that it had a brain of more than 800 c.c.

是猿类还是人类？

布鲁姆，鲁滨逊

编者按

达特的汤恩头骨被确定为南方古猿——一种介于猿类与人类之间的中间类型的代表——而不是猿类，这在很大程度上要归因于罗伯特·布鲁姆的研究以及他从1936年开始发现的人科化石。本文中布鲁姆和他的同事鲁滨逊将之前关于迩人（现在为南方古猿）以及更为粗壮的傍人的工作进行了总结。一些学者认为这些化石接近于人类，而另一些学者则认为它们更像猿类，布鲁姆和鲁滨逊承认这种激烈的争论长期存在着，在一些人看来，中间类型“猿人”的命名是一种折中的办法。布鲁姆和鲁滨逊称所有那些实际看过化石的人都会有这样一种感觉：他们看到的是介于猿类和人类之间的某种中间类型。

1925年，达特教授宣布发现了一种新型高等灵长类动物，这种灵长类动物似乎是介于猿类与人类之间的某种中间类型。这便是他称为南方古猿非洲种的汤恩幼儿的头骨。多年以来人们对此一直存在着很大的争议：我们这部分人认为这个小头骨所属的生物类型与人类祖先具有密切的亲缘关系，而另外一些人则认为它只是猿类的一个变种，与黑猩猩有亲缘关系；而黑猩猩经过平行进化，在许多方面已具有与人类相似的特征。

自1936年以来，我们已经取得了大量的新发现。通过许多成年头骨和骨残骸，使人们认识了这类高等灵长类动物，这些成年头骨和骨残骸的类型多种多样，我们认为应该将其归为不同的属和种。

在过去的两年中，我们已经发现了大量基本完整的头骨，为我们描绘了一幅人类起源的新图景。当只知道我们所谓的“猿人”头骨的脑量在450毫升～650毫升之间时，那些说它们只是猿类并与人类没有任何密切亲缘关系的人似乎还有一些根据，但是现在我们发现了脑量达到750毫升、800毫升甚至可能为1,000毫升的头骨，那么我们正在讨论的生物似乎就是一些人声称的人类。

最近，我们发现了5件具有较大脑量的头骨。一件是年幼个体的头骨，其脑量约为600毫升，另一件年幼个体头骨的脑量约为700毫升或750毫升。之后我们得到了两件几乎完整的女性头骨，我们估计其脑量约为800毫升或850毫升。每件头骨都缺少枕骨，但除此以外，尽管稍微有些破碎基本上还是完整的。复原出一件未破碎的头骨尚需一些时间，但是我们可以肯定地认为其脑量大于800毫升。

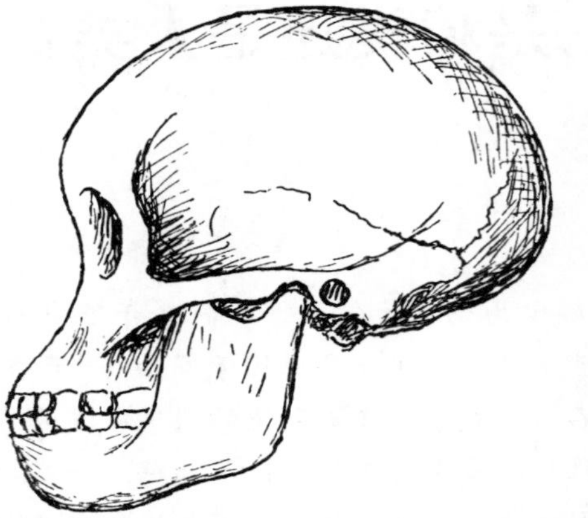

Fig. 1. Attempted restoration of seven-year-old male *Paranthropus crassidens* ($\frac{1}{3}$ natural size). The skull is almost complete, but the top is much crushed down on the base. The mandible is drawn from the jaw of another child. As restored the brain would be more than 700 c.c.

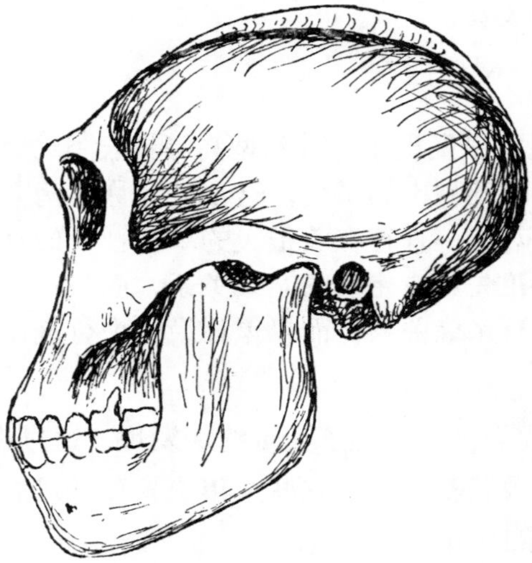

Fig. 2. Restoration of skull of female *Paranthropus crassidens* ($\frac{1}{3}$ natural size). The skull is satisfactorily known except the occiput, but is considerably crushed. The mandible is perfect, but is that of another individual. As restored the brain would be more than 800 c.c.

In structure the skulls are very interesting. The face is flat and broad. Above the eyes is a transverse supraorbital ridge; but it is more slender than in Pekin man, and a little like that of *Pithecanthropus*. There is practically no brow. The temporal muscles must have been relatively very large, and they passed up to the top of the skull as in male gorillas, and were separated by a bony sagittal crest rising about 12 mm. above the general surface of the skull. The ear region and the glenoid are almost typically human, and there is a large mastoid process and well-marked mastoid notch.

The palate and teeth are essentially human, and the incisors and canines would be accepted by most dentists as human teeth.

We have a perfect female mandible with all the teeth in perfect condition and a number

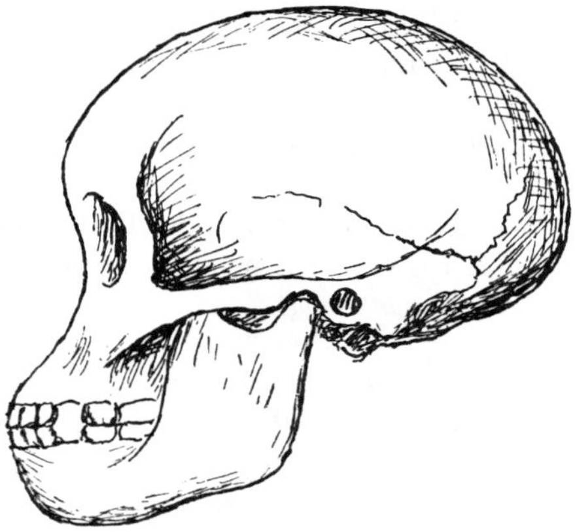

图 1. 对7岁男性傍人粗齿种的尝试复原图（真实尺寸的$\frac{1}{3}$）。该头骨基本完整，但是颅底前部有破碎。下颌骨是根据另一个幼儿的颌骨画出来的。复原之后，该头骨脑量超过700 毫升。

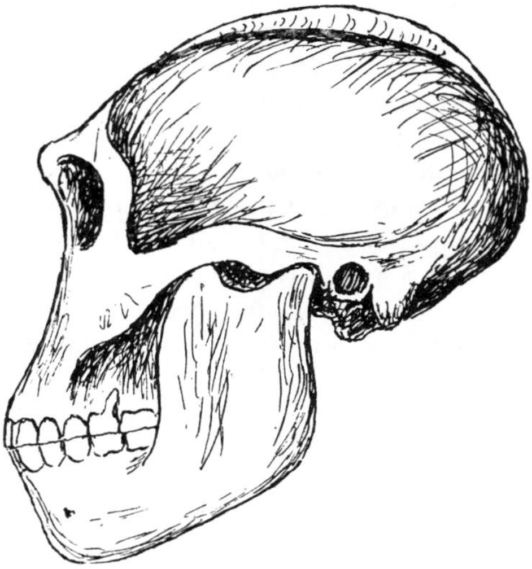

图2. 女性傍人粗齿种头骨的复原图（真实尺寸的$\frac{1}{3}$）。除枕骨外，人们对该头骨有了充分的认识，但是其破碎程度相当严重。下颌骨保存得很好，但属于另外一个个体。复原之后得到该头骨的脑量应超过800 毫升。

这些头骨的结构非常引人注意。面部扁平而宽阔。眼上方是一个横向的眶上嵴，但是比北京人的更加纤细，与爪哇猿人的有点像。几乎没有眉毛。其颞肌肯定相对比较大，一直延伸到头骨的顶部，就像在雄性大猩猩中一样，高于头骨全表面约12 毫米的一个矢状脊将颞肌分开。耳区和下颌关节盂几乎是典型的人类类型，并且有一个大的乳突和明显的乳突切迹。

腭和牙齿实质而言是人类的，大部分牙科专家认为切牙和犬齿也属于人类的牙齿。

我们有一件完整的女性下颌骨，所有牙齿都保存得很好，还有许多其他颌骨也

of other jaws in fairly good condition. One striking feature is that all the jaws have some indication of a chin, and one has a typical human chin with a well-marked mental prominence. If we did not have the whole symphysis, which is very thick, and the molar teeth, which are certainly those of *Paranthropus*, we might suspect this jaw to be that of a *Homo*.

Then we have a very fine pelvis. It has a large, wide ilium, practically human and not at all ape-like, with an ischium that is not human and which also differs considerably from that of the Sterkfontein ape-man *Plesianthropus*.

When Dart described the Taungs ape-man the large majority of men of science in the northern hemisphere were of opinion that it was an anthropoid ape allied to the chimpanzee and gorilla. One went so far as to call it a "dwarf gorilla". But soon one or two came to the conclusion that, if an anthropoid ape, it is the one known that is nearest to man. But most anatomists apparently took little interest in the skull.

In 1936 the senior author started a search for an adult skull, as the child skull did not seem to be understood; and a fairly good skull of an adult allied to the Taungs child was found on August 17 at Sterkfontein. This was made the type of *Plesianthropus transvaalensis*. Two years later another type of skull was found at Kromdraai, and named *Paranthropus robustus*. Some anatomists in Britain and America assumed it as probable that the two adult skulls were merely adults of the Taungs species. Then in Novermber 1948 another new type was discovered at Swartkrans and called *Paranthropus crassidens*. Even now there are, we believe, many who consider that all our types are at most only species of *Australopithecus*, and a few still hold that they are all anthropoid apes. A considerable number of men of science from America and Europe have visited South Africa to examine our specimens, and we think all who have taken this trouble have gone back convinced that at least we have the remains of beings that were much more human in structure than any known living or fossil apes.

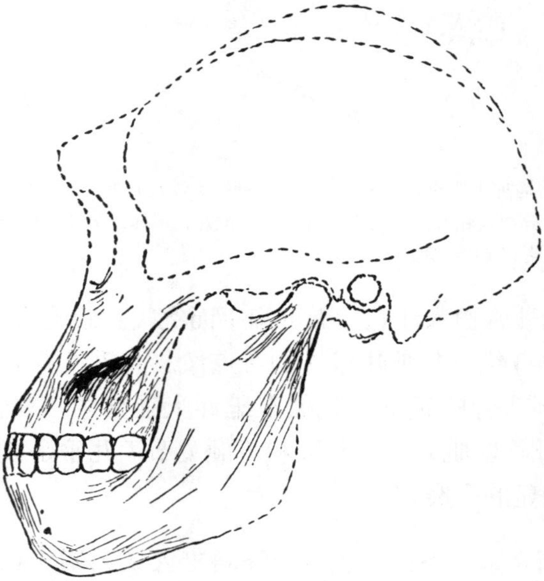

Fig. 3. Restoration of skull of male Swartkrans ape-man *Paranthropus crassidens* ($\frac{1}{3}$ natural size). Only lower jaw and face are known. As restored the brain would be about 1,000 c.c., and thus well within the human range

保存得相当完好。所有颌骨都有一个显著的特征，即具有一些颏的迹象；其中一个具有典型的人颏特征，带有明显的颏凸。如果没有粗壮的联合部以及那些肯定属于傍人属的臼齿，我们可能会怀疑这个颌骨属于人属。

之后我们发现了一个很好的骨盆。它有一个大而宽的髂骨，该髂骨实际上是人类的而根本不类似猿类的；它还有一个坐骨，该坐骨不是人类的，与斯泰克方丹猿人——迩人的坐骨差异也很大。

当达特描述汤恩猿人时，北半球科学界的大多数人认为它是一种与黑猩猩和大猩猩具有亲缘关系的类人猿。有人甚至称它为“矮小大猩猩”。但是不久之后，有一两个人得出结论称，如果是类人猿的话，那么它就是当前已知的最接近人类的类人猿了。但是大多数解剖学家显然对这个头骨没有什么兴趣。

由于大家似乎并没有弄明白年幼个体的头骨，1936 年本文第一作者开始了对成年个体头骨的寻找；8 月 17 日在斯泰克方丹发现了一件保存相当好的与汤恩幼儿有亲缘关系的成年头骨。认为是德兰士瓦迩人。两年后在克罗姆德拉伊又发现了另一种类型的头骨，并将其命名为粗壮傍人。英国和美国的一些解剖学家认为这两个成年头骨可能仅仅是汤恩种类的成年个体。之后在 1948 年 11 月，在斯瓦特克朗斯发现了另外一种新类型，将其命名为傍人粗齿种。我们相信即使在现在，仍有许多人认为我们发现的所有类型至多不过是南方古猿的一些种类，还有一些人仍然认为它们都是类人猿。来自美国和欧洲科学界的许多人士都到访过南非来查验我们的标本，我们认为所有不辞辛苦这么做的人回去之后都至少会相信，我们拥有的生物化石在结构上比任何已知的现存猿类或化石猿类都更接近于人类。

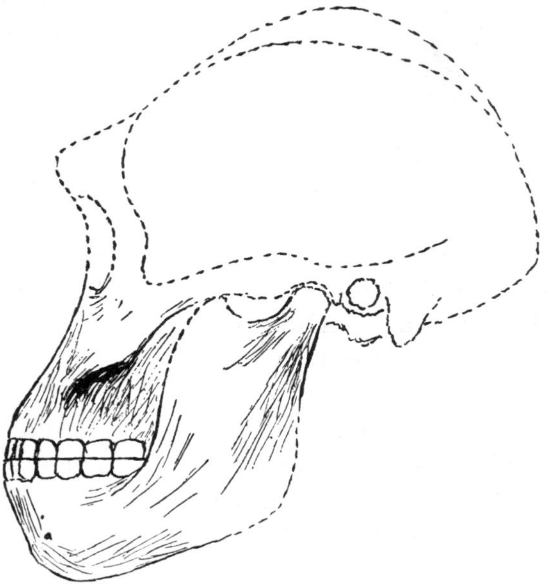

图3. 男性斯瓦特克朗斯猿人——傍人粗齿种头骨的复原图（真实尺寸的$\frac{1}{3}$）。只有下颌骨和面部是已知的。复原之后得到的该头骨脑量约为1,000 毫升，因而完全处于人类脑量的范围之内。

Opinions still differ considerably. Some have argued that all our ape-men are true human beings. Some—a very few, we believe—consider they are anthropoid apes. Probably most prefer to wait, and call them ape-men.

Plesianthropus has a female with a brain of about 500 c.c., and this seems to us a brain scarcely large enough to entitle it to human status—though it may be in the human line.

Paranthropus crassidens we now know fairly well. It has a brain of about 800-850 c.c. in the female, and perhaps more than 1,000 c.c. in the male. Even in the female it has a large bony sagittal crest. It has milk teeth differing so much from those of *Plesianthropus* and *Australopithecus* as to seem to confirm the correctness of placing it in a distinct genus. Its pelvis is also different in important details from those of both *Plesianthropus* and man.

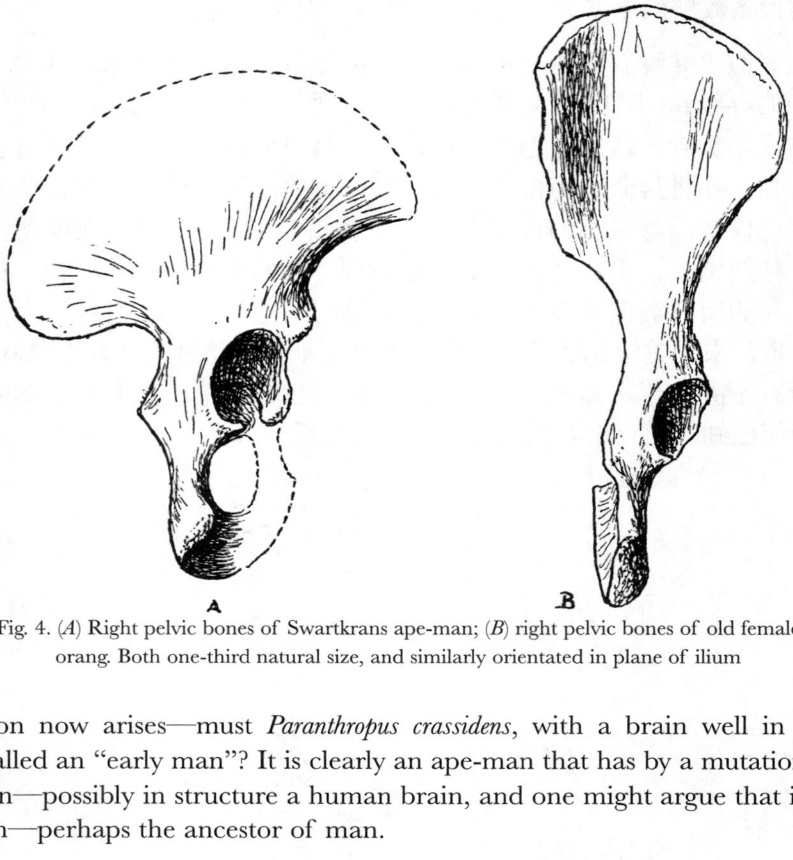

Fig. 4. (*A*) Right pelvic bones of Swartkrans ape-man; (*B*) right pelvic bones of old female orang. Both one-third natural size, and similarly orientated in plane of ilium

The question now arises—must *Paranthropus crassidens*, with a brain well in the human range, be called an "early man"? It is clearly an ape-man that has by a mutation developed a large brain—possibly in structure a human brain, and one might argue that it is an early type of man—perhaps the ancestor of man.

Again, the teeth seem to solve our problem. *Australopithecus* and *Plesianthropus* have remarkable milk pre-molar teeth. Man has exactly the same type. But *Paranthropus* has a more primitive type, so that it seems more probable that man (*Homo*) has evolved from a *Plesianthropus*-like type than from a *Paranthropus*.

Possibly we are correct in assuming that there lived in South Africa a million or perhaps two million years ago a family of higher primates, not closely related to the living

目前观点仍存在很大的分歧。有些人认为，我们所有的猿人都是真正的人类。有一些人认为它们只是类人猿，我们相信这部分人只占极少数。可能大多数人更倾向于观望，并暂时称它们为猿人。

迩人标本中有一件女性头骨，其脑量约为 500 毫升，在我们看来，这样的脑量尚不足以称其为人类——尽管它可能处于人类世系中。

现在我们对傍人粗齿种已经了解得非常清楚了。其女性的脑量约为 800 毫升 ~ 850 毫升，男性可能大于 1,000 毫升。即使女性也有巨大的矢状脊。它的乳齿与迩人和南方古猿的差别如此之大，因此似乎可以确认将其归为一个不同的属是正确的。它的骨盆在很多重要细节上也与迩人和人类的不同。

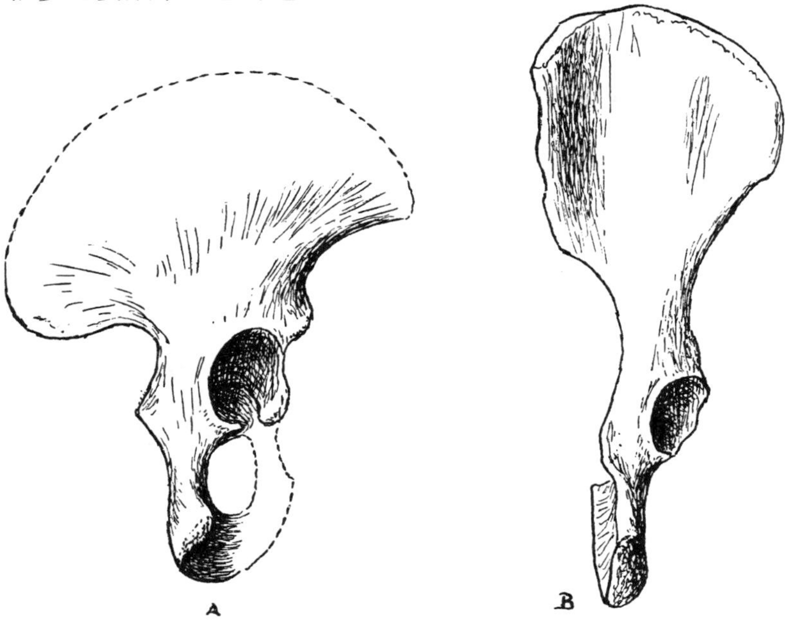

图 4.（*A*）斯瓦特克朗斯猿人的右侧骨盆骨骼；（*B*）老年雌性猩猩的右侧骨盆骨骼。这两幅图都为真实尺寸的$\frac{1}{3}$，并且同样都是从髂骨平面看到的视图。

现在问题产生了——脑量正好处于人类范围内的傍人粗齿种一定要称为“早期人类”吗？很明显，猿人有一个由于发生突变而发育形成的脑——在结构上可能是人类的脑，甚至有些人可能会认为它是一种早期人类的类型——或许是人类的祖先。

那么，牙齿似乎能帮助我们解决问题。南方古猿和迩人具有显著的乳前臼齿。人类也拥有相同类型的牙齿。但是傍人的牙齿类型更为原始，因此人类（人属）似乎更可能是从一种类似迩人的类型进化而来的，而不是从傍人进化而来的。

我们的以下推测可能是正确的：即一百万年或可能两百万年前在南非居住着高等灵长类动物家族，它们与现存的类人猿没有密切的亲缘关系，但有可能是从一种

anthropoids, but perhaps evolved from a very early anthropoid or even a pre-anthropoid by a different line, that this line early became bipedal and soon used the hands for tools and weapons, and that one branch of this family, about Upper Pliocene times, gave rise to man. There is no doubt the family varied greatly, and the safest conclusion to which we can at present come is that of the writer in *The Times* of July 28, who says: "It seems clear that the *Australopithecinae* as revealed up to now were 'almost man', and their presence in the Transvaal a million years ago strongly reinforces the possibility that something which we should recognize as man was first evolved in Africa".

(**166**, 843-844; 1950)

R. Broom and J. T. Robinson: Transvaal Museum, Pretoria.

非常早的类人猿或甚至是从一种不同世系的前类人动物进化而来的，这一世系很早就成为了两足动物并且不久就会用双手使用工具和武器，大概在上新世晚期这一家族的一个分支演化成了人类。毫无疑问，这个家族发生了巨大的变异，目前我们能够得出的最保险的结论正如 7 月 28 日《泰晤士报》上的一个作者所说的："似乎很清楚的是，目前为止的研究表明南方古猿亚科'几乎就是人类'，一百万年前它们在德兰士瓦的存在大大增强了这样的可能性：我们应该认定为人类的这一生物最早是从非洲进化而来的。"

（刘皓芳 翻译；冯兴无 审稿）

Spiral Growth on Carborundum Crystal Faces

A. R. Verma

Editor's Note

The British physicist Charles Frank suggested in 1949 that growing crystals might develop so-called screw dislocations, in which misalignments of the regular rows of atoms create defects in the stacking of layers in the form of a spiral-staircase arrangement that twists around a central core. This would produce spiral-like patterns on the crystal surface. Something of this sort was reported the following year on the surface of beryl, but Frank's idea received its most solid confirmation from these two papers, by Ajit Ram Verma at Royal Holloway College just outside London in England, and by Severin Amelinckx at the University of Gent in Belgium. Both studied carborundum (silicon carbide), and both coated the surface with a thin layer of silver, improving the visibility of the surface structure and enabling the step height to be measured by light reflection. The measurements confirmed that successive spirals step up by a single "unit cell" of the crystal structure, as Frank's theory required.

IN 1949 Frank[1,2] pointed out the possibility that growth of crystals at low supersaturations, essential for good crystals, could take place because of the formation of dislocations in the crystal so that any real crystal should have a number of dislocations with a screw component, terminating on the face. When growth takes place on these exposed molecular terraces, the edges of these layers develop into spirals centred on the dislocation.

Griffin[3] has observed these "monomolecular" layers on the (1010) face of a beryl crystal, and has shown by multiple-beam interferometry that the height of these steps is less than 34 A., that is, less than four unit cells of the crystal. It was inferred that these steps are only one unit cell high.

In the present investigation, numerous "growth spirals" have been observed on the faces of carborundum and measured with the aid of phase-contrast microscopy and multiple-beam interferometry.

Carborundum[4] occurs in at least eight known types, one of which is cubic, whereas the rest are either hexagonal or rhombohedral and have identical layers but differ in their arrangement and are uniquely distinguished by the number of layers in the unit cell. The crystals studied here are of type I (rhombohedral, fifteen layers, with lattice parameter $c = 37.7$ A.), and type II (hexagonal, six layers, $c = 15.1$ A.).

These spirals were studied by coating the crystal faces with a thin film of silver of reflectivity nearly 90 percent, deposited by thermal evaporation, and then examining these

碳化硅晶体表面的螺旋生长

维尔马

编者按

英国物理学家查尔斯·弗兰克在1949年指出，生长着的晶体可能形成所谓的螺旋位错，该位错是指晶体在逐层叠加过程中，以绕中心核旋转的螺旋梯排列的形式呈现的由原子规则排列失准造成的晶格缺陷。这会在晶体表面产生螺旋形花纹。虽然次年有报道称在绿柱石表面发现了这种花纹，但令弗兰克的观点得到最可靠的确证则有赖于以下两人的文章：英国伦敦近郊皇家哈洛威学院的阿吉特·拉姆·维尔马和比利时根特大学的塞韦林·阿梅林克斯。这两位学者研究的都是碳化硅，并且都在晶体表面薄薄地覆盖一层银以提高表面结构的可见度并由此通过光反射测量台阶的高度。测量结果证实了弗兰克的理论，即连续的螺旋状台阶的高度值确实是晶体结构中的一个“晶胞”的高度。

弗兰克[1,2]在1949年指出，在低度过饱和条件下——这对形成优质晶体是必要的——晶体有可能生长是因为晶体中位错的形成，所以任何真实晶体中都应该存在大量含有终止于表面的螺旋位错。当晶体的生长发生在这些暴露出来的分子台阶中时，这些分子层的边缘就会形成以位错为中心的螺旋。

格里芬[3]曾在绿柱石晶体（1010）面上观测到这些“单分子”层，并且采用多光束干涉法得出这些台阶高度小于34埃，也就是说，小于晶体中4个晶胞的高度。由此我们可推测这些台阶只有一个晶胞的高度。

在目前的研究中，已在碳化硅晶体表面观测到大量“生长螺旋”，并且借助相差显微技术和多光束干涉法对其进行了测定。

碳化硅晶体[4]至少存在8种已知的类型，除一种立方晶系外，其余均属于六方晶系或斜方晶系，并且具有相同的层但排列方式不同，唯一能区分它们的是其晶胞中层的数目。本文研究的是类型I（斜方晶系，15层，晶格参数 $c = 37.7$ 埃）和类型II（六方晶系，6层，$c = 15.1$ 埃）的晶体。

研究上述螺旋的方法是通过热蒸发沉积的方式在晶体表面薄薄地覆盖一层反射

faces in reflexion.

Theory shows that for growth taking place from vapour, the ledge extending from the point of emergence of the dislocation to the crystal boundary has a rate of advance independent of the crystallographic orientation, thus forming a simple Archimedean spiral which can be calculated and from which the constant of spacing between turns can be predicted. These predictions have been completely confirmed numerically by the circular spirals shown in Fig. 1.

Fig. 1-Fig. 4

The dependence of the rate of advance of a growth front on the orientation of the step line should impose a characteristic distortion of the growth of spirals, exhibiting the crystal symmetry. In accordance with this, Fig. 2 shows a hexagonal spiral (crystal type II). The straight edges correspond to a sharp minimum in the growth-rate as a function of orientation.

The complex growth patterns predicted for two or more screw dislocations ending on a crystal face and depending on the property of growth fronts which annihilate each other where the two edges meet are illustrated in Fig. 1. Thus for two screw dislocations of opposite hand, with the unfolding of the two spirals the ledges starting from one terminate on the other, generating closed loops.

Various other growth patterns for two, three and larger numbers of dislocations ending on crystal faces to type I and type II have been photographed and explained.

Interlacing of hexagonal spirals observed on a crystal face of type II is illustrated in Fig. 3.

The observed density of dislocations varies widely on different specimens, ranging from a few to a maximum of $\sim 10^4$ per sq. cm. On any crystal they are predominantly of one hand.

率约为 90% 的银，然后检测这些表面的反射情况。

理论表明，对于气相条件下的生长，从位错出现的位置向晶体边界扩展的晶体阶壁具有一种独立于晶体学取向的推进速率，因此会形成一种简单的阿基米德螺线。这种螺线可由计算得出，并且其中各圈之间的间隔常数是可以预测的。这些预测已由图 1 所示的圆形螺线在数值上得到完全确证。

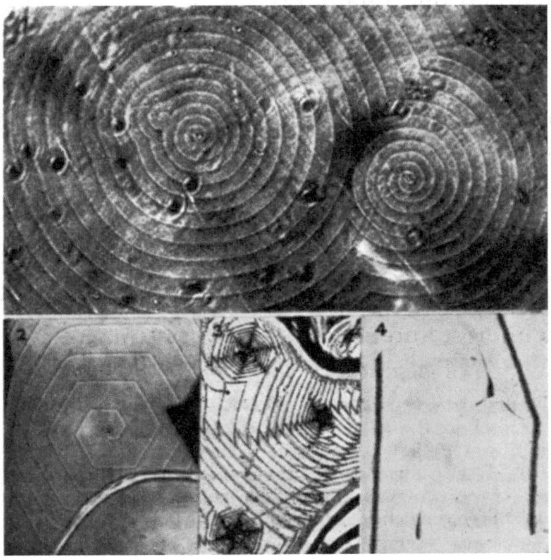

图 1~ 图 4

生长阵面的推进速率对阶梯线取向的依赖性会迫使螺线生长产生一种特征性的扭曲，体现出晶体的对称性。与此对应的就是图 2 显示的六方螺旋（类型 II 晶体）。作为阶梯线取向的函数，生长速率极小值与螺线的直线形边对应。

对两个或更多终止于晶体表面并且依赖于生长阵面性质的复杂生长模式，如图 1 所示，此生长阵面在两个边缘相遇的位置相互抵消。因此，对于手性相反的两个螺旋位错，随着两个螺旋的展开，晶体阶壁都以对方的一端作为自己另一端的起点，从而形成闭合的环。

对于终止于类型 I 和类型 II 晶体表面的两个、三个或更多位错，我们已经对它们其他的多种生长模式拍摄了照片并对其加以解释。

图 3 所示的为在类型 II 晶体表面观测到的六方螺旋的交织。

不同样品观测到的位错密度变化很大，其范围从每平方厘米只有几个到最多约有 10^4 个。对于任意一种晶体，其位错方向总是以某一手性方向为主。

The calculated radius of the critical nucleus is 2 μ and the supersaturation 0.2 percent.

To measure the step height of these spirals, multiple-beam interference (Tolansky[5]) has been employed. Fig. 4 shows the Fizeau fringes for λ 5,461, passing over a circular spiral, in which the height can be accurately measured; and as the number of turns is readily visible, the height of each single step can be deduced with precision. Analogous measurements have been made also with fringes of equal chromatic order. The step heights on a type II crystal measured from two different spirals are respectively 15.2 A. and 15.1 A., with a maximum uncertainty of 2 A. It is already known from X-ray analysis that, for type II, $c = 15.1$ A. Thus it has been proved here that the step is a single unit-cell high.

The observation of spiral markings on carborundum has already been reported[6]. The observed shapes of these spirals are in accordance with the predictions of theory, and their step height is equal to that of a unit cell, showing that these are growth spirals originating from screw dislocations.

A more detailed account of this work has been communicated elsewhere. I am grateful to Prof. S. Tolansky for his interest and encouragement in the course of this work, and to the British Council for the award of a scholarship.

(**167**, 939; 1951)

Ajit Ram Verma: Royal Holloway College, Englefield Green, Surrey.

References:

1. Burton, Cabrera and Frank, *Nature*, **163**, 398 (1949).
2. Frank, F. C., Farad. Soc. Discuss., Crystal Growth, No. 5(1949).
3. Griffin, L. J., *Phil. Mag.*, **41**, 196 (1950).
4. Ramsdell, L. S., *Amer. Min.*, **32**, 64 (1947).
5. Tolansky, S., "Multiple-beam Interferometry of Surfaces and Films" (Oxford Univ. Press, 1948).
6. Mellor, J. W., "A Comprehensive Treatise on Inorganic and Theoretical Chemistry", **5**, 879 (1924).

临界核的计算半径为 2 微米，其过饱和度为 0.2%。

采用多光束干涉法（托兰斯基[5]）测定这些螺旋的台阶高度。图 4 显示了波长 λ 为 5,461 埃的斐索条纹（越过圆形螺线），螺线的高度可由此得到精确测定；并且由于圈数易于观测，因此我们可以精确地推测出每一个台阶的高度。也通过等色级条纹方法进行了类似的测量。从两种不同螺旋中测得类型 II 晶体的台阶高度分别为 15.2 埃和 15.1 埃，最大不确定度为 2 埃。根据 X 射线分析已经得知，类型 II 晶体 $c = 15.1$ 埃。因此，台阶只有一个晶胞的高度就得到证实。

对碳化硅表面螺纹的观测已经有过报道[6]。所观测到的这些螺旋的形状与之前的理论预期是一致的，而且其台阶高度等于一个晶胞的高度，这表明它们是起源于螺旋位错的生长螺旋。

关于这项研究的更为详细的说明已在其他地方发表。在此，我要感谢托兰斯基教授对于本研究工作给予的关心和鼓励，以及英国文化协会的奖学金。

（王耀杨 翻译；李芝芬 审稿）

Determination of the Absolute Configuration of Optically Active Compounds by Means of X-Rays

J. M. Bijvoet *et al.*

Editor's Note

It was known since the nineteenth century that many organic molecules come in two "chiral" forms or enantiomers, identical except for being mirror images, like left and right hands. But there was no way to determine which handedness a given enantiomer had. Conventional X-ray crystallography could reveal the positions of atoms from the distances between them—but the latter are identical for enantiomers. Here Johannes Bijvoet and coworkers in Utrecht overcome that problem by measuring the phases as well as the angles of scattered X-ray beams from chiral tartaric acid. They find that, by good fortune, the configuration fits with the one designated historically, which was previously just an arbitrary convention with an even chance of conforming to reality.

J. H. VAN'T HOFF extended the structural formulae of organic chemistry to include spatial configuration ("La chimie dans l'espace" (1874), the aliphatic carbon atom with hydrogen or other atoms at the corners of a tetrahedron surrounding it). X-ray analysis has determined the exact configurations and the interatomic distances accurately to within a hundredth of an angstrom unit.

Optically active compounds are not superimposable and are the inverted image of each other. Now it is a remarkable fact that while all details of such configurations can be determined, it yet remained unsolved, whether model or inversion corresponds with a given—say the dextrorotatory—compound. Our present investigation was concerned with this question.

It is impossible to determine absolute configurations by chemical means, which show only the relationship between different structures. These relationships would not alter in any respect if every optically active compound should possess its inverted configuration. Absolute configurations—introduced for the sake of expressing relationship—were based on mere convention. Emil Fischer attributed the configuration of Fig. 2*b* to natural, dextrorotatory, tartaric acid—with an even chance that this choice would fit the real situation.

Of the physical methods of determining absolute configuration, the theoretical calculation of the rotatory power is the most obvious and that most studied; hitherto, the results, however, have lacked conclusiveness. Recently, a discussion of the relation between crystal structure and face development has been put forward. As to the X-ray method, X-rays

用X射线方法测定光学活性化合物的绝对构型

比沃特等

编者按

众所周知，自从19世纪以来，许多有机分子以“手性”形式或者对映异构体两两出现，除了互为镜像外，它们完全一致，就像人的左手和右手；但是没有方法能够确定给定对映异构体是左手性还是右手性。传统的X射线晶体学能够通过原子间的距离来显示原子的位置，但是对于对映异构体，原子间的距离完全一样。本文中乌得勒支的约翰内斯·比沃特及其合作者们通过检测手性酒石酸散射的X射线束的相位和角度解决了这一难题。幸运的是，他们发现这一构型和之前定义的构型吻合，虽然之前定义的构型完全是随机的，与事实相符的可能性为50%。

范特霍夫将有机化学的结构式扩展，使其包含空间构型（《立体化学论》(1874年)，脂肪族碳原子上连接的氢或者其他原子处于它周围的四面体顶点上）。X射线分析已确定了正确的构型以及精确到1%埃的原子间的距离。

光学活性化合物是不能彼此重叠的而是互为翻转的镜像。现在一个值得我们注意的事实是即使能够测定这类构型的全部细节，仍然有问题尚未解决，无法知道一个给定的——比如右旋性的——化合物对应的究竟是其原型还是翻转像。我们现在的研究就是关于这一问题的。

用化学方法无法测定绝对构型，该方法只能说明不同结构之间的关系。如果每种光学活性化合物具有自身翻转构型，这些关系不会有任何改变。为表示关系而引入的绝对构型，仅仅是基于人为约定。埃米尔·费歇尔将图2*b*所示的构型称为天然右旋酒石酸，这种选择与事实相符的可能性为50%。

在测定绝对构型的物理方法中，旋光率的理论计算是最直接的，也是研究得最充分的一种理论；不过到目前为止，仍然缺少决定性的结果。最近，一场晶体结构与面生长之间关系的讨论得以开展。至于X射线方法，通常认为X射线无法测定绝

are not supposed to be able to determine absolute configuration as they measure the interatomic distances, which do not differ for model and inversion.

This condition may be illustrated by the simple schematic diffraction experiments indicated in Fig. 1. Compared with *(a)*, the diffraction object in *(b)* has been inverted. The path (phase) differences for each pair of atoms involved in the same direction of diffraction *(p)* remains unchanged (except for sign); hence the resultant interference effect will be the same for both conditions. The removal of this equivalence is the essential point of the determination of absolute configuration by X-rays.

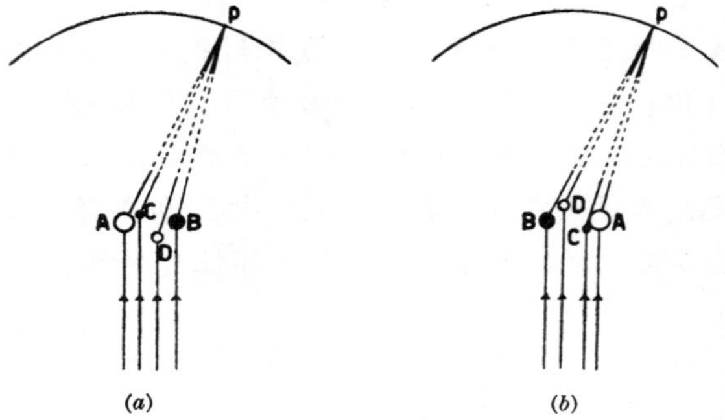

Fig. 1. Equal phase differences (except for sign) for model and inversion in the same direction of diffraction. By introducing a phase-lag in the scattering of one of the atoms, this equivalence is removed

A phase-lag can be introduced into the primary scattering process by one of the atoms[1], say atom *A*. This is achieved by using X-rays of a wave-length that just excites atom *A*. Again, for the conditions *(a)* and *(b)*, compare the phase differences operative in the diffraction *p*. Consider the phase difference between the waves scattered by the atoms *A* and *B*. In *(a)* the characteristic phase-lag in the scattering of atom *A* is seen to be connected with the longer light path, in case *(b)* with the shorter. Hence, the total phase difference operative in the interference of the waves scattered by *A* and *B* will no longer be opposite, and the diffraction intensities will differ for these two conditions. (In the crystal diffraction, besides the inequality $I^{a}_{hkl} \neq I^{b}_{hkl}$ (*a* and *b* denoting the two optical antipodes) the following relation exists: $I^{a}_{hkl} = I^{b}_{\bar{h}\bar{k}\bar{l}}$. According to the latter relation, the films of optical antipodes do not differ in diffraction intensities, but only in their succession on Weissenberg diagrams with fixed rotation sense of the crystal.)

This difference of corresponding diffractions, which vanishes for X-rays of arbitrary wave-length, has been observed in the case of sodium rubidium tartrate using zirconium K_{α} rays which just excite the rubidium atom[2]. It enabled us, analogous to the case discussed above, to decide between the diffracting model and its inversion. The result is that Emil Fischer's *convention*, which assigned the configuration of Fig. 2 to the dextrorotatory acid, *appears to answer to reality.*

对构型，因为它们测量的原子间的距离在原型和翻转像中并无差别。

这种情况可以通过图 1 所示简单的衍射实验示意图加以说明。相对于（a）而言，（b）中的衍射物体被翻转过来。在相同衍射方向（p）上的每对原子的路径（相位）差保持不变（除符号不同外）；因此在这两种情况下所产生的干涉效应将是一样的。去除这一相等关系是用 X 射线测定绝对构型的关键。

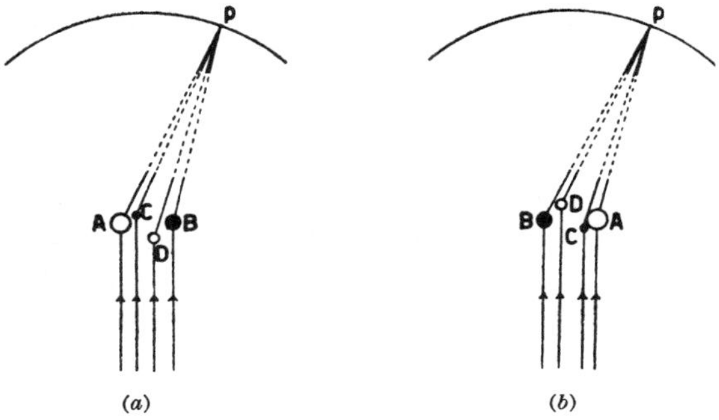

图 1. 原型与翻转像在同一衍射方向上具有相等的相位差（除符号不同外）。通过在某一原子的散射中引入相位滞后去除这一相等关系。

可以在某一个原子（比如原子 A）的初级散射过程引入一个相位滞后[1]。通过使用波长刚好可以激发原子 A 的 X 射线来实现这一点。再次比较（a）和（b）两种情况下衍射 p 中产生的相位差。考虑被原子 A 和 B 散射的电磁波的相位差。在（a）中，A 原子散射的特征性的相位滞后被认为与较长的光程有关，在（b）中则与较短光程有关。因此，被 A 和 B 散射的电磁波的干涉中产生的总相位差将不再相反，并且这两种情况下的衍射强度将会有所不同。（在晶体衍射中，除了不等关系 $I^{a}_{hkl} \neq I^{b}_{hkl}$（$a$ 和 b 代表两种光学对映体）之外，还存在下列关系：$I^{a}_{hkl} = I^{b}_{\bar{h}\bar{k}\bar{l}}$。根据后一关系，在衍射强度上光学对映体的影像并无差别，而只是在于它们在固定的晶体旋转方向得到的魏森堡图上的演替。）

用刚好可以激发铷原子[2]的锆 K_{α} 射线对酒石酸铷钠进行衍射实验，可以观测到相应的衍射差异——这一差异对于任意其他波长的 X 射线都不会出现。与上述讨论的情况类似，这一差异使我们能够区分衍射原型及其翻转像。结果是埃米尔·费歇尔的**约定**——将图 2 中的构型指定为右旋的酸——**看来与事实相符**。

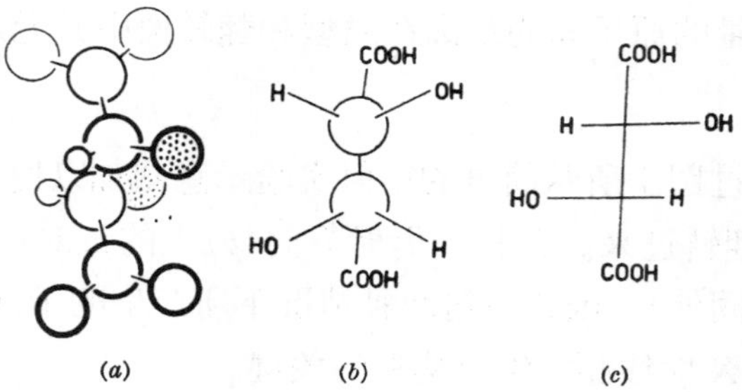

Fig. 2. Absolute configuration of natural dextrorotatory tartaric acid
a, As determined by X-rays in sodium rubidium tartrate.
b, In normalized configuration by rotating around single bonds.
c, In projection.

Obviously, the agreement between conventional and real model then also embraces all compounds, the configurations of which—relative to tartaric acid—have been determined. Details are given in ref. 2 and in a forthcoming paper in *Acta Crystallographica.* (A preliminary account was given by one of the authors (J. M. B.) at a conference in Pennsylvania State College in April 1950.)

The question of nomenclature is beyond the scope of our investigation. Absolute configuration determined, the standard substance for which hitherto a configuration had to be assumed becomes a redundant concept. The problem of nomenclature now concerns given configurations, and requires a notation which denotes these configurations in an unambiguous and if possible self-explanatory way. The usual notations like D_s or L_g for dextrorotatory tartaric acid, based on chemical relations, seems rather unsatisfactory from the latter point of view. For a recent study of the problem reference should be made to the literature[3].

We wish to thank the Netherlands Organization for Pure Research (Z.W.O.) for its support of this investigation.

(**168**, 271-272; 1951)

J. M. Bijvoet, A. F. Peerdeman and A. J. van Bommel: van't Hoff Laboratory, University of Utrecht.

References:

1. von Laue, M., *Ann. Physik*, 50, 33 (1916). Coster, D., Knol, K. S., and Prins, J., *Z. Phys.*, 63, 345 (1930). See also James, R. W., "The Optical Principles of the Diffraction of X-Rays", chapter 4 (1948).
2. Bijvoet, J. M., *Proc. Roy. Acad. Amsterdam*, 52, 313 (1949). Peerdeman, A. F., van Bommel, A. J., and Bijvoet, J. M., *ibid.*, B, 54, 16 (1951).
3. Cahn, R. S., and Ingold, C. K., *J. Chem. Soc.*, 612 (1951).

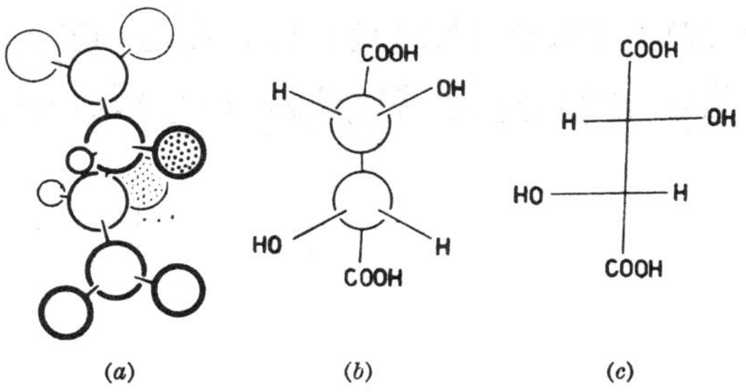

图 2. 天然右旋酒石酸的绝对构型
a，用 X 射线方法从酒石酸铷钠盐测得的结果。
b，通过绕单键旋转得到的标准化构型。
c，投影图。

显然，人为约定原型与真实原型之间的一致性也适用于所有化合物，因为它们的构型是相对于酒石酸而确定的。在参考文献 2 与一篇即将发表于《晶体学报》的文章中给出了研究细节。（其中的一位作者（约翰内斯·比沃特）于 1950 年 4 月在宾夕法尼亚州立大学的一次研讨会上给出了初步说明。）

命名法的问题已超出了我们的研究范围。一旦测定了绝对构型，迄今仍需假定其构型的标准物质就成为一个多余的概念。现在，命名法的问题涉及给定的构型，并且需要一套符号以一种清楚而且（如果可能的话）一目了然的方式表示这些构型。从后一角度来看，基于化学关系的常用符号，比如用 D_s 或 L_g 表示右旋酒石酸看起来相当地难以令人满意。关于此问题的一项近期研究可以参考有关文献 [3]。

我们要感谢荷兰纯理论研究提升组织对本项研究的支持。

（王耀杨 翻译；李芝芬 审稿）

Evidence for the Pauling-Corey α-Helix in Synthetic Polypeptides

W. Cochran and F. H. C. Crick

Editor's Note

In 1951 Linus Pauling and Robert Corey proposed that the molecular chains of proteins are commonly compacted into helical structures called α-helices. Here William Cochran and Francis Crick at the Cavendish Laboratory of Cambridge University provide evidence of these structures in a synthetic peptide (a kind of model protein), using X-ray crystallography. This and related work at the same time confirmed the hypothesis of Pauling and Corey. The α-helix is now known to be one of the key elements in the "secondary structure" of proteins, by which means the long polypeptide chain is folded into a compact, functional shape.

WE have calculated, in collaboration with Dr. V. Vand[1], the Fourier transform (or continuous structure factor) of an atom repeated at regular intervals on an infinite helix. The properties of the transform are such that it will usually be possible to predict the general character of X-ray scattering by any structure based on a regular succession of similar groups of atoms arranged in a helical manner. In particular, the type of X-ray diffraction picture given by the synthetic polypeptide poly-γ-methyl-L-glutamate, which has been prepared in a highly crystalline form by Dr. C. H. Bamford and his colleagues in the Research Laboratories, Courtaulds, Ltd., Maidenhead, is so readily explained on this basis as to leave little doubt that the Pauling-Corey α-helix[2], or some close approximation to it, exists in this polypeptide. Pauling and Corey[2] have already shown this correspondence in the equatorial plane; it is shown here that the correspondence extends over the whole of the diffraction pattern.

We quote here the value of the transform which applies when the axial distance between successive turns of the helix is P, the axial distance between the successive atoms lying on the helix is p, and the structure so formed is repeated exactly in an axial distance c. (For the latter condition to be possible, P/p must be expressible as the ratio of whole numbers.) In this case, the transform is restricted to planes in reciprocal space which are perpendicular to the axis of the helix, and occur at heights $\zeta = l/c$, where l is an integer. In crystallographic nomenclature, these are the layer lines corresponding to a unit cell of length c. On the lth such plane the transform has the value:

$$F\left(R,\psi,\frac{l}{c}\right) = f\sum_n J_n(2\pi Rr)\exp\left[in\left(\psi + \frac{\pi}{2}\right)\right]. \tag{1}$$

(R, ψ, ζ) are the cylindrical co-ordinates of a point in reciprocal space, f is the atomic scattering factor, and J_n is the Bessel function of order n; r is the radius of the helix on which the set of atoms lies, the axes in real space being chosen so that one atom lies at

合成多肽中存在鲍林–科里α螺旋的证据

科克伦，克里克

编者按

1951 年，莱纳斯·鲍林和罗伯特·科里提出蛋白质的分子链通常会形成被称为 α 螺旋的紧密的螺旋结构。在本文中，剑桥大学卡文迪什实验室的威廉·科克伦和弗朗西斯·克里克利用 X 射线晶体学方法，给出了这种结构在合成多肽（蛋白质的一种形式）中存在的证据。此项工作以及同一时期的相关工作证实了鲍林和科里的假说。现在 α 螺旋被认为是蛋白质“二级结构”的关键要素之一，通过这种方式，长的多肽链被折叠成了一个紧凑的、具有功能的形状。

通过与范特博士合作[1]，我们已经计算出在无限螺旋结构中按照固定间距重复排列的单个原子的傅里叶变换（或连续结构因子）。该变换的性质是：对于任意基于相似原子基团连续规则排列成螺旋形式的结构，傅里叶变换通常都可以推测出该结构的 X 射线散射结果所具有的总体特征。尤其是，合成多肽聚–γ–甲基–L–谷氨酸酯所给出的 X 射线衍射图样，在上述理论基础上可以很容易地得到解释，该多肽中无疑存在鲍林–科里 α 螺旋或者某种与之极为类似的结构，这种高度晶态的多肽由位于梅登黑德的考陶尔兹有限公司研究实验室的班福德博士及其同事合成。鲍林和科里[2]已经指出了在赤道平面上的这种对应关系；这里要说明的是，这种对应关系能够拓展到整个衍射图中。

在这个变换中，我们设位于螺旋中相邻两圈之间的轴距为 P，位于螺旋中相邻原子之间的轴距为 p，而这样形成的结构精确地按轴距 c 周期性重复排列。（为保证后一情况成立，P/p 必须用整数比来表示。）在这种情况下，变换只限于与螺旋轴垂直的倒易空间中的平面，而且出现在高度 $\zeta = l/c$ 处，其中 l 为整数。用晶体学术语来讲，它们是对应于长度为 c 的单位晶胞的层线。在第 l 个这种晶面上，变换的数值为：

$$F\left(R,\psi,\frac{l}{c}\right) = f\sum_{n} J_n(2\pi Rr)\exp\left[in\left(\psi+\frac{\pi}{2}\right)\right] \tag{1}$$

(R, ψ, ζ) 为倒易空间中一点的柱坐标，f 为原子的散射因子，J_n 为 n 阶贝塞尔函数；r 为原子组所在螺旋的半径，选取正空间中的轴使得一个原子位于（r，0，0）。对于

(r, 0, 0). For a given value of l, the sum in equation (1) is to be taken over all integer values of n which are solutions of the equation,

$$\frac{n}{P} + \frac{m}{p} = \frac{l}{c}, \tag{2}$$

m being any integer[1].

Thus only certain Bessel functions contribute to a particular layer line. This is illustrated in the accompanying table for the case of poly-γ-methyl-L-glutamate, for which Pauling and Corey[2] suggested $P = 5.4$ A., $p = 1.5$ A. and $c = 27$ A. The first column lists the number, l, of the layer line, while the second gives the orders (n) of the Bessel functions which contribute to it (for simplicity only the lowest two values of n are given for each layer line).

Value of l for the layer line	Lowest two values of n allowed by theory			Observed average strength of layer line(ref. 4)
0	0		±18	strong
1	−7		+11	
2	+4		−14	*weak
3	−3		+15	very weak
4	+8		−10	
5	+1		−17	medium
6	−6		+12	
7	+5		−13	
8	−2		+16	weak
9		±9		
10	+2		−16	weak
11	−5		+13	
12	+6		−12	
13	−1		+17	very weak
14	−8		+10	
15	+3		−15	
16	−4		+14	
17	+7		−11	
18	0		+18	medium
19	−7		+11	
20	+4		−14	
21	−3		+15	
22	+8		−10	
23	+1		−17	trace
24	−6		+12	
25	+5		−13	
26	−2		+16	trace
27		±9		
28	+2		−16	trace

Layers not described are absent.

*(10$\bar{1}$2), the reflexion having the smallest value of R, is absent.

给定的 l 值，方程（1）中的求和将取遍下列方程式中 n 的所有整数解：

$$\frac{n}{P}+\frac{m}{p}=\frac{l}{c} \tag{2}$$

其中 m 为任意整数[1]。

因此对于某一特定层线而言，只有特定的贝塞尔函数有贡献。下表以聚–γ–甲基–L–谷氨酸酯为例对此进行了说明，鲍林和科里[2]认为 $P=5.4$ Å，$p=1.5$ Å，$c=27$ Å。表中第一列为层线编号 l，第二列为对其有贡献的贝塞尔函数的阶数 n（为简明起见，对于每一层线只给出最小的两个 n 值）。

层线编号 l	理论范围内两个最小 n 值			层线的平均观测强度（参考文献 4）
0	0		±18	强
1	−7		+11	
2	+4		−14	* 弱
3	−3		+15	很弱
4	+8		−10	
5	+1		−17	中
6	−6		+12	
7	+5		−13	
8	−2		+16	弱
9		±9		
10	+2		−16	弱
11	−5		+13	
12	+6		−12	
13	−1		+17	很弱
14	−8		+10	
15	+3		−15	
16	−4		+14	
17	+7		−11	
18	0		+18	中等
19	−7		+11	
20	+4		−14	
21	−3		+15	
22	+8		−10	
23	+1		−17	痕量
24	−6		+12	
25	+5		−13	
26	−2		+16	痕量
27		±9		
28	+2		−16	痕量

没有描述的层是不出现的。

* 有最小 R 值的反射的（1012）层不出现。

Now there is, of course, more than one set of atoms in the polypeptide, but for all of them, P, p and c are the same, although r is different. The basis of our prediction is that a reflexion will be absent if the contribution of all sets of atoms to it is very small, and that on the average it will be strong if all sets of atoms make a large contribution.

It is a property of Bessel functions of higher order, illustrated in the graph, that they remain very small until a certain value of $2\pi Rr$ is reached, and that this point recedes from the origin as the order increases. Now, whatever the precise form of the chain, the value of r for any atom cannot be greater than about 8 A. because of the packing of the chains. This sets a limit to the value of $2\pi Rr$ within the part of the transform covered by the observed diffraction picture ($R < 0.3$ A.$^{-1}$ for $l \neq 0$). No set of atoms can make an appreciable contribution to the amplitude of a reflexion occurring on a layer line with which only high-order Bessel functions are associated, because $2\pi Rr$ comes within the very low part of the curve in the graph.

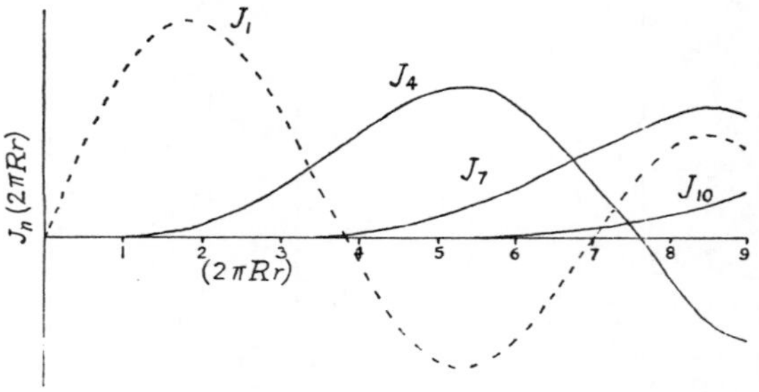

The march of higher-order Bessel functions(with J_1 added dashed)

We should therefore predict that layer lines to which only high-order Bessel functions contribute would be weak or absent, and that those to which very low orders contribute would be strong.

These predictions are strikingly borne out by the experimental data[4] summarized in the last column of the table. The significant Bessel functions involved in the first twenty-eight layer lines are shown in the second column, and, as will be seen, only layer lines associated with a function of order 4 or less are represented. This limiting value of 4 is less than might have been expected, and this fact suggests that the contribution of the side-chains to any reflexion is small, probably due to their large thermal motion.

In addition, the theory predicts (as can also be shown by a simpler approach) that meridional reflexions can occur only on layer lines which involve Bessel functions of order zero; that is, at reciprocal spacings of multiples of 1/1.5 A.$^{-1}$. This had previously been pointed out by Perutz[3] when reporting the strong meridional 1.5 A. reflexion.

We have therefore no doubt that the structure of poly-γ-methyl-L-glutamate is based on a helix of eighteen residues in five turns and 27 A., or a helix which approximates to this

当然，由于多肽分子中有不止一组原子，就总体而言虽然它们的 r 是不同的，但 P、p 和 c 都是相同的。我们所做推测的基础是，如果所有原子组对于反射的贡献都很小，反射就不会出现，一般情况下，若所有原子组都有明显贡献则反射会很强。

图中呈现出较高阶贝塞尔函数的一个性质，即它们在达到一个特定的 $2\pi Rr$ 值之前其数值一直很小，且该点会随着阶数增大而远离原点。无论链以何种精确的形式存在，任何原子的 r 值都会因链的堆积而无法超过 8 Å 左右。$2\pi Rr$ 的值在变换部分内被限定在一个区间内，这一部分涵盖于观测到的衍射图像之中（$R<0.3$ Å^{-1}，$l\neq 0$）。对于只与高阶贝塞尔函数有关的层线上发生的反射，所有原子组都不能对其强度做出显著的贡献，因为 $2\pi Rr$ 处于图中曲线较低的那部分。

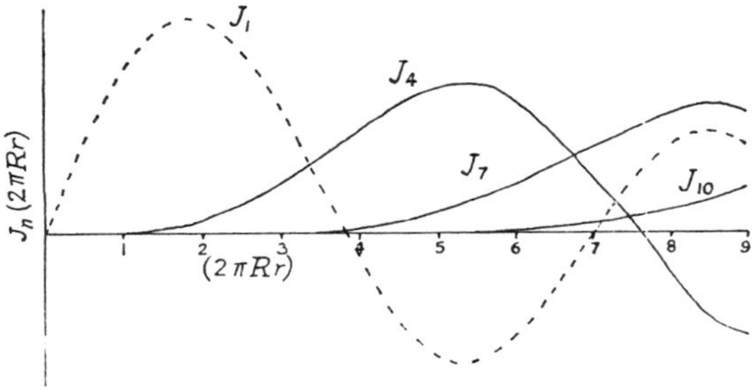

较高阶贝塞尔函数的演变（J_1 为虚线）

因此我们可以推测，那些只由高阶贝塞尔函数贡献的层线将会很弱甚至不出现，而那些由低阶贝塞尔函数贡献的层线则会很强。

由表中最后一列汇总的实验数据 [4] 可知，上述推测得到了惊人的证实。第二列数据为与前 28 条层线有关的有效贝塞尔函数，并且正如我们将要看到的那样，只有与阶数小于或等于 4 的函数有关的层线才会被呈现出来。4 这个极限值可能比预期值要小，这就意味着侧链对于任何反射的贡献都较小，这可能归因于它们大规模的热运动。

此外根据理论推测（通过一个较简便方法也能表明）只有在与零阶贝塞尔函数有关的层线上，即处于倍数为 1/1.5 Å^{-1} 的倒易空间时，才有可能产生子午线反射。佩鲁茨 [3] 在报告子午线 1.5 Å 的强反射时曾指出过这一点。

因此我们确信聚–γ–甲基–L–谷氨酸酯的结构是基于一条由 18 个残基旋转 5 圈而形成的轴距为 27 Å 的螺旋，或者是非常近似于该结构的一条螺旋。由于鲍林和科

very closely. As the structure proposed by Pauling and Corey[2] satisfies these conditions and is also stereochemically very satisfactory, it seems to us highly probable that it is correct.

We should like to thank Dr. Bamford and his colleagues for allowing us to quote their experimental results in advance of publication, and Sir Lawrence Bragg and Dr. M. Perutz for the stimulus which their interest in this work has provided.

(**169**, 234-235; 1952)

W. Cochran: Crystallographic Laboratory, Cavendish Laboratory, Cambridge.

F. H. C. Crick: Medical Research Council Unit for the Study of the Molecular Structure of Biological Systems, Cavendish Laboratory, Cambridge, Dec. 14.

References:

1. Cochran, W., Crick, F. H. C., and Vand. V. (to be published).
2. Pauling, L., and Corey, R. B., *Proc. U.S. Nat. Acad. Sci.*, 37, 241 (1951).
3. Perutz, M. F., *Nature*, 167, 1053 (1951).
4. Bamford, C. H., Brown, L., Elliott, A., Hanby, W. E., and Trotter, I. F. (to be published).

里[2]提出的结构满足这些条件，并且从立体化学的角度看也是令人满意的，因此我们认为这个结论极有可能是正确的。

班福德博士及其同事们准许我们引用他们尚未发表的实验结果，劳伦斯·布拉格爵士和佩鲁茨博士对这项研究的关注给我们提供了动力，我们对此表示感谢。

（王耀杨 翻译；顾孝诚 审稿）

A Structure for Deoxyribose Nucleic Acid

J. D. Watson and F. H. C. Crick

Editor's Note

This short paper is probably the most famous Nature has ever published. By the early 1950s it was becoming clear that the genes responsible for inherited traits reside on the biochemical polymer DNA. Watson and Crick used measurements from X-ray crystallography, along with chemical reasoning, to propose a molecular structure for DNA in which two polymer strands are intertwined in a double helix. The result was striking not just for its beauty and elegance but because, as the researchers laconically say, "the specific pairing we have postulated immediately suggests a possible copying mechanism for the genetic material"—that is, a means by which DNA is replicated. This marked the beginning of modern genomics.

WE wish to suggest a structure for the salt of deoxyribose nucleic acid (D.N.A.). This structure has novel features which are of considerable biological interest.

A structure for nucleic acid has already been proposed by Pauling and Corey[1]. They kindly made their manuscript available to us in advance of publication. Their model consists of three intertwined chains, with the phosphates near the fibre axis, and the bases on the outside. In our opinion, this structure is unsatisfactory for two reasons: (1) We believe that the material which gives the X-ray diagrams is the salt, not the free acid. Without the acidic hydrogen atoms it is not clear what forces would hold the structure together, especially as the negatively charged phosphates near the axis will repel each other. (2) Some of the van der Waals distances appear to be too small.

Another three-chain structure has also been suggested by Fraser (in the press). In his model the phosphates are on the outside and the bases on the inside, linked together by hydrogen bonds. This structure as described is rather ill-defined, and for this reason we shall not comment on it.

We wish to put forward a radically different structure for the salt of deoxyribose nucleic acid. This structure has two helical chains each coiled round the same axis (see diagram). We have made the usual chemical assumptions, namely, that each chain consists of phosphate diester groups joining β-D-deoxyribofuranose residues with 3′, 5′ linkages. The two chains (but not their bases) are related by a dyad perpendicular to the fibre axis. Both chains follow right-handed helices, but owing to the dyad the sequences of the atoms in the two chains run in opposite directions. Each chain loosely resembles Furberg's[2] model No. 1; that is, the bases are on the inside of the helix and the phosphates on the outside. The configuration of the sugar and the atoms near it is close to Furberg's "standard

脱氧核糖核酸的结构

沃森，克里克

编者按

这篇简短的文章可能是《自然》有史以来发表的最著名的文章。在20世纪50年代初期，人们越来越清楚地认识到，具有遗传特征的基因存在于生化多聚体DNA上。沃森和克里克利用X射线晶体学的测量结果和化学推理，提出了DNA的一种分子结构模型，即DNA分子是由两条聚合链缠绕而成的双螺旋结构。这一结果之所以令人震惊，不只是因为双螺旋结构的优雅和美丽，而且正如研究者所指出的，“我们提出的这种特定配对原则立即揭示了遗传物质一种可能的复制机制。”——也就是说，DNA复制的一种方式。它标志着现代基因组学的开端。

我们希望提出脱氧核糖核酸（DNA）盐的一种结构。这种结构的新特性具有重要的生物学意义。

鲍林和科里已经提出了核酸的一种结构[1]。他们在原稿发表之前慷慨地将其提供给我们。他们的模型由三条彼此缠绕的链组成，磷酸基团位于长链的中心轴附近，而碱基则位于外侧。在我们看来，该结构不太令人满意，理由有两点：(1) 我们认为，给出X射线图的物质是盐而不是游离酸。在没有酸性氢原子的情况下，使该结构维系在一起的力并不明确，尤其是中心轴附近带负电荷的磷酸基团会彼此排斥。(2) 某些范德华距离显得过小。

弗雷泽提出了另外一种三链式结构（即将发表）。在他的模型中，磷酸基团位于外侧而碱基位于内侧，通过氢键连接在一起。他对这种结构的描述非常不清楚，因此我们不会对其作任何评论。

我们要提出的是一种完全不同的脱氧核糖核酸盐的结构。这种结构有两条螺旋链，围绕同一中心轴相互缠绕（见示意图）。我们采用了一般的化学假设，即每条链由磷酸二酯基团组成，这些基团通过3′、5′连接与β–D–脱氧呋喃核糖残基连接起来。两条链（而不是它们的碱基）通过一个与中心轴垂直的二分体相连接。两条链都是右手螺旋，不过由于成对出现，两条链上的原子顺序方向相反。各条链大致类似于富尔贝里[2]的一号模型，也就是说，碱基位于螺旋的内侧，而磷酸基团位于外侧。糖及其邻近原子的构型类似于富尔贝里的“标准构型”，糖分子大致上垂直于与之相连的碱基。每条链在 z 轴方向上，每隔3.4 Å就有一个残基。我们假定同一链上的

configuration", the sugar being roughly perpendicular to the attached base. There is a residue on each chain every 3.4 A. in the *z*-direction. We have assumed an angle of 36° between adjacent residues in the same chain, so that the structure repeats after 10 residues on each chain, that is, after 34 A. The distance of a phosphorus atom from the fibre axis is 10 A. As the phosphates are on the outside, cations have easy access to them.

The structure is an open one, and its water content is rather high. At lower water contents we would expect the bases to tilt so that the structure could become more compact.

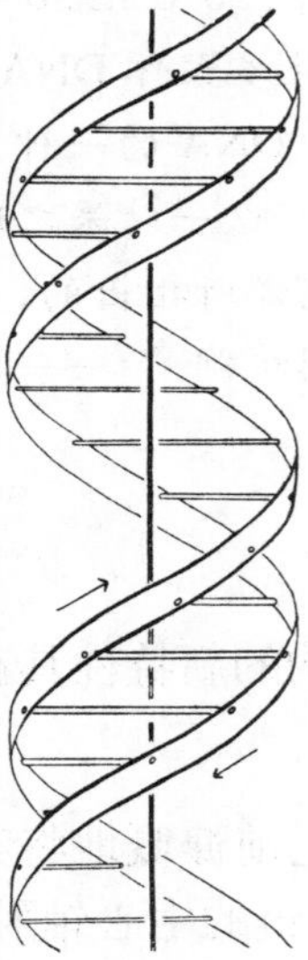

This figure is purely diagrammatic. The two ribbons symbolize the two phosphate-sugar chains, and the horizontal rods the pairs of bases holding the chains together. The vertical line marks the fibre axis

The novel feature of the structure is the manner in which the two chains are held together by the purine and pyrimidine bases. The planes of the bases are perpendicular to the fibre axis. They are joined together in pairs, a single base from one chain being hydrogen-bonded to a single base from the other chain, so that the two lie side by side with identical *z*-co-ordinates. One of the pair must be a purine and the other a pyrimidine for bonding to occur. The hydrogen bonds are made as follows: purine position 1 to pyrimidine position 1; purine position 6 to pyrimidine position 6.

If it is assumed that the bases only occur in the structure in the most plausible tautomeric forms (that is, with the keto rather than the enol configurations) it is found that only specific pairs of bases can bond together. These pairs are: adenine (purine) with thymine (pyrimidine), and guanine (purine) with cytosine (pyrimidine).

In other words, if an adenine forms one member of a pair, on either chain, then on these assumptions the other member must be thymine; similarly for guanine and cytosine. The sequence of bases on a single chain does not appear to be restricted in any way. However, if only specific pairs of bases can be formed, it follows that if the sequence of bases on one chain is given, then the sequence on the other chain is automatically determined.

It has been found experimentally[3,4] that the ratio of the amounts of adenine to thymine, and the ratio of guanine to cytosine, are always very close to unity for deoxyribose nucleic acid.

It is probably impossible to build this structure with a ribose sugar in place of the deoxyribose, as the extra oxygen atom would make too close a van der Waals contact.

The previously published X-ray data[5,6] on deoxyribose nucleic acid are insufficient for

相邻残基间的夹角为 36°，因此每条链上每 10 个残基，即 34 Å，就出现一次螺旋结构重复。磷原子与中心轴之间的距离为 10 Å。由于磷酸基团位于外侧，阳离子很容易接近它们。

这种结构尚未完全确定，其含水量相当高。在含水量低时，我们预计碱基会发生倾斜从而结构变得更加紧凑。

这种结构的新颖之处在于两条链通过嘌呤与嘧啶碱基连接在一起。碱基平面垂直于中心轴。碱基成对连接在一起，一条链上的一个碱基与另一条链上的一个碱基通过氢键结合，因此两个并排的碱基具有相同的 z 轴坐标。要产生这种氢键，其中一个碱基必须是嘌呤，另一个则必须是嘧啶。嘌呤的 1 位和嘧啶的 1 位之间以及嘌呤的 6 位和嘧啶的 6 位之间形成氢键。

如果假定碱基处于互变异构结构中最可能的构型（也就是说，处于酮式而不是烯醇式构型），可以发现，只有特定的碱基对可以结合在一起。这些碱基对是：腺嘌呤（嘌呤）与胸腺嘧啶（嘧啶），鸟嘌呤（嘌呤）与胞嘧啶（嘧啶）。

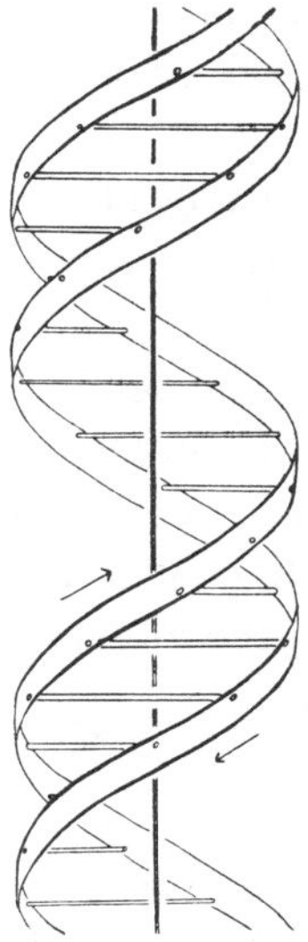

这仅仅是个示意图。两条丝带代表两条磷酸–糖链，而横线代表将链连接起来的碱基对。垂直线标示出中心轴。

换句话说，根据上述假定，如果一个碱基对中某一链上是一个腺嘌呤，那么另一链上与之对应的必定是一个胸腺嘧啶；鸟嘌呤和胞嘧啶也是类似情况。一条单链上的碱基顺序看来是不受任何限制的，但是，如果只有特定的碱基之间能够形成碱基对，那么如果给定某条链上碱基的顺序，另一条链的碱基顺序就自然确定了。

已经通过实验发现 [3,4]，对于脱氧核糖核酸而言，腺嘌呤与胸腺嘧啶数量的比值以及鸟嘌呤和胞嘧啶数量的比值总是非常接近 1 的。

如果用核糖代替脱氧核糖，很可能无法建立这种结构，因为多出来的氧原子将导致范德华接触过于紧密。

以前发表的关于脱氧核糖核酸的 X 射线数据 [5,6] 还不足以对我们的结构进行严格的检验。就我们所知，我们的结构与实验数据粗略吻合，不过在更多精确的结果

a rigorous test of our structure. So far as we can tell, it is roughly compatible with the experimental data, but it must be regarded as unproved until it has been checked against more exact results. Some of these are given in the following communications. We were not aware of the details of the results presented there when we devised our structure, which rests mainly though not entirely on published experimental data and stereochemical arguments.

It has not escaped our notice that the specific pairing we have postulated immediately suggests a possible copying mechanism for the genetic material.

Full details of the structure, including the conditions assumed in building it, together with a set of co-ordinates for the atoms, will be published elsewhere.

We are much indebted to Dr. Jerry Donohue for constant advice and criticism, especially on interatomic distances. We have also been stimulated by a knowledge of the general nature of the unpublished experimental results and ideas of Dr. M. H. F. Wilkins, Dr. R. E. Franklin and their co-workers at King's College, London. One of us (J. D. W.) has been aided by a fellowship from the National Foundation for Infantile Paralysis.

(**171**, 737-738; 1953)

J. D. Watson and F. H. C. Crick: Medical Research Council Unit for the Study of the Molecular Structure of Biological Systems, Cavendish Laboratory, Cambridge, April 2.

References:

1. Pauling, L., and Corey, R. B., *Nature*, **171**, 346 (1953); *Proc. U.S. Nat. Acad. Sci.*, **39**, 84 (1953).
2. Furberg, S., *Acta Chem. Scand.*, **6**, 634 (1952).
3. Chargaff, E., for references see Zamenhof, S., Brawerman, G., and Chargaff, E., *Biochim. et Biophys. Acta*, **9**, 402 (1952).
4. Wyatt. G. R., *J. Gen. Physiol.*, **36**, 201 (1952).
5. Astbury, W. T., Symp. Soc. Exp. Biol. 1, Nucleic Acid, 66 (Camb. Univ. Press, 1947).
6. Wilkins, M. H. F., and Randall, J. T., *Biochim. et Biophys. Acta*, **10**, 192 (1953).

核查之前，我们还必须把它视为未经证实的。一些核查工作将在后面的通讯文章中给出。在我们设计结构时，我们还不清楚该工作结果的细节，我们的结构主要（但不是完全）依赖于已发表的实验数据和立体化学证据。

我们还注意到，我们提出的这种特定配对原则立即揭示了遗传物质一种可能的复制机制。

该结构的完整细节，包括建立此结构所用的假设条件以及一套原子坐标，将在其他地方发表。

我们非常感谢杰里·多诺霍博士长期以来的建议和批评，尤其是关于原子间距离的问题。我们还从伦敦国王学院的威尔金斯博士、富兰克林博士及其同事们未发表的实验结果与观点所包含的一般属性的知识中获得了启发。我们中的一员（沃森）由国家小儿麻痹症基金会资助。

（王耀杨 翻译；王晓晨 审稿）

Molecular Structure of Deoxypentose Nucleic Acids

M. H. F. Wilkins *et al.*

Editor's Note

James Watson and Francis Crick's famous paper describing the structure of DNA was accompanied by this contribution from their collaborator Maurice Wilkins and his coworkers at King's College in London. It describes the evidence from X-ray diffraction that the DNA molecule has a helical structure, a crucial aspect of the picture presented by Watson and Crick. Indeed, the researchers mention the "reasonable agreement" with that model. The analysis in this paper draws on the experimental work of Rosalind Franklin and Raymond Gosling, described in the following paper.

WHILE the biological properties of deoxypentose nucleic acid suggest a molecular structure containing great complexity, X-ray diffraction studies described here (cf. Astbury[1]) show the basic molecular configuration has great simplicity. The purpose of this communication is to describe, in a preliminary way, some of the experimental evidence for the polynucleotide chain configuration being helical, and existing in this form when in the natural state. A fuller account of the work will be published shortly.

The structure of deoxypentose nucleic acid is the same in all species (although the nitrogen base ratios alter considerably) in nucleoprotein, extracted or in cells, and in purified nucleate. The same linear group of polynucleotide chains may pack together parallel in different ways to give crystalline[1-3], semi-crystalline or paracrystalline material. In all cases the X-ray diffraction photograph consists of two regions, one determined largely by the regular spacing of nucleotides along the chain, and the other by the longer spacings of the chain configuration. The sequence of different nitrogen bases along the chain is not made visible.

Oriented paracrystalline deoxypentose nucleic acid ("structure *B*" in the following communication by Franklin and Gosling) gives a fibre diagram as shown in Fig. 1 (cf. ref. 4). Astbury suggested that the strong 3.4-A. reflexion corresponded to the internucleotide repeat along the fibre axis. The ~34 A. layer lines, however, are not due to a repeat of a polynucleotide composition, but to the chain configuration repeat, which causes strong diffraction as the nucleotide chains have higher density than the interstitial water. The absence of reflexions on or near the meridian immediately suggests a helical structure with axis parallel to fibre length.

脱氧戊糖核酸的分子结构

威尔金斯等

编者按

詹姆斯·沃森和弗朗西斯·克里克在他们所发表的著名文章中描述了DNA的结构，这一科研成果也有他们的合作者——伦敦国王学院的莫里斯·威尔金斯及其同事们的贡献。这篇文章描述了由X射线衍射所得到的证据，即DNA分子的螺旋结构——这是由沃森和克里克描绘的图景中的重要方面。的确，这些研究者们提到其结构和螺旋模型具有“合理的一致性”。这篇文章中的分析部分是依据罗莎琳德·富兰克林和雷蒙德·戈斯林的实验工作得到的，这将在下一篇文章中提到。

尽管脱氧戊糖核酸的生物学性质暗示其分子结构极为复杂，但这里所描述的X射线衍射研究（参见阿斯特伯里的研究[1]）却表明其基本分子构型非常简单。这篇通讯文章的目的是为了初步地描述一些实验证据，证明多核苷酸链的构型为螺形，并且以这种形式存在于自然状态中。对这一工作更完整的记述不久即将发表。

不管是在提取的或者细胞内的核蛋白中，还是处于纯化的核酸盐状态下，所有物种中的脱氧戊糖核酸都具有相同的结构（尽管含氮碱基的比例有显著差异）。一组相同的线性的多核苷酸链能够以不同方式平行排列在一起，形成晶态[1-3]、半晶态或类晶态物质。在所有情况下，X射线衍射照片都包含两个区域，其中一个区域很大程度上取决于沿着这条链排列规则的核苷酸间距，另一个区域则取决于长链构型的更大排列间距。沿着链延伸方向，不同含氮碱基的排列顺序目前还无法观测到。

图1（参见参考文献4）显示的是脱氧戊糖核酸的有序类晶态（富兰克林与戈斯林在后面的通讯文章中所说的“*B*型结构”）所给出的纤维衍射图。阿斯特伯里提出，强烈的3.4Å反射对应于沿纤维轴方向核苷酸之间的重复间距。但是，约为34Å的层线不是由于多核苷酸组分的重复，而是对应于链状构型的重复，正是这种链状构型的重复造成了强烈衍射，因为核苷酸链具有比间隙水更高的密度。在子午线及其附近没有出现反射，直接说明了脱氧戊糖核酸是螺旋轴平行于纤维轴方向的螺旋结构。

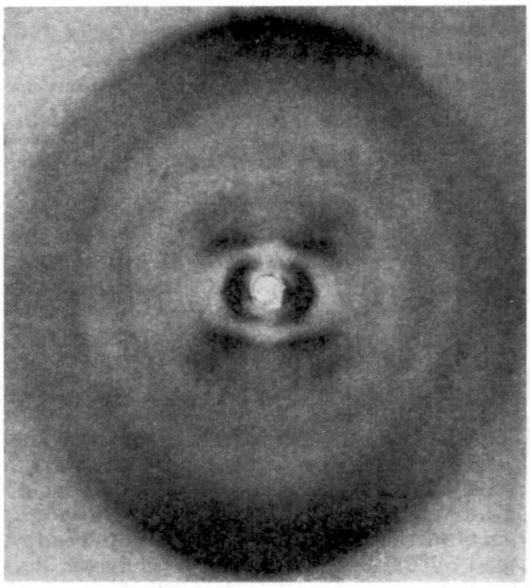

Fig. 1 . Fibre diagram of deoxypentose nucleic acid from *B. coli*
Fibre axis vertical

Diffraction by Helices

It may be shown[5] (also Stokes, unpublished) that the intensity distribution in the diffraction pattern of a series of points equally spaced along a helix is given by the squares of Bessel functions. A uniform continuous helix gives a series of layer lines of spacing corresponding to the helix pitch, the intensity distribution along the *n*th layer line being proportional to the square of J_n, the *n*th order Bessel function. A straight line may be drawn approximately through the innermost maxima of each Bessel function and the origin. The angle this line makes with the equator is roughly equal to the angle between an element of the helix and the helix axis. If a unit repeats n times along the helix there will be a meridional reflexion (J_0^2) on the *n*th layer line. The helical configuration produces side-bands on this fundamental frequency, the effect[5] being to reproduce the intensity distribution about the origin around the new origin, on the *n*th layer line, corresponding to *C* in Fig. 2.

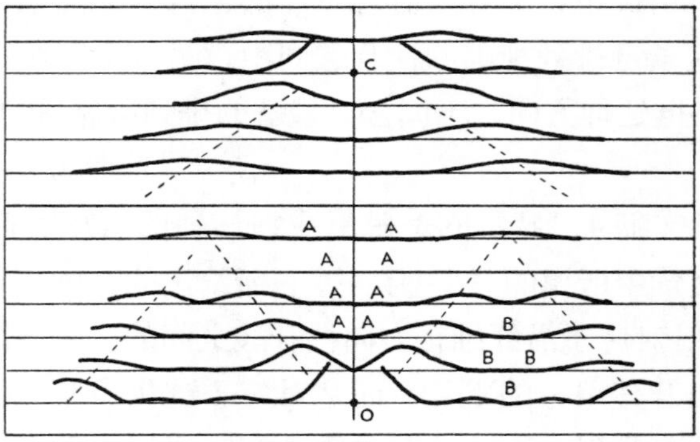

Fig. 2. Diffraction pattern of system of helices corresponding to structure of deoxypentose nucleic acid. The squares of Bessel functions are plotted about 0 on the equator and on the first, second, third and fifth layer lines for half of the nucleotide mass at 20 A. diameter and remainder distributed along a radius, the mass at a given radius being proportional to the radius. About *C* on the tenth layer line similar functions are plotted for an outer diameter of 12 A.

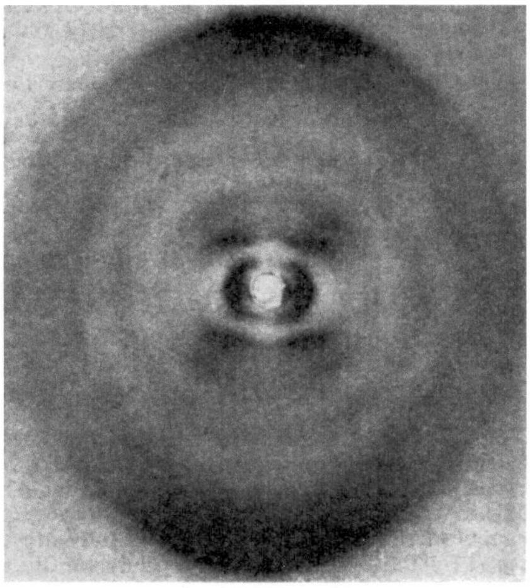

图 1. 大肠杆菌的脱氧戊糖核酸的纤维图
纤维轴垂直于纸面

由螺旋产生的衍射

有文章指出[5]沿螺旋等间距排列的一系列点所产生的衍射图案，其强度分布可以由贝塞尔函数的平方给出（斯托克斯也有此观点但未发表）。一条均一连续的螺旋会给出一系列层线，层线间距对应于螺旋的螺距。第 n 层线的强度分布正比于 J_n 的平方，J_n 为 n 阶贝塞尔函数。通过每个贝塞尔函数最内部的极大值点和原点可以近似地画出一条直线。这条直线与赤道的夹角近似等于螺旋的一个元件与螺旋轴的夹角。如果一个单元沿着螺旋重复 n 次，就会在第 n 层线出现一个子午反射（J_0^2）。螺旋构型在此基频上则会产生边频带，其效应[5]是在第 n 层线上围绕新原点复制出原点周围的强度分布，对应于图 2 中的 C。

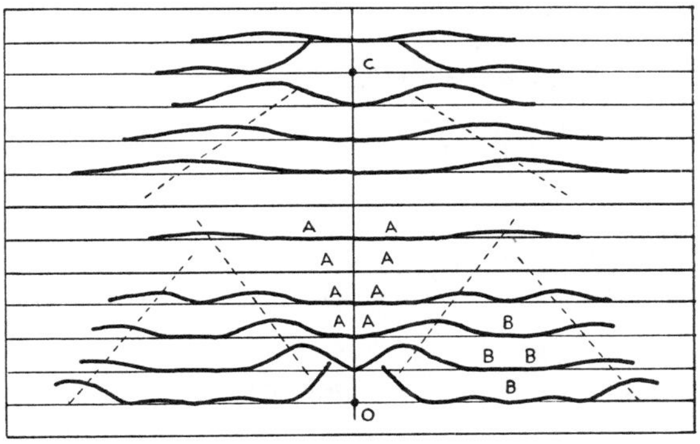

图 2. 对应于脱氧戊糖核酸结构的螺旋体系的衍射图案。贝塞尔函数的平方值在赤道线上围绕 0 作图，而在第 1、2、3 和 5 层线上按照直径 20 Å 的核苷酸质量的一半计算，其余部分则沿径向分布，因为在一给定半径下的质量均与该半径成正比。第 10 层线的 C 点附近的函数图是根据 12 Å 外径的核苷酸画出的。

We will now briefly analyse in physical terms some of the effects of the shape and size of the repeat unit or nucleotide on the diffraction pattern. First, if the nucleotide consists of a unit having circular symmetry about an axis parallel to the helix axis, the whole diffraction pattern is modified by the form factor of the nucleotide. Second, if the nucleotide consists of a series of points on a radius at right-angles to the helix axis, the phases of radiation scattered by the helices of different diameter passing through each point are the same. Summation of the corresponding Bessel functions gives reinforcement for the innermost maxima and, in general, owing to phase difference, cancellation of all other maxima. Such a system of helices (corresponding to a spiral staircase with the core removed) diffracts mainly over a limited angular range, behaving, in fact, like a periodic arrangement of flat plates inclined at a fixed angle to the axis. Third, if the nucleotide is extended as an arc of a circle in a plane at right-angles to the helix axis, and with centre at the axis, the intensity of the system of Bessel function layer-line streaks emanating from the origin is modified owing to the phase differences of radiation from the helices drawn through each point on the nucleotide. The form factor is that of the series of points in which the helices intersect a plane drawn through the helix axis. This part of the diffraction pattern is then repeated as a whole with origin at *C* (Fig. 2). Hence this aspect of nucleotide shape affects the central and peripheral regions of each layer line differently.

Interpretation of the X-Ray Photograph

It must first be decided whether the structure consists of essentially one helix giving an intensity distribution along the layer lines corresponding to J_1, J_2, J_3 ..., or two similar co-axial helices of twice the above size and relatively displaced along the axis a distance equal to half the pitch giving J_2, J_4, J_6 ..., or three helices, etc. Examination of the width of the layer-line streaks suggests the intensities correspond more closely to J_1^2, J_2^2, J_3^2 than to J_2^2, J_4^2, J_6^2 ... Hence the dominant helix has a pitch of ~34 A., and, from the angle of the helix, its diameter is found to be ~20 A. The strong equatorial reflexion at ~17 A. suggests that the helices have a maximum diameter of ~20 A. and are hexagonally packed with little interpenetration. Apart from the width of the Bessel function streaks, the possibility of the helices having twice the above dimensions is also made unlikely by the absence of an equatorial reflexion at ~34 A. To obtain a reasonable number of nucleotides per unit volume in the fibre, two or three intertwined coaxial helices are required, there being ten nucleotides on one turn of each helix.

The absence of reflexions on or near the meridian (an empty region *AAA* on Fig. 2) is a direct consequence of the helical structure. On the photograph there is also a relatively empty region on and near the equator, corresponding to region *BBB* on Fig. 2. As discussed above, this absence of secondary Bessel function maxima can be produced by a radial distribution of the nucleotide shape. To make the layer-line streaks sufficiently narrow, it is necessary to place a large fraction of the nucleotide mass at ~20 A. diameter. In Fig. 2 the squares of Bessel functions are plotted for half the mass at 20 A. diameter, and the rest distributed along a radius, the mass at a given radius being proportional to the radius.

现在我们将用物理学概念简要分析一下重复单元或核苷酸的形状与大小对衍射图案的一些影响。第一，如果核苷酸由具有圆形对称性的单元组成，且其对称轴平行于螺旋的中心轴，那么整个衍射图案就会受到核苷酸的形状因子的影响。第二，如果核苷酸是由一系列点组成，且这些点位于与螺旋轴成直角的半径方向上，那么通过每个点的不同直径的螺旋所散射出来的辐射的相位角就是相同的。相应的贝塞尔函数的加和就会使最内部的极大值获得增强，一般来说，还会由于相位差而抵消所有其他极大值。这种螺旋体系（对应于去除了中心部分的螺旋式楼梯）主要在有限的角度范围内产生衍射，这样的体系实际上很类似于与中心轴有固定夹角的平板的周期性排列。第三，如果核苷酸在与螺旋中心轴垂直的平面内伸展成一段圆弧，且其圆心位于轴上，那么，从原点发射出的贝塞尔函数层线条纹系统的强度就会由于通过核苷酸上每一点的各条螺旋所产生的辐射具有相位差而改变。形状因子与螺旋线和通过螺旋轴的平面相交所得的一系列点有关。这部分衍射图案将会以 *C* 为原点（图 2）整体重复。因此，核苷酸形状的这一因素对于每一层线的中心和外围区域会产生不同的影响。

对 X 射线照片的解释

首先必须确定，该结构本质上是由一条螺旋组成而使得沿层线的强度分布与 J_1、J_2、J_3…相对应，还是由两条类似的同轴螺旋组成，其大小为上述单条螺旋的两倍，相应地沿着螺旋轴每半个螺距间隔处的强度分布变成了 J_2、J_4、J_6…，或者甚至是由三条螺旋组成，诸如此类。对层线条纹宽度的检测表明，强度分布更接近 J_1^2、J_2^2、J_3^2，而不是 J_2^2、J_4^2、J_6^2…。因此，绝大部分螺旋的螺距大约是 34 Å，并且通过螺旋角可以得到其直径大约是 20 Å。约 17 Å 处的强烈的赤道反射表明，螺旋的最大直径约为 20 Å，并为六方堆积且很少相互穿插。除了贝塞尔函数条纹的宽度这一证据之外，在约 34 Å 处没有赤道反射出现也能说明尺寸上两倍于单条螺旋是不太可能的。但要使螺旋纤维中每单位体积里核苷酸的数目比较合理，又需要两条或三条相互缠绕成同轴螺旋，因为单条螺旋每一周有 10 个核苷酸。

这种螺旋结构的直接结果就是在子午线处及其附近没有反射（图 2 中 *AAA* 处的空白区域）。在照片上，赤道处及其附近也有一个相对空白的区域，对应于图 2 中的 *BBB* 区域。如同上面讨论过的，核苷酸放射状分布的外形可以导致次级贝塞尔函数极大值的缺失。要使层线条纹变得足够窄，就必须把核苷酸的大部分质量置于直径为 20 Å 处。图 2 中贝塞尔函数的平方是根据直径为 20 Å 处的核苷酸质量的一半来作图的，其余部分则沿径向分布，在给定半径下的质量与该半径成正比。

On the zero layer line there appears to be a marked J_{10}^2, and on the first, second and third layer lines, $J_9^2 + J_{12}^2$, $J_8^2 + J_{12}^2$, etc., respectively. This means that, in projection on a plane at right-angles to the fibre axis, the outer part of the nucleotide is relatively concentrated, giving rise to high-density regions spaced *c.* 6 A. apart around the circumference of a circle of 20 A. diameter. On the fifth layer line two J_5 functions overlap and produce a strong reflexion. On the sixth, seventh and eighth layer lines the maxima correspond to a helix of diameter ~12 A. Apparently it is only the central region of the helix structure which is well divided by the 3.4-A. spacing, the outer parts of the nucleotide overlapping to form a continuous helix. This suggests the presence of nitrogen bases arranged like a pile of pennies[1] in the central regions of the helical system.

There is a marked absence of reflexions on layer lines beyond the tenth. Disorientation in the specimen will cause more extension along the layer lines of the Bessel function streaks on the eleventh, twelfth and thirteenth layer lines than on the ninth, eighth and seventh. For this reason the reflexions on the higher-order layer lines will be less readily visible. The form factor of the nucleotide is also probably causing diminution of intensity in this region. Tilting of the nitrogen bases could have such an effect.

Reflexions on the equator are rather inadequate for determination of the radial distribution of density in the helical system. There are, however, indications that a high-density shell, as suggested above, occurs at diameter ~20 A.

The material is apparently not completely paracrystalline, as sharp spots appear in the central region of the second layer line, indicating a partial degree of order of the helical units relative to one another in the direction of the helix axis. Photographs similar to Fig. 1 have been obtained from sodium nucleate from calf and pig thymus, wheat germ, herring sperm, human tissue and T_2 bacteriophage. The most marked correspondence with Fig. 2 is shown by the exceptional photograph obtained by our colleagues, R. E. Franklin and R. G. Gosling, from calf thymus deoxypentose nucleate (see following communication).

It must be stressed that some of the above discussion is not without ambiguity, but in general there appears to be reasonable agreement between the experimental data and the kind of model described by Watson and Crick (see also preceding communication).

It is interesting to note that if there are ten phosphate groups arranged on each helix of diameter 20 A. and pitch 34 A., the phosphate ester backbone chain is in an almost fully extended state. Hence, when sodium nucleate fibres are stretched[3], the helix is evidently extended in length like a spiral spring in tension.

Structure *in vivo*

The biological significance of a two-chain nucleic acid unit has been noted (see preceding communication). The evidence that the helical structure discussed above does, in fact, exist in intact biological systems is briefly as follows:

在第 0 层线，似乎出现了显著的 J_{10}^2，而在第 1、2 和 3 层线则分别出现了显著的 $J_9^2+J_{12}^2$、$J_8^2+J_{12}^2$ 等。这意味着，在与纤维轴垂直的平面上的投影图中，核苷酸外围部分相对比较浓缩，从而形成了与直径 20 Å 的圆周相距约 6 Å 处环绕的高密度分布区。在第 5 层线上，两个 J_5 函数重叠并产生一个强反射。第 6、7 和 8 层线上的极大值对应于直径约为 12 Å 的螺旋。很显然，只有螺旋结构的中间区域才按照 3.4 Å 的间距很好地排列，核苷酸的外围部分相互重叠形成一条连续的螺旋。这意味着，在螺旋体系的中间区域，含氮碱基就像一摞便士硬币[1]般地排布着。

第 10 层线以上明显缺乏反射。样品的无序性会导致第 11、12 和 13 层线上贝塞尔函数条纹比在第 9、8 和 7 层线上更宽。由于这个原因，位于较高层线上的反射就会比较难观测到。核苷酸的形状因子也可能会导致这一区域反射强度降低。含氮碱基的倾斜可能也会产生这种效应。

赤道上的反射强度更低，有点不足以确定螺旋体系中密度的径向分布。不过如前所述，有迹象表明在直径约为 20 Å 处有一个高密度壳层。

被检测的样品显然不是完全的类晶态，因为在第 2 层线的中心区域出现了明显的斑点，这意味着在螺旋中心轴方向上各个螺旋单元彼此间的排布表现出一定程度的有序性。利用其他来源（如来自于小牛或猪的胸腺、麦芽、鲱鱼的精子，人体组织或 T_2 噬菌体）的核酸钠盐也都得到了类似于图 1 的照片。我们的同事富兰克林和戈斯林利用小牛胸腺中的脱氧戊糖核酸盐得到了异常漂亮的衍射照片（参见后一篇通讯文章），该照片和图 2 具有非常显著的一致性。

必须强调的是，上述讨论中或许不无含糊之处，但是大体上看，实验数据和沃森与克里克所描述的那种模型（参见前一篇通讯文章）之间具有合理的一致性。

有趣的是，如果在直径为 20 Å、螺距为 34 Å 的螺旋的每一圈内安置 10 个磷酸基团，那么磷酸酯骨架就几乎处于完全伸展的状态。因此，当使核酸钠盐长链伸展开时，螺旋就会明显变长[3]，如同受到牵拉的螺旋形弹簧。

在体内的结构

人们注意到了双链核酸单元具有重要的生物学意义（参见前面的通讯文章）。实际上，前面所论述的螺旋结构在完整无损的生物体内确实存在，证据可以简述如下：

Sperm heads. It may be shown that the intensity of the X-ray spectra from crystalline sperm heads is determined by the helical form-function in Fig. 2. Centrifuged trout semen give the same pattern as the dried and rehydrated or washed sperm heads used previously[6]. The sperm head fibre diagram is also given by extracted or synthetic[1] nucleoprotamine or extracted calf thymus nucleohistone.

Bacteriophage. Centrifuged wet pellets of T_2 phage photographed with X-rays while sealed in a cell with mica windows give a diffraction pattern containing the main features of paracrystalline sodium nucleate as distinct from that of crystalline nucleoprotein. This confirms current ideas of phage structure.

Transforming principle (in collaboration with H. Ephrussi-Taylor). Active deoxypentose nucleate allowed to dry at ~60 percent humidity has the same crystalline structure as certain samples[3] of sodium thymonucleate.

We wish to thank Prof. J. T. Randall for encouragement; Profs. E. Chargaff, R. Signer, J. A. V. Butler and Drs. J. D. Watson, J. D. Smith, L. Hamilton, J. C. White and G. R. Wyatt for supplying material without which this work would have been impossible; also Drs. J. D. Watson and Mr. F. H. C. Crick for stimulation, and our colleagues R. E. Franklin, R. G. Gosling, G. L. Brown and W. E. Seeds for discussion. One of us (H. R. W.) wishes to acknowledge the award of a University of Wales Fellowship.

(**171**, 738-740; 1953)

M. H. F. Wilkins: Medical Research Council Biophysics, Research Unit.
A. R. Stokes and H. R. Wilson: Wheatstone Physics Laboratory, King's College, London, April 2.

References:

1. Astbury. W. T., Symp. Soc. Exp. Biol., 1, Nucleic Acid (Cambridge Univ. Press, 1947).
2. Riley, D. P., and Oster, G., *Biochim. et Biophys. Acta*, 7, 526 (1951).
3. Wilkins, M. H. F., Gosling, R. G., and Seeds, W. E., *Nature*, **167**, 759 (1951).
4. Astbury, W. T., and Bell, F. O., Cold Spring Harb. Symp. Quant. Biol., **6**, 109 (1938).
5. Cochran, W., Crick, F. H. C., and Vand, V., *Acta Cryst.*, **5**, 581 (1952).
6. Wilkins, M. H. F., and Randall, J. T., *Biochim. et Biophys. Acta*, **10**, 192 (1953).

精子头部 有数据表明，晶态的精子头部的X射线谱的强度是由图2中那样的螺旋形式函数决定的。经离心分离的鲑鱼精液给出的衍射图案与先前使用干燥并且重新水合的精子头部或经漂洗的精子头部得到的图案是一样的[6]。提取的或人工合成[1]的鱼精蛋白或者提取的小牛胸腺核组蛋白也给出了精子头部的纤维衍射图。

噬菌体 将 T_2 噬菌体离心得到的湿的片状沉淀物封闭在带有云母窗的样品盒中，它给出的衍射图像具有类晶态核酸钠盐的主要特征，这与结晶态核蛋白的特征迥然不同。这一结果确认了目前关于噬菌体结构的观点。

转化要素（与伊弗鲁西–泰勒合作） 在约60%湿度下干燥得到具有活性的脱氧戊糖核酸盐，与胸腺核酸钠盐的某些样品[3]具有相同的晶体结构。

我们要衷心感谢兰德尔教授对我们的鼓励，感谢查加夫教授、西格纳教授、巴特勒教授、沃森博士、史密斯博士、哈密顿博士、怀特博士以及怀亚特博士，没有他们所提供的各种材料我们就不可能做这项工作，我们还要感谢沃森博士和克里克先生的激励，以及我们的同事富兰克林、戈斯林、布朗和西兹所提供的讨论。我们中的一员（威尔逊）对威尔士大学所授予的奖学金表示感谢。

（王耀杨 翻译；顾孝诚 审稿）

Molecular Configuration in Sodium Thymonucleate

R. E. Franklin and R. G. Gosling

Editor's Note

This paper reports the X-ray crysyallographic work on DNA by Rosalind Franklin and Raymond Gosling at King's College London, which furnished James Watson and Francis Crick with the crucial information for deducing how DNA is structured. Franklin and Gosling realise not only that DNA is helical but also that the sugar and base groups, part of the molecular building blocks, must point inwards towards the helix axis, contrary to an earlier helical model proposed by Linus Pauling. Franklin, who died from ovarian cancer only five years later, has been considered unfairly sidelined in the discovery of DNA's structure, not least because of the way she was dismissively described by James Watson in his account of the story in the book *The Double Helix*.

SODIUM thymonucleate fibres give two distinct types of X-ray diagram. The first corresponds to a crystalline form, structure *A*, obtained at about 75 percent relative humidity; a study of this is described in detail elsewhere[1]. At higher humidities a different structure, structure *B*, showing a lower degree of order, appears and persists over a wide range of ambient humidity. The change from *A* to *B* is reversible. The water content of structure *B* fibres which undergo this reversible change may vary from 40-50 percent to several hundred percent of the dry weight. Moreover, some fibres never show structure *A*, and in these structure *B* can be obtained with an even lower water content.

The X-ray diagram of structure *B* (see photograph) shows in striking manner the features characteristic of helical structures, first worked out in this laboratory by Stokes (unpublished) and by Crick, Cochran and Vand[2]. Stokes and Wilkins were the first to propose such structures for nucleic acid as a result of direct studies of nucleic acid fibres, although a helical structure had been previously suggested by Furberg (thesis, London, 1949) on the basis of X-ray studies of nucleosides and nucleotides.

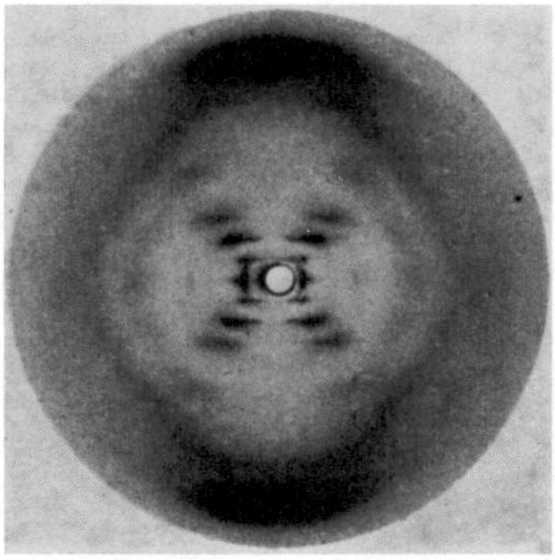

Sodium deoxyribose nucleate from calf thymus. Structure *B*

胸腺核酸钠盐的分子构型

富兰克林，戈斯林

编者按

这篇文章报道了伦敦国王学院的罗莎琳德·富兰克林和雷蒙德·戈斯林对DNA进行的X射线晶体学研究，该项研究为詹姆斯·沃森和弗朗西斯·克里克推断DNA结构提供了关键信息。富兰克林和戈斯林认识到不仅DNA是螺旋结构的，而且核糖和碱基基团作为分子构建基元的一部分，必须向内指向螺旋轴。这与莱纳斯·鲍林早先提出的螺旋模型相反。仅仅5年后富兰克林就死于卵巢癌，人们认为她在DNA结构的发现中被不公正地边缘化了，尤其是詹姆斯·沃森在其叙述DNA发现故事的《双螺旋》一书中曾对她做了轻蔑的排斥性描述。

胸腺核酸钠盐的纤维会产生两种不同类型的X射线图。第一种对应于在相对湿度大约为75%时得到的*A*型结构晶体形态，对它的研究在别处有详细的描述[1]。在更高湿度条件下出现的另一种*B*型结构有序性较低，能在较大范围的环境湿度下出现并且保持构型不变。从*A*型结构到*B*型结构的变化是可逆的。经历这种可逆变化后的*B*型结构纤维，其含水量可为干重的40%~50%到百分之几百不等。此外，某些纤维根本不会出现*A*型结构，但在这些纤维中可以得到含水量很低的*B*型结构。

*B*型结构的X射线图（见照片）非常突出地表现了螺旋结构的代表性特征，这些特征是由斯托克斯（未发表）以及克里克、科克伦和范特等人在本实验室首先得到的。斯托克斯和威尔金斯基于对核酸纤维的直接研究，首先提出核酸有此结构，而早先富尔贝里（参见其博士论文，伦敦，1949年）基于对核苷与核苷酸的X射线研究也提出过一种螺旋结构。

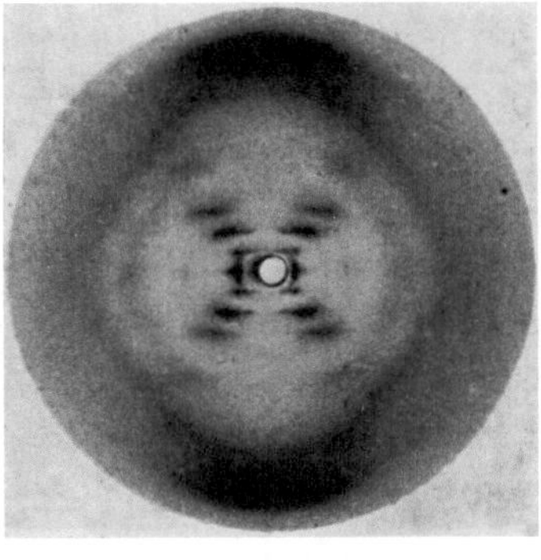

小牛胸腺的脱氧核糖核酸钠盐，*B*型结构。

While the X-ray evidence cannot, at present, be taken as direct proof that the structure is helical, other considerations discussed below make the existence of a helical structure highly probable.

Structure *B* is derived from the crystalline structure *A* when the sodium thymonucleate fibres take up quantities of water in excess of about 40 percent of their weight. The change is accompanied by an increase of about 30 percent in the length of the fibre, and by a substantial re-arrangement of the molecule. It therefore seems reasonable to suppose that in structure *B* the structural units of sodium thymonucleate (molecules on groups of molecules) are relatively free from the influence of neighbouring molecules, each unit being shielded by a sheath of water. Each unit is then free to take up its leastenergy configuration independently of its neighbours and, in view of the nature of the long-chain molecules involved, it is highly likely that the general form will be helical[3]. If we adopt the hypothesis of a helical structure, it is immediately possible, from the X-ray diagram of structure *B*, to make certain deductions as to the nature and dimensions of the helix.

The innermost maxima on the first, second, third and fifth layer lines lie approximately on straight lines radiating from the origin. For a smooth single-strand helix the structure factor on the *n*th layer line is given by:

$$F_n = J_n(2\pi rR)\exp i\, n(\psi + \tfrac{1}{2}\pi),$$

where $J_n(u)$ is the *n*th-order Bessel function of u, r is the radius of the helix, and R and ψ are the radial and azimuthal co-ordinates in reciprocal space[2]; this expression leads to an approximately linear array of intensity maxima of the type observed, corresponding to the first maxima in the functions J_1, J_2, J_3, etc.

If, instead of a smooth helix, we consider a series of residues equally spaced along the helix, the transform in the general case treated by Crick, Cochran and Vand is more complicated. But if there is a whole number, m, of residues per turn, the form of the transform is as for a smooth helix with the addition, only, of the same pattern repeated with its origin at heights mc^*, $2mc^*$ ... etc. (c is the fibreaxis period).

In the present case the fibre-axis period is 34 A. and the very strong reflexion at 3.4 A. lies on the tenth layer line. Moreover, lines of maxima radiating from the 3.4-A. reflexion as from the origin are visible on the fifth and lower layer lines, having a J_5 maximum coincident with that of the origin series on the fifth layer line. (The strong outer streaks which apparently radiate from the 3.4-A. maximum are not, however, so easily explained.) This suggests strongly that there are exactly 10 residues per turn of the helix. If this is so, then from a measurement of R_n the position of the first maximum on the *n*th layer line (for $n \leqslant 5$), the radius of the helix, can be obtained. In the present instance, measurements of R_1, R_2, R_3 and R_5 all lead to values of r of about 10 A.

目前虽然 X 射线研究的证据还不能直接证明该结构为螺旋形，但下面讨论中对其他方面的思考使螺旋结构的存在大有可能。

当胸腺核酸钠盐的纤维吸收了超过其自身重量 40%的水分时，晶态的 A 型结构就变为 B 型结构。这一变化还伴随着纤维长度 30%的增加，以及实质性的分子重排。由此我们有理由认为在 B 型结构中，胸腺核酸钠盐的结构单元（分子群中的分子）基本上不受邻近分子的影响，因为每个结构单元都被一层水分子层屏蔽。每个单元都可以独立自由地采取不依赖于邻近分子的最低能量状态的构型，另外考虑到结构中长链分子的性质，其总体形状很有可能就是螺旋形的[3]。如果我们采纳螺旋结构的假说，那么根据 B 型结构的 X 射线图，我们立刻就可以对螺旋的实质与尺度做出某些推论。

在第 1、2、3 和第 5 层线上最内部的极大值近似地分布在从原点辐射出来的一条直线上。对于一个平滑的单链螺旋来说，位于第 n 层线上的结构因子可以由下式给出：

$$F_n = J_n(2\pi rR)\exp i\,n(\psi + \tfrac{1}{2}\pi)$$

其中，$J_n(u)$ 是 u 的 n 阶贝塞尔函数，r 是螺旋的半径，而 R 和 ψ 分别是倒易空间中的径向坐标和方位角坐标[2]。该表达式导致所观测到的强度极大值形成近似线性排列的形式，这些极大值对应于 J_1、J_2、J_3 等函数的第一个极大值。

如果我们在考虑沿着螺旋等间距排布的一系列残基，而不是把它们当作一条平滑的螺旋来处理，那么克里克、科克伦和范特所采用的变换通常情况下会更复杂。不过，要是每周螺旋中的残基数 m 是整数，那么变换的形式就只是在一条平滑螺旋的基础上，在高度为 mc^*、$2mc^*\cdots$（c 为纤维轴周期）等处为新原点重复添加相同的图案就行了。

在目前情况下，纤维轴周期为 34 Å，而在 3.4 Å 处出现的极强的反射位于第 10 层线上。此外，由 3.4 Å 反射所产生的极大辐射线与来自原点的相似，可以在第 5 层线和序号更低的层线上看到，这些辐射线具有 J_5 极大值，这与第 5 层线上原有辐射线的极大值是一致的。（不过，靠外的明显是从 3.4 Å 极大值辐射而来的较强条纹还不易解释。）这有力地暗示着螺旋的每一周刚好有 10 个残基。如果确实如此，那么通过测量第 n 层线上第一极大值的位置 R_n（$n \leqslant 5$），就能够得出螺旋的半径。在目前的例子中，根据测量得到的 R_1、R_2、R_3 和 R_5 推算出的螺旋半径 r 的值都大约是 10 Å。

Since this linear array of maxima is one of the strongest features of the X-ray diagram, we must conclude that a crystallographically important part of the molecule lies on a helix of this diameter. This can only be the phosphate groups or phosphorus atoms.

If ten phosphorus atoms lie on one turn of a helix of radius 10 A., the distance between neighbouring phosphorus atoms in a molecule is 7.1 A. This corresponds to the P . . . P distance in a fully extended molecule, and therefore provides a further indication that the phosphates lie on the outside of the structural unit.

Thus, our conclusions differ from those of Pauling and Corey[4], who proposed for the nucleic acids a helical structure in which the phosphate groups form a dense core.

We must now consider briefly the equatorial reflexions. For a single helix the series of equatorial maxima should correspond to the maxima in $J_0(2\pi rR)$. The maxima on our photograph do not, however, fit this function for the value of r deduced above. There is a very strong reflexion at about 24 A. and then only a faint sharp reflexion at 9.0 A. and two diffuse bands around 5.5 A. and 4.0 A. This lack of agreement is , however, to be expected, for we know that the helix so far considered can only be the most important member of a series of coaxial helices of different radii; the non-phosphate parts of the molecule will lie on inner co-axial helices, and it can be shown that, whereas these will not appreciably influence the innermost maxima on the layer lines, they may have the effect of destroying or shifting both the equatorial maxima and the outer maxima on other layer lines.

Thus, if the structure is helical, we find that the phosphate groups or phosphorus atoms lie on a helix of diameter about 20 A., and the sugar and base groups must accordingly be turned inwards towards the helical axis.

Considerations of density show, however, that a cylindrical repeat unit of height 34 A. and diameter 20 A. must contain many more than ten nucleotides.

Since structure *B* often exists in fibres with low water content, it seems that the density of the helical unit cannot differ greatly from that of dry sodium thymonucleate, 1.63 $gm./cm.^3$ [1,5], the water in fibres of high water-content being situated outside the structural unit. On this basis we find that a cylinder of radius 10 A. and height 34 A. would contain thirty-two nucleotides. However, there might possibly be some slight interpenetration of the cylindrical units in the dry state making their effective radius rather less. It is therefore difficult to decide, on the basis of density measurements alone, whether one repeating unit contains ten nucleotides on each of two or on each of three co-axial molecules. (If the effective radius were 8 A. the cylinder would contain twenty nucleotides.) Two other arguments, however, make it highly probable that there are only two co-axial molecules.

First, a study of the Patterson function of structure *A*, using superposition methods, has indicated[6] that there are only two chains passing through a primitive unit cell in this

既然极大值形成线性排列是 X 射线图最突出的特征之一，那么我们应当得出结论：该分子中在晶体学方面最重要的部分一定位于具有这一直径的螺旋上。它们只可能是磷酸基团或者磷原子。

如果 10 个磷原子分布在半径为 10 Å 的螺旋的一周上，那么分子中相邻磷原子之间的距离就是 7.1 Å。这对应于完全伸展的分子中的磷原子之间的距离，从而为磷酸基团位于结构单元的外侧提供了进一步的证明。

因此我们的结论不同于鲍林和科里[4]，他们认为在核酸的螺旋结构中磷酸基团形成了致密的内核。

现在我们必须简要地考虑一下赤道反射。对于单链螺旋来说，赤道处极大值系列应该对应于 $J_0(2\pi rR)$ 的极大值。不过，如果 r 取前面推算得到的数值，我们照片上的极大值并不符合这一函数关系。在约 24 Å 附近有一极强的反射，然后在 9.0 Å 处只有一个微弱且尖锐的反射，另外在约 5.5 Å 和 4.0 Å 附近有两个弥散的反射带。不过，这种不一致是意料之中的，因为我们知道，迄今所考虑的螺旋只可能是一系列不同半径的同轴螺旋中最重要的一个成员而已。分子中的非磷酸盐部分将位于靠内部的同轴螺旋上，并且可以证明，尽管这些部分不会明显影响层线上的最内部的极大值，但它们可以造成破坏或移动赤道极大值以及其他层线上靠外围的其他极大值的效果。

因此，如果结构是螺旋形的，我们就会发现磷酸基团或磷原子位于一个直径约为 20 Å 的螺旋上，因而，糖和碱基基团必定只能转向内部朝向螺旋轴。

但是，考虑到密度，一个高为 34 Å、直径为 20 Å 的圆柱状重复单元中必定包含远不止 10 个核苷酸。

由于 *B* 型结构经常存在于含水量低的纤维中，螺旋单元的密度似乎不会和干的胸腺核酸钠盐的密度（1.63 mg/cm^3）[1,5] 相差很多，因为在含水量较高的纤维中，水分子是位于结构单元外部的。基于这些考虑，我们发现一个半径为 10 Å、高为 34 Å 的圆柱体中能容纳 32 个核苷酸。不过，处于干燥状态时，圆柱状单元之间也有可能存在某些轻微的相互穿插，使其有效半径稍小。因此，单纯靠密度测量，难以断定包含 10 个核苷酸的一个重要单元是在两个或三个同轴分子的每个分子上。（如果有效半径为 8 Å，相应地圆柱中应该包含 20 个核苷酸。）不过，另外两个论据使得只有两个同轴分子的看法显得颇有可能。

首先，通过叠加法对 *A* 型结构的帕特森函数进行的研究表明[6]，在此结构中，只有两条链穿过一个素晶胞。由于 $A \rightleftharpoons B$ 的可逆变换很容易实现，那么 *B* 型结构中

structure. Since the $A \rightleftharpoons B$ transformation is readily reversible, it seems very unlikely that the molecules would be grouped in threes in structure *B*. Secondly, from measurements on the X-ray diagram of structure *B* it can readily be shown that, whether the number of chains per unit is two or three, the chains are not equally spaced along the fibre axis. For example, three equally spaced chains would mean that the *n*th layer line depended on J_{3n}, and would lead to a helix of diameter about 60 A. This is many times larger than the primitive unit cell in structure *A*, and absurdly large in relation to the dimensions of nucleotides. Three unequally spaced chains, on the other hand, would be crystallographically non-equivalent, and this, again, seems unlikely. It therefore seems probable that there are only two co-axial molecules and that these are unequally spaced along the fibre axis.

Thus, while we do not attempt to offer a complete interpretation of the fibre-diagram of structure *B*, we may state the following conclusions. The structure is probably helical. The phosphate groups lie on the outside of the structural unit, on a helix of diameter about 20 A. The structural unit probably consists of two co-axial molecules which are not equally spaced along the fibre axis, their mutual displacement being such as to account for the variation of observed intensities of the innermost maxima on the layer lines; if one molecule is displaced from the other by about three-eighths of the fibre-axis period, this would account for the absence of the fourth layer line maxima and the weakness of the sixth. Thus our general ideas are not inconsistent with the model proposed by Watson and Crick in the preceding communication.

The conclusion that the phosphate groups lie on the outside of the structural unit has been reached previously by quite other reasoning[1]. Two principal lines of argument were invoked. The first derives from the work of Gulland and his collaborators[7], who showed that even in aqueous solution the —CO and —NH_2 groups of the bases are inaccessible and cannot be titrated, whereas the phosphate groups are fully accessible. The second is based on our own observations[1] on the way in which the structural units in structures *A* and *B* are progressively separated by an excess of water, the process being a continuous one which leads to the formation first of a gel and ultimately to a solution. The hygroscopic part of the molecule may be presumed to lie in the phosphate groups ($(C_2H_5O)_2PO_2Na$ and $(C_3H_7O)_2PO_2Na$ are highly hygroscopic[8]), and the simplest explanation of the above process is that these groups lie on the outside of the structural units. Moreover, the ready availability of the phosphate groups for interaction with proteins can most easily be explained in this way.

We are grateful to Prof. J. T. Randall for his interest and to Drs. F. H. C. Crick, A. R. Stokes and M. H. F. Wilkins for discussion. One of us (R. E. F.) acknowledges the award of a Turner and Newall Fellowship.

(**171**, 740-741; 1953)

的分子就不大可能是以三个分子为一组。其次，根据对 *B* 型结构的 X 射线图的测量，可以很容易地看出，无论每个单元中有两条链还是三条链，这些链都不可能是沿着纤维轴等间距排布的。比如说，三条等间距排布的链意味着第 n 层线由 J_{3n} 决定，这将会得出一个直径约为 60 Å 的螺旋。这比 *A* 型结构中的素晶胞要大好几倍，相对于核苷酸的尺寸来说更是大得不合情理。另一方面，三条不等间距排布的链在晶体学上是不等效的，因此看起来也不大可能。由此看来，可能只有两个同轴分子，并且它们是沿着纤维轴不等间距排布的。

因此，我们虽然并未对 *B* 型结构的纤维图提供一个完整详尽的解释，但还是可以陈述如下结论：该结构很可能是螺旋形的。磷酸基团位于结构单元的外侧，在直径大约为 20 Å 的螺旋上。结构单元很可能是由两个同轴分子沿纤维轴不等间距排布形成的，它们之间的相互位移正好可以解释层线上最内部极大值的观测强度的差异。如果一个分子与另一个分子间的位移约为纤维轴周期的 $\frac{3}{8}$，那就可以解释为何第 4 层线极大值缺失和第 6 层线的强度非常微弱。因此，我们的基本观点与沃森和克里克在前面的通讯文章中提出的模型没有矛盾。

此前已经依据其他一些完全不同的推论[1]得到了磷酸基团位于结构单元外侧这一结论。这主要借助于两条主要论据。第一条论据来自于格兰德及其同事的工作[7]。他们证明，即使是在水溶液中，碱基中的羰基和氨基也是不可及的，并且都无法进行滴定。而磷酸基团却是完全可及的。第二条论据是基于我们自己的观测[1]：即 *A* 型结构和 *B* 型结构中的结构单元如何逐步被过量的水分开。在这一连续过程中，首先形成凝胶，最终成为溶液。可以假定分子中的吸水部分位于磷酸基团处（$(C_2H_5O)_2PO_2Na$ 和 $(C_3H_7O)_2PO_2Na$ 都是高度吸湿的[8]），那么对上述过程最简单的解释就是这些基团位于结构单元的外侧。此外，磷酸基团可以很容易地与蛋白质发生相互作用，这一现象也可以非常容易地以此方式作出解释。

我们要感谢兰德尔教授的关注，以及克里克博士、斯托克斯博士和威尔金斯博士等人与我们讨论。我们中的一员（富兰克林）对特纳和纽沃尔研究基金的支持表示感谢。

（王耀杨 翻译；顾孝诚 审稿）

Rosalind E. Franklin and R. G. Gosling: Wheatstone Physics Laboratory, King's College, London, April 2.

References:

1. Franklin, R. E., and Gosling, R. G. (in the press).
2. Cochran, W., Crick, F. H. C., and Vand, V., *Acta Cryst.*, **5**, 501 (1952).
3. Pauling, L., Corey, R. B., and Bransom, H. R., *Proc. U.S. Nat. Acad. Sci.*, **37**, 205 (1951).
4. Pauling, L., and Corey, R. B., *Proc. U.S. Nat. Acad. Sci.*, **39**, 84 (1953).
5. Astbury, W. T., Cold Spring Harbor Symp. on Quant. Biol., **12**, 56 (1947).
6. Franklin, R. E., and Gosling, R. G. (to be published).
7. Gulland, J. M., and Jordan, D. O., Cold Spring Harbor Symp. on Quant. Biol., **12**, 5(1947).
8. Drushel, W. A., and Felty, A. R., *Chem. Zent.*, **89**, 1016 (1918).

Genetical Implications of the Structure of Deoxyribonucleic Acid

J. D. Watson and F. H. C. Crick

Editor's Note

The short paper by James Watson and Francis Crick the previous month, postulating a structure for DNA, only hinted at what this structure implied for genetics and heredity. Here the two researchers expand on what they have in mind. They show that the two strands of the double helix are held together by weak bonds called hydrogen bonds, which specifically bind each of the four "nucleotide bases" with a complementary partner that has a well-fitting shape. "If the actual order of the bases on one of the pair of chains were given, one could write down the exact order of the bases on the other one", they say. So each strand may act as a template for assembling its complement, enabling replication that passes on the genetic material encoded in the sequence of bases.

THE importance of deoxyribonucleic acid (DNA) within living cells is undisputed. It is found in all dividing cells, largely if not entirely in the nucleus, where it is an essential constituent of the chromosomes. Many lines of evidence indicate that it is the carrier of a part of (if not all) the genetic specificity of the chromosomes and thus of the gene itself. Until now, however, no evidence has been presented to show how it might carry out the essential operation required of a genetic material, that of exact self-duplication.

We have recently proposed a structure[1] for the salt of deoxyribonucleic acid which, if correct, immediately suggests a mechanism for its self-duplication. X-ray evidence obtained by the workers at King's College, London[2], and presented at the same time, gives qualitative support to our structure and is incompatible with all previously proposed structures[3]. Though the structure will not be completely proved until a more extensive comparison has been made with the X-ray data, we now feel sufficient confidence in its general correctness to discuss its genetical implications. In doing so we are assuming that fibres of the salt of deoxyribonucleic acid are not artefacts arising in the method of preparation, since it has been shown by Wilkins and his co-workers that similar X-ray patterns are obtained from both the isolated fibres and certain intact biological materials such as sperm head and bacteriophage particles[2,4].

The chemical formula of deoxyribonucleic acid is now well established. The molecule is a very long chain, the backbone of which consists of a regular alternation of sugar and phosphate groups, as shown in Fig. 1. To each sugar is attached a nitrogenous base, which can be of four different types. (We have considered 5-methyl cytosine to be equivalent to cytosine, since either can fit equally well into our structure.) Two of the possible bases—adenine and guanine—are purines, and the other two—thymine and cytosine—are pyrimidines. So far as is known, the sequence of bases along the chain is irregular. The monomer unit, consisting of phosphate, sugar and base, is known as a nucleotide.

脱氧核糖核酸结构的遗传学意义

沃森，克里克

编者按

在本文发表的一个月前，詹姆斯·沃森和弗朗西斯·克里克发表了一篇短文，提出了DNA的一种结构，当时仅仅暗示了这种结构对于遗传学及遗传的意义。本文中两位研究者进一步阐述了他们的想法。他们指出，双螺旋的两条链是由一种叫做氢键的弱键连接在一起的，其中氢键将四个“核苷酸碱基”与具有良好拟合形状的互补核苷酸碱基特异性地结合在一起。他们指出“如果给出其中一条链的确切的碱基顺序，那么我们就能准确写出另一条链的碱基顺序”。因此，每条链都可以作为其互补链的模板，使得由碱基序列编码的遗传物质能够复制下去。

活细胞中脱氧核糖核酸（DNA）的重要性是无可争议的。在一切分裂着的细胞中，DNA大部分（如果不是全部）存在于细胞核中，是染色体的重要组成成分。许多证据表明，DNA是部分（如果不是全部）染色体遗传特异性或者说基因本身的载体。但是，到目前为止还没有证据能够指出它是如何完成遗传物质所必需的精确的自我复制的。

最近，我们提出了脱氧核糖核酸盐的一种结构[1]，如果这一结构是正确的，那它立即揭示了DNA自我复制的机制。与此同时，伦敦国王学院的研究人员得到的X射线的数据对我们的结构也提供了定性的支持[2]，该数据与以前提出过的各种结构都不一致[3]。虽然在对X射线数据进行更广泛深入的比较之前我们提出的结构还不能被完全证实，但是现在我们有足够的信心认为，讨论其遗传学意义是基本正确的。为此，我们认为样品的制备方法并不会使脱氧核糖核酸盐的纤维结构出现人为假象，这是因为威尔金斯及其同事们已经发现，分离纯化的纤维与某些完整无损的生物材料，如精子头部和噬菌体颗粒等，能够得到类似的X射线衍射图样[2,4]。

现在我们已经完全确定了脱氧核糖核酸的化学组成。其分子是一条很长的链，糖和磷酸基团规则交替排列组成了它的骨架，如图1所示。每一个糖分子与一个含氮碱基相连，碱基有四种不同的类型。（我们认为5–甲基胞嘧啶与胞嘧啶是等同的，因为它们同样都适合于我们的结构中碱基所在位置。）碱基中有两种属于嘌呤，它们是鸟嘌呤和腺嘌呤，另外两种属于嘧啶，它们是胸腺嘧啶和胞嘧啶。就目前所知，分子长链上的碱基序列是无规则的。由磷酸基团、糖和碱基组成的单体单元被称为核苷酸。

The first feature of our structure which is of biological interest is that it consists not of one chain, but of two. These two chains are both coiled around a common fibre axis, as is shown diagrammatically in Fig. 2. It has often been assumed that since there was only one chain in the chemical formula there would only be one in the structural unit. However, the density, taken with the X-ray evidence[2], suggests very strongly that there are two.

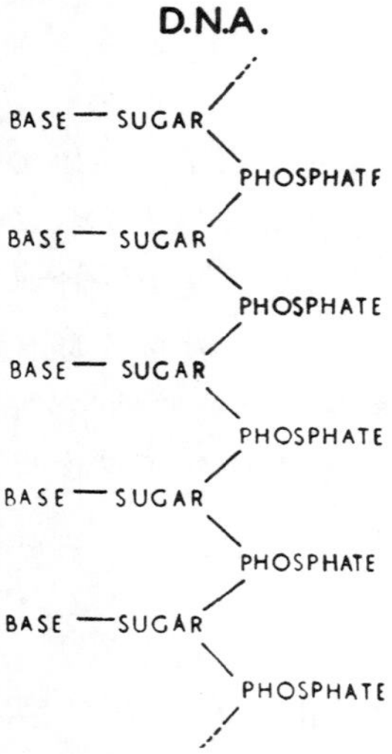

Fig. 1. Chemical formula of a single chain of deoxyribonucleic acid

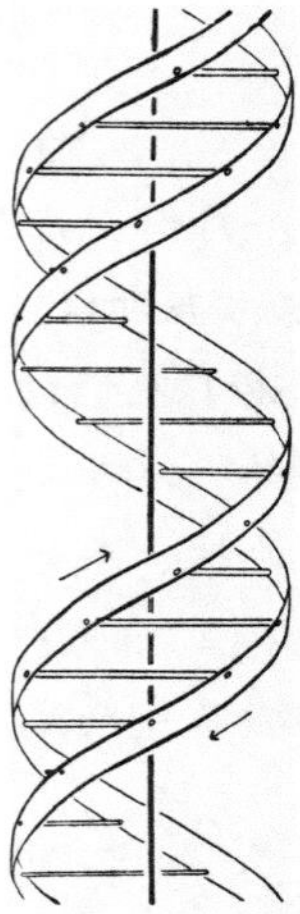

Fig. 2. This figure is purely diagrammatic. The two ribbons symbolize the two phosphate-sugar chains, and the horizontal rods the pairs of bases holding the chains together. The vertical line marks the fibre axis

The other biologically important feature is the manner in which the two chains are held together. This is done by hydrogen bonds between the bases, as shown schematically in Fig. 3. The bases are joined together in pairs, a single base from one chain being hydrogen-bonded to a single base from the other. The important point is that only certain pairs of bases will fit into the structure. One member of a pair must be a purine and the other a pyrimidine in order to bridge between the two chains. If a pair consisted of two purines, for example, there would not be room for it.

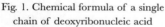

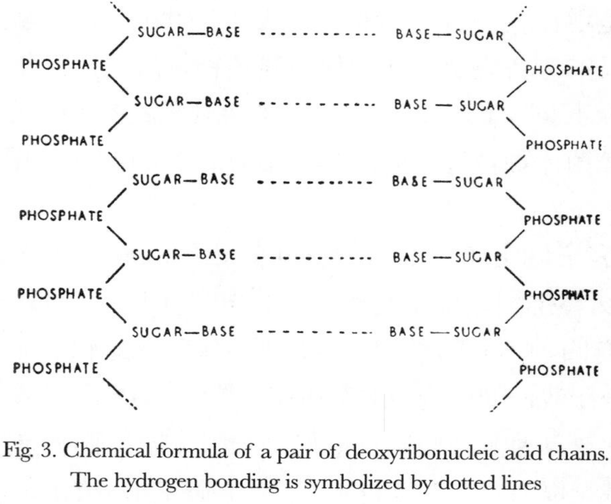

Fig. 3. Chemical formula of a pair of deoxyribonucleic acid chains. The hydrogen bonding is symbolized by dotted lines

我们这种具有生物学意义的结构的首要特点，在于它是由双链而不是由单链组成。两条链围绕一个共同的中心轴缠绕在一起，如图 2 所示。此前人们一直认为，既然 DNA 在化学组成上只是一条链，那么其结构单元也应该只有一条链。然而，X 射线衍射结果中的密度值 [2] 有力地表明它有两条链。

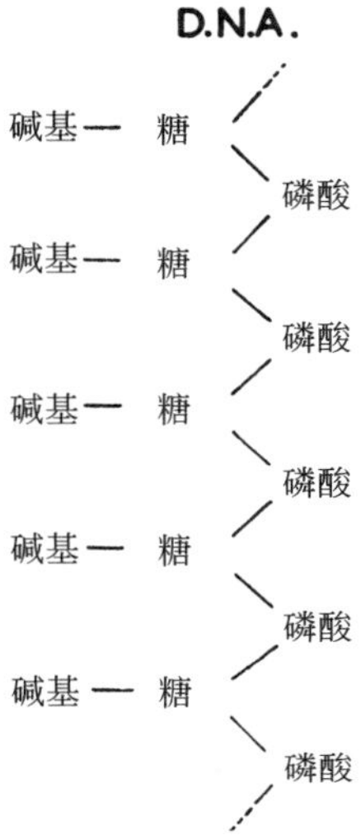

图 1. 单链脱氧核糖核酸的化学式

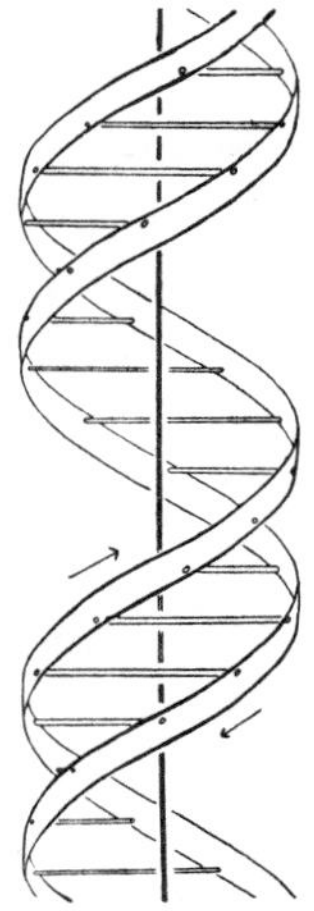

图 2. 这仅仅是个示意图。两条丝带代表两条磷酸–糖链，而横线代表将链连接起来的碱基对。垂直线标示出中心轴。

另外一个具有重要生物学意义的特点是两条链结合在一起的方式。双链是通过碱基之间的氢键结合在一起的，如图 3 所示。碱基之间配对结合在一起，一条链上的一个碱基与另一条链上的一个碱基通过氢键结合。值得注意的是，在这个结构中只有特定的碱基对可以匹配这个结构。为了将两条链桥接起来，碱基对中的一个是嘌呤则另一个必须是嘧啶。如果一个碱基对是由两个嘌呤组成的，那将没有空间容纳这个碱基对。

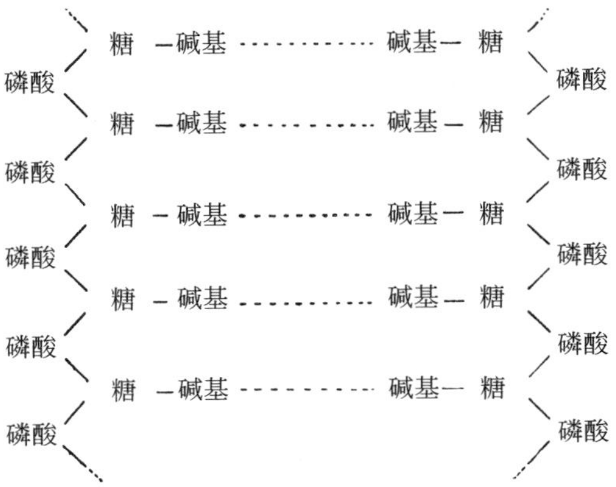

图 3. 双链脱氧核糖核酸的化学式。虚线代表氢键。

We believe that the bases will be present almost entirely in their most probable tautomeric forms. If this is true, the conditions for forming hydrogen bonds are more restrictive, and the only pairs of bases possible are:

adenine with thymine;
guanine with cytosine.

The way in which these are joined together is shown in Figs. 4 and 5. A given pair can be either way round. Adenine, for example, can occur on either chain; but when it does, its partner on the other chain must always be thymine.

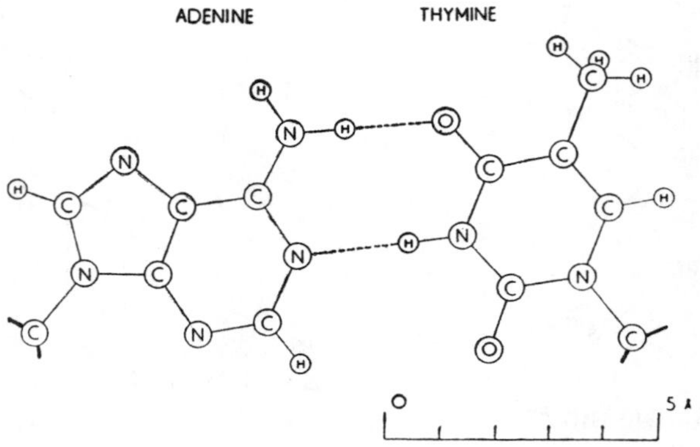

Fig. 4. Pairing of adenine and thymine. Hydrogen bonds are shown dotted. One carbon atom of each sugar is shown

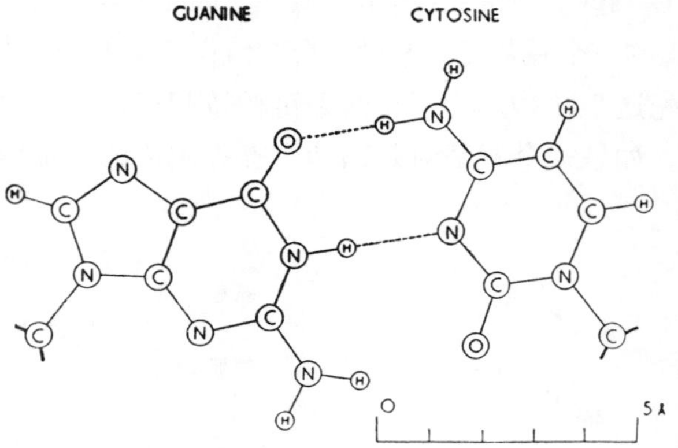

Fig. 5. Pairing of guanine and cytosine. Hydrogen bonds are shown dotted. One carbon atom of each sugar is shown

This pairing is strongly supported by the recent analytical results[5], which show that for all sources of deoxyribonucleic acid examined the amount of adenine is close to the amount of thymine, and the amount of guanine close to the amount of cytosine, although the cross-ratio (the ratio of adenine to guanine) can vary from one source to another. Indeed, if the sequence of bases on one chain is irregular, it is difficult to explain these analytical

我们认为，碱基几乎全部以其最可能出现的互变异构体形式存在。如果事实确实如此，那么形成氢键的条件将会受到更多的限制，可能的碱基配对就会只有两种：

腺嘌呤和胸腺嘧啶；

鸟嘌呤和胞嘧啶。

它们的结合方式如图 4 和图 5 所示。对于给定的一个碱基对，正反配对都是可以的。例如，腺嘌呤可以出现在任意一条链上，但是另一条链上与它配对的一定是胸腺嘧啶。

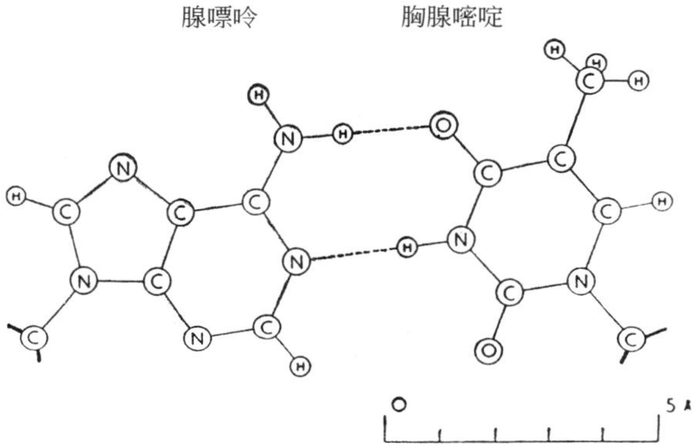

图 4. 腺嘌呤和胸腺嘧啶之间的配对。虚线代表氢键。图中只标出了每个糖基中的一个碳原子。

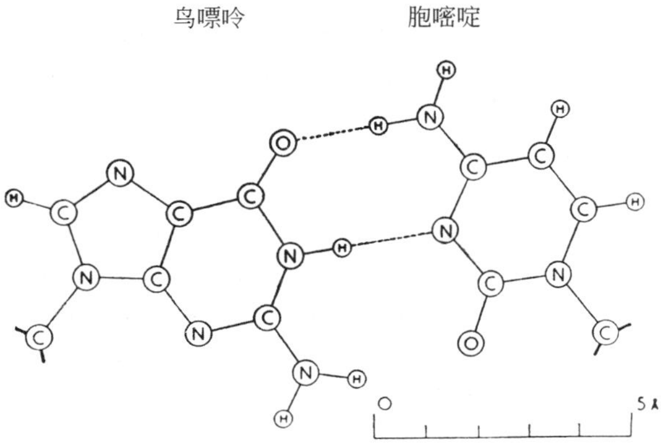

图 5. 鸟嘌呤和胞嘧啶之间的配对。虚线代表氢键。图中只标出了每个糖基中的一个碳原子。

最近的分析结果有力地支持了这种配对方式[5]，这些结果显示，虽然交叉比率（腺嘌呤与鸟嘌呤的比率）随样品来源的不同而不同，但在被检测的各种来源的脱氧核糖核酸中，腺嘌呤的量总是接近于胸腺嘧啶的量，鸟嘌呤的量总是接近于胞嘧啶的量。实际上，如果一条链上的碱基序列是无规则的，那么除非用我们提出的这种配对原则，

results except by the sort of pairing we have suggested.

The phosphate-sugar backbone of our model is completely regular, but any sequence of the pairs of bases can fit into the structure. It follows that in a long molecule many different permutations are possible, and it therefore seems likely that the precise sequence of the bases is the code which carries the genetical information. If the actual order of the bases on one of the pair of chains were given, one could write down the exact order of the bases on the other one, because of the specific pairing. Thus one chain is, as it were, the complement of the other, and it is this feature which suggests how the deoxyribonucleic acid molecule might duplicate itself.

Previous discussions of self-duplication have usually involved the concept of a template, or mould. Either the template was supposed to copy itself directly or it was to produce a "negative", which in its turn was to act as a template and produce the original "positive" once again. In no case has it been explained in detail how it would do this in terms of atoms and molecules.

Now our model for deoxyribonucleic acid is, in effect, a *pair* of templates, each of which is complementary to the other. We imagine that prior to duplication the hydrogen bonds are broken, and the two chains unwind and separate. Each chain then acts as a template for the formation on to itself of a new companion chain, so that eventually we shall have *two* pairs of chains, where we only had one before. Moreover, the sequence of the pairs of bases will have been duplicated exactly.

A study of our model suggests that this duplication could be done most simply if the single chain (or the relevant portion of it) takes up the helical configuration. We imagine that at this stage in the life of the cell, free nucleotides, strictly polynucleotide precursors, are available in quantity. From time to time the base of a free nucleotide will join up by hydrogen bonds to one of the bases on the chain already formed. We now postulate that the polymerization of these monomers to form a new chain is only possible if the resulting chain can form the proposed structure. This is plausible, because steric reasons would not allow nucleotides "crystallized" on to the first chain to approach one another in such a way that they could be joined together into a new chain, unless they were those nucleotides which were necessary to form our structure. Whether a special enzyme is required to carry out the polymerization, or whether the single helical chain already formed acts effectively as an enzyme, remains to be seen.

Since the two chains in our model are intertwined, it is essential for them to untwist if they are to separate. As they make one complete turn around each other in 34 A., there will be about 150 turns per million molecular weight, so that whatever the precise structure of the chromosome a considerable amount of uncoiling would be necessary. It is well known from microscopic observation that much coiling and uncoiling occurs during mitosis, and though this is on a much larger scale it probably reflects similar processes on a molecular level. Although it is difficult at the moment to see how these processes occur without

否则很难解释这些分析结果。

在我们的模型中，磷酸基–糖骨架是完全规则的，在这种结构中任何碱基对序列都是合适的。由此可以断定，在大分子中可能存在许多种不同的碱基排列方式，因此，这似乎表明精确的碱基序列就是携带遗传信息的密码。如果双链中一条链的碱基序列是已知的，那么我们就可以准确写出另一条链的碱基序列，因为碱基之间的配对是特异的。因此，一条链是另一条链的互补链，正是这个特点向我们揭示了脱氧核糖核酸分子是如何自我复制的。

此前关于自我复制的讨论常常涉及模板或者模具的概念。人们认为，或者是模板直接自我复制，或者是模板产生一个“负链”，此“负链”反过来又作为模板再产生一条原来的“正链”。但是任何论述都没能详细解释复制过程在原子和分子水平上是如何进行的。

实际上，我们的脱氧核糖核酸模型可以看作一**对**模板，它们之间是互补的。我们猜想，在复制之前氢键断裂，两条链解开并彼此分离。然后分别以每条链为模板，合成一条与之互补的新链，最终我们就得到了**两**对链，而在复制之前只有一对链。此外，碱基对的顺序将会被完全准确地复制下来。

深入研究我们的模型可以发现，如果单条链（或者单条链上的相应部分）为螺旋构型，复制就可以非常简单地进行。我们猜想，在细胞周期中的这个阶段，胞内存在大量游离核苷酸（严格来讲应该是多核苷酸的前体）。游离核苷酸的碱基不时地通过氢键与链上的某个碱基相结合。我们现在可以推断，只有当形成上述结构时这些单体才可能聚合形成一条新链。这应该是合理的，因为从空间上来看，除非结合到初始链上的核苷酸能形成我们所提出的结构的核苷酸，否则，它们是不可能“结晶”到初始链上并相互接近而连在一起形成一条新链的。至于是否需要一种专一性的酶来催化聚合过程，或者已形成的单股螺旋链是否可以有效地发挥酶的作用，这还需要进一步的研究。

在我们的模型中两条链是相互缠绕的，因此，要分离它们就必须解开螺旋。两条链每 34 Å 缠绕一周，按此计算，分子量为 100 万的 DNA 约有 150 个螺旋，因此，无论染色体具有怎样精确的结构，其复制过程中一定会发生大量解链。根据显微镜观察的结果，人们已经知道在有丝分裂过程中发生大量的螺旋化和解螺旋化，尽管这是在一个更大的尺度上，但是它很可能反映出在分子水平上也存在类似的过程。虽然此刻还没有弄清各个过程的关联性，很难确定它们是如何发生的，但是我们认

everything getting tangled, we do not feel that this objection will be insuperable.

Our structure, as described[1], is an open one. There is room between the pair of polynucleotide chains (see Fig. 2) for a polypeptide chain to wind around the same helical axis. It may be significant that the distance between adjacent phosphorus atoms, 7.1 A., is close to the repeat of a fully extended polypeptide chain. We think it probable that in the sperm head, and in artificial nucleoproteins, the polypeptide chain occupies this position. The relative weakness of the second layer-line in the published X-ray pictures[3a,4] is crudely compatible with such an idea. The function of the protein might well be to control the coiling and uncoiling, to assist in holding a single polynucleotide chain in a helical configuration, or some other non-specific function.

Our model suggests possible explanations for a number of other phenomena. For example, spontaneous mutation may be due to a base occasionally occurring in one of its less likely tautomeric forms. Again, the pairing between homologous chromosomes at meiosis may depend on pairing between specific bases. We shall discuss these ideas in detail elsewhere.

For the moment, the general scheme we have proposed for the reproduction of deoxyribonucleic acid must be regarded as speculative. Even if it is correct, it is clear from what we have said that much remains to be discovered before the picture of genetic duplication can be described in detail. What are the polynucleotide precursors? What makes the pair of chains unwind and separate? What is the precise role of the protein? Is the chromosome one long pair of deoxyribonucleic acid chains, or does it consist of patches of the acid joined together by protein?

Despite these uncertainties we feel that our proposed structure for deoxyribonucleic acid may help to solve one of the fundamental biological problems—the molecular basis of the template needed for genetic replication. The hypothesis we are suggesting is that the template is the pattern of bases formed by one chain of the deoxyribonucleic acid and that the gene contains a complementary pair of such templates.

One of us (J. D. W.) has been aided by a fellowship from the National Foundation for Infantile Paralysis (U.S.A.).

(**171**, 964-967; 1953)

J. D. Watson and F. H. C. Crick: Medical Research Council Unit for the Study of the Molecular Structure of Biological Systems, Cavendish Laboratory, Cambridge.

References:

1. Watson, J. D., and Crick, F. H. C., *Nature*, 171, 737 (1953).

2. Wilkins, M. H. F., Stokes, A. R., and Wilson, H. R., *Nature*, 171, 738 (1953). Franklin, R. E., and Gosling, R. G., *Nature*, 171, 740 (1953).

3. (*a*) Astbury, W. T., Symp. No. 1 Soc. Exp. Biol., 66 (1947). (*b*) Furberg, S., *Acta Chem. Scand.*, 6, 634 (1952). (*c*) Pauling, L., and Corey, R. B., *Nature*, 171, 346 (1953);

为这一障碍并非是不可克服的。

正如前文所述[1]，我们提出的结构是尚未确定的。在一对多核苷酸链之间有一定的空间（见图 2），可使一条多肽链围绕同一螺旋轴缠绕。相邻磷原子之间的距离为 7.1 Å，与一条完全伸展的多肽链中重复单元之间的距离非常接近，这可能很重要。我们认为，在精子头部和人工合成的核蛋白中，多肽链很可能占据了这个位置。在已经发表的 X 射线衍射图片中二级衍射线相对较弱的现象[3a,4]与我们的这一观点粗略吻合。蛋白质的功能可能是控制螺旋和解螺旋，协助维持多核苷酸单链的螺旋构型，或者行使其他非特异性的功能。

我们的模型也可以解释其他的一些现象。比如，自发突变可能是由于某个碱基偶尔变为它的一种可能性较小的互变异构体形式。此外，减数分裂期间同源染色体之间的配对可能依赖于特定碱基之间的配对。我们将在另外的文章中详细讨论这些观点。

目前，应当将我们提出的关于脱氧核糖核酸复制的基本方案看作一种推测。即便这种推测是正确的，从我们此前的论述中也能清楚地看到，在能详细描述遗传物质复制的全景之前，还有许多问题需要我们去探索。多核苷酸的前体是什么？什么使得配对的双链解螺旋并相互分离？蛋白质的确切作用是什么？染色体到底是一条很长的脱氧核糖核酸双链，还是由通过蛋白质连接起来的许多个脱氧核糖核酸双链的片段组成的？

尽管这些问题还没有确定的答案，但是我们认为我们提出的脱氧核糖核酸的结构可能有助于解决一个最基本的生物学问题——遗传物质复制所需模板的分子基础。我们提出的假说是，复制所需的模板就是一条脱氧核糖核酸链上形成的碱基序列模式，而基因则包括了一对互补的模板链。

我们中的一员（沃森）由国家小儿麻痹症基金会资助。

（郑建全 翻译；王晓晨 审稿）

Proc. U.S. Nat. Acad. Sci., **39**, 84 (1953). (*d*) Fraser, R. D. B. (in preparation).

4. Wilkins, M. H. F., and Randall, J. T., *Biochim. et Biophys. Acta*, **10**, 192 (1953).

5. Chargaff, E., for references see Zamenhof, S., Brawerman, G., and Chargaff, E., *Biochim. et Biophys. Acta*, **9**, 402 (1952). Wyatt, G. R., *J. Gen. Physiol.*, **36**, 201 (1952).

Piltdown Man

Editor's Note

The discovery of a modern-looking skull with a primitive jaw at Piltdown in southern England in 1912 caused a sensation. As the years passed, *Eoanthropus dawsoni*—the name given to this "missing link"—looked increasingly out of step with discoveries from Africa and Asia, showing early hominids with primitive skulls and modern-looking teeth. This news report in *Nature* is an account of a paper by J. S. Weiner and colleagues (*Bulletin of the British Museum* (*Natural History*) 2, No. 3, 1953) in which the Piltdown finds are comprehensively revealed as forgeries. The skull was admittedly ancient, although still of a modern human. The jaw came from a modern ape, the teeth abraded mechanically. Both had been stained to look old.

A CRITICAL re-examination of all the Piltdown specimens was undertaken this year by the British Museum (Natural History) in conjunction with the Department of Anatomy, University of Oxford. The results, published over the names of Dr. J. S. Weiner, Dr. K. P. Oakley and Prof. W. E. Le Gros Clark, demonstrate clearly that the jaw and the canine tooth are in fact deliberate frauds (*Bull. Brit. Mus.* (*Nat. Hist.*), **2**, No. **3**; 1953). The Piltdown brain-case must still be regarded as a genuine fossil (an Upper Pleistocenc variety of modern man). The jawbone and tooth which had been falsely associated with this human cranium were so entirely out of character that, even when allowance was made for different parts of the human skull having evolved at different rates, it became increasingly difficult as time went on to reconcile them with the evidence of human evolution obtained elsewhere. The removal of the "ape-jawed Piltdown man (*Eoanthropus*)" from the fossil record thus actually clarifies the problem of human ancestry.

In their remarkably flat wear the molar teeth in the Piltdown jawbone rèsemble man rather than ape. Microscopical examination of these flatly worn surfaces showed that they are due to artificial abrasion and not to natural wear. The canine is a young tooth with incomplete root, so the fact that it has been worn right down to the pulp cavity, as in an aged individual, is only explicable by artificial abrasion.

Re-determination of the fluorine content of all the specimens, using an improved technique, has shown that whereas the brain-case contains the same amount of fluorine as some local Upper Pleistocene fossils, the jawbone and the canine contain no more than modern specimens. The organic content of all the specimens has also been determined. The jawbone and the canine contain as much nitrogen as fresh bones and teeth; but the brain-case contains only the small quantity expected in Upper Pleistocene fossils.

皮尔当人

编者按

1912 年在英国南部皮尔当发现一件具有原始下颌骨、看起来像现代人类的头骨，这一发现引起一场轰动。随着时间的流逝，道森曙人——为这个“缺失环节”所取的名字，看起来与出自非洲和亚洲的发现越来越不一致，道森曙人展现的早期人科动物具有原始的头骨和看起来像现代人类的牙齿。《自然》上的这篇消息报道是对韦纳及其同事的论文（《大英博物馆公报（自然探究）》第 2 卷，第 3 期；1953 年）的一个说明，揭示了皮尔当发现完全是造假。虽然该头骨属于现代人类，但不可否认它是相当古老的。其颌骨来自于现代猿类，牙齿经过机械打磨。为了看起来古老一些，它们都经过了人工染色。

今年大英博物馆（自然分馆）联合牛津大学解剖学系共同对所有的皮尔当样本进行了批判性的重新审查。以韦纳博士、奥克利博士和勒格罗·克拉克教授的名义发表的审查结果明确地证实了颌骨以及犬齿实际上是刻意伪造的（《大英博物馆公报（自然探究）》，第 2 卷，第 3 期；1953 年）。该皮尔当脑颅一定仍被当作一个真正的化石（一种上更新世时期的现代人类物种）。即使认同人类头骨的不同部分是以不同速率进化的，颌骨和牙齿与该人类颅骨虚假地关联在一起完全不相称，以至于随着时间的流逝，想要使它们与在其他地方获得的人类进化证据相吻合变得越来越困难。因而从化石记录中将“具有猿类颌的皮尔当人（曙人）”去除，实际上就能阐明人类祖先的问题了。

皮尔当人下颌骨上磨损面非常平坦的臼齿，与人类的相似，而非与猿类的相似。对这些平坦的磨损面进行的显微镜检验表明，它们是人工磨损形成的而非自然磨损形成的。犬齿是一颗年轻的牙齿，具有不完整的牙根，所以它表现出来的像在一个老年个体中见到的磨损径直向下到牙髓腔的情况只能通过人工磨损来解释了。

使用一种改进的技术对所有样本的氟含量进行了重新检测，结果表明尽管脑颅与当地上更新世一些化石的氟含量相同，但颌骨和犬齿的氟含量却不超过现代样本。所有样本的有机物含量也已得到检测。颌骨和犬齿的含氮量与新鲜骨和牙齿的相同，但是脑颅中的含量很少，正如在上更新世化石中预期的那样。

Finally, evidence has been found which indicates that the jawbone was artificially stained by iron salts and potassium dichromate prior to its being "discovered" by the excavators. Some who were at first sceptical about the association of the human brain-case with an ape-like jaw and canine tooth became convinced that it was a genuine association, and not a fortuitous one, when it was announced that remains of another individual had been found at a second site. Tests applied to the two pieces of skull bone alleged to be from the second site show that whereas one piece is fossilized and probably belongs to the skull from the first site, the other piece is comparatively modern and has been artificially stained in an attempt to match it in colour. A molar tooth reputed to be from this second site shows signs of artificial abrasion and almost certainly came from the original "Piltdown mandible".

The tests and other investigations reported above were carried out jointly in the Departments of Geology and Mineralogy of the British Museum, in the Department of Anatomy and the Clarendon Laboratory, University of Oxford, and in the Department of the Government Chemist, London.

These investigations serve to confirm the doubts expressed by certain men of science during the controversy which raged for some years after the original discovery in 1912. For example, exactly forty years ago, Prof. D. Waterston, then professor of anatomy in King's College, London, after superimposing tracings of the radiograms of the Piltdown mandible and that of a chimpanzee, wrote (*Nature*, **92**, 319; 1913): "The similarity of the specimens brought out in this way is very striking, for the outlines are practically identical. … The cranial fragments of the Piltdown skull, on the other hand, are in practically all their details essentially human. If that be so it seems to me to be as inconsequent to refer the mandible and the cranium to the same individual as it would be to articulate a chimpanzee foot with the bones of an essentially human thigh and leg". A similar view was expressed by Mr. G. Miller, jun., in the United States after systematic comparison of the casts of the Piltdown fossils with the corresponding bones of men and apes.

(**172**, 981-982; 1953)

最终，已发现的一些证据表明颌骨在被挖掘者“发现”之前，就已用铁盐和重铬酸钾进行了人工染色。当宣布在别的地点发现了另一个体的残骸时，起初对人类脑颅与类似猿类的颌骨和犬齿之间的关联表示怀疑的那些人开始相信这是一个真实的而非偶然的关联。对宣称是来自第二地点的两件头骨进行的检测表明，尽管其中一件头骨是石化的并且可能是来自于第一地点的头骨，但另一件却相对现代些，已进行了人工染色，以使该头骨与其他头骨在颜色上匹配。一颗号称是来自第二地点的臼齿表现出了人工磨损的迹象，几乎肯定它来自于最初的“皮尔当下颌骨”。

以上报道的这些检测和其他调查是由大英博物馆地质学与矿物学部、牛津大学解剖学系和克拉伦登实验室、伦敦政府化学部联合完成的。

这些调查证实了在 1912 年最初发现之后争议盛行的几年里一些科学工作者提出的质疑。例如，正是 40 年前，时为伦敦国王学院解剖学系教授的沃特斯顿在将皮尔当下颌骨的射线照相扫描图与黑猩猩的叠加之后，写道（《自然》，92 卷，319 页；1913 年）：“以这种方式呈现的这些样本的相似性很明显，因为其轮廓几乎一样……另一方面，皮尔当头骨的颅骨破片几乎在所有细节方面实质上都是人类的。如果果真如此，那么在我看来推断该下颌骨和颅骨属于同一个体是不合理的，正如将一只黑猩猩的脚与实质上是人类的大腿和小腿的骨头合成一个关节一样不合情理”。美国的小米勒先生在对皮尔当化石模型和相应的人类及猿类的骨进行了系统比较之后，表达了相似的观点。

（刘皓芳 翻译；吴新智 胡荣 审稿）

Chemical Examination of the Piltdown Implements

K. P. Oakley and J. S. Weiner

Editor's Note

Following their revelations this same year that the supposedly ancient pre-human remains from Piltdown in southern England were forgeries, Joseph Sidney Weiner and Kenneth Oakley here add a further twist. Not only had all the bones been stained to look old, but also had some of the supposed flint artefacts too. Staining might have had the purpose of hardening bone, the better to preserve it—but there is no possible reason for staining flint artefacts except to deceive. These revelations were a bitter blow to some established names in anthropology, who had fallen for the deception. The identity of the forger has, however, never been conclusively proven.

IN the report[1] on the main results of our re-examination of the Piltdown material, we gave reasons for regarding the chromate staining of the *mandible* as indicating a deliberate attempt to match a modern bone with the mineralized cranial fragments. The actual composition of this bone (3.9 percent nitrogen, less than 0.03 percent fluorine) suffices to prove its modernity; but the chromate staining, combined with the artificially abraded appearance of the molars, indicates that it is not only modern but also fraudulent.

In case there is any lingering doubt that the Piltdown finds are in part fraudulent, we think that one other fact now brought to light should be published immediately. Suspecting that some of the so-called implements[2] reported from the site might have been "doctored", we asked Mr. E. T. Hall, of the Clarendon Laboratory, Oxford, to test the composition of their surface stains by means of his X-ray spectrographic method of analysis. He has reported to us that the stains on these flints are entirely ferruginous, with one notable exception. The triangular flint (Reg. No. E. 606) recovered *in situ* from the layer immediately overlying the skull horizon[3] is chromate stained. When this stain is removed in acid the flint appears greyish-white. It is indistinguishable from a mechanically broken piece of flint such as one might encounter on the surface of any ploughed field in "Chalk-land".

Whereas a bone might have been dipped in a solution of potassium dichromate with the sole purpose of trying to harden it, a flint would only have been treated in that way by a forger requiring it to be of a certain colour.

(**172**, 1110; 1953)

K. P. Oakley: Department of Geology, British Museum (Nat. Hist.), London, S.W.7.

对皮尔当工具进行的化学检验

奥克利，韦纳

编者按

这一年，韦纳和奥克利先是揭露了发现于英格兰南部皮尔当的所谓古代前人类化石是一个骗局，随后他们又对此做了进一步的验证。不仅所有的骨经过了染色处理以使其看起来陈旧，而且一些之前被猜测是燧石的石器也经过了同样的处理。给骨染色可能是为了使其硬化以便于保存，但是给燧石石器染色的原因就只能是为了欺骗了。这次揭露事件使一些著名的人类学家受到沉重的一击，并因这个骗局而声名扫地。但是伪造者的身份至今仍未得到充分证实。

通过对皮尔当样品重新进行检验，我们认为对**下颌骨**进行铬酸盐染色表明伪造者蓄意使这件现代的骨与矿化的颅骨破片相匹配，在这份包含了主要结果的检验报告中[1]，我们给出了得出这样结论的依据。该骨骼的实际组分（3.9%的氮，不到0.03%的氟）足以证实其现代性；但是铬酸盐染色以及臼齿表面受到过人工磨损表明，该样本不仅是现代的，而且还带有欺诈性。

为了避免有人怀疑皮尔当发现带有部分欺诈性，我们认为应该立即将新发现的另一个事实公之于众。由于怀疑报告发现于该遗址的所谓的工具[2]可能被“做过手脚”，所以我们请求牛津大学克拉伦登实验室的霍尔先生用X射线光谱分析方法对其表面的染料进行了检验。他在报告中称，这些燧石表面的染料全部含铁，但是有一个显著的例外。在头骨所在层位[3]紧上方的地层原位发掘出的三角形燧石（登记编号E.606）是铬酸盐染色。当用酸将这种染料去除时，燧石呈现出灰白色。这与燧石由于机械断裂而形成的碎片的颜色非常相似，这在任意一块“白垩质土地”上被犁过的田野中都可以见到。

用重铬酸钾溶液浸泡骨可能只是为了使其硬化，但是用这种方法处理燧石的目的则只有一个，即伪造者为了使其呈现出某种特定的颜色。

（刘皓芳 崔娅铭 翻译；吴新智 审稿）

J. S. Weiner: Department of Anatomy, University of Oxford. Nov. 24.

References:

1. Weiner, J. S., Oakley, K. P., and Clark, W. E. Le Gros, *Bull. Brit. Mus.* (*Nat. Hist.*), Geol. Ser., **2**, No. 3 (1953).
2. Doubts about their genuineness were expressed in 1949 in a handbook of the British Museum (Nat. Hist.), "Man the Tool-Maker", 1st edit., pp. 69-70.
3. Dawson, C., and Woodward, A. S., *Quart. J. Geol. Soc. Lond.*, **69**, 122, footnote 1, pl. xvi, fig. 2 (1913).

Pithecanthropus, Meganthropus and the Australopithechinae*

G. H. R. von Koenigswald

Editor's Note

The flourish of African hominid discovery in the 1930s and '40s came after the discovery of the Pithecanthropines in China and Java. Here Gustav Heinrich Ralph von Koenigswald—an expert on these Asian forms—compares the Asian record with the newly discovered Australopithecines from Africa. He disputes claims that the Australopithecines were capable of technology, showing that their brains were small and they had many apelike features. The Pithecanthropines looked much more modern and had larger brains relative to their body mass. Later work vindicated this view: the Pithecanthropines are now all assigned to *Homo erectus*, the first human of modern aspect. Presciently, von Koenigswald suspected that Australopithecines and Pithecanthropines shared a common ancestry: but in 1954 no trace of such ancestry existed.

A VERY important group of higher Primates has been discovered in Africa, the Australopithecinae[1]. They include *Australopithecus*, *Plesianthropus* and *Paranthropus* from South and most probably "*Meganthropus africanus*"[2] from East Africa. The position of *Telanthropus* from the *Plesianthropus* layers of Swartkrans is still under dispute.

The large amount of material now at hand leaves no doubt that the Australopithecinae are members of the Hominidae. With this group they share the upright gait, which can be concluded from the pelvis, used by *Plesianthropus* and *Paranthropus*, and several important peculiarities of the skull and the dentition. The *Australopithecus* from Makapansgat owes the name "*prometheus*" to Dart's suggestion that he knew the use of fire, which, however, was disputed by Broom[3]. Dart has also suggested that certain battered ungulate humeri from the same site are evidence of a "predatory implemental technique"[4]; however, exactly the same type of damage is caused by hyaenas[5], which are also known from Makapansgat[6].

The oldest known, undoubtedly human beings, are the *Pithecanthropi* of Asia, including *Pithecanthropus*, *Sinanthropus* and *Meganthropus*. Do the Australopithecinae represent an ancestral type? Are they really older and more primitive?

First of all, the known Australopithecinae are, geologically, not older than *Meganthropus* and *Pithecanthropus modjokertensis* (not *Pithecanthropus robustus*) from the Lower Pleistocence of Java[7]. In at least two of the South African sites, Kromdraai and Swartkrans, the horse,

* Summary of a lecture given at University College, London, on March 12.

爪哇猿人、魁人与南方古猿亚科*

孔尼华

编者按

继在中国和爪哇发现猿人之后，20 世纪 30 年代和 40 年代在非洲出现了发现人科的高潮。本文中，研究亚洲猿人类群的专家古斯塔夫·海因里希·拉尔夫·孔尼华将亚洲的猿人与在非洲新发现的南方古猿亚科进行比较。结果显示南方古猿亚科的脑量小并且具有许多类似猿类的特征，他对南方古猿亚科能掌握技术这一说法表示怀疑。而爪哇猿人看起来更加现代并且相对于它们的体重来说，其脑量较大。后来的研究证明了这一看法：现在，爪哇猿人都被归属于直立人，它们是最早的有现代人模样的人类。孔尼华很有预见性地推测南方古猿亚科和猿人亚科拥有共同的祖先，但是在 1954 年还没有找到这一祖先存在的任何痕迹。

在非洲出土了一组非常重要的高等灵长类类群，即南方古猿亚科 [1]。它们包括来自南非的南方古猿、迩人和傍人，也很有可能包括来自东非的“非洲魁人”[2]。在斯瓦特克朗斯的迩人层位出土的远人的分类地位尚存在争议。

现在手头上的大量材料毫无疑问地表明南方古猿亚科属于人科。它们和这个群体都具有直立行走的特征（这一点可以根据迩人和傍人的骨盆推断出），头骨和齿系有着一些重要的特点。达特认为马卡潘斯盖的南方古猿会使用火，因此将其命名为“普罗米修斯”，而布鲁姆则对这一点表示了异议 [3]。达特还认为某些来自同一遗址的被磨损的有蹄类肱骨可以作为“捕食工具技术”的证据 [4]；然而，马卡潘斯盖 [6] 的证据表明，鬣狗 [5] 可以造成同种类型的损伤。

已知最古老的、确定无疑的人类是亚洲的猿人，包括爪哇猿人、中国猿人和魁人。那么南方古猿亚科是否代表了一种祖先类型？它们真的更古老更原始吗？

首先，从地质学角度而言，已知的南方古猿亚科并不比爪哇下更新世的魁人和莫佐克托猿人（不是粗壮猿人）更古老 [7]。至少在南非的克罗姆德拉伊和斯瓦特克

* 3 月 12 日在伦敦大学学院发表的一篇演讲的摘要。

Equus, is found, which is the best guide fossil for the Pleistocene, and at Sterkfontein and Swarkrans we find an extinct carnivore, *Lycyaena*, which even in Europe existed until the Villafranchian[8]. There is no definite proof that any of the other sites is really of Pliocene age.

The best-known hominid from the Lower Pleistocene of Java is *Pithecanthropus modjokertensis*. This form has retained the "simian gap", which is a very primitive characteristic which might be expected in an early human forerunner; for Remane, in a very careful study, has shown that even in the dentition of modern man there are peculiarities due to his forerunners having much better developed canines[9]. This gap has already disappeared in the full-grown Australopithecinae—although it seems to be present in the deciduous dentition of *Australopithecus africanus*; but while this *Pithecanthropus* in spite of the primitive dentition possesses a typical human entrance to the nose with a well-developed nasal septum, in the Australopithecinae—I quote from a description of *Paranthropus crassidens*—"except that the inner parts of the premaxillaries pass considerably further back, the resemblance of this region to that of the chimpanzee is considerable"[10].

The incisors in *Pithecanthropus* are well developed. In the Australopithecinae they are much reduced, in some cases even below the minimum values known for modern man. Minimum values for central incisors are, for *Paranthropus crassidens* and *Homo sapiens*, upper 7.5 and 8.0 mm., lower 5.0 and 4.6 mm., respectively. The relative values are much higher, as the average length for the first lower molar in *crassidens* is 15.0 mm., in modern man 11.1 mm. The canines are of about the same size in both groups.

In modern man the first lower premolar is only a little smaller than the second (in some Eskimos we still find the reverse), the average being 0.3 mm. But it is 1.3 mm. in *Paranthropus crassidens*. In *Sinanthropus* the first premolar is largest, also in *Meganthropus*, and generally in all anthropoids. This surely is the primitive condition. As a whole, in the Australopithecinae the incisor-canine-premolar group is more reduced not only as in *Pithecanthropus* but also more than in modern man. In connexion with this reduction, the dental arcade shows a typical shortening, which has been demonstrated by Le Gros Clark[11].

In spite of all these specializations, the roots of the premolars in *Paranthropus* do not differ in number from those observed generally in the anthropoids. In the lower jaw the second premolar has two roots, and in the upper jaw the first and the second both have three. In *Pithecanthropus* the lower premolar in question is single-rooted, the first upper has three and the second two roots. In modern man two roots in the second lower premolar are extremely rare (one case was observed among 2,089 specimens), while three separate roots occur in the first upper premolar in 3 percent, three roots in the second in only 0.3 percent, two in 3.5 percent of specimens[12].

朗斯这两处遗址发现了马属动物，这是更新世时期最好的指示性化石了，而在斯泰克方丹和斯瓦特克朗斯，我们则发现了一种已灭绝的食肉动物狼鬣狗，这种动物即使在欧洲也一直生存到维拉方期[8]。还没有确凿的证据表明其他任何遗址真正属于上新世。

爪哇下更新世时期最著名的人科是莫佐克托猿人。它们保留了“猿的齿隙”，这是一种可能存在于早期人类祖先的非常原始的特征。雷马内通过一次非常细致的研究发现，即使在现代人的齿系中，也存在由于其祖先具有发育良好得多的犬齿而产生的一些特点[9]。尽管这种齿隙在南方古猿非洲种的乳齿齿系中可能存在，但在发育完全的南方古猿亚科中已经消失了。另外这种爪哇猿人尽管其齿系是原始的，却具有典型的人类的鼻腔入口和发育完好的鼻中隔，而在南方古猿亚科中，“除了前颌骨的内部部分大幅向后延伸外，这一区域与黑猩猩的还是具有很大的相似性的”（引自对傍人粗齿种的描述）[10]。

爪哇猿人的门齿发育良好。南方古猿亚科门齿的发育情况则差得多，有些情况下，甚至低于现代人已知的最小值。傍人粗齿种和智人的上中门齿的最小值分别是7.5毫米和8.0毫米，下中门齿的最小值分别为5.0毫米和4.6毫米。相关数值要高得多，就如傍人粗齿种的第一下臼齿的平均长度是15.0毫米，而现代人的是11.1毫米。两个群体的犬齿大小基本相同。

现代人的第一下前臼齿只比第二下前臼齿略小一点（在某些爱斯基摩人中，我们还发现了相反的情况），平均值是0.3毫米，但是傍人粗齿种的平均值是1.3毫米。中国猿人的第一前臼齿最大，魁人也是，所有的类人猿一般也如此。因此这肯定是原始状态。总体上来说，南方古猿亚科的门齿－犬齿－前臼齿群不仅像爪哇猿人的一样大大减小了，而且比现代人减小的还要多。齿弓也相应显示出典型的缩短现象，勒格罗·克拉克已证实这一点[11]。

尽管存在以上这些特殊之处，傍人的前臼齿齿根数量与在类人猿中观察到的普遍数目并无差异。下颌骨的第二前臼齿有2个齿根，而上颌骨的第一前臼齿和第二前臼齿都有3个齿根。此处讨论的爪哇猿人下前臼齿是单根的，而第一上前臼齿有3个齿根，第二上前臼齿有2个齿根。在现代人中，第二下前臼齿有2个齿根的情况极为少见（2,089个标本中只观察到1例），而第一上前臼齿有3个独立齿根的情况发生的比例为3%，第二上前臼齿有3个齿根的情况发生的比例仅为0.3%，有2个齿根的比例为3.5%[12]。

In the relative size of the molars, the increase in size from the first to the last lower molar, and in the upper jaw the second molar being larger than the first, *Pithecanthropus* shows the same primitive conditions as the Australopithecinae and the anthropoids. There is, however, a tendency for the last upper molar in *Paranthropus crassidens* to be enlarged; this is not found either in the Hominidae (in modern man this molar is often completely reduced) or in the anthropoids.

The deciduous dentition is of great value for the determination of the phylogenetic position. In *Sinanthropus* as in *Pithecanthropus modjokertensis* the first lower deciduous molar has two main cusps—as also the chimpanzee and the orang; in the first form the entoconid is absent, as is common in the anthropoids, in the second very faint. Complete absence of the entoconid in modern man is found in about 2 percent of specimens only. In the Australopithecinae this cusp is not only developed to the same degree as in modern man (in *Australopithecus africanus* this point is not so clear), but there is also a tendency towards a complete molarization of this tooth, which reaches a maximum in *Plesianthropus transvaalensis* for the upper and in *Paranthropus robustus* for the lower molar; in the latter form, except for its size, this tooth is indistinguishable from the second deciduous molar. There is a certain amount of variability in modern man; but extreme conditions like these have not been observed in a vast collection of modern teeth at our disposal (Bolk Collection, Amsterdam.)

This comparison already reveals so many features which must be regarded as a sign of over-specialization that they exclude the Australopithecinae from the ancestorship not only of *Pithecanthropus* but also of *Homo sapiens*.

A greater resemblance exists between the Australopithecinae and the imperfectly known *Meganthropus* from Java; so much so that recently Robinson has included the Javanese species in the same group[2]. He shows that, especially in the formation of the symphysis, there is a very great resemblance, and he mentions the occurrence of a mental spine in a certain specimen of *Paranthropus crassidens*. We are looking forward with great interest to his final publication.

There are, however, some differences, in which *Meganthropus* is more primitive. There is the basic pattern of the premolars and the first molar, which still have an undivided ridge between protoconid and metaconid, conditions which I could not detect in any of the South African species. The same is true of the presence of a paraconid on the second lower deciduous molar. The first lower premolar is of a more oval outline in the Australopithecinae, whereas in *Meganthropus* it is more angular, as in *Sinanthropus* and Heidelberg man.

The dental arch is probably very similar in both forms, as is evident from a new find, discovered last year[13]. This specimen, however, is crushed, and therefore not reliable.

There is not a single feature in the original *Meganthropus* jaw fragment which cannot be

爪哇猿人在以下方面显示出了与南方古猿亚科和类人猿同样的原始特征，包括臼齿的相对大小，从第一颗下臼齿到最后一颗下臼齿逐渐增大，以及上颌第二臼齿比第一臼齿大。但是傍人粗齿种的最后一颗上臼齿有增大的趋势，在人科（现代人的这一臼齿经常是完全缺少的）和类人猿中都没有发现这种现象。

乳齿齿系的研究对于确定物种的演化发展地位非常有价值。中国猿人和莫佐克托猿人的第一下乳臼齿具有 2 个主齿尖，在黑猩猩和猩猩中也是如此。第一种类型没有下内尖，这点在类人猿中很常见，在第二种类型中，下内尖很弱。观察的样本中，现代人的下内尖完全消失的情况仅为约 2%。南方古猿亚科的这一齿尖不仅达到了与现代人相同的发育程度（南方古猿非洲种中这一点尚未确定），而且这颗牙齿也具有完全臼齿化的趋势，这种趋势在德兰士瓦迩人的上臼齿和粗壮傍人的下臼齿中达到了最大的程度。后一类型中，除了牙齿的大小，很难依据其他特征将这颗牙与第二乳臼齿区分开来。现代人虽然存在一定程度的变异，但是在我们研究的大量现代牙齿中并没有观察到像这样的极端情况（博尔克收编，阿姆斯特丹）。

这一比较已经揭示了如此多的特征，它们必定被认为是过度特化的迹象，这足以将南方古猿亚科从爪哇猿人和智人的祖先中排除出去了。

南方古猿亚科与尚不完全清楚的爪哇魁人之间存在更大的相似性，它们之间的相似性如此之多，以至于最近鲁滨逊将爪哇的这个物种纳入了与南方古猿亚科相同的类群之中[2]。他指出二者具有非常大的相似性，尤其是在（纤维软骨）骨联合形成方面，他还提到了傍人粗齿种的一些标本中出现了颏棘。我们正怀着极大的兴趣期待他最终发表的结果。

但是也有一些差异表明魁人更加原始。它们具有最基本的前臼齿和第一臼齿模式，在下原尖和下后尖之间有尚未分开的脊，这是我在其他南非物种中都没有发现的。第二下乳磨牙有一个下前尖。南方古猿亚科的第一下前臼齿的轮廓比较椭圆，而魁人的第一前臼齿有较多的棱角，在中国猿人和海德堡人中也是如此。

去年的一个新发现表明这两种类型的齿弓可能非常相似[13]，但是这个样本已经压碎了，所以结果并不可靠。

最初发现的魁人颌骨破片上没有一个特征能与其他原始人类的颌骨匹配。南方

matched with other primitive human jaws. In the corresponding part of the *Australopithecus* mandible the two-rooted second premolar must already be regarded as a sign that it belongs to a different category. In fossil human jaws this condition has never been observed; in modern man it occurs in less than 0.02 percent of specimens. When more is known of *Meganthropus*, it will probably be found that there are more differences of significance.

However, there can be no doubt that *Meganthropus* and the Australopithecinae have a common ancestor. Such a form must have still had the "simian gap"—*vide Pithecanthropus*—relatively large canines and incisors, large first lower premolars, and a primitive deciduous dentition. Therefore, it will not fall into the group of the Australopithecinea *s. str.*, and for that reason I cannot agree with Robinson, who claims that the Australopithecinae are "ancestral to he euhominid group" (see ref. 2, p. 37).

Within this latter group there is a very strong tendency towards a reduction of the dentition, and parallel with it an exaggerated increase in brain capacity (Table 1). The same mesiodistal lengths are for *Plesianthropus transvaalensis* 44.0 mm., and for *Paranthropus crassidens* (average) no less than 48.4 mm., respectively.

Table 1. Mesiodistal length of the three lower molars

Lower Pleistocene:	*Meganthropus*	44.0 mm.
	Pithecanthropus modjokertensis	39.5 mm.
Middle Pleistocene:	*Sinanthropus pekinensis* (G)	37.7 mm.
	Homo heidelbergensis	36.5 mm.
Upper Pleistocene:	*Homo neanderthalensis* (Spy II)	34.0 mm.
Recent:	*Homo sapiens* (White, average)	32.5 mm.

Also in regard to the brain capacity the conditions seem fundamentally different. The capacity of the Australopithecinae is a controversial question; Broom gives estimates up to more than 1,000 c.c.[14], and Schepers even calculates "cephalization coefficients" (see Schepers, ref. 14). Let us not forget that only a single skull can be measured, *Plesianthropus* V, and that here the capacity is only 482 c.c.

Most probably in their absolute brain capacity the Australopithecinae bridge the gap which exists between the largest brain of the anthropoids (gorilla with 585 c.c.) and the smallest of the Hominidae (*Pithecanthropus erectus* II with 775 c.c.). There is, however, this important difference: the greatest brain capacity in the Australopithecinae goes together with the largest molars, whereas in man it goes with the smallest molars. We have tried to express this relation in a brain-molar coefficient[15]—brain capacity in cubic centimeters divided by the mesiodistal length of the three upper molars in millimetres, both measurements taken on the same skull—the results of which are given in Table 2.

古猿下颌骨相应部分的第二前臼齿具有 2 个齿根，这肯定早已被认为是它属于不同分类单元的标志。在化石人类的颌骨中，则从未见到过这种情况，它在现代人中的发生比例低于 0.02%。在对魁人有了更多的了解之后,可能会发现更多有意义的差异。

然而,毫无疑问魁人和南方古猿亚科具有共同的祖先。这一类型肯定还具有“猿的齿隙”（参看爪哇猿人）、相对较大的犬齿和门齿、大的第一下前臼齿，以及原始的乳齿齿系。因此不应该将其归到狭义的南方古猿亚科组群中，这就是我不能同意鲁滨逊意见的原因，他认为南方古猿亚科是“真正人类群体的祖先”（见参考文献 2，第 37 页）。

表 1 中年代较晚的组群齿系减小的趋势非常明显，与之相对应，脑量增加也十分明显。德兰士瓦迩人和傍人粗齿种（平均值）的近中远中径分别是 44.0 毫米和不低于 48.4 毫米。

表 1. 三颗下臼齿的近中远中径

下更新世	魁人	44.0 毫米
	莫佐克托猿人	39.5 毫米
中更新世	中国猿人北京种 (G)	37.7 毫米
	海德堡人	36.5 毫米
上更新世	尼安德特人 (Spy II)	34.0 毫米
近期	智人（白种人，均值）	32.5 毫米

至于脑量，情况似乎从根本上不同。南方古猿亚科的脑量尚存争议，布鲁姆估计其大于 1,000 毫升 [14]，舍佩尔斯甚至计算出了“脑发育系数”（见舍佩尔斯，参考文献 14)。但希望大家不要忘记，只能测量迩人 V 号这唯一一件头骨，其脑量只有 482 毫升。

南方古猿亚科很有可能在绝对脑量方面填补了类人猿的最大脑量（大猩猩是 585 毫升）和人科的最小脑量（直立猿人 II 的脑量是 775 毫升）之间存在的空缺。然而,这里有一个重要的差异,即南方古猿亚科的最大脑量与最大臼齿是同时出现的,而在人类中最大脑量却与最小臼齿一起出现。我们曾经尝试用脑 – 臼齿系数来表示这种关系 [15]，即用以立方厘米为单位的脑量除以以毫米为单位的三颗上臼齿的近中远中径，这两个数据都是对同一头骨测量得到的，结果见表 2。

Table 2. Brain-Molar Coefficients
(The numbers in brackets indicate the number of skulls measured)

Chimpanzee (7)	10.9-13.9	Average: 11.8
Orang (16)	9.8-12.4	10.9
Gorilla (10)	9.0-13.0	11.7
Plesianthropus V	13.4	
Pithecanthropus modjokertensis	25.8	
Pithecanthropus erectus	24.3	
Sinanthropus pekinensis XI	34.2	
Homo neanderthalensis (Steinheim)	36.7	
Homo sapiens (Europeans, 10)	33.5-57.1	47.3

As we expected, the modern anthropoids form a homogeneous group. The values for *Pithecanthropus* are estimates: a capacity of 1,000 c.c. was estimated by Weidenreich for the skull of *modjokertensis*, and for *erectus* we have used a dentition, not yet described, from a different individual. In Table 2 the anthropoids are sharply separated from the Hominidae; *Plesianthropus* is not intermediate, since it comes within the range of the anthropoids.

This coefficient has still another advantage. If we take a maximum of about 15 for the anthropoids, then the Australopithecinae with their large molars will still remain within the anthropoid group, even with a brain capacity of more than 700 c.c.

Two specimens of the large *Plesianthropus* from Swartkrans have a well-developed sagittal creast[15], which is not found in the smaller species. Apart from the fact that this must be taken as a sign of a limited brain capacity, it is to be noted that a sagittal crest in the anthropoids depends upon the absolute size of the species. It is absent from the small gibbon, very rare in male chimpanzees, normal in male oranges and practically always present in the male and often in the large female gorillas. That this structure appears among the Australopithecinae under the same conditions is a very important parallel to the anthropoids, and a significant difference from the Hominidae.

Thus the Australopithecinae apparently are a group of the Hominidae, which most probably did not rise much above the "anthropoid" level. The reduction of the dentition only affects the face; their increase in brain capacity is slight and depends upon the absolute size of the species; the possession of a sagittal crest in the large specimen parallels the development of the same structure in the anthropoids. It seems that towards the end of the Pliocene period the early Hominidae were separated into several branches—Australopithecinae in Africa, *Gigantopithecus* (and undescribed forms) in China, Pithecanthropi in Asia—and that only one of them, the Pithecanthropi, by a harmonious reduction of the whole dentition and—this is the most important point—by an exaggerated and accelerated increase of the brain capacity, gave rise to the Hominidae, of which group we are the most human members.

(**173**, 795-797; 1954)

表 2. 脑 – 臼齿系数

（括号中的数字表示测量的头骨编号）

黑猩猩 (7)	10.9~13.9	均值：11.8
猩猩 (16)	9.8~12.4	10.9
大猩猩 (10)	9.0~13.0	11.7
迩人 V	13.4	
莫佐克托猿人	25.8	
直立猿人	24.3	
中国猿人北京种 XI	34.2	
尼安德特人（施泰因海姆）	36.7	
智人 (欧洲人 , 10)	33.5~57.1	47.3

正如我们所期望的，现代类人猿形成了一个同质类群。爪哇猿人的估计值如下：魏登瑞根据莫佐克托猿人的头骨估计其脑量为 1,000 毫升，而对于直立猿人，我们则使用另外一个个体尚未被描述过的齿系来进行估算。表 2 中，类人猿明显与人科分离开了；迩人并不是介于中间，而是落在了类人猿的范围之内。

这一系数还有另外一个优点。如果我们对类人猿取最大值（大约 15），那么即使南方古猿亚科的脑量超过 700 毫升，这些具有大臼齿的南方古猿亚科也将依然位列于类人猿类群内。

斯瓦特克朗斯的两个大型迩人样本具有发育完好的矢状脊[15]，这一特征还没有在较小的物种中发现过。这肯定可以看作有限脑量的标志，此外还应该说明的是，类人猿的矢状脊取决于物种个体的绝对大小。小长臂猿没有这种矢状脊，在雄性黑猩猩中这种情况也很少见，而雄性猩猩中则很常见，实际上，雄性大猩猩总存在矢状脊，大型雌性大猩猩也常具有矢状脊。在同等条件下，南方古猿亚科中出现的这种结构与类人猿非常一致，而与人科则具有显著差异。

因此，很明显南方古猿亚科是人科的一个组群，很有可能在发生上它们并不比“类人猿”高等很多。齿系的减小只会影响到面部；它们脑量增加的幅度微小且依赖于物种个体的绝对大小；大型样本所具有的矢状脊与类人猿中同样结构的发育情况一致。可能在接近上新世末期时，早期人科分化成了几个支系——非洲的南方古猿亚科、中国的巨猿（以及其他没有描述过的类型）、亚洲的猿人，其中只有一种，即猿人的全齿系匀称地减小，另外最重要的一点是，其脑量以一种惊人的速度加速变大，由此产生了人科，在这一组群中，我们人类是最主要的成员。

（刘皓芳 崔娅铭 翻译；吴新智 审稿）

G. H. R. von Koenigswald: University of Utrecht.

References:

1. Gregory, W. K., and Hellman, M., *Ann. Transvaal Mus.*, **19**, 339 (1939).
2. Robinson, J. T., *Amer. J. Phys. Anthrop.*, **11**, 1 (1953).
3. Broom, R., "Finding the Missing Link", 74 (London, 1950).
4. Dart, R. A., *Amer. J. Phys. Anthrop.*, 7, 1 (1949).
5. Zapfe, H., *Palaeobiologica*, 7, 111 (1939).
6. Toerien, M. J., *S. Afric. J. Sci.*, **48**, 293 (1952).
7. von Koenigswald, G. H. R., Rep. Int. Geol. Congr. Great Britain 1948, part IX, 59 (1950).
8. del Campana, D., *Palaeontologia Italica*, **19**,189 (1913).
9. Remane, A., *Z. f. Anat. u. Entwicklungsgesch.*, **82**, 391 (1927).
10. Broom, R., and Robinson, J. T., *Transvaal Mus. Mem.*, **6**, 1 (1952).
11. Clark, W. E. Le Gros, *J. Roy. Anthrop. Inst.*, **80**, 37 (1952).
12. Visser, J. B., Diss. Zurich, 1 (1948).
13. Marks, P., *Madjalah Ilum Alam Untuk Indonesia*, **109**, 26 (1953).
14. Broom, R., Robinson, J. T., and Schepers, *Transvaal Mus. Mem.*, **4**, 1 (1950).
15. von Koenigswald, G. H. R., *Proc. Kon. Ned. Akad. Wetensch.*, B, **56**, 403 and 427 (1953): **57**, 85 (1954).

Structural Changes in Muscle during Contraction: Interference Microscopy of Living Muscle Fibres

A. F. Huxley and R. Niedergerke

Editor's Note

Here physiologists Andrew Huxley and Rolf Niedergerke from the University of Cambridge show that muscle fibres shorten as a result of the sliding between two sets of filaments containing the proteins myosin and actin. The researchers use interference microscopy to show that the width of thick, myosin-containing filaments called "*A*-bands" remain constant during muscle contraction, implying that the thin, actin-containing filaments of the "*I*-band" slide into the *A*-band when muscle shortens. The paper was published back-to-back with a manuscript by English biologists Hugh Huxley and Jean Hanson from the Massachusetts Institute of Technology, who used light microscopy to independently arrive at similar results. Together these studies lead to the "sliding filament" model of muscle, which is still widely accepted today.

IN spite of the numerous investigations which have been made into the changes of the striations of muscle when it contracts, there is little agreement at the present day on either the nature or the significance of these changes. Several factors contribute to this unsatisfactory position. The only contractions that could be studied in living muscle by the earlier workers[1] were the slow waves that occur in freshly isolated insect fibres; the broad striations and small diameter of these fibres are favourable for the interpretation of the microscope image, but the local nature of the contractions and the difficulty of applying passive stretch make it impossible to say whether the changes seen in the striations are accompaniments of "activation", of tension development or of shortening. Observations on fixed material, whether with visible light or with the electron microscope, are also subject to this limitation as well as to the uncertainties in the effect of the fixative. Isolated fibres from frog muscle, however, give satisfactory propagated twitches and tetani, in which activation is complete very early after the first stimulus[2], while tension develops more slowly even if the contraction is isometric, and changes of length, both during stimulation and in the resting muscle, can be controlled by holding the tendon ends. This preparation therefore provides a basis for correlating visible changes with the sequence of events which take place during a contraction, and Buchthal and his colleagues[3] have endeavoured to exploit this possibility. Their conclusions are, however, open to the objection that they used the ordinary light microscope, which cannot be expected to provide a reliable image of unstained striations (alternate bands of high and low refractive index) the repeat distance of which is 2-3 μ, in a fibre of 50-100 μ diameter.

肌肉收缩时的结构变化：使用干涉显微镜观察活体肌纤维

赫胥黎，尼德格克

编者按

在这篇文章中，剑桥大学的生理学家安德鲁·赫胥黎和罗尔夫·尼德格克指出，肌纤维缩短是由包含肌球蛋白和肌动蛋白的两套细丝间的滑动造成的。研究者利用干涉显微镜发现包含肌球蛋白丝的粗的 *A* 带的宽度在肌肉收缩过程中保持恒定，这暗示着当肌肉缩短时包含肌动蛋白丝的细的“*I* 带”滑入 *A* 带。紧随这篇文章之后的是来自麻省理工学院的英国生物学家休·赫胥黎和琼·汉森完成的一篇来稿，他们利用光学显微镜独立地得到了相同的结论。综合这些研究结果所得出的肌纤维“滑动细丝”模型至今仍被广泛认可。

尽管人们已经对肌肉收缩过程中肌肉条纹的变化进行了大量的研究，但是目前关于这些变化的本质或其重要性几乎没有取得一致的意见。这种并不令人满意的局面是由许多因素造成的。早期的研究人员[1]只能从新鲜分离的昆虫肌纤维的慢波中研究活体肌肉的收缩；这些肌纤维的条纹宽、直径小，适合用显微镜进行观察，但是由于其收缩存在局域性以及被动拉伸困难，研究人员无法分辨出条纹的变化是与纤维的“激活”、拉伸还是与缩短相伴随。对于固定材料的观察，无论用光学显微镜还是电子显微镜，也受这种限制的影响，而且固定效果也会带来不确定性。然而，从青蛙肌肉中分离出来的肌纤维则具有良好的颤搐和强直性收缩的能力，在这种肌纤维中，第一次刺激后激活能够很快完成[2]，而拉伸出现得更加缓慢（即使肌肉是等张收缩），并且在刺激过程中和静止肌肉中肌纤维长度的变化都可以通过固定肌腱的两端来控制。因此，这一准备工作为肉眼可见的变化同收缩过程中事件发生的顺序关联起来提供了根据，布克塔尔及其同事们在这方面作了尝试[3]。但是他们的结论容易受到质疑，因为他们使用的普通光学显微镜不能提供一张未染色的条纹（具有高折射率和低折射率的交替带）的可靠图片，在直径为 50 微米 ~100 微米的纤维中，这些条纹的重复距离为 2 微米 ~3 微米。

The phase-contrast microscope is equally unsuitable for a specimen of these dimensions; but an interference microscope in which the reference beam does not traverse the specimen would be expected to give a satisfactory "optical section" of the fibre. An instrument of this kind was therefore built, the optical components being made to our specification by Messrs. R. and J. Beck. The basic principle was first described by Smith[4] (see also Huxley[5]), but further developments were incorporated to allow a water-immersion objective of n.a. 0.9 to be used. Gross refraction effects due to the cylindrical shape of the fibre were abolished by adding serum albumin to the Ringer's solution to bring its refractive index close to the average value for the fibre contents. A solid cone of illumination, n.a. 0.5-0.6, was always employed. Under these conditions, the fibre was completely invisible with ordinary light, but with the interference arrangement an excellent image of the striations (and also of sarcoplasm, nuclei and granules) was obtained. The contrast between *A*-(higher refractive index) and *I*-bands could be controlled or reversed by changing the background path-difference between the two beams; the measured widths of the bands were independent of this adjustment (Fig. 1). The fibre was photographed on moving film by a series of ten flashes from a discharge tube at intervals of about 20 msec., and could be stimulated by pulses of current synchronized with these flashes.

(*a*)

−

(*b*)

+

10 μ

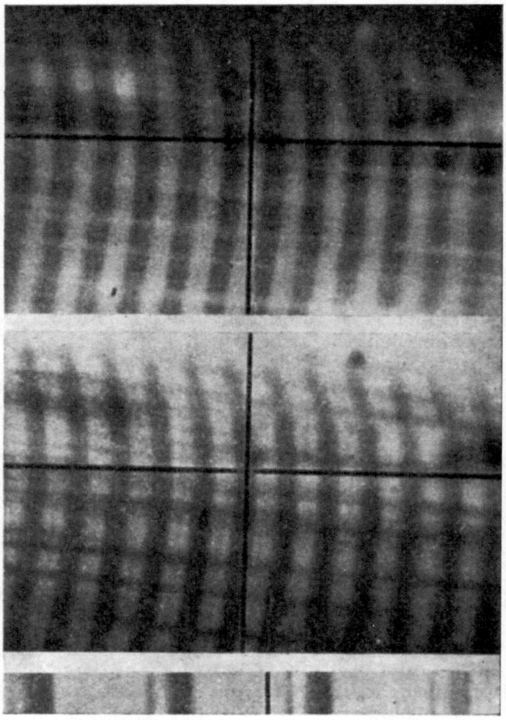

Fig. 1. Muscle fibre in negative (*a*) and positive (*b*) contrast. *A*-bands (higher refractive index) light in (*a*), dark in (*b*). Note that the threads of sarcoplasm have a refractive index slightly higher than even the *A*-bands. Sarcomere length, 3.0 μ

Passive stretch. The sarcomere length *s* could be changed by passive stretch or release from

相差显微镜同样不适合观察这种尺度的样品，而干涉显微镜则有可能给出一个令人满意的肌纤维"光学切片"，其参考光束并不穿透样品。因此，我们制造了这种类型的仪器，理查德·贝克先生和约瑟夫·贝克先生按照我们的要求制造了光学元件。史密斯首先描述了其基本原理[4]（也参考了赫胥黎的工作[5]），但我们对其进行了进一步改造，添加了一个数值孔径为 0.9 的水浸物镜。通过向林格液中添加血清白蛋白，以使溶液的折射率接近肌纤维含量的平均值来消除圆柱形肌纤维所带来的总折射效应。通常使用数值孔径为 0.5~0.6 的圆锥形聚光镜。在此条件下，用普通光源完全观察不到肌纤维，但是使用相干模式则可以获得极好的条纹图像（还有肌浆、细胞核以及颗粒体的图像）。可以通过改变两个光束之间的背景路径差来控制或者颠倒 *A* 带（折射率较高）和 *I* 带之间的明暗对比，这种调节不会影响带的测量宽度（图 1）。通过一个放电管以每隔约 20 毫秒闪光 10 次的速度进行系列闪拍，将纤维图像照到移动的底片上，信号可以通过与这些闪拍同步的脉冲电流而得到加强。

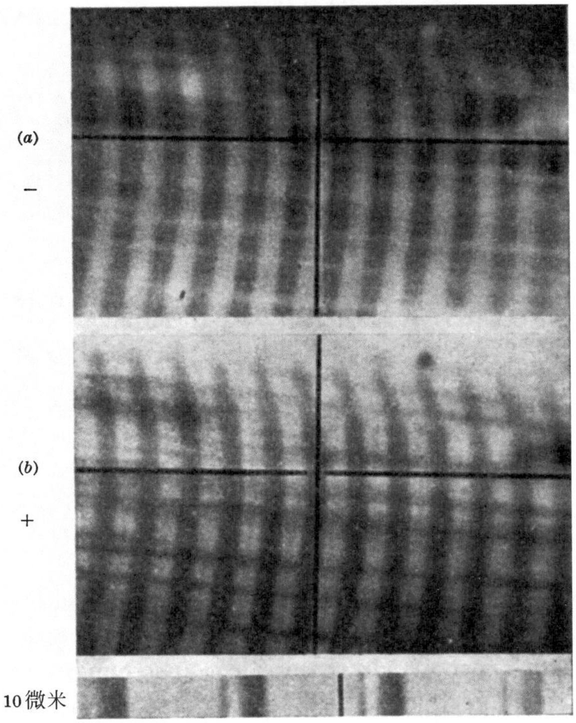

图 1. 肌纤维的负反差（*a*）和正反差（*b*）图片。（*a*）图中亮的部分和（*b*）图中暗的部分是 *A* 带（折射率较高）。请注意肌浆丝的折射率甚至比 *A* 带略高。肌节长度为 3.0 微米。

被动拉伸　通过被动拉伸或者松弛，肌节长度 *s* 能够从大约 2.0 微米变化到

about 2.0 to 4.2 μ, the value at the extended length in the body being 2.5 μ[6]. Almost the whole of this change of length took place in the *I*-bands (Fig. 2). The measured width of each *A*-band remained constant at 1.4-1.5 μ except for a fall to about 1.3 μ as *s* was reduced in the range 2.5-2.0 μ; but this fall may well not be real, as its amount is less than the resolving power of the optical system. When a fibre was stretched rapidly (20-30 percent in 5 msec.) the new ratio of *A*- to *I*-band widths appeared to be established without delay (less than 2 msec.).

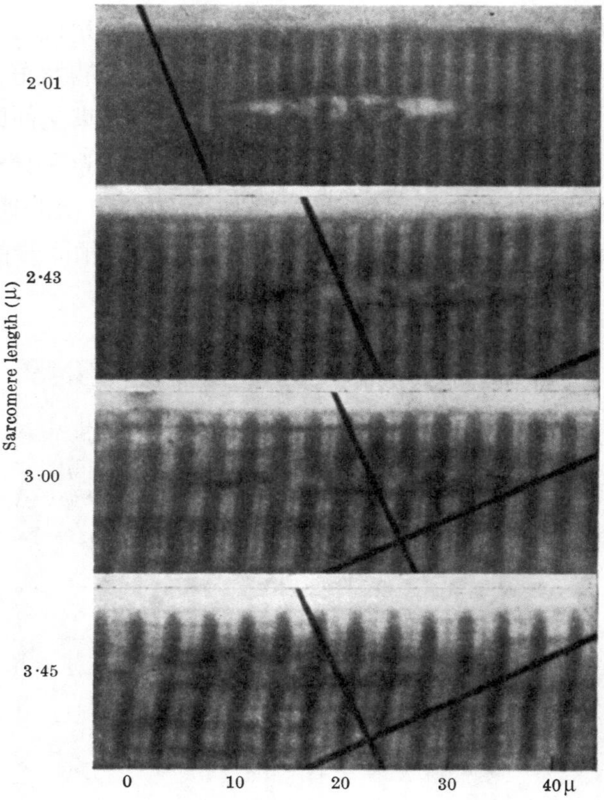

Fig. 2. Passive stretch of a muscle fibre. Positive contrast (*A*-bands dark). Sarcomere lengths indicated beside the photographs. Almost all the change of length is in the *I*-bands (light)

Isometric twitches. Fibres were stimulated at a wide range of lengths with the tendon ends held stationary, and the twitch tensions, measured simultaneously with the *RCA* 5734 transducer, were normal. No change in the widths of the bands could be detected, except that when slight shortening of the region of the fibre in the field of view took place the changes were similar to those in isotonic shortening of the same extent.

Isotonic contractions (Fig. 3). Fibres were photographed during twitches and short tetani under isotonic conditions, with various initial lengths up to 3.2 μ per sarcomere. As in passive shortening, it was the *I*-bands that became narrower, the band-width of *A* being constant down to a sarcomere length of s = 2.5 μ and falling only slightly down to s = 2.0 μ.

4.2 微米，在体内延伸长度值为 2.5 微米[6]。几乎全部的肌节长度的变化都产生于 *I* 带（图 2）。每个 *A* 带的测量宽度均恒定维持在 1.4 微米 ~1.5 微米，只有 *s* 降到 2.5 微米 ~2.0 微米时 *A* 带的测量宽度才会降到 1.3 微米左右；但是这种下降很可能是不真实的，因为它的数值低于光学系统的分辨率。当肌纤维被快速拉伸时（5 毫秒内拉伸 20 %~30%），*A* 带与 *I* 带宽度新的比值也会即时确立（延迟在 2 毫秒以内）。

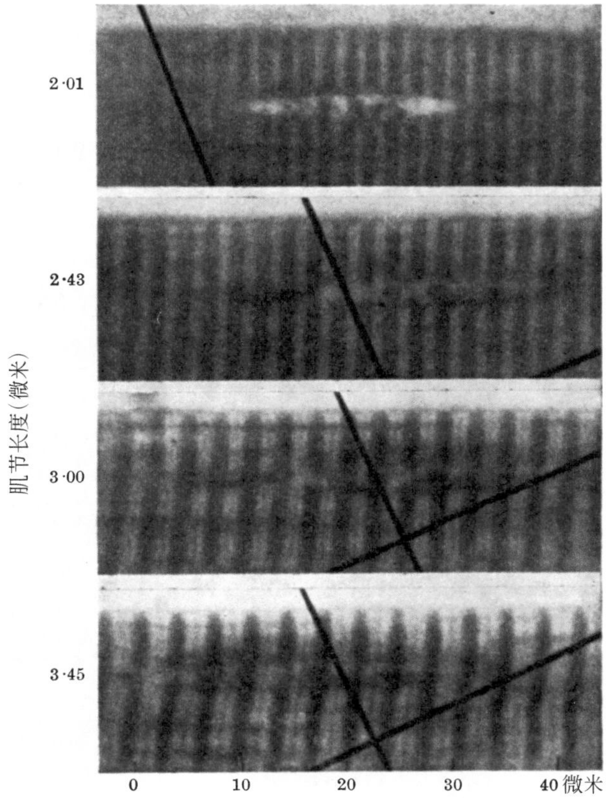

图 2. 肌纤维的被动拉伸。此图为正反差成像（*A* 带为暗的部分）。肌节长度在图旁标注出来。几乎所有长度的改变都产生于 *I* 带（亮的部分）。

等长颤搐　固定两端肌腱并刺激肌纤维使其处于不同长度，同时用 *RCA* 5734 换能器检测它的颤搐张力，发现其均处于正常范围。但是检测不到条带宽度的变化，只有当视野内肌纤维区域发生轻微缩短时，这样的变化才与同等程度的等张缩短中的变化类似。

等张收缩（图 3）　在等张条件下，对处于颤搐和短促的强直性收缩过程中具有不同起始长度的肌纤维（肌节长度长达 3.2 微米）进行了拍照。和被动缩短时一样，*I* 带变窄，当肌节长度 *s* 缩短到 2.5 微米时，*A* 带的宽度维持恒定；当肌节长度 *s* 缩短到 2.0 微米时，*A* 带的宽度略微下降。在进一步的收缩中，用电影摄影研究了持续

On further shortening, studied largely by ciné photography of slow contractions induced by constant-current stimulation, *A*-band width decreased definitely in all cases; but there were additional phenomena which were not the same in every experiment. The following sets of changes were observed on several occasions:

(*a*) Striations became extremely faint on shortening beyond a sarcomere length of about 1.8 μ (cf. Speidel[7]).

(*b*) The dense band narrowed to about half the sarcomere length, after which both bands narrowed in proportion.

(*c*) At $s = 1.8$ μ, a very narrow dense band was visible at the centre of the former *A*-band, and on shortening to $s = 1.7$ μ additional dense lines appeared midway between these (cf. Jordan's observations on stained preparations[8]).

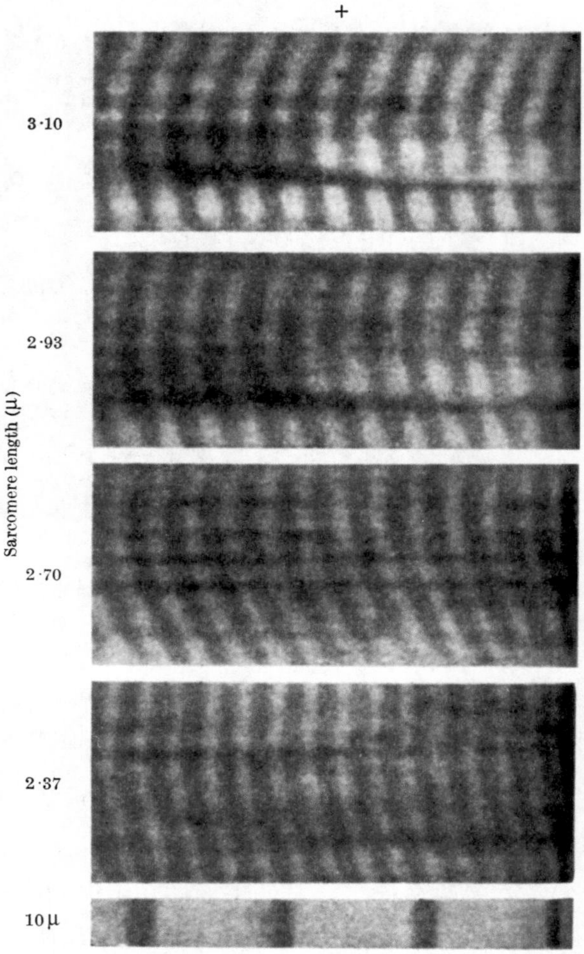

Fig. 3. Muscle fibre during a short isotonic tetanus. Positive contrast (*A*-bands dark). As in passive stretch (Fig. 2), the *A*-bands remain of almost constant width

的电流刺激所引发的慢速收缩，在所有实验中 *A* 带宽度显著变窄；不过在各个实验组中也存在另外一些不同的实验现象。以下是多次观察到的变化：

（*a*）当缩短超出一个肌节长度（约 1.8 微米）时，条纹会变得非常模糊（参见斯派德尔[7]）。

（*b*）致密条带收缩到约半个肌节长度后，两条带成比例缩短。

（*c*）当 s=1.8 微米时，在前面的 *A* 带的中心可以看见一条非常窄的致密条带，当缩短到 s=1.7 微米时，在两个致密条带中间又会出现一条致密的线（参见乔丹对染色样品的观察[8]）。

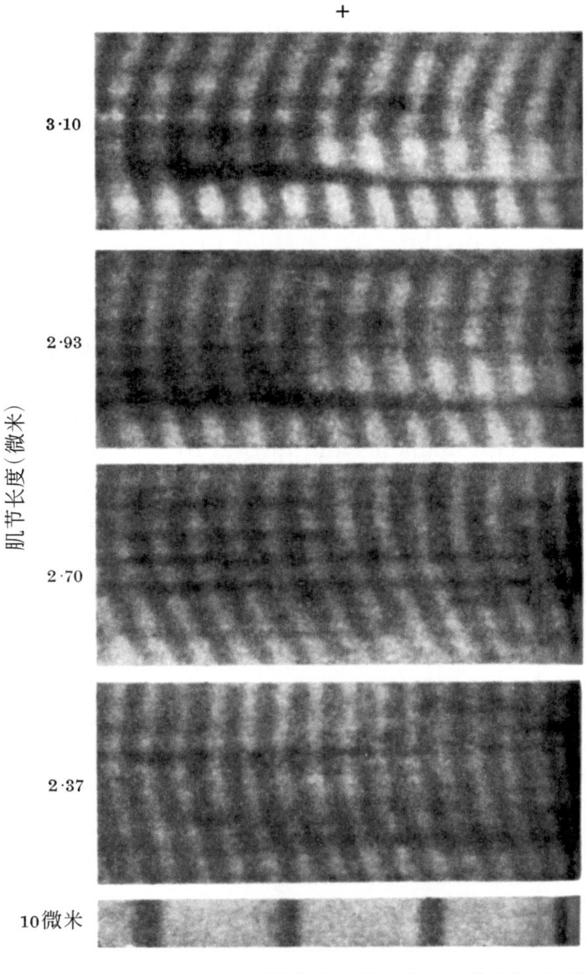

图 3. 肌纤维在短时间内等张强直性收缩时的照片。此图为正反差成像（*A* 带为暗的部分）。当被动拉伸时（图 2），*A* 带的宽度几乎维持不变。

The similarity of the changes during passive shortening and during isotonic contraction, and the absence of change during isometric twitches, show that the changes in the ratio of widths of the *A*- and *I*-band depend simply on the length of the fibre, and are unaffected by "activation" or by tension development as such. The approximate constancy of *A*-band width under a wide range of conditions (including shortening within the physiological range) agrees with the observations of Krause and of Engelmann[1], and also with those of H. E. Huxley and J. Hanson on separated myofibrils reported in the accompanying communication, though it is in conflict with the results of Buchthal *et al.*[3]. The natural conclusion, that the material which gives the *A*-bands their high refractive index and also their birefringence is in the form of submicroscopic rods of definite length, was put forward by Krause, and receives strong support from the observations reported here. The identification of this material as myosin[9], and the existence of filaments (presumably actin) extending through the *I*-bands and into the adjacent *A*-bands, as shown in many electron microscope studies, makes very attractive the hypothesis that during contraction the actin filaments are drawn into the *A*-bands, between the rodlets of myosin. (This point of view was reached independently by ourselves and by H. E. Huxley and Jean Hanson in the summer of 1953. It has already been mentioned by one of those authors[10] and is further discussed by them in the accompanying article.)

If a relative force between actin and myosin is generated at each of a series of points in the region of overlap in each sarcomere, then the tension per filament should be proportional to the number of these points, and therefore to the width of this zone of overlap. If the myosin rods are 1.5 μ long and the actin filaments 2.0 μ, the isometric tetanus tension should fall linearly as the fibre is stretched over the range of sarcomere lengths from 2.0 to 3.5 μ; this is in fair agreement with observation[11]. In arthropod striated muscle, there is a wide range of sarcomere lengths *in situ*, and narrowness of striation appears to be correlated with high speed of contraction[12]. This would be expected if the relative velocity between actin filaments and myosin rods in any one zone of overlap were the same for muscles of different sarcomere lengths, since the number of sarcomeres shortening in series per unit length is inversely proportional to sarcomere length. On this basis it would also be expected that the muscle with longer sarcomeres would be capable of producing a greater tension, but we are not aware of any experimental results on this point.

(**173**, 971-973; 1954)

A. F. Huxley and R. Niedergerke: Physiological Laboratory, University of Cambridge.

References:

1. Krause, W., "Die motorischen Endplatten der qnergestreiften Muskelfasern" (Hahn, Hannover, 1869). Engelmann. T. W., *Pflüg. Arch. ges. Physiol.*, **23**, 571 (1880). Rollett, A., *Denkschr. Akad. Wiss. Wien*, **58**, 41 (1891). Hürthle, K., *Pflüg. Arch. ges. Physiol.*, **126**, 1 (1909).

2. Hill, A. V., *Proc. Roy. Soc.*, B, **136**, 399 (1949).

3. Buchthal, F., Knappeis, G. G., and Lindhard, J., *Skand. Arch Physiol.*, **73**, 163 (1936). Buchthal, F., and Knappeis, G. G., *Acta Physiol. Scand.*, **6**, 123 (1943).

4. Smith, F. H., prov. Pat. Spec. No. 21996 (1947); complete Pat. Spec. No. 639014 (1950).

被动缩短和等张收缩过程中变化的相似性以及等长颤搐过程中没有变化都表明 *A* 带与 *I* 带宽度之比的改变仅仅取决于肌纤维的长度，而不受“激活”或拉伸这类因素的影响。*A* 带宽度在多种条件下（包括在生理范围内的缩短）几乎都保持恒定，这虽然与布克塔尔等人 [3] 的实验结果矛盾，但是与克劳斯和恩格尔曼 [1] 的观察结果一致，也与赫胥黎和汉森在随后的文章中对分离出的肌原纤维的研究结果一致。本文观察到的现象强有力地支持了克劳斯提出的结论，即 *A* 带的高折射率和双折射性是由长度一定的亚显微棒状物质造成的。这种物质被证明是肌球蛋白 [9]，而且在许多电子显微镜研究中都观察到有一种细丝（可能是肌动蛋白）贯穿 *I* 带并进入相邻的 *A* 带中。基于这些发现，我们提出了一个很有吸引力的假设，即在收缩过程中，肌动蛋白丝被牵拉进肌球蛋白棒形结构间的 *A* 带。（这一观点由我们组和赫胥黎及琼·汉森在 1953 年夏天分别独立提出。在随后的文章中他们进行了深入的探讨，并且他们中有一位作者已经提及过这一观点 [10]。）

如果肌动蛋白与肌球蛋白之间的相对作用力产生于每个肌节中重叠部分的一系列接触点，那么每根细丝的张力应该与这些接触点的数量成正比，并因此与重叠区域的宽度成正比。如果肌球蛋白棒长 1.5 微米，肌动蛋白丝长 2.0 微米，那么当肌纤维拉伸到超过肌节长度达 2.0 微米 ~3.5 微米时，等长强直性收缩张力应该呈线性下降，这与实验结果非常一致 [11]。在节肢动物体内，横纹肌的肌节长度差别很大，并且窄条纹似乎与高收缩速度有关 [12]。由于每单位长度上连续缩短的肌节数目与肌节长度成反比，我们可以猜想，对于具有不同肌节长度的肌肉，任何重叠区域中肌动蛋白丝和肌球蛋白棒间的相对速度是相同的。在这个基础上，我们也可以预期肌肉的肌节越长，肌肉所能产生的张力也应该越大，不过关于这一点我们还不知道任何实验结果。

（张锦彬 翻译；周筠梅 审稿）

5. Huxley, A. F., *J. Physiol.*, **117**, 52*P* (1952).
6. Sandow, A., *J. Cell. Comp. Physiol.*, **9**, 37 (1936).
7. Speidel, C. C., *Amer. J. Anat.*, **65**, 471 (1939).
8. Jordan, H. E., *Amer. J. Anat.*, **55**, 117 (1934).
9. Hasselbach, W., *Z. Naturforsch.*, **8b**, 449 (1953). Hanson, J., and Huxley, H. E., *Nature*, **172**, 530 (1953).
10. Huxley, H. E., *Biochim. Biophys. Acta*, **12**, 387 (1953).
11. Ramsey, R. W., and Street, S. F., *J. Cell. Comp. Physiol.*, **15**, 11 (1940).
12. Jasper, H. H., and Pezard, A., *C. R. Acad. Sci., Paris*, **198**, 499 (1934).

Changes in the Cross-Striations of Muscle during Contraction and Stretch and Their Structural Interpretation

H. Huxley and J. Hanson

Editor's Note

In this paper, British biologists Hugh Huxley and Jean Hanson from the Massachusetts Institute of Technology use light microscopy to establish a sliding filament model of muscle contraction. The two researchers had previously shown that myosin is located in the thick filaments of the "*A*-band", whilst actin is located in the thin filaments of the "*I*-band". Here they photograph striated muscle fibres contracting on microscope slides and establish that the width of the *A*-band remains constant. They also show that the driving force behind muscle contraction is the splitting (hydrolysis) of molecules of ATP.

IN recent papers[1-3], we have described evidence concerning the location and arrangement of the two principal structural proteins, actin and myosin, in striated muscle at rest length. This evidence indicates that myosin is located in the anisotropic or *A*-bands, in the form of longitudinal filaments about 110 A. in diameter, spaced out in a hexagonal array 440 A. apart; these filaments are continuous from end to end of the *A*-band, and appear to be responsible for its high density and birefringence. Actin, on the other hand, is present in both the *A*-bands and the relatively isotropic or *I*-bands, in the form of filaments about 40 A. in diameter; these extend from the *Z*-lines, through the *I*-bands, and into the *A*-bands, where they lie between the myosin filaments and terminate on either side of the *H*-zone; the myosin filaments seem to have a somewhat greater thickness in this zone. Hasselbach[4] has reached similar conclusions about the location of actin and myosin, though his concept of the details of their arrangement is different from ours. We shall now describe evidence that during stretch, and during contraction down to about 65 percent of rest length, the length of the *A*-bands remains constant within the limits of accuracy of our measurements (5-10 percent), the changes in length of the muscle being taken up by changes in the length of the *I*-bands alone; further shortening beyond the point where the *I*-bands vanish (about 65 percent of the rest length) is accompanied by the formation of contraction bands where the *A*-bands have come into contact with the *Z*-lines. These changes appear to take place by a process in which actin filaments slide out of or into the parallel array of myosin filaments in the *A*-bands; as shortening proceeds, the actin filaments fold up in the *A*-band, and this folding continues after the *I*-bands have been fully retracted. The myosin filaments remain at constant length until forced to shorten by excessive contraction of the sarcomeres.

肌肉收缩与拉伸过程中的横纹变化及结构上的解释

赫胥黎，汉森

编者按

在这篇文章中，来自麻省理工学院的英国生物学家休·赫胥黎和琼·汉森通过光学显微镜建立了肌肉收缩的滑动细丝模型。之前这两位研究者指出肌球蛋白位于“*A* 带”的粗肌丝中，而肌动蛋白位于“*I* 带”的细肌丝中。本文中他们通过对显微镜载玻片上的横纹肌纤维收缩过程进行拍照，证明了 *A* 带的宽度保持恒定。他们也指出肌肉收缩的动力是 ATP 分子裂解（水解）。

在最近的几篇文章中[1-3]，我们描述了关于两个主要的结构蛋白——肌动蛋白和肌球蛋白——在静息长度的横纹肌中的位置和排布方式的证据。这个证据表明肌球蛋白位于各向异性带或 *A* 带中，以直径约为 110 埃的纵向细丝形式存在，组成相互之间间隔 440 埃的六边形。从 *A* 带的这一端到那一端，这些细丝是连续的，使得 *A* 带具有高密度性和双折射性的特点。另一方面，肌动蛋白在 *A* 带和相对呈现为各向同性带或 *I* 带中都有分布。肌动蛋白相互聚集成直径约 40 埃的细丝，这些细丝从 *Z* 线开始伸展，穿过 *I* 带，进入 *A* 带。肌动蛋白丝位于肌球蛋白丝之间并终止于 *H* 区任何一边。在 *H* 区中，肌球蛋白丝的密度似乎更高。关于肌动蛋白和肌球蛋白的位置，哈塞尔巴赫[4]也得到类似的结论，不过这一结论在肌球蛋白与肌动蛋白的具体排布方式上与我们的模型有一定的差异。现在我们将给出证据，即在肌肉拉伸和收缩到静息长度的 65%的过程中，在我们测量的精度范围内（5% ~10%），*A* 带的长度始终保持不变；而肌纤维长度的变化都源自 *I* 带长度的改变。当肌纤维继续缩短到 *I* 带消失时（约为静息长度的 65%）会伴随形成收缩带，*A* 带与 *Z* 线在此相接触。这些变化似乎是由肌动蛋白丝滑出或滑进平行排布于 *A* 带的肌球蛋白丝而引起的：当肌肉收缩时，肌动蛋白丝折叠进 *A* 带中，在 *I* 带完全收缩之后这个过程还会继续进行；而肌球蛋白丝的长度保持不变，直到肌节过度收缩时才被迫缩短。

Previous work on the changes in cross-striation accompanying stretch or contraction (reviewed by Jordan[5] and Buchthal, Knappeis and Lindhard[6]) has given results which in general we consider to be unreliable, for the following reasons. Observations made on intact muscle fibres in conventional light microscopes are liable to be misleading because of optical artefacts due to the thickness of the fibres. (This difficulty has been surmounted by the technique described by A. F. Huxley and R. Niedergerke in the accompanying paper.) Furthermore, normal contraction is so rapid that the changes taking place *during* the process are difficult to see and record. If fixed and sectioned material is used, it is possible to avoid optical artefacts and the necessity for rapid observation, but other kinds of artefacts are introduced. In spite of all these considerations, a number of workers, notably Speidel[7], have given accounts of changes of band pattern during stretch and contraction which we recognize as generally correct; but they do not establish the details of the changes with the precision necessary for satisfactory interpretation.

In order to avoid optical artefacts, we have used isolated myofibrils about 2 μ in diameter prepared by blending glycerol-extracted rabbit psoas muscle[8]. They are admirable objects for high-resolution microscopy in phase-contrast illumination or polarized light, and will contract when treated with adenosine triphosphate[9]. This contraction is a much slower process than contraction *in vivo*, and therefore provides favourable circumstances for detailed observation of the band changes taking place. The evidence that the mechanism of contraction in glycerol-extracted muscle treated with adenosine triphosphate is similar to that of normal contraction in living muscle has already been adequately discussed by Szent-Györgyi[8] and Weber and Portzehl[10]. We have also devised a simple technique for stretching isolated fibrils during observation. A suspension of fibrils, mounted as a very thin layer on a slide under a coverslip, is examined in the microscope until a fibril is found with one end embedded in a fibre fragment adhering to the coverslip, and its other end in a fragment attached to the slide. Movement of the coverslip in the appropriate direction will then produce the desired stretch or will permit the fibril to shorten if adenosine triphosphate is present. Very small movements can be produced with great ease by gentle pressure on the edge of the coverslip, for the thin layer of liquid provides smooth and highly viscous lubrication.

Photographs used for measurement were taken on microfile film at a magnification of ×370 or ×550, and an apochromatic phase-contrast objective of n.a. 1.15 was employed.

Contraction

We have studied and obtained photographic records of the details of contraction in the following systems:

以前曾有人对肌肉拉伸或收缩过程中的横纹变化进行过研究（参见乔丹[5]以及布克塔尔、纳培斯和林哈德[6]的综述），并取得了一些结果，但总体上我们认为这些结果是不可靠的，原因如下：由于肌纤维本身的厚度，使用普通光学显微镜对完整的肌纤维进行观察很容易被光学假象误导。（这一难题已经被赫胥黎和尼德格克在相关文章中所述的技术克服。）此外，肌肉的收缩是一个非常迅速的过程，人们很难对这个过程中发生的变化进行观察和记录。如果将样品固定并切片后再观察，虽然可以避免光学假象和需要快速观察的问题，但又引入了其他假象。尽管存在这些难题，许多研究人员特别是斯派德尔[7]对肌肉拉伸和收缩过程中条带样式的变化还是给出了解释，并且给出了我们认为大体正确的结论。但是，由于他们没有描述出具有足够精度的变化细节，所以未给出令人满意的解释。

为了避免出现光学假象，我们用混合甘油抽提的方法从兔腰大肌[8]中分离出直径约2微米的肌原纤维。这种纤维保持了收缩活性（在加入腺苷三磷酸后可以收缩[9]），非常适合用高分辨率相差显微镜或偏振光显微镜来观察。与体内收缩相比，这种收缩是一个较为缓慢的过程，因此为详细观察发生的条带变化提供了有利的条件。森特–哲尔吉[8]、韦伯和波策尔[10]已经充分论证了通过甘油抽提的肌肉在加入腺苷三磷酸后收缩的机制和活体肌肉正常收缩机制相似的证据。在观察中我们还设计了一种简单的拉伸分离的纤维的方法。我们首先将肌原纤维悬浮液滴到载玻片上，然后盖上盖玻片，使之铺展成很薄的一层。在显微镜下观察，寻找一端连在盖玻片上而另一端连在载玻片上的肌原纤维。往适宜的方向移动盖玻片就会产生期望的拉伸，或者在腺苷三磷酸存在的情况下肌原纤维将缩短。由于液体的薄层具有平滑和高黏的润滑作用，因此轻压盖玻片的边缘就可以很容易地产生小的位移。

所有的图片都是使用微缩胶片进行拍摄的，放大倍数为370倍或550倍。使用的是数值孔径为1.15的消色相差物镜。

收　缩

在下列系统中我们对肌肉收缩过程的细节进行了研究，并获得了一些图片记录：

(1) Fibrils contracting freely at room temperature (about 22 °C.) in 5×10^{-4} *M* adenosine triphosphate, 0.1 *M* potassium chloride, 10^{-3} *M* magnesium chloride, *p*H 7.0.

(2) Fibrils contracting freely at room temperature in a series of steps achieved by irrigating them with a succession of small amounts of a very dilute solution of adenosine triphosphate (5×10^{-6} *M*), irrigation being stopped as soon as the required degree of shortening had taken place.

(3) Fibrils contracting freely at a low temperature (about 2 °C.) in adenosine triphosphate in the almost complete absence of magnesium ions, when shortening takes place very slowly.

(4) Fibrils contracting as in (1) but held at both ends so that shortening is controlled.

Cinephotography was used for system 1; but in systems 2-4 it was possible to take "still" photographs on fine-grain film. In the first three systems the fibrils were contracting against virtually zero load and showed identical changes of band pattern. System 4 provided information about isometric contraction, and it was found that the changes of band pattern differed in some details from those recorded during contraction against zero load.

During contraction of single fibrils against zero load, we have observed the following changes in band patterns (illustrated in Figs. 1-4). The *I*-bands shorten from a resting length of approximately 0.8 μ until they disappear completely. During this process, the length of the *A*-bands remains constant at approximately 1.5 μ. Changes of density within the *A*-band do, however, occur. The *H*-zone, originally of low density, first becomes indistinguishable from the rest of the *A*-band, and is then replaced (at about 85 percent rest length) by a narrow zone which is denser than the rest of the *A*-band. At a slightly shorter sarcomere length (about 80 percent rest length), a very dense line becomes visible at either end of the *A*-band. The overall density of the *A*-bands decreases as the fibril diameter increases during shortening. When the *I*-bands disappear at about 65 percent rest length, contraction bands form at the lines of contact of adjacent *A*-bands. It is interesting to note that contraction down to 65 percent of the rest length covers the usual range of physiological shortening. With the further shortening which can usually be produced in isolated fibrils, the contraction bands become denser; during this process (or in some cases just before the *I*-bands disappear) the dense zone in the middle of the sarcomere splits into two lines which merge with the incoming contraction bands at approximately 30 percent rest length.

（1）室温（约 22 ℃）下，在含有 5×10^{-4} 摩尔 / 升腺苷三磷酸、0.1 摩尔 / 升氯化钾和 10^{-3} 摩尔 / 升氯化镁的 pH 值为 7.0 的溶液中肌原纤维自由收缩。

（2）连续使用少量低浓度（5×10^{-6} 摩尔 / 升）的腺苷三磷酸冲洗肌原纤维，当纤维缩短到目的长度时停止冲洗，通过这一系列步骤能获得室温下肌原纤维的自由收缩。

（3）在低温（约 2 ℃）、几乎没有镁离子的条件下，加入腺苷三磷酸后观察肌原纤维的自由收缩（此时肌原纤维的收缩会非常缓慢）。

（4）肌原纤维收缩，如同系统（1），但要固定肌原纤维的两端以便控制收缩。

我们在系统（1）中使用了电影摄影技术，但在系统（2）~（4）中则可以用微粒胶片拍摄“静态”照片。在前三个实验中，肌原纤维实际上都是在零负载的条件下进行自由收缩，因此呈现出一致的条带样式的变化。系统（4）提供了关于等长收缩的信息，其呈现出的条带样式的变化与零负载条件下条带样式的变化在一些细节上有所不同。

我们观察到单个肌原纤维在零负载下收缩时，其条带样式呈现出下列变化，如图 1~图4 所示。*I* 带从约为 0.8 微米的静息长度逐渐缩短直至它们完全消失，而 *A* 带的长度则始终保持恒定（约为 1.5 微米）。但在这个过程中，*A* 带的密度确实发生了变化。*A* 带中原本密度较低的 *H* 区在收缩后与 *A* 带中其他区域的界限开始变得不明显。当收缩至约为静息长度的 85%时，*H* 带被一条很窄的比 *A* 带其他部位密度都大的带所取代。当肌节的长度收缩到约为静息长度的 80%时，在 *A* 带的两端会出现一条高密度的线。肌原纤维的直径随着收缩过程逐渐变大，而 *A* 带的总密度呈逐渐减小的趋势。此外，*I* 带收缩至约为静息长度的 65%时会消失，在与相邻的 *A* 带接触的地方会出现一条新的收缩带。有趣的是，我们注意到，达到静息长度的 65% 的收缩覆盖了生理状态下肌肉收缩的通常范围。分离得到的肌原纤维还可以进一步缩短，这使得收缩带的密度变得更高。在这个过程中（或者在 *I* 带恰好要消失前的一些情况下），肌节中部的密度区域分裂成两条带，当收缩到约为静息长度的 30% 时，这两条带会与新形成的收缩带合并。

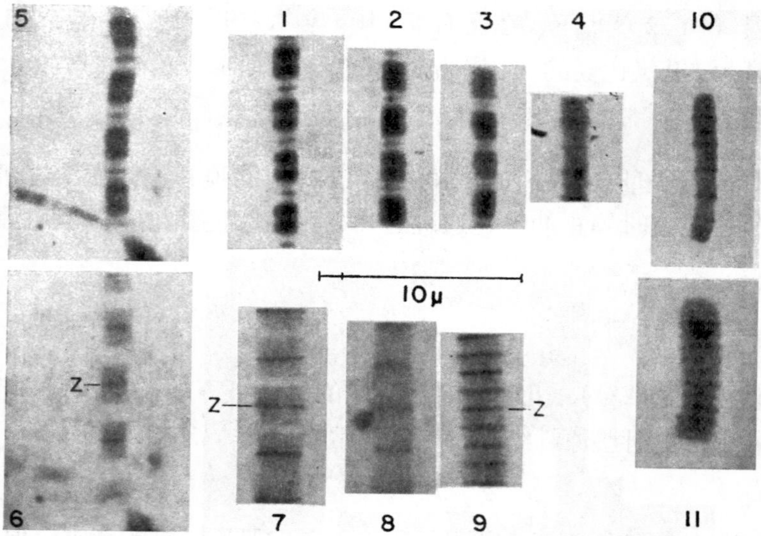

Myofibrils photographed in phase contrast. Magnification, 4,000 ×. Photographs of extracted fibrils are printed so as to give adequate contrast, and the fibrils are in fact much less dense than they appear here

Figs. 1-4. The same four sarcomeres of one fibril photographed during contraction induced by adenosine triphosphate from rest length down to 50 percent rest length, when contraction bands have formed

Figs. 5 and 6. Stretched fibril (115 percent rest length) before (Fig. 5) and after (Fig. 6) extraction of myosin

Figs.7, 8 and 9. Fibrils after extraction of myosin. Fig. 7: rest length. Fig. 8: 90 percent rest length. Fig. 9: 75 percent rest length

Figs. 10 and 11. Fibril with contraction bands (50 percent rest length) before (Fig. 10) and after (Fig. 11) extraction of myosin

Fibrils prepared from muscle which was allowed to shorten to equilibrium length (~80 percent rest length) before glycerol extraction usually lack the *H*-zones characteristic of rest-length fibrils, and have correspondingly shorter sarcomere lengths. Suspensions of untreated fibrils also include some specimens with sarcomere lengths down to about 65 percent of the rest length. Contraction presumably took place while the muscle was still excitable before glycerol extraction. Such fibrils exhibit the same characteristic band patterns and band lengths as those recorded for each sarcomere length during contraction induced by adenosine triphosphate.

During isometric contraction of isolated fibrils in adenosine triphosphate (achieved by holding the ends of the fibrils) the lengths of the *A*- and *I*-bands do not change. However, a narrow dark zone appears in the centre of the *A*-band (as in free contraction) as though some translation of material within the sarcomere were taking place, presumably accompanied by stretch of a series elastic component. This phenomenon is not observed in fibrils that are attached along their whole length to the coverslip or slide.

Stretch

We have found that isolated fibrils can stretch by two different processes, depending on

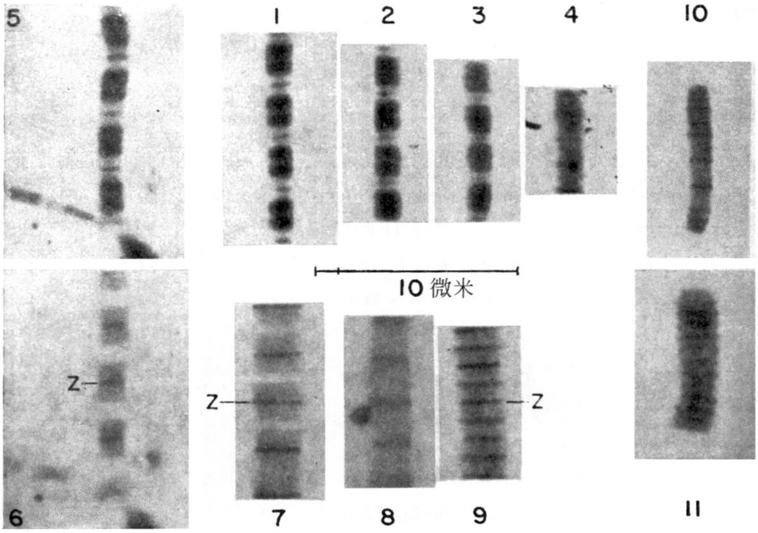

使用相差显微镜对肌原纤维进行 4,000 倍放大拍摄。为了获得适当的对比度，我们将提取的肌原纤维的照片打印了出来。实际观察到的肌原纤维的密度比图中所示的要低一些。

图 1~ 图 4. 在腺苷三磷酸的诱导下，同一肌原纤维的 4 个肌节在不同收缩程度时的照片，由静息长度一直收缩到静息长度的 50%（此时收缩带已经形成）。

图 5 和图 6. 肌球蛋白被抽提前（图 5）和被抽提后（图 6 ）拉伸的肌原纤维（静息长度的 115%）。

图 7、图 8 和图 9. 肌球蛋白被抽提后的肌原纤维。图 7 : 静息长度；图 8 : 静息长度的 90% ；图 9 : 静息长度的 75%。

图 10 和图 11. 肌球蛋白被抽提前（图 10）和被抽提后（图 11）具有收缩带的肌原纤维（静息长度的 50%）。

在甘油抽提前，从缩短到平衡长度（约为静息长度的 80%）的肌肉中制备出来的肌原纤维通常缺少静息长度的肌原纤维特征性的 *H* 区。相应地，其肌节长度也较短；未处理过的肌原纤维的悬浮液中也含有长度只有静息长度 65% 的肌节。收缩可能发生在甘油抽提前肌肉仍具有应激性时。这些肌原纤维显示了同样的特征性条带样式和条带长度，这与腺苷三磷酸诱导的收缩中各肌节长度的记录结果一致。

分离得到的肌原纤维在腺苷三磷酸的诱导下发生等长收缩（通过固定肌原纤维的两端来实现）时，其 *A* 带和 *I* 带的长度并没有发生改变。但是，在 *A* 带的中央会出现一个窄的暗区(与自由收缩类似)。这似乎表明在肌节中发生了某种物质的移动，并且很可能是伴随着串联弹性组分的拉伸。在全长都被连在盖玻片或载玻片上的纤维中未观察到这一现象。

拉　伸

我们发现可以通过两种不同的途径拉伸分离得到的肌原纤维，这取决于肌原纤

whether the fibril has been "plasticized"[10], or whether it is being extended while in rigor or while it is exerting a large contractile force. In each case, however, only the *I*-bands change in length; the *A*-bands remain at constant length.

If fibrils are stretched at 2°C., in the absence of magnesium ions and in the presence of rather high concentrations of adenosine triphosphate (about 10^{-2} *M*)—conditions which favour the plasticizing action of adenosine triphosphate rather than its contracting effect[10]—then the *I*-bands increase in length. The length of the *A*-band remains unchanged, but its central region becomes somewhat less dense, as though the *H*-zone were lengthening; the length of this less dense region increases as stretch proceeds. This process is perfectly reversible: stretched fibrils can be allowed to shorten until contraction bands form, and then re-extended.

If fibrils are stretched without any previous treatment, or in the presence of 10^{-4} *M* adenosine triphosphate and 10^{-3} *M* magnesium chloride at room temperature, when contraction is strong, then it is still the *I*-bands alone which increase in length. However, this increase is now not accompanied by any decrease in density of the central part of the *A*-band; on the other hand, the *Z*-lines now become appreciably fainter in spite of the fact that the diameter of the fibril is decreasing. (In the first type of stretch the *Z*-lines remain normal.) This suggests that some stretch is occurring in the region of the *Z*-line. This type of extension is also reversible.

We believe that the second type of stretch extends the series elastic component (Hill[11]), whereas the first type of stretch produces semi-plastic extension as in relaxed muscle.

The appearance of stretched muscle has also been investigated by examining fibrils prepared from fibres which were stretched immediately after removal from the rabbit. Such preparations contain a very high proportion of fibrils with long *I*-bands and the characteristic long zone of low density in the middle of each *A*-band (Fig. 5). We have made several hundred measurements of the lengths of *A*- and *I*-bands on such fibrils and can detect no significant difference in the lengths of *A*-bands from those found in fibrils with the shorter *I*-bands typical of rest length. These observations provide some evidence that the band pattern changes associated with stretch in whole living muscle fibres are similar to those seen in isolated fibrils which have been plasticized. Much more powerful evidence for this is described in the accompanying paper by A. F. Huxley and R. Niedergerke, to whom we are indebted for early reports of their results.

Myosin Extraction after Stretch and after Contraction

We have extracted myosin from fibrils of different sarcomere lengths by methods similar to those described previously[3]. In these earlier studies a dark zone always remained in the centre of the *A*-band of rest-length fibrils after extraction, although the density of the rest of the *A*-band was reduced to that of the *I*-band. Electron microscope studies showed that the dark band still contained the thicker filaments which elsewhere in the *A*-band had been removed. Hasselbach[4] has shown that this dark band disappears during prolonged

维是否已经被“塑料化”[10]，或者是否在强直状态下或正施加很强的收缩力时被拉伸。但不论哪种情况，只有 *I* 带的长度发生了变化，*A* 带的长度保持不变。

如果在 2 ℃的不含有镁离子但含有相当高浓度的腺苷三磷酸（约 0.01摩尔 / 升）溶液中（这种条件下腺苷三磷酸会促进肌原纤维的塑料化而不会使其发生收缩）拉伸肌原纤维，那么 *I* 带的长度会增加[10]。*A* 带的长度保持不变，但中央区域的颜色变浅，好像 *H* 区伸长了一样。随着拉伸的进行，颜色变浅的区域的长度也随之增加。这一过程是完全可逆的：拉伸过的肌原纤维还可以缩短直到形成收缩带，之后还可以重新伸展。

如果没有预先对肌原纤维进行处理，或者在室温下含有 10^{-4} 摩尔 / 升腺苷三磷酸和 10^{-3} 摩尔 / 升氯化镁的溶液中就进行拉伸（此时肌原纤维会发生强烈收缩），那么仍然只有 *I* 带的长度增加。但此时这种增加并没有伴随 *A* 带中央区域的密度减小。另一方面，尽管肌原纤维的直径变小，*Z* 线却明显变得有点模糊（在第一种拉伸情况下，*Z* 线并不会发生变化）。这表明 *Z* 线所在的区域也被拉伸。这一过程也是可逆的。

我们认为第二种类型的拉伸拉长了串联弹性组分（参见希尔[11]），而第一种类型的拉伸使得肌原纤维出现了像松弛肌肉中那样的半塑料式的拉长。

通过检测刚从兔子中分离出来就立即进行拉伸的肌原纤维，我们也研究了肌肉拉伸的现象。如图 5 所示，我们发现很大比例的肌原纤维中都含有长的 *I* 带，同时在每条 *A* 带中央都具有特征性的长的低密度区。我们对这类肌原纤维中的 *A* 带和 *I* 带的长度进行了数百次测量，结果发现这些肌原纤维中 *A* 带的长度与在静息长度下具有典型的短的 *I* 带的肌原纤维中 *A* 带长度相比没有明显的不同。这些现象证明了在生物活体内的肌纤维中和在塑料化后分离得到的肌原纤维中肌小节受到拉伸时条带样式的变化是相同的。关于这一点更有力的证据参见赫胥黎和尼德格克的相关文章，他们实验结果的早期报告让我们很受益。

在拉伸和收缩后抽提肌球蛋白

采用与前述类似的方法[3]，我们将肌节长度不同的肌原纤维中的肌球蛋白抽提出来。虽然其余 *A* 带的密度减小到与 *I* 带近似，但是在早期的研究中人们还是可以发现抽提后静息长度下 *A* 带的中央存在一个暗区。利用电子显微镜进行观察可以发现，*A* 带中其他区域的粗丝都消失了，唯独暗带中仍有保留。哈塞尔巴赫[4]研究表明延长肌球蛋白抽提过程会使暗带消失。我们发现使用 pH 值为 7.0 的含有 0.1 摩尔 / 升

myosin extraction, and we have found that this process can be accelerated by using 0.1 *M* pyrophosphate, 10^{-3} *M* magnesium chloride, *p*H 7.0. Accordingly, in the present studies we have employed this method for extracting all the myosin.

The appearance of fibrils extracted at different degrees of stretch and contraction is shown in Figs. 6-9 and 11. The "ghost" fibril consists of a faint backbone structure (which we believe consists largely of actin) the density of which is about the same as that of the original *I*-bands; the *Z*-lines are also still visible. In fibrils at rest length, an apparent gap is observed in place of the original *H*-zone (Fig. 7). In stretched fibrils, where there was originally a longer zone of low density in the centre of the *A*-band, the length of the gap is correspondingly greater (Fig. 6). The ghost fibrils are, however, still structurally continuous; stretched fibrils shorten spontaneously to a little less than rest length during extraction unless stuck to slide or coverslip; they may be reversibly extended again. This can be done with great ease, and it is apparent that only a very weak force opposes such a stretch; the gap elongates in the process, but the length of the material extending from the *Z*-line to the edge of the gap remains constant; that is, no stretching of an elastic component in the *I*-band region now occurs.

The ghosts obtained from contracted fibrils in which the *H*-zones had just disappeared have no gaps in the centres of the sarcomeres (Fig. 8). Fibrils which had shortened until dark lines appeared in the middle of the *A*-bands retain these lines after thorough extraction of myosin (Fig. 9); these dark lines are also present in ghosts from more strongly contracted fibrils (Fig. 11).

None of these "ghosts" will contract when treated with adenosine triphosphate.

Electron Microscopy

We have made a preliminary examination in the electron microscope of thin sections of stretched, contracted and myosin-extracted muscles prepared by the methods described elsewhere[2,12], and we have obtained results which, so far as they go, are in complete agreement with those obtained by light microscopy. This technique does not readily permit of reliable measurements of the lengths of sarcomeres or bands, for, apart from fixation artefacts, an unknown amount of compression is always present in even the best thin sections. In sections of stretched muscle, the majority of the *A*-bands show the characteristic long central region of low density (also observed by Philpott and Szent-Györgyi[13]); we find that the secondary array of thin (40 A.) filaments[2] is absent from this zone. In stretched muscle which has been subjected to myosin extraction the thick (110 A.) primary filaments are absent, and gaps apparently exist between the groups of thin (40 A.) filaments associated with successive *Z*-lines. In sections of glycerol-extracted muscle contracted in adenosine triphosphate, we have observed the same variety of band patterns seen in the light microscope. Up to the point where the *I*-bands disappear, the primary array of thick filaments remains apparently unchanged; and when contraction bands have been formed, the primary filaments between them are still straight. Our fixation of the secondary filaments has not yet been sufficiently good to allow us to describe adequately

焦磷酸盐和 10^{-3} 摩尔 / 升氯化镁的溶液可以加速这一过程。相应地，在这篇文章中，我们采用这种方法来抽提所有的肌球蛋白。

图 6 ~ 图 9 以及图 11 显示了抽提后处于不同程度的拉伸和收缩状态的肌原纤维。“鬼影”肌原纤维包含一个非常模糊的骨架结构（我们认为主要由肌动蛋白组成），其密度大约和之前的 *I* 带相同。与此同时，*Z* 线仍然清晰可见。在处于静息长度的肌原纤维中，原先是 *H* 区的地方出现了一个明显的间隙（图 7），而在被拉伸的肌纤维中，在 *A* 带中央原本是长的低密度区的地方，相应地出现了更大的间隙（图 6）。然而鬼影纤维在结构上仍然是连续的，被拉伸的肌原纤维在抽提时会自动缩短到比静息长度稍微小一点的长度（除非肌原纤维粘在载玻片或盖玻片上）。它们还可以被再次拉长。这很容易做到，显然仅微弱的力就能阻碍这样的拉伸；并且伴随着拉伸我们可以观察到 *H* 带中的间隙逐渐变大，但从 *Z* 线到这一间隙边缘的距离则保持不变，也就是说，此时 *I* 带中的弹性组分没有被拉伸。

从 *H* 区刚刚消失了的处于收缩状态的肌原纤维中得到的鬼影纤维在肌节的中央没有间隙（图 8）。那些能缩短到暗线处（存在于 *A* 带中间）的肌原纤维在经过对肌球蛋白的彻底抽提后，这些线仍然存在（图 9）。来自收缩程度更强烈的肌原纤维的鬼影纤维中也可以观察到这些暗线（图 11）。

这些“鬼影”纤维在腺苷三磷酸的作用下都不会产生收缩反应。

电子显微镜

我们使用电子显微镜分别对拉伸、收缩以及抽提肌球蛋白后的肌肉薄切片进行了初步检测，制备方法在其他文章中有所提及 [2,12]，并且得到了与用光学显微镜观察完全一致的结果。不过，由于固定过程中会产生假象，以及即使在最薄的切片中样品也会不可避免地发生不同程度的收缩，因此这种方法不能可靠地测量肌节或条带的长度。在对拉伸的肌肉切片进行观察时，我们发现绝大多数 *A* 带具有特征性的长的低密度中央区域（菲尔波特和森特–哲尔吉也观察到相同的结果 [13]），并且在这个区域内没有直径为 40 埃的细肌丝 [2]。在抽提掉肌球蛋白后被拉伸的肌肉中，直径为 110 埃的粗肌丝也消失了，并且在细肌丝和 *Z* 线之间出现了明显的间隙区域。同样的，在对甘油抽提后由腺苷三磷酸诱导而收缩的肌原纤维的切片进行观察时，我们也得到了与使用光学显微镜观察到的相一致的条带样式。直到 *I* 带消失，粗肌丝的排布并未明显改变。当收缩带形成后，粗肌丝仍然是直的。受固定方法所限，我们只能观察到细丝在肌肉收缩过程中相对于 *A* 带发生了平移，但无法对这一过程中的其他细微变化进行充分的阐述。然而，在对活体肌细胞进行拉伸实验时可以观察到长度

any changes, apart from translation into the *A*-bands, that may have taken place in them during contraction. During stretch of living muscle, however, the approximately 400-A. axial period seems to remain unchanged; a similar result was obtained by low-angle X-ray diffraction studies[1].

Conclusions

We believe that most of these changes in the cross-striations of muscle during stretch and contraction may be adequately described in terms of the following fairly simple model: The backbone of the muscle fibril is made up of actin filaments which extend from the *Z*-line up to one side of the *H*-zone, where they are attached to an elastic component (*not* the series elastic component) which for convenience we will call the *S*-filaments. The *S*-filaments provide continuity between the set of actin filaments associated with one *Z*-line and that associated with the next. The series elastic component is provided either by the actin filaments themselves or, more probably, by their mode of attachment to the *Z*-line. Myosin filaments extend from one end of the *A*-band, through the *H*-zone, to the other end of the *A*-band, and their length is unaltered by stretch or by contraction down to the point where the sarcomere length is equal to the length of the *A*-band; when contraction beyond this point takes place, the ends of the myosin filaments fold up and contraction bands form. Thus myosin and actin filaments lie side by side in the *A*-band and, in the absence of adenosine triphosphate, cross-linkages will form between them; the *S*-filaments are attached to the myosin filaments in the centre of the *A*-band by some more permanent cross-linkages.

In this model, plastic stretch takes place when the actin filaments are partly withdrawn from the *A*-band, leaving a long lighter central region and stretching the *S*-filaments in the process. Only the *I*-bands and the *H*-zones increase in length, the length of *A*-band remaining constant. This process would be inhibited by cross-linkages between the actin and myosin filaments; there is good evidence[10] that muscles are only readily extensible when such linkages are absent. When they are present, stretch would take place by extension of the series elastic component; in our model, this would again lead to an increase in the length of the *I*-band, but in this case no change in the length of the *H*-zone would take place. Contraction takes place in this model when the actin filaments are drawn into the *A*-band (until the *H*-zone is filled up) and are then folded up in some way to produce more extensive shortening. Thus, when the model is allowed to shorten, only the *I*-bands decrease in length until adjacent *A*-bands are pulled into contact with the *Z*-lines. When contraction is isometric, translation of actin filaments into the *A*-bands is accompanied by stretch of the series elastic component. It will be seen that in both stretch and contraction the behaviour of this model reproduces the observed behaviour of muscle quite faithfully.

A possible driving force for contraction in this model might be the formation of actin-myosin linkages when adenosine triphosphate, having previously displaced actin from myosin, is enzymatically split by the myosin. In this way, the actin filaments might be

约为 400 埃的轴心区并未发生变化。通过小角度的 X 射线衍射实验 [1] 也可以得到类似的结果。

结　论

我们认为用下列非常简单的模型就可以描述肌肉拉伸和收缩过程中横纹所呈现出的变化：肌原纤维的骨架由肌动蛋白丝组成，它们从 *Z* 线开始伸展到 *H* 带边缘，在此它们与一种弹性组分相连（**不是**串联弹性组分），为简便起见称之为 *S* 细丝。这些 *S* 细丝使得相邻 *Z* 线的肌动蛋白丝相互连接起来。串联弹性组分可能是由肌动蛋白丝本身提供的，更有可能是由于它们与 *Z* 线连接的方式不同而产生的。肌球蛋白丝从 *A* 带的一端开始伸展，穿过 *H* 区直到 *A* 带的另一端结束，并且其长度在肌肉拉伸或收缩到肌节长度和 *A* 带长度相等的时候都不会改变；只有当肌节的长度缩短到比 *A* 带还短时，肌球蛋白的末端才会折叠起来形成收缩带。因此，肌球蛋白和肌动蛋白丝在 *A* 带中是紧挨着的，在没有腺苷三磷酸的情况下，它们之间会形成桥连；同时 *S* 细丝也会通过某种永久性的桥连与 *A* 带中央的肌球蛋白丝相连。

在这个模型中，当肌动蛋白丝从 *A* 带中部分滑出时会产生可塑性拉伸，使 *H* 区伸长并且颜色变浅，*S* 细丝也伸长。只有 *I* 带和 *H* 区的长度增加，*A* 带本身的长度保持恒定。肌动蛋白丝与肌球蛋白丝之间的桥连可以抑制该过程，并且有充分的证据表明只有未发生这样的桥接时肌肉才易于拉伸 [10]。在发生桥接时，拉伸可以通过串联弹性组分的拉长来完成。在我们的模型中，这会再次导致 *I* 带长度增加，但在实验中我们发现 *H* 区的长度并未发生变化。在我们的模型中，肌肉收缩时肌动蛋白丝向 *A* 带中滑入，直到完全进入 *H* 区，然后以某种方式折叠以产生更大规模的收缩。因此当肌肉收缩时只有 *I* 带的长度缩短，直到相邻的 *A* 带与 *Z* 线重合。在等长收缩中，伴随着肌动蛋白丝向 *A* 带中滑入，串联弹性组分也相应地被拉伸。无论肌肉拉伸还是收缩，上述模型都和观察到的肌肉的行为吻合得很好。

关于该模型中肌肉收缩的动力，我们认为其可能主要源自于肌动蛋白与肌球蛋白之间桥接的形成。当腺苷三磷酸被肌球蛋白酶解时，肌动蛋白从肌球蛋白中移出，按照这个途径肌动蛋白丝可能被拉入到肌球蛋白束之中以便暴露出尽可能多的活性

drawn into the array of myosin filaments in order to present to them as many active groups for actomyosin formation as possible; furthermore, if the structure of actin is such that a greater number of active groups could be opposed to those on the myosin by, for example, a coiling of the actin filaments, then even greater degrees of shortening could be produced by essentially the same mechanism. The model will remain contracted as long as the splitting of adenosine triphosphate continues; it will relax if the splitting stops and more adenosine triphosphate diffuses in, breaking actomyosin linkages and allowing the muscle to be re-extended. However, our results by no means require that contraction and relaxation be brought about in this way; and indeed, in the light of recent studies on actin[14,15], it would not be surprising if other processes are also involved. Furthermore, our results cannot exclude the possibility that repetitive configurational changes take place within the myosin filaments during contraction, unaccompanied by any overall change in the length of those filaments, and that these changes somehow bring about the observed movement of the actin filaments into the *A*-band.

These results will be described in greater detail elsewhere. We are much indebted to Prof. Francis O. Schmitt for his encouragement of this work, and to the Commonwealth Fund and the Rockefeller Foundation for their support.

(**173**, 973-976; 1954)

H. Huxley and J. Hanson: Department of Biology, Massachusetts Institute of Technology, Cambridge, Massachusetts.

References:

1. Huxley, H. E., *Proc. Roy. Soc.*, B, **141**, 59 (1953).
2. Huxley, H. E., *Biochim. Biophys. Acta*, **12**, 387 (1953).
3. Hanson, J., and Huxley, H. E., *Nature*, **172**, 530 (1953).
4. Hasselbach, W., *Z. Naturforsch.*, 8b, 449 (1953).
5. Jordan, H. E., *Amer. J. Anat.*, **27**, 1 (1920); "Physiological Reviews", **13**, 301 (1933).
6. Buchthal, F., Knappeis, G. G., and Lindhard, J., *Skand. Arch. Physiol.*, **73**, 163 (1936).
7. Speidel, C. C., *Amer. J. Anat.*, **65**, 471 (1939).
8. Szent-Györgyi, A., "Chemistry of Muscular Contraction" (2nd edit., Academic Press, N. Y., 1951).
9. Hanson, J., *Nature*, **169**, 530 (1952).
10. Weber, H. H., and Portzehl, H., "Advances in Protein Chemistry", 7, 161 (1952); "Progress in Biophysics" (in the press); we are indebted to Prof. Weber and to the Editors for allowing us to read this article.
11. Hill, A. V., *Proc. Roy. Soc.*, B, **137**, 273 (1950).
12. Hodge, A. J., Huxley, H. E., and Spiro, D., *J. Histo. and Cyto. Chem.*, **2**, 54 (1954).
13. Philpott, D., and Szent-Györgyi, A., *Biochim. Biophys. Acta*, **12**, 128 (1953).
14. Straub, F. B., and Feuer, G., *Biochim. Biophys. Acta*, **4**, 455 (1950).
15. Tsao, T.-C., *Biochim. Biophys. Acta*, **11**, 236 (1953).

基团来形成肌动球蛋白。另外，如果肌动蛋白的结构允许足够多的活性基团暴露给肌球蛋白的活性基团（比如通过肌动蛋白丝的自身卷曲），那么便可以通过同样的机制进行更进一步的收缩。只要腺苷三磷酸不断地被水解，这种收缩过程就将一直持续下去。当腺苷三磷酸停止水解时，肌肉将松弛，更多的腺苷三磷酸扩散进入纤维，破坏肌动球蛋白的桥接，从而允许肌肉再度延伸。不过，我们并不认为肌肉收缩和松弛一定按照上述机制发生，事实上，根据最近的一些关于肌动蛋白的研究结果，即使肌肉的收缩还包含其他的过程也不足为奇[14,15]。此外，我们不排除在收缩过程中肌球蛋白丝的构象发生重复改变的可能性，而并不伴随那些细丝总长度的变化，也不排除这些构象变化在一定程度上可能导致所观察到的肌动蛋白丝进入 *A* 带的运动。

我们会在别处对上述实验结果进行更详尽的描述。我们非常感谢弗朗西斯·施米特教授对本工作的鼓励，也非常感谢联邦基金和洛克菲勒基金会对我们工作的资助。

（张锦彬 翻译；周筠梅 审稿）

Man-Made Diamonds

F. P. Bundy *et al.*

Editor's Note

Scientists had long known that both graphite and diamond are forms of pure carbon in which the atoms are linked in different patterns. This seemed to offer the prospect of converting cheap graphite into diamond. But that transformation requires very high pressures and temperatures, as found where diamonds are formed in the Earth. This conversion was attempted since the late nineteenth century, but was first reported in this paper by Francis Bundy and colleagues at the General Electric laboratories in Schenectady. They squeezed graphite to pressures of 50-100,000 atmospheres at over 1200 °C. This made human-made diamond available for the first time; GE began to sell it by 1957. Synthetic diamond is now widely used in abrasive and cutting tools.

IN the 1920's it was quite widely believed that diamond had been made from carbon under conditions of high heat and great pressure. The story was indeed one to capture the imagination. It involved famous chemists, a thoroughly fascinating subject and very striking experimental techniques.

In the recent past, however, informed scientists soberly agree that there has been no certain example of diamond production in the laboratory. More than a century of claims and counterclaims for the synthesis of diamond attest to the fascination of the subject and the extreme difficulty of the experimental techniques. Henri Moissan dissolved sugar charcoal in molten iron and quenched the solution in cold water in order to crystallize the carbon under the great internal pressure supposedly generated by contraction as the mass cooled from the outside. When the metal was dissolved from the solidified melt, there remained traces of transparent material having optical properties similar to those of diamond and giving some carbon dioxide upon combustion. Moissan therefore believed he had made diamond.

In 1880, J. B. Hannay reported he had made diamonds by heating a mixture of hydrocarbons, bone oil and lithium at red heat in sealed wroughtiron tubes. The project was said to be fraught with great difficulty because of exploding tubes; only three out of eighty held. Hannay's identification of his diamonds seemed very conclusive, since it even included a density of 3.5 and a carbon analysis of 97.85 percent.

Sir Charles Parsons tried for thirty years to synthesize diamonds, including in his experiments many attempts to duplicate the work of Moissan and Hannay. At first Parsons thought he had succeeded; but later, having some doubts, he scrupulously re-investigated all his work on the subject. Parsons's new work clearly demonstrated how he had been

人造金刚石

邦迪等

编者按

科学家们早已知道石墨和金刚石都是由纯碳元素组成，但其中原子的结合方式不同。这似乎为我们提供了将廉价石墨转化为金刚石的希望，但这个转化需要具备如同在地壳内形成金刚石时的那种超高压高温条件。自 19 世纪后期以来，科学家就试图进行这种转化，但位于斯克内克塔迪通用电气实验室的弗朗西斯·邦迪及其同事们在这篇文章中首次对此转化进行了报道。他们在温度超过 1,200 ℃，压强为 50~100,000 个大气压的条件下对石墨进行挤压。这是第一次制造出人造金刚石；通用电气公司于 1957 年开始出售这种人造金刚石。现在人造金刚石已广泛应用于研磨和切割工具上。

20 世纪 20 年代，人们普遍认为在高温高压下碳已能转化为金刚石。事实上这不过是一个引人遐想的故事罢了。这涉及一些著名的化学家、一个极其引人入胜的课题和一些十分惊人的实验技术。

然而就在不久之前，一些学识广博的科学家审慎地认可目前在实验室尚无实现金刚石人工合成的确切案例。一个多世纪以来，那些关于成功合成金刚石的声明与反驳充分证实了这一课题的魅力和实验技术的高难度。亨利·穆瓦桑将糖炭溶于熔融的铁中再在冷水中进行淬火，目的是使碳在极高的内压下结晶，据推测，这种压力来自于大块物质外部受冷而产生的收缩。将凝固在熔体中的金属溶解之后，残余物中有微量的透明物质，其光学性质与金刚石相似，并且燃烧后生成二氧化碳。穆瓦桑由此确信他成功合成了金刚石。

1880 年，汉内报道称，他将碳氢化合物、骨油和锂的混合物置于密封的锻造铁管中加热至炽热从而合成了金刚石。据说这个实验由于铁管易于爆炸而颇具难度；因此用于实验的 80 个铁管只有 3 个成功。汉内对他合成的金刚石所做的鉴定似乎非常令人信服，因为他甚至测得了密度为 3.5 克 / 厘米 ^{3} 和碳含量为 97.85%。

查尔斯·帕森斯爵士为合成金刚石花费了 30 年心血，多次试图重复穆瓦桑与汉内的实验。一开始帕森斯以为自己成功了；但是后来出现了一些疑问，于是他重新谨慎地研究了他对这一课题所做的全部工作。他的新研究明确地表明他被严重地误

misled into regarding as diamond various transparent, singly refracting minerals (spinels) which were very resistant to chemical reagents and would not burn. He finally concluded that neither he nor anyone else had ever succeeded in making diamonds in the laboratory.

The early claims to diamond synthesis were again reviewed by Prof. N. V. Sidgwick, of Oxford, in 1950, and Henry Eyring, of the University of Utah, in 1952. These authorities conclude that the synthesis of diamond in the laboratory has never been shown to be a success, and that thermodynamic considerations make it seem improbable that diamonds could have been formed under the conditions used in the experiments reported.

For a full account of the arguments the reader is referred to an extensive literature on the subject, a bibliography[1-24] for which is appended*.

Suggestions from Thermodynamics

The phase diagram for carbon as now understood is plotted in Fig. 1. Only the boundary between graphite and its vapour at low pressure is accurately established by experimental measurements. The boundaries at higher pressures between graphite, vapour and liquid are based on the work of Basset, and are not fully accepted.

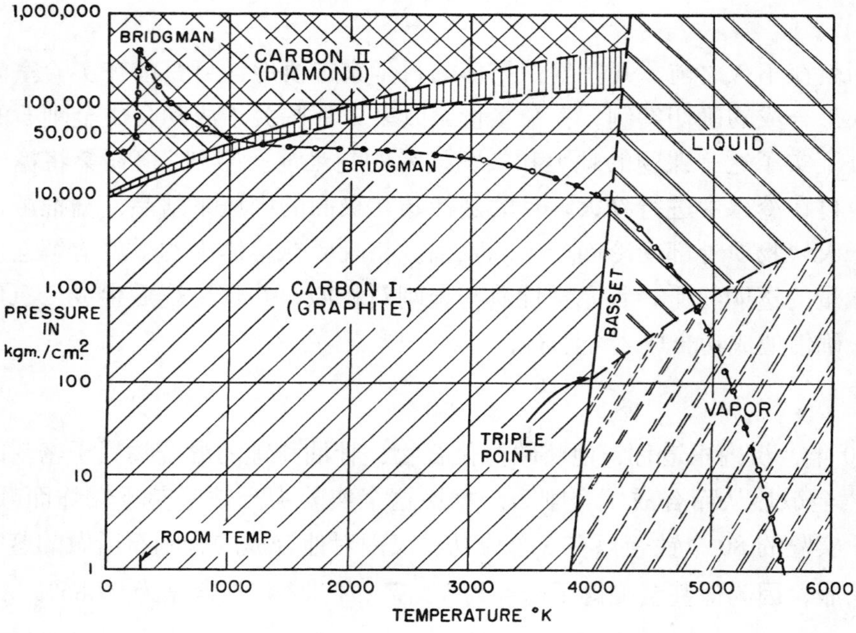

Fig. 1. Phase diagram of carbon

* References centring about the claims of Hannay and of Moissan, which are the major ones, are dealt with chronologically. Earlier references extending back to 1828 are considered in J. W. Mellor's "Comprehensive Treatise on Inorganic and Theoretical Chemistry", Vol. 5 (Longmans, Green and Co., London, 1924).

导了。他原先认为金刚石就是透明的单折光的矿物（尖晶石），对化学试剂表现出很强的惰性且不可燃。他最终推断出无论是他还是其他任何人均未在实验室中成功合成金刚石。

牛津大学的西奇威克教授以及犹他大学的亨利·艾林分别于1950年和1952年再次评述了早期关于成功合成金刚石的声明。这些专家认为实验室中的金刚石合成从未获得过成功，并且从热力学的角度考虑，在实验报告中所描述的条件下不可能实现金刚石的人工合成。

为详尽解释这一争论，读者可参考有关这一课题的大量文献，本文附有参考文献[1-24]*。

热力学启发

图1显示的是目前我们所获悉的碳的相图。只有低压下石墨的固气平衡线是通过实验测量精确绘制的。在较高压强条件下石墨相、液相和气相平衡线均是根据巴塞的研究工作而绘制的，但尚未获得完全认可。

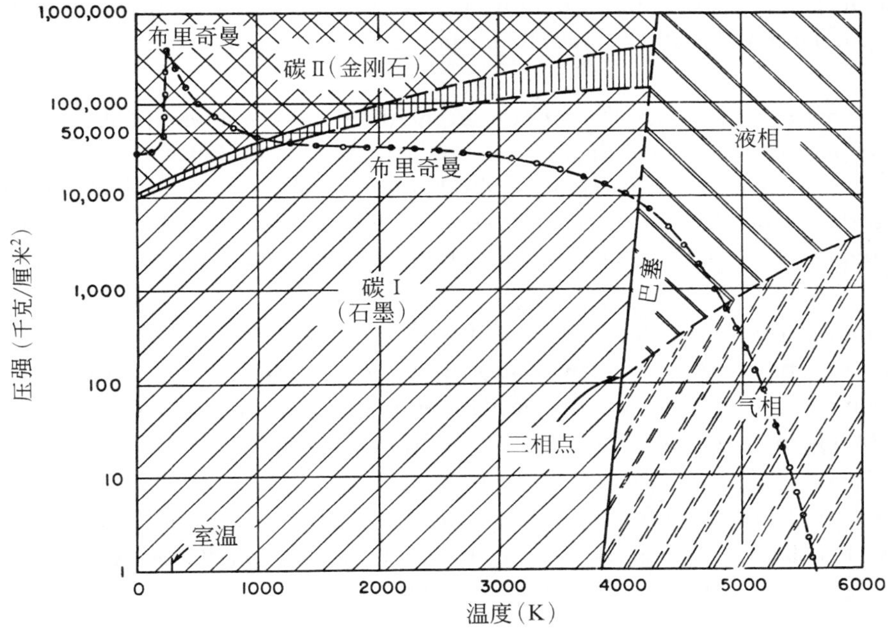

图1. 碳的相图

---

* 参考文献按时间顺序列出，集中了汉内和穆瓦桑在这一领域的主要著作。更早的文献可追溯到1828年，这在梅勒《无机和理论化学总论》第5卷（朗曼格林出版公司，伦敦，1924年）中被提到过。

The location of the boundary between the graphite and diamond-stable regions has very little direct experimental evidence at present. The position of the lower temperature part of this boundary was calculated by thermodynamic methods by Rossini and Jessup[25] of the U. S. Bureau of Standards in 1938. The higher temperature part of the boundary shown by broken lines is purely extrapolated from the other part, as the physical data have never been obtained.

The chain-line running across the diagram shows the upper limits of pressure and temperature that are known to have been reached in controlled experiments (this excludes atom bombs) according to the published literature. Prof. P. W. Bridgman, of Harvard University, is the outstanding investigator in this field, working up to more than 400,000 atmospheres at room temperature. He also held temperatures near 3,000° K. at 30,000 kgm./cm.^{2} for very short intervals of time.

The diagram shows that Bridgman has operated well up into the diamond-stable region and has tried many times to synthesize diamonds but without success. He has stated in several of his papers that the reason for his lack of success is that at the relatively low temperatures at which his experiments were carried out the rates of reaction were negligible. He recognized the necessity of going to higher temperatures; but he had not developed apparatus capable of operating at these high pressures and temperatures simultaneously. The maximum conditions he has reported in this direction were 30,000 kgm./cm.^{2} and 2,200°-3,000° K. for periods of one or two seconds.

Bridgman[19] attempted to establish a point on the diamond-graphite equilibrium curve in a series of experiments in which diamonds were heated to about 2,500° K. for a few seconds at pressures which were increased until the diamonds failed to graphitize. This pressure was reached at 30,000 kgm./cm.^{2}. He suggested in his paper that this point, 30,000 kgm./cm.^{2} and 2,500° K., might lie near the diamond-graphite equilibrium curve.

In Bridgman's experiment the possibility that pressure reduced the rate of conversion of diamond to graphite cannot be ruled out. If so, the diamonds would fail to graphitize at 30,000 kgm./cm.^{2} in the few seconds at high temperature available. If this be the case, the point 30,000 kgm./cm.^{2} and 2,500° K. is still within the graphite region of stability.

The known evidence about the thermodynamic stability for diamond and graphite led us to believe that diamonds could be formed in the pressure region 30,000-100,000 kgm./cm.^{2} at temperatures somewhere in the range of 1,000°-3,000° K.

Pressure Vessels

Practically all known ultra-high-pressure generators are based on the principle of pushing a piston into a cylinder that encloses the substance to be subjected to the pressure. The main factor which limits the maximum pressures that can be reached within vessels is the

目前几乎没有多少直接的实验证据能够确定石墨稳定区与金刚石稳定区之间平衡线的位置。该平衡线低温部分的位置是由美国标准局的罗西尼和杰瑟普[25]在1938年用热力学方法计算得出的。平衡线的高温部分以虚线表示，完全是靠其他部分的数据外推得到的，因为目前我们还无法得到这部分的物理数据。

相图中的点划线是在已知可控的实验（原子弹除外）中所能达到的压强和温度的上限，这些数据来自于已经发表的文献。哈佛大学的布里奇曼教授是这一领域的杰出研究者，他在室温下逐渐加压获得超过400,000个大气压。他还能在30,000千克 / 厘米^{2}的压强下将温度在很短时间内控制在3,000 K上下。

由相图可以看出，布里奇曼的实验条件已经位于金刚石稳定区之中，他曾多次尝试合成金刚石但均未成功。在他的多篇论文中他阐述过自己失败的原因，即实验过程中的温度相对过低从而导致反应速率几乎为零。他承认更高的温度条件是必不可少的；但他没有研制出同时能在如此高压高温条件下工作的实验装置。他报道了在这一研究方向上的极限条件：压强为30,000千克 / 厘米^{2}时温度在2,200 K ~ 3,000 K间保持1秒或2秒。

布里奇曼[19]试图通过一系列实验在金刚石–石墨两相平衡线上确定一个点，将金刚石加热到约2,500 K温度下，在几秒钟内对金刚石持续加压，但金刚石并未转化为石墨。实验中压强达到30,000千克 / 厘米^2。他在论文中指出，这个压强为30,000千克 / 厘米^2、温度为2,500 K的点可能位于金刚石–石墨两相平衡线附近。

在布里奇曼的实验中，我们还不能排除这种可能性，即压强会降低金刚石转化为石墨的速率。如果是这样的话，在30,000千克 / 厘米^{2}的压强和可获得的几秒钟高温条件下，金刚石就不可能转化为石墨。如果就是这种情况，那么压强为30,000千克 / 厘米^2、温度为2,500 K这个点还是位于石墨稳定区中。

关于金刚石和石墨热力学稳定性的已知证据使我们相信，在压强处于30,000千克 / 厘米^2 ~ 100,000千克 / 厘米^{2}区间而温度为1,000 K ~ 3,000 K中某点时，是能够形成金刚石的。

压力容器

实际上所有已知的超高压发生器都是基于同样的原理，即将活塞推入圆筒中从而使其中的实验对象受到高压。容器内能达到的最大压强主要取决于其制造材料的

strength of materials. The strongest steels in the most favourable form and size (piano wire, for example) have ultimate tensile strengths of the order of 14,000-21,000 kgm./cm.^{2}. Sintered carbides, such as "Carboloy", have compressive strengths of the order of 50,000 kgm./cm.^{2} or more. The pressure required for reasonably rapid synthesis of diamond was thought by our group to be above the compressive strength of "Carboloy" in the range 50,000-100,000 kgm./cm.^{2}.

Merely making the walls thicker on a pressure vessel contributes very little to its pressure-holding ability after a certain wall thickness is reached. By using multiple support bands on the cylinder part (a technique used years ago in making large gun barrels), and special sealing gasket devices between the piston and cylinder, Bridgman had developed pressure vessels good for 50,000 kgm./cm.^{2} at room temperature. At high temperatures, materials get weaker and in general the attainable pressures are lower.

By developing some new ways of distributing stress and giving support to critical parts, our research group has succeeded in developing pressure vessels that operate at pressures up to at least 100,000 kgm./cm.^{2} and temperatures in excess of 2,300°K. for hours of continuous operation.

Calibration of Pressures and Temperatures

Pressures of this magnitude are calibrated by making use of four of the electrical resistance transitions observed by P. W. Bridgman[26] in the pressure region up to 80,000 kgm./cm.^{2}. The transitions are bismuth 25,400, thallium 45,000, caesium 55,000 and barium at 80,000 kgm./cm.^{2}. For pressures greater than 80,000 kgm./cm.^{2}, the melting point of germanium as a function of pressure was used. It was found to decrease linearly with pressure to press loads corresponding to 100,000 kgm./cm.^{2}.

Temperatures inside the pressure cells are measured by use of thermocouples, melting points of materials, change of electrical resistance of wires, Curie points of magnetic materials, thermocolour paints, etc.

Region now Available for Research

In Fig. 2 appears a pressure-temperature diagram, with linear scales on both axes, showing the new region of exploratory research which has been opened up by the development of our new high-pressure and high-temperature apparatus. Note that the newly attainable region covers about as much area as does all the region previously attainable.

强度。最坚硬的钢材在最适合的形状和大小时（例如钢琴丝），其极限抗张强度的数量级可达 14,000 千克 / 厘米^2 ~ 21,000 千克 / 厘米^2。烧结碳化物的耐压强度的数量级可达 50,000 千克 / 厘米^2 甚至更高，例如“卡波洛依”硬质合金。我们研究小组认为，合理快速合成金刚石所需的压强应在 50,000 千克 / 厘米^2 ~ 100,000 千克 / 厘米^2 范围内，而这超过了“卡波洛依”硬质合金的耐压强度。

在压力容器的器壁达到某一特定的厚度之后，仅靠增加器壁厚度很难再增强其耐压能力。通过给圆筒部分套上多重支承板（这是多年以前制造大型炮筒时使用的技术），并在活塞与圆筒之间加上密封垫圈，布里奇曼制造出的压力容器能在室温下承受 50,000 千克 / 厘米^2 的压强。高温时材料的强度会减弱，可达到的压强一般也会随之变低一些。

我们研究小组新开发了一些分散压力和加固关键部位的方法，现制造出的压力容器能在压强至少达到 100,000 千克 / 厘米^2 和温度高于 2,300 K 的条件下持续正常工作几个小时。

压强和温度的校准

布里奇曼[26] 在高达 80,000 千克 / 厘米^2 的压强区域内观测到电阻跃迁，通过 4 种电阻跃迁来校准如此大的压强。跃迁具体值为：铋在 25,400 千克 / 厘米^2，铊在 45,000 千克 / 厘米^2，铯在 55,000 千克 / 厘米^2，钡在 80,000 千克 / 厘米^2。在超过 80,000 千克 / 厘米^2 时，锗的熔点与压强的变化有关。但是我们发现，当压强接近 100,000 千克 / 厘米^2 时，其熔点会随施加的压强升高而线性地下降。

压力传感器内的温度可以通过热电偶、物质的熔点、导线电阻的变化、磁性材料的居里点和热致变色颜料等来测定。

目前研究所能达到的区域

图 2 为压强–温度关系图，两个坐标轴上有线性标度，其中显示了我们利用开发的新型高温高压装置进行探索性研究所测得的新的区域。请注意，这个新区域基本包含了以前研究所能达到的全部区域。

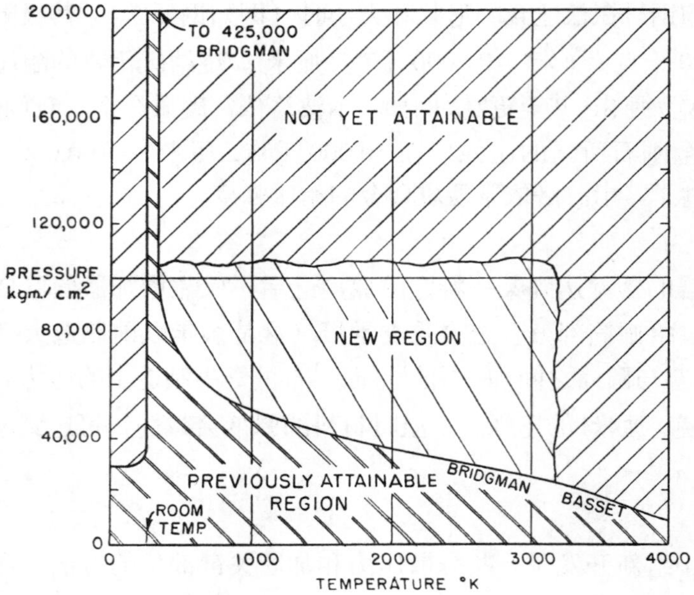

Fig. 2. New region of pressure and temperature available for research

Diamond Synthesis

The new region of attainable pressure and temperature extended well into the diamond-stable region as defined in Fig. 1. Under these supposed diamond-stable conditions, processes were discovered which yielded diamonds ranging in size from less than 100 microns to more than 1 mm. along an edge. The various processes have been independently repeated more than one hundred times by a number of workers in this Company. Each time crystals were grown which pass the critical tests for identification with diamond. The present chamber sizes permit the synthesis of up to about $\frac{1}{4}$ carat of diamond material.

It is not necessary to introduce diamond seeds. Nucleation and growth occur spontaneously and profusely when diamond-stable conditions are reached. In some of the early successful work, diamond seeds were added; but growth occurred independently and apart from the added seed. In a few cases under special conditions, some growth has occurred on the seed crystals.

The man-made diamonds form in many of the different crystal habits found in Nature. These include octahedra, tetrahedra and dodecahedra. Some typical forms are shown in Fig. 3.

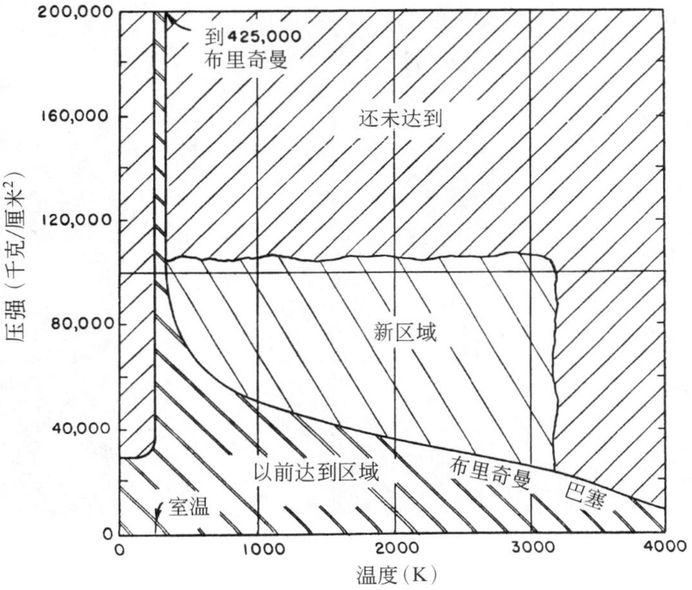

图 2. 研究中所能达到的新的压强和温度区域

金刚石合成

最新能达到的压强和温度区域很好地扩展到了图1中所示的金刚石稳定区域。在这些假定的金刚石稳定的条件下，我们已经找到了一些方法成功合成了金刚石，其边长大小从不足100微米到超过1毫米。本公司的多位员工对各种工艺流程共进行了一百多次独立的重复实验。每次合成的晶体都通过了金刚石鉴定中的几项关键性实验。当前实验设备的容积可允许合成 $\frac{1}{4}$ 克拉左右的金刚石材料。

人们认为引入金刚石籽晶并不是一个必要的步骤。因为当满足金刚石稳定的条件时，晶核的形成与晶体的生长可以自发地大量进行。我们在一些早期成功的实验中植入一些金刚石籽晶；但实际上晶体生长是独立的，与植入的籽晶无关。在少数特殊条件下，一些晶体在籽晶上生长。

我们发现人造金刚石在自然界中存在多种不同形式的结晶形态，其中包括八面体、四面体和十二面体。一些典型形态如图 3 所示。

Fig. 3. Man-made diamonds. (*a*) 1-mm. diamond shown with phonograph needle. (*b*) 0.2-0.5mm. octahedra

Proof that Diamonds were Made

The proof that diamonds were made was based on the following conclusive tests:

(1) Identity of crystal structure of man-made diamonds to natural diamonds as determined by X-ray diffraction patterns (Fig. 4).

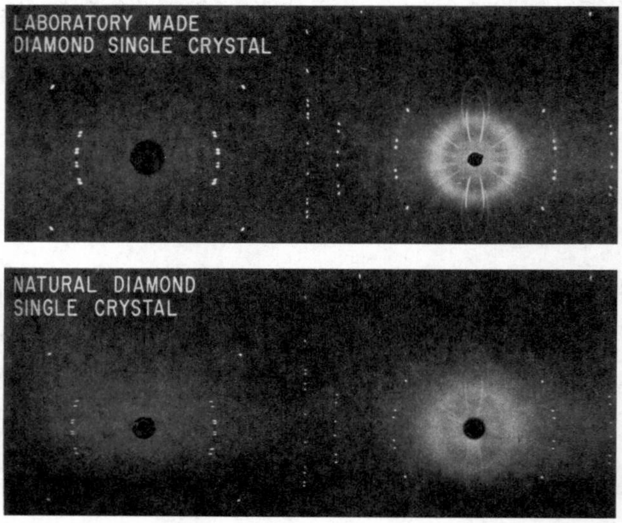

Fig. 4. X-ray diffraction patterns of man-made and natural diamond (powder camera photograph)

(2) Chemical analysis to show that crystals made were composed of carbon. Those analysed were 86 percent carbon, 14 percent inorganic ash identified with the growing media.

(*a*) (*b*)

图 3. 人造金刚石。(*a*) 与留声机针一起展示的 1 毫米大小的金刚石。
(*b*) 0.2 毫米 ~ 0.5 毫米大小的八面体晶形。

成功合成金刚石的证据

成功合成金刚石的证据基于下列结论性的检测结果：

(1) X 射线衍射图（图 4）表明，人造金刚石与天然金刚石的晶体结构是一致的。

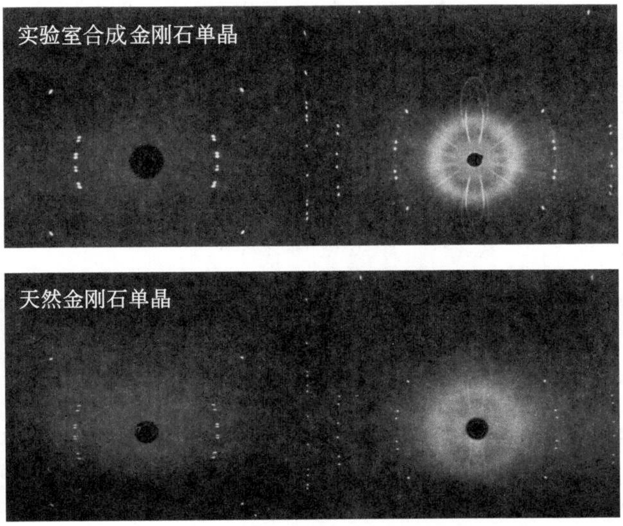

图 4. 人造金刚石和天然金刚石的 X 射线衍射图（粉末照相相片）

(2) 化学分析表明人造金刚石由碳组成。分析结果 86% 为碳，14% 为与生长介质一致的无机物粉尘。

(3) Hardness tests. The laboratory-made diamonds were hard enough to scratch the hardest face, the 111 face, of natural diamond (Fig. 5).

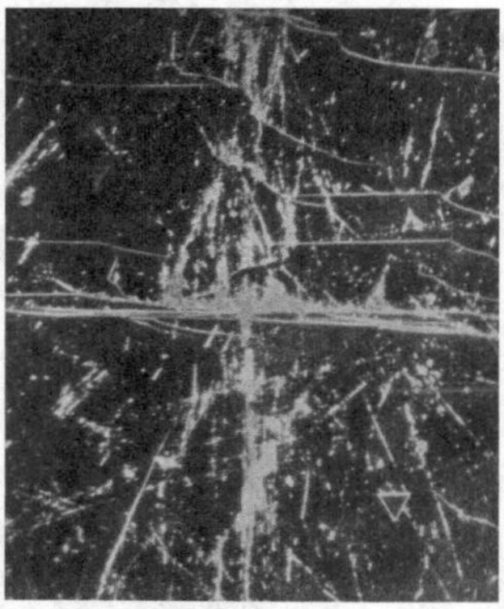

Fig. 5. Scratches made on natural diamond 111 face with man-made diamonds. A large number of scratches appear in a generally vertical direction down through the centre of the picture. The horizontal marks are growth steps on the crystal face. The triangular pit in the lower right-hand corner is also a typical growth mark found on diamond faces.

(4) Repeatability. The synthesis of diamond has been repeated, entirely independently, by a number of workers in the General Electric Company. The diamonds so made pass the above conclusive tests for diamonds.

In addition, it was shown that the index of refraction for the man-made crystals was within the range 2.40-2.50. Mineral compilations[27] list five isotropic minerals having a refractive index near this range. Natural diamond is one of them and its value is 2.419. The other four are:

	Index of refraction	Mohs' hardness
Franklinite, (Zn, Fe, Mn) O · (Fe, Mn)$_2$O$_3$	2.36±	6
Perovskite, CaO · TiO$_2$	2.38±	5.5
Sphalerite, (Zn, Fe)S	2.428	3.5-4
Eglestonite, Hg$_2$Cl$_2$, Hg$_2$O	2.49±	2.3

These four are ruled out as possibilities by the other critical tests.

The result of more than four years effort in this laboratory has been the development of equipment capable of holding pressures and temperatures in the diamond-stable region for hours at a time. Synthesis of diamond has been accomplished more than a hundred times. A number of people have independently repeated the various diamond-making processes successfully. These laboratory-made diamonds can scratch natural diamonds and have a crystal structure identical with natural diamonds.

(**176**, 51-55; 1955)

（3）硬度检测。实验室内人造金刚石硬到足以划伤天然金刚石上最硬的 111 晶面（图 5）。

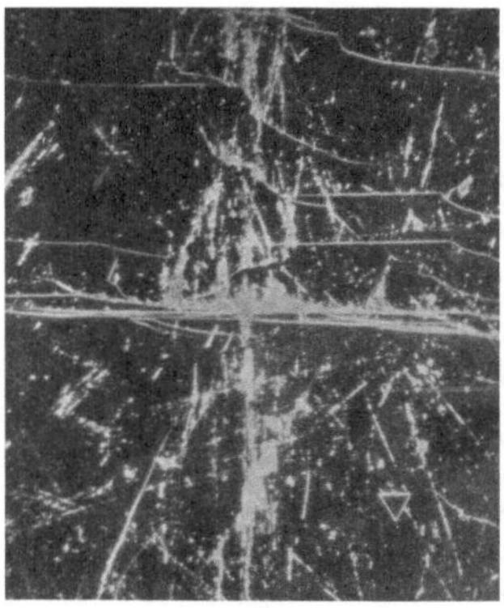

图 5. 人造金刚石在天然金刚石的 111 晶面上的划痕。图片中心显示有大量基本处于垂直方向上的划痕。水平标记为晶面上的生长阶。右下角的三角形凹痕也是金刚石晶面上发现的典型的生长标志。

（4）重复性。通用电气公司的多位员工对金刚石合成实验进行了完全独立的重复。他们制得的金刚石都通过了上述结论性的检测。

另外，实验结果还显示人造晶体的折射率在 2.40~2.50 之间。矿物汇编[27]中列出了 5 种各向同性的矿物的折射率在该范围附近。天然金刚石是其中之一，其折射率为 2.419，另外 4 种是：

	折射率	莫氏硬度
锌铁矿，$(Zn, Fe, Mn)O \cdot (Fe, Mn)_2O_3$	2.36 ±	6
钙钛矿，$CaO \cdot TiO_2$	2.38 ±	5.5
闪锌矿，$(Zn, Fe)S$	2.428	3.5~4
氯汞矿，Hg_2Cl_2, Hg_2O	2.49 ±	2.3

通过其他的关键性实验排除了这 4 种矿物的可能性。

经过四年多的努力，本实验室研制出的实验装置能在金刚石稳定区内的压力和温度下一次持续几个小时。合成金刚石已经重复实现了一百多次。很多人都已独立并成功地重复了金刚石的各种合成过程。这些实验室内的人造金刚石可以划伤天然金刚石，并且具有与天然金刚石相同的晶体结构。

（王耀杨 翻译；李芝芬 审稿）

F. P. Bundy, H. T. Hall, H. M. Strong and R. H. Wentorf, jun.: Research Laboratory, General Electric Company, Schenectady, New York.

References:

1. Hannay, J. B., *Proc. Roy. Soc.*, **30**, 188 (1880), or *Chem. News*, **41**, 106 (1880).
2. Story-Maskelyne, N., *The Times*, Feb. 20, 1880, or *Chem. News*, **41**, 97 (1880).
3. Hannay, J. B., *Proc. Roy. Soc.*, **30**, 450 (1880), or *Nature*, **22**, 255 (1880).
4. Moissan, H., *C.R. Acad. Sci., Paris*, **118**, 320 (1894), and **123**, 206, 210 (1896).
5. Hannay, J. B., *Chem. News*, **86**, 173 (1902).
6. Crookes, W., "Diamonds" (London, 1909).
7. Ruff, O., *Z. anorg. allgem. Chem.*, **99**, 73 (1917).
8. Parsons, C. A., *Proc. Roy. Soc.*, **79**, 532 (1907); *J. Inst. Metals*, **20**, 5 (1918); *Phil. Trans.*, A, **220**, 67 (1920).
9. LeChatelier, H., "Leçons sur le carbone", p. 24 (Paris, 1926).
10. Desch, C. H., *Nature*, **121**, 799 (1928).
11. Hershey, J. W., *Trans. Kansas Acad. Sci.*, **31**, 52 (1929), and **40**, 109 (1937); "The Book of Diamonds" (Hearthside Press, 1940).
12. Bannister, F. A., and Lonsdale, K., *Nature*, **151**, 334 (1943); *Mineral Mag.*, **26**, 309 (1943).
13. Desch, C. H., *Nature*, **152**, 148 (1943).
14. Rayleigh, Lord, *Nature*, **152**, 597 (1943).
15. Travers, M. W., *Nature*, **152**, 726 (1943).
16. French, J. W., *Nature*, **153**, 112 (1944).
17. Lonsdale, K., *Nature*, **153**, 669 (1944).
18. Mellor, D. P., *J. Chem. Phys.*, **15**, 525 (1947); *Research*, **2**, 314 (1949).
19. Bridgman, P. W., *J. Chem. Phys.*, **15**, 92 (1947).
20. Rossini, F. D., "Chemical Thermodynamics", 453 (Wiley, 1950).
21. Sidgwick, N. V., "Chemical Elements and Their Compounds", **1**, 491-3 (Clarendon Press, Oxford, 1950).
22. Moeller, T., "Inorganic Chemistry", 669 (Wiley, 1952).
23. Eyring, H., and Cagle, jun., F. W., *Z. Elektrochem.*, **56**, 480 (1952).
24. Neuhaus, A., *Angew. Chem.*, **66**, 525 (1954).
25. Rossini, F. D., and Jessup, R. S., *J. Res. Nat. Bur. Stand.*, **21**, 491 (1938).
26. Bridgman, P. W., *Proc. Amer. Acad. Arts and Sci.*, **81**, 165 (1952).
27. Palache, Berman and Frondel, "Dana's System of Mineralogy" (J. Wiley, 1951).

Errors in Diamond Synthesis

H. P. Bovenkerk *et al.*

Editor's Note

This postscript to the synthesis of artificial diamond, reported in *Nature* in 1955, adds an intriguing twist to the story. A team at General Electric in Schenectady, New York, including most of those who did the original work, reanalysed the first diamond "grown" using their method of compressing carbon materials to high pressures under high-temperature conditions. They find that this "synthetic diamond" is not actually synthetic at all, but a fragment of natural diamond. How it got into the initial sample is not clear. The finding in no way invalidated the earlier work, in which unambiguously artificial diamonds were subsequently made. But the misattribution, say the researchers, serendipitously gave them faith that they were on the right track.

SIR —In 1955, some of us announced the first reproducible synthesis of diamond[1], details of which were subsequently published[2]. These results marked the beginning of the present synthetic-diamond industry. But from the outset there were doubts in our team as to whether the first diamond grown by our technique (which we will call the run 151 diamond) was truly synthetic at all, or whether it was instead just a fragment of a natural diamond seed that got into the experiment inadvertently. We have now reanalysed the run 151 diamond using modern spectroscopic techniques and have found that it is indeed a small piece of a natural type Ia diamond.

In the early 1950s four of us (H. P. B., F. P. B., H. M. S. and R. H. W.), together with H. T. Hall, developed an approach to diamond synthesis at high pressures and temperatures. The pressure scale used in our experiments was Bridgman's "resistance-jump" scale, which was suspected to be in error in absolute terms above 30 kbar or so. The proximity of our experimental conditions to the calculated graphite-diamond phase boundary was therefore uncertain.

The run 151 diamond appeared in an experiment using apparatus made of hard steel. According to the Bridgman "resistance" scale, the pressure in this run was about 53 kbar, within the diamond stability field[3]. But later developments revealed that the true pressure could not have been much above 42 kbar, which is insufficient to stabilize diamond.

To investigate the true nature of the run 151 diamond, we recently removed it from the GE archives, cleaned it with acids and rinsed it with water. An infrared absorption spectrum was measured using an IR PLAN microscope attached to a Nicolet 740 FTIR spectrometer. The portion of this spectrum shown in the figure resembles that of a natural nitrogen-containing type Ia diamond[4]. In particular, there are coincidences of the

金刚石合成中的失误

博文科克等

编者按

本篇是针对 1955 年在《自然》上发表的关于人造金刚石的合成的补充说明，文章为该故事增添了一段引人入胜的曲折情节。参与最初工作的大部分研究人员隶属于通用电气公司（位于美国纽约州的斯克内克塔迪）的一个研究小组，他们对当时“长出的”第一块金刚石进行了重新分析。这块金刚石是在高温高压条件下用压缩碳材料的方法制得的。他们发现这一“合成金刚石”事实上完全不是合成的，而是天然金刚石的一个碎片。至于它是如何进入到最初的实验样品的仍不清楚。这一发现一点也没否定之前的工作，因为毫无疑问他们随后的确合成出了人造金刚石。相关研究人员表示，对这一错误的偶然判定却使得他们坚信他们在正确的轨道上。

在 1955 年，我们中的一些人宣布了第一次可重复地合成金刚石[1]，有关此合成的详细资料随后予以发表[2]。这些结果标志着当前合成金刚石工业的开端；但是从一开始我们的研究小组中就存在着这样的疑虑：用我们的技术所生长出来的第一块金刚石（我们将其称为 151 轮金刚石）确实是真的合成的呢？还是只是由于我们的疏忽而引入实验中的天然金刚石籽晶的碎片？现在，我们用当代光谱技术重新分析了 151 轮金刚石，发现它确实是天然 Ia 型金刚石的小碎片。

20 世纪 50 年代早期，我们中的四位（博文科克、邦迪、斯特朗和小温托夫）与霍尔一起研制了一种在高温高压下合成金刚石的方法。在我们的实验中所用的压力标度是布里奇曼的“阻抗跳跃”标度，该标度被认为在大约超过 30 千巴时其绝对值有误差，因此在我们的实验条件下由计算所得的石墨－金刚石相界的近似度是不确定的。

151 轮金刚石是在用硬钢制成的装置中进行实验得到的。根据布里奇曼的“阻抗”标度，这一轮反应的压强约为 53 千巴，处于金刚石的稳定区域[3]之中；但是后来的研究进展表明其真正的压强不大可能远远超过 42 千巴，而 42 千巴并不足以稳定金刚石。

为了研究 151 轮金刚石的真正本质，最近，我们将它从通用电气公司的档案部门中取出，用酸溶液对其进行清洗并用水漂洗。用装配有 IR PLAN 显微镜的尼高力 740 傅里叶变换红外光谱仪进行了红外吸收光谱的测定。图中所显示的这部分光谱类似于天然的含氮 Ia 型金刚石[4]的光谱。尤其是在以下几处存在着吸收光谱

absorption bands at about 1,365 cm^{-1} (related to nitrogen platelets), 1,330 cm^{-1} (a Raman frequency, rendered infrared-active by defects and impurities), 1,280 cm^{-1} (from nitrogen in the "A" aggregate form) and 1,175 cm^{-1} (from nitrogen in the "B" aggregate form). We also show the spectrum of a typical nitrogen-containing synthetic type Ib diamond, which has characteristic bands at 1,130 and 1,343 cm^{-1} (ref. 5); neither of these bands is seen in the run 151 diamond. We conclude that the run 151 diamond is a small piece of a natural type Ia diamond.

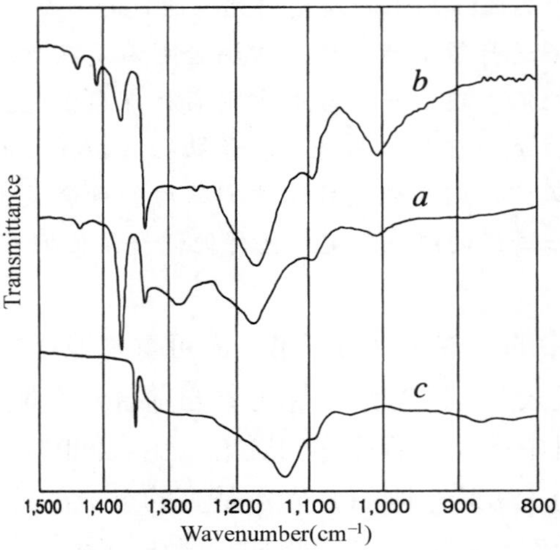

Infrared absorption spectra of: *a*, run 151 diamond; *b*, a type Ia natural diamond with "B"-form nitrogen; *c*, a typical synthesized diamond (type Ib).

How the natural diamond got into the run 151 experiment is not clear, although it came to light only a week later, when the iron pellet from the run was being polished for metallographic examination. After we found this diamond and took it to be synthetic, Hall used a similar synthetic system of iron/iron sulphide/graphite in his "belt" apparatus, which used a carbide piston and cylinder to achieve high pressures[6]. This led to further successful runs and ultimately to the development of the process for synthesizing diamonds at high pressures and temperatures from graphite reacted with molten group VIII metals and alloys, which we described fully in 1959[2] (after a US Department of Defense secrecy order had been lifted). Our mistake was therefore clearly a most serendipitous one, as it provided the impetus to experiment with that system at higher pressures, leading quickly to the "right" and "reproducible" results.

(**365**, 19; 1993)

H. P. Bovenkerk, F. P. Bundy, R. M. Chrenko, P. J. Codella, H. M Strong and R. H. Wentorf Jr: GE Corporate Research and Development, Schenectady, New York 12301, USA.

带的一致性：位于约 1,365 厘米$^{-1}$ 处（与片晶氮相相关）、1,330 厘米$^{-1}$ 处（拉曼频率，由于缺陷和杂质而获得红外活性）、1,280 厘米$^{-1}$ 处（来自“A”型聚集态中的氮）和 1,175 厘米$^{-1}$ 处（来自“B”型聚集态中的氮）。我们还指出：典型的含氮 Ib 型合成金刚石光谱具有位于 1,130 厘米$^{-1}$ 和 1,343 厘米$^{-1}$ 处的特征带 (参考文献 5)，而在 151 轮金刚石中这些带都是看不到的。因此，我们断定 151 轮金刚石是天然 Ia 型金刚石的小碎片。

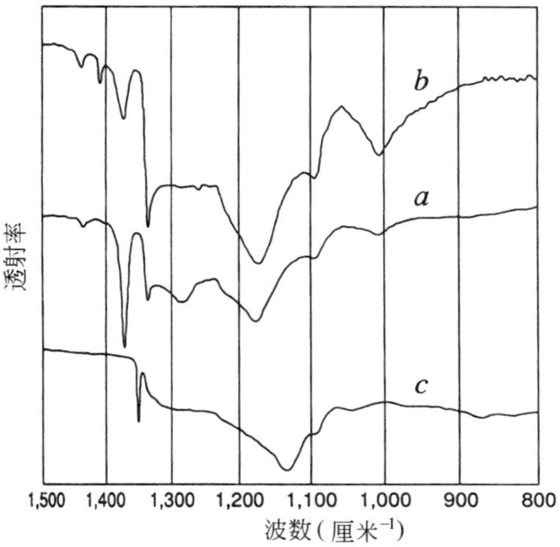

红外吸收光谱：*a*，151 轮金刚石；*b*，含“B”型氮的 Ia 型天然金刚石；*c*，典型的合成金刚石（Ib 型）。

虽然只在一个星期后发现，为了进行金相学检测该轮实验中的铁丸被抛光了，但是我们仍然不清楚天然金刚石是如何进入 151 轮实验中的。在我们发现这种金刚石并将其视为合成产物之后，霍尔在他的“带”装置中使用了铁 / 黄铁矿 / 石墨的类似合成体系，其中使用了一种碳化物活塞和圆筒以获取高压 [6]。由此取得了随后的多轮成功并且最终发展了在高压高温下用石墨与熔融的第 VIII 族金属和合金反应以合成金刚石的工艺，在 1959 年我们对其进行了完整的描述 [2]（在美国国防部撤销其保密等级之后）。由此可以清晰地看到，我们的失误是一种非常幸运的偶然性，因为它为我们在更高压强系统下进行实验提供了推动力，引导我们很快地获得了“正确的”和“可重复的”结果。

（王耀杨 翻译；李芝芬 审稿）

References:
1. Bundy, F. P., Hall, H. T., Strongm, H. M, and Wentorf, R. H. Jr., *Nature,* **176**, 51-54 (1955).

2. Bovenkerk, H. P., Bundy, F. P., Hall, H. T., Strong, H. M., and Wentorf, R. H. Jr., *Nature,* **184**, 1094-1098 (1959).

3. Strong, H. M., *Am. J. Phys.*, **57**, 794-802 (1989).

4. Clark, C. D., Mitchell, E. W. J., and Parsons, B. J., in *The Properties of Diamond* (ed. Field, J. E.), 28 (Academic. London, 1979).

5. Chrenko, R. M., Tuft, R. E., and Strong, H. M., *Nature,* **270**, 141-144 (1977).

6. Hall. H. T. *Rev. sci. Instr.*, **31**, 125-131 (1960).

Correlation between Photons in Two Coherent Beams of Light

R. Hanbury-Brown and R. Q. Twiss

Editor's Note

In classical interferometry, phase differences between two interacting light beams probe differences in their travelled paths. In the early 1950s, Robert Hanbury-Brown and Richard Twiss proposed that a new means of interferometry, using only the intensity (not the phase) of light, could be used to estimate the angular size of distant stars. Here they report a laboratory demonstration of the effect. The result illustrated the quantum" bunching" of photons—the tendency for photons in two separate, coherent beams to arrive together at two detectors. The Hanbury-Brown Twiss effect now refers generally to any correlation or anti-correlation in the intensities of signals measured by two detectors from a beam of particles. Intensity interferometry has become an important technique in nuclear and particle physics.

IN an earlier paper[1], we have described a new type of interferometer which has been used to measure the angular diameter of radio stars[2]. In this instrument the signals from two aerials A_1 and A_2 (Fig. 1*a*) are detected independently and the correlation between the low-frequency outputs of the detectors is recorded. The relative phases of the two radio signals are therefore lost, and only the correlation in their intensity fluctuations is measured; so that the principle differs radically from that of the familiar Michelson interferometer where the signals are combined before detection and where their relative phase must be preserved.

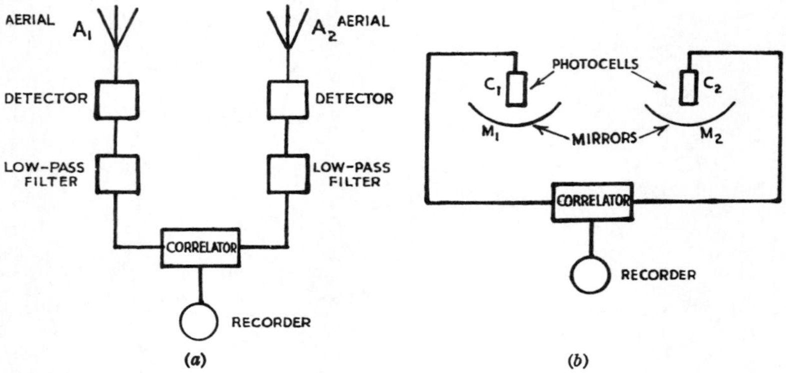

Fig. 1. A new type of radio interferometer (*a*), together with its analogue (*b*) at optical wave-lengths

This new system was developed for use with very long base-lines, and experimentally it has proved to be largely free of the effects of ionospheric scintillation[2]. These advantages led us to suggest[1] that the principle might be applied to the measurement of the angular

两个相干光束中光子间的相关性

汉伯里-布朗，特威斯

编者按

在经典的干涉技术中，由两个相互作用光束之间的相位差可以探查出它们传播路径的不同。20 世纪 50 年代早期，罗伯特·汉伯里-布朗和理查德·特威斯提出了一种新的干涉测量法，此方法仅仅利用光强（非相位）就可以估测遥远恒星的角大小。本文中他们报道了对这种效应所做的实验论证。结果阐释了光子的量子“聚束”效应——两束独立的相干光束中的光子有同时到达两个探测器的趋势。现在，汉伯里-布朗-特威斯效应一般是指使用两个探测器测量出的从一个粒子束发出的信号强度之间的任何相关性或者反相关性。强度干涉法已经成为核物理以及粒子物理中一项重要的技术。

在一篇早期的论文中[1]，我们描述了一台新型的干涉仪，它已被用于测量射电星的角直径[2]。用这台仪器分别检测来自 A_1 和 A_2 两个天线（如图 1*a* 所示）的信号，并记录检测器低频输出之间的相关系数。因此我们没有测量到两个射电信号的相对相位，而仅测量到它们强度起伏的相关系数；这种原理与常见的迈克尔逊干涉仪的原理有根本上的差异，因为后者的信号是在检测前合成的，从而必然保留它们的相对相位。

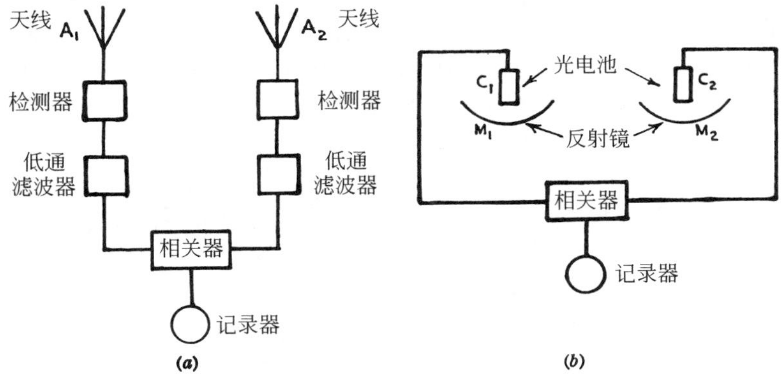

图 1. 新型射电干涉仪 (*a*) 及其在光学波段的类似设备 (*b*)

开发这套新系统是为了利用甚长基线，实验证明它在很大程度上不受电离层闪烁效应的影响[2]。鉴于这套系统的优点，我们提出[1]从原理上它可以用于测量目视

diameter of visual stars. Thus one could replace the two aerials by two mirrors M_1, M_2 (Fig. 1*b*) and the radio-frequency detectors by photoelectric cells C_1, C_2, and measure, as a function of the separation of the mirrors, the correlation between the fluctuations in the currents from the cells when illuminated by a star.

It is, of course, essential to the operation of such a system that the time of arrival of photons at the two photocathodes should be correlated when the light beams incident upon the two mirrors are coherent. However, so far as we know, this fundamental effect has never been directly observed with light, and indeed its very existence has been questioned. Furthermore, it was by no means certain that the correlation would be fully preserved in the process of photoelectric emission. For these reasons a laboratory experiment was carried out as described below.

The apparatus is shown in outline in Fig. 2. A light source was formed by a small rectangular aperture, 0.13 mm. × 0.15 mm. in cross-section, on which the image of a high-pressure mercury are was focused. The 4,358 A. line was isolated by a system of filters, and the beam was divided by the half-silvered mirror M to illuminate the cathodes of the photomultipliers C_1, C_2. The two cathodes were at a distance of 2.65 m. from the source and their areas were limited by identical rectangular apertures O_1, O_2, 9.0 mm. × 8.5 mm. in cross-section. (It can be shown that for this type of instrument the two cathodes need not be located at precisely equal distances from the source. In the present case their distances were adjusted to be roughly equal to an accuracy of about 1 cm.) In order that the degree of coherence of the two light beams might be varied at will, the photomultiplier C_1, was mounted on a horizontal slide which could be traversed normal to the incident light. The two cathode apertures, as viewed from the source, could thus be superimposed or separated by any amount up to about three times their own width. The fluctuations in the output currents from the photomultipliers were amplified over the band 3-27 Mc./s. and multiplied together in a linear mixer. The average value of the product, which was recorded on the revolution counter of an integrating motor, gave a measure of the correlation in the fluctuations. To obtain a significant result it was necessary to integrate for periods of the order of one hour, so very great care had to be taken in the design of the electronic equipment to eliminate the effects of drift, of interference and of amplifier noise.

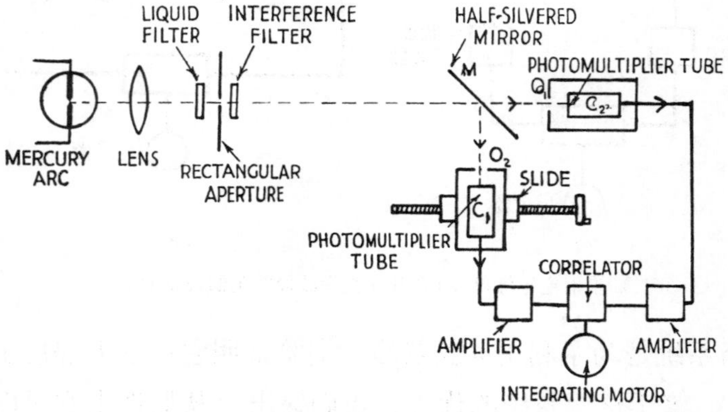

Fig. 2. Simplified diagram of the apparatus

恒星的角直径。因此我们可以用 M_1 和 M_2 两面反射镜来代替 A_1 和 A_2 两根天线（如图 1*b* 所示），用光电池 C_1 和 C_2 作为射频检测器，将测量到的由恒星照射导致的电池中电流起伏间的相关系数作为反射镜间距的函数。

当然，当入射到两个反射镜上的光束有相干性时，光子到达两个光电阴极的时间应该是相关的，这对于这套系统的运行是很有必要的。然而，据我们所知，目前尚未用光直接观测到这个基本效应，况且此效应存在与否还存在疑问。此外，在光电发射过程中，无法确定是否完全保留着这种相关性。为此，我们开展了下列实验。

图 2 展示了此套装置的概略图。一个截面为 0.13 毫米 × 0.15 毫米的小矩形孔径形成光源，高压汞灯在此截面上聚焦成像。我们通过滤波系统将 4,358 埃的谱线分离出来，光束通过半透半反分束镜 *M* 被分成两束，分别照射在光电倍增管 C_1 和 C_2 的阴极上。这两个阴极与光源相距 2.65 米，它们的面积受到截面为 9.0 毫米 ×8.5 毫米的相同矩形孔径 O_1 和 O_2 的限制。（可以证明这类仪器的两个阴极与光源之间的距离并不需要精确相等。在目前的实验中，它们的距离只是大致相等，精度约为 1 厘米。）为了使两束光束的相干度可以任意改变，光电倍增管 C_1 装在水平轨道上，这样光电倍增管 C_1 可以在垂直于入射光的方向上移动。因此从光源看来，两个阴极孔径能叠加或分离到最大可达约为其自身宽度 3 倍的任何量值。在 3 兆周 / 秒 ~27 兆周 / 秒波段内来自光电倍增管的输出电流的起伏被放大，并在线性混频器中倍增。在积分电机的旋转计数器上记录乘积的平均值，并对起伏相关系数进行度量。为了得到有意义的结果，必须要对量级 1 小时的周期进行积分，所以我们非常精心地设计了电子装置，从而消除由漂移、干涉和放大器噪声所造成的影响。

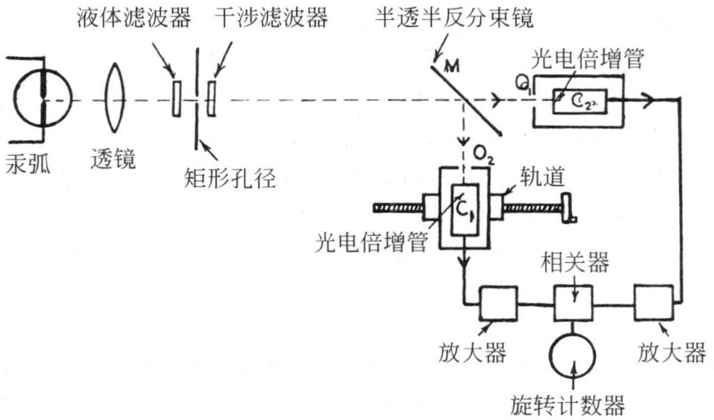

图 2. 装置的简化图

Assuming that the probability of emission of a photoelectron is proportional to the square of the amplitude of the incident light, one can use classical electromagnetic wave theory to calculate the correlation between the fluctuations in the current from the two cathodes. On this assumption it can be shown that, with the two cathodes superimposed, the correlation $S(0)$ is given by:

$$S(0) = A \cdot T \cdot b_v \mathrm{f}\left(\frac{a_1 \theta_1 \pi}{\lambda_0}\right) \cdot \mathrm{f}\left(\frac{a_2 \theta_2 \pi}{\lambda_0}\right) \int \alpha^2(v) \cdot n_0^2(v) \cdot dv \tag{1}$$

It can also be shown that the associated root-mean-square fluctuations N are given by:

$$N = A \cdot T \cdot \frac{2m}{m-1} \cdot b_v (b_v T)^{-\frac{1}{2}} \int \alpha(v) \cdot n_0(v) \cdot dv \tag{2}$$

where A is a constant of proportionality depending on the amplifier gain, etc.; T is the time of observation; $\alpha(v)$ is the quantum efficiency of the photocathodes at a frequency v; $n_0(v)$ is the number of quanta incident on a photocathode per second, per cycle bandwidth; b_v is the bandwidth of the amplifiers; $m/(m-1)$ is the familiar excess noise introduced by secondary multiplication; a_1, a_2 are the horizontal and vertical dimensions of the photocathode apertures; θ_1, θ_2 are the angular dimensions of the source as viewed from the photocathodes; and λ_0 is the mean wave-length of the light. The integrals are taken over the complete optical spectrum and the phototubes are assumed to be identical. The factor $\mathrm{f}\left(\frac{a\theta\pi}{\lambda_0}\right)$ is determined by the dimensionless parameter η defined by

$$\eta = a\theta/\lambda_0 \tag{3}$$

which is a measure of the degree to which the light is coherent over a photocathode. When $\eta \ll 1$, as for a point source, $\mathrm{f}(\eta)$ is effectively unity; however, in the laboratory experiment it proved convenient to make η_1, η_2 of the order of unity in order to increase the light incident on the cathodes and thereby improve the ratio of signal to noise. The corresponding values of $\mathrm{f}(\eta_1)$, $\mathrm{f}(\eta_2)$ were 0.62 and 0.69 respectively.

When the centres of the cathodes, as viewed from the source, are displaced horizontally by a distance d, the theoretical value of the correlation decreases in a manner dependent upon the dimensionless parameters, η_1 and d/a_1. In the simple case where $\eta_1 \ll 1$, which would apply to an experiment on a visual star, it can be shown that $S(d)$, the correlation as a function of d, is proportional to the square of the Fourier transform of the intensity distribution across the equivalent line source. However, when $\eta \geqslant 1$, as in the present experiment, the correlation is determined effectively by the apparent overlap of the cathodes and does not depend critically on the actual width of the source. For this reason no attempt was made in the present experiment to measure the apparent angular size of the source.

The initial observations were taken with the photocathodes effectively superimposed ($d = 0$) and with varying intensities of illumination. In all cases a positive correlation was observed which completely disappeared, as expected, when the separation of the photocathodes

假设发射一个光电子的概率与入射光的振幅的平方成正比，我们可以用经典电磁波理论计算来自两个阴极的电流起伏之间的相关系数。根据这个假设我们可以证明，两个阴极叠加，相关系数 $S(0)$ 由下式表示：

$$S(0) = A \cdot T \cdot b_v \mathrm{f}\left(\frac{a_1\theta_1\pi}{\lambda_0}\right) \cdot \mathrm{f}\left(\frac{a_2\theta_2\pi}{\lambda_0}\right) \int \alpha^2(v) \cdot n_0^2(v) \cdot \mathrm{d}v \tag{1}$$

同样地，相应的方均根涨落 N 由下式给出：

$$N = A \cdot T \cdot \frac{2m}{m-1} \cdot b_v (b_v T)^{-\frac{1}{2}} \int \alpha(v) \cdot n_0(v) \cdot \mathrm{d}v \tag{2}$$

式中 A 是与放大器增益等有关的比例常数；T 是观测时间；$\alpha(v)$ 是光电阴极在频率 v 处的量子效率；$n_0(v)$ 是每秒钟每周带宽入射到光电阴极上的量子数；b_v 是放大器的带宽；$m/(m-1)$ 是次级倍增引入的常见过量噪声；a_1 和 a_2 是光电阴极孔径的水平尺寸和垂直尺寸；θ_1 和 θ_2 是从光电阴极来看光源的角尺寸；λ_0 是光的平均波长。在假定光电管完全相同的情况下，对整个光谱积分。因子 $\mathrm{f}\left(\frac{a\theta\pi}{\lambda_0}\right)$ 由无量纲参数 η 决定，η 的定义为：

$$\eta = a\theta/\lambda_0 \tag{3}$$

这是光在光电阴极范围内相干度的度量。当 $\eta \ll 1$ 时，对于点光源，$\mathrm{f}(\eta)$ 可有效地认定为单位 1；然而，在实验室中做实验时，可方便地证明：设置 η_1 和 η_2 为单位 1 的数量级，以增加阴极上的入射光，从而提高信噪比。此时对应的 $\mathrm{f}(\eta_1)$ 和 $\mathrm{f}(\eta_2)$ 的值分别是 0.62 和 0.69。

当从源处看阴极的中心水平方向上位移距离为 d 时，相关系数的理论值会降低，它的多少与无量纲参量 η_1 和 d/a_1 有关。在简单情况下 $\eta_1 \ll 1$，将其用于可视恒星的实验上，可以证明相关系数 $S(d)$ 作为 d 的函数与等效线源上强度分布的傅里叶变换的平方成正比。然而，当 $\eta \geqslant 1$ 时，正如在目前的实验中一样，相关系数是由阴极的表观叠加有效决定的，而并不严格地依赖于源处的实际宽度。因此，在目前的实验中我们并不试图测量源的视角大小。

最初的实验观测是在光电阴极有效地叠加 $(d=0)$ 以及改变照明强度下进行的。在我们所预期的所有情况下，当光电阴极相距很远时，观测到相关系数为正的情

was large. In these first experiments the quantum efficiency of the photocathodes was too low to give a satisfactory ratio of signal to noise. However, when an improved type of photomultiplier became available with an appreciably higher quantum efficiency, it was possible to make a quantitative test of the theory.

A set of four runs, each of 90 min. duration, was made with the cathodes superimposed ($d = 0$), the counter readings being recorded at 5-min. intervals. From these readings an estimate was made of N_e, the root mean square deviation in the final reading $S(0)$ of the counter, and the observed values of $S_e(0)/N_e$ are shown in column 2 of Table 1. The results are given as a ratio in order to eliminate the factor A in equations (1) and (2), which is affected by changes in the gain of the equipment. For each run the factor

$$\frac{m-1}{m}\int \alpha^2(\nu)\, n_0^2(\nu) d\nu \Big/ \int \alpha(\nu)\, n_0(\nu)\, d\nu$$

was determined from measurements of the spectrum of the incident light and of the d.c. current, gain and output noise of the photomultipliers; the corresponding theoretical values of $S(0)/N$ are shown in the second column of Table 1. In a typical case, the photomultiplier gain was 3×10^5, the output current was 140 μamp., the quantum efficiency $\alpha(\nu_0)$ was of the order of 15 percent and $n_0(\nu_0)$ was of the order of 3×10^{-3}. After each run a comparison run was taken with the centres of the photocathodes, as viewed from the source, separated by twice their width ($d = 2a$), in which position the theoretical correlation is virtually zero. The ratio of $S_e(d)$, the counter reading after 90 minutes, to N_e, the root mean square deviation, is shown in the third column of Table 1.

Table 1. Comparison between the Theoretical and Experimental Values of the Correlation

	Cathodes superimposed ($d = 0$)		Cathodes separated ($d = 2a = 1.8$ cm.)	
	Experimental ratio of correlation to r.m.s. deviation $S_e(0)/N_e$	Theoretical ratio of correlation to r.m.s. deviation $S(0)/N$	Experimental ratio of correlation to r.m.s. deviation $S_e(d)/N_e$	Theoretical ratio of correlation to r.m.s. deviation $S(d)/N$
1	+7.4	+8.4	−0.4	~0
2	+6.6	+8.0	+0.5	~0
3	+7.6	+8.4	+1.7	~0
4	+4.2	+5.2	−0.3	~0

The results shown in Table 1 confirm that correlation is observed when the cathodes are superimposed but not when they are widely separated. However, it may be noted that the correlations observed with $d = 0$ are consistently lower than those predicted theoretically. The discrepancy may not be significant but, if it is real, it was possibly caused by defects in the optical system. In particular, the image of the arc showed striations due to imperfections in the glass bulb of the lamp; this implies that unwanted differential phase-shifts were being introduced which would tend to reduce the observed correlation.

况完全消失。在第一批实验中，光电阴极的量子效率太低，以致没有得到令人满意的信噪比。然而，当我们采用具有较高量子效率的改进型光电倍增管时，就能进行这个理论的定量检验。

我们所做的观测 4 次为一组、每次持续时间为 90 分钟，是在阴极叠加 ($d=0$) 时进行的。计数器以 5 分钟为时间间隔进行记录。根据这些读数，我们对 N_e 做出估测，其中 N_e 为计数器最终读数 $S(0)$ 的均方根偏差，将 $S_e(0)/N_e$ 的观测值列入表 1 的第 1 列内。为了消除 (1) 式和 (2) 式中的因子 A，结果以比值的形式给出，此比值受装置增益变化的影响。对每次测量的因子如下式所示：

$$\frac{m-1}{m}\int\alpha^2(v)n_0^2(v)\mathrm{d}v\Big/\int\alpha(v)n_0(v)\mathrm{d}v$$

这是由入射光的光谱、直流电流、增益和光电倍增管的输出噪声所决定的；表 1 的第 2 列内示出了 $S(0)/N$ 相应的理论值。在典型情况下，光电倍增管的增益是 3×10^5，输出电流是 140 微安，量子效率 $\alpha(v_0)$ 的数量级为 15%，$n_0(v_0)$ 的数量级为 3×10^{-3}。在每次测量之后，在光电阴极中心做一次对比测量，从源处看两阴极之间的距离为自身宽度的两倍 ($d=2a$)，在光电阴极中心时理论修正实际上为零。表 1 的第 3 列内列出的是 $S_e(d)$ 与 N_e 的比值，其中 $S_e(d)$ 是 90 分钟后的计数器读数，N_e 是均方根偏差。

表 1. 相关系数的理论值和实验值之间的比较

阴极叠加 ($d=0$)		阴极分离 ($d=2a=1.8$ 厘米)	
相关系数与均方根偏差的实验比 $S_e(0)/N_e$	相关系数与均方根偏差的理论比 $S(0)/N$	相关系数与均方根偏差的实验比 $S_e(d)/N_e$	相关系数与均方根偏差的理论比 $S(d)/N$
1　+7.4	+8.4	−0.4	~0
2　+6.6	+8.0	+0.5	~0
3　+7.6	+8.4	+1.7	~0
4　+4.2	+5.2	−0.3	~0

表 1 中所示的结果证实了在阴极叠加时可观测到相关性，但当阴极相距甚远时未观测到相关性。然而可以注意到的是，距离 $d=0$ 时实验所观测到的相关系数比理论上预料的数值一致偏低。这个差异可能并不重要，但如果事实如此，那么它可能是由光学系统中的缺陷引起的。尤其是灯的玻璃泡中的不完善性引起弧光的像呈现辉纹，这意味着引入了多余的微分相移，它们往往会降低观测到的相关系数。

This experiment shows beyond question that the photons in two coherent beams of light are correlated, and that this correlation is preserved in the process of photoelectric emission. Furthermore, the quantitative results are in fair agreement with those predicted by classical electromagnetic wave theory and the correspondence principle. It follows that the fundamental principle of the interferometer represented in Fig. 1*b* is sound, and it is proposed to examine in further detail its application to visual astronomy. The basic mathematical theory together with a description of the electronic apparatus used in the laboratory experiment will be given later.

We thank the Director of Jodrell Bank for making available the necessary facilities, the Superintendent of the Services Electronics Research Laboratory for the loan of equipment, and Mr. J. Rodda, of the Ediswan Co., for the use of two experimental phototubes. One of us wishes to thank the Admiralty for permission to submit this communication for publication.

(**177**, 27-29; 1956)

R. Hanbury-Brown: University of Manchester, Jodrell Bank Experimental Station.
R. Q. Twiss: Services Electronics Research Laboratory, Baldock.

References:

1. Hanbury Brown, R., and Twiss, R. Q., *Phil. Mag.*, 45, 663 (1954).
2. Jennison, R. C., and Das Gupta, M. K., *Phil. Mag.* (in the press).

这项实验表明，两束相干光的两个光子之间的相关性是毫无疑问的，这种相关性存在于光电发射的过程中。此外，定量结果与经典电磁波理论及相应原理的预料吻合得相当好。图 1*b* 所示干涉仪的基本原理是正确的，建议在目视天文学的应用中进行进一步详细的检验。基本数学理论与用于实验室的电子学装置的描述将在以后一起给出。

我们感谢焦德雷尔班克天文台台长允许我们使用所需的实验设备，同时对电子服务研究实验室的负责人所提供的实验设备表示感谢，还要对爱迪斯旺公司的罗达先生所提供的两个光电管表示感谢。我们当中的一位作者对英国海军部同意将此文予以发表表示感谢。

（沈乃澂 翻译；熊秉衡 审稿）

Chinese Astronomical Clockwork

J. Needham *et al.*

Editor's Note

Joseph Needham was born in 1900, the son of a leading physician in London. He studied medicine and biochemistry at the University of London but in the mid-1930s he encountered three young people visiting his laboratory from China and became deeply interested in the history of Chinese science. One of the visitors was Lu Gwei-djen, the daughter of a Chinese pharmacist, who taught him classical Chinese. Needham and Lu spent the period 1942-46 in China where he was director of the Sino-British Science Cooperation Office. Here he formed a working relationship with Wang Ling, a distinguished historian who remained a close collaborator. The main product of his Chinese work was a series of 23 volumes entitled *Science and Civilisation in China*. Needham died in 1995. This article is presumably one of the those collected for his mammoth work.

IT is generally agreed that the invention of the mechanical clock was one of the most important turning-points in the history of science and thechnology. According to the view accepted until recently[1-4], the problem of slowing down the rotation of a wheel to keep a constant speed continuously in time with the apparent diurnal rotation of the heavens was first solved in Europe in the early fourteenth century A.D. Trains of gearing were then combined with the verge and foliot escapement and powered by a falling weight. Recent research has shown, however, that these first mechanical time-keepers were not so much an innovation as has been supposed[5]. They descended, in fact, from a long series of complicated astronomical "clocks", planetary models, mechanically-rotated star-maps and similar devices designed primarily for exhibition and demonstration rather than accurate time-keeping. Although such devices are of the greatest interest as the earliest complex scientific machines, it has not hitherto been possible to adduce more than a few fragmentary remains, and literary descriptions tantalizingly incomplete, which lack sufficient detail for clear understanding of the mechanical principles involved. But the examination of certain medieval Chinese texts, the relevance of which has not been realized, has now permitted us to establish the existence of a long tradition of astronomical clock-making in China between the seventh and the fourteenth centuries A.D.

The key text is the "Hsin I Hsiang Fa Yao" [New Design for a (Mechanized) Armillary (Sphere) and (Celestial) Globe], written by Su Sung in A.D. 1090, the appropriate sections of which we have fully translated. This describes in great detail an astronomical clock of large size (Figs. 1 and 2) powered not by a falling weight, but by a scoop-wheel using water or mercury. Besides the rotation of the sphere and globe by trains of gear-wheels, the clock embodied elaborate time-keeping jack-work. The escapement consisted of a weigh-bridge

中国的天文钟

李约瑟等

编者按

李约瑟出生于1900年，是伦敦一个首席医生的儿子。他在伦敦大学学习医学和生物化学，然而在20世纪30年代中期，他遇到了三个参观他实验室的中国年轻人，开始对中国科学的历史产生了浓厚的兴趣。其中一个来访者鲁桂珍是一位中国药师的女儿，教他学习文言文。1942年～1946年间李约瑟和鲁桂珍在中国工作，李约瑟时任中英科学合作馆馆长。在这里他结识了出色的历史学家王铃，并保持密切的合作关系。他在中国工作的主要成果是出版了一套23卷的、名为《中国科学技术史》的书。1995年李约瑟逝世。这篇文章可能是他当时庞大工作中的一部分。

人们通常将机械钟的发明看作科技史上最重要的转折点之一。按照最近才被人们广为接受的观点[1-4]，在公元14世纪早期欧洲人首先解决了机械钟转轮变慢的问题，从而使钟表保持恒定的速率，与大自然的日夜变化相一致。他们将一系列传动装置与带有摆轮心轴与原始平衡摆的擒纵装置结合起来，然后用落锤提供动力。然而，最近的研究表明，这些最早的计时器并非如之前认为的那样富有创新性[5]。事实上，这些钟表起源于一系列复杂的天文“钟”、行星模型、机械转动星图以及类似的装置，这些设计最初是为了演示而不是为了精确计时。尽管这些装置作为最早的复杂的科学机械具有重要的意义，但是迄今只能引证少量破碎的遗物以及残缺到令人着急的文字描述，要想清楚全面地理解其中的机械原理，还缺乏足够的资料。然而，阅读那些人们尚未意识到存在关联的中世纪的中国史料，使我们承认在公元7世纪到14世纪中国已经存在着悠久的天文钟制造传统。

这方面的主要书籍是公元1090年苏颂撰写的《新仪象法要》（对浑天仪和天球仪的新设计），我们已将相关的章节全部翻译。这本书详细描述了一种尺寸很大的天文钟（图1和图2），它不是由落锤，而是由水或水银驱动的水斗轮提供动力。除了一系列传动转轮装置带动浑天仪和天球仪的球体旋转外，该钟具有精确的守时机制。擒纵装置包括一个衡桥，用于在水斗充满前托住水斗防止其下降；还包括一个撞击

which prevented the fall of each scoop until full, and a trip-lever and parallel linkage system which checked the rotation of the wheel at another point. An anti-recoil device was also built in. The basic principle involved is thus more like the anchor escapement of the late seventeenth century than the verge and foliot type, although the time-keeping is, of course, governed mainly by the flow of water rather than by the escapement action itself. This type of effect is therefore the "missing link" between the time-keeping properties of a steady flow of liquid and those of mechanically produced oscillations. So complete is the description, which has yielded more than a hundred and fifty technical terms of eleventh-century mechanics, that it has been possible to prepare detailed working drawings of the clock (Figs. 3 and 4).

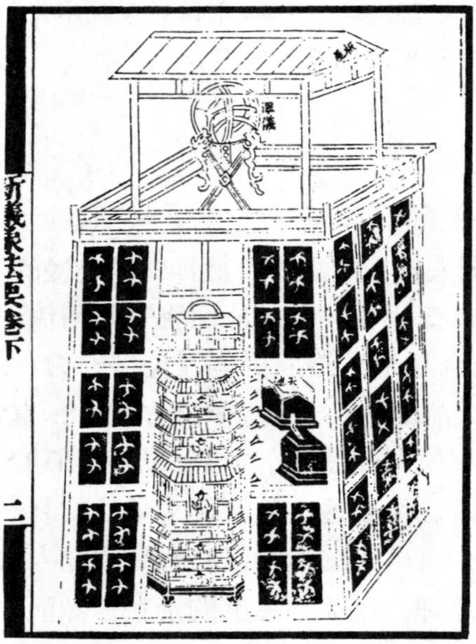

Fig. 1

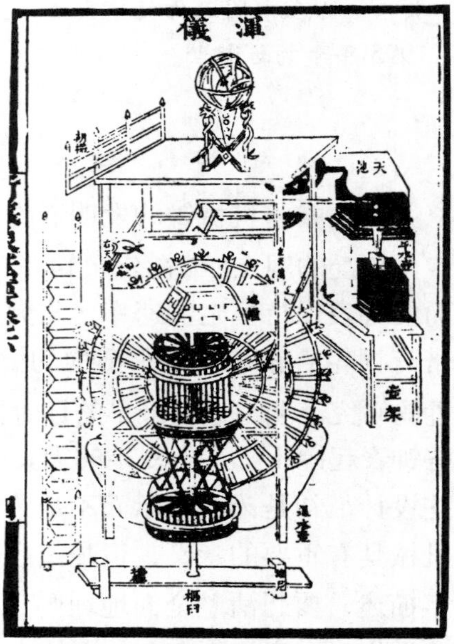

Fig. 2

Fig. 1. Astronomical clock of A.D. 1088 from Su Sung's "Hsin I Hsiang Fa Yao", ch. 3, p. 2*a*. External appearance. The armillary sphere on the platform above, the celestial globe in the upper chamber of the tower, and the pagoda with the time-announcing jacks below this. On the right, the housing removed to show the water-tanks. Estimated total height about 30 ft.

Fig. 2. The same as Fig. 1. General view of the works. Vertical shaft with jack-wheels in the foreground, behind this the driving-wheel with its scoops. Water-tanks on the right, part of the anti-recoil device on the left at the top. Escapement not shown in this diagram, though the device above the wheel is probably intended for part of it

杆和平行连杆系统，用于在另一点检查转轮的转动。还装有一个抗反冲装置。因此，整个驱动系统的基本原理更加类似于 17 世纪晚期的锚状擒纵装置而非使用摆轮心轴和原始平衡摆的类型，虽然守时主要是由水流而不是擒纵装置本身驱动的。因此，在稳定液体流守时性能和机械振荡守时性能之间，这种效应类型是二者之间“缺失的一环”。史料对于这一机械钟装置的记录非常完备，其中包含了 11 世纪的 150 多个机械部件，使得我们能够给出详细的时钟机械工作示意图（图 3 和图 4）。

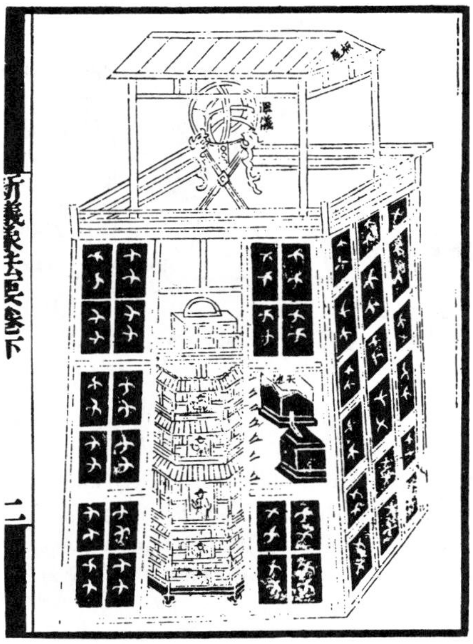

图 1

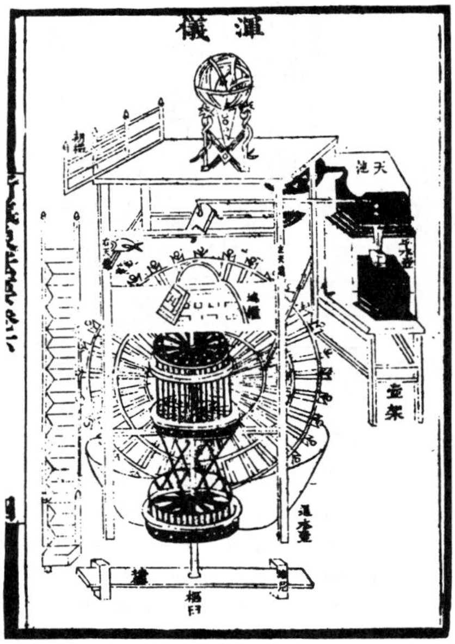

图 2

图 1. 公元 1088 年苏颂在《新仪象法要》中记载的天文钟的外观图（第 3 章第 2*a* 页）。浑天仪位于最上面的平台上，天球仪位于塔内上层，具有报时功能的支架塔位于塔内下层。图中右侧去除了房屋外层，以显示出水箱。整个装置的高度大约为 30 英尺。

图 2. 同图 1 一样给出了装置的内部结构纵览。装置前面装有支架轮和立轴，后面是驱动轮及其水车。右侧装有水箱，左上方露出部分抗反冲装置。图中未给出擒纵装置，但转动轮上方的装置可能是擒纵装置的一部分。

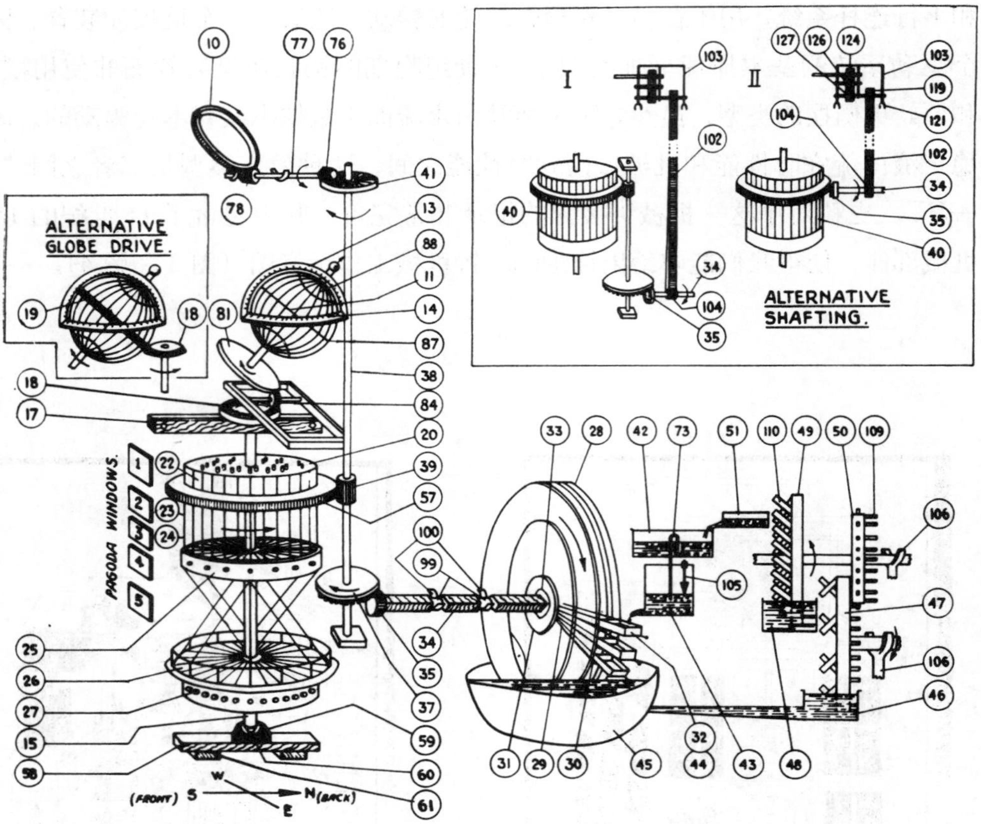

Fig. 3

Fig. 3. General reconstruction. The numbers indicate technical terms which will be given and explained in the full publication. Gearing at the top of the jack-wheel shaft on the left drives the celestial globe. The long shaft rotating the armillary sphere was in later models replaced by successively shorter chain drives, as shown in the inset. On the right are the two norlas which raised the water to the uppermost reservoir, sufficient for twenty-four hours running. (*Drawn by Angel*)

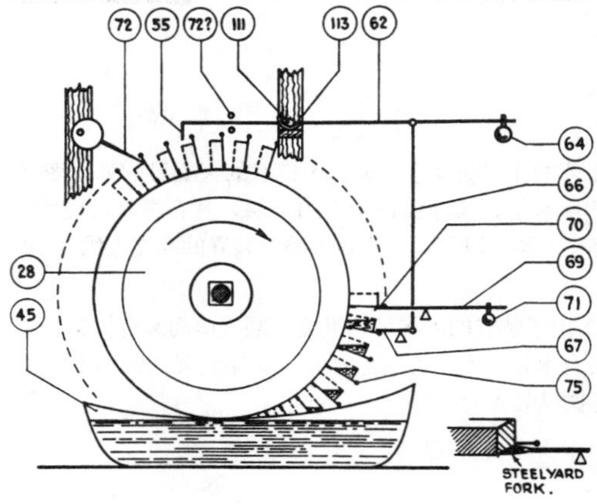

Fig. 4

Fig. 4. Diagram of the escapement, with its weigh-bridge and parallel linkwork. The clepsydra flow delivered into the scoop at 70. (*Drawn by Angel*)

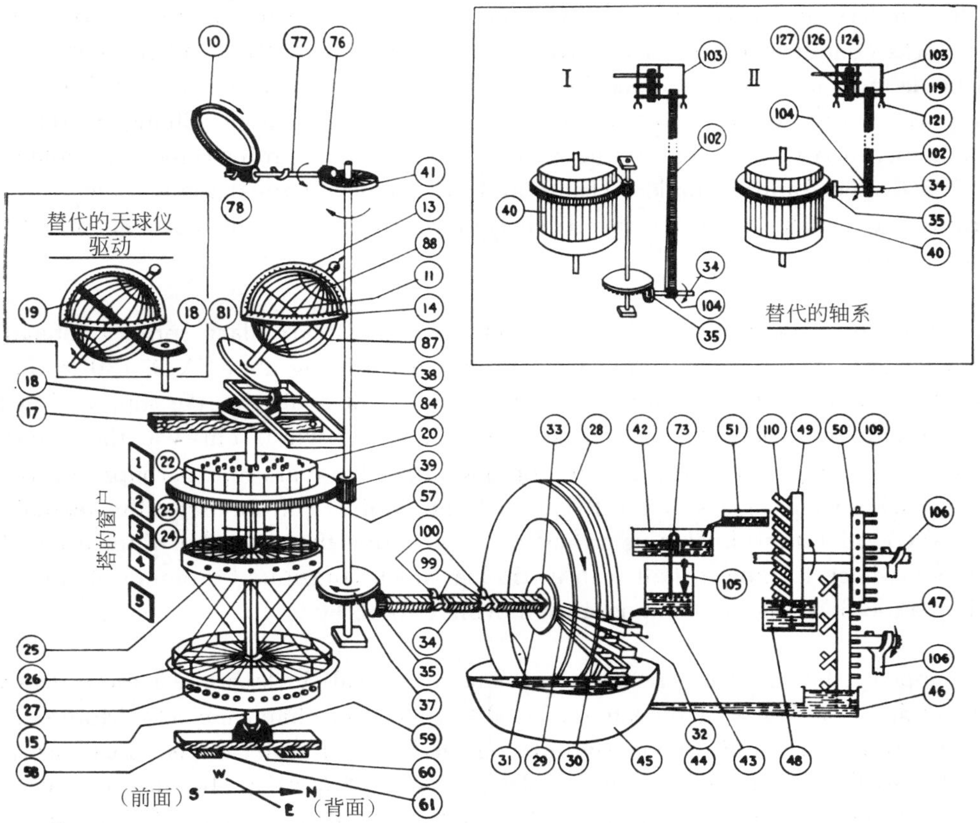

图 3

图 3. 中国天文钟结构的复原重建图。将在以后完整的出版物中给出并解释图中数字代表的部件。图中左侧位于支架轮轴顶部的传动装置用于驱动天球仪。如插入框图所示，用于转动浑天仪的长杆在后续的模型中被更短的链式传动替代了。图中右侧是两个轮轴，用于将水汲取到最高处的储水槽，从而保证系统 24 小时连续运转。（本图由安杰尔绘制）

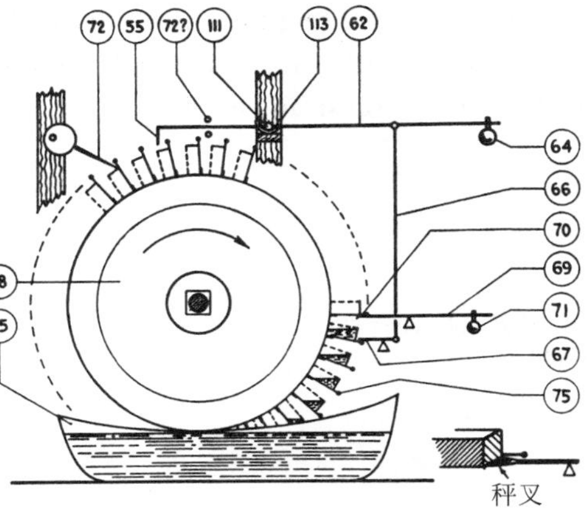

图 4

图 4. 擒纵装置示意图，包括衡桥装置和平行连杆系统。漏壶的水流从标号 70 的位置流入水斗。（本图由安杰尔绘制）

The full understanding of this text has enabled us to interpret many descriptions of other clocks contained partly in the dynastic histories and partly in other sources, some from books now lost, but preserved in the "Yü Hai" encyclopaedia of A.D. 1267. Thus an important astronomical clock driven by mercury was built by Chang Ssu-Hsün, a Szechuanese, in A.D. 979. The tradition seems to start with an instrument completed in A.D. 725 by the Tantric monk, I-Hsing, and an engineer named Liang Ling-Tsan, the description of which would not have been comprehensible without thorough prior study of Su Sung's text.

Earlier texts describe celestial globes or demonstrational armillary spheres rotated by clepsydra water. These range from the work of Chang Hêng about A.D. 130 to that of Kêng Hsün about 590, but evidence of any escapement is absent. We supposed at first that these employed only the sinking float of a large clepsydra. This was the system of the Hellenistic anaphoric clock with its rotating astrolabic dial[6], and perhaps also of the famous striking water-clocks of the Byzantine[7] and Arabic[8] culture-areas. But textual and historical considerations incline us rather to the view that the clepsydra water dripped on to a scoop-wheel, turning a shaft with a trip-lug which constituted a pinion of one. This acted on a toothed ring on the apparatus, moving it tooth by tooth.

It thus appears that the Chinese tradition of astronomical clockwork was more nearly in the direct line of ancestry of the late medieval European mechanical clocks. Moreover, the detailed description of this previously unrecognized type of water-driven clock has made it possible to find similar devices incompletely described (perhaps because incompletely known) in Indian[9], Arabic and Hispano-Moorish[10] texts. Of the transmission of influences little can as yet be said, though there are indications that the European centuries just preceding the fourteenth knew devices with water-powered and mechanically checked driving-wheels[11]. This would suggest that the time of transmission was rather that of "the Crusades" (as in the case of the wind-mill) than that of the Marco Polo.

All the texts now translated, with commentary and discussion, will, it is hoped, be published as a special monograph by the Antiquarian Horological Society, to which the results of the investigation have been communicated.

(177, 600-602; 1956)

Joseph Needham: F.R.S., Caius College, Cambridge.
Wang Ling: Trinity College, Cambridge.
Derek J. Price: Christ's College, Cambridge.

References:

1. Beckmann, J., "A History of Inventions, Discoveries, etc.", vol. 1, pp. 340 ff. (Bohn, London, 1846).
2. Usher, A. P., "A History of Mechanical Inventions", pp. 191 ff., 304 ff., 2nd edit. (Harvard Univ. Press, Cambridge, Mass., 1954).
3. Frémont, C., "Origine de 1'Horloge à Poids" (Études Expérimentales de Technologie Industrielle, No. 47; Paris, 1915).

对苏颂一文的全面理解使我们得以理解部分王朝史书上或其他书上记载的对其他各种钟的描述，虽然其中一些书目已失传，但其内容在《玉海》百科全书（成书于公元 1267 年）中保留了下来。公元 979 年，一位名叫张思训的四川人建造了一座用水银驱动的天文钟。公元 725 年，密宗高僧一行和一位名叫梁令瓒的工程师制造了一个钟，这似乎是制钟历史的开始。如果没有对苏颂一文深入的研究，就不会对这些描述有充分的理解。

更早的史料记载了用漏壶中的水驱动的天球仪或演示用的浑天仪。从大约公元 130 年张衡到大约公元 590 年耿询都进行了这方面的工作，但是史料中没有任何擒纵装置的内容。起初我们推测，这些装置只使用了大漏壶中的浮子结构。就类似于装有转动拨号星盘的希腊式浮子升降钟[6]，也可能类似拜占庭[7]和阿拉伯地区[8]著名的水钟。但是考虑到原文记载和具体历史条件，我们倾向于以下观点：漏壶中的水滴到斗式水车上，触动附有凸缘开关的传动轴，从而驱动系统相互啮合转动。

综上所述，中国古代的天文钟可能就是欧洲中世纪晚期机械钟的直系祖先。此外，对这种以前未获认可、靠水驱动的天文钟的详细描述，使我们可能在印度[9]、阿拉伯和西班牙摩尔[10]的史料中也会找到描述不完整的（可能是由于我们不完全知晓）类似装置。虽然欧洲直到 14 世纪才掌握了水驱动和机械驱动轮装置[11]，但是这种传播的影响迄今还很难说。这表明，中国时钟制造术传到欧洲的时间是在“十字军”东征的时候（和风车一样），而不是马可波罗时代。

目前我们已经翻译完毕所有相关的史料，添加了注释和讨论，并与古钟协会进行了沟通，希望他们将其作为一本特别专著出版。

（金世超 翻译；沈志侠 审稿）

4. Howgrave-Graham, R. P., "Some Clocks and Jacks, with Notes on the History of Horology", *Archaeologia*, 77, 257 (1927). Baillie, G. H., "Watches" (Methuen, London, 1929).

5. Price, D. J., "Clockwork before the Clock", *Horological J.*, **97**, 810 (1955); and **98**, 31 (1956).

6. Vitruvius, IX. 8. Cf. Drachmann, A. G., "The Plane Astrolabe and the Anaphoric Clock", *Centaurus*, **3**, 183 (1954).

7. Diels, H., "Über die von Prokop beschriebene Kunstuhr von Gaza; mit einem Anhang enthaltende Text und Übersetzung d. *ekphrasis horologiou* des Prokopios von Gaza", *Abhandlungen d. preuss. Akad. Wiss.* (Phil.-Hist. Kl.), No. 7 (1917).

8. Wiedemann, E., and Hauser, F., "Über die Uhren im Bereich der islamischen Kultur", *Nova Acia* (*Abhandlungen d. K. Leop.-Carol. deutschen Akad. d. Naturforsch.*) Halle, **100**, No. 5 (1915).

9. Burgess, E., "The Sürya-Siddhānta, a. Textbook of Hindu Astronomy", pp. 282, 298, 305 ff., edit. Phanindralal Gangooly (University, Calcutta, 1935).

10. Rico y Sinobas, M., "Libros del Saber de Astronomia del Rey D. Alfonso X de Castilla" (Aguado, Madrid, 1864).

11. Drover, C. B., "A Mediaeval Monastic Water-Clock", *Antiquarian Horology* (Dec. 1954).

Structure of Vitamin B_{12}

D. C. Hodgkin *et al.*

Editor's Note

Vitamin B_{12} was first identified in 1948 as the active ingredient in liver extracts used to treat pernicious anaemia. It was later manufactured by fermentation of bacteria, but chemists wondered whether it might be synthesized directly by chemical means. This required knowledge of the molecular structure of vitamin B_{12}. As a very complicated organic molecule, it posed a fearsome challenge to the usual method of structure determination, X-ray crystallography. That challenge is met in this paper by Dorothy Hodgkin of Oxford University and her colleagues, which was a key factor in Hodgkin's 1964 Nobel Prize in chemistry. The results show where every atom sits, enabling chemists in the USA and Switzerland to synthesize the compound between 1965 and 1972.

SINCE our communication in August 1955[1], we have carried our refinement of the structure of vitamin B_{12} a critical stage further. Four more calculations of the electron density distribution have been made, one for the wet B_{12} crystals, two for air-dried B_{12} crystals and one for the hexacarboxylic acid.

In Fig. 1 are shown the electron density peaks over all the atoms of the B_{12} molecule as it appears from our present calculations in the wet crystals. These peaks are rather lower than those observed for the hexacarboylic acid owing to the smaller number of X-ray reflextions given by the larger molecule in proportion to its size. But they serve to show the relative positions of all the atoms in space of this very complex molecule within probably as little as 0.3 A. Similar evidence has been obtained for air-dried B_{12}; for both crystals the reliability indices in the latest structure factor calculations, 36.1 and 30.6 percent, respectively, are now low enough to indicate that the solution we have reached is likely to be essentially correct.

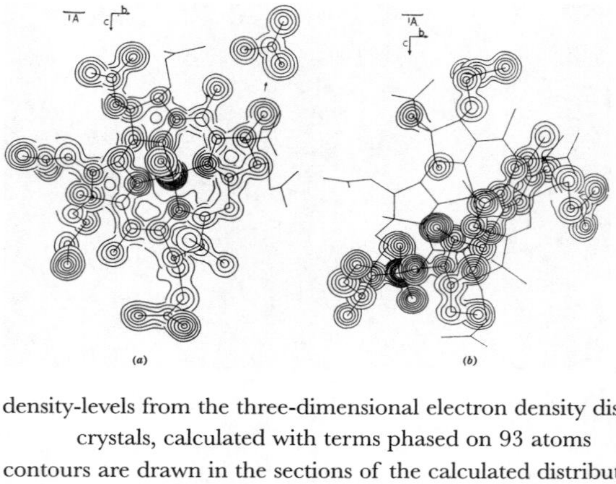

Fig. 1. Electron density-levels from the three-dimensional electron density distribution for wet B_{12} crystals, calculated with terms phased on 93 atoms

Here, and in Fig. 4, the contours are drawn in the sections of the calculated distribution parallel with the *a* place, passing at or near the atomic positions. Owing to the complexity of the molecule, complete contours for every atom are not given and the figure is divided into two parts. (*a*) shows the cobalt-containing nucleus and cyanide group; (*b*) the benziminazole, sugar, phosphate and propanolamine groups, the side chains being divided between the two. The acetamide chain on ring *B* is inset. The contour interval is 1 $e/A.^3$

维生素B_{12}的结构

霍奇金等

编者按

1948 年，科学家们首次发现了维生素 B_{12}，它是从肝脏提取物中分离得到的活性成分，用来治疗恶性贫血。后来又利用细菌发酵方法生产出维生素 B_{12}，但化学家一直尝试通过化学方法直接合成这种化学物质。这就需要了解维生素 B_{12} 的分子结构。作为一种非常复杂的有机分子，利用常规的 X 射线晶体衍射分析法测定其结构是极其具有挑战性的。这篇文章的作者牛津大学的多萝西·霍奇金及其同事们就遇到了这样的挑战，这也是霍奇金获得 1964 年诺贝尔化学奖的关键因素。维生素 B_{12} 分子中每个原子位置的确定为美国和瑞士的化学家在 1965 年～1972 年间合成该化合物提供了依据。

自从 1955 年 8 月发表维生素 B_{12} 的结构以来[1]，我们又对其进行了修正，并取得了关键性进展。我们已经获得了四种样品的电子密度分布的计算结果，包括一种含水维生素 B_{12} 晶体、两种无水维生素 B_{12} 晶体和一种六羧酸晶体。

图 1 所示的是含水维生素 B_{12} 晶体分子上所有原子的电子密度峰，该图是依照我们目前对含水维生素 B_{12} 晶体的计算结果绘制的。这些峰值比在六羧酸晶体上观察到的强度低得多。因为分子越大，X 射线反射的数量就越少，与分子的大小成比例。但是这些峰值表明这个非常复杂的分子上所有原子的空间相对位置可能仅有 0.3 Å。在无水维生素 B_{12} 晶体上也得到了类似的结果。在最新的结构因子计算中，含水和无水两种晶体可靠因子值分别为 36.1% 和 30.6%，数据目前已经非常低，足以表明我们所使用的方法基本正确。

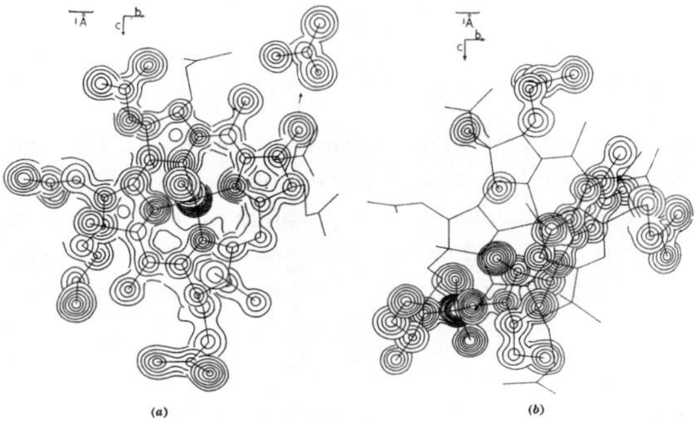

图 1. 含水维生素 B_{12} 的电子密度分布水平图，数据来自三维的电子密度分布，通过计算 93 个原子的相位项获得。

图 1 和图 4 显示的轮廓是计算获得的部分电子密度分布图，该图平行于 *a* 平面（经过原子或者邻近原子位置）。因为这个分子比较复杂，所以每个原子的完整轮廓不能一次性描绘出来，而是分成了两个部分：(*a*) 显示的是含钴核心和氰基基团；(*b*) 显示的是苯并咪唑、糖、磷酸酯和丙醇胺基团，侧链则被分割到这两部分中。*B* 环的乙酰胺侧链是内嵌的。图中的轮廓间隔为：1 e/Å^3。

The molecule that appears is very beautifully composed, not far from spherical in form, with all the more chemically reactive groups on its surface. It is drawn in projection in Fig. 2. It is built around the two planes of the benziminazole nucleus and the central cobalt-containing nucleus, which are nearly at right angles to each other. The ribose ring turns in a position nearly normal to the benziminazole group, which permits its easy linking through the phosphate, propanolamine, and propionic acid residues to ring *D* of the planar group. The benziminazole nucleus is packed in on either side by the propionamide side-chains in the extended, staggered configuration, attached to rings *A* and *B*; the side-chain on ring *C*, in the gauche configuration, lies above the ribose ring. All the acetamide residues project from the opposite side of the nucleus to the propionamide residues, towards the cyanide group. It is an interesting point that one of them—that on ring *B*—swings round the carbon-carbon single bond from a position directed away from, to one in contact with, the cyanide group, when the crystals are removed from their mother liquor; this permits the rather closer packing of the molecules found in the air-dried crystals. Throughout the molecule, as shown by Figs. 1 and 2, the atomic positions found conform in a most convincing way with the stereochemical rules established by the study of simpler molecules.

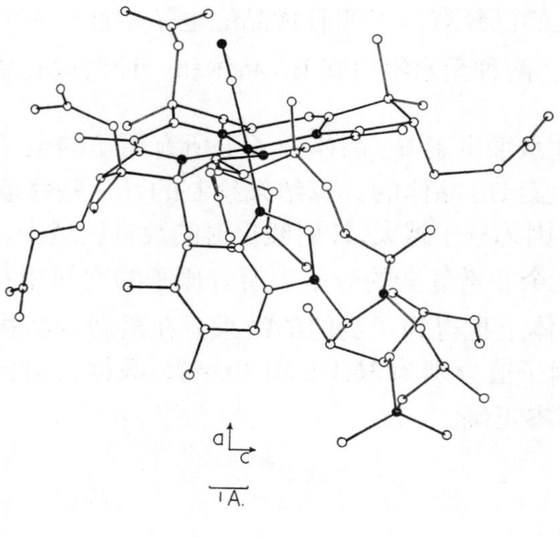

Fig. 2. The atomic positions found in the molecule of vitamin B_{12}. These are shown as derived in the wet crystals, projected on the *b* plane. To distinguish different parts of the molecule, bonds within the cobalt containing nucleus, benziminzole and cyanide groups are shown in black, together with the cobalt and phosphorus atoms and the nitrogen atoms of the nucleus, benziminazole, propanolamine and cyanide groups

It now seems reasonably certain that we should formulate vitamin B_{12}, $C_{63}H_{88}O_{14}N_{14}PCo$, as in I, and the hexacarboxylic acid as in II, with six double bonds in the inner ring of the central nucleus; these can form a resonating system by intervention of the cobalt atom as illustrated by III. Some evidence in support of this has been obtained by theoretical calculations[2], by spectroscopic measurements[3] and from further chemical studies[4]. Our own evidence for this formulation is the geometrical form of the nucleus, which is illustrated by

维生素 B_{12} 分子的组成非常巧妙，其造型近似球状，并且所有的化学反应活性基团都分布在其表面上。图 2 所示为投影图。它由两个面构成，分别是苯并咪唑核心和中间含钴核心，这两个面相互间夹角接近为直角。核糖环转向特定的位置以接近苯并咪唑基团，这样利于磷酸酯、丙醇胺和丙酸残基与 *D* 环平面的基团相连接。苯并咪唑核心要么堆积在由 *A* 环和 *B* 环上的丙酰胺侧链形成的伸展且相互交错的构型的同侧，要么堆积在由位于核糖环上面的 *C* 环丙酰胺侧链形成的邻位交叉构型的一侧。所有的乙酰胺残基都是沿着氰基方向从核心相反一侧投向丙酰胺残基。令人感兴趣的一点是，从母液中分离晶体时，*B* 环上的乙酰胺残基会绕着碳 – 碳单键旋转，从定向地远离氰基的位置转到与氰基相近的位置，这使得无水晶体形成更紧凑的分子结构。图 1 和图 2 所示为维生素 B_{12} 整体分子结构，确定的原子位置符合那些根据较简单分子的研究建立起来的立体化学规则，因此这个结果是非常令人信服的。

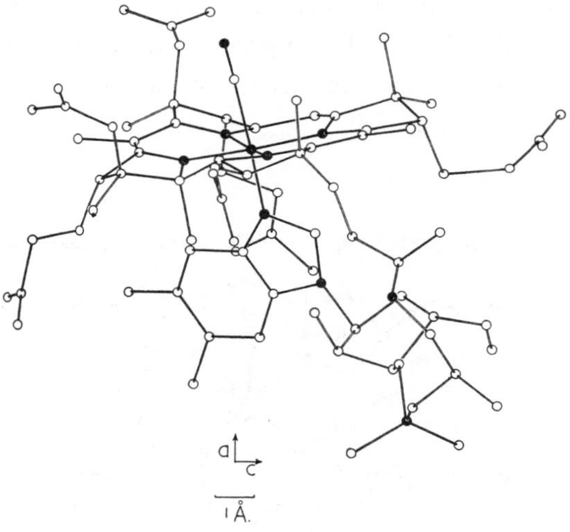

图 2. 含水维生素 B_{12} 晶体中发现的原子位置。这些位置都是通过投射到 *b* 平面上获得的。为了区分该分子的不同部分，用黑实线表示含钴核心、苯并咪唑和氰基基团内的化学键，用黑色实心点表示钴原子、磷原子，以及含钴核心、苯并咪唑、丙醇胺和氰基上的氮原子。

现在我们推导出维生素 B_{12} 的化学式为 $C_{63}H_{88}O_{14}N_{14}PCo$，如（I）所示，这看起来是很合理的；六羧酸的化学式如（II）所示，其中央核的内环含有 6 个双键。这些双键可以形成烯键共轭系统并与钴原子发生络合，如（III）所示。通过理论计算 [2]、光谱测量 [3] 与更进一步的化学研究 [4] 获得的一些证据能够支持这个结论。我们用于支持这个化学式的证据来源于核心的几何学形状，如图 3 所示，此外，这三种

Fig. 3, and which is closely similar in all three crystals studied. The interatomic distances shown in this figure are derived from the latest calculations on the hexacarboxylic acid and are not individually very precise; in other parts of the molecule distances differing by as much as 0.16 A. from accepted bond-lengths have been found. But it is notable that in the region N_6-N_{18} *all* the bond-lengths are shorter than normal single bond distances; their average value, 1.36 A., is similar to that found in the phthalocyanines[5]. The positions of C_{29} and C_{30}, one or other of which would be expected to be out of the plane of the central ring system if only five double bonds were present, are even more significant. In the hexacarboxylic acid they appeared at all stages of the refinement to be within 0.2 A. of this plane, but in the B_{12} crystals themselves their positions were at first more confused, particularly C_{29}. As a critical test, accordingly, this atom was omitted from the phasing calculations used for the latest electron distribution calculated for air-dried B_{12}. It has now appeared, as Fig. 4 shows, as a small but clearly defined peak at a site which is closely equivalent to that found in the hexacarboxylic acid along the line Co to C_8. There is still some departure from planar character in this region of the inner nucleus in both wet and air-dried crystals, but this seems to affect N_{10}, C_9 and C_8 as much as C_{29}. If real, it may be a consequence of a small amount of compression from the benziminazole nucleus, which is in contact with these atoms. It is, in any event, not of the geometrical form that would be expected if C_8 were reduced.

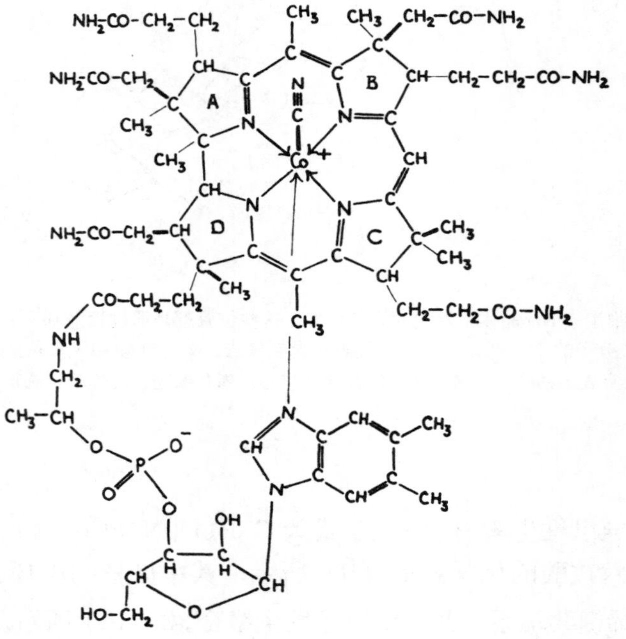

(I)

晶体的研究结果都极为相似。图中显示的是通过最新的计算方法获得的六羧酸分子中原子间的距离，但单个数据不是很准确；这个分子中其他部分的间距与已经被发现并被接受的键长相比最多相差 0.16 Å。但值得注意的是在 N_6~N_{18} 区域内**所有**的键长都比正常单键的键长短。它们的平均键长为 1.36 Å，类似于在酞菁中发现的键长[5]。如果只存在 5 个双键，那么 C_{29} 和 C_{30} 这两个位置不管哪一个都会偏离中心环系统平面，甚至比其他位置偏离得更为明显。对于六羧酸，在整个修正过程中，这两个位置总会在这个平面 0.2 Å 范围内显现。但是对于维生素 B_{12} 晶体，它们的位置起初非常模糊，尤其是 C_{29}。因此，在进行关键实验的相位计算时，我们忽略这个原子，然后再计算无水的维生素 B_{12} 最新电子分布。如图 4 所示，现在我们可以很清楚地看到，沿着钴和 C_8 的连线，有一个细小但又清晰可辨的峰，与六羧酸上发现的近乎完全一致。在含水和无水的结晶中，内部核心区域的平面特征仍然存在着一定的偏离，但对 N_{10}、C_9 和 C_8 的影响程度与 C_{29} 差不多。如果真是这样，将会产生的一个结果是与这些原子相连接的苯并咪唑核心会出现少量压缩现象。无论如何，如果 C_8 不存在的话，那么这个分子也就不会形成几何学的形状了。

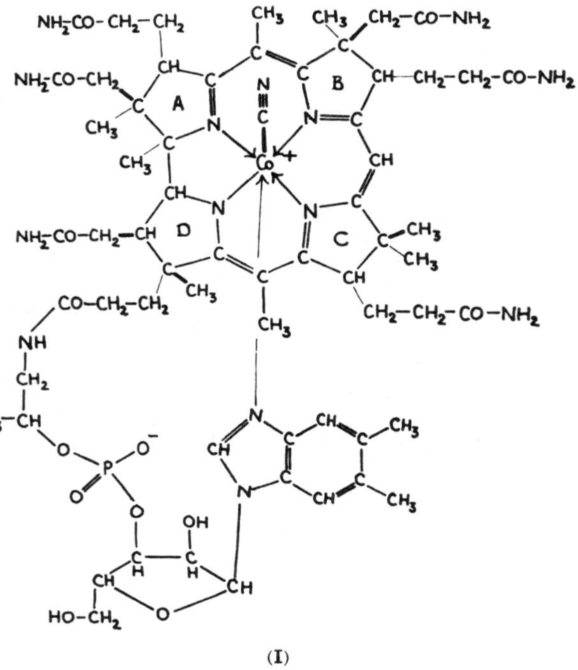

(I)

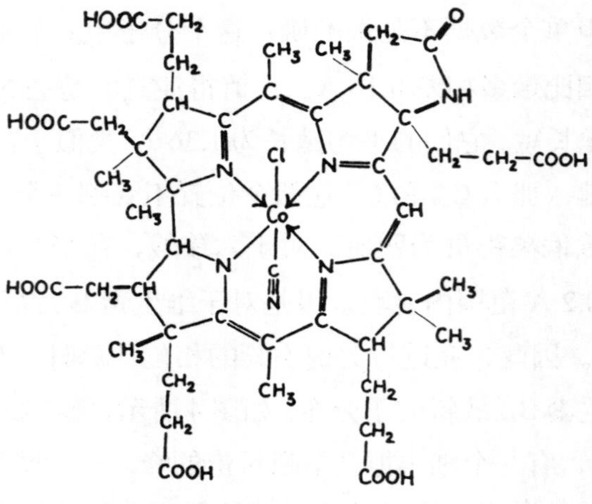
HOOC–CH2
CH2
CH3
CH3
CH2–C=O
NH
CH
C
HOOC–CH2
N
Cl
N=C
CH2–CH2–COOH
CH3
CH3
Co
CH
CH
N
C
N
N
C
HOOC–CH2–CH
CH3
CH3
CH3
CH
CH2
CH3
CH2
CH2
CH2
COOH
COOH

(II)

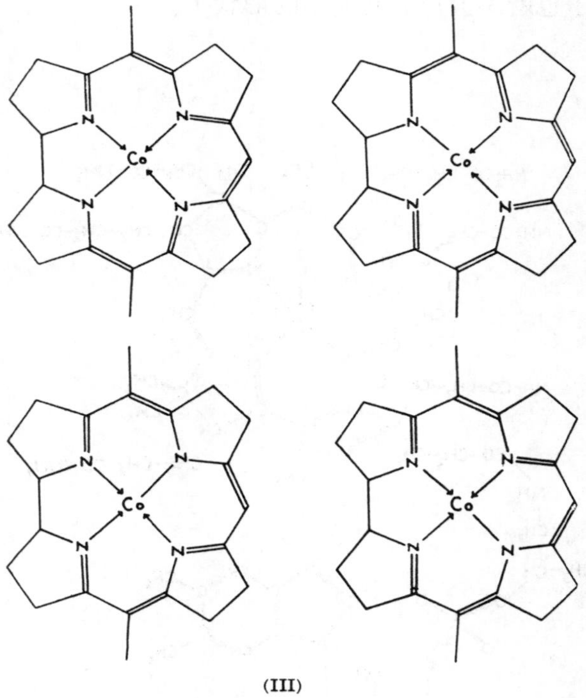
N
N
Co
N
N

(III)

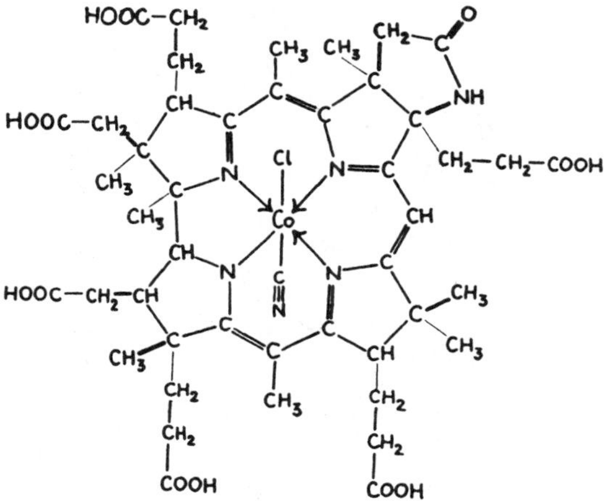
HOOC—CH2
CH2
CH3
CH3
CH2—C=O
NH
HOOC—CH2
CH
C
N
Cl
N=C
CH2—CH2—COOH
CH3
Co
CH
HOOC—CH2—CH
C
N
CH3
CH3
CH2
CH2
COOH
CH2
CH2
COOH

(II)

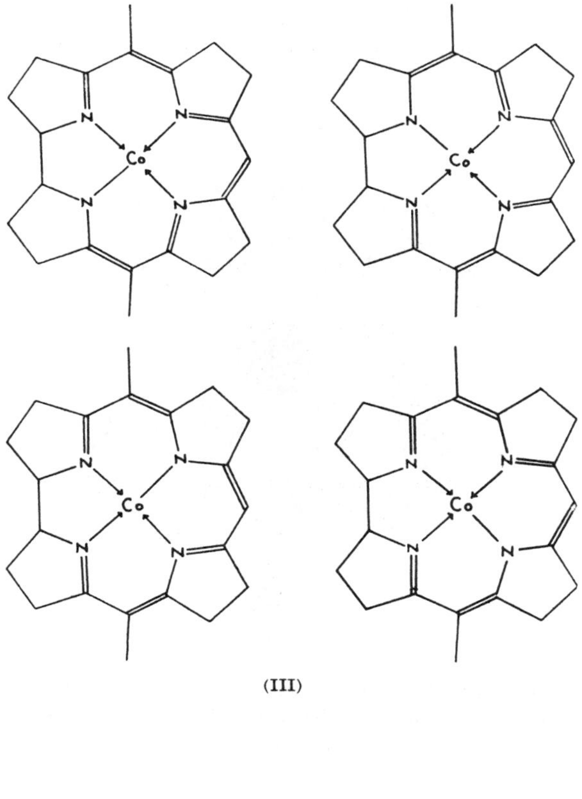
N
Co

(III)

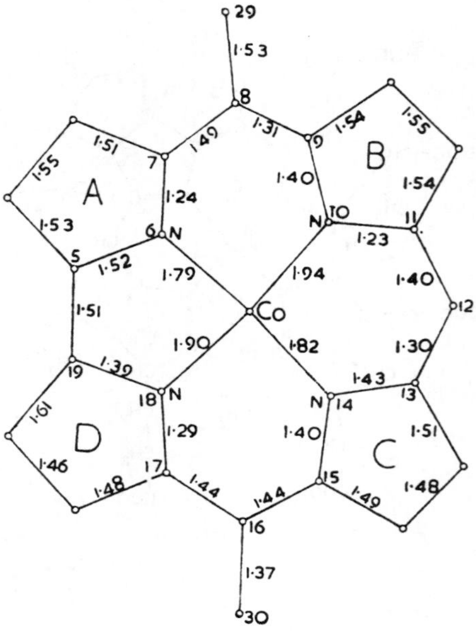

Fig. 3. Interatomic distances found in the inner nucleus of the hexacarboxylic acid, derived from nine refinements of the calculated electron density distribution

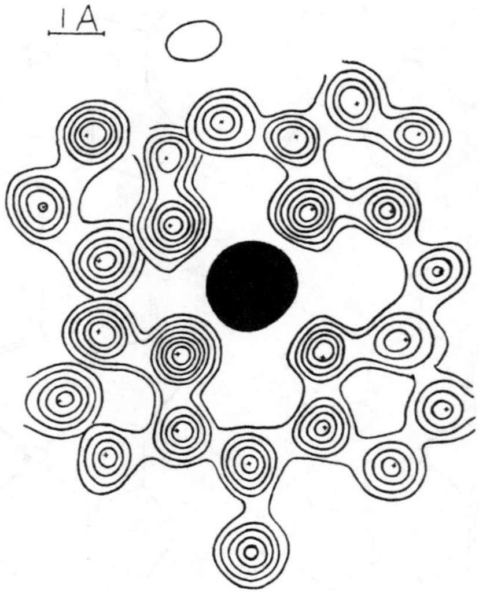

Fig. 4. Electron density peaks over the nucleus in air-dried vitamin B_{12}, derived from the three-dimensional electron density distribution calculated with terms phased on 95 atoms (Princeton data)

The crystal structures of the different B_{12} compounds are still not completely solved; many of the water molecules which occupy space between the vitamin molecules have been placed, but not all. Still further small adjustments are to be expected on continued

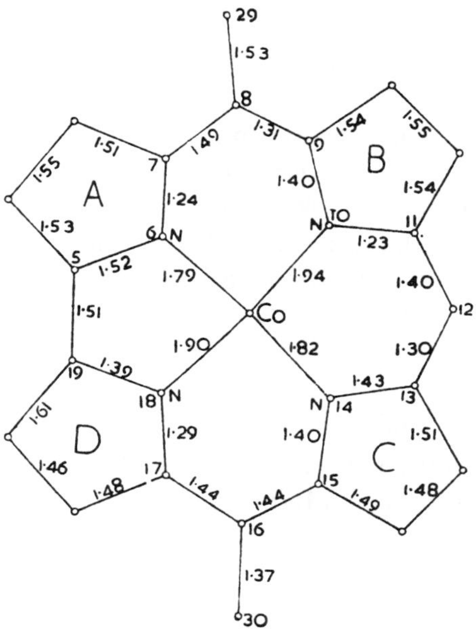

图 3. 六羧酸中内部核心内的原子间距。对计算得到的电子密度分布共进行了 9 次修正。

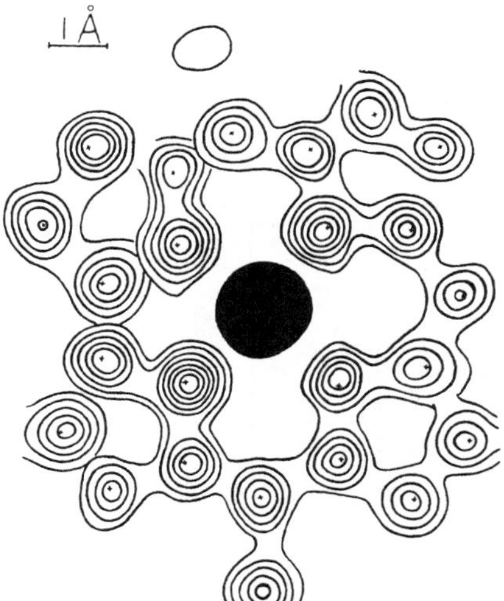

图 4. 无水的维生素 B_{12} 核心上面的电子密度峰。数据来自三维的电子密度分布，是对分子中 95 个原子的相位项进行计算得到的（数据来自普林斯顿）。

目前对不同维生素 B_{12} 化合物的晶体结构还不完全清楚。位于维生素分子间隙的许多结晶水分子都已确定，但并不是全部。我们仍然期望在所测量的原子位置的

refinement of the atomic positions observed. We hope that future calculations will add still greater precision and certainty to our knowledge of the structure of the molecule.

The latest series of calculations on wet B_{12} were carried out on the University of Manchester electronic computer through the generous co-operation of Dr. D. W. J. Cruickshank, Miss Diana Pilling and Mr. J. F. P. Donavan, of the University of Leeds. Those on air-dried B_{12} and on the hexacarboxylic acid were made on the National Bureau of Standards automatic computer in Los Angeles, supported by the United States Office of Naval Research.

Again we acknowledge the very generous support given this research by the Nuffield Foundation, and materials and help given us by Dr. E. Lester Smith, Glaxo Laboratories, Ltd., and Dr. K. Folkers, Merck Laboratories. Two of us (J. P. and J. K.) received grants from the Department of Scientific and Industrial Research.

(**178**, 64-66; 1956)

D. C. Hodgkin, F.R.S., J. Kamper, M. Mackay and J. Pickworth: Oxford.
K. N. Trueblood: Los Angeles.
J. G. White: Princeton.

References:

1. *Nature*, **176**, 325 (1955).
2. Orgel, L. E. (private communication).
3. Beaven, G. H., and Johnson, E. A., *Nature*, **176**, 1264 (1955).
4. Todd, A. R. (private communication).
5. Robertson, J. M., *J. Chem. Soc.*, 1195 (1936). Robertson, J. M., and Woodward, I., *ibid.*, 219 (1937).

持续修正方面作进一步的细小调整。我们也希望未来的计算会更加精确和明确，使我们对这个分子的结构更加了解。

最近这些基于含水维生素 B_{12} 的一系列计算工作是在曼彻斯特大学的电子计算机上进行的，也是在与利兹大学的克鲁克香克博士、黛安娜·皮林女士和多纳文先生的大力合作下进行的。基于无水维生素 B_{12} 和六羧酸计算的工作是在位于洛杉矶的美国国家标准局的自动计算机上进行的，其经费由美国海军研究办公室支付。

我们还要感谢纳菲尔德基金会对这项研究工作的大力支持，感谢葛兰素化学药品公司的莱斯特·史密斯博士提供了实验材料并给予帮助，也感谢默克实验室的福克斯博士的帮助。此外，我们中的两人（珍妮·皮克沃思和珍妮弗·坎珀）也得到了科学及工业研究署的资助。

（刘振明 翻译；吕扬 审稿）

The Neutrino

F. Reines and C. L. Cowan

Editor's Note

The existence of the subatomic particle called the neutrino had been inferred in the early 1930s chiefly as a result of work by Enrico Fermi in Rome and Wolfgang Pauli in Zurich from the phenomenon of radioactive beta-decay: it was supposed to be a particle with insignificant mass and no electric charge. Frederick Reines and Clyde L. Cowan at the Los Alamos Scientific Laboratory, acknowledging that nuclear reactors should be powerful sources of neutrinos, here described an experiment to demonstrate the existence of neutrinos by their interaction with protons (provided by a large tank of water) and their individual conversion into photons which were to be measured by an array of photoscintillators. The use of photoscintillators for detecting neutrinos produced in analogous nuclear reactions has become standard practice. In the 1980s, however, it became clear that there are three different kinds of neutrinos and that even those studied by Reines and Cowan may have a small mass.

EACH new discovery of natural science broadens our knowledge and deepens our understanding of the physical universe; but at times these advances raise new and even more fundamental questions than those which they answer. Such was the case with the discovery and investigation of the radioactive process termed "beta decay". In this process an atomic nucleus spontaneously emits either a negative or positive electron, and in so doing it becomes a different element with the same mass number but with a nuclear charge different from that of the parent element by one electronic charge. As might be expected, intensive investigation of this interesting alchemy of Nature has shed much light on problems concerning the atomic nucleus. A new question arose at the beginning, however, when it was found that accompanying beta decay there was an unaccountable loss of energy from the decaying nucleus[1], and that one could do nothing to the apparatus in which the decay occurred to trap this lost energy[2]. One possible explanation was that the conservation laws (upon which the entire structure of modern science is built) were not valid when applied to regions of subatomic dimensions. Another novel explanation, but one which would maintain the integrity of the conservation laws, was a proposal by Wolfgang Pauli in 1933 which hypothesized a new and fundamental particle[3] to account for the loss of energy from the nucleus. This particle would be emitted by the nucleus simultaneously with the electron, would carry with it no electric charge, but would carry the missing energy and momentum—escaping from the laboratory equipment without detection.

The concept of this ghostly particle was used by Enrico Fermi (who named it the "neutrino") to build his quantitative theory of nuclear beta decay[4]. As is well known, the theory, with but little modification, has enjoyed increasing success in application to nuclear

中微子

莱因斯，考恩

编者按

20 世纪 30 年代初期，罗马的恩里科·费米和苏黎世的沃尔夫冈·泡利根据放射性β衰变现象得到的研究结果，推测出被称为中微子的亚原子粒子的存在，他们认为该粒子质量极小且不带电荷。洛斯阿拉莫斯科学实验室的弗雷德里克·莱因斯和克莱德·考恩认为，核反应堆是强大的中微子源，本文中他们描述了一个证明中微子存在的实验，实验中质子（由一大箱水提供）与中微子相互作用，使中微子转换为光子，并用光闪烁体阵列对光子进行测量。如今用光闪烁体检测这类核反应中产生的中微子已成为标准方法。然而，直到 20 世纪 80 年代人们才逐渐清楚存在三种不同类型的中微子以及莱因斯和考恩研究的那些中微子也可能具有微小的质量。

自然科学的每项新发现都扩展了我们的知识，加深了我们对物质世界的了解；但是与它们所解决的问题相比，这些进展有时会引出一些新的甚至更基本的问题。放射性“β 衰变”过程的发现和研究就是这样一个例子。在这个过程中，原子核自发地发射一个负电子或正电子，这样它就变成了一个与母元素质量数相同但相差一个电子电荷的不同元素。正如所预料的那样，对自然界这一有趣的神奇过程的深入研究阐明了关于原子核的一些问题。然而随即出现的一个新问题是：人们发现伴随着β 衰变，衰变核 [1] 中有无法解释的能量损失；并且人们无法通过改善发生衰变的装置来捕获这些损失的能量 [2]。一种可能的解释是，守恒定律（现代科学的整个结构建立在这个定律之上）应用到亚原子尺度时不再成立。沃尔夫冈·泡利于 1933 年提出另一种新奇的但能继续遵守守恒定律的解释，他假设存在一类新的基本粒子 [3] 对应于损失的核能量。核在发射电子的同时发射出这类粒子，该粒子不带电荷，但是带有丢失的那部分能量和动量，即实验装置未检测到的那部分能量和动量。

恩里科·费米在构建他的核 β 衰变定量理论 [4] 时，采用了这个如幽灵般的粒子的概念（他称之为“中微子”）。众所周知，这个理论作了微小修正后应用到核问题

problems and has itself constituted one of the most convincing arguments in favour of the acceptance of Pauli's proposal. Many additional experimental tests have been devised, however, which have served to strengthen the neutrino hypothesis; and also to provide information as to its properties. The very characteristic of the particle which makes the proposal plausible—its ability to carry off energy and momentum without detection—has limited these tests to the measurement of the observable details of the decay process itself: the energy spectra, momentum vectors and energy states associated with the emitted electron and with the recoiling daughter nucleus[5]. So, for example, an upper limit has been set on the rest mass of the neutrino equal to 1/500 of the rest mass of the electron by careful measurement of the beta-energy spectrum from tritium decay near its end point[6], and it is commonly assumed that the neutrino rest mass is identically zero.

While there is no theoretical reason for the expectation of a finite neutrino rest mass, there is some expectation for a small but finite neutrino magnetic moment of perhaps as much as 10^{-10} Bohr magneton based on a consideration of possible virtual states in which the neutrino may exist effectively dissociated into other particles[7]. An upper limit of 2×10^{-9} electron Bohr magneton has been set on the magnetic moment by calculations concerning the maximum assignable heat transfer to the Earth by neutrinos from the Sun[8]. We have recently obtained an improved upper limit of 10^{-9} electron Bohr magneton using a large scintillation detector near a fission reactor at the Savannah River Plant of the United States Atomic Energy Commission. The counting rate of single pulses in an energy range of 0.1-0.3 MeV. in 370 gallons of liquid scintillator was observed, and all changes due to reactor power changes were assigned to possible electron recoils in the liquid through magnetic moment interaction with neutrinos. It is hoped that this limit may be further improved by lowering the gamma-ray and neutron background at the detector.

The Pauli-Fermi theory not only requires the neutrino to carry energy and linear momentum from beta-decaying nuclei but also angular momentum, or "spin". The simplest of beta-decay processes, the decay of the free neutron[9], illustrates this:

$$n^0 \rightarrow p^+ + \beta^- + \nu_- \qquad (1)$$

As the neutron, proton and beta particle all carry half-integral spin, it is necessary to assign a spin quantum number of 1/2 to the neutrino to balance the angular momenta of equation (1), where any two of the three product particles must be oriented with spin vectors antiparallel. As all four of the particles in equation (1) are, therefore, fermions and should obey the Dirac relativistic Wave equations for spin 1/2 particles, there are presumably antiparticles corresponding to each, of which as yet only the anti-electron (or positron) and the antiproton have been identified. The antiparticle corresponding to the neutrino in equation (1) may be obtained by rearrangement of the terms in the following manner:

$$p^+ \rightarrow n^0 + \beta^+ + \nu_+ \qquad (2)$$

中已经取得了越来越多的成功,并成为支持泡利观点的最令人信服的论据之一。此外，还设计了许多别的实验测试，这些测试巩固了中微子假设，并提供了中微子性质的信息。这种粒子具有带走能量和动量而不被检测到的本领，这表明之前提出的解释可能是正确的。也正是这一特性限制了这些测试只能测量衰变过程本身可观测的细节：与发射的电子和反冲子核[5]相关的能谱、动量矢量和能态。例如，通过仔细测量接近端点的氚衰变的 β 能谱[6]，得到中微子静止质量的上限为电子的静止质量的 1/500，通常可以假定中微子的静止质量恒等于零。

然而预测中微子确定的静止质量并无理论上的根据，但考虑到中微子可能存在的虚态（中微子在这种虚态中可以分裂为其他粒子[7]），可以预测中微子具有很小且确定的磁矩，大小可能为 10^{-10} 玻尔磁子。通过计算中微子从太阳[8]到地球所传送的最大可转让热量，得到磁矩的上限可取为 2×10^{-9} 电子玻尔磁子。最近我们在美国原子能委员会萨凡纳河工厂的裂变反应堆附近使用大的闪烁探测器，得到改进上限值为 10^{-9} 电子玻尔磁子。在 370 加仑的液体闪烁器内，观测到了 0.1 兆电子伏 ~0.3 兆电子伏能量区间内单脉冲的计数率，通过与中微子的磁矩相互作用，由反应堆功率变化引起的所有变化都被归因于液体中可能的电子反冲。我们希望通过降低探测器中 γ 射线和中子的背景，可以进一步改进这个上限。

泡利–费米理论不仅要求中微子从 β 衰变核带走能量和线性动量，而且还要求带走角动量,即“自旋”。最简单的 β 衰变过程就是自由中子的衰变[9],可用下式说明：

$$n^0 \rightarrow p^+ + \beta^- + \nu_- \tag{1}$$

因中子、质子和 β 粒子都带有半整数的自旋，为了式 (1) 中的角动量平衡（式中三个产物粒子中的任何两个必须自旋反平行），必须赋予中微子一个量子数为 1/2 的自旋。因为式 (1) 中四个粒子全都是费米子，所以应遵从自旋为 1/2 的粒子的狄拉克相对论波动方程。每个粒子都可能存在相应的反粒子，但只有反电子（或称为正电子）和反质子已被确认。式 (1) 的中微子相应的反粒子可以通过把这几项重排而获得：

$$p^+ \rightarrow n^0 + \beta^+ + \nu_+ \tag{2}$$

This process is observed in positron decay of proton-rich radioactive nuclides where the proton and daughter neutron are both constituent nucleons. Further rearrangement results in the reaction:

$$\beta^{-} + p^{+} \rightarrow n^{0} + \nu_{+} \tag{3}$$

This is descriptive of the capture of an electron from one of the inner atomic shells by a nuclear proton and is equivalent to equation (2). The question of the identity of the neutrino, ν_{+}, appearing in equations (2) and (3) with the neutrino, ν_{-}, appearing in equation (1) thus arises. With no finite mass or magnetic moment yet measured for either of the neutrinos, one is under no compulsion to assume that they are not in fact identical. The rule of algebraic conservation of fermions, which states that fermions are produced or disappear in particle-antiparticle pairs, requires the ν_{-}, of equation (1) to be named "antineutrino", since it is emitted with a negative electron. The identity or non-identity of the neutrino, ν_{+}, and the antineutrino, ν_{-}, although of no observable significance in single beta decay, should be amenable to test by measurement of the decay constant for double beta decay of certain shielded isotopes. This process was studied theoretically by M. Goeppert-Mayer[10] for the case in which neutrinos are not identical with antineutrinos and by Furry[11] for the case in which the two neutrinos are identical, as proposed by Majorana[12]. Double beta decay is typified by the possible decay of neodymium-150:

$$^{150}\text{Nd} \rightarrow {}^{150}\text{Sm} + 2\beta^{-} + 2\nu_{-}\ \text{(Dirac-Mayer)} \tag{4a}$$
$$^{150}\text{Nd} \rightarrow {}^{150}\text{Sm} + 2\beta^{-}\ \text{(Majorana-Furry)} \tag{4b}$$

If the neutrino and antineutrino are identical, then the virtual emission of one neutrino and its immediate re-absorption by the nucleus are equivalent to the real emission of two neutrinos, and equation (4*b*) is applicable. This cancellation is not possible if the neutrino and antineutrino differ. The half-lives for processes such as equation (4) have been shown by Primakoff[13] and by Konopinski[14] to be quite different in the two cases, of the order 10^{19} years for equation (4*a*) and 10^{15}years for equation (4*b*), where 5.4 MeV. is available for the decay. Furthermore, a line spectrum for the total energy of the two beta particles is to be expected for the Majorana-Furry case (equation 4*b*).

That a decay period consistent with equation (4*b*) does not exist has been shown for a number of shielded isotopes[15], first by Kalkstein and Libby, then by Fireman and Schwartzer for tin-124; by Awschalom for calcium-48; and our associates and us for neodymium-150. In the neodymium-150 experiment, a lower limit of 4×10^{18} years (corresponding to one standard deviation in the background) was set on the mean life against Majorana-Furry decay. This limit is to be compared with a reasonable value on this hypothesis of 1.3×10^{15} years and one calculated for identical neutrinos (using most severe assumptions) to be 6×10^{17} years. The conclusion remains that the neutrino and antineutrino are distinct particles with an as yet undetected "difference". This conclusion is further supported by the negative results of an experiment recently reported by R. Davis[16] employing the reaction:

这个过程是在丰质子放射性核素的正电子衰变中观测到的，其中质子和中子都是核子的组成成分。进一步的重排引起了如下反应：

$$\beta^- + p^+ \rightarrow n^0 + \nu_+ \tag{3}$$

与式 (2) 类似，这是一个核内质子从原子内壳层捕获电子的描述。这导致了一个问题，即式 (2) 和式 (3) 中的中微子 ν_+ 与式 (1) 中的中微子 ν_- 是否相同。目前二者的质量和磁矩都还没有确定的测量值，我们更倾向于认为它们实际上是相同的。费米子代数上的守恒法则表示，费米子是通过粒子–反粒子对成对产生或消失的，由于式 (1) 的 ν_- 是伴随一个负电子发射的，因此应被称为“反中微子”。尽管中微子 ν_+ 和反中微子 ν_- 是否相同这个问题在单一的 β 衰变中并无重要观测结果，但却易于通过测量某些屏蔽同位素的双 β 衰变的衰变常数来检验。梅耶夫人 [10] 在理论上对这个过程做了研究，认为中微子和反中微子并不相同，而弗里 [11] 的研究则认为马约拉纳 [12] 的观点是正确的，即两类中微子是相同的。以钕-150 的可能衰变表征双 β 衰变：

$$^{150}\mathrm{Nd} \rightarrow {}^{150}\mathrm{Sm} + 2\beta^- + 2\nu_- \text{（狄拉克–梅耶夫人）} \tag{4a}$$

$$^{150}\mathrm{Nd} \rightarrow {}^{150}\mathrm{Sm} + 2\beta^- \text{（马约拉纳–弗里）} \tag{4b}$$

如果中微子和反中微子是相同的，则一个中微子的虚发射和它立即被原子核重新吸收等效于两个中微子的实发射，可用式 (4*b*) 来表示。如果中微子和反中微子并不相同，便不可能存在这种抵消。对于式 (4) 所表达过程的半衰期，普里马科夫 [13] 和科诺平斯基 [14] 在两种情况下给出的结果完全不同，其中式 (4*a*) 的量级为 10^{19} 年，式 (4*b*) 的量级为 10^{15} 年，衰变可用的能量为 5.4 兆电子伏。此外，对于马约拉纳–弗里 (式 4*b*) 的情况，可以预期得到两个 β 粒子总能量的线谱。

一些屏蔽同位素表明，与式 (4*b*) 相一致的衰变周期并不存在 [15]。卡尔克施泰因和利比以及法尔曼和施瓦策先后在锡-124 中发现了这一点，阿沙洛姆在钙-48 中以及我们和我们的同事在铷-150 中也发现了这一点。在钕-150 的实验中，马约拉纳–弗里衰变的平均寿命下限被设置为 4×10^{18} 年（对应于背景中的一倍标准偏差）。这个极限可以与基于合理假设的值 1.3×10^{15} 年以及相同中微子情况下计算（用最严格的假设）的值 6×10^{17} 年进行比较。这个结论依旧认为中微子和反中微子是不同的粒子，只是至今尚未检测到它们之间的“差异”。戴维斯 [16] 最近报道的实验负结果进一步支持了这个结论，他采用以下反应：

$$^{37}Cl + \nu_{+} \rightarrow {}^{37}A + \beta^{-} \tag{5}$$

The chlorine target was supplied by 1,000 gallons of carbon tetrachloride placed near a large reactor, and the liquid was tested for the presence of argon-37. Fission fragments, being rich in neutrons, should emit only the antineutrino, ν_{-}.

While careful reasoning from experimental evidence gathered about all terms in the beta-decay process—except the neutrino—may support the inference that a neutrino exists, its reality can only be demonstrated conclusively by a direct observation of the neutrino itself. If the neutrino is a real particle carrying the missing energy and momentum from the site of a beta decay, then the discovery of these missing items at some other place would demonstrate its reality. Thus, if negative beta decays as in equation (1) could be associated at another location with the inverse reaction:

$$\nu_{-} + p^{+} \rightarrow \beta^{+} + n^{0} \tag{6}$$

which is observed to occur at the predicted rate, the case would be closed. An expression for this reaction cross-section has been obtained by application of the principle of detailed balancing to equation (1), knowing the decay constant and electron energy spectrum for the beta decay of free neutrons:

$$\sigma = \left(\frac{G^2}{2r}\right)\left(\frac{\hbar}{mc}\right)^2\left(\frac{p}{mc}\right)^2\left(\frac{1}{v/c}\right)^2 (\text{cm.}^2) \tag{7}$$

where σ is the cross-section in cm.^{2}; G^2 ($=44\times10^{-24}$) is the dimensionless lumped beta-coupling constant based on neutron decay[9]; and p, m and v are the momentum, mass and speed of the emitted positron, respectively, c is the speed of light, and $2\pi\hbar$ is Planck's constant, all in c.g.s. units. For neutrinos of 3-MeV. energy incident on free protons, this cross-section is 10^{-43} cm.^{2}. Explicit solution of equation (6) for the cross-section as a function of the neutrino energy yields:

$$\sigma = 1.0 \times 10^{-44} \times (E - a)\sqrt{(E - a)^2 - 1}\,(\text{cm.}^2) \tag{8}$$

where $a+1$ ($=3.53$) is the threshold for the reaction and E is the neutrino energy, both in units of $m_e c^2$. The threshold for a proton bound in a nucleus is higher by an amount equal to the energy difference between the target and daughter nuclei. It is interesting to note that the penetrability of matter is given by equation (8) to be infinite for neutrinos with low energies ($E<a+1$) and is very large for neutrinos of only a few MeV., the mean free path for absorption being measured in the latter case in terms comparable to the radius of the universe.

Equation (6) may be employed in an experiment in which a large number of hydrogen atoms are provided as targets for an intense neutrino flux and are watched by a detector capable of recording the simultaneous production of a positron and a neutron. Such a

$$^{37}Cl + \nu_+ \rightarrow {}^{37}A + \beta^- \tag{5}$$

将 1,000 加仑的四氯化碳放置在大反应堆的附近作为氯靶，然后检验液体中是否存在氩-37。富含中子的裂变碎片应仅发射反中微子 ν_-。

根据β衰变过程各方面聚集的实验证据（除中微子外）的审慎推理可以支持存在中微子这一结论，而是否真实存在只能通过对中微子进行直接观测才能证明。如果中微子是一个真实的粒子，且携带β衰变位置处丢失的能量和动量，那么若在另一地点发现这些丢失的能量和动量便可以证明它真实存在。因此，如果式 (1) 中的负β衰变能与另一地点的下列逆反应（观测发现该逆反应以预期的速率发生）相关：

$$\nu_- + p^+ \rightarrow \beta^+ + n^0 \tag{6}$$

那么这个问题就解决了。已知自由中子β衰变的衰变常数和电子能谱，将细致平衡原理应用于式 (1)，可以得到这个反应截面的表达式：

$$\sigma = \left(\frac{G^2}{2r}\right)\left(\frac{\hbar}{mc}\right)^2\left(\frac{p}{mc}\right)^2\left(\frac{1}{v/c}\right)^2(厘米^2) \tag{7}$$

式中截面 σ 的单位为厘米²；G^2(值为 44×10^{-24}) 是基于中子衰变 [9] 的无量纲集总β耦合常数；p、m 和 v 分别是发射的正电子的动量、质量和速度，c 是光速，$2\pi\hbar$ 是普朗克常数，所有量都采用厘米 · 克 · 秒制单位。对于入射到自由质子上能量为 3 兆电子伏的中微子而言，这个截面是 10^{-43} 厘米²。式 (6) 中截面的精确解是中微子能量的函数：

$$\sigma = 1.0 \times 10^{-44} \times (E - a)\sqrt{(E - a)^2 - 1}(厘米^2) \tag{8}$$

式中 $a+1$ (值为 3.53) 是反应的阈值，E 是中微子能量，两者都以 m_ec^2 为单位。束缚在核内的质子的阈值会随着靶与子核之间的能量差的增加而增高。有趣的是，我们注意到由式 (8) 可知，低能 ($E<a+1$) 的中微子对物质的穿透力无限大，仅有几兆电子伏的中微子的穿透力都很大，测得的吸收平均自由程可与宇宙的半径相比。

式 (6) 可以应用到如下实验：大量的氢原子作为强中微子流的靶，并用一个能够记录同时产生的正电子和中子的探测器进行监测。多兆瓦反应堆中的裂变碎片的

direct experiment is made possible by the availability of high beta-decay rates of fission fragments in multi-megawatt reactors and advances in detection techniques through the use of liquid scintillators. An estimate of the neutrino flux available from large reactors shows that a few protons should undergo reaction (6) per hour in 50 litres of water placed near the reactor. The problem, then, is to observe these events with reasonable efficiency against the background of reactor neutrons and gamma-rays, natural radioactivity and cosmic rays. In an experiment conducted at the Hanford Plant of the Atomic Energy Commission by us[17] in 1953, an attempt was made in this direction. The target protons were supplied by 300 litres of liquid scintillator (toluene plus trace amounts of terphenyl, and alpha-naphtha-phenyloxayole in which cadmium propionate was dissolved). A delayed coincidence-rate of pairs of pulses, the first of each pair being assignable to the positron and the second to a neutron capture in cadmium, of 0.4 ± 0.2 counts per minute was observed, in agreement with the predicted rate, and with a large reduction in the backgrounds mentioned above. The signal-to-total-background ratio, however, was still very low (1/20), rendering further testing of the signal impractical and leaving the results tentative. On the basis of the Hanford experience it was felt that the detection problem was soluble in a definitive manner, and a second experiment was designed[18] with the view of further reduction of backgrounds and providing means for checking each term of equation (6) independently.

Fig. 1 is a schematic diagram of the detection scheme employed in this experiment. The sequence of events pictured is as follows: a neutrino from the decay of a fission fragment in a reactor causes a target proton to be changed into a neutron with the simultaneous emission of a positron. The positron is captured by an electron in the target water, emitting two 0.51-MeV. annihilation gamma-rays, which are detected simultaneously by counters I and II. The neutron moderates and diffuses for several microseconds and is finally captured by the cadmium giving a few gamma rays (totalling 9 MeV.), which are again detected by I and II. Thus we have a prompt coincidence followed in several microseconds by a second prompt coincidence, providing a very distinctive sequence of events.

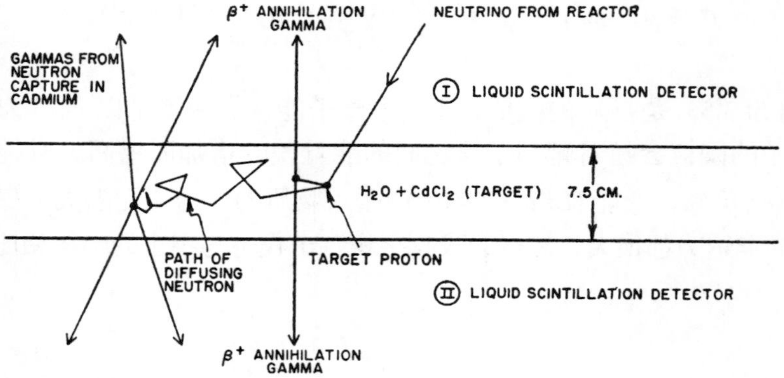

Fig. 1. Schematic diagram of neutrino detector

高 β 衰变速率的可用性，以及通过使用液体闪烁器而带来的检测技术的改进，最终使得这类直接实验得以实施。对来自大反应堆的中微子流的估计表明，反应堆附近放置的 50 升水中每小时有几个质子发生反应 (6)。问题是如何排除反应堆中的中子和 γ 射线、天然放射性和宇宙射线的背景的影响，合理有效地观测这些结果。1953 年，我们[17] 在原子能委员会的汉福特场地进行的实验中，对这方面进行了尝试。我们用 300 升的液体闪烁器（内含甲苯和微量三联苯的混合物以及溶解了丙酸镉的α–挥发油–苯基）提供靶质子。观测到脉冲对的延迟速率为每分钟 0.4 ± 0.2 个计数（每对的第一个可归为正电子，第二个可归为在镉中俘获的中子），该观测速率与预测速率相符，而且前面提到的背景影响也大大减小。然而，信号与整个背景的比仍然很低 (1/20)，因而进一步测试还不现实，结果也只是暂时性的。在汉福特经验的基础上，我们认为可以以一种确定的方式解决检测问题，综合考虑了进一步减小背景因素的目的之后，设计了第二个实验[18]，该实验可以独立检验式 (6) 中的每一项。

图 1 是实验采用的检测方案的示意图。图示事件的发生顺序如下：从反应堆的裂变碎片中衰变得到的中微子使靶质子转变为中子，同时发射出一个正电子。正电子被靶水中的电子俘获，并发射两束 0.51 兆电子伏的湮没 γ 射线，被计数器 I 和 II 同时检测到。中子在几微秒内减速和扩散，最终被镉俘获并发射一些 γ 射线（总能量为 9 兆电子伏），这些射线再次被计数器 I 和 II 检测到。因此，我们得到一个瞬间符合，几微秒后，又得到第二个瞬间符合，从而形成了一个非常独特的事件序列。

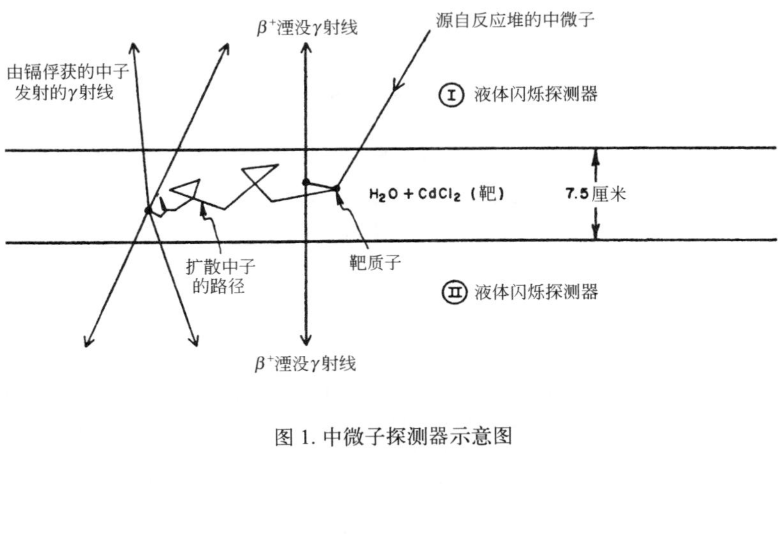

图 1. 中微子探测器示意图

The over-all size of the equipment was set by the number of events expected per hour per litre of water, and the detection efficiency one could hope to achieve. A primary factor in the design geometry and detection efficiency was the absorption of the positron annihilation radiation by the target water itself. Experimentation and calculations showed that an optimum water thickness was 7.5 cm. Since the over-all efficiency dictated a target volume of about 200 litres to yield several counts per hour, two target tanks were used, each measuring 1.9 m. ×1.3 m. × 0.07 m. The depth of the liquid scintillation detector (61 cm.) was such as to absorb the cadmium-capture gamma-rays with good efficiency and transmit the resultant light to the ends of the detector with minimal loss. The scintillating liquid (triethylbenzene, terphenyl and POPOP wave-length shifter) were viewed from the ends of each detector tank by 110 5-in. Dumont photomultiplier tubes, a number determined primarily by the amount of light emitted in a scintillation. The complete detector consisted of a "club sandwich" arrangement employing two target tanks between three detector tanks, comprising two essentially independent triads which used the centre detector tank in common. The entire detector was encased in a lead-paraffin shield and located deep underground near one of the Savannah River Plant production reactors of the United States Atomic Energy Commission. Signals from the detectors were transmitted via coaxial cables to an electronics trailer located outside the reactor building. The pulses were analysed by pulse-height and time-coincidence circuits and, when acceptable, were recorded photographically as traces on triple-beam oscilloscopes. Fig. 2 is a record of an event in the bottom triad. The entire system was calibrated using a plutonium-beryllium neutron source and a dissolved copper-64 positron source in the target tanks; and standardized pulsers were used to check for stability of the electronics external to the detector itself. The response of the detector to cosmic ray μ-mesons was also employed as a check on its performance. After running for 1,371 hr., including both reactor-up and reactor-down time, it was observed[19] that:

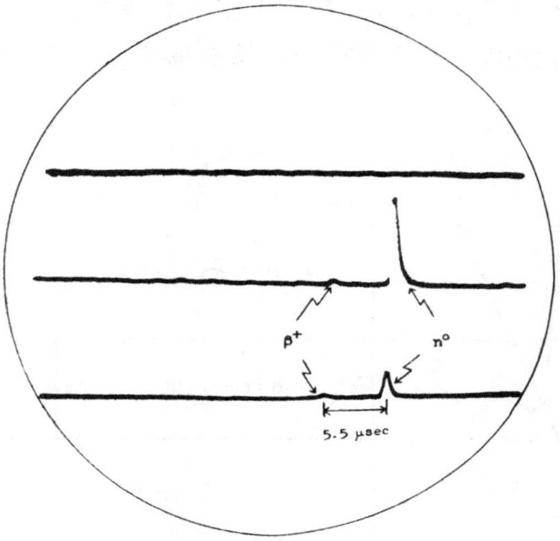

Fig. 2. A characteristic record. Each of the three oscilloscope traces shown corresponds to a detector tank. The event recorded occurred in the bottom triad. First seen in coincidence are the "positron" annihilation gamma-ray pulses in each tank followed in 5.5 μsec. by the larger "neutron" pulses. The amplification was chosen in this case to enable measurement of the neutron pulses. A second oscilloscope with higher amplification was operated in parallel to enable measurement of the positron pulses

根据预测的每小时每升水中的事件数以及我们希望得到的探测效率来设置实验装置的总尺寸。设计几何形状和探测效率的一个主要影响因素是靶水本身对正电子湮灭辐射的吸收。实验和计算表明，水的最佳厚度为 7.5 厘米。由于整个效率需要约 200 升的靶以保证每小时产生几个计数，因此需要两个尺寸为 1.9 米 × 1.3 米 × 0.07 米的靶箱。液体闪烁探测器的深度 (61 厘米) 可以保证高效率地吸收镉俘获的 γ 射线，并以最小的损耗传输 γ 射线产生的光到探测器终端。用 110 个 5 英寸的杜蒙特光电倍增管从每个探测箱的端部观察闪烁液体（三乙基苯、三联苯和 POPOP 波长变换剂），其中光电倍增管的数量主要取决于闪烁体中发射光子的数量。完整的检测器是一个“总汇三明治”式的组合，即在三个探测箱之间放置两个靶箱，从而构成了两个基本独立但共同使用中心探测箱的三件套。整个探测器装在一个铅–石蜡保护箱内，并放置在深层地下，位于美国原子能委员会的萨凡纳河工厂的一个生产堆附近。检测信号通过同轴电缆传输到位于反应堆建筑外的电子仪器拖车上。通过脉冲–高度以及时间符合电路来分析脉冲，当接收到脉冲时，用照相方法将脉冲记录为三踪示波器上的径迹。图 2 是三件套底部一个事件的记录结果。用靶箱中的钚–铍中子源和溶解的铜-64 正电子源校准整个系统；用标准化的脉冲发生器检测探测器以外的电子设备的稳定性。还通过探测器对宇宙射线中 μ 介子的响应检验它自身的性能。在运行 1,371 小时后（包括反应堆功率增长的时间和反应堆功率下降的时间），观测结果 [19] 如下：

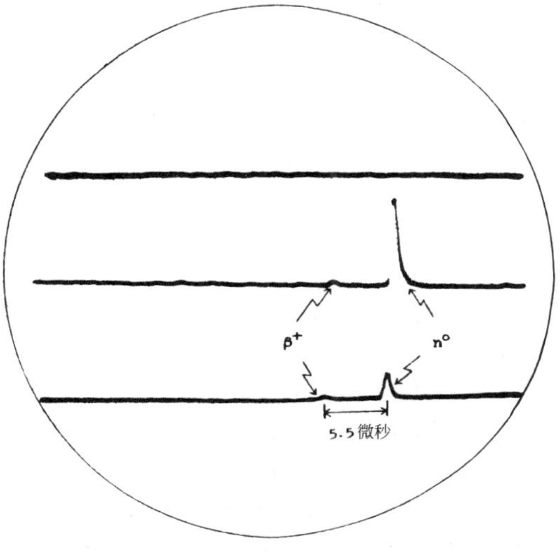

图2. 一次特征记录。显示的三条示波器径迹分制对应三个探测箱。记录的这个事件发生在底部的三件套。在符合中首先见到的是每个探测箱中的“正电子”湮没γ射线脉冲，5.5微秒后，出现较大的“中子”脉冲。在这种情况下，选用能测量中子脉冲的放大倍数。并行运行的第二台示波器的放大倍数更大，用以测量正电子脉冲。

(1) A signal dependent upon reactor-power, 2.88±0.22 counts/hr. in agreement with the predicted[20] cross-section (6×10^{-44} cm.^{2}), was measured with a signal-to-reactor associated accidental background in excess of 20/1. The signal-to-reactor independent background ratio was 3/1.

(2) Dilution of the light water solution in the target tank with heavy water to yield a proton density of one-half normal caused the reactor signal to drop to one-half its former rate. The efficiency of neutron detection measured with the plutonium-beryllium source was unchanged.

(3) The first pulse of the pair was shown to be positron annihilation radiation by subjecting it to a number of tests: its spectrum agreed with the spectrum of positron annihilation radiation from copper-64 dissolved in the water, and it was absorbed in the expected manner by thin lead sheets inserted between the target tank and one detector.

(4) The second pulse of the pair was identified as due to the capture in cadmium of a neutron born simultaneously with the positron by virtue of its capture-time distribution as compared both with calculations and observations with a neutron source. The second pulse spectrum was consistent with that of cadmium-capture gamma-rays, and removal of the cadmium resulted in disappearance of the reactor signal.

(5) Reactor-associated radiations such as neutrons and gamma-rays were ruled out as the source of the signal by two kinds of experiment. In the first, a strong americium-beryllium neutron source was placed outside the detector shield and was not only found very inefficient in producing acceptable delayed coincidences but was also found to produce a first-pulse spectrum which was unlike the required signal in that it was monotonically decreasing with increasing energy. In the second experiment an additional shield, which provided an attenuation factor of at least 10 for reactor neutrons and gamma-rays, was observed to cause no change in the reactor signal outside the statistical fluctuations quoted in (1).

Completion of the term-by-term checks of equation (6) thus demonstrated that the free neutrino is observable in the near vicinity of a high-power fission reactor.

The availability of neutrinos from reactors in sufficiently intense fluxes has opened a number of interesting possibilities. One arises from the use of heavy water to dilute the proton target as described above. This test was valid because the threshold for the neutrino interaction with the deuteron is higher by 2.2 MeV., the binding energy of the deuteron, than the threshold energy for equation (6), and the cross-section is for this reason an order of magnitude smaller; other considerations reduce it still further. The neutrino-deuteron interaction is itself, however, of interest, as two alternatives arise:

$$\nu_- + D \rightarrow \beta^+ + n + n \qquad (8a)$$

$$\nu_- + D \rightarrow \beta^+ + n_2 \qquad (8b)$$

(1) 取决于反应堆功率的信号，为 2.88 ± 0.22 个计数 / 小时，是用超过 20/1 的信号–反应堆偶然背景比测量的，与预计[20]的截面 (6×10^{-44} 厘米^2) 相一致。信号–反应堆的独立背景比为 3/1。

(2) 用重水稀释靶箱内的轻水溶液从而使质子密度为正常情况下的一半，这样可使反应堆信号的速率下降到其以前的一半。而用钚–铍源测量的中子检测效率不变。

(3) 通过一些实验表明，这对脉冲中的第一个脉冲是正电子湮没辐射形成的：其光谱与水中溶解的铜-64 的正电子湮没辐射谱一致，并以预期的方式被插放在靶箱和探测器间的薄铅板吸收。

(4) 这对脉冲中的第二个脉冲是由与正电子同时产生的中子经延迟后在镉中俘获产生的，这可由其俘获时间分布与中子源的计算和观测结果相比较来确定。第二个脉冲的谱与镉俘获 γ 射线谱一致，移除镉将导致反应堆的信号也随之消失。

(5) 对于与反应堆有关的辐射，例如中子和 γ 射线，有两类实验可将它们排除在信号来源之外。在第一类实验中，在检测器保护箱外放置一个强镅–铍中子源，我们发现它不仅在产生可接收的延迟符合方面效率很低，而且它产生的第一个脉冲谱并不像要求的信号那样随着能量的增高单调下降。在第二类实验中，一个附加的保护箱为反应堆的中子和 γ 射线提供了一个至少为 10 的衰减因子，观测发现除了影响到式 (1) 统计涨落外，它并不引起反应堆的信号变化。

因此，对式 (6) 的逐项检测结果表明，在高能裂变反应堆附近能观测到自由中微子。

来自反应堆的高通量中微子的可用性带来了许多有趣的可能性。其中一个源于前面提到的用重水稀释质子靶。这个试验是成立的，因为中微子与氘核相互作用的阈能比式 (6) 的阈能高 2.2 兆电子伏，这个值正是氘核的结合能，因此截面小一个量级；如果考虑到其他因素，其值可能还会进一步减小。然而中微子–氘的相互作用本身就很有意义，得到下面两个反应：

$$\nu_{-} + D \rightarrow \beta^{+} + n + n \tag{8a}$$
$$\nu_{-} + D \rightarrow \beta^{+} + n_2 \tag{8b}$$

where n_2 is the bound state of the bineutron[21], as yet unobserved. If reaction (8*a*) were observed to occur, then a careful measurement of its rate relative to the rate of reaction (6) and a knowledge of the fission neutrino spectrum should enable a direct determination of the ratio of the Fermi and Gamow-Teller coupling constants in beta decay. This follows from the fact that the coupling constant in equation (6) includes a mixture of both types, whereas in (8*a*) it is composed of the Gamow-Teller constant alone. If, on the other hand, equation (8*b*) were observed, not only would these considerations hold, but also the existence of a bound state of the bineutron, which would necessarily be a singlet state (antiparallel spins) because of the Pauli exclusion principle, would bear directly on the question of the dependence of nuclear forces on charge. This follows because the singlet state of the (n, p) system is known to be unbound. As the two neutrons in equation (8*a*) can possess only a few kilovolts of energy when produced by fission-fragment neutrinos, and as they leave the event in antiparallel spin states, the conditions seem favourable for the formation of bineutrons, even if the binding energy were only tens of kilovolts.

Since the proposal of the neutrino hypothesis by Pauli and its success in Fermi's theory of nuclear beta decay, the particle has been called upon to play similar parts in the observed decay of a number of different mesons[22]. The question arises as to the identity of these neutrino-like particles with the neutrino of nucleon decay. It is to be noted that in nuclear beta decay the initial and final nuclei both quite obviously interact strongly with nuclei. This is not the case in (π, μ) decay, where the emission of a "neutrino" converts the interaction of the heavy particles with nuclei from strong to weak. Furthermore, despite the apparent equality of the nuclear beta-decay matrix elements with those associated with (μ, β) decay, both the initial and final products of the latter interact weakly with nuclei.

The neutrino is the smallest bit of material reality ever conceived of by man; the largest is the universe. To attempt to understand something of one in terms of the other is to attempt to span the dimension in which lie all manifestations of natural law. Yet even now, despite our shadowy knowledge of these limits, problems arise to try the imagination in such an attempt. If nuclear reactions played a part in a cataclysmic birth of the universe as we assume, what fraction of the primordial energy was quickly drained into the irreversible neutrino field? Are these neutrinos—untouched by anything from almost the beginning of time—trapped by the common gravitational field of the universe, and if so, what is their present density, their energy spectrum and angular distribution? Do neutrinos and antineutrinos exist in equal numbers? If the neutrino has zero rest mass, is it to be considered with "matter" particles in discussing its gravitational potential, or with electromagnetic radiation? The problem of detecting these cosmic end-products of all nuclear energy generation processes and the measurement of their characteristics presents a great challenge to the physics of today.

式中 n_2 是双中子[21]的束缚态，不过目前尚未观测到。如果观测到反应 (8a) 发生，则精确测量其反应速率与式 (6) 反应速率之比，并应用裂变中微子谱的知识，将能直接测定在 β 衰变中费米常数与伽莫夫 – 特勒耦合常数的比值。这是因为：式 (6) 中的耦合常数包含上述两个常数，而式 (8a) 仅包含伽莫夫 – 特勒常数。另一方面，如果观测到式 (8b) 表示的反应，则不仅这些考虑成立，而且双中子束缚态 (根据泡利不相容原理这个束缚态必然是一个单重态，即反平行自旋) 的存在将直接影响到核力是否依赖于电荷这一问题。这是因为已经知道 (n, p) 体系的单重态是非束缚的。由于式 (8a) 中由裂变碎片中的中微子产生的两个中子仅具有几千伏的能量，而且事件结束时它们处于自旋反平行态，因此条件似乎对双中子的形成十分有利，即使结合能仅几十千伏。

自从泡利提出中微子假设并且在费米的核 β 衰变理论上取得成功后，这种粒子已经被认为在观测到的许多不同介子[22]的衰变中发挥着类似的作用。然而存在一个问题，即这些类中微子粒子与核子衰变的中微子是否是同一种粒子。我们注意到在核 β 衰变中，最初的核和最终的核均与原子核有明显的强相互作用。而在 (π, μ) 衰变中并不是这种情况，其中“中微子”的发射使重粒子与核的相互作用从强变弱。此外，尽管核 β 衰变矩阵元与那些 (μ, β) 衰变矩阵元明显相等，但是后者的最初产物和最终产物与核只有很弱的相互作用。

人们曾认为，中微子是最小的物质实体；最大的是宇宙。试图用一事物来理解另一事物，就是希望横跨自然定律所有表现形式的尺度。然而，尽管现在我们对这些极限的知识还是模糊不清，但仍在试图通过想象解决这些问题。如果核反应在我们假定的宇宙的剧烈的诞生过程中发挥作用，那么有多少比重的初始能量快速地流入不可逆的中微子场中？这些中微子几乎从时间一开始就不与任何物质接触，那么它们会被宇宙普通的引力场捕获吗？如果答案是肯定的，那么它们现在的密度有多大，它们的能谱和角度分布又如何？中微子和反中微子以相等数量存在吗？如果中微子的静止质量为零，那么在讨论其引力势时，它是作为“物质”粒子还是电磁辐射来考虑？所有核能产生过程的宇宙最终产物的探测及其特性的测量，对当今的物理学无疑是一个重大的挑战。

The known properties of the neutrino are summarized below.

Properties of the Neutrino

Spin	$1/2\hbar$.
Mass	<1/500 electron mass, if any.
Charge	0.
Magnetic moment	$<10^{-9}$ Bohr magneton
Cross-section for reaction	$\nu_{-}+p^{+}\rightarrow\beta^{+}+n^{0}$ at 3 MeV. $=10^{-43}$ cm.^{2}. Neutrino ν_{+} not identical with antineutrino ν_{-}

Our work and that of our associates reported in this paper were supported by the United States Atomic Energy Commission.

(**178**, 446-449; 1956)

Frederick Reines and Clyde L. Cowan, jun.: University of California, Los Alamos Scientific Laboratory, Los Alamos, New Mexico.

References:

1. Chadwick discovered that the beta spectrum was continuous. L. Meitner suggested in 1922 that a quantized nucleus should not be expected to emit a continuous spectrum, and Ellis found non-conservation of energy from experiments on the emitted electron. Chadwick, J., *Verh. Deutsch. Phys. Ges.*, **16**, 383 (1914). Ellis, C. D., Internat. Conf. on Phys., **16**, 209 (1934).
2. Ellis and Wooster, *Proc. Roy. Soc.*, A, **117**, 109 (1927). Chadwick, J., and Lea, D. E., *Proc. Camb. Phil. Soc.*, **30**, 59 (1934); Nahmias, M. E., *Proc. Camb. Phil. Soc.*, **31**, 99 (1935). Wu, C. S., *Phys. Rev.*, **59**, 481 (1941).
3. Pauli, W., in "Rapports du Septième Conseil de Physique Solvay", Brussels, 1933 (Gauthier-Villars, Paris, 1934).
4. Fermi, E., *Z. Phys.*, **88**, 161 (1934).
5. We do not attempt here to describe the many beautiful and difficult, recoil experiments in which recoils of neutrino-emitting nuclei (~8-200 eV.) have been measured. A summary can be found in an article by O. Kofoed-Hansen in Siegbahn's "Beta and Gamma-Ray Spectroscopy" (Interscience Publishers, Inc., New York, 1955).
6. Langer, L. M., and Moffat, R. J. D., *Phys. Rev.*, **88**, 689 (1952). Hamilton, Alford and Gross, *Phys. Rev.*, **92**, 1521 (1953). This question is treated in detail in an article by C. S. Wu in Siegbahn (*op. cit.*). We quote Dr. Wu's most conservatively estimated limit.
7. Houtermans, F. G., and Thirring, W., *Helv. Phys. Acta*, **27**, 81 (1954). H. A. Bethe has given the relationship between the recoil electron spectrum and the energy and magnetic moment of a neutrino in *Proc. Camb. Phil. Soc.*, **31**, 108 (1935).
8. Crane, H. R., *Revs. Mod. Phys.*, **20**, 278 (1948). This article also summarizes neutrino detection attempts to 1948. The status of the neutrino in 1936 is given by H. A. Bethe and R. F. Bacher. *Revs. Mod. Phys.*, **8**, 82 (1936).
9. Snell, A. H., and Miller, L. C., *Phys. Rev.*, **74**, 1714 A (1948). Snell, A. H., Pleasanton, F., and McCord, R. V., *Phys. Rev.*, **78**, 310 (1950). Robson, J. M., *Phys. Rev.*, **78**, 311 (1950); **83**, 349 (1951).
10. Goeppert-Mayer, M., *Phys. Rev.*, **48**, 512 (1935).
11. Furry, W. H., *Phys. Rev.*, **56**, 1184 (1939).
12. Majorana, E., *Nuovo Cimento*, **14**, 171 (1937).
13. Primakoff, H., *Phys. Rev.*, **85**, 888 (1952).
14. Konopinski, E. J., Los Alamos Report *LAMS* 1949 (1955).
15. Kalkstein, M. I., and Libby, W. F., *Phys. Rev.*, **85**, 368 (1952). Fireman, E. L., and Schwartzer, D., *Phys. Rev.*, **86**, 451 (1952). Awschalom, M., *Phys. Rev.*, **101**, 1041 (1956). Cowan, jun., C. L., Harrison, F. B., Langer, L. M., and Reines, F., *Nuovo Cimento*, **3**, 649 (1956).
16. Davis, jun., R., Contributed Paper, American Physical Society, Washington, D. C., Meeting, 1956. This experiment was originally suggested by Pontecorvo and considered by Alvarez in a report *UCRL*-328 (1949).
17. Reines, F., and Cowan, jun., C. L., *Phys. Rev.*, **90**, 492 (1953); **92**, 830 (1953).
18. Cowan, jun., C. L., and Reines, F., Invited Paper, American Physical Society, New York Meeting, January 1954.
19. Cowan, jun., C. L., and Reines, F., Postdeadline Paper, American Physical Society, New Haven Meeting, June 1956. Cowan, Reines, Harrison, Kruse and McGuire, *Science*, **124**, 103 (1956).
20. The neutrino spectrum was deduced from the spectrum of beta-radiation from fission fragments as measured by C. O. Muehlhause at the Brookhaven National Laboratory. Dr. Muehlhause kindly communicated his results to us in advance of publication.
21. The evidence for and against the existence of a "bineutron", also called "dineutron", is discussed by B. T. Feld in his article on the neutron in the volume edited by E. Segrè entitled "Experimental Nuclear Physics", 2 (John Wiley and Sons, Inc., New York, 1953).
22. Oneda, S., and Wakasa, A., discuss the question of classes of interactions between the elementary particles in *Nuclear Phys.*, **1**, 445 (1956).

中微子的已知性质概括如下：

中微子的性质

自旋	$1/2\hbar$.
质量	即使有，< 1/500 电子质量
电荷	0
磁矩	$< 10^{-9}$ 玻尔磁子
反应截面	在 3 兆电子伏时，$\nu_{-}+p^{+} \rightarrow \beta^{+}+n^{0}$ 截面为 10^{-43} 厘米^2。中微子 ν_{+} 与反中微子 ν_{-} 不相同

我们的工作以及本文中涉及的我们同事的工作得到美国原子能委员会的支持。

（沈乃澂 翻译；尚仁成 审稿）

A Test of a New Type of Stellar Interferometer on Sirius

R. Hanbury-Brown and R. Q. Twiss

Editor's Note

Robert Hanbury-Brown and Richard Twiss had recently demonstrated that photons in two separate but coherent beams of light tend to arrive together at two distinct detectors. Here they show how this effect could be applied in stellar interferometry, which measures the size (the angular diameter, or angle subtended by lines to each edge) of stars. Testing the technique for the star Sirius, they eventually found a signal indicating an angular size for the star of 0.0063 seconds of arc. This was the first measurement of the angular diameter of Sirius, and showed how the quantum nature of light could be put to advantage in extremely sensitive interferometry.

WE have recently described[1] a laboratory experiment which established that the time of arrival of photons in coherent beams of light is correlated, and we pointed out that this phenomenon might be utilized in an interferometer to measure the apparent angular diameter of bright visual stars.

The astronomical value of such an instrument, which might be called an "intensity" interferometer, lies in its great potential resolving power, the maximum usable base-line being governed by the limitations of electronic rather than of optical technique. In particular, it should be possible to use it with base-lines of hundreds, if not thousands of feet, which are needed to resolve even the nearest of the *W*-, *O*- and *B*-type stars. It is for these stars that the measurements would be of particular interest since the theoretical estimates of their diameters are the most uncertain.

The first test of the new technique was made on Sirius (α Canis Majoris A), since this was the only star bright enough to give a workable signal-to-noise ratio with our preliminary equipment.

The basic equipment of the interferometer is shown schematically in Fig. 1. It consisted of two mirrors M_1, M_2, which focused light on to the cathodes of the photomultipliers P_1, P_2 and which were guided manually on to the star by means of an optical sight mounted on a remote-control column. The intensity fluctuations in the anode currents of the photomultipliers were amplified over the band 5-45 Mc./s., which excluded the scintillation frequencies, and a suitable delay was inserted into one or other of the amplifiers to compensate for the difference in the time of arrival of the light from the star at the two mirrors. The outputs from these amplifiers were multiplied together in a linear mixer and, after further amplification in a system where special precautions were taken to eliminate the effects of drift; the average value of the product was recorded

一种新型恒星光干涉法对天狼星的测试

汉伯里–布朗，特威斯

编者按

最近，罗伯特·汉伯里–布朗和理查德·特威斯演示了两个分离的但是在相干光束中的光子能够同时到达两个不同的探测器。在本文中他们介绍了如何将这一原理运用到恒星干涉法中来测量恒星的大小（即角直径，或沿视线指向恒星边缘所形成的张角）。他们运用该技术测试天狼星，最终发现信号显示该恒星的角大小为 0.0063 角秒。这是首次测量天狼星的角直径，也显示了光的量子性质是如何发挥高敏感干涉测量法的优势的。

我们最近记述的实验[1]证明，相干光束中光子的到达时间是相关的。我们指出，这个现象可以应用在干涉仪测量可见亮星的视角直径上。

这种被称为“强度”干涉仪的设备在天文学方面的意义在于其超强的潜在分辨率，其最大可用基线受电子学技术而不是受光学技术的限制。尤其是用几百英尺而非几千英尺的基线时，这种仪器甚至可以分辨最接近的 *W* 型、*O* 型和 *B* 型星。正是由于这类恒星直径的理论值具有很大的不确定性，所以我们特别关注这种测量方法。

由于天狼星（大犬座 α 星 A）是唯一一颗明亮到足以用我们早期实验设备就能给出可用信噪比的恒星，所以利用该项新技术对天狼星进行了首次测试。

干涉仪的基本装置如图 1 所示。其中，两面反射镜 M_1、M_2 将光束汇聚到光电倍增管 P_1、P_2 的阴极上。这两面反射镜通过人工操作安装在远程控制栏上的光学瞄准器来对准所选恒星。在光电倍增管阳极电流中，在 5 兆周 / 秒 ~45 兆周 / 秒的波段内强度起伏（不包括闪烁频率）被放大，并向其中任何一个放大器内置入恰当的延迟时间，来补偿恒星的光到达两面反射镜时所产生的时间差。在一个采取了特殊预防措施以消除漂移影响的系统中，信号被进一步放大；其后在一个线性混频器中将放大器的输出叠加在一起。结果的平均值记录在一个积分电动机的转数计上。该测量读数直观地给出了光束到达两面反射镜产生的强度起伏的相关系数。然而，读数的大小依

on the revolution counter of an integrating motor. The readings of this counter gave a direct measure of the correlation between the intensity fluctuations in the light received at the two mirrors; however, the magnitude of the readings depended upon the gain of the equipment, and for this reason the r.m.s. value of the fluctuations at the input to the correlation motor was also recorded by a second motor. Since the readings of both revolution counters depend in the same manner upon the gain, it was possible to eliminate the effects of changes in amplification by expressing all results as the ratio of the integrated correlation to the r.m.s. fluctuations, or uncertainty in the final value. The same procedure was also followed in the laboratory experiment described in a previous communication[1].

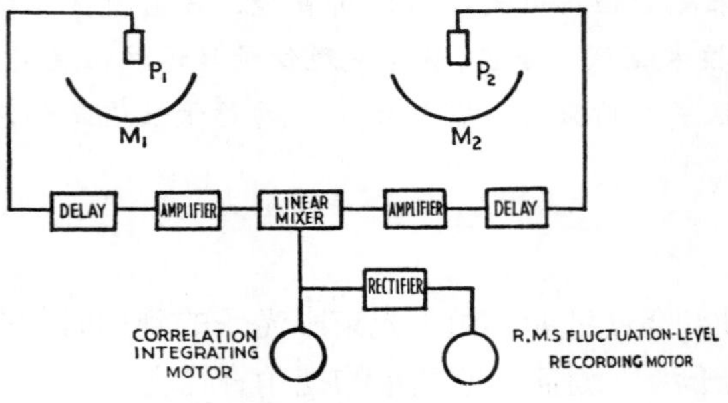

Fig. 1. Simplified diagram of the apparatus

There is no necessity in an "intensity" interferometer to form a good optical image of the star. It is essential only that the mirrors should focus the light from the star on to a small area, so that the photocathodes may be stopped down by diaphragms to the point where the background light from the night sky is relatively insignificant. In the present case, the two mirrors were the reflectors of two standard searchlights, 156 cm. in diameter and 65 cm. in focal length, which focused the light into an area 8 mm. in diameter. However, for observations of Sirius, the circular diaphragms limiting the cathode areas of the photomultipliers (*R.C.A.* type 6342) were made as large as possible, namely, 2.5 cm. in diameter, thereby reducing the precision with which the mirrors had to be guided.

The first series of observations was made with the shortest possible base-line. The searchlights were placed north and south, 6.1 metres apart, and observations were made while Sirius was within 2 hr. of transit. Since the experiments were all carried out at Jodrell Bank, lat. 53° 14′ N., the elevation of the star varied between $15\frac{1}{2}°$ and 20°, and the average length of the base-line projected normal to the star was 2.5 metres; at this short distance Sirius should not be appreciably resolved.

Throughout the observations the average d.c. current in each photomultiplier was recorded every 5 min., together with the readings of the revolution counters on both the integrating motors. The small contributions to the photomultiplier currents due to the night-sky background were measured at the beginning and end of each run. The gains of the photomultipliers were also measured and were found to remain practically constant over periods of several hours.

赖于设备增益，因此，均方根起伏值在输入相关电动机时也被记录在了另一个电动机中。因为两个转数计的读数以相同的方式依赖于增益，所以将所有结果表示为积分相关值与均方根起伏值（即最终值的不确定性）的比值，可能可以消除在信号放大过程中变化的影响。与以前的通讯 [1] 中描述的实验室实验步骤相同。

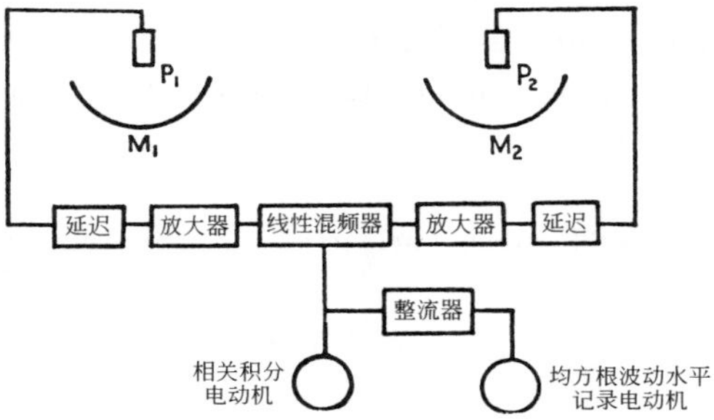

图 1. 仪器结构简图

用“强度”干涉仪进行测量时不必形成一张很好的恒星光学图像；只有当反射镜将星光聚集到很小的区域内时才是必要的，可用光阑使光电阴极缩小光圈至夜空的背景光相对而言可忽略的地步。在此情况中，两面反射镜是两个标准探照灯的反射面，直径为 156 厘米，焦距为 65 厘米，能够将光束聚集在一个直径为 8 毫米的区域内。然而，在观测天狼星时，限制光电倍增管（*R.C.A.* 6342 型）阴极区域的圆形光阑的直径可大至 2.5 厘米，因此降低了控制反射镜所要达到的精确度。

第一批观测采用了尽可能最短的基线。探照灯分别放置在相距 6.1 米的南北两侧，在天狼星位于中天的两个小时内进行了观测。因为实验全部是在北纬 53° 14′的焦德雷尔班克天文台进行的，所以天狼星的地平高度在 15.5° 和 20° 之间变化，垂直于星体的基线投影的平均长度是 2.5 米，在如此近的距离内不会明显地分辨出天狼星。

在观测的整个过程中，每隔 5 分钟就记录一次每个光电倍增管的平均直流电流以及两个积分电机上转数计的读数。在每次观测的开始和结束时，测量夜空的背景光对光电倍增管电流的微小影响。我们也测量了光电倍增管的增益，结果发现实际上它在几个小时内保持恒定。

In order to ensure that any correlation observed was not due to internal drifts in the equipment, or to coupling between the photomultipliers or amplifier systems, dummy runs of several hours duration were made before and after every observation; for these runs the photomultiplier in each mirror was illuminated by a small lamp mounted inside a detachable cap over the photocathode. In no case was any significant correlation observed.

In this initial stage of the experiment, observations were attempted on every night in the first and last quarters of the Moon in the months of November and December 1955; the period around the full moon was avoided because the background light was then too high. During these months a total observation time of 5 hr. 45 min. was obtained, an approximately equal period being lost due to failure of the searchlight control equipment. The experimental value for the integrated correlation $C(d)$ at the end of the observations is given in the line 3 of Table 1. The value of $C(d)$ is the ratio of the change in the reading of the counter on the correlation motor to the associated r.m.s. uncertainty in this reading.

Table 1. Comparison between Theoretical and Observed Correlation

1. Base-line in metres	2.5 (N.S.)	5.54 (E.W.)	7.27 (E.W.)	9.20 (E.W.)
2. Observing time (min.)	345	285	280	170
3. Observed ratio of integrated correlation to r.m.s. deviation: $C(d)$	+8.50	+3.59	+2.65	+0.83
4. Theoretical ratio of integrated correlation to r.m.s. deviation, assuming star has an angular diameter of 0.0063″: $C(d)$	+9.35	+4.11	+2.89	+1.67
5. Theoretical ratio of integrated correlation to r.m.s. deviation, assuming star is a point source : $C(o)$	+10.15	+5.63	+5.06	+4.40
6. Theoretical normalized correlation coefficient for star of diameter 0.0063″: $\Gamma^2(d)$	0.92	0.73	0.57	0.38
7. Observed normalized correlation coefficient with associated probable errors : $\Gamma^2(d)$	0.84±0.07	0.64±0.12	0.52±0.13	0.19±0.15

In the second stage of the experiment the spacing between the mirrors was increased and observations were carried out with east-west base-lines of 5.6, 7.3 and 9.2 metres. These measurements were made on all possible nights during the period January-March 1956, and a total observing time of $12\frac{1}{4}$ hr. was obtained. The observed values of the integrated correlation $C(d)$ are shown in line 3 of Table 1.

As a final check that there was no significant contribution to the observed correlation from any other source of light in the sky, such as the Čerenkov component from cosmic rays[2], a series of observations was made with the mirrors close together and exposed to the night sky alone. No significant correlation was observed over a period of several hours.

The results have been used to derive an experimental value for the apparent angular diameter of Sirius. The four measured values of $C(d)$ were compared with theoretical values for uniformly illuminated disks of different angular sizes, and the best fit to the observations was found by minimizing the sum of the squares of the residuals weighted

为了确保任何观测得到的相关系数不是由于仪器的内部漂移或者光电倍增管和放大器系统之间的耦合作用所致，在每次观测前和观测后都要进行几个小时的试运行。运行时，通过光电阴极上方活盖内的一个小灯照射每个反射镜的光电倍增管。在任何情况下都没有观测到任何显著的相关性。

在该实验初期阶段，我们试图在 1955 年的 11 月及 12 月的上弦月和下弦月的每个夜晚都进行观测。满月那段时间没有观测，因为夜空背景光过亮。在这两个月里观测时间总计达 5 小时 45 分，由于探照灯控制系统的失灵而浪费的观测时间与其大致相同。观测结束后综合相关系数 $C(d)$ 的实验值列在表 1 的第 3 行中。$C(d)$ 是相关电机的计数器读数与该读数的均方根不确定性之间的比值。

表 1. 理论相关系数和观测得到的相关系数之间的比较

1．基线长度（单位：米）	2.5 （南北向）	5.54 （东西向）	7.27 （东西向）	9.20 （东西向）
2．观测时间（单位：分钟）	345	285	280	170
3．综合相关系数与均方根偏差的观测比：$C(d)$	+8.50	+3.59	+2.65	+0.83
4．假设恒星角直径为 0.0063″时，综合相关系数与均方根偏差的理论比：$C(d)$	+9.35	+4.11	+2.89	+1.67
5．假设恒星是点光源时，综合相关系数与均方根偏差的理论比：$C(o)$	+10.15	+5.63	+5.06	+4.40
6．角直径为 0.0063″恒星的理论归一化相关系数：$\Gamma^2(d)$	0.92	0.73	0.57	0.38
7．观测得到的理论归一化相关系数及其相应可能误差：$\Gamma^2(d)$	0.84 ± 0.07	0.64 ± 0.12	0.52 ± 0.13	0.19 ± 0.15

在该实验的第二阶段，增加两面反射镜之间的间距，在东西向基线为 5.6 米、7.3 米和 9.2 米时进行观测。1956 年 1 月到 3 月期间在所有可观测夜晚进行观测，总计观测时间达 12.25 小时。观测得到的综合相关系数 $C(d)$ 列在表 1 第 3 行中。

将天空中其他光源（如宇宙线的切伦科夫辐射 [2]）对观测得到的相关系数没有显著的影响作为最后的检验，我们进行了一系列观测，将反射镜紧靠在一起并只对着夜空单独曝光，在连续的几个小时时间段并没有观测到显著的相关性。

现已用这些结果来推导天狼星视角直径的实验值。将 $C(d)$ 的 4 个观测值与从不同角大小的均匀照射圆盘得到的理论值进行比较，可得当各点的观测误差加权平方和最小时，与观测结果拟合得最好。在比较时，假设圆盘的角直径和 $C(o)$（零基线时的相关系数）的值都是未知的，并且考虑了每点的不同光通量和观测时间。因此，

by the observational error at each point. In making this comparison, both the angular diameter of the disk and the value of $C(o)$, the correlation at zero base-line, were assumed to be unknown, and account was taken of the different light flux and observing time for each point. Thus the final experimental value for the diameter depends only on the relative values of $C(d)$ at the different base-lines, and rests on the assumption that these relative values are independent of systematic errors in the equipment or in the method of computing $C(d)$ for the models. The best fit to the observations was given by a disk of angular diameter 0.0068″ with a probable error of ±0.0005″.

The angular diameter of Sirius, which is a star of spectral type *A*1 and photovisual magnitude −1.43, has never been measured directly; but if we assume that the star radiates like a uniform disk and that the effective black body temperature[3,4] and bolometric correction are 10,300°K. and −0.60, respectively, it can be shown that the apparent angular diameter is 0.0063″, a result not likely to be in error by more than 10 percent. (In this calculation the effective temperature, bolometric magnitude and apparent angular diameter of the Sun were taken as 5,785°K., −26.95, and 1,919″, respectively.) Thus it follows that the experimental value for the angular diameter given above does not differ significantly from the value predicted from astrophysical theory.

A detailed comparison of the absolute values of the observed correlation with those expected theoretically has also been made, and the results are given in Table 1 and in Fig. 2. In making this comparison, it is convenient to define a normalized correlation coefficient $\Gamma^2(d)$, which is independent of observing time, light flux and the characteristics of the equipment, where $\Gamma^2(d)=C(d)/C(o)$ and $C(d)$ is the correlation with a base-line of length d, and $C(o)$ is the correlation which would be observed with zero base-line under the same conditions of light flux and observing time. The theoretical values of $\Gamma^2(d)$ for a uniformly illuminated disk of diameter 0.0063″ are shown in line 6 of Table 1. For monochromatic radiation it is simple to evaluate $\Gamma^2(d)$, since it can be shown[5] that it is proportional to the square of the Fourier transform of the intensity distribution across the equivalent strip source; however, in the present case, where the light band-width is large, the values of $\Gamma^2(d)$ were calculated by numerical integration.

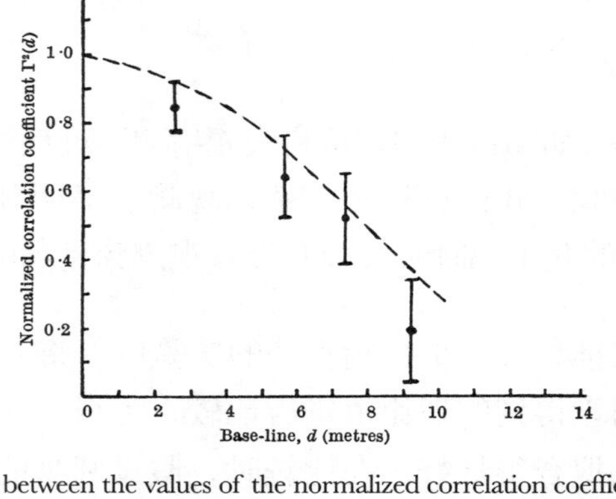

Fig. 2. Comparison between the values of the normalized correlation coefficient $\Gamma^2(d)$ observed from Sirius and the theoretical values for a star of angular diameter 0.0063″. The errors shown are the probable errors of the observations

基于这些相关的数值与设备的系统误差无关或与计算 $C(d)$ 模型的计算方法也无关的假设，直径最终的实验值只取决于不同基线下 $C(d)$ 的相对值。与观测值拟合的最好的是角直径为 0.0068″的圆盘，误差可能为 ±0.0005″。

天狼星的光谱型是 $A1$ 型，仿视星等是 –1.43。至今没有直接测出其角直径；但是如果我们假设该恒星像一均匀圆盘一样辐射，且有效黑体温度[3,4]和热星等改正分别是 10,300 K 和 –0.60，则可得视角直径为 0.0063″，该结果的误差不太可能超过 10%。（在该计算过程中，太阳的有效温度、热星等和角直径取值分别为 5,785 K、–26.95 和 1,919″。）因此可以看出，以上给出的角直径的实验值和由天体物理学理论预测的数值并没有很大的差异。

观测得到的相关系数的绝对值和理论上得到的预期值之间的详细比较见表 1 和图 2。在比较时，定义一个归一化相关系数 $\Gamma^2(d)$ 是方便的，$\Gamma^2(d)=C(d)/C(o)$。该系数与观测时间、光通量和设备的特性无关。其中，$C(d)$ 是基线长度为 d 时的相关系数，$C(o)$ 是在光通量和观测时间相同的条件下基线为零时观测得到的相关系数。表 1 的第 6 行列出了一个角直径为 0.0063″均匀辐射圆盘的 $\Gamma^2(d)$ 理论值。因为已知 $\Gamma^2(d)$ 与等价条形光源强度分布的傅立叶变换的平方成比例[5]，所以用单色辐射估计 $\Gamma^2(d)$ 是很简单的。然而，真实的情况是光束的带宽很宽，所以 $\Gamma^2(d)$ 值由数值积分得到。

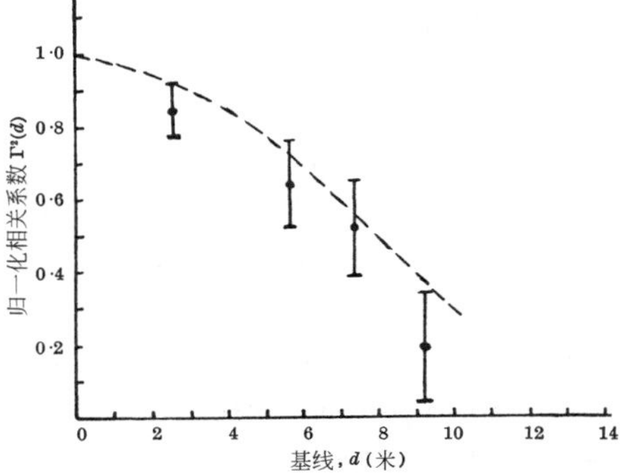

图 2. 观测天狼星所得归一化相关系数 $\Gamma^2(d)$ 和角直径为 0.0063″的恒星的理论值之间的比较。图中所示误差为观测中可能产生的误差。

The theoretical values of $C(o)$, given in line 5, were calculated for the conditions of light flux and observing time appropriate to each base-line by means of equations (1) and (2) of our previous communication[1] (though in the present experiment the r.m.s. fluctuations were smaller by a factor $1/\sqrt{2}$ than the value given in the previous paper, which refers to an alternative electronic technique). The most important quantities in this calculation are the gains and output currents of the photomultipliers and the band-widths of the amplifiers; but it is also necessary to make a small correction for the combined spectral characteristics of the photocathodes, the atmospheric attenuation, the star and the mirrors. Finally, in line 4 of Table 1 the theoretical values of the correlation $C(d)$ are shown; they were calculated from the theoretical values of $C(o)$ and $\Gamma^2(d)$ by means of the relation given above.

The correlation observed at the shortest base-line (2.5m.) can be used as a rough test of the effects of atmospheric scintillation on the equipment, since the corresponding theoretical value depends only on well-known quantities and is almost independent of the angular diameter of the star. Throughout the observations Sirius was seen to be scintillating violently, although the corresponding fluctuations in the d.c. anode currents of the photomultiplier tubes, which were smoothed with a time constant of about 0.1 sec., were only of the order of ±10 percent, as might be expected with mirrors large by normal telescope standards. Nevertheless, the observed correlation $C(d)=+8.50$ does not differ significantly from the calculated value of +9.35, and it follows that it cannot be greatly affected by scintillation.

The experimental values of $C(d)$ obtained at the four base-lines may be compared with the corresponding theoretical values $C(d)$ by means of lines 3 and 4 of Table 1. However, it is more convenient, since these values depend upon the different values of observing time and light flux at each base-line, to normalize the observed values of $C(d)$ by the corresponding values of $C(o)$, so as to give the normalized correlation coefficients $\Gamma^2(d)$ shown in line 7. In Fig. 2 these experimental values of $\Gamma^2(d)$ are shown together with their probable errors, and may be compared with the broken curve, which gives the theoretical values for a uniform disk of 0.0063″. It can be seen that both the relative and absolute values of $\Gamma^2(d)$ are in reasonable agreement with theory, and that within the rather wide limits of this preliminary test there is no significant difference between the correlation predicted and observed.

In assessing the potentialities of the technique described here, it is important to note that, although the measurements took five months to complete, the visibility was so poor that the total observing time was only 18 hr., while in this limited period additional absorption of 0.25-0.75 magnitudes due to haze or thin cloud was often present. If the observations had been made at a latitude where Sirius transits close to the zenith, the improved signal-to-noise ratio, due to decreased atmospheric absorption, would have made it possible to obtain the same data in a total observing time of about four hours.

表 1 中第 5 行给出 $C(o)$ 的理论值是通过对应于各基线长度的光通量和观测时间，运用我们以前研究 [1] 中给出的式（1）和式（2）计算出来的（尽管现在实验得到的均方根起伏是以前文章中涉及其他电子技术给出值的 $1/\sqrt{2}$）。在这一计算中最重要的量是光电倍增器的输出电流和增益以及放大器的带宽；但是对光阴极、大气衰减、恒星和反射镜的联合光谱特征做一些微小的修正也是很必要的。最后，在表 1 第 4 行中给出了 $C(d)$ 的理论值，这些值是用 $C(o)$ 和 $\Gamma^2(d)$ 的理论值通过上文给出的相互关系计算得到的。

由于相对应的理论值只和已知量有关而与恒星的角直径几乎无关，在最短基线（2.5 米）情况下观测得到的相关系数可以作为大气闪烁对该设备影响的一个粗略测试。整个观测过程中，天狼星看起来闪烁得厉害，尽管在光电倍增管阳极的直流电中（时间常数约为 0.1 秒时电流平稳），在反射镜比正常望远镜大的情况下，预期相应的起伏只有 ±10% 的量级。然而，观测得到的相关系数 $C(d)$=+8.50 和计算值 +9.35 相差不大，这表明闪烁对观测结果没有产生很大影响。

对表 1 中第 3 行、第 4 行 4 种不同基线情况下得到的相关系数 $C(d)$ 的实验值和相对应的理论值进行比较。然而，由于这些数据和在每一基线处不同的观测时间值和光通量值有关，所以更为方便的是用相对应的值 $C(o)$ 对观测值 $C(d)$ 进行归一化，以便得到表 1 第 7 行给出的归一化相关系数 $\Gamma^2(d)$。在图 2 中，给出了 $\Gamma^2(d)$ 的实验值及其各自的可能误差，并可以和角直径为 0.0063″ 均匀圆盘理论值的虚线进行比较。我们可以看出，$\Gamma^2(d)$ 的相对值及绝对值都与理论吻合，而且在这种初步的测试的较宽限制下，理论预测和观测分别得到的相关系数并没有显著差异。

在评估本文所描述的这种技术的潜能时，值得我们注意的是尽管该测量工作耗费了 5 个月的时间才完成，但能见度太低以至于总观测时间只有 18 小时，同时在这一有限的时期内，由于常常有雾或薄云造成了 0.25~0.75 星等的额外吸收。如果在天狼星的中天靠近天顶的纬度地区进行观测，由于减少了大气吸收的影响，信噪比提高，这样也许在总共 4 个小时的观测时间内得到等量的数据信息。

Thus, despite their tentative nature, the results of this preliminary test show definitely that a practical stellar interferometer could be designed on the principles described above. Admittedly such an instrument would require the use of large mirrors. Judging from the results of this test experiment, where the peak quantum efficiency of the phototubes was about 16 percent and the overall bandwidth of the amplifiers was about 38 Mc./s., one would need mirrors at least 3 metres in diameter to measure a star, near the zenith, with an apparent photographic magnitude +1.5. Mirrors of at least 6 metres in diameter would be required to measure stars of mag. +3, and an increase in size would also be needed for stars at low elevation because of atmospheric absorption. However, the optical properties of such mirrors need be no better than those of searchlight reflectors, and their diameters could be decreased if the overall band-width of the photomultipliers and the electronic apparatus could be increased, or if photocathodes with higher quantum efficiencies become available. It must also be noted that the technique of using two mirrors, as described here, would probably be restricted to stars of spectral type earlier than *G*, since cooler stars of adequate apparent magnitude would be partially resolved by the individual mirrors.

The results of the present experiment also confirm the theoretical prediction[6] that an "intensity" interferometer should be substantially unaffected by atmospheric scintillation. This expectation is also supported by experience with a radio "intensity" interferometer[5,7,8] which proved to be virtually independent of ionospheric scintillation. It is also to be expected that the technique should be capable of giving an extremely high resolving power. Without further experience it is impossible to estimate the maximum practical length of the base-line; however, it is to be expected that the resolving power could be at least one hundred times greater than the highest value so far employed in astronomy, and that almost any star of sufficient apparent magnitude could be resolved.

We thank the Director of Jodrell Bank for making available the necessary facilities, the Superintendent of the Services Electronics Research Laboratory for the loan of much of the equipment, and Dr. J. G. Davies for his assistance with setting up the searchlights. One of us (R. Q. T.) wishes to thank the Admiralty for permission to submit this communication for publication.

(**178**, 1046-1048; 1956)

R. Hanbury-Brown: Jodrell Bank Experimental Station, University of Manchester.
R. Q. Twiss: Services Electronics Research Laboratory, Baldock.

References:

1. Hanbury Brown, R., and Twiss, R. Q., *Nature*, 177, 27 (1956).

2. Galbraith, W., and Jelley, J. V., *J. Atmos. Terr. Phys.*, **6**, 250 (1955).

3. Kuiper, G. P., *Astrophys. J.*, **88**, 429 (1938).

4. Keenan, P. C., and Morgan, W. W., "Astrophysics", edit. J. A. Hynek (McGraw-Hill, New York, 1951).

5. Hanbury Brown, R., and Twiss, R. Q., *Phil. Mag.*, **45**, 663 (1954).

6. Twiss, R. Q., and Hanbury Brown, R. (in preparation).

7. Hanbury Brown, R., Jennison, R. C., and Das Gupta, M. K., *Nature*, **170**, 1061 (1952).

8. Jennison, R. C., and Das Gupta, M. K., *Phil. Mag.*, 1, viii, 55 (1956).

因此，尽管这一初步测试具有一定的尝试性，但是其结果确实表明：可以用上述原理设计一个实际的恒星干涉仪，但是我们需要承认，这样的观测需要更大的反射镜。根据本次测试实验结果，当光电管的峰值量子效率约为 16%、放大器的总带宽约为 38 兆周 / 秒时，如果所选星体位于天顶、视照相星等为 +1.5，则至少需要直径为 3 米的反射镜。如果所测量星是 +3 等星，则需要至少直径为 6 米的反射镜。由于大气吸收的作用，观测星体的地平高度越低，所需反射镜的直径也就越大。然而，这些反射镜的光学性质只需要和探照灯反射面一样即可。而且，如果光电倍增管和其他电子器件的总带宽增加或者光电阴极的量子效率进一步提高并可用，那么反射镜的直径可以相应减小。需要指出的是，上述两面反射镜的观测技术仅仅适用于光谱型早于 G 型恒星的恒星。因为有足够视星等的较冷恒星可以用单面反射镜部分分辨。

现阶段的实验结果也证明了理论上预期的结果 [6]，即这种“强度”干涉仪基本上不会受到大气闪烁的影响。用无线电“强度”干涉仪的实验结果 [5,7,8] 也支持这一预期结果：实际上无线电干涉仪的观测和电离层的闪烁无关。人们还希望这种技术可以达到更高的分辨率。没有进一步的实验就想要预估出基线实际最大长度是不可能的；然而，人们预期该技术的分辨率至少能提高到目前天文学领域内分辨率最高值的 100 倍。这样一来，就都能够分辨几乎所有有足够视星等的恒星。

我们感谢焦德雷尔班克天文台的主管提供可用的必要仪器，电子服务研究实验室的负责人借给我们大部分的实验设备，以及戴维斯博士在探照灯放置上给予的帮助。我们中的特威斯非常感谢英国海军部批准此内容发表。

（冯翀 翻译；蒋世仰 审稿）

Production of High Temperatures and Nuclear Reactions in a Gas Discharge

P. C. Thonemann *et al.*

Editor's Note

The first hydrogen bomb, which derived energy from nuclear fusion rather than fission, was detonated in 1952. Two years later, physicists began trying to bring controlled nuclear fusion into the laboratory. Here Peter Thonemann and colleagues report on initial experiments with a device called the ZETA, a toroidal chamber 3 metres in diameter holding a dilute plasma. They were attempting to heat that plasma to temperatures approaching those in the Sun by using powerful bursts of current. The team describe encouraging initial results, but would later find that numerous plasma instabilities foiled the scheme's ultimate success. Today, more than 50 years later, a wide variety of plasma instabilities still put practical fusion energy out of reach.

Introduction

THE basic conditions which must be established before a thermonuclear reactor is possible are, first, the containment of a high-temperature gas so that it is isolated from the walls of the surrounding vessel, and second, the attainment of temperatures sufficiently high for nuclear reactions to take place between the light elements. These two conditions are interdependent. Poor containment results in energy losses so large that gas temperatures much exceeding 10^6 °K. are unattainable.

The experimental apparatus described was designed to study the containment of ionized hydrogen (or deuterium) by the magnetic field associated with the current flowing in the gas and to reach temperatures sufficiently high for nuclear reactions to be detectable using deuterium. This apparatus, known as ZETA, was built at the Atomic Energy Research Establishment Harwell.

The principles underlying the containment of a high-temperature gas by means of the "pinch effect" have been discussed by a number of authors[1-3].

The constricted gas discharge formed by passing a high current through a low-pressure gas, while isolating the gas from the tube walls for short periods of time, rapidly develops instabilities and distortions which lead to bombardment of the walls by electrons and positive ions. The consequent cooling and recombination make it impossible to maintain high temperatures except for a transient period[4-8]. These instabilities can be suppressed by the combination of an axial magnetic field parallel to the direction of the discharge current and by the fields produced by eddy currents induced in the surrounding metal walls when the current channel changes its position.

气体放电中产生的高温和核反应

索恩曼等

编者按

1952 年第一颗氢弹爆炸，其能量来自于核聚变而不是核裂变。两年后，物理学家开始尝试将可控的核聚变引入实验室。本文中彼得·索恩曼及其同事报道了最初的实验，在实验中他们使用一个叫 ZETA 的装置，这个装置是一个直径为 3 米并装有稀薄等离子体的环形腔。他们试图通过强大的电流爆发加热等离子体使其温度接近太阳的温度。这个小组描述了令人振奋的初步结果，但不久发现大量的等离子体的不稳定性阻碍了课题的最终成功。五十多年后的今天，多种等离子体的不稳定性仍然阻碍着聚变能的应用。

引　言

在成功建立热核反应堆前必须具备的基本条件是：第一，约束高温气体，确保将其与周围的容器壁隔离开；第二，达到足够高的温度，使轻元素间能发生核反应。这两个条件是相互依存的。不好的约束条件会使能量损失太大，以致气体温度难以达到远大于 10^6 K 的温度。

设计的实验装置通过与气体中电流相关的磁场来研究电离氢(或氘)的约束情况，该装置能达到可以用氘检测是否发生核反应所需的足够高的温度。这台在哈威尔原子能研究中心建立的装置被称为 ZETA。

许多作者 [1-3] 已讨论了用“箍缩效应”方法约束高温气体的原理。

短时间内将气体与管壁隔离开时，在低压气体中通过强电流产生的压缩气体放电会很快变得不稳定并发生变形，这会导致电子或正离子轰击壁。除非在过渡周期 [4-8]，否则随后的冷却和复合将使等离子体不可能保持高温。这些不稳定性可以通过平行于放电电流方向的轴向磁场的叠加和电流通道改变位置时在周围金属壁感生的涡旋电流产生的磁场来加以抑制。

Theoretical studies of discharge stability in the presence of an axial magnetic field have been published[9-12], together with experimental evidence for stability in a straight discharge tube[13].

The preliminary results reported in this article show that relatively long-time stability can be achieved in a toroidal metal-walled tube. The neutron yield and the kinetic ion temperatures have been measured over a limited range of conditions. The nuclear reaction-rates observed are not inconsistent with those expected from a thermonuclear process.

Apparatus

ZETA is a ring-shaped discharge tube of aluminium, 1-m. bore and 3-m. mean diameter, containing gas at low pressure. The gas, usually at a pressure of about 10^{-4} mm. of mercury, is made weakly conducting by a radio-frequency discharge. The toroidal ionized gas plasma forms the secondary of a large iron-cored pulse transformer. A condenser bank, storing up to a maximum of 5×10^5 joules, is discharged into the primary of the transformer, and produces a unidirectional current pulse in the gas up to a maximum of 200,000 amp. The current pulse in the gas lasts for about 4 msec. and is repeated every 10 sec. A steady axial magnetic field is generated by current-carrying coils wound on the torus. This field can be varied from zero to 400 gauss.

Fig. 1 shows the discharge tube assembled with the transformer. A vacuum spectrograph can be seen connected to the torus body.

Fig. 1. Photograph of ZETA. The apparatus is enclosed in a room with concrete walls 3 ft. thick for radiation shielding

Electrical Characteristics

Typical current and voltage oscillograms are shown in Fig. 2. The top trace is the "voltage

轴向磁场存在时放电稳定度的理论研究[9-12]，以及在直线放电管中稳定性的实验证据[13]现已发表。

本文中报道的初步结果表明，在环形的金属壁管中能实现较长时间的稳定。在有限范围的条件下，已测量了中子产生和离子动力学温度。观测到的核反应速率并没有与热核过程预期的结果相矛盾。

装　置

ZETA 是一个铝的环形放电管，管径为 1 米，平均直径为 3 米，内装有低压气体。通常气体的压强约为 10^{-4} 毫米汞柱，射频放电使其具有弱的导电性。环形电离的气体等离子体形成了一个大铁芯的脉冲变压器的次级。电容器储备了最大为 5×10^5 焦的能量，它放电到变压器的初级，在气体中产生一个单向的最大值为 200,000 安的电流脉冲。在气体中的电流脉冲持续约 4 毫秒，每 10 秒重复一次。稳定的轴向磁场是由绕在环上的载流线圈产生的。磁场从 0 变到 400 高斯。

图 1 显示了装有变压器的放电管。可以看到环流器主体与一台真空光谱仪连接。

图 1. ZETA 的照片。为了屏蔽辐射，装置密封在 3 英尺厚的混凝土墙的室内。

电 学 特 性

图 2 是电流和电压的特征波形图。上面的轨迹是用放电管包围的铁芯环绕的回

per turn" measured by a loop around the iron core enclosed by the discharge tube. The length of the discharge path is approximately 1,000 cm. so that the initial electric field at the boundary of the ionized gas is about 2 V. per cm. The primary winding is short-circuited when the voltage per turn is zero, thus preventing the charge on the condensers reversing. The second trace shows the current flowing in the gas, which persists for about 2 msec. after the transformer primary is short-circuited.

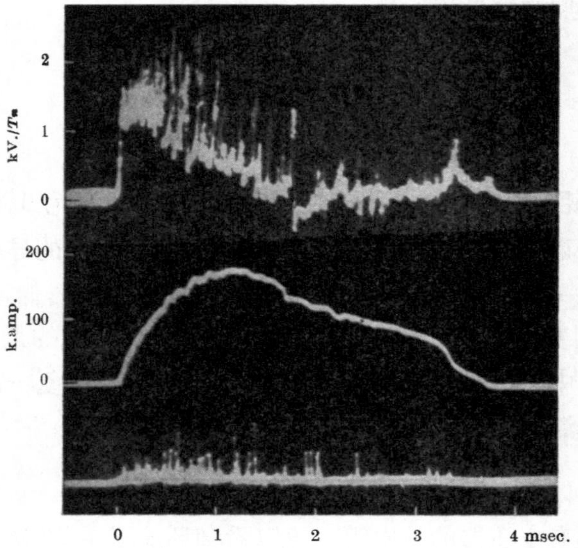

Fig. 2 Oscillograph recordings of the voltage per turn of the transformer, and the secondary current I_S. The lower trace shows the pulses produced by proton recoil in a scintillation neutron counter. Conditions: gas, deuterium +5 percent nitrogen + 10 percent oxygen; pressure, 0.13×10^{-3} mm. mercury; axial field, 160 gauss

As the current decreases the plasma expands until it reaches the walls. It is then cooled. A sudden increase in resistance accompanies this process and the consequent increase in $|dI/dt|$ produces a severe voltage transient which may rise to tens of kilovolts. Destructive voltage transients of this type are suppressed by the addition of 5 percent nitrogen without affecting the neutron yield.

Stability

Measurements with magnetic field-probes and Langmuir probes, together with streak photographs of the current channel taken through a slit in the vacuum vessel, show the current channel to be quasi-stable and clear of the walls for the greater part of the current pulse. Fig. 3 is a reproduction of a streak picture of a helium discharge. The limit of the black area represents the internal diameter of the tube. The light recorded is that of the spark lines of impurities and of (He II) 4,686 A. Streak pictures taken of discharges in deuterium are difficult to interpret as the light is emitted by neutral atoms and by impurity ions released into the current channel from the walls.

路测量的“每匝的电压”。放电路程的长度近似为 1,000 厘米，因此，在电离气体边界的初始电场约为 2 伏 / 厘米。当每匝的电压为零时，初级线圈被短路，因此避免了电容器的电荷反向。第二个轨迹显示了气体中的电流，它在变压器初级线圈短路后持续约 2 毫秒。

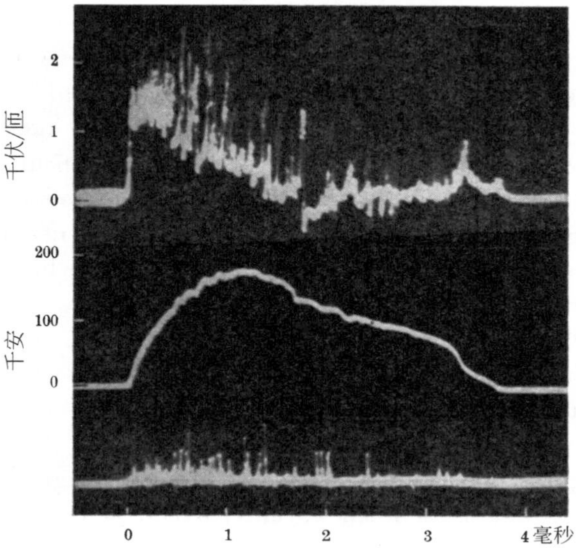

图 2. 示波器记录的变压器每匝电压以及次级电流 I_S。下方的径迹显示的是在闪烁中子计数器中质子反冲产生的脉冲。条件：气体，氘 +5% 氮 +10% 氧；气压，0.13×10^{-3} 毫米汞柱；轴向场为 160 高斯。

当电流减小时，等离子体扩展直到它到达器壁，然后冷却。伴随这一过程，电阻突然增大，$|dI/dt|$ 相继增大，产生瞬间急剧增长的电压，它可以增高到几十千伏。通过附加不影响中子产生的 5% 的氮可抑制这类破坏性电压瞬变。

稳 定 度

由磁场探针和朗缪尔探针进行的测量与通过真空容器的狭缝拍摄的电流通道的条纹照片一起可知，电流通道是准稳定的并且显示大部分的电流脉冲没有接触管壁。图 3 是氩放电的条纹图的重现。黑色区域的边界代表了管的内径。记录的光是杂质和 4,686 埃 (He II) 的火花放电谱线。氘放电的条纹图难以解释为光是由中性原子和从器壁进入电流通道的杂质离子所发射的。

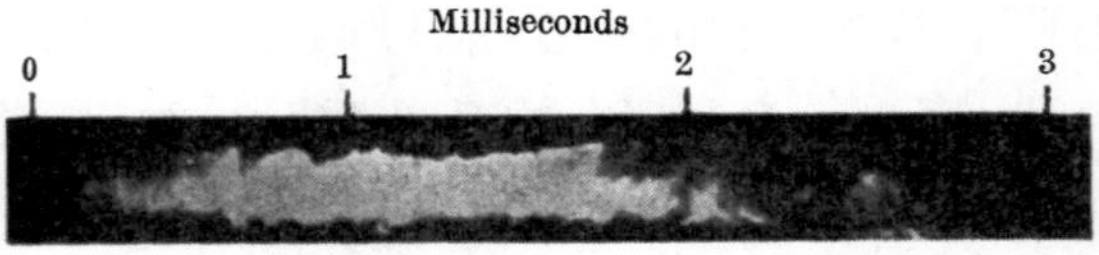

Fig. 3. Streak picture of a helium discharge. Conditions: initial gas pressure 0.25×10^{-3} mm. mercury; axial field 160 gauss; peak current, 130 k.amp. The tube walls lie at the boundary of the dark region

The centre of the current channel is displaced towards the outer wall due to the tendency of the ring current to expand. This expansion is opposed by eddy currents in the metal walls, which are of 1-in. thick aluminium. Measurements of the internal magnetic fields in the plasma are reproducible and show that the axial magnetic field, B_z , is trapped in the gas. On the axis it increases to approximately ten times the initial value. In general, the resultant lines of magnetic force due to the B_θ and B_z components are helical and vary in pitch over the cross-section of the plasma. The stability of a discharge with this magnetic-field configuration has not been treated theoretically.

The presence of the magnetic field-probe, which is 1 in. in diameter, greatly increases the discharge resistance and reduces the production of neutrons.

The diameter of the current channel estimated from the magnetic-field measurements and the streak photographs is between 20 and 40 cm. at peak current. Transmission measurements with 4-mm. microwaves demonstrate that the electron density is greater than 6×10^{13} cm.$^{-3}$. This density is consistent with the assumption that all the gas present is ionized and contained in the current channel.

High-Energy Radiations

Neutron emission arising from the D-D reaction is observed for gas currents in deuterium in excess of 84 k.amp. Emission occurs for a period of about 1 msec., centred about the peak current.

Table 1 shows the average number of neutrons emitted per pulse as the peak current is increased.

Table 1

Conditions: gas D_2 + 5 percent N_2. Pressure: 0.12×10^{-3} mm. B_z= 160 gauss

Current (k.amp.)	Total neutron yield per pulse	T_c (calc.)
84	0.4×10^4	2.4×10^4 °K.
117	3.1	2.9
126	9.2	3.3
135	14.2	3.6
141	26.5	3.8
150	41.6	4.0
177	108	4.5
178	125	4.6
187	134	4.65

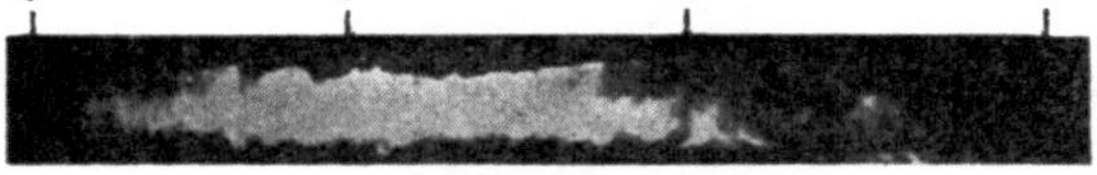

图 3. 氦放电的条纹图。条件：初始气压为 0.25×10^{-3} 毫米汞柱；轴向磁场为 160 高斯；峰值电流为 130 千安。管壁位于黑色区边缘。

电流通道的中心会由于环形电流扩张的趋势而移向外壁。这种扩张受到 1 英寸厚铝金属壁中涡旋电流的抵制。等离子体内的磁场测量是可重复的，测量还显示轴向磁场 B_z 局限于气体中。在轴上，它增大到约初始值的十倍。通常由 B_θ 和 B_z 分量产生的磁力线是螺旋形的，螺旋间距随等离子体截面变化。理论上尚未对具有这类形状的磁场的放电稳定度作过处理。

磁场探针直径为 1 英寸，极大地增加了放电电阻并减少了中子的产生。

从磁场测量和条纹照片估计的电流通道在峰值电流处的直径在 20 厘米 ~40 厘米之间。通过使用 4 毫米微波的透射测量表明，电子密度大于 6×10^{13} 厘米$^{-3}$。这个密度与所有气体是电离的并包含在电流通道中的假设一致。

高 能 辐 射

在氘的气体电流超过84 千安时观测D-D反应产生的中子发射，发现发射集中在峰值电流附近，时间约为1毫秒。

表 1 显示了在峰值电流增高时每个脉冲发射的平均中子数。

表 1

条件：气体 D_2+5% N_2；气压：0.12×10^{-3} 毫米汞柱；B_z = 160 高斯

电流（千安）	每个脉冲产生的总中子数	T_c（计算值）
84	0.4×10^4	2.4×10^4 K
117	3.1	2.9
126	9.2	3.3
135	14.2	3.6
141	26.5	3.8
150	41.6	4.0
177	108	4.5
178	125	4.6
187	134	4.65

Fig. 4 is a histogram showing the average rate of neutron emission during the current pulse.

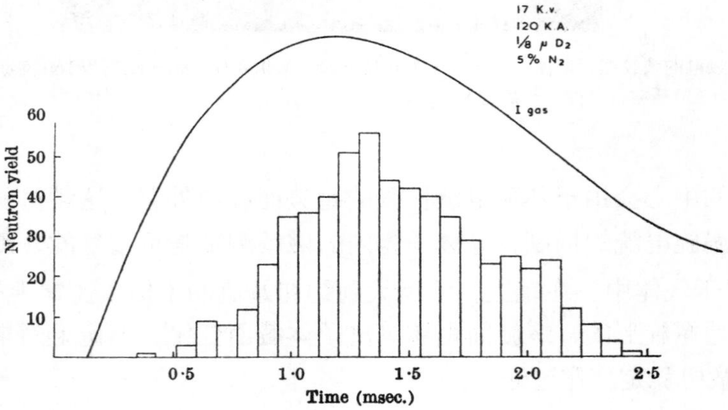

Fig. 4 Histogram showing the number of neutrons counted at various times during the current pulse

The third column of Table 1 gives the temperatures required to produce the observed neutron yields assuming a thermonuclear process. In calculating these figures, it has been assumed that the current channel is 20 cm. in diameter, emits neutrons uniformly for a period of 1 msec. and all the deuterium initially present is contained in the current channel. Since the reaction rate is an extremely sensitive function of temperature, variations in these parameters do not greatly affect the calculated temperature T_c. A comparison is made of the calculated and spectroscopically observed temperatures in Fig. 6.

Within the pressure-range investigated (0.8-10.0×10^{-4} mm.) the neutron yield decreased with increasing pressure. Neutrons were observed when 25 percent of the gas initially present was nitrogen, but the yield was much reduced.

The results obtained with a directional neutron counter moved around the torus showed that, within a factor of two, the neutron emission was uniform and did not arise from localized sources.

No correlation is found between the time of neutron emission and the voltage fluctuations during the current pulse. However, neutrons are produced at the large voltage transient at the end of the pulse, but these can be eliminated by the addition of nitrogen gas.

X-rays are observed towards the beginning of the current pulse. Their average energy lies in the range 20-30 kV. and on the average some 10^5 quanta per pulse are emitted by the whole tube. The number and energy of the X-ray quanta are insensitive to gas pressure and current, but increase in intensity as the axial magnetic field is increased.

图 4 为在电流脉冲周期内中子发射的平均速率的直方图。

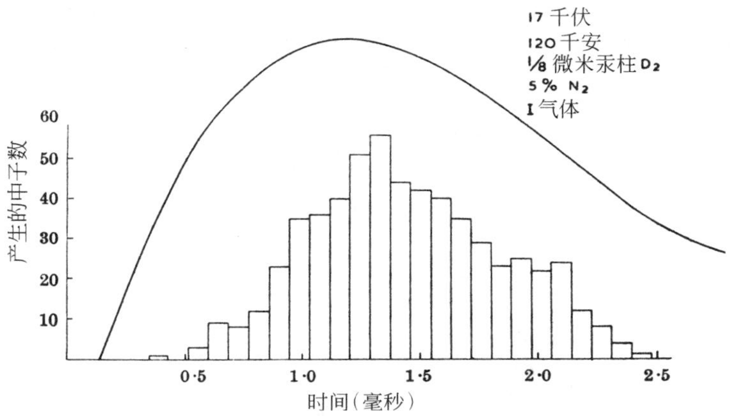

图 4. 电流脉冲周期内不同时间的中子计数的直方图

表 1 的第三列给出了假定的热核过程产生观测到的中子数所需的温度。在计算这些值时假定，电流通道的直径是 20 厘米，在 1 毫秒期间内均匀地发射中子，并且所有最初存在的氘均在电流通道内。由于反应速率是一个对温度极其灵敏的函数，这些参量的变化并不会对计算的温度 T_c 产生很大的影响。在图 6 中对计算的温度与光谱仪上观测到的温度做了对比。

在所研究的气压范围内 (0.8×10^{-4} 毫米汞柱 ~ 10.0×10^{-4} 毫米汞柱)，随着压强增高，产生的中子将会减少。最初存在的气体中 25% 是氮气时，观测到了中子，但中子产额大大减少。

用沿环流器运动的定向中子计数器得到的结果表明，在最大值与最小值相差不到两倍的意义上，中子发射是均匀的，并不是由局域源产生的。

在中子发射时间和电流脉冲期间的电压起伏之间并没有发现相关性。然而，中子是在脉冲末端的大电压瞬态时产生的，但这可以通过添加氮气来消除。

在电流脉冲起始时观测到 X 射线，其平均能量在 20 千伏 ~ 30 千伏范围内，整个管平均每个脉冲发射 10^5 个量子。X 射线量子的数量和能量对于气压和电流并不敏感，但是强度随轴向磁场的增大而增强。

Spectroscopic Observations

Both arc and spark line intensities vary greatly over the period of the pulse. In general, emission lines of normal atoms and ions up to three times ionized have a maximum intensity before peak current. Fig. 5 shows the intensity variation of (He II) 4,686 A. and (O V) 2,781 A.

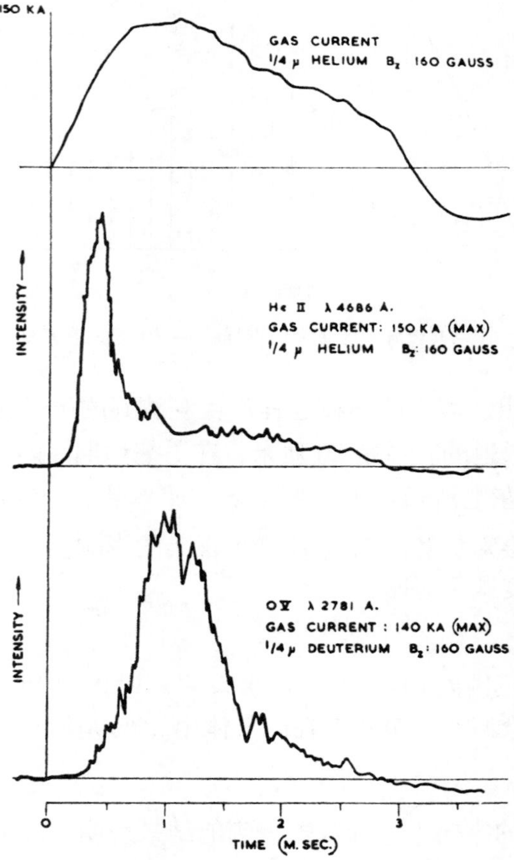

Fig. 5. The two lower traces are photomultiplier records of the intensity variation of two selected spark lines during the current pulse

The Doppler broadening of spark lines emitted in a radial direction is used for estimating the kinetic ion temperature of deuterium and neon discharges. Small quantities of oxygen and nitrogen introduced into deuterium discharges provide spark lines in a convenient part of the spectrum. The breadth of the lines is of the order of 1 A. and can be measured with a quartz spectrograph having a dispersion of 20 A./mm. Calculations show that both Stark and Zeeman effects make a negligible contribution to the line-breadth. Mass motion may contribute to the observed broadening to an appreciable extent, but both probe and streak records show no evidence of gross motion. The contribution to the line breadths of small-scale instabilities and turbulence remains to be measured.

光谱观测

弧光和火花放电谱线的强度在脉冲周期内变化都很大。通常正常的原子和三次电离的离子的发射谱线在峰值电流前有一个最大强度。图 5 显示了 4,686 埃 (He II) 和 2,781(O V) 埃的谱线强度变化。

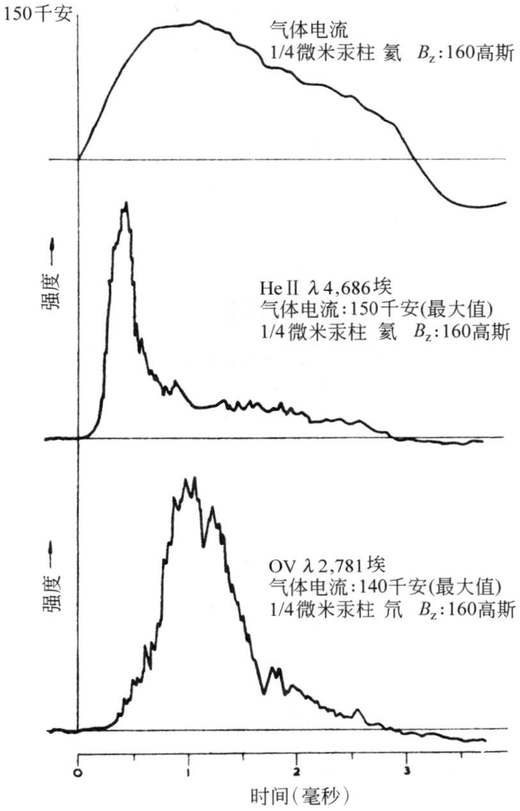

图 5. 图中下方的两条径迹是光电倍增管记录的在电流脉冲期间选择的火花放电的两个谱线强度的变化

径向发射的火花放电谱线的多普勒展宽可用来估计氘和氖放电的运动学离子温度。引入到氘放电中的少量氧和氮，在谱线适当部分提供火花放电谱线。谱线宽度是 1 埃的量级，可以用色散为 20 埃 / 毫米的石英光谱仪测量。计算表明，斯塔克效应和塞曼效应对线宽的影响可忽略不计。集体运动可能有助于谱线增宽变显著，但探针和条纹记录均没有证据显示总体运动。小范围的不稳定性及扰动对谱线宽度的影响尚有待测量。

Some 300 emission lines have been identified in the wave-length range 400-2,500 A. The most prominent are those oxygen, nitrogen, aluminium and carbon. Strong lines of (O VI) are recorded. In this wave-length range more than 400 lines remain unidentified.

The (O V) line has been used for Doppler breadth determination without time resolution as it has a maximum intensity in the neighbourhood of peak current. For (N IV) 3,479 A. this is not so, and light was admitted to the spectrograph for a period of 1 msec. centred about peak current.

The kinetic temperatures obtained by observation of (O V) and (N IV) lines as a function of peak current are shown in Fig. 6. The ion temperatures are found to decrease with increasing initial pressure of deuterium. No satisfactory measurement of electron temperature has yet been made.

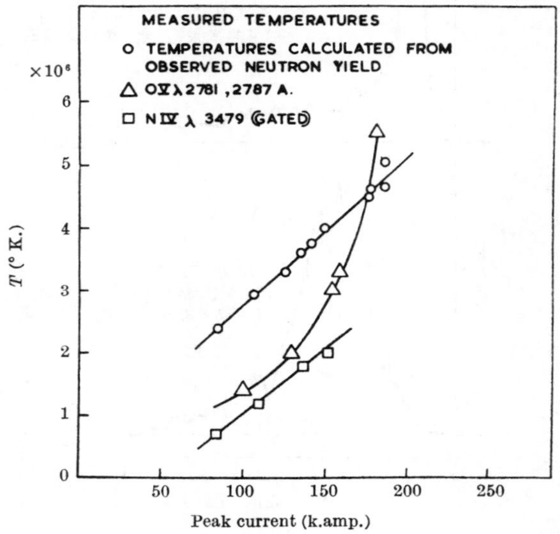

Fig. 6. Ion temperature as a function of peak current determined from the Doppler broadening of (O V) and (N IV). Conditions: initial gas pressure, 0.13×10^{-3} mm. deuterium and 5 percent nitrogen; B_z=160 gauss. The temperature of the deuterium gas, estimated from the observed neutron yield, is shown for comparison

Conclusion

These preliminary results demonstrate that it is possible to produce a stable highly ionized plasma isolated from the walls of a toroidal tube. Hydrogen gas has been maintained in a state of virtually complete ionization with a particle density lying between 10^{13} and 10^{14} per cm.^{3} , for times of milliseconds. The mean energy of the ions in the plasma is certainly of the order of 300 eV., and there are many indications that the electron temperature is of the same order. The containment time and the high electrical conductivity are both adequate for the detailed study of magnetohydrodynamical processes.

在波长为400埃~2,500埃的范围内，约300条发射谱线已被确认。最显著的是氧、氮、铝和碳的发射谱线。其中，记录了(O VI)的强谱线。在这个波长区间内，还有400多条谱线有待确认。

由于(O V)谱线在峰值电流附近有最大的强度，它已被用于测定无时间分辨的多普勒宽度。(N IV) 3,479埃并不是这样，光在峰值电流中心1毫秒范围内被放入到光谱仪中。

图6显示了根据(O V)和(N IV)谱线的观测得出的动力学温度，它是峰值电流的函数。发现离子温度随氘的最初压强的增高而降低。对电子温度尚未得到满意的测量结果。

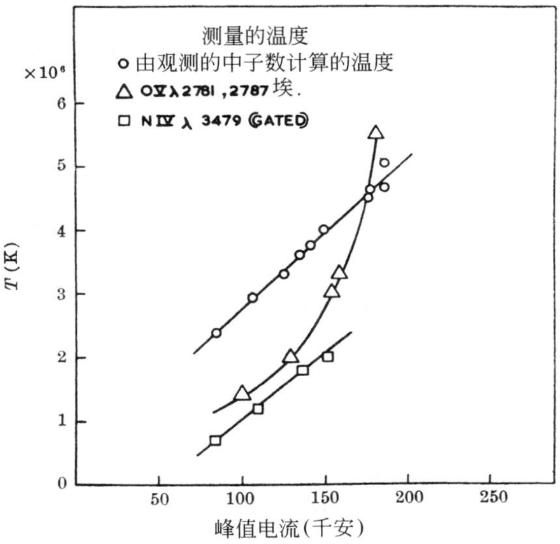

图6. 根据(O V)和(N IV)的多普勒展宽确定的离子温度作为峰值电流的函数。条件：最初气压为0.13×10^{-3}毫米汞柱的氘和5%的氮；B_z=160高斯。作为对比，图中还给出了根据观测的中子产生估计的氘气体的温度。

结　论

这些初步结果表明，可以产生与螺旋管壁隔离的稳定的高度电离等离子体。在几毫秒时间内，氢气体维持完全电离的状态，其粒子密度在每立方厘米10^{13}至10^{14}之间。等离子体内的离子平均能量量级为300电子伏，许多事实表明，电子的温度处于相同量级。约束时间和高电导对于详尽研究磁流体力学过程都是合适的。

To identify a thermonuclear process it is necessary to show that random collisions in the gas between deuterium ions are responsible for the nuclear reactions. In principle, this can be done by calculating the velocity distribution of the reacting deuterium ions from an exact determination of both the energy and direction of emission of the neutrons. The neutron flux so far obtained is insufficient to attain the desired accuracy of measurement.

Investigations leading up to the present results have been constantly encouraged and supported by Sir John Cockcroft and the late Lord Cherwell. The theoretical investigations have been directed by Dr. W. B. Thompson, of the Theoretical Physics Division.

A major part of the engineering design and construction of ZETA was done by the Metropolitan-Vickers Electrical Co., Ltd.

(**181**, 217-220; 1958)

P. C. Thonemann, E. P. Butt, R. Carruthers, A. N. Dellis, D. W. Fry, A. Gibson, G. N. Harding, D. J. Lees, R. W. P. McWhirter, R. S. Pease, S. A. Ramsden and S. Ward: Atomic Energy Research Establishment, Harwell.

References:

1. Post, B. F., *Rev. Mod. Phys.*, **28**, 338 (1956).

2. Pease, R. S., *Proc. Phys. Soc.*, B, **70**, 11 (1957).

3. Burkhart, L. C., Dunaway, B. E., Mather, J. W., Phillips, J. A., Sawyer, G. A., Stratton, T. F., Stovall, E. J., and Tuck, J. L., *J. App. Phys.*, **28**, 519 (1957).

4. Kurchatov, I. V., *Atomnaya Energiya*, **1**, No. 3, 65 (1956). English translation, *J. Nuclear Energy*, **4**, 198 (1957).

5. Artaimovitch, L. A., Andrianov, A. M., Bazilevakaya, O. A., Prokhorov, YU. G. and Filippov, N. V., *Atomnaya Energiya*, **1**, No. 3, 76 (1956). English translation, *J. Nuclear Energy*, **4**, 203 (1957).

6. Colgate, S.
7. Berglund, S., Nilsson, R., Ohlin, P., Siegbahn, K., Sundstrom, T., and Svennerstedt, S., *Nuclear Instruments*, **1**, 233 (1957).
8. Curran, S., and Allen, K. W.

(6–8:) Proc. 3rd Int. Conf. on Ionization Phenomena in Gases, Venice (1957).

9. Shrafranov, V. D., *Atomnaya Energiya*, **1**, No. 5, 38 (1956). English translation, *J. Nuclear Energy*, **5**, 86 (1957).

10. Tayler, R. J., *Proc. Phys. Soc.*, B, **70**, 1049 (1957).

11. Bosenbluth, M.
12. Bickerton, R. J.

(11–12:) Proc. 3rd Int. Conf. on Ionization Phenomena in Gases, Venice (1957).

13. Bezba chenko, A. L., Golovin, I. N., Ivanov D. P., Kirillov, V. D., Yavlinsky, N. A., *Atomnaya Energiya*, **1**, No. 5, 26 (1956). English translation, *J. Nuclear Energy*, **5**, 71 (1957).

为了确认热核过程，必须说明核反应是由气体中氘离子之间随机碰撞引起的。原则上，这一点可以通过计算反应氘粒子的速率分布得到，速率分布又可以通过中子能量和发射方向的精确测定而得到。至今得出的中子通量还不足以获得所要求的测量精确度。

为获得现有结果所做的研究得到了约翰·考克饶夫爵士和已故的彻韦尔勋爵不断的鼓励和支持。理论研究得到了理论物理部的汤普森博士的指导。

工程设计的主要部分和 ZETA 的构建是由茂伟电气公司完成的。

（沈乃澂 翻译；尚仁成 审稿）

Co-operative Phenomena in Hot Plasmas

L. Spitzer, jun.

Editor's Note

The new experiments producing high-temperature plasmas in the ZETA device at Harwell not only shed light on the potential for controlled fusion energy, but also provided an opportunity for studying plasma physics in extreme conditions. Here physicist Lyman Spitzer reports on a mystery evident in the ZETA data: an anomalously fast rise in the temperature of positive ions, which in theory should gain energy more slowly through collisions with hot electrons. These findings indicated that physicists still had much to learn about the rich dynamics within plasmas, and the many collective instabilities which drive it. This theme of the overwhelming collective complexity of dynamical behaviour would be a common one in plasma physics for the next half century.

THE interesting results described by Thonemann and his co-workers in the preceding article provide not only an important step forward in the controlled release of thermonuclear energy, but also a challenging problem in the dynamics of fully ionized gases or plasmas. The spectroscopic line profiles and the neutron counts provide incontrovertible evidence for the acceleration of the positive ions. However, theory would seem to indicate that electron-ion collisions are inadequate to explain the observed rate of heating, and some unknown mechanism would appear to be involved.

The rate at which the positive-ion temperature increases, as a result of electron-ion collisions, has been given elsewhere[1]. It has been suggested, both in Great Britain and in the United States, that this process might be inadequate to explain the rate at which positive ions gain energy in certain electrical discharges. A relatively simple procedure, due to Stix[2], may be used to set an upper limit to the rate at which positive ions are heated by electron-ion collisions. In this method the rate of heating is made a maximum by setting the electron temperature equal to three times the ion temperature, T_i, and setting the electron density equal to a constant, n_e, corresponding to complete ionization and concentration within the discharge channel of all the gas initially present in the tube. On this basis (with $\ln\Lambda$ set equal to 15, see ref. 1) T_i is given by the relation

$$T_i^{3/2} = 1.71 \times 10^{-2} n_e t \qquad (1)$$

where T_i is in degrees K., n_e in electrons per cm.^{3}, and t in seconds.

To determine the density in the ZETA experiments, we compute the radius, r_d, of the discharge channel on the assumption that the flux of the axial magnetic field, B_z, is held constant in the gas during the contraction, and that the field, B_θ, due to the current equals the compressed axial field at the boundary of the discharge. As a result of the high

热等离子体中的协同现象

小斯皮策

编者按

在哈威尔的 ZETA 设备上产生高温等离子体的新实验不仅为可控核聚变的研究带来一线光明，同时也为我们提供了一个研究极端条件下等离子体物理的机会。本文中物理学家赖曼·斯皮策指出了 ZETA 数据中一个谜团：正离子温度异常地快速上升，而理论上来说，由于它与热电子相互碰撞，因此获得能量的速率应该更加缓慢。这些发现说明，物理学家们对于等离子体内丰富的动力学现象以及导致这种现象的众多集体不稳定性仍需进一步的探索。在此后的半个世纪的时间里，动力学行为这个错综复杂且极具挑战性的问题成为等离子体物理中一个很常见的研究主题。

索恩曼及其同事们在先前的文章中阐述了一个很有意思的结果，这个结果不仅说明我们在热核能量的可控释放中迈出了重要的一步，而且还提出了一个极具挑战性的有关完全电离的气体（即等离子体）的动力学问题。光谱线剖面和中子数提供了与正离子加速相矛盾的证据。然而，理论显示仅靠电子–离子碰撞并不足以解释观测到的升温速率，其中应该包含某些未知的机制。

在之前的一篇文章[1]中，我曾提到正离子温度升高的速率是由电子–离子碰撞导致的。然而在英国和美国都有人提出，这个碰撞过程不足以解释正离子在释放电荷后获得能量的速率。斯蒂克斯[2]提出了一个相对简单的过程，可以用来确定电子–离子碰撞所导致的正离子升温的速率上限。在这种方法中，将电子温度取为离子温度 T_i 的三倍，设定电子密度为一常数 n_e，相当于完全电离并且管内最初存在的所有气体都浓缩在放电通道内，在这些条件下可以得到加热速率的最大值。据此 ($\ln\Lambda$ 取为 15，见参考文献 1)，T_i 由下列关系式给出：

$$T_i^{3/2} = 1.71 \times 10^{-2} n_e t \tag{1}$$

式中，T_i 的单位是 K，n_e 的单位是每立方厘米的电子数，t 的单位是秒。

为了测定 ZETA 实验中的密度，我们在下面两个假设的基础上计算了放电通道的半径 r_d。一是假定在收缩过程中轴向磁场 B_z 方向上的通量保持不变，二是假定由电流产生的磁场 B_θ 等于放电界面上被压缩的轴向磁场。由于 ZETA 实现了高温，因

temperatures achieved in ZETA, appreciable leakage of axial flux out of the discharge does not appear to be possible. Neglect of the finite gas pressure decreases the computed channel radius, increases n_e and again makes the rate of increase of T_i a maximum. On these assumptions, values of r_d have been computed for two currents, and an initial B_z of 160 gauss, and are listed in the second column of Table 1.

Table 1

I (amp.)	r_d (cm.)	n_e (cm.$^{-3}$)	T_i (°K.)	t (theor.)	t (obs.)
126,000	16	8.6×10^{13}	3.3×10^{6}	4.0×10^{-3}	1.0×10^{-3}
140,000	14	1.1×10^{14}	2.5×10^{6}	2.0×10^{-3}	1.0×10^{-3}

These values of r_d are consistent with those cited by the Harwell group. The values of n_e in the third column correspond to complete ionization of all the deuterium initially present in the torus, at a pressure of $1/8\mu$, and its concentration in the current channel. The value of T_i for the lower current in column 4 is taken from Table 1 in the article by Thonemann *et al.*, and is based on the neutron yield. The value of T_i at the higher current is the temperature obtained from the Doppler width of the O V triplet, as shown in Fig. 6 of the Harwell article. The ion temperature obtained from the neutron yield under this condition is about 50 percent greater, but no information is available on the time at which the neutrons appear in this case. In the fifth column are given the values of the time, in seconds, required for the positive ions to reach this temperature, computed from equation 1.

For comparison, the final column lists the observed times, in seconds, at which the positive-ion energies reach the values corresponding to the fourth column. For the lesser current, this is the time at which the neutron yield reaches half its peak value as shown in Fig. 4 of the paper from Harwell. For the greater value of current, t (obs.) is set equal to the time at which the O V radiation reaches its peak intensity, as shown in Fig. 5 of the Harwell paper. The simplifications made have tended to reduce t (theor.), and the correct value may be about an order of magnitude greater than given in Table 1. Thus the discrepancy seems real. There does not appear to be any simple model, based on a quiescent plasma, which is consistent with the observed rapid heating of the positive ions.

Following a suggestion by the Harwell group as to the importance of non-thermal heating processes, Stix[2] in 1956 arrived at conclusions similar to the above from experimental results obtained at Project Matterhorn. A discharge was produced in helium gas in a stainless-steel race-track tube of 10 cm. diameter and 240 cm. axial length, with an initial pressure of 0.63μ and an externally produced axial field of 19,000 gauss. The magnetic field was arranged so that intersection of the outer lines of force with material walls restricted the discharge to a channel of 5 cm. diameter. A loop voltage of 300 V. was applied around an iron transformer threading the race-track, and a maximum current of 8,000 amp. observed; since this current produces only a minor perturbation in the magnetic field, there was no pinching of the discharge. Time-resolved spectroscopic profiles of the He II line, λ 4,686, indicated that the kinetic temperature of these ions increased to 1.2×10^6 degrees K. in 1.5×10^{-4} sec., as compared to a theoretical maximum

此基本不会出现放电造成的轴向磁通量的明显泄漏。忽略有限的气压使得计算出的通道半径变小，并使 n_e 增大，最后使 T_i 的增长率达到最大值。基于这些假设，对两个电流强度下的 r_d 值进行计算，最初的 B_z 为 160 高斯，计算结果详见表 1 的第二列。

表 1

I（安）	r_d（厘米）	n_e（厘米$^{-3}$）	T_i (K)	t（理论值）	t（观测值）
126,000	16	8.6×10^{13}	3.3×10^{6}	4.0×10^{-3}	1.0×10^{-3}
140,000	14	1.1×10^{14}	2.5×10^{6}	2.0×10^{-3}	1.0×10^{-3}

这些 r_d 的值与哈威尔小组引用的数值是一致的。在第三列中 n_e 的值对应的是最初存在于环内的所有氘在气压为 1/8 微米汞柱时完全电离并浓缩在电流通道内的情况。第四列中较低电流下的 T_i 值取自索恩曼等人的论文中的表 1，它是根据中子产额而得出的。较高电流下的 T_i 值是根据哈威尔小组的论文中图 6 所示的 O V 三重线的多普勒宽度而得出的。在这种条件下，根据中子产额得到的离子温度升高了约 50%，但还无法确定在这种情况下中子是什么时候开始产生的。在第五列中给出了以秒为单位的时间的值，这是根据式 (1) 计算出的正离子达到这个温度所需要的时间。

为了进行比较，最后一列给出了以秒为单位的观测时间，在这个时间内正离子能量达到第四列的温度所对应的值。对于较小电流的情况，这是中子产额达到其峰值一半时所用的时间，如哈威尔小组的论文中图 4 所示。对于较大电流的情况，t(观测值) 取 O V 辐射值达到其峰值强度时所用的时间，如哈威尔小组的论文中图 5 所示。这种简化常常使得 t(理论值) 偏小，修正值可能会比表 1 给出的值大约大一个数量级。因此差异看起来确实存在。似乎并没有能和观测到的阳离子的快速加热相吻合的基于静等离子体的任何简单模型。

1956 年，按哈威尔小组关于非热效应的加热过程的重要性所提出的建议，斯蒂克斯 [2] 得到了与马特峰计划的实验结果相类似的结论。在直径 10 厘米、轴长 240 厘米充满氦气的不锈钢环形管中进行放电，其初始气压为 0.63 微米汞柱，外部产生的轴向磁场为 19,000 高斯。磁场的分布使得外部的磁力线与材料壁交叉从而将放电限制在直径为 5 厘米的通道内。将 300 伏回路电压加在穿过粒子轨道的铁变压器周围，观测到的最大电流为 8,000 安；因为电流在磁场中只产生了较小的扰动，所以并不存在放电的箍缩。λ 为 4,686 埃的氦 II 线的时间分辨光谱图表明，这些离子的动力学温度在 1.5×10^{-4} 秒内增高到 1.2×10^{6}K，而理论上在这一时间内所能达到的最大值

value of 0.8×10^6 degrees in this same time-interval.

It has been known since the work by Langmuir[3] that electrons in a conventional gas discharge approach a Maxwellian distribution much more rapidly than can be explained by inter-particle collisions. Recent research by Gabor and his collaborators[4] has shown that oscillations generated in the plasma sheath are responsible for much of this effect, but the detailed mechanism is still unexplained. Possibly the high ion energies observed in ZETA represent a phenomenon related to Langmuir's paradox. To analyse the possible processes involved, such as oscillations, shocks, hydromagnetic turbulences, etc., it would be helpful to obtain information on the extent to which the positive-ion velocities are thermalized, that is, on how nearly the distribution function is isotropic and Maxwellian. Evidently detailed experimental investigations of these cooperative effects in hot plasmas will be of great interest in basic physics.

(**181**, 221-222; 1958)

Lyman Spitzer: Princeton University.

References:

1. Spitzer, L., "Physics of Fully Ionized Gases" (Interscience Publishers, 1956, Section 5.3).
2. Stix, T., Talk at Berkeley, California (February 20-23, 1957).
3. Langmuir, I., *Phys. Rev.*, **26**, 585 (1925); *Z. Phys.*, **46**, 271 (1928).
4. Gabor, D., Ash, E. A., and Dracott, D., *Nature*, **176**, 916 (1955).

是 0.8×10^6 K。

依据朗缪尔[3]的工作我们知道，在传统的气体放电中，电子以极快的速率达到麦克斯韦分布而单纯用粒子间的相互碰撞无法对此进行解释。最近盖伯及其同事们[4]的研究表明，这种效应主要是由等离子体鞘层中产生的振荡造成的，但具体的机制还无法解释。在 ZETA 中观测到的高离子能也许代表了一种与朗缪尔悖论相关的现象。为了分析可能包含的过程（例如振荡、冲击、磁流体湍流等），有必要收集与正离子速度被热能化的程度有关的信息，即分布函数在多大程度上接近于各向同性和麦克斯韦分布。显然，对热等离子体中协同效应的详细情况的实验研究，将是基础物理学科中一个非常有趣的课题。

（沈乃澂 翻译；尚仁成 审稿）

A Three-Dimensional Model of the Myoglobin Molecule Obtained by X-Ray Analysis

J. C. Kendrew *et al.*

Editor's Note

Although X-ray diffraction had been used since the beginning of the twentieth century to analyse the structure of crystalline materials such as common salt, it had not yielded much information about the properties of materials involved in living things. Progress was made only after the Second World War in Europe. This paper reports the structure of the molecule called myoglobin, used by animals of all kinds for storing oxygen. The principal authors are John Kendrew and David Phillips. Their success in producing the first structure of a real-life protein depended on a technique developed by Max Perutz involving the attachment of various heavy atoms such as mercury to the protein molecule being studied. Kendrew and Perutz received the Nobel Prize for Chemistry in 1962.

MYOGLOBIN is a typical globular protein, and is found in many animal cells. Like haemoglobin, it combines reversibly with molecular oxygen; but whereas the role of haemoglobin is to transport oxygen in the blood stream, that of myoglobin is to store it temporarily within the cells (a function particularly important in diving animals such as whales, seals and penguins, the dark red tissues of which contain large amounts of myoglobin, and which have been our principal sources of the protein). Both molecules include a non-protein moiety, consisting of an iron-porphyrin complex known as the haem group, and it is this group which actually combines with oxygen; haemoglobin, with a molecular weight of 67,000, contains four haem groups, whereas myoglobin has only one. This, together with about 152 amino-acid residues, makes up a molecular weight of 17,000, so that myoglobin is one of the smaller proteins. Its small size was one of the main reasons for our choice of myoglobin as a subject for X-ray analysis.

In describing a protein it is now common to distinguish the primary, secondary and tertiary structures. The *primary structure* is simply the order, or sequence, of the amino-acid residues along the polypeptide chains. This was first determined by Sanger using chemical techniques for the protein insulin[1], and has since been elucidated for a number of peptides and, in part, for one or two other small proteins. The *secondary structure* is the type of folding, coiling or puckering adopted by the polypeptide chain: the α-helix and the pleated sheet are examples. Secondary structure has been assigned in broad outline to a number of fibrous proteins such as silk, keratin and collagen; but we are ignorant of the nature of the secondary structure of any globular protein. True, there is suggestive evidence, though as yet no proof, that α-helices occur in globular proteins, to an extent which is difficult to gauge quantitatively in any particular case. The *tertiary structure* is the way in which the

利用X射线分析获得肌红蛋白分子的三维模型

肯德鲁等

编者按

尽管早在20世纪初X射线衍射就已用于分析食盐等晶体物质的结构，但是对于生物体相关物质的性质并没有给出太多信息。直到第二次世界大战之后，这种情况才在欧洲有所改善。这篇文章报道了肌红蛋白（即各种动物用以储存氧气的物质）分子的结构。本文的主要作者是约翰·肯德鲁和戴维·菲利普斯。他们能够成功得到第一个生物体内蛋白质的结构，是借助了马克斯·佩鲁茨所开发的技术，即令汞等重原子附着于所研究的蛋白质分子上。肯德鲁和佩鲁茨获得了1962年的诺贝尔化学奖。

肌红蛋白是一种典型的球状蛋白质，存在于多种动物细胞之中。如同血红蛋白一样，它可以与氧分子可逆地结合；不过血红蛋白的作用是在血液流动过程中传输氧气，而肌红蛋白则是将氧气临时储存于细胞之中（这对鲸、海豹和企鹅等潜水动物来说是一种特别重要的功能，富含大量肌红蛋白的暗红色组织是我们获得这种蛋白质的主要来源）。两种分子中都含有非蛋白部分，由被称为血红素分子的铁－卟啉配合物组成，而实际上与氧结合的正是这个血红素分子。分子量为67,000的血红蛋白中含有四个血红素分子，而肌红蛋白中只含有一个血红素分子。这个血红素分子再加上大约152个氨基酸残基，总分子量合为17,000，因此肌红蛋白是一种较小的蛋白质。我们选择肌红蛋白作为X射线分析对象的主要理由之一就是它的尺寸小。

在描述蛋白质时，通常要识别其一级、二级和三级结构。**一级结构**是指多肽链中氨基酸残基的排列顺序。桑格首先借助化学手段确定了胰岛素蛋白的一级结构[1]，此后又有很多种多肽物质的一级结构被阐明，另外有一两种其他小蛋白质的部分一级结构也被解析。**二级结构**是指多肽链采取的折叠、卷曲或皱折的类型，例如α螺旋和折叠片。丝蛋白、角蛋白与胶原蛋白等多种纤维蛋白的二级结构已经有了大概轮廓，但我们对任何球状蛋白的二级结构的本质一无所知。当然，有一些尚未被证实的暗示性证据表明，α螺旋存在于球状蛋白中，但是在各种具体事例中其含量还难以定量地确定。**三级结构**是指三维蛋白质分子的折叠和卷曲的多肽链在空间中形成的排布方式。要完全解释蛋白质的化学和物理性质，必须了解上述三个层次的结构，

folded or coiled polypeptide chains are disposed to form the protein molecule as a three-dimensional object, in space. The chemical and physical properties of a protein cannot be fully interpreted until all three levels of structure are understood, for these properties depend on the spatial relationships between the amino-acids, and these in turn depend on the tertiary and secondary structures as much as on the primary.

Only X-ray diffraction methods seem capable, even in principle, of unravelling the tertiary and secondary structures. But the great efforts which have been devoted to the study of proteins by X-rays, while achieving successes in clarifying the secondary (though not yet the tertiary) structures of fibrous proteins, have hitherto paid small dividends among the metabolically more important globular, or crystalline, proteins. Progress here has been slow because globular proteins are much more complicated than the organic molecules which are the normal objects of X-ray analysis (not counting hydrogens, myoglobin contains 1,200 atoms, whereas the most complicated molecule the structure of which has been completely determined by X-rays, vitamin B_{12}, contains 93). Until five years ago, no one knew how, in practice, the complete structure of a crystalline protein might be found by X-rays, and it was realized that the methods then in vogue among protein crystallographers could at best give the most sketchy indications about the structure of the molecule. This situation was transformed by the discovery, made by Perutz and his colleagues[2], that heavy atoms could be attached to protein molecules in specific sites and that the resulting complexes gave diffraction patterns sufficiently different from normal to enable a classical method of structure analysis, the so-called "method of isomorphous replacement", to be used to determine the relative phases of the reflexions. This method can most easily be applied in two dimensions, giving a projection of the contents of the unit cell along one of its axes. Perutz attached a *p*-chloromercuri-benzoate molecule to each of two free sulphydryl groups in haemoglobin and used the resulting changes in certain of the reflexions to prepare a projection along the *y*-axis of the unit cell[3]. Disappointingly, the projection was largely uninterpretable. This was because the thickness of the molecule along the axis of projection was 63 A. (corresponding to some 40 atomic diameters), so that the various features of the molecule were superposed in inextricable confusion, and even at the increased resolution of 2.7 A. it has proved impossible to disentangle them[4]. It was clear that further progress could only be made if the analysis were extended to three dimensions. As we shall see, this involves the collection of many more observations and the production of three or four different isomorphous replacements of the same unit cell, a requirement which presents great technical difficulties in most proteins.

The present article describes the application, at low resolution, of the isomorphous replacement method in three dimensions to type *A* crystals of sperm whale myoglobin[5]. The result is a three-dimensional Fourier, or electron-density, map of the unit cell, which for the first time reveals the general nature of the tertiary structure of a protein molecule.

Isomorphous Replacement in Myoglobin

No type of myoglobin has yet been found to contain free sulphydryl groups, so that the method of attaching heavy atoms used by Perutz for haemoglobin could not be employed.

因为这些性质取决于氨基酸分子之间的空间关系，而这些空间关系则不仅取决于蛋白质的一级结构，同样也取决于二级结构和三级结构。

一般而言，也只有 X 射线衍射的方法可以揭示二级和三级结构。尽管在阐明纤维蛋白二级结构（三级结构还不清楚）时 X 射线衍射方法取得了成功，但对于了解那些在新陈代谢过程中作用更为重要的球状蛋白或结晶蛋白，虽然投入了巨大的努力却仍然所获甚少。这一领域的进展缓慢，是由于球状蛋白分子比 X 射线分析的一般对象——有机分子结构复杂很多（不考虑氢原子，肌红蛋白中还有 1,200 个原子，而采用 X 射线方法完全确定结构的最复杂的分子——维生素 B_{12} 仅有 93 个原子）。五年前还没有人知道如何实际利用 X 射线方法来获得结晶蛋白的完整结构，而当时蛋白质晶体学家常用的方法最多只能对分子结构给出极为粗略的描述。佩鲁茨及其同事[2]的发现改变了这种情况。他们发现，重原子可以结合到蛋白质分子中特定的位置上，所得到的复合物给出了明显不同于普通蛋白质的衍射图案，这使得我们可以用一种名为“同晶置换方法”的经典结构分析方法确定其相对相位。这一方法可以很容易地用于二维分析，给出晶胞沿着某一轴向的投影图。佩鲁茨把对氯汞苯甲酸分子连接到血红蛋白分子中两个游离的巯基上，并利用某些反射的变化来获得晶胞沿 y 轴方向的投影图[3]。令人遗憾的是，得到的投影图在很大程度上无法得到解释。这是因为分子在投影轴方向上的厚度为 63 Å（相当于大约四十个原子的直径），因此分子中的各种信息彼此重叠，导致了无法解释的混乱状况[4]，即使将分辨率提高到 2.7 Å 也还是一样。很明显，只有取得新的进展后，才能将这种分析方法扩展到三维分析。就如同我们即将看到的，这将涉及更多观测结果的收集与同一晶胞的 3~4 种同晶置换晶体的制备支持，上述需求对于大多数蛋白质来说意味着巨大的技术困难。

本文介绍的是在低分辨率下研究抹香鲸肌红蛋白[5] *A* 型晶体三维结构时同晶置换方法的应用。所得到的结果是晶胞的三维傅里叶谱图，或电子密度图，这是首次揭示蛋白质分子三级结构的一般特征。

肌红蛋白的同晶置换

迄今为止还没有发现任何一种肌红蛋白中具有游离的巯基，因此佩鲁茨将重原子结合到血红蛋白上的方法无法应用。最终，我们通过将肌红蛋白与重金属离子

Eventually, we were able to attach several heavy atoms to the myoglobin molecule at different specific sites by crystallizing it with a variety of heavy ions chosen because they might be expected, on general chemical grounds, to possess affinity for protein side-chains. X-ray, rather than chemical, methods were used to determine whether combination had taken place, and, if so, whether the ligand was situated predominantly at a single site on the surface of the molecule. Among others, the following ligands were found to combine in a way suitable for the present purpose: (i) potassium mercuri-iodide and auri-iodide; (ii) silver nitrate, potassium auri-chloride; (iii) *p*-chloromercuri-benzene sulphonate; (iv) mercury diammine ($Hg(NH_3)^{2+}$, prepared by dissolving mercuric oxide in hot strong ammonium sulphate), *p*-choro-aniline; (v) *p*-iodo-phenylhydroxylamine. Each group of ligands combined specifically at a particular site, five distinct sites being found in all. The substituted phenylhydroxylamine is a specific reagent for the iron atom of the haem group[6], and may be assumed to combine with that group; in none of the other ligands have we any certain knowledge of the mechanism of attachment or of the chemical nature of the site involved.

Methods of X-ray Analysis

Type *A* crystals of myoglobin are monoclinic (space group $P2_1$) and contain two protein molecules per unit cell. Only the $h0l$ reflexions are "real", that is, can be regarded as having relative phase angles limited to 0 or π, or positive or negative signs, rather than general phases; when introduced into a Fourier synthesis, these reflexions give a projection of the contents of the cell along its y-axis. In two dimensions the analysis followed lines[7] similar to that of haemoglobin. First, the heavy atom was located by carrying out a so-called difference-Patterson synthesis; if all the heavy atoms are located at the same site on every molecule in the crystal, this synthesis will contain only one peak, from the position of which the x-and z-co-ordinates of the heavy atom can be deduced, and the signs of the $h0l$ reflexions determined. These signs were cross-checked by repeating the analysis for each separate isomorphous replacement in turn; we are sure of almost all of them to a resolution of 4 A., and of most to 1.9 A. Using the signs, together with the measured amplitudes, we may, finally, compute an electron-density projection of the contents of the unit cell along y; but, as in haemoglobin and for the same reasons, the projection is in most respects uninterpretable (even though here the axis of projection is only 31A.). On the other hand, knowledge of the signs of the $h0l$ reflexions to high resolution enabled us to determine the x- and z-co-ordinates of all the heavy atoms with some precision. This was the starting point for the three-dimensional analysis now to be described.

In three dimensions the procedure is much more lengthy because all the general reflexions hkl must be included in the synthesis, and more complicated because these reflexions may have any relative phase angles, not only 0 or π. Furthermore, we need to know all three co-ordinates of the heavy atoms; the two-dimensional analysis gives x and z, but to find y is more difficult, and details of the methods used will be published elsewhere, including among others two proposed by Perutz[8] and one proposed by Bragg[9]. Finally, a formal ambiguity enters into the deduction of general phase angles if only one isomorphous

形成共晶，使几种重原子分别结合到肌红蛋白分子的几个特定位置上，选取重金属离子的依据是，按照一般的化学原理来考虑，可以预期它们与蛋白质分子侧链间具有亲和力。我们采用X射线衍射方法，而不是化学方法，来确定结合是否发生，并且如果结合的话，是否绝大多数重金属离子位于分子表面某一特定的位置上。在实验中，我们发现下列配体可以按上述要求方式与肌红蛋白结合：(i) 碘汞酸钾和碘金酸钾；(ii) 硝酸银，氯金酸钾；(iii) 对氯汞苯磺酸；(iv) 二氨合汞离子 $(Hg(NH_3)^{2+}$，将氧化汞溶解于热的浓硫酸铵中即可制得)，对氯苯胺；(v) 对碘苯羟胺。每组配体与某一特定的位置结合，总计有五个不同的位置。取代后的苯基羟胺对于血红素分子[6]中的铁原子来说是一种特效试剂，可以假定它是与血红素分子相结合的。对于其他配体来说，我们对其与肌红蛋白结合的机制和相关位置的化学特征都一无所知。

X 射线分析方法

肌红蛋白的 A 型晶体属于单斜晶系（空间群 $P2_1$），每个晶胞中含有 2 个蛋白质分子。只有 $h0l$ 反射线是“真正有用的”，也就是说，它们的相对相位角取值仅限于 0 或 π，于是有或正或负的符号，而不同于一般的相位；对这些反射线进行傅里叶合成后可以得到晶胞内分子沿 y 轴方向的投影图。二维分析的过程与对血红蛋白的分析过程类似[7]。首先，通过名为差值帕特森合成的方法对重原子进行定位。如果不同晶体分子中，所有重原子都位于相同位置，该合成结果将只包含一个峰位置，从峰的位置可以推算出重原子的 x 坐标和 z 坐标，并确定 $h0l$ 反射线的正负号。依次对每种同晶置换晶体重复进行同样的分析，即可得到正负号校验结果。我们确信几乎所有信息分辨率均能达到 4 Å，其中大多数能达到 1.9 Å。利用正负号与测得的结构振幅数据，我们可以计算出晶胞内沿 y 轴方向的电子密度投影图。但是与血红蛋白一样，由于相同的理由，所得的投影在很大程度上是无法解释的（尽管我们这里的投影轴仅有 31 Å）。另一方面，对高分辨率下 $h0l$ 反射线正负号的了解，使我们能够以一定的精度来确定所有重原子的 x 坐标和 z 坐标。这就是我们将要介绍的三维分析的起点。

在三维情况下，分析过程要漫长得多，因为进行合成时必须包括所有一般的 hkl 反射线，再加上这些反射线可能具有不仅限于 0 和 π 的任意的相对相位角，所以分析过程变得更为复杂。此外，我们需要知道重原子的三个坐标位置，缺一不可。二维分析给出了 x 坐标和 z 坐标，但是确定 y 坐标要困难得多。所用方法的细节将在其他地方发表，其中包括佩鲁茨[8]提出的两种方法和布拉格[9]提出的一种方法。最后，如果只有一种同晶置换晶体，那么对一般相角的推断就会出现形式上的不确定性。

replacement is available; this can be resolved by using several replacements[10], such as are available in the present case. Once the phases of the general reflexions have been determined, one can carry out a three-dimensional Fourier synthesis which will be a representation of the electron density at every point in the unit cell.

Before such a programme is embarked upon, however, the resolution to be aimed at must be decided. The number of reflexions needed, and hence the amount of labour, is proportional to the cube of the resolution. To resolve individual atoms it would be necessary to include at least all terms of the series with spacings greater than 1.5 A.—some 20,000 in all; and it is to be remembered that the intensities of all the reflexions would have to be measured for *each* isomorphous derivative. Besides this, introduction of a heavy group may cause slight distortion of the crystal lattice; as the resolution is increased, this distortion has an increasingly serious effect on the accuracy of phase determination. In the present stage of the analysis the most urgent objective was an electron-density map detailed enough to show the general layout of the molecule—in other words, its tertiary structure. If the α-helix, or something like it, forms the basis of the structure, we need only work to a resolution sufficient to show up a helical chain as a rod of high electron density. For this purpose we require only reflexions with spacings greater than about 6 A. ; in all there are some 400 of these, of which about 100 are *h0l*'s already investigated in the two-dimensional study. The Fourier synthesis described here is computed from these 400 reflexions only, and is in consequence blurred; besides this, it is distorted by an unknown amount of experimental error, believed to be small but at the moment difficult to estimate. Thus while the general features of the synthesis are undoubtedly correct, there may be some spurious detail which will require correction at a later stage.

The Three-dimensional Fourier Synthesis

The synthesis was computed in 70 min. on the EDSAC Mark I electronic computer at Cambridge (as a check, parts of the computation were repeated on DEUCE at the National Physical Laboratory). It is in the form of sixteen sections perpendicular to *y* and spaced nearly 2 A. apart; these must be piled on top of one another to represent the electron density throughout the cell, containing two myoglobin molecules together with associated mother liquor (which amounts to nearly half the whole). Unfortunately, the synthesis cannot be so represented within the two-dimensional pages of a journal; furthermore, if the sections are displayed side by side, they give no useful idea of the structure they represent. The examples reproduced in Fig. 1 illustrate some of the more striking features.

如果像本文实例一样使用多种同晶置换晶体[10]，就可以克服这个问题。一旦确定了一般反射线的相位，就可以进行三维傅里叶综合分析，获得结果代表了晶胞内每一点的电子密度。

不过，在开始进行这些处理之前，必须先确定需要达到的分辨率。所需反射线的数量以及与此对应的工作量正比于分辨率的立方。要分辨出每个原子，必须至少包含所有间距大于 1.5 Å 的反射线，总共约有 20,000 个。另外我们还必须记得对**每一种**同晶衍生物测定其全部反射线的强度。除此之外，重金属元素的引入还可能导致晶格的轻微变形。随着分辨率的提高，这种变形将对相位确定的精确性产生越来越严重的影响。对于现阶段的分析工作而言，最紧迫的任务是得到一张足以显示出分子的一般轮廓（即分子的三级结构）的电子密度图。如果构成分子结构的基础是 α 螺旋或者类似的结构，那么我们只需要分辨率达到让螺旋链以一根高电子密度链的形式显现出来即可。为了达到这个目的，我们就只需要那些间距超过 6 Å 的反射线，这总共约有 400 个，而且其中约有 100 个是 $h0l$ 反射线，它们在研究二维情况时已经探讨了。这里所描述的傅里叶合成，是只对这 400 个左右的反射线进行计算得到的，因此是模糊的。此外，处理过程还受到某种大小未知的实验误差干扰，虽然我们认为它的影响不大，但是目前还难以估计这一误差。因此，尽管结果中的一般特征无疑是正确的，但其中可能还会存在细节问题，需要在下一步的研究中给予校正。

三维傅里叶合成

使用剑桥的 EDSAC（电子延迟存储自动计算机）Mark I 型电子计算机，70 分钟内完成合成计算（在国家物理实验室的 DEUCE 即通用电子数字计算机上对部分计算进行了重复检验）。获得结果是垂直于 y 轴的相互间隔大约 2 Å 的 16 个断层面。必须将这些断层面彼此叠放起来才能表示整体晶胞的电子密度，这包括两个肌红蛋白分子和其间结合的母液（约占全部的一半）。不幸的是，合成的结果无法在杂志的二维纸面上进行展示。另外，要将那些断层面合并排列，它们也不能真实地显示它们代表的结构。图 1 中展示的断层面图表现了一些很显著的特征。

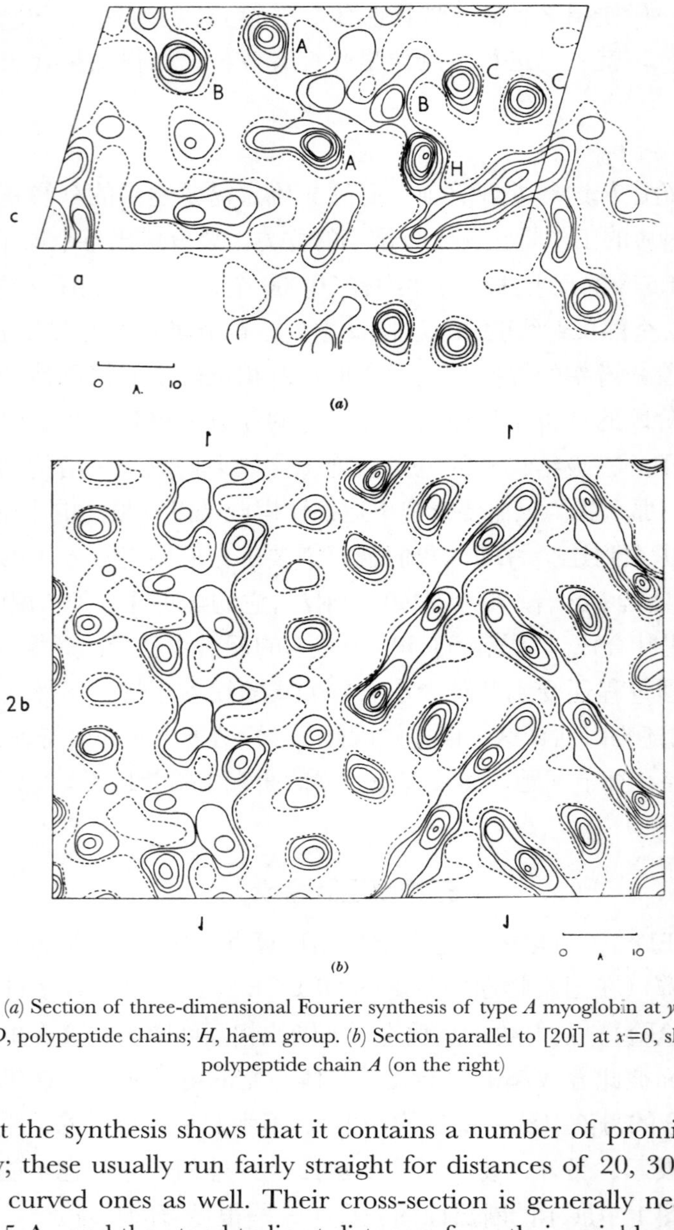

Fig. 1. (*a*) Section of three-dimensional Fourier synthesis of type *A* myoglobin at $y = -1/8b$. *A-D*, polypeptide chains; *H*, haem group. (*b*) Section parallel to [20$\bar{1}$] at x=0, showing polypeptide chain *A* (on the right)

A first glance at the synthesis shows that it contains a number of prominent rods of high electron density; these usually run fairly straight for distances of 20, 30 or 40 A., though there are some curved ones as well. Their cross-section is generally nearly circular, their diameter about 5 A., and they tend to lie at distances from their neighbours of 8-10 A. (axis to axis). In some instances two segments of rod are joined by fairly sharp corners. Fig. 1*a* shows several rods—three of them (*A*, *B* and *C*) cross the plane of the section almost at right angles, while one (*D*) lies nearly in that plane. *D* is part of a nearly straight segment of chain about 40 A. long, of which some 20 A. is visible in this section. It seems virtually certain that these rods of high density are the polypeptide chains themselves—indeed, it is hard to think of any other features of the structure which they could possibly be. Their circular cross-section is what would be expected if the configuration were helical, and the electron density along their axes is of the right order for a helical arrangement such as the

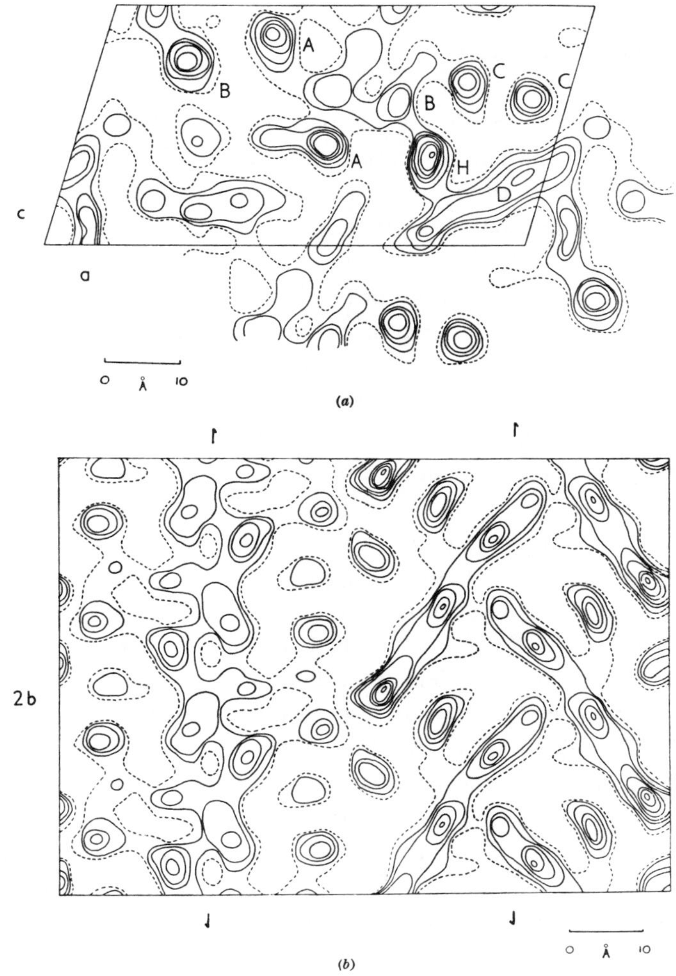

图 1.（*a*）*A* 型肌红蛋白进行三维傅里叶合成时位于 $y = -1/8b$ 处的断层面。*A*~*D* 代表不同的多肽链，*H* 代表血红素分子。（*b*）位于 $x = 0$ 处与 [20$\bar{1}$] 平行的断层面，显示了多肽链 *A*（右边）。

初步考察合成的结果，可以看出其中包含了许多明显的高电子密度链。它们通常会比较直地延伸 20 Å、30 Å 或 40 Å 的距离，尽管其中也有一些弯曲的链。它们的断层面一般近于圆形，直径约为 5 Å，它们倾向于以 8 Å~10 Å 的间距（轴与轴之间）排列。在某些地方，电子密度链的两个片断是以很尖锐的拐角连接。图 1*a* 显示了几个高电子密度链，其中三条（*A*、*B* 和 *C*）几乎垂直地穿过该断层面，而另一条（*D*）基本是平躺在该断层面上。*D* 是一段长约 40 Å 近乎笔直的链中的一部分，在这个断层面中可以看到其中约 20 Å 的部分。基本上可以确定，这些高电子密度链就是多肽链，事实上也很难认为它们会是结构中的其他部分。对于螺旋构型来说，就像预期的那样，其截面是圆形的，而且沿着轴向的电子密度分布也符合像 α 螺旋那样的螺

α-helix. The various rods in the structure are intertwined in a very complex manner, the nature of which we shall describe later.

Another prominent feature is a single disk-shaped region of high electron density which reaches a peak value greater than at any other point in the cell. A section through this disk is shown at *H* in Fig. 1*a*. We identify this feature as the haem group itself, for the following reasons: (i) the haem group is a flat disk of about the same size; (ii) its centre is occupied by an iron atom and therefore has a higher electron density than any other point in the whole molecule; (iii) a difference-Fourier projection of the *p*-iodo-phenylhydroxylamine derivative shows that, at least in *y*-projection, the position of the iodine atom is near that of our group; this is what we should expect, since this reagent specifically combines with the haem group; (iv) the orientation of the disk corresponds, as closely as the limited resolution of the map allows one to determine it, with the orientation of the haem group deduced from measurements of electron spin resonance[5,11].

We cannot understand the structure of the molecules in the crystal unless we can decide where one ends and its neighbours begin. In a protein crystal the interstices are occupied by mother liquor, in this case strong ammonium sulphate. the electron density of which is nearly equal to the average for the whole cell. Hence it is to be expected that in the intermolecular regions the electron density will be near average (the density of coiled polypeptide chains is much above average, and that of side-chains well below). It should also be fairly uniform; these regions should not be crossed by major features such as polypeptide chains. Using these criteria, it is possible to outline the whole molecule with minor uncertainties. It was gratifying to find that the result agreed very well, in projection, with a salt-water difference-Fourier projection made as part of the two-dimensional programme (for the principles involved, see ref. 12). Moreover, the dimensions of the molecule agreed closely with those deduced from packing considerations in various types of unit cell.

The Myoglobin Molecule

We are now in a position to study the tertiary structure of a single myoglobin molecule separated from its neighbours. Fig. 2 illustrates various views of a three-dimensional model constructed to show the regions of high electron density in the isolated molecule. Several points must be noticed. First, the model shows only the general distribution of dense regions. The core of a helical polypeptide chain would be such a region; but if the chain were pulled out, into a β-configuration, for example, its mean density would drop to near the average for the cell and the chain would fade out at this resolution. Similarly, side-chains should, in general, scarcely show up, so that the polypeptide rods in the model must be imagined as clothed in an invisible integument of side-chains, so thick that neighbouring chains in reality touch. Third, features other than polypeptide chains may be responsible for some of the regions of high density; patches of adsorbed salt, for example. Fourth, the surface chosen to demarcate a molecule cannot be traced everywhere with certainty, so it is possible that the molecule shown contains parts of its neighbours, and correspondingly lacks part of its own substance.

旋形排布的顺序。结构中的各种链以极为复杂的方式缠绕在一起，我们将在后面描述这一方式的特征。

另一个显著特征是存在一个单独的圆盘形高电子密度区域，其电子密度比晶胞内其他任何位置都高。图 1*a* 中 *H* 显示的就是穿过该圆盘的一个断层面。我们认为这一特征应该是血红素分子才有的：(i) 血红素分子具有平面结构；(ii) 中心被一个铁原子占据，因此电子密度比整个分子中其他任何部位都要高；(iii) 对碘苯羟胺衍生物的差值傅里叶投影图中显示，至少在沿 *y* 轴方向的投影图中，碘原子的位置是在这一基团附近，既然该试剂特异性地与血红素分子结合，那这一结果就和我们预期的是一致的；(iv) 在电子密度图有限的分辨率允许的范围内，我们得到的该电子密度图最准确的取向与利用电子自旋共振方法测量后推断出来的血红素分子的取向是一致的[5,11]。

要理解晶体中分子的结构，必须先确定哪里是分子的末端位置和哪里是分子的起点位置。在蛋白质晶体结构中，空隙被母液即浓的硫酸铵溶液占据，其电子密度与整个晶胞的平均值近乎相等。因此可以预计，分子间区域的电子密度接近平均值（卷曲的多肽链的密度大大高于平均值，而侧链的密度则明显低于平均值）。并且这些区域的分布应该是非常均匀的，且不应与多肽链的主要区域交叉。根据这些原则就有可能以较小的不确定性勾画出分子的轮廓。令人欣慰的是，我们发现投影图中的结果与作为二维程序（其中所涉及的原理请参见参考文献 12）一部分的盐水差值傅里叶投影图吻合得非常好。此外，分子的尺寸与对各种类型晶胞进行填充所得出的结果十分吻合。

肌红蛋白分子

现在我们可以开始研究与其邻近分子隔开的单个肌红蛋白分子的三级结构。图 2 给出了三维分子模型的不同视角，这一模型显示了单个分子中的高电子密度区域。有几点是必须要注意的。首先，模型显示的只是高电子密度区域的大致分布。那些螺旋形多肽链的核心应该是这样的区域，但是如果多肽链伸展开，例如转变为 β 构型，那它们的平均电子密度将降低到晶胞电子密度的平均值附近，此时这些多肽链在该分辨率下就看不到了。与此类似，侧链基本上很难显示出来，因此要将模型中的多肽链想象成被一层不可见的侧链外壳所覆盖，这一外壳非常厚以至于邻近的链实际上是彼此接触的。第三，除多肽链之外的其他部分也可能对某些高密度区域有贡献，例如吸附盐分形成的斑点。第四，所选取的作为分子边界的表面并不是处处准确，因此显示出的分子中有可能包含其邻近分子的部分，同样也可能缺少其自身的某些部分。

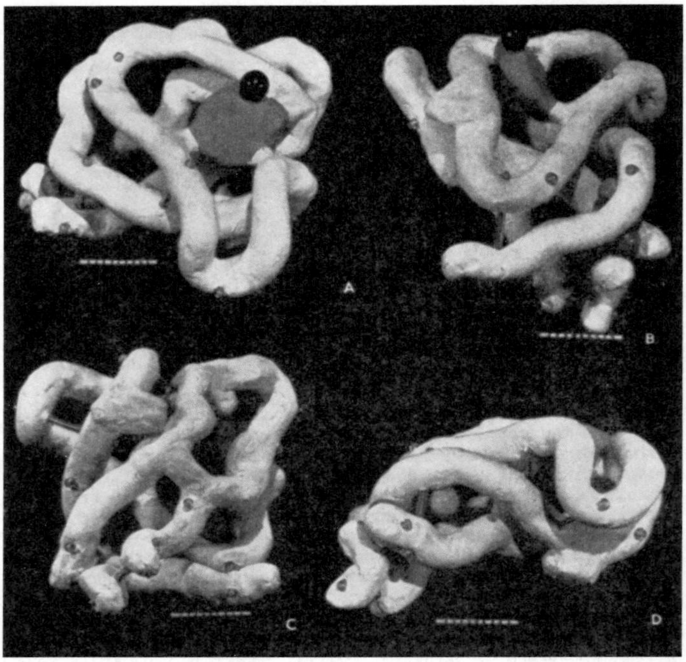

Fig. 2. Photographs of a model of the myoglobin molecule. Polypeptide chains are white; the grey disk is the haem group. The three spheres show positions at which heavy atoms were attached to the molecule (black: Hg of *p*-chloro-mercuri-benzene-sulphonate; dark grey: Hg of mercury diammine; light grey: Au of auri-chloride). The marks on the scale are 1 A. apart

Making due allowance for these difficulties, we may note the main features. It is known[13] that myoglobin has only one terminal amino-group: it is simplest to suppose that it consists of a single polypeptide chain. This chain is folded to form a flat disk of dimensions about 43 A. × 35 A. × 23 A. Within the disk chains pursue a complicated course, turning through large angles and generally behaving so irregularly that it is difficult to describe the arrangement in simple terms; but we note the strong tendency for neighbouring chains to lie 8-10 A. apart in spite of the irregularity. One might loosely say that the molecule consists of two layers of chains, the predominant directions of which are nearly at right angles in the two layers. If we attempt to trace a single continuous chain throughout the model, we soon run into difficulties and ambiguities, because we must follow it around corners, and it is precisely at corners that the chain must lose the tightly packed configuration which alone makes it visible at this resolution (an α-helix, for example, cannot turn corners without its helical configuration being disrupted). Also, there are several apparent bridges between neighbouring chains, perhaps due to the apposition of bulky side-chains. The model is certainly compatible with a single continuous chain, but there are at least two alternative ways of tracing it through the molecule, and it will not be possible to ascertain which (if either) is correct until the resolution has been improved. Of the secondary structure we can see virtually nothing directly at this stage. Owing to the corners, the chain cannot be in helical configuration through out; in fact, the total length of chain in the model is 300 A., whereas an α-helix of 152 residues would be only 228 A.

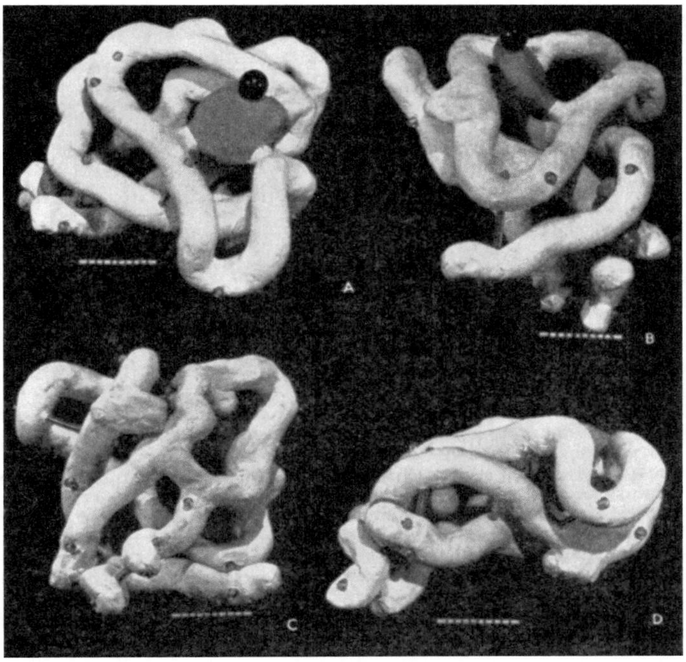

图 2. 肌红蛋白分子模型的照片。白色代表多肽链，灰色圆盘代表血红素分子。三个球指示出重原子在分子表面结合的位置（黑色的是对氯汞苯磺酸中的汞，深灰色的是二氨合汞离子中的汞，浅灰色的是氯金酸中的金）。图中标尺均代表 1 Å。

适当考虑这些问题之后，我们就可以关注主要的特征了。我们已经知道 [13] 肌红蛋白中只有一个末端氨基，因此很容易推断出它只包含一条多肽链。这条链通过折叠形成了尺寸为 43 Å × 35 Å × 23 Å 的扁圆盘。在圆盘内链经过大角度的转折缠绕出一条很复杂的线，由于这些缠绕基本上都过于无规则而难以用简单的词汇描述其排布情况。尽管有如此的不规则性，但我们还是可以看到一个明显的趋势即邻近链是以 8 Å~10 Å 的间隔排列的。不太严格地说，分子是由两层链组成的，两层中链的主要排列方向接近垂直。如果我们试图追踪单独一条贯穿模型的连续的链，那么我们很快就会陷入困难和迷茫之中。因为我们进行追踪时必须绕过拐角，而恰恰是在拐角处，这条链一定会丧失其紧密排列的构型，而现有的分辨率条件下只有紧密排列的构型是可见的（例如 α 螺旋结构，它在不破坏螺旋构型的前提下是无法转过拐角的）。另外，邻近链之间有明显的几处桥接，可能是由于大侧链的相互靠近。这一模型无疑是与一条单独连续链相吻合的，但是至少存在两种贯穿追踪整个分子的方式，而且要是不改进分辨率的话就不大可能确定究竟哪一种方式是正确的（如果其中某一种是正确的话）。实际上目前我们还不能直接看到任何二级结构的信息。由于拐角的存在，链不可能始终保持螺旋构型。实际上，模型中链的总长度为 300 Å，而一

long. The 300 A. might correspond, for example, to 70 percent α-helix and 30 percent fully extended chain, but of course intermediate configurations are probably present, too. The haem group is held in the structure by links to at least four neighbouring chains; nevertheless, one side of it is readily accessible from the environment to oxygen and to larger reagents such as *p*-iodo-phenylhydroxylamine (in the difference Fourier projection of this complex, referred to above, the position of the iodine atom indicates that the ligand is attached to the outside of the group). Clearly, however, the model cannot at present be correlated in detail with what we know of the chemistry of myoglobin; this must await further refinement.

Perhaps the most remarkable features of the molecule are its complexity and its lack of symmetry. The arrangement seems to be almost totally lacking in the kind of regularities which one instinctively anticipates, and it is more complicated than has been predicated by any theory of protein structure. Though the detailed principles of construction do not yet emerge, we may hope that they will do so at a later stage of the analysis. We are at present engaged in extending the resolution to 3 A., which should show us something of the secondary structure; we anticipate that still further extensions will later be possible—eventually, perhaps, to the point of revealing even the primary structure.

Full details of this work will be published elsewhere. We wish to record our debt to Miss Mary Pinkerton for assistance of all kinds; to the Mathematical Laboratory, University of Cambridge, for computing facilities on the EDSAC; to Dr. J. S. Rollett and the National Physical Laboratory for similar facilities on the DEUCE; to Mrs. Joan Blows and Miss Ann Mansfield for assistance in computing; for fellowships to the U.S. Public Health Service (H. W.), the Merck Fellowship Board (R. G. P.), the U.S. National Science Foundation (R. G. P. and H. M. D.), and the Rockefeller Foundation (H. M. D.); and to Sir Lawrence Bragg for his interest and encouragement. Finally, we wish to express our profound gratitude to the Rockefeller Foundation, which has actively supported this research from its earliest beginnings.

(**181**, 662-666; 1958)

J. C. Kendrew, G. Bodo, H. M. Dintzis, R. G. Parrish and H. Wyckoff: Medical Research Council Unit for Molecular Biology, Cavendish Laboratory, Cambridge.

D. C. Phillips: Davy Faraday Laboratory, The Royal Institution, London.

References:

1. Sanger, F., and Tuppy, H., *Biochem. J.*, **49**, 481(1951). Sanger, F., and Thompson, E. O. P., *ibid.*, **53**, 353, 366 (1953).
2. Green, D. W., Ingram, V. M., and Perutz, M. F., *Proc. Roy. Soc.*, A, **225**, 287 (1954).
3. Bragg, W. L., and Perutz, M. F., *Proc. Roy. Soc.*, A, **225**, 315 (1954).
4. Dintzis, H. M., Cullis, A. F., and Perutz, M. F. (in the press).
5. Kendrew, J. C., and Parrish, R. G., *Proc. Roy. Soc.*, A, **238**, 305 (1956).
6. Jung, F., *Naturwiss.*, **28**, 264 (1940). Keilin, D., and Hartree, E. F., *Nature*, **151**, 390 (1943).
7. Bluhm, M. M., Bodo, G., Dintzis, H. M., and Kendrew, J. C. (in the press).

条由 152 个残基组成的 α 螺旋的长度只有 228 Å。300 Å 的链长可能对应于多种构型，例如 70% α 螺旋构型和 30%完全伸展的构型，当然中间构型很可能也是存在的。血红素分子通过与至少四条邻近链的连接而被固定于结构中。不过，它的一面很容易与环境中的氧或对碘苯羟胺这样的较大试剂接触（在上面提到过的复合物的差分傅里叶投影图中，碘原子的位置表明配体结合到了血红素分子的外表面）。不过很明显，目前该模型在细节上还不能与我们所知的肌红蛋白的化学性质结合起来，这有待于下一步的改进。

也许分子最显著的特征就是具有复杂性和缺乏对称性。看起来，排列形式几乎完全不具有人们通常所期望的规律性，而且它比任何蛋白质结构理论所预测的还要复杂。尽管还没有找到详细的构造原理，但我们希望能在下一阶段的分析中给出。目前我们正设法将分辨率提高到 3 Å，这样我们将能看到某些二级结构的信息。我们期待未来还能有更进一步的提高，最终也许能达到揭示出一级结构的程度。

这一工作的完整细节将发表在其他地方。在这里我们要感谢为我们提供了各种帮助的玛丽 · 平克顿小姐，感谢允许我们在 EDSAC 上进行计算的剑桥大学数学实验室，感谢允许我们在 DEUCE 上进行同样计算的罗利特博士和英国国家物理实验室，感谢琼 · 布洛斯夫人和安 · 曼斯菲尔德小姐帮助我们进行计算。我们还要对美国公共卫生署（威科夫）、默克基金委员会（帕里什）、美国国家科学基金会（帕里什和丹特齐斯）和洛克菲勒基金会（丹特齐斯），对劳伦斯 · 布拉格爵士所给予的关注和鼓励表示感谢。最后，我们要向从一开始就给我们这项研究提供积极帮助的洛克菲勒基金会致以深切的谢意。

（王耀杨 翻译；吕扬 审稿）

8. Perutz, M. F., *Acta Cryst.*, **9**, 867(1956).
9. Bragg, W. L. (in the press).
10. Bokhoven, C., Schoone, J. C., and Bijvoet, J. M., *Acta Cryst.*, **4**, 275 (1951).
11. Ingram, D. J. E., and Kendrew, J. C., *Nature*, **178**, 905 (1956).
12. Bragg, W. L., and Perutz, M. F., *Acta Cryst.*, **5**, 277(1952).
13. Schmid, K., *Helv. Chim. Acta*, **32**, 105 (1949). Ingram, V. M. (unpublished work).

Sexually Mature Individuals of *Xenopus laevis* from the Transplantation of Single Somatic Nuclei

Gurdon *et al.*

Editor's Note

Here British developmental biologist John Gurdon and colleagues describe the production of the first sexually mature cloned animals, specifically frogs. Gurdon transferred nuclei from embryonic tadpole cells into unfertilized frog eggs, which went on to develop normally. A few years later he cloned frogs from adult cells, demonstrating irrefutably that nuclei from mature, differentiated cells could have their developmental clock reprogrammed. Gurdon's work paved the way for future somatic-cell nuclear-transfer experiments, including the arrival of Dolly, the first mammal to be cloned from an adult cell, nearly 40 years later. Today, somatic-cell nuclear-transfer experiments are still shedding light on the plasticity of the genome, as well as offering a route for the production of stem cells.

A method of testing the potentialities of nuclei from embryonic cells has been described by Briggs and King[1]. The method consists of transferring a nucleus from an embryonic cell into an enucleated and unfertilized egg of the same species. King and Briggs[2], who have performed their experiments on *Rana pipiens*, found that normal tadpoles resulted from eggs with transplanted nuclei in about 35 percent of cases in which the nuclei were taken from blastulae, but in only about 6 percent of cases in which the nuclei were taken from late gastrula endoderm; they have not reported normal development from nuclei of post-neurulae or later stages.

We have performed similar experiments on *Xenopus laevis*. In this species we do not enucleate the eggs, because the female pronucleus participates in the development of only a very few of the transplanted eggs; these cases can be recognized by the use of a nuclear marker[3], and are excluded from our results. The marker is introduced by taking donor nuclei from a stock of mutant individuals having only one nucleolus in all cells, as opposed to wild-type individuals in which all cells contain potentially two nucleoli. Large series of observations and measurements show no differences in the embryonic development, viability, growth-rate, and fertility between mutant individuals and their wild-type full sibs. The host eggs are taken from the wild-type stock and the female pronucleus introduces an additional nucleolar organizer when it participates in development. The origin of the nuclei in transplant-tadpoles can be interpreted with certainty by knowing the ploidy and number of nucleoli.

We have found that the great majority of normal tadpoles resulting from transferred nuclei

源于单个体细胞核移植的非洲爪蟾性成熟个体

格登等

编者按

本文中，英国发育生物学家约翰·格登和他的同事们描述了第一批性成熟克隆动物——特别是成蛙的产生。格登将处于胚胎时期的蝌蚪细胞的细胞核移植到未受精的蛙卵中，该蛙卵能继续正常发育。数年后，他用成体细胞获得了克隆蛙，这无可辩驳地证明了来自成熟的、已发生分化的细胞的细胞核可以重新编排其发育时钟。格登的工作为后来的体细胞核移植实验铺平了道路，其中包括在近 40 年之后由成体细胞克隆而来的第一只哺乳动物——多利羊的诞生。目前，体细胞核移植实验依然清楚地表明基因组具有可塑性，同时也成为获得干细胞的一条途径。

布里格斯和金[1]描述过一种可以用来检测胚胎细胞的细胞核潜能的方法。该方法是将胚胎细胞中的细胞核移植到同种生物未受精的去核卵细胞中。金和布里格斯[2]曾经用美洲豹蛙来做这个实验，他们发现采用来自囊胚期细胞的细胞核进行移植的实验中约有 35% 的个体可以发育成正常的蝌蚪，但是采用来自原肠胚后期内胚层细胞的细胞核进行移植的实验中只有约 6% 的个体可以发育成蝌蚪，他们没有报道来自神经胚后期或更晚时期的细胞核能够正常发育。

我们利用非洲爪蟾进行了类似的实验。对于这一物种我们并没有将卵细胞去核，因为卵原核仅参与了一部分移植卵的发育。通过应用细胞核标记能够证明这些情况[3]，而且我们的结果不包括这些情况。我们用来引入标记的供体细胞核来自所有细胞中只含有一个核仁的突变体库，与之相对应的野生型个体的所有细胞含两个潜在的核仁。大量的观察和测量结果表明，突变个体及其野生型全同胞在胚胎发育、生存能力、生长速度和繁殖力方面并无差别。实验中所用的受体卵细胞来自于野生型个体，卵原核参与发育时会引入一个额外的核仁形成区。核移植蝌蚪体内细胞核来源一定可以通过获知其染色体组倍数以及核仁的数目来确定。

我们发现通过核移植得到的正常蝌蚪中绝大多数都能进行正常的变态发育。年

pass through metamorphosis normally. The older frogs appear to be sexually mature males and females; the rate of growth and sexual differentiation is similar in transplant-embryos and controls. In order to test the capacity of gametogenesis in transplant-individuals, we hope shortly to breed from these. Immature oocytes were found in one transplant-frog which died two months after metamorphosis.

As with *Rana pipiens*, the proportion of normal development obtainable from transferred nuclei decreases with increasing age of the donor embryo. *Xenopus laevis* gives a smaller proportion of normal development from blastula nuclei than *Rana pipiens*, but on the other hand normal development can be obtained from much later donor stages; a prehatching tadpole (Nieuwkoop[4] stage 32, endoderm) was the most advanced stage of donor from which a normal individual was obtained, but this was accidentally killed shortly before metamorphosis. We have also a few frogs from nuclei which have been transferred twice (serial transfers).

Table 1 gives the numbers of metamorphosed frogs that have been obtained from different germ-layers and developmental stages of donor embryos. When transplanting endoderm nuclei from post-neurula stages care has been taken to avoid using nuclei from the region of the presumptive germ-cells.

Table 1. Metamorphosed Frogs which Resulted from Transplanted Nuclei

Donors			Transplants		
			Metamorphosed frogs		
Stage	Germ-layer	Total transfers	No.	Percentage of total	Percentage of normal late blastulae
Mid and late blastula	Ectoderm	565	17	3.0	12
	Endoderm	159	12	7.5	16
Early gastrula	Ectoderm	94	7	7.5	40
	Endoderm	287	12	4.2	15
Late gastrula	Ectoderm	26	2	7.7	33
	Endoderm	185	11	5.9	16.5
Neural folds	Ectoderm	9	0	0	0 out of 1
	Mesoderm	325	4	1.2	6
	Endoderm	137	7	5.1	14
Tail bud	Endoderm	163	4	2.5	9
Muscular response	Endoderm	287	1	0.35	3
Pre-hatching tadpoles	Endoderm	357	0	0	0 out of 70
Total		2,594	77		

When considering our results it is important to appreciate that the normal development of eggs with transferred nuclei may mean either that the nuclei were undifferentiated and totipotent, or that they were differentiated, but were able to return to a totipotent state as a result of developing again in the cytoplasm of an uncleaved egg.

长个体似乎已经发育为性成熟的雄性和雌性个体。核移植胚胎与对照组胚胎的生长速率与性别的分化类似。为了检测核移植个体的配子形成能力，我们希望这些个体能够快速繁殖。我们曾经在一只核移植蛙体内发现未发育成熟的卵母细胞，这只蛙在变态发育两个月后死亡。

与美洲豹蛙的实验结果一样，核移植后能进行正常发育的个体所占比例随着供体胚胎年龄的增加而减小。与美洲豹蛙相比，采用非洲爪蟾的囊胚期细胞核进行核移植得到的能正常发育的个体所占比例则相对较低。但另一方面，我们用发育时期更晚一些的胚胎细胞作供体进行核移植后能获得正常发育的个体，而孵化前的蝌蚪（尼乌科普[4]，32 发育期，内胚层）是能获得正常个体的最晚时期的供体，但是这一个体在即将进行变态发育前意外死亡了。我们也有一些成体蛙，它们的核已经被移植了两次（即连续移植）。

表 1 给出了通过移植处于不同胚层和不同发育阶段的供体胚胎获得的变态发育的蛙的数量。在对神经胚后期的内胚层细胞核进行移植时应注意避免使用那些位于将来可能发育成生殖细胞的区域的细胞核。

表 1. 核移植获得的变态发育的蛙

供体			移植个体		
			变态发育的蛙数量		
发育时期	胚层	移植总数	数目	占总数百分比	能发育到囊胚晚期个体占总数百分比
囊胚中晚期	外胚层	565	17	3.0	12
	内胚层	159	12	7.5	16
原肠早期	外胚层	94	7	7.5	40
	内胚层	287	12	4.2	15
原肠晚期	外胚层	26	2	7.7	33
	内胚层	185	11	5.9	16.5
神经褶期	外胚层	9	0	0	0（总数为 1）
	中胚层	325	4	1.2	6
	内胚层	137	7	5.1	14
尾芽期	内胚层	163	4	2.5	9
肌肉效应期	内胚层	287	1	0.35	3
孵化前蝌蚪	内胚层	357	0	0	0（总数为 70）
总数		2,594	77		

在我们的实验结果中有一点是十分重要的，即带有移植核的卵细胞能够正常发育，这可能意味着用来移植的核是尚未分化的而且是全能的，或者是已经分化了的细胞核在尚未分裂的卵细胞质中重新发育而使得细胞的全能性得到恢复。

Our results may be summarized as follows: (1) It is possible to transplant nuclei without impairing their ability to bring about normal development. (2) Some nuclei are capable of giving normal development very shortly before the organ of which they are part becomes functional; normal development was obtained from presumptive somite nuclei nine hours before the first muscular responses. (3) Normal development results from nuclei of more advanced donor stages in *Xenopus* than in *Rana pipiens*. (4) A number of monozygotic frogs have been obtained from single donors.

It may now become possible to breed from our sexually mature individuals which have developed from single somatic nuclei, and to test their genetic qualities.

We gratefully acknowledge the technical assistance of Miss A. Jewkes. This work has been made possible by contributions from the British Empire Cancer Campaign (M. F. and T. R. E.) and the Medical Research Council (J. B. G.).

(**182**, 64-65; 1958)

J. B. Gurdon, T. R. Elsdale and M. Fischberg: Department of Zoology and Comparative Anatomy, University Museum, Oxford, May 9.

References:

1. Briggs, R., and King, T. J., *J. Exp. Zool.*, **122**, 485 (1953).
2. King, T. J., and Briggs, R., Cold Spring Harbor Symp., **21**, 271 (1956).
3. Elsdale, T. R., Fischberg, M., and Smith, S., *Exp. Cell Res.* (in the press).
4. Nieuwkoop, P. D., and Faber, J., "Normal Table of *Xenopus laevis*" (1956).

我们的结果总结如下：(1) 在不损害实现其正常发育能力的条件下进行细胞核移植是可能的；(2) 在胚胎发育过程中，即将进行部分功能分化的器官的细胞核具有使核移植个体正常发育的能力；在第一次肌肉效应前 9 小时，我们用即将发育为体节的细胞核进行移植获得的个体仍能正常发育；(3) 与美洲豹蛙相比，用发育时期更晚的爪蟾胚胎细胞核进行移植后获得的个体仍能正常发育；(4) 我们在单个细胞核移植的实验中，获得了一些同卵双生的成蛙。

现在，我们有可能对由单个体细胞核发育来的性成熟爪蟾个体进行繁殖，并检验它们的遗传学特性。

我们诚挚地感谢朱克斯小姐的技术协助。同时这项工作也是得到了大英帝国癌症运动组织（菲施贝格和埃尔斯代尔）以及医学研究理事会（格登）的支持才得以实现的。

（苏慧 翻译；刘京国 审稿）

A New Fossil Skull from Olduvai

L. S. B. Leakey

Editor's Note

Louis Leakey almost single-handedly made Africa the site of choice for palaeontological exploration from the 1930s to the present. He was born in Kenya, educated at Cambridge, England, and appointed director of the Coryndon Museum in Nairobi in 1945. In 1959, he reported the discovery of a new fossil skull from the Olduvai Gorge in Kenya, a part of the East African Rift Valley. His first estimate of the age of the skull was 600,000 years, based largely on geological evidence, but this has since been corrected to 1.75 million years. Apart from his original work, Leakey founded a dynasty of African paleontologists. The discovery reported here was made by his wife Mary. His second son Richard Leakey became a later collaborator and was joined by his wife Meave and eventually his daughter Louise.

ON July 17, at Olduvai Gorge in Tanganyika Territory, at Site *FLK*, my wife found a fossil hominid skull, at a depth of approximately 22 ft. below the upper limit of Bed I. The skull was in the process of being eroded out on the slopes, and it was only because this erosion had already exposed part of the specimen that the discovery was possible. Excavations were begun on the site the following day and continued until August 6. As a result, an almost complete skull of a hominid was discovered. This skull was found to be associated with a well-defined living floor of the Oldowan, pre-Chelles-Acheul, culture.

Upon the living floor, in addition to Oldowan tools and waste flakes, there were the fossilized broken and splintered bones of the animals that formed part of the diet of the makers of this most primitive stone-age culture. It has not yet been possible to study the fauna found on this living floor; but it can be said that it includes birds, amphibians, reptiles such as snakes and lizards, many rodents and also immature examples of two genera of extinct pigs, as well as antelope bones, jaws and teeth.

It is of special importance to note that whereas the bones of the larger animals have all been broken and scattered. The hominid skull was found as a single unit within the space of approximately one square foot by about six inches deep. Even fragile bones like the nasals are preserved. The expansion and contraction of the bentonitic clay, upon which the skull rested and in which it was partly embedded, had resulted, over the years, in its breaking up into small fragments which have had to be pieced together. The bones, however, are not in any way warped or distorted. A large number of fragments still remain to be pieced together.

This very great difference between the condition of the hominid skull and that of the

来自奥杜威的新的头骨化石

利基

编者按

路易斯·利基几乎是仅凭一己之力就使非洲成为了从20世纪30年代到现在普遍选择的古生物学研究之地。利基出生于肯尼亚，后就读于英国剑桥大学，1945年被任命为内罗毕科里登博物馆的馆长。1959年他报道在肯尼亚的奥杜威峡谷（东非大裂谷的一段）发现了一件新的头骨化石。最初他主要依据地质学方面的证据，估算出该头骨的年代距今约为60万年，不过现已更正为175万年。除了他自己进行创造性的研究工作外，利基的家人也成为这一领域的权威，成就了一个非洲古生物学的家族研究。本篇报道中的发现是由他的妻子玛丽完成的。后来，他的二儿子理查德·利基也加入到这项工作之中，接着理查德的妻子梅亚维也加入进来，最后理查德的女儿路易丝也成为这项研究中的一员。

7月17日，在坦噶尼喀地区奥杜威峡谷的*FLK*遗址中第I层上界之下深约22英尺的地方，我的妻子发现了一件人科化石的头骨。在斜坡上的头骨正处于被侵蚀出来的过程之中，正是因为受到了侵蚀令标本有一部分已经被暴露出来，使得发现它成为可能。次日我们便开始对这个遗址进行挖掘，并一直持续到8月6日。结果我们发现了一件近乎完整的人科的头骨。发现该头骨与奥杜威文化（前舍利–阿舍利文化）的一个清晰可辨的生活面具有紧密的联系。

在这个生活面中，除了奥杜威文化的工具及废弃的破片之外，还有已石化的破碎的或裂成破片的动物的骨。这些动物是这个最为原始的石器时代文化创造者们的部分食物。现在还不可能对在这个生活面上发现的动物群进行研究；但可以说这个动物群包括鸟、两栖动物、爬行动物（比如蛇与蜥蜴）、许多啮齿动物，还有两类已灭绝的猪的未成年个体，以及羚羊的骨、颌骨及牙齿。

有一点特别重要，那就是我们注意到稍大的动物的骨全破碎了，散落四处；但这一人科的头骨却是一个独立的实体，埋在约1平方英尺、6英寸深的空间内。甚至像鼻骨这样易碎的骨都被保存了下来。头骨位于膨润土之上，且部分包埋在膨润土之中。多年来，由于膨润土的胀缩作用，导致头骨破裂成了小破片，于是我们不得不把它们拼在一起。不过，骨没有发生任何翘曲或变形。至今仍有大量破片有待拼凑起来。

在这一生活面上，人科动物头骨的状态与动物的骨的状态（所有动物的骨全是

animal bones on the same living floor (all of which had been deliberately broken up) seems to indicate clearly that this skull represents one of the hominids who occupied the living site; who made and used the tools and who ate the animals. There is no reason whatever, in this case, to believe that the skull represents the victim of a cannibalistic feast by some hypothetical more advanced type of man. Had we found only fragments of skull, or fragments of jaw, we should not have taken such a positive view of this.

It therefore seems that we have, in this skull, an actual representative of the type of "man" who made the Oldowan pre-Chelles-Acheul culture.

This skull has a great many resemblances to the known members of the sub-family of Australopithecinae. Some scientists recognize only one genus, namely, *Australopithecus*, and treat Broom's *Paranthropus* as a synonym; others consider that the demonstrable differences are of such a nature that both genera are valid. Personally, having recently re-examined all the material of the two genera, in Johannesburg and Pretoria, I accept both as valid.

The Olduvai skull is patently a member of the sub-family Australopithecinae, and in certain respects it recalls the genus *Paranthropus*. In particular, this is the case in respect of the presence of the sagittal crest, the great reduction in the size of the canines and the incisors, the relatively straight line of these teeth at the front of the palate, the position of the nasal spines and the flatness of the forehead. In certain other characters, the new skull resembles more closely the genus *Australopithecus*, for example in respect of the high cranial vault, the deeper palate and the reduction of the upper third molars to a size smaller than the second, all of which are features to be found in *Australopithecus* but not in *Paranthropus*.

The very close examination and direct comparisons which I have personally made in South Africa have convinced me that, on the basis of our present state of knowledge, the new skull from Olduvai, while clearly a member of the Australopithecinae, differs from both *Australopithecus* and *Paranthropus* much more than these two genera differ from each other.

I am not in favour of creating too many new generic names among the Hominidae; but I believe that it is desirable to place the new find in a separate and distinct genus. I therefore propose to name the new skull *Zinjanthropus boisei*. This generic name derives from the word "Zinj", which is the ancient name for East Africa as a whole, which is the specific name is in honour of Mr. Charles Boise, whose constant encouragement and financial help ever since 1948 have made this and other important discoveries possible. I would also like to acknowledge the generous help received, from time to time, from the Wenner-Gren Foundation and the Wilkie Trust.

The following is the preliminary diagnosis of the new genus and the new species:

人为蓄意弄碎的）之间的差别非常大，这似乎清楚地表明该头骨代表了占据这块生存地的人科中的一员；他们制造并使用工具，以动物为食。既然如此，我们没有理由去相信这块头骨代表的是一些假想的进化水平更高的人类同类相食的受害者。即使我们只发现头骨破片或颌骨破片，我们也不应该采纳上述看法。

因此，该头骨似乎确实代表了一种“人”，他们创造了奥杜威前舍利–阿舍利文化。

该头骨与南方古猿亚科已知成员的头骨相比有许多相似点。一些科学家认为仅存在南方古猿属这一个属，并把布鲁姆的傍人属当作同物异名；而其他科学家认为两个属之间显而易见的差异性表明这两个属都是成立的。最近我在约翰内斯堡与比勒陀利亚重新考察了这两个属的全部资料，个人认为应该分作两个属。

显然奥杜威头骨属于南方古猿亚科的成员，且在某些方面与傍人属相似。这尤其表现在以下方面：具有矢状脊，犬齿与门齿的大小减小很多，这些牙齿在腭前基本呈直线排列，鼻棘的位置，前额扁平。这件新头骨的某些其他特点更近似于南方古猿属，例如：头骨穹隆高，腭较深，第三上臼齿的大小减小到比第二臼齿还要小。所有这些特点都可以在南方古猿属中发现，而在傍人属中则找不到。

我亲自在南非进行了十分仔细的检查，并进行了直接对比，在我们目前知识水平基础上，我确信来自奥杜威的新头骨显然是南方古猿亚科的成员，其与南方古猿属及傍人属的差异度远远大于这两个属之间的差异度。

我不赞同在人科之下创立太多新属名；但我认为应该将这件新发现的头骨归为一个独立、不同的属。因此我建议命名这一新头骨为鲍氏东非人。属名来源于单词“Zinj”，是整个东非的古名，而种名是为了纪念查尔斯·鲍伊斯，自 1948 年来，是他的不断鼓励与资金支持才使得这个重要的发现及其他重要的发现成为可能。我还要对不时收到的来自温纳–格伦基金会与威尔基信托基金会的慷慨资助表示感谢。

以下是新属与新种的初步鉴定：

Zinjanthropus gen. nov. :

Genotype: a young male with third molars not yet in wear and sutures relatively open, from *FLK* I, Olduvai.

A new genus of the Hominidae, sub-family Australopithecinae, which exhibits the following major differences from the genera *Australopithecus* and *Paranthropus*:

(*a*) in males a nuchal crest is developed as a continuous ridge across the occipital bone;

(*b*) the inion, despite the great evidence of muscularity, is set lower (when the skull is in the Frankfurt plane) than in the other two genera;

(*c*) the posterior wall of the occipital bone rises more steeply to form, with the parietals, a very high-vaulted posterior region of the skull;

(*d*) the foramen magnum is less elongate and has a more horizontal position than in *Australopithecus* (in the curshed skulls of *Paranthropus* it is not possible to be quite sure of the plane of the foramen magnum);

(*e*) the presence of a very massive horizontal ridge or torus above the mastoids. This is much more marked than the normal type of supra-mastoid crest;

(*f*) the mastoids are more similar to those seen in present-day man, both in size and shape;

(*g*) the presence of a strong wide shelf above the external auditory meatus, posterior to the jugal element of the temporal bone;

(*h*) the shape and form of the tympanic plate, whether seen in *norma lateralis* or in *norma basalis*. In this character the new skull has similarities with the Far Eastern genus *Pithecanthropus*;

(*i*) the very great pneumatosis of the whole of the mastoid region of the temporal bones, which even invades the squamosal elements;

(*j*) the massiveness of the jugal element of the temporal bone relative to the total size of the temporal bone;

(*k*) the way in which the parietals rise almost vertically behind the squamous elements of the temporal before bending over to become a dome;

(*l*) the relative thinness of the parietals in comparison with the occipitals and the temporals;

东非人新属：

正型标本：年轻男性，第三臼齿还没有磨损，骨缝相对不闭合，出土于奥杜威 *FLK* 遗址第 I 层。

人科南方古猿亚科的一个新属与南方古猿属和傍人属相比，其表现出来的主要不同点如下：

(*a*) 男性的项脊发育成一个横跨枕骨的连续骨脊；

(*b*) 枕外隆凸点，尽管存在强有力的证据证明其肌肉强壮，但当将这一头骨置于法兰克福平面的位置时此测点低于其他两个属的；

(*c*) 枕骨后壁向上陡倾，与顶骨一起形成拱起程度很高的头骨后区；

(*d*) 枕骨大孔延伸得不长，相比于南方古猿它处于更加水平的位置上（在压碎了的傍人头骨上，不可能确定枕骨大孔所在的平面）；

(*e*) 在乳突之上有十分巨大的水平脊或圆枕。这比正常类型的乳突上脊要明显得多；

(*f*) 乳突的大小与形状都更类似于现在的人类所呈现的乳突；

(*g*) 在外耳道上方，颞骨颧突后面出现了强而宽阔的猿板；

(*h*) 不论是从侧面看还是从底部看，鼓板的形态与形状都与远东爪哇猿人属相似；

(*i*) 颞骨的整个乳突区气窦很大，甚至侵入鳞部；

(*j*) 相对于颞骨的总体尺寸，颞骨颧突很硕壮；

(*k*) 在颞骨的鳞部之后，顶骨几乎是垂直升起，之后弯曲形成一个圆顶；

(*l*) 与枕骨及颞骨相比，顶骨相对较薄；

(*m*) the very prominent and keeled anterior margin of the crests on the frontal bone for the anterior segment of the temporal muscles in the region of the post-orbital constriction (even the most muscular male *Paranthropus* exhibits nothing comparable);

(*n*) the very unusual position of the nasion, which is on the most anterior part of the skull, instead of being behind and below the glabella region;

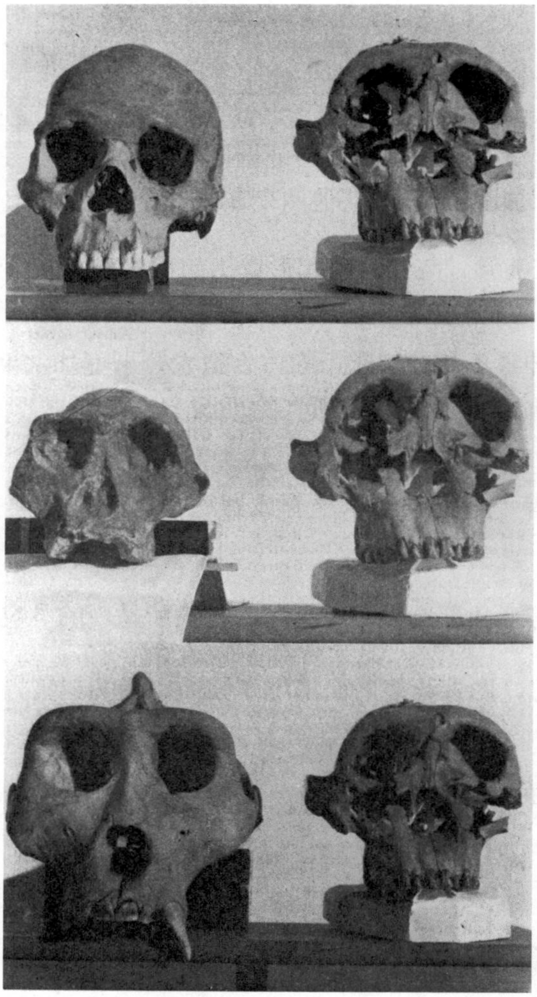

Fig. 1. *Above*: The new skull compared with the skull of an Australian aboriginal. Note the very long face, the architecture of the malar region, the unusual nasal bones, the torus above the mastoid, the sagittal and nuchal crests. *Middle*: The new skull compared with a cast of the most complete adult of *Australopithecus*. Note the difference in the size and shape of the face, the shape of the tympanic plate, the low position of the inion, the huge mastoid, as well as the difference in the shape of the malar region and the supra-orbital area. *Below*: The new skull seen next to that of a gorilla

(*m*) 眶后缩狭区供颞肌前段附着的额骨上的脊的前缘十分突出，呈龙骨状突起（甚至肌肉最强健的男性傍人也没有可与之比较的结构）；

(*n*) 鼻根点位置尤为与众不同，是在头骨的最前部，而不是在眉间点区的后下方；

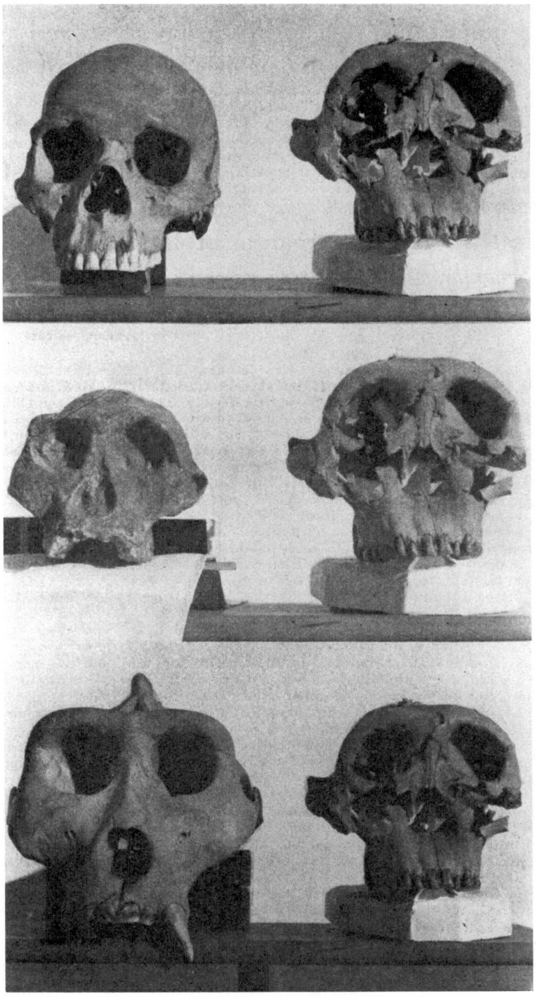

图 1. **上**：新头骨与澳大利亚土著人头骨的比较。注意其很长的脸、颧骨区的构造、与众不同的鼻骨、乳突上方的圆枕骨、矢状脊与项脊。**中**：新头骨与最完整的成年南方古猿的铸模型比较。注意面部形状和大小的差异、鼓板形状、位置低的枕外隆凸点、巨大的乳突，以及颊部与眶上部形状的差异。**下**：新头骨与大猩猩的头骨的比较。

(*o*) the very great absolute and also relative width of the inter-orbital area, with which may be associated the shape of the nasal bones, which are much wider at the top than at their inferior margin;

(*p*) the whole shape and position of the external orbital angle elements of the frontal bone;

(*q*) the very deep palate which is even more markedly like that of *Homo* than in *Australopithecus*, and is quite unlike the form seen is *Paranthropus*, except in respect of the more or less straight canine-incisor line which has already been commented on, as a character recalling *Paranthropus*;

(*r*) the conformation of the malar-maxillary area of the cheek. In all known members of the genera *Australopithecus* and *Paranthropus* there is a buttress of bone which runs down from the malar towards the alveolar margin of the maxilla in about the region of the fourth premolar; in *Zinjanthropus* this buttress is wholly absent and the form of architecture of this region is that which is found in *Homo*;

(*s*) the very great area of muscle attachment on the inferior margin of the malars;

(*t*) the relatively greater reduction of the canines in comparison with the molar-premolar series than is seen even in *Paranthropus*; where it is a marked character.

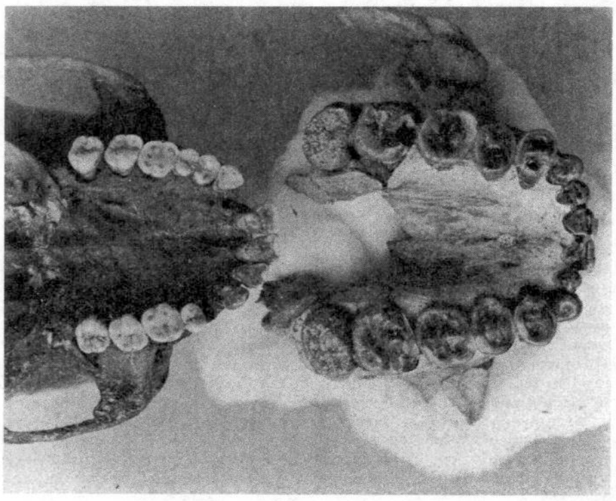

Fig. 2. The palate of the new skull compared with that of an East African native

Zinjanthropus boisei sp. nov.

A species of *Zinjanthropus* in which the males are far more massive than the most massive male *Paranthropus*. The face is also excessively long. Males have a sagittal crest, at least posteriorly. Upper third molars smaller than the second.

The above is only a preliminary diagnosis of the genus *Zinjanthropus* species *boisei*. It is recognized that, if and when further material is found, the diagnosis will need both enlarging and possibly modifying.

(*o*) 眶间区的绝对宽度、相对宽度都相当大，可能与鼻骨的形状有关，其顶部比其下缘宽得多。

(*p*) 额骨眼眶外侧角部分的位置与整体形状；

(*q*) 腭很深，其与人属的相似程度明显更甚于与南方古猿属的相似程度，并完全不同于在傍人属中所见到的形式，除了犬齿–门牙排列大致呈直线，这一特点与傍人属的特点相似，这在上文已经提到过；

(*r*) 脸颊的颧骨–上颌骨部位的构造。南方古猿属与傍人属的所有已知成员都有壁柱状的构造，它从颧骨一直延伸到大约是第四前臼齿部位的上颌骨牙槽边缘；东非人完全没有这种壁柱状的构造，该部位的结构与人属完全相同；

(*s*) 颧骨下缘肌肉附着的面积很大；

(*t*) 与臼齿–前臼齿齿系相比，犬齿相对减小的程度甚至比傍人的还要大；这是一个显著的特点。

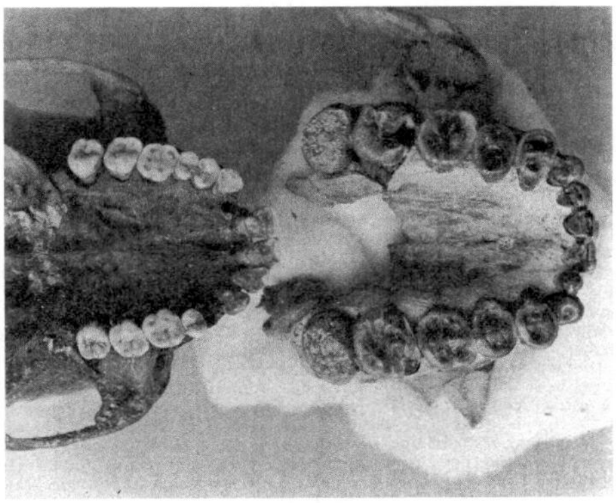

图 2. 新头骨的腭与东非本地人的腭的对比

鲍氏东非人新种：

男性东非人比最魁梧的男性傍人还要魁梧得多。面部也相当长。男性有矢状脊，至少在后部是这样。第三上臼齿比第二臼齿小。

上述仅是对鲍氏东非人的初步鉴定。我们认识到，如果发现了进一步的材料，将需要对鉴定要点进行补充并可能进行修改。

The whole question of generic value is one which is relative. There are some who maintain that *Australopithecus* and *Paranthropus* are not generically distinct, and who will wish to treat *Zinjanthropus* as a third, but less specialized, species of a single genus; but the differences seem to be too great for this.

I must now turn to the absolute and relative geological age of the new skull. As stated earlier, *Zinjanthropus* comes from Olduvai Gorge, about 22 ft. below the upper limit of Bed I. It was found in association with tools of the Oldowan culture, on a living floor and with associated fauna.

In the past it has been customary to regard Olduvai Bed I as a part of the Middle Pleistocene, not differentiation it from Bed II. During the last few years, however, detailed excavations at sites *BK* II, *SHK* II and *HWK* II have shown that there is a constant and well-marked break between the top of Bed I and the base of Bed II. It is incidentally on this clearly defined land surface that Chellean Stage I living sites are found.

There has also been found a great deal of new faunal evidence, and it is now clear that the fauna of Olduvai Bed I is the same as that of Omo, and that both are generally of the same age as that of Taungs. In other words, it is now necessary to regard Olduvai Bed I as representing the upper half of the Villafranchian and not the lower part of the Middle Pleistocene. So far as relative dating is concerned, it now seems clear that in the Far East the Djetis beds belong to the Middle, rather than to the Lower, Pleistocene, so that the new Olduvai skull would be older than the oldest *Pithecanthropus*.

In South Africa, the deposits at Taungs and Sterkfontein are now regarded as belonging to the upper part of the Lower Pleistocene; they must therefore be regarded as generally contemporary with Olduvai Bed I. The Makapan beds are a little younger, in all probability, while Swartkrans is of Middle Pleistocene age, as are the upper beds at Sterkfonten which are now yielding stone tools.

With the Taungs child, therefore, and the *Australopithecus* fossils from the lower beds at Sterkfontein, the new find represents one of the earliest Hominidae, with the Olduvai skull as the oldest yet discovered maker of stone tools.

属的价值问题是比较而言的。有些人坚持认为南方古猿属与傍人属不是两个区别明显的属，他们想要将东非人看成是与上二者同一个属的第三个较欠特化的种。但这样做的话，它们之间的差异似乎太大了。

现在我必须开始讨论新头骨的绝对地质年龄与相对地质年龄。正如前文所述，东非人来自奥杜威峡谷第I层上界之下深约22英尺的地方。在同一生活面上还发现了属于奥杜威文化的工具以及动物群。

过去一直习惯把奥杜威第I层作为中更新世的一部分，没有把它与第II层进行区分。不过最近几年，在遗址*BK* II、*SHK* II及*HWK* II所进行的详细的挖掘显示，在第I层的顶部与第II层的底部之间存在一个稳定和明显的间断。在这个界限清楚的地表上偶然发现了舍利文化第I期的生命活动遗址。

人们还发现了新动物群存在的大量证据，现在已经清楚奥杜威第I层的动物群与奥莫的动物群相同，而且这二者的年代与汤恩头骨的年代大体相同。换言之，现在应该用奥杜威第I层来代表维拉方期的上半部分，而不是中更新世的下部。就相对年代而言，似乎可以明确地认为远东的哲蒂斯地层属于中更新世，而不是下更新世，因此奥杜威新头骨比最古老的猿人属还要古老。

在南非，现在认为汤恩与斯泰克方丹的堆积物属于下更新世的晚期；因此通常认为它们与奥杜威第I层的时代相同。很可能马卡潘地层更年轻一点，而斯瓦特克朗斯和斯泰克方丹的上部地层（现已出土了石器）都属于中更新世。

因此，与汤恩小孩及来自斯泰克方丹下部地层的南方古猿化石一样，新发现的头骨代表了最早的人科中的一员，奥杜威头骨代表了迄今为止被发现的最早的石器制造者。

The following approximate measurements will indicate the size of the new specimen.

Length from inion to glabella	about 174 mm.
Greatest breadth at supra-mastoid torus	,, 138 mm.
Greatest breadth of brain case on squamosal element of the temporal bones	,, 118 mm.
Height (in Frankfurt plane) from basion to a point vertically above it in the sagittal plane	,, 98 mm.
External orbital angle width	,, 122 mm.
Inter-orbital width	,, 32.5 mm.
Post-orbital width	,, 88 mm.
Palate-length from front of incisors to a line joining back of third molars	,, 84 mm.
Palate-width at second molars	,, 82 mm.
Palate-width at third premolars	,, 62 mm.
Length of molar-premolar series	,, 72 mm.
Teeth measurements: *M*3: 21×16 mm.; *M*2: 21×17 mm.; *M*1: 18×15.5 mm.; *PM*4: 18×12 mm.; *PM*3: 17×11.5 mm.; *C*: 9.5×9 mm.; *C*2: 7×7 mm.; *C*1(both damaged but about 10×8 mm.).	

(**184**, 491-493; 1959)

L. S. B. Leakey: Coryndon Museum, Nairobi.

以下的测量近似值表明了这一新标本的大小。

枕骨隆凸点到眉间的长度	大约 174 毫米
圆枕上乳突处的最大宽度	大约 138 毫米
在颞骨鳞部脑颅的最大宽度	大约 118 毫米
当颅骨处于法兰克福平面时，从枕骨大孔前缘点到在矢状面上垂直于它的一点的高度	大约 98 毫米
眼眶外角的宽度	大约 122 毫米
眶间宽度	大约 32.5 毫米
眶后宽度	大约 88 毫米
从门齿前面到第三臼齿背面连接线的腭长度	大约 84 毫米
在第二臼齿的腭宽度	大约 82 毫米
在第三前臼齿的腭宽度	大约 62 毫米
臼齿－前臼齿齿系的长度	大约 72 毫米
牙齿的测量值： *M*3：21 × 16 毫米；*M*2：21 × 17 毫米；*M*1：18 × 15.5 毫米；*PM*4：18 × 12 毫米；*PM*3：17 × 11.5 毫米；*C*: 9.5 × 9 毫米；C2：7 × 7 毫米；*C*1（都损坏了，但大约是 10 × 8 毫米）。	

（田晓阳 翻译；吴新智 胡荣 审稿）

The Affinities of the New Olduvai Australopithecine

Editor's Note

The shift of focus from southern to eastern Africa in the search for human origins was so abrupt that it can be dated precisely—to 15 August 1959, when *Nature* published Louis Leakey's discovery of a super-robust australopithecine from Olduvai Gorge in Tanzania. Coming at the end of decades of fruitless search, Leakey named his find *Zinjanthropus boisei*—or "Nutcracker Man", for its enormous teeth. Reviewing the find in *Nature* the following May, John T. Robinson—Broom's longtime co-author on many papers about South African australopithecines—suggested that *Zinjanthropus* was not as distinct as Leakey had proposed, suggesting that it might be referred to *Paranthropus*. Robinson's comments stuck—Nutcracker Man is now known as *Paranthropus boisei*.

Responding to J. T. Robinson's critique, Leakey responded in characteristically robust style. Although "Zinj" was similar to *Paranthropus*, it was, Leakey maintained, sufficiently different to be deserving of generic rank. This was clearly more than a trivial academic spat over names: it had taken decades for Leakey to discover a significant fossil hominid, and Robinson might have been worried about a newcomer in a field previously dominated by Broom and himself, and sought to put the interloper in his place. Such battles were not the first to have happened in palaeoanthropology, and they would not be the last.

DR. L. S. B. Leakey recently reported in *Nature*[1] the discovery of an essentially complete hominid skull without mandible from site *FLK* at Olduvai Gorge. He regards the specimen as an australopithecine that differs more from either of the two known genera, *Australopithecus* and *Paranthropus*, than these two differ from each other. He therefore erected the genus *Zinjanthropus* to accommodate the new specimen.

The description consists largely of a list of twenty "major" differences between the new specimen and the two previously known genera. Some of these points cannot be dealt with as they are briefly stated in terms which are not useful by themselves for comparison. Others, for example, continuous nuchal crest, enlargement of the mastoid area, prominent temporal lines, large areas for masseter attachment, etc., do not each represent a separate difference; all are reflexions of the fact that this specimen is a little larger and more muscular than the known South African specimens of *Paranthropus*. In at least one case (nuchal crest) comparison with the latter specimens is not possible since there is no known male specimen with the relevant area preserved. The remainder are not real differences and will be dealt with briefly:

新型奥杜威南方古猿亚科的亲缘关系

编者按

当《自然》杂志刊载了路易斯·利基在坦桑尼亚奥杜威峡谷发现超级粗壮的南方古猿亚科后，关注人类起源的目光由南非迅速转移到了东非，这一转变非常突然，甚至可以精确到1959年8月15日这一天。在经过数十年徒劳的探索后，利基将其发现的南方古猿命名为鲍氏东非人，又由于其具有硕大的牙齿因此被称为“胡桃钳人”。次年5月，在回顾《自然》杂志上发表的成果时，约翰·鲁滨逊（曾与布鲁姆合作发表过多篇关于南方古猿的论文）认为，这个东非人并没有利基所认为的那样特别，而可能与傍人有关。鲁滨逊的观点后来被证实是正确的，胡桃钳人现在被称为鲍氏傍人。

利基以其特有的粗壮风格对鲁滨逊的批评做出了回应。利基坚持认为，尽管“东非人”与傍人类似，但它们仍然存在非常大的差异从而不能将二者归为同一个属。这显然不仅仅是一个微不足道的关于命名的学术争论：利基耗费了数十年的时间发现了这一具有重要意义的人科化石，而鲁滨逊可能对这个闯入原本由布鲁姆和他自己主导的领域的外来者感到很烦恼，并想挫挫闯入者的傲气。在古人类学领域，这类纷争不是第一次发生，也不会是最后一次。

利基博士最近在《自然》杂志[1]上报道称在奥杜威峡谷的*FLK*遗址发现了一件人科的头骨，该头骨基本完整，但没有下颌骨。他认为该标本属于南方古猿亚科，但不同于两个已知属（南方古猿属和傍人属）中的任何一个，它与这两个属之间的差异要大于这两个属彼此间的差异。因此他为这件新标本建立了东非人这个新属。

关于这件新标本的描述主要包括新标本和那两个先前已知的属之间的20个“较大的”差异。其中一些差异表述得过于简单，我们无法进行探讨，并且这些差异本身也不利于进行比较。其他的如连续的项脊、乳突骨区的增大、凸出的颞线、咀嚼肌附着区的增大等等，并不是每一项都代表独立的区分特征，所有这些现象都反映了一个事实：这件标本比已知的南非傍人标本稍大一些且肌肉更强健。此外，至少有一项（项脊）是不可能与后一种标本进行比较的，因为没有已知男性标本的相关部位被保存下来。余下的部分没有实质性的差别，因此只作简短的探讨：

(1) The inion is lower relative to the Frankfort plane: In both *Australopithecus* and *Paranthropus* the base of the external occipital protuberance is almost exactly in the Frankfort plane, as seems to be the case with the Olduvai specimen.

(2) The posterior wall of the occipital bone rises more steeply to form, with the parietals, a very high-vaulted posterior region of the skull: This is also the case in *Paranthropus*, less so in *Australopithecus*. *Paranthropus* has an almost spheroidal brain-case which is relatively low and narrow anteriorly but steep-sided and higher posteriorly. *Australopithecus* has a brain-case more nearly like that of a dolichocephalic modern hominine. The Olduvai specimen has the *Paranthropus* type of brain-case.

(3) The form of the tympanic plate is different: Dr. Leakey demonstrated this point to me on the specimen to make clear his meaning. This feature is variable in *Paranthropus* and includes an instance of close resemblance to the Olduvai specimen. The observed range of variation is illustrated in Fig. 1. Being thus variable, it is in any event a feature of low phyletic valence.

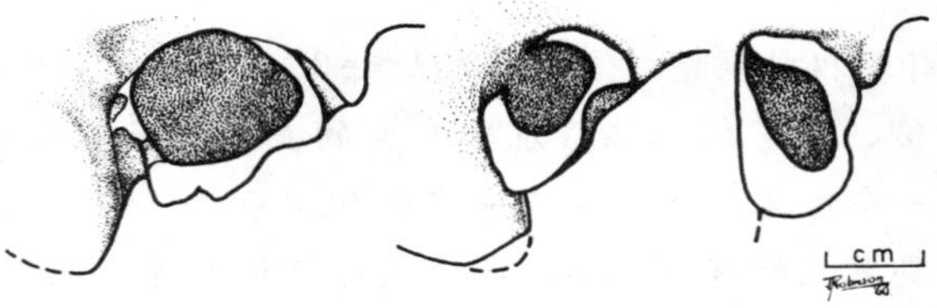

Fig. 1. Variation of the tympanic bone at the lateral end of the external auditory meatus in *Paranthropus* from Swartkrans (*SK* 48, *SK* 52 and *SK* 848). The Olduvai specimen resembles in this feature the condition illustrated in the middle diagram

(4) The very unusual position of the nasin—almost coinciding with glabella: This is true of *Paranthropus* and in at least some cases of *Australopithecus* also. In *Paranthropus*, as in the Olduvai specimen, the nasals are relatively very wide near the nasion.

(5) The very great absolute and also relative width of the inter-orbital area. The proportionate width of the inter-orbital area to that between the external orbital angles is 26.6 in the Olduvai specimen; 26.2(*SK* 846), 25.3(*SK* 48) in two specimens of *Paranthropus*. A single specimen of *Australopithecus* gave a value of 24.1, while a random sample of eight modern human skulls gave a range of 23.4-30.5. No taxonomic significance can therefore be attached to this point on the present evidence.

(6) The very deep palate which is even more markedly like that of *Homo* than *Australopithecus*, and is quite unlike the form seen in *Paranthropus*: In *Homo*, the degree of vaulting of the hard palate is variable, but the difference in depth at the incisive fossa and the back of the palate is normally relatively slight. This is true also of *Australopithecus*. The palate of *Paranthropus* differs in that it slopes more markedly; that is, there is always an appreciable difference between the anterior and posterior depths—in some cases there

（1）相对于眶耳平面，枕外隆凸点较低：南方古猿与傍人的枕外隆凸点底部几乎都在眶耳平面上，这似乎与奥杜威标本是一样的。

（2）枕骨后壁向上陡倾，与顶骨形成拱起程度很高的头骨后区：傍人的情况也是如此，而南方古猿的拱起程度则欠缺一些。傍人的头盖骨类似于球体，其前部相对较低而窄，但侧面陡，后部较高。南方古猿的头盖骨与脸长的现代人类的更为相似。奥杜威标本的头盖骨类型与傍人的一样。

（3）鼓板的形态不同：利基博士利用标本清楚地论述了这一观点。这一特征在南方古猿中是变化的，且存在与奥杜威标本非常类似的情况。所观察到的变化范围如图 1 所示。就因为存在这样的变化，在任何情况下，这个特征在种系发生上的价值都不高。

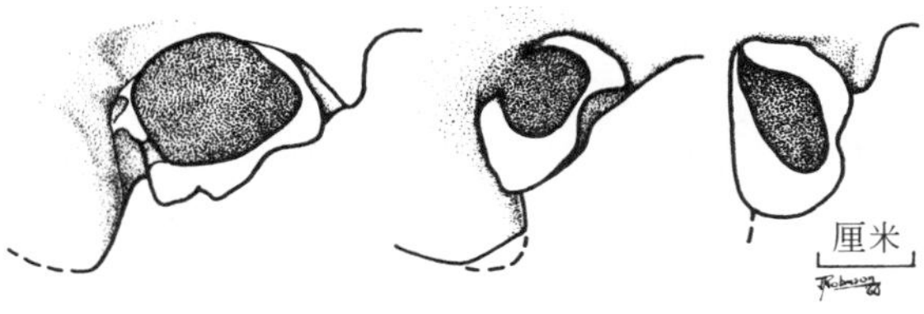

图 1. 源于斯瓦特克朗斯的傍人外耳道侧端耳鼓骨处的差异（*SK* 48、*SK* 52 和 *SK* 848），奥杜威标本的特征与本图中间所示的情形类似。

（4）鼻根点的位置几乎与眉间点一致，这点非常罕见：傍人的情况就是如此，至少有些南方古猿也是如此。像奥杜威标本一样，傍人的鼻骨在鼻根点附近相对很宽。

（5）眶间区的绝对宽度和相对宽度都非常大。奥杜威标本眶间区对外眶角的宽度比为 26.6；傍人的两个标本是 26.2（*SK* 846）与 25.3（*SK* 48）。单个南方古猿标本的比值为 24.1，而随机抽样出来的 8 个现代人类头骨的样本的比值范围为 23.4~30.5。因此就现有证据看这一点不具有分类学上的意义。

（6）腭很深，明显更类似于人属的腭，而不是南方古猿属的腭，并且与傍人属中所见的腭十分不同：人属的硬腭的拱形程度是有差异的，但门齿窝与腭后端的深度差异通常相对较小。南方古猿属的情况也是如此。傍人属的腭的不同点在于其倾斜更为明显；也就是说，前部与后部间的深度总是有明显的差异——有时前部一点也不深，有时前部明显很深。奥杜威标本的特征是：与前部深度相比后部深度相对

is no depth at all anteriorly, in others the anterior depth is appreciable. The Olduvai specimen shares this characteristic of relatively much greater posterior compared to anterior depth, reflecting the *Paranthropus* condition, not that of *Homo* and *Australopithecus*.

(7) The shape and arrangement of the zygomatic process of the maxilla: The Olduvai specimen has a relatively poorly developed zygomatic process, the lower border of which passes almost horizontally from the zygo-maxillary suture to the main body of the maxilla. In some specimens of *Paranthropus* the process passes from the zygo-maxillary suture downward and medial-ward at a fairly sharp angle like an inverted flying buttress. However, *SK* 52, of the same dental age as the Olduvai specimen, has a trace only of the buttress and *SK* 846 (mature adult) has no trace of it, as in the Olduvai specimen.

(8) The relatively greater reduction of the canines in comparison with the molar-premolar series than is seen even in *Paranthropus*: As the marked change of proportion between anterior and cheek teeth occurs in *Paranthropus* and the Olduvai specimen between canine and P^3, the degree of reduction can be measured by the ratio between the modules of these two teeth. The ratio for the Olduvai specimen is 64.9 while that for three specimens of *Paranthropus* ranges from 61.8 to 78.8.

(9) In the species diagnosis Leakey refers to the presence of a sagittal crest "at least posteriorly". The reason for this statement is not clear, since the crest occupies a position identical to that in *Paranthropus*—on roughly the middle third of the distance between glabella and inion. In neither form is the sagittal crest known to reach as far back as the planum occipitale or even the posterior part of the sagittal suture.

It seems to me that the most fruitful approach to an understanding of the australopithecine skull, within the framework of hominid structure, is in terms of diet and the nature of the dentition. *Australopithecus*, as an omnivore eating at least a moderate amount of flesh, has a dental apparatus very similar to that of the older hominines. The relative sizes of the teeth along the tooth row are closely similar, as is the arrangement of the dental arcades. The anterior teeth, especially the canines, are well developed, but the post-canine ones only moderately so. The skulls are also similarly constructed except for the relatively small cranium, compared to the face, of *Australopithecus*.

In *Paranthropus* the situation is very different. Here the anterior teeth, set in an almost straight line across the front of the palate, are appreciably reduced in size compared to those of *Australopithecus*, while the post-canine teeth are appreciably larger. This difference in arrangement and proportion is very striking and is characterized by the very small canine tooth set firmly against a massive premolar. All this must clearly have functional meaning. The massive crushing and grinding teeth, the relatively unimportant anterior teeth and frequent damage to the enamel which could only have been caused by small, very hard particles (presumably grit), and the large size of the animal suggest a predominantly vegetarian diet. Concentration of heavy dental function in the post-canine region has strongly modified the skull architecture. The massive cheek teeth, especially

较大，所反映出的是傍人属的特征，而非人属或南方古猿属的特征。

（7）上颌骨颧突的走向与形状：奥杜威标本的上颌骨颧突发育相对较差。它的下缘几乎水平地从颧骨－上颌骨骨缝延伸到上颌骨的主体。一些傍人标本的上颌骨颧突从颧骨－上颌骨骨缝向下和沿中间成锐角穿过，犹如一个倒转的飞拱。然而，尽管 *SK* 52 与奥杜威标本的齿龄相同，但仅有少许壁柱状构造的痕迹，而 *SK* 846（成熟个体）和奥杜威标本一样没有壁柱状构造的痕迹。

（8）与臼齿－前臼齿齿系相比，犬齿明显减小，甚至比傍人减小得还明显：前齿与颊齿间的大小比例在傍人和奥杜威标本（犬齿与第三上前臼齿间）中发生了明显变化，因此退化的程度可以通过测量这两颗牙齿模数之间的比率获得。奥杜威标本的比率是 64.9，而 3 个傍人标本的比率从 61.8 到 78.8 不等。

（9）在种一级的鉴定上，利基认为“至少在后部”出现了矢状脊。这一条所依据的理由是不清晰的，因为奥杜威标本矢状脊的分布位置与傍人的一致，大约位于眉间点与枕外隆凸点之间的中部三分之一处。已知的矢状脊没有一种形式是向后延伸远至枕平面或甚至到矢状缝的后部。

在我看来，在人科系统框架内了解该南方古猿头骨的最有效的方法是分析南方古猿的食性和齿系之间的特征。南方古猿作为一种杂食动物至少会吃适量的肉，其牙齿构造十分类似于较早的人亚科成员。同一齿列中牙齿的相对大小非常相似，沿齿弓排列。前齿尤其是犬齿发育完好，但是犬齿后的牙齿仅为中度发育。头骨的构造也非常相似，只是南方古猿的颅骨与面部相比相对较小而已。

傍人的情况则非常不同。与南方古猿相比，沿着腭前部几乎呈直线横向排列的前齿明显变小，而颊齿明显较大。这种差异在排列和比例上是非常明显的，这表现为非常小的犬齿牢牢地紧挨着粗大的前臼齿。所有这些特征一定具有非常重要的功能学意义。粗大的用来压碎和研磨食物的牙齿、相对不重要的前齿、只可能是由十分坚硬的小颗粒（可能是粗砂）所引起的常见的牙釉质的损坏以及庞大的体型，都表明以素食为主。牙齿的主要功能集中在后犬齿区，这对头骨的结构有很大的影响。粗大的颊齿尤其是臼齿的齿根系统发育得很完善，因此生长在粗壮的骨头上并且腭的后部相对较深。由于咀嚼力很大、腭很厚、颌骨特别是支撑颊齿的地方粗大，因

the molars, have strongly developed root systems and hence are set in heavy bone, and the back of the palate is relatively deep. Owing to the heavy chewing forces, the palate is thick, the jaws are massive, especially where supporting the cheek teeth, the zygomatic arches are strongly built, the circumorbital bone is strong in the stressed areas, the strongly stressed pillars on either side of the pyriform aperture are thick and the medial and lateral pterygoid plates, especially the latter, are large and strong. However, the large dental battery requires heavy musculature to operate it—hence further changes from the *Australopithecus* and hominine pattern. The areas of origin and insertion of these muscles are sturdy; hence the large surface area of the mandibular ramus, the massive zygomatic arch—which also is widely spaced from the brain-case to allow for the very large temporal muscle—large medial and lateral pterygoid plates, clearly defined temporal lines, sagittal crest and apparent prominence of the supraorbital tori. The large muscles associated with the large and chunky animal result in well-defined muscular ridges on the occiput and the prominence of the mastoid area—assisted by the large temporal muscles which necessitate appreciable lateral extension of the zygomatic arch. It is probable also that the large temporal muscles have influenced the shape of the brain-case anteriorly to help produce the low and narrow shape characteristic of *Paranthropus*. As is usual in relatively massive skulls where large surface area is necessary, some reduction of weight has occurred by increased pneumatism. The mastoid region (not the mastoid process alone) is strongly cellular and the air spaces in the skull base, the maxillae and the frontal bone are all very large.

The curious and characteristic features of the *Paranthropus* skull, which parallel some of those of the gorilla skull and mark it off so clearly from that of *Australopithecus*, are all functionally related and determined largely by the specialized diet of this creature as compared to all other known hominids. These functional and structural differences indicate clear adaptational differences between the two forms and hence also differences of evolutionary direction. In modern systematics, adaptational differences of this order and nature are normally accorded generic rank.

The features of the Olduvai specimen fit the *Paranthropus* pattern as here outlined very accurately—the differences being almost entirely of the sort shown to be variable within a single population by the sample of nearly 200 specimens of *Paranthropus* now in the collections of the Transvaal Museum. The chief feature of the Olduvai form which does not fall within the observed range of variation of this collection is size. The best size comparison is with the only male specimen with good teeth which has P^3-M^1 preserved in sequence and is of the same dental age as the Olduvai specimen. The latter is only 8.4 percent larger. The average percentage difference for five skull and dental series dimensions compared to those of a fully adult female skull is 17.4 percent. As Schultz has shown in a number of papers, intra-specific veriation in measurable primate anatomical characters can often greatly exceed the above values.

The validity of separate specific status is not clear on the basis of the single specimen, and it is perhaps wisest to leave it as distinct. In the light of the above analysis, however,

此颧弓构造结实，围眶骨受力区坚硬，梨状口任一边上的强受力柱粗，中间的翼状板与侧面的翼状板特别是后者又大又结实。但是粗大的齿列需要强大的肌肉组织来控制，因此傍人与南方古猿及人亚科的头骨结构之间产生了进一步的差异。这些肌肉的起点区与附着区非常强健；因此，下颌支的表面积较大，颧弓较粗大（它与头盖骨之间的宽距能允许宽大的颞肌存在），中间和侧面的翼状板大，颞线、矢状脊界线清楚，眶上圆枕明显凸出。体形大而强壮的动物所特有的发达肌肉导致枕骨的肌肉脊清晰以及乳突区凸起，并伴有发达的颞肌，这使得颧弓明显侧向伸展。发达的颞肌可能已经影响了傍人头盖骨前部的形状，并致使其变得低而窄。通常情况下，肌肉在头骨上附着的面积增大必然需要相应地增大头骨的体积，因此通过增加头骨中的气室来减轻头骨的重量。乳突区（不仅仅是乳突）呈多孔状，头骨基部、上颌骨和额骨中的气室都非常大。

傍人头骨具有奇特而典型的特征，与一些大猩猩头骨非常相近但与南方古猿头骨明显不同。通过与所有其他已知的人科成员相比发现，这些特征在功能上是密切相关的，并且主要是由其特定的食性决定的。这些功能上与结构上的不同清晰地表明了两种类型之间的适应性差异，因此在进化方向上也是有差异的。在现代分类学上，适应性演化差异和特性具有属一级的分类意义。

奥杜威标本的形态符合傍人属的特征，此处概括得已非常准确——即奥杜威标本所反映的形态差异基本没有超出德兰士瓦博物馆现有藏品中约 200 个傍人标本所体现的形态变异范围。奥杜威标本明显超出藏品所观测的变异范围的特征是它的大小。若进行大小的比较，就必须是一个男性标本，并且该标本的牙齿从第三上前臼齿－第一上臼齿依次保存完好，且齿龄与奥杜威标本相同。后者仅大 8.4%。和完全成熟的女性标本的头骨相比，5 件头骨与齿系大小的平均百分数差为 17.4%。正如舒尔茨在很多文章里所叙述的那样，可测量的灵长类动物解剖特性的种内变化值经常大大超出上述值。

由于奥杜威标本只有一件，因此无法确定种一级的区别，也许最明智的方法是把奥杜威标本作为一个独立的种。但是综上所述，把它放到独立的属的位置似乎既

separate generic status seems unwarranted and biologically unmeaningful. I therefore propose that the name of the Olduvai form be *Paranthropus boisei* (Leakey).

J. T. Robinson

(**186**, 456-458; 1960)

* * *

THE exact taxonomic label that should be applied to the skull that I have named *Zinjanthropus*, from Olduvai, and which I described in *Nature* of August 15, 1959, seems to me relatively unimportant at the moment. Inevitably, different scientific workers have different ideas of what characters justify specific, generic, and even superfamilial rank. After all, this is purely a question of artificial labels.

Dr. Robinson and I agree that *Zinjanthropus boisei* is closely related to the Australopithecinae; we agree that it has certain resemblances to *Paranthropus*, and we disagree mainly in that he believes the differences to be insufficient to justify separate generic rank, while I think they do.

It is hard enough to reach agreement among zoologists on the taxonomic status of living primates, under conditions in which we possess the skull, skeleton, skin and viscera for study, and it will always be much more difficult to do so when we have only fossils to guide us. I can only say that the very considerable additional work that I have done on the *Zinjanthropus* skull since my preliminary report in *Nature* has greatly strengthened my view that it is entirely different from *Australopithecus* and *Paranthropus*, differing from both these genera more than they do from each other.

I do not feel that any useful purpose would be served by entering into a long discussion with Dr. Robinson in *Nature* at present, since the more detailed study of the Olduvai skull which is now in hand will not, I hope, be too long delayed. However, Dr. Robinson makes certain statements which may mislead those who read them, unless I comment on them. I will therefore do so as briefly as possible.

First of all, whereas in *Paranthropus* and *Australopithecus* (as Dr. Robinson says) the external occipital protuberance lies more or less on the Frankfort plane, in *Zinjanthropus* it lies below it.

Robinson's description of the brain case of *Paranthropus* as "almost spheroidal", but also "relatively low and narrow anteriorly but steep-sided and higher posteriorly", does not seem to make sense, for the two statements seem to cancel each other out. In any event, such a combined description does not fit the brain case of *Zinjanthropus*.

没有实质的根据又没有生物学意义。因此我建议将利基发现的奥杜威标本更名为鲍氏傍人。

鲁滨逊

（田晓阳 翻译；董为 审稿）

* * *

在 1959 年 8 月 15 日的《自然》杂志上，我对我所命名的来自奥杜威的东非人头骨进行了描述，此刻对我来说，应该附于此头骨准确的分类学标签并不是最重要的。然而不可避免的是，不同的科学工作者对于用什么样的特征界定种、属甚至是超科的分类阶元持有不同的观点。毕竟，这纯粹是一个人为分类的问题。

鲁滨逊博士和我都认为鲍氏东非人与南方古猿亚科有很近的亲缘关系；我们也都认为其与傍人属有某些相似之处，而我们观点的分歧主要是，他认为这些差异不足以将其归为一个独立的属，而我认为可以。

即使在有头骨、骨骼、皮肤以及内脏用于研究的条件下，让动物学家们对现存的灵长类动物进行分类并达成共识都是很难的，更何况当我们只能以化石为依据的时候，这种共识就更难达成了。我只能说，自从在《自然》杂志发表了那篇最初的报道之后，我又对这一东非人头骨进行了大量的工作，这些工作都极大地支持了我的观点，即它与南方古猿属和傍人属是完全不同的，它与这两个属之间的差异要大于这两个属彼此之间的差异。

我觉得，现在与鲁滨逊博士在《自然》杂志上展开长篇的讨论并不会产生任何有用的效果，因为我不希望现在手头上对奥杜威头骨进行更为详细的研究工作因此而被耽搁得太久。然而，鲁滨逊博士发表的一些陈述可能会误导读者，所以我不得不发表一下评论。因此我会尽可能简短地进行一些说明。

首先，（正如鲁滨逊博士所说）傍人和南方古猿的枕外隆凸点大体位于眶耳平面上，然而在东非人中其位于该平面之下。

鲁滨逊对傍人脑颅的描述是“类似于球体”，但“其前部相对较低而窄，但侧面陡，后部较高”，这似乎不具有任何意义，因为这两个陈述是自相矛盾的。任何情况下，它们都不能共同用来描述东非人的脑颅。

Robinson illustrates the range of the tympanic plate (see in profile), in *Paranthropus*. None of these three illustrations closely resembles the tympanic plate of *Zinjanthropus*, although the one to the left appears to be rather closer than the middle one.

Without knowing the points at which Robinson measures inter-orbital width and external orbital width, I cannot comment upon his comparisons of his *Paranthropus* figures with mine for *Zinjanthropus*.

As to the morphology of the palate, I do not know upon what evidence Robinson is basing his statement, since I have published no measurements of the palatal depth in *Zinjanthropus*. I must repeat, however, quite categorically, that the morphology of the *Zinjanthropus* palate in no way resembles that of *Paranthropus*.

I cannot accept Robinson's statement that the zygomatic process of the maxilla in *Zinjanthropus* is "relatively poorly developed"; I would say rather, as I have said before, that it is developed in an entirely different morphological manner from *Paranthropus*.

As regards the position of the sagittal crest, in *Zinjanthropus* it ceases to be a crest and divides into two temporal lines well behind the line drawn vertically through the ear when the skull is on the Frankfort plane. In *Paranthropus* (in all the published photographs), the sagittal crest extends a long way forward of such a vertical line through the ear when the skull is on the Frankfort plane, and it is therefore wrong to say, as Robinson does, that "the crest occupies a position identical to that in *Paranthropus*".

Finally, I do not understand the significance of a comparison of "the ratio between the modules of these two teeth", that is, the canine and P^3. Robinson has defined a module as the sum of the length and breadth of a tooth divided by two, and I am at a complete loss to understand how the ratios of modules can have any significance. It must be obvious that one can have on one band a canine tooth 16 mm. long and 6 mm. wide (module equals 11), and a premolar 9 mm. long and 7 mm. wide (module equals 8), while in another specimen one could have a canine which measured 11 mm. × 11 mm., and a premolar which was only 5 mm. long and 11 mm. wide, yet the ratio of the modules in the two sets of teeth would be identical, but completely without significance.

In any event, the ratio between the canine and the premolar alone cannot have any bearing upon the relation of the canine size to the total molar-premolar series, unless the premolar bears a constant relation to the total post canine series.

I therefore repeat my statement that in *Zinjanthropus* there is a relatively greater reduction of the canines in comparison with the total molar-premolar series than is seen in *Paranthropus*, and maintain that Robinson has in no way disproved this statement.

I agree with Robinson that we need to study the *Australopithecus* skull structure and

鲁滨逊描绘了傍人的鼓板变异范围（见侧面图）。然而这三个图示均不与东非人的鼓板相类似，尽管左边那个看起来比中间那个更接近一些。

因为不知道鲁滨逊测量眼窝间宽度和眼窝外宽度的测量点，所以对于他得到的傍人数值与我的东非人数值进行的比较，我不作出任何评论。

至于腭的形态，我不知道鲁滨逊的陈述基于什么证据，因为我从未发表过任何关于东非人腭厚度的测量结果。但是我必须重申的是，我非常确定东非人的腭形态与傍人的绝对没有相似之处。

鲁滨逊认为东非人的上颌骨颧突“发育相对较差”，我不认同这一说法；我想说的是，正如我之前已经说过的，它是以一种与傍人完全不同的形态学方式发育的。

至于矢状脊的位置，在东非人中它不再是一道脊，而是分成了两条颞线，当头骨位于眶耳平面时，这两条颞线恰好位于垂直经过耳所画出的直线的后面。在傍人中（在所有已发表的照片中），矢状脊延伸了很长一段距离，当头骨位于眶耳平面时，其位于过耳垂直线的前方，因此鲁滨逊所说的“矢状脊的分布位置与傍人的是一致的”是错误的。

最后，我不理解对“这两颗牙齿模数之间的比率”进行比较的意义何在，即对犬齿和第三上前臼齿进行的比较。鲁滨逊将这种模数定义为一枚牙齿的长度和宽度的总和除以 2，我完全不能理解这种模数的比值到底有什么意义。很显然，一个个体可能具有一枚长 16 毫米、宽 6 毫米的犬齿（模数等于 11）以及一枚长 9 毫米、宽 7 毫米的前臼齿（模数等于 8），然而别的标本可能具有长 11 毫米、宽 11 毫米的犬齿以及一枚仅仅长 5 毫米、宽 11 毫米的前臼齿，尽管这两套牙齿的模数比值相同，但完全没有意义。

无论如何，对犬齿大小与全部臼齿－前臼齿齿系的关系来说，单个的犬齿和前臼齿间的比值并不具备任何意义，除非前臼齿与全部的后犬齿齿系间具有某种恒定的关系。

因此，我重申一下我的观点，就全部臼齿－前臼齿齿系的比较而言，在东非人中犬齿的退化比在傍人中看到的退化相对来说幅度更大，并且我认为鲁滨逊无法反驳我的这一观点。

鲁滨逊认为，我们需要依据其食性和生活方式研究南方古猿的头骨结构和齿系，

dentition in terms of diet and mode of life, and I shall certainly do so as far as *Zinjanthropus* is concerned in my fuller report.

L. S. B. Leakey

(**186**, 458; 1960)

J. T. Robinson: Transvaal Museum, Pretoria.
L. S. B. Leakey: Coryndon Museum, Nairobi, Kenya.

Reference:

1. *Nature*, **184**, 491 (1959).

对此我表示赞同，并且在对东非人进行更完整的报道中，我肯定会这么做。

利基

（刘皓芳 翻译；董为 审稿）

Stimulated Optical Radiation in Ruby

T. H. Maiman

Editor's Note

Albert Einstein identified the phenomenon of the stimulated emission of radiation early in the 20th century—how radiation of a particular frequency could stimulate more of the same to be emitted in an excited medium. Here Theodore Maiman of the Hughes Research Laboratories in California reported the first observation of the effect in a cube of ruby with ends coated with reflective silver. These mirrors create an "optical cavity" within which light bounces back and forth to stimulate emission from chromium ions in an electronically excited state. This "light amplification by stimulated emission of radiation" was the first basic demonstration of the principles of laser action.

SCHAWLOW and Townes[1] have proposed a technique for the generation of very monochromatic radiation in the infra-red optical region of the spectrum using an alkali vapour as the active medium. Javan[2] and Sanders[3] have discussed proposals involving electron-excited gaseous systems. In this laboratory an optical pumping technique has been successfully applied to a fluorescent solid resulting in the attainment of negative temperatures and stimulated optical emission at a wave-length of 6,943 Å.; the active material used was ruby (chromium in corundum).

A simplified energy-level diagram for triply ionized chromium in this crystal is shown in Fig. 1. When this material is irradiated with energy at a wave-length of about 5,500 Å., chromium ions are excited to the $^4F_2$ state and then quickly lose some of their excitation energy through non-radiative transitions to the ^2E state[4]. This state then slowly decays by spontaneously emitting a sharp doublet the components of which at 300°K. are at 6,943 Å. and 6,929 Å.(Fig. 2*a*). Under very intense excitation the population of this metastable state (^2E) can become greater than that of the ground-state; this is the condition for negative temperatures and consequently amplification via stimulated emission.

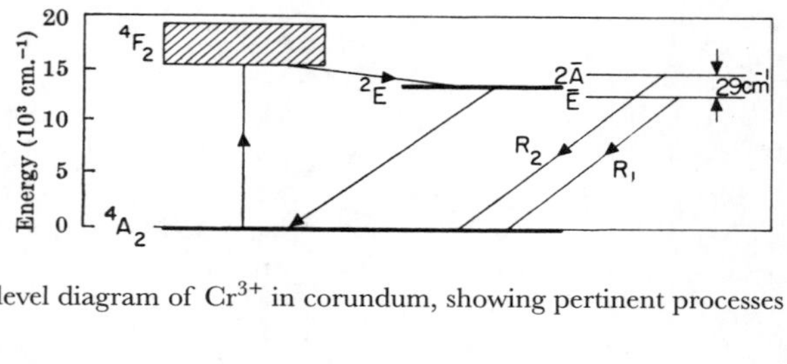

Fig. 1. Energy-level diagram of Cr^{3+} in corundum, showing pertinent processes

红宝石中的受激光辐射

梅曼

编者按

在20世纪初，阿尔伯特·爱因斯坦指出存在受激辐射跃迁现象，即一种特定频率的辐射是怎样从受激发介质中激发出更多同样频率的辐射的。这篇文章中，加利福尼亚州休斯研究实验室的西奥多·梅曼利用一块红宝石首次观察到了这种现象。这块红宝石的两端镀着反射型银膜，因此而形成的镜子构成了一个“光学谐振腔”，在这个“光学谐振腔”中光束反复地将处于激发态的镉离子激发并辐射出来。“受激辐射的光放大”是关于激光原理的第一次基本说明。

肖洛和汤斯[1]提出了一种以碱金属蒸气作为工作介质产生单色性极高的红外光辐射的技术。贾范[2]和桑德斯[3]也讨论了在电子激发气体中产生这种辐射的若干方案。在本实验室中，我们已经成功地将光泵浦技术用于固体荧光材料中，并以此获得了负温度及波长为6,943埃的受激光辐射，其中所用的工作介质是红宝石（含铬的刚玉）。

图1给出的是该晶体中三价铬离子的能级结构简图。当我们用波长约为5,500埃的能量照射此材料时，铬离子被激发到 $^4F_2$ 态，然后通过非辐射跃迁迅速损失部分激发能而跃迁到 ^2E 态[4]。随后这个能态通过自发辐射而缓慢衰变，辐射产生了明锐的双线，它们在温度为300 K时的波长分别是6,943埃和6,929埃（图2*a*所示）。在高强度的激发条件下，处于亚稳态（^2E）的粒子数将多于处于基态的粒子数，这就是产生负温度的条件，并最终导致受激辐射的光放大。

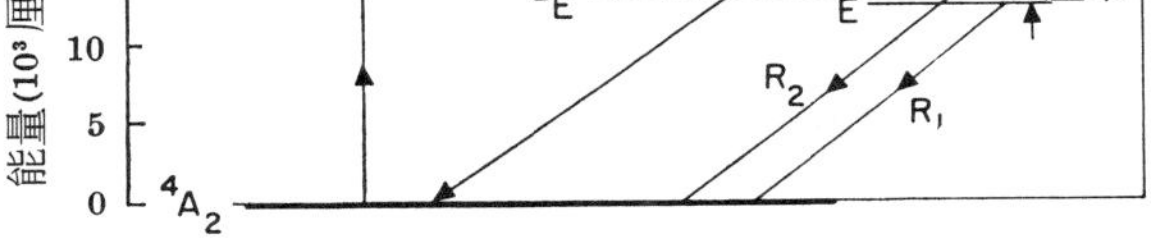

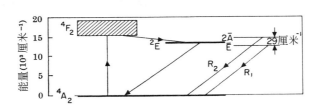

图1. 刚玉中 Cr^{3+} 的能级图及相关的跃迁过程

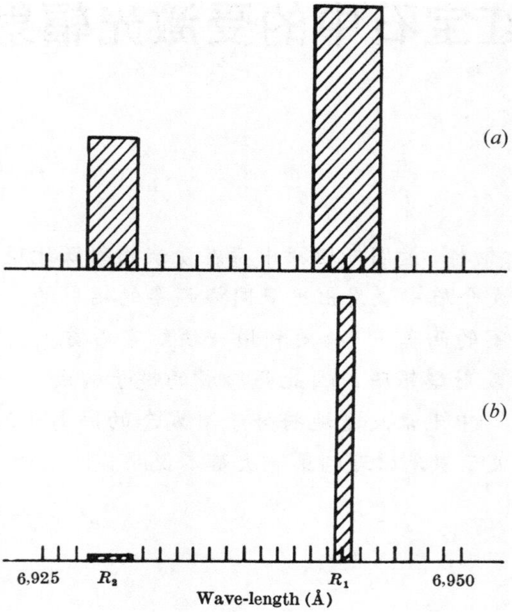

Fig. 2. Emission spectrum of ruby: *a*, low-power excitation; *b*, high-power excitation

To demonstrate the above effect a ruby crystal of 1-cm. dimensions coated on two parallel faces with silver was irradiated by a high-power flash lamp; the emission spectrum obtained under thesse conditions is shown is Fig. 2*b*. These results can be explained on the basis that negative temperatures were produced and regenerative amplification ensued. I expect, in principle, a considerably greater ($\sim 10^8$) reduction in line width when mode selection techniques are used[1].

I gratefully acknowledge helpful discussions with G. Birnbaum, R. W. Hellwarth, L. C. Levitt, and R. A. Satten and am indebted to I. J. D'Haenens and C. K. Asawa for technical assistance in obtaining the measurements.

(**187**, 493-494; 1960)

T. H. Maiman: Hughes Research Laboratories, A Division of Hughes Aircraft Co., Malibu, California.

References:

1. Schawlow, A. L., and Townes, C. H., *Phys. Rev.*, 112, 1940 (1958).
2. Javan, A., *Phys. Rev. Letters*, 3, 87 (1959).
3. Sanders, J. H., *Phys. Rev. Letters*, 3, 86 (1959).
4. Maiman, T. H., *Phys. Rev. Letters*, 4, 564 (1960).

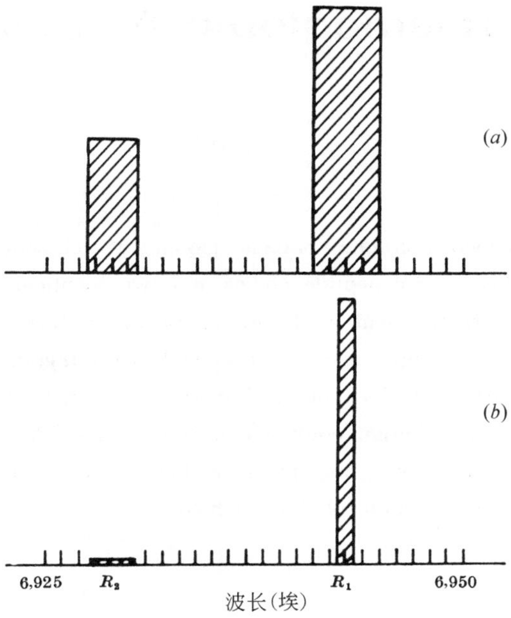

图 2. 红宝石的发射谱：*a*, 低功率激发；*b*, 高功率激发

为了演示上述效应，我们用高功率的闪光灯照射一块尺寸为 1 厘米且两个平行表面都镀了银膜的红宝石晶体，在这种条件下得到的发射谱如图 2*b* 所示。这些结果可以用负温度的产生以及随后的再生放大来解释。我预期，原则上当采用模式选择技术时 [1] 谱线宽度将会有显著的（约 10^8）减小。

我非常感谢伯恩鲍姆、赫尔沃思、莱维特和萨滕与我进行了非常有益的讨论，也感谢黑内斯和浅轮（C. K. Asawa）等人在测量中提供的技术帮助。

（沈乃澂 翻译；尚仁成 审稿）

Four Adult Haemoglobin Types in One Person

C. Baglioni and V. M. Ingram

Editor's Note

By the 1960s the molecular structure of haemoglobin was well known: normal adult haemoglobin contains two identical α polypeptide chains and two identical β chains. German American biologist Vernon M. Ingram had used electrophoresis to show how amino-acid substitutions could produce disease-causing haemoglobin variants. Here Ingram, with Corrado Baglioni from the Massachusetts Institute of Technology, describes the analysis of a blood sample from a single patient containing four different adult haemoglobin types. Three were abnormal, containing various amino-acid substitutions, and the researchers use this information to make assumptions about how the haemoglobin molecule is assembled.

THE normal adult type of human haemoglobin (A) is a single molecular species with the chemical constitution $\alpha_2^A\beta_2^A$ (ref. 1). Such a molecule contains two identical α polypeptide chains and two identical β chains. It has been shown that the genetically controlled abnormal human haemoglobins previously examined contain an abnormal α or an abnormal β chain, carrying an amino-acid substitution[2,3]; for example, lysine for glutamic acid in the β chain of haemoglobin C, $\alpha_2^A\beta_2^C$ (ref. 4). We wish to report the results of chemical studies on four adult haemoglobin components[5] found in a single individual, D. K. P.; her haemoglobins turned out to be normal in both peptide chains, abnormal in one or other chain and abnormal in both chains, respectively. Apart from their genetic interest, these findings allow us to make certain deductions about the mode of assembly of the haemoglobin molecule.

The blood sample from this patient, D. K. P., became available to us through the kindness of Dr. L. M. Tocantins and Miss J. Atwater of Philadelphia. They have already described[5] the occurrence of four haemoglobins in approximately equal amounts in this blood, together with their clinical findings. The haemoglobins are electrophoretically distinct at *p*H 8.6; they have been called[5] haemoglobins A, G, C and X, which is the order of migration, with A as the fastest component. Electrophoretic comparison with authentic specimens is the basis for naming the first three haemoglobins; haemoglobin X was unknown and the slowest haemoglobin yet described. The haemoglobin G was found by these authors[5] to behave identically with a specimen of G from Dr. Schneider. It may therefore be identical with the haemoglobin G of Lehmann and Edington[6] and with the G_{Ib} (for G_{Ibadan}) recently described by Shooter *et al.*[7], and found by them to be abnormal in the α chain. On the other hand, D. K. P.'s haemoglobin G is different from the G of Schwartz *et al.*[3,8] which carries a substitution of glycine for glutamic acid in the β peptide chain.

一人体内的四种成人血红蛋白

巴廖尼，英格拉姆

编者按

20 世纪 60 年代，血红蛋白的分子结构已为人们所熟知。正常成人血红蛋白包括两条相同的 α 多肽链和两条相同的 β 多肽链。美籍德裔生物学家弗农·英格拉姆运用电泳方法进行的研究显示氨基酸替换可以产生多种致病的血红蛋白变异体。本文中英格拉姆与来自麻省理工学院的科拉多·巴廖尼合作，对血液中存在四种不同的成人血红蛋白的一名患者的血样进行了分析，结果发现其中三种血红蛋白是存在各种不同的氨基酸替换的异常血红蛋白，并在此基础上提出了血红蛋白分子组装机制的假说。

正常成人型人血红蛋白 A 是化学组成为 $\alpha_2^A\beta_2^A$（参考文献 1）的单分子化合物，这个分子包括两条相同的 α 多肽链和两条相同的 β 多肽链。以前的研究表明，由遗传因素引起的人异常血红蛋白中往往存在一条异常的携带氨基酸替换的 α 链或 β 链[2,3]。例如血红蛋白 C，$\alpha_2^A\beta_2^C$（参考文献 4）的 β 链上一个谷氨酸就被一个赖氨酸所取代。我们对一名女性（D. K. P.）体内发现的四种成人血红蛋白组分[5]进行了化学分析，发现其中有的血红蛋白的两条链都正常，有的一条链发生了变异，而有的两条链都发生了变异。这些发现除了具有遗传意义外，还可以让我们据此对血红蛋白分子的组装模式做出确切的推论。

费城的托坎廷斯医生和阿特沃特小姐慷慨地为我们提供了患者 D. K. P. 的血液样本，他们叙述了该患者的临床表现，并指出该患者血液样本中存在着四种几乎等量的血红蛋白[5]。由于这四种血红蛋白在 pH 值为 8.6 时电泳迁移率不同，它们分别被命名为血红蛋白 A、G、C 和 X[5]，字母表示蛋白迁移顺序，A 表示迁移速度最快的蛋白组分。其中，前三种血红蛋白是根据与各自迁移率相同的标准蛋白样本来命名的，而 X 组分是一个未知的血红蛋白，在目前已知的所有血红蛋白中迁移最慢。他们还发现[5]血红蛋白 G 的性质与施奈德医生所研究的 G 样本是一致的。因此，它很可能与莱曼和埃丁顿[6]描述的血红蛋白 G 以及舒特等人[7]最近描述的血红蛋白 G_{Ib}（即 $G_{伊巴丹}$）是同一种物质，其 α 链发生异常。另一方面，这一血红蛋白 G 组分又不同于施瓦茨等人[3,8]描述的血红蛋白 G，后者 β 链上的一个谷氨酸残基被甘氨酸残基所取代。

The original characterization of haemoglobins A, G, C and X was done by paper electrophoresis[5]. We have been able to confirm the presence of the four components by starch-gel electrophoresis[9] at *p*H 8.6 in 0.02 *M* veronal buffer (see Fig. 1). The four proteins were also separated by electrophoresis on a starch block[10] in the same buffer. The relative amounts (percent) recovered were: A, 35; G, 27; C, 23; X, 15.

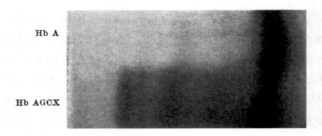

Fig. 1. Starch-gel electrophoresis of D. K. P.'s haemoglobin at *p*H 8.6 in 0.05 *M* veronal buffer

Each haemoglobin was digested with trypsin and fingerprinted[11]. Haemoglobin A appeared to be completely normal (Fig. 2) and haemoglobin C showed only the expected absence[4] of peptide 4 and its replacement by two new peptides, C-4*a* and C-4*b* (C-4*b* = haemoglobin C tryptic peptide 4*b*). These peptides were isolated, hydrolysed and their amino-acid content analysed. The results confirmed the glutamic acid to lysine substitution previously reported for haemoglobin C[4]. It appears, therefore, that D. K. P.'s haemoglobin C is authentic haemoglobin C.

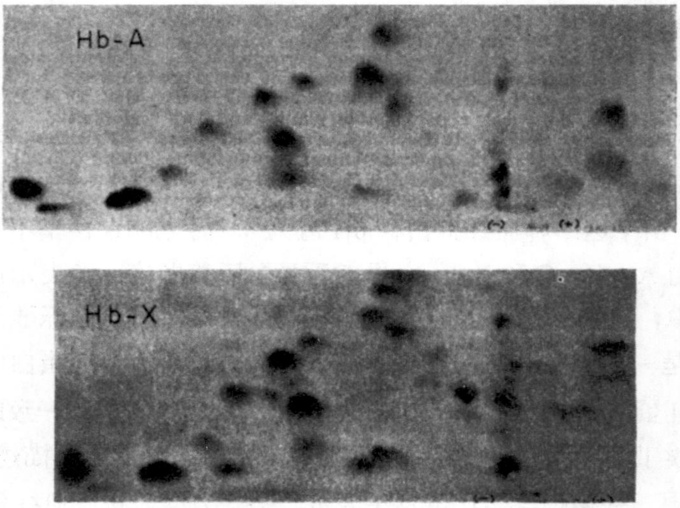

(*a*)

在之前的研究中，已经通过纸电泳法对血红蛋白 A、G、C 和 X 的初步性质进行了分析 [5]。我们采用淀粉胶电泳 [9]（pH 值为 8.6 的含 0.02 摩尔 / 升巴比妥的缓冲液）的方法来证实这四种血红蛋白的存在（见图 1）。在同样的缓冲体系下进行淀粉阻滞电泳 [10]，也能够成功地将这四种血红蛋白分离开。可以看出它们的相对含量分别是：A，35%；G，27%；C，23%；X，15%。

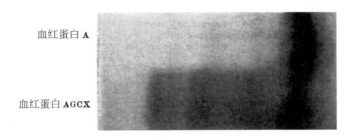

图 1. D. K. P. 血红蛋白的淀粉胶电泳图（pH 值为 8.6 的含 0.05 摩尔 / 升巴比妥缓冲液）

用胰蛋白酶消化各个血红蛋白后进行指纹印迹分析 [11]，结果表明血红蛋白 A 可能是完全正常的（图 2），而血红蛋白 C 出现了我们所预期的结果，即肽段 4 缺失并被两个新肽段 C-4*a* 和 C-4*b* 所取代（C-4*b* 代表血红蛋白 C 的胰蛋白酶消化肽段 4*b*）。将这些肽段分离、水解后进行氨基酸分析，结果表明其肽链上的一个谷氨酸被一个赖氨酸所取代，这也证实了之前的一篇关于血红蛋白 C 的报道 [4]。因此，D. K. P. 的 C 组分可能就是血红蛋白 C。

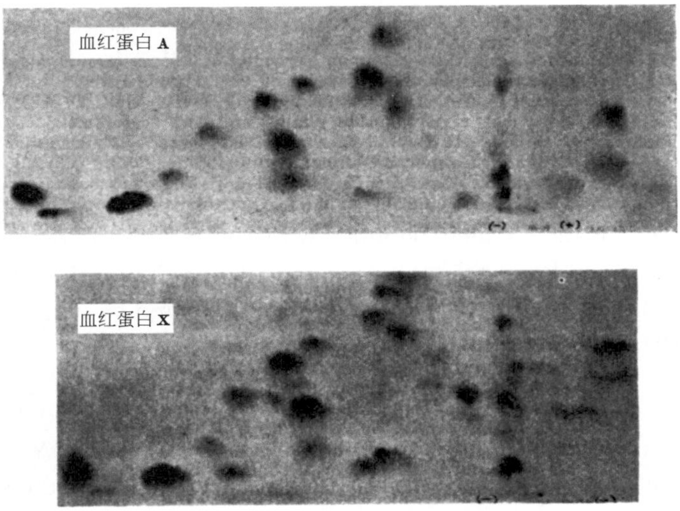

(*a*)

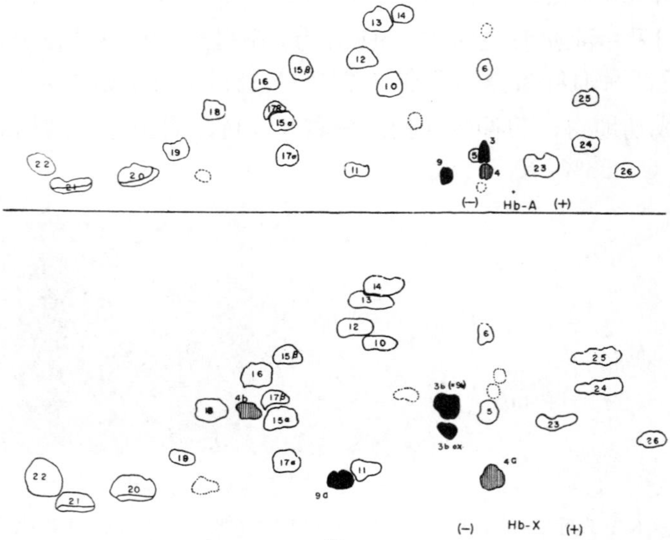

(b)

Fig. 2. Photographs (a) and tracings (b) of fingerprints (ref. 11) of haemoglobins A and X. Electrophoresis was in the usual buffer but on a cooled brass plate at about 30 V./cm. for 2.5 hr. Ascending chromatography is in pyridine: isoamyl alcohol: water—35:35:30 by volume (ref. 18). The methionine residue in G-3*b* is often partially oxidized to the corresponding sulphoxide peptide with a different chromatographic mobility. Such an oxidized peptide is referred to as "G-3*b* ox". Peptides A-4, C-4*a* and C-4*b* are marked by a vertical shading. Peptides A-3, G-3*b*, G-3*b* ox and G-9*a* are marked in black

Fingerprints[11] of D. K. P.'s haemoglobin G were more difficult to interpret. The fingerprinting technique had to be modified to make it more sensitive. Isolated peptide bands from paper ionophoresis at *p*H 6.4 are compared side by side by a second ionophoresis on Whatman No. 3*MM* paper in a *p*H 4.7 buffer. It eventually appeared that in haemoglobin G, two normal peptides—A-3 and A-9—had been replaced by three new peptides. No other changes have so far been detected.

The following relationship for these five peptides was established by means of quantitative amino-acid analyses of the isolated peptides with the Spinco model Moore and Stein automatic analyser, by endgroup determinations with the dinitrophenol procedures[12], by stepwise degradation with the Edman-Sjøquist procedure[13] and by fingerprinting[11] of some of the peptides after their digestion with elastase[14].

The haemoglobin A peptides A-3 and A-9 differ only in that A-9 has an additional N-terminal lysine residue; we may write A-9 = Lys-(A-3). The Lys-(A-3) bond in such a peptide would be attacked by trypsin only slowly; hence yields of peptides A-9 and A-3 were found to be variable.

(1) In D. K. P.'s haemoglobin G, an asparagine residue in peptide A-3 (and A-9) has been

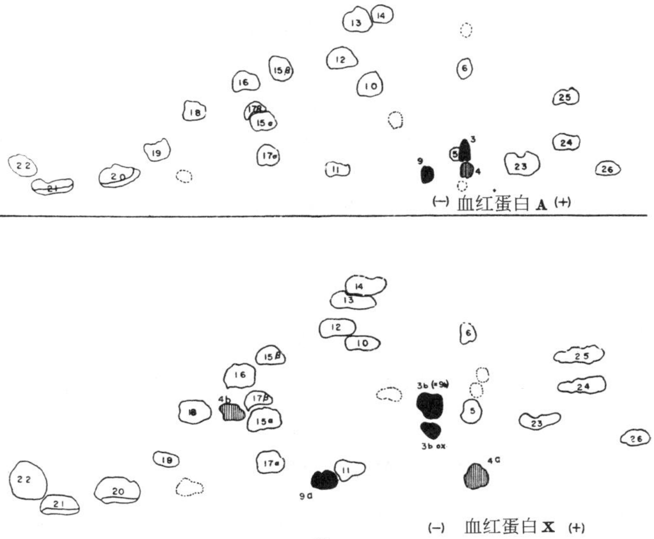

(b)

图 2. 血红蛋白 A 和血红蛋白 X 的指纹印迹图谱（参考文献 11）的原图（*a*）和摹图（*b*）。在冷却的铜板上，于常规缓冲液中 30 伏特 / 厘米恒压电泳 2.5 小时。之后在嘧啶 : 异戊醇 : 水（体积比 35:35:30）（参考文献 18）的混合溶液中完成上行层析。由于 G-3*b* 肽段上的甲硫氨酸残基常常被部分氧化为亚砜，因此其层析样点迁移率会不同，我们将此氧化肽段表示为“G-3*b* ox”。用竖线区域来表示肽段 A-4、C-4*a* 和 C-4*b*。用黑色区域来表示肽段 A-3、G-3*b*、G-3*b* ox 和 G-9*a*。

相比之下，D. K. P. 的血红蛋白 G 的指纹印迹 [11] 结果解析起来要更困难一些。我们需要对指纹印迹技术进行一些改进以提高其灵敏度。首先，利用纸电泳的方法在 pH 值为 6.4 时将多肽段初步分离，然后将分离开的多肽条带并排转移到 3*MM* 号沃特曼滤纸上，之后在 pH 值为 4.7 的缓冲液中进行二次电泳分离。结果表明血红蛋白 G 的 A-3 和 A-9 这两条正常肽段被三个新的肽段取代了。除此之外没发现其他变化。

之后，我们通过下列方法来研究上述五种肽段间的相互关系。采用特种设备公司生产的穆尔和斯坦自动分析仪对分离肽段进行定量氨基酸分析，用二硝基酚法 [12] 测定末端基团，利用埃德曼–舍奎斯特法 [13] 逐步降解肽段，并在弹性蛋白酶消化后采用指纹印迹法 [11] 分析其中的部分肽段 [14]。

血红蛋白 A 的肽段 A-3 和 A-9 之间的区别只是后者的 N 末端多了一个赖氨酸残基，可以将这一关系表示为 A-9 = Lys-(A-3)。胰蛋白酶只能缓慢地攻击这个肽段中 Lys-(A-3) 之间的肽键，因此消化产生的 A-9 和 A-3 的量并不恒定。

(1) D. K. P. 的血红蛋白 G 的肽段 A-3（和 A-9）上的一个天冬酰胺残基被一个

replaced by lysine; hence a new trypsin-sensitive bond has appeared which results in the appearance of an additional tryptic peptide. Therefore we can write:

$$A\text{-}3 \rightarrow G\text{-}3a + G\text{-}3b$$
$$A\text{-}9 \rightarrow G\text{-}9a + G\text{-}3b\ (= G\text{-}9b).$$

Of course, peptide G-9*a* = Lys-(G-3*a*), as illustrated in Fig. 3.

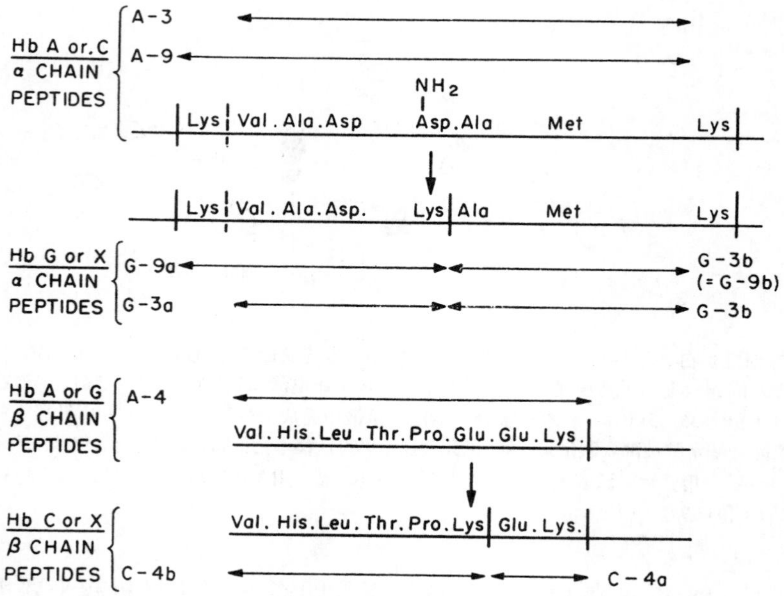

Fig. 3. Diagrammatic representation of the peptides obtained by the action of trypsin on the α- or β-chains of haemoglobins A, G, C, X. See text for the explanation of the relationship between peptide A-3 and A-9 and between G-3*a* and G-9*a*. In the lower part of the figure it can be seen that peptides A-4 and C-4*b* are at the N-terminus of the β-chains (ref. 19) of haemoglobins A and C. Peptide A-9 contains 29 amino-acid residues, peptide G-9*a* has 8

(2) It so happens that peptide G-3*b* contains methionine, which in the course of fingerprinting is to some extent oxidized to the sulphoxide. The resultant peptide "G-3*b* ox" is definitely identifiable, since it is separated in chromatography. Peptides A-3 and A-9 (and for that matter A-25) show the same oxidation phenomenon.

Haemoglobin X was also digested and fingerprinted[11]. It is clear from the results (Figs. 2 and 3) that haemoglobin X contains the abnormal peptides characteristic of both haemoglobin C and G. Peptide A-4 (β chain) is replaced by the two haemoglobin C peptides C-4*a* and C-4*b*. Peptides A-3 and A-9 (α chain) are replaced by the three haemoglobin G peptides G-3*a*, G-9*a* and G-3*b*. Haemoglobin X is therefore a naturally occurring adult haemoglobin which is abnormal in both its α and its β chains. Such doubly abnormal haemoglobins have been prepared *in vitro* by Itano and Robinson[15] using dissociation and re-association of suitable mixtures of singly abnormal human haemoglobins.

赖氨酸残基所取代，从而增加了一个胰蛋白酶敏感位点，于是就产生了一个额外的胰蛋白酶水解片段。我们可以这样表述：

$$A\text{-}3 \rightarrow G\text{-}3a + G\text{-}3b$$
$$A\text{-}9 \rightarrow G\text{-}9a + G\text{-}3b\ (= G\text{-}9b)$$

当然，如图 3 所示，肽段 G-9*a* 就是 Lys-(G-3*a*)。

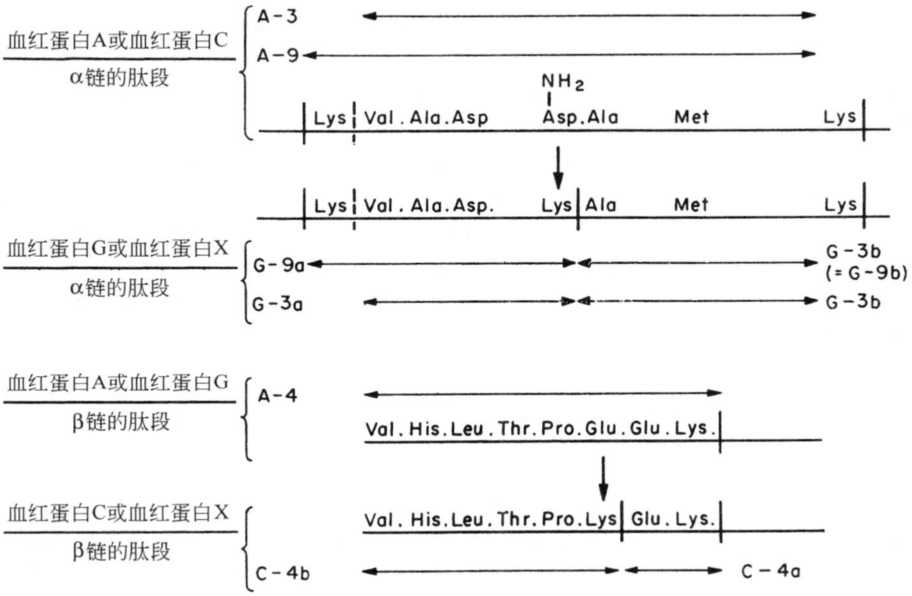

图 3. 血红蛋白 A、G、C 和 X 的 α 链或 β 链经胰蛋白酶消化后得到的肽段的分析图。肽段 A-3 和 A-9 的关系以及肽段 G-3*a* 和 G-9*a* 的关系说明见正文。我们可以从靠下方的图上看出，肽段 A-4 和 C-4*b* 位于血红蛋白 A 和血红蛋白 C 的 β 链的 N 末端（参考文献 19）。肽段 A-9 含有 29 个氨基酸残基，肽段 G-9*a* 含有 8 个氨基酸残基。

（2）肽段 G-3*b* 刚好包含甲硫氨酸，在指纹印迹过程中，甲硫氨酸残基会一定程度地被氧化为亚砜，由此产生的“G-3*b* ox”可以通过层析法进行分离与鉴定。肽段 A-3 和 A-9（以及 A-25）也存在着同样的氧化现象。

血红蛋白 X 也被消化并进行指纹印迹分析 [11]，从实验结果（图 2 和图 3）可以很明显地看出血红蛋白 X 含有异常肽段，其特征与血红蛋白 C 和血红蛋白 G 的异常肽段相似。其肽段 A-4（β 链）被血红蛋白 C 的两个肽段 C-4*a* 和 C-4*b* 所取代，肽段 A-3 和 A-9（α 链）被血红蛋白 G 的三个肽段 G-3*a*、G-9*a* 和 G-3*b* 所取代。因此，血红蛋白 X 是自然产生的 α 链和 β 链均异常的成人血红蛋白。板野和鲁滨逊 [15] 在体外将人的单链异常血红蛋白分散再重组后，得到了这样的双链异常血红蛋白 X。

One can now write the constitution of D. K. P.'s four haemoglobins as follows:

$$\text{Haemoglobin A} = \alpha_2^A\beta_2^A$$
$$\text{Haemoglobin G} = \alpha_2^G\beta_2^A$$
$$\text{Haemoglobin C} = \alpha_2^A\beta_2^C$$
$$\text{Haemoglobin X} = \alpha_2^G\beta_2^C$$

We would deduce from these findings that D. K. P.'s genotype is $\alpha^A/\alpha^G\ \beta^C/\beta^A$ (see also in refs. 16 and 17). It has also been suggested before by Atwater *et al.*[5] that D. K. P. is doubly heterozygous for the G and C abnormalities. Apparently, each gene causes the manufacture of the peptide chain characteristic of it; thus, the α^A gene produces α^A chains, the α^G gene produces α^G chains with lysine in place of asparagine in peptide A-3, and so on. We must next assume that each chain dimerizes as soon as it is formed; $2\alpha^A \rightarrow \alpha_2^A$ and $2\alpha^G \rightarrow \alpha_2^G$. This must be so, since no real hybrids, such as $\alpha^A\alpha^G\beta_2^A$, etc., are produced, although all these chains are present inside the same cells. Finally, the four types of subunit seem to assemble to complete molecules in a random fashion, leading to the four haemoglobins:

$$\alpha_2^A+\alpha_2^G+\beta_2^A+\beta_2^C \rightarrow \alpha_2^A\beta_2^A+\alpha_2^G\beta_2^A+\alpha_2^A\beta_2^C+A_2^G\beta_2^C.$$

It is important to realize the random nature of this final step in the assembly of the molecule, in contrast to the previous dimerization step, which is specific. The fact that the four haemoglobins occur in roughly equal amounts, with A predominating, implies that at least in this patient the rate of manufacture of the different chains is only slightly different. As in the other abnormal human haemoglobins, the phenotype corresponding to each gene is expressed and the product of all of them is to be found within the same cell.

Rather similar chemical results are being obtained by Dr. Park Gerald, Boston, working with an apparently unrelated patient who possesses four haemoglobins called at present A, D, C and X. However, the four components are not nearly in equal amounts, haemoglobins C and X greatly predominating. It will be interesting to see whether these haemoglobins D and X are identical chemically with D. K. P.'s haemoglobins G and X and why the proportions are so different. Very recently, Raper *et al.*[20] reported briefly on the occurrence of A, G, C, X in one patient, with X abnormal in both chains. The relationship between their haemoglobins and ours remains to be determined.

Full details of our experiments have been submitted for publication.

We wish to thank Miss Jean Atwater and Dr. L. M. Tocantins for their help and interest. We would also like to acknowledge the help of Miss Marianne Schick, who performed

现在 D. K. P. 的四种血红蛋白的构成可以描述如下：

血红蛋白 A = $\alpha_2^A\beta_2^A$
血红蛋白 G = $\alpha_2^G\beta_2^A$
血红蛋白 C = $\alpha_2^A\beta_2^C$
血红蛋白 X = $\alpha_2^G\beta_2^C$

根据这些结果我们可以推断出 D. K. P. 血红蛋白的基因型是 α^A/α^G β^C/β^A（也见参考文献 16、17）。阿特沃特等人[5] 之前也认为 D. K. P. 的异常血红蛋白 G 和血红蛋白 C 是双杂合子。肽链的特征显然取决于编码它的基因；因此，基因 α^A 决定 α^A 链，基因 α^G 决定 α^G 链以及肽段 A-3 上的赖氨酸残基取代天冬酰胺残基等。又由于同一细胞内虽然同时含有四种肽链但并不存在真正的杂合子（如 $\alpha^A\alpha^G\beta_2^A$ 等），我们可以推测出每条肽链一旦合成就会二聚体化，即 $2\alpha^A \rightarrow \alpha_2^A$ 和 $2\alpha^G \rightarrow \alpha_2^G$。最终这四种亚基似乎能够随机组装成这四种血红蛋白：

$$\alpha_2^A+\alpha_2^G+\beta_2^A+\beta_2^C \rightarrow \alpha_2^A\beta_2^A+\alpha_2^G\beta_2^A+\alpha_2^A\beta_2^C+A_2^G\beta_2^C$$

与先前独特的二聚体化步骤相比，能认识到血红蛋白分子组装过程中最后一步的随机性是重要的。事实上，四种血红蛋白中除了 A 组分的含量高一些以外，其他三种出现的概率是大致相等的，这表明人体内各种肽链的含量相差甚微，至少在该患者体内如此。与其他人的异常血红蛋白一样，对应每个基因的表型都会表达出来，并且它们所有的产物都能在同类细胞中检测到。

波士顿的帕克·杰拉尔德医生获得了非常相似的化学实验结果，他的研究对象是一名无血缘关系的患者，该患者具有四种血红蛋白，目前分别被称为血红蛋白 A、D、C 和 X。但这四种血红蛋白的含量不尽相同，其中血红蛋白 C 和 X 要远多于 A 和 D。值得关注的是，该患者的血红蛋白 D 和 X 在化学性质方面是否等同于 D. K. P. 的血红蛋白 G 和 X？它们各自的含量为什么会存在这样的差距？最近雷珀等人[20] 简要报道了一名患者体内同时存在血红蛋白 A、G、C 和 X，其中 X 为双链异常血红蛋白。这些报道中的血红蛋白和我们所研究的四种血红蛋白之间到底是什么样的关系，这一点还有待进一步研究。

有关我们研究的全部细节已经提交并等待发表。

我们向琼·阿特沃特小姐和托坎廷斯医生对本研究的帮助与关注表示感谢，并感谢玛丽安娜·希克小姐为我们进行了定量氨基酸分析。同时，这项工作还得到了

the quantitative amino-acid analysis. This work has been supported by a grant from the Institute for Arthritis and Metabolic Diseases, U.S. Public Health Service.

(**189**, 465-467; 1961)

C. Baglioni and V. M. Ingram: Division of Biochemistry, Department of Biology, Massachusetts Institute of Technology.

References:

1. Rhinesmith, H. W., Schroeder, W. A., and Pauling, L., *J. Amer. Chem. Soc.*, 79, 4682 (1957). Rhinesmith, H. W., Schroeder, W. A., and Martin, N., *ibid*, **80**, 3358 (1958).
2. Hunt, J. A., and Ingram, V. M., CIBA Found. Symp. Biochem. Human Genetics (Naples), 114 (1959).
3. Hill, R. L., and Schwartz, H. C., *Nature*, **184**, 642 (1959).
4. Hunt, J. A., and Ingram, V. M., *Nature*, **181**, 1062 (1958).
5. Atwater, J., Schwartz, I. R., and Tocantins, L. M., *Blood*, **15**, 901 (1960).
6. Edington, G. M., and Lehmann, H., *Lancet*, **267**, 173 (1954).
7. Shooter, E. M., Skinner, E. R., Garlick, J. P., and Barnicot, N. A., *Brit. J. Haematol.*, **6**, 140 (1960).
8. Schwartz, H. C., Spaet, J. H., Zuelzer, W. W., Neel, J. V., Robinson, A. R., and Kaufman, S. F., *Blood*, **12**, 238 (1957).
9. Smithies, O., *Biochem. J.*, **61**, 629 (1955).
10. Kunkel, H. G., and Wallenius, G., *Science*, **122**, 788 (1955).
11. Ingram, V. M., *Biochim. Biophys. Acta*, **28**, 539 (1958).
12. Sanger, F., and Tuppy, H., *Biochem. J.*, **49**, 465 (1951).
13. Sjøquist, J., *Arkiv Kemi*, **14**, 291, 323 (1959).
14. Naughton, M. A., and Sanger, F., *Biochem. J.*, **70**, 4*p* (1958).
15. Itano, H. A., and Robinson, E., *Nature*, **183**, 1799 (1959).
16. Ingram, V. M., and Stretton, A. O. W., *Nature*, **184**, 1903 (1959).
17. Ingram, V. M., "Haemoglobin and Its Abnormalities", C. C. Thomas, 1961 (in the press).
18. Wittmann, H. G. (personal communication).
19. Hunt, J. A., and Ingram, V. M., *Nature*, **184**, 640 (1959).
20. Raper, A. B., Gammack, D. B., Huchns, E. R., and Shooter, E. M., *Biochem. J.*, 77. 10*P* (1960).

美国公共卫生署关节炎和代谢疾病研究所的资助。

（高如丽 翻译；金侠 审稿）

Gene Action in the *X*-Chromosome of the Mouse (*Mus musculus* L.)

M. F. Lyon

Editor's Note

In 1960, geneticists Susumu Ohno and T. S. Hauschka studied a variety of female mouse cells, and reported that one of the two *X*-chromosomes always appeared different. Here English geneticist Mary F. Lyon suggests these condensed *X*-chromosomes can be of maternal or paternal origin in different cells of the same animal, and that they are genetically inactive. This could, she explained, account for the mottled appearance of female mice heterozygous for coat colour genes. The Lyon hypothesis, now widely accepted, states that in female mammals, one copy of the *X*-chromosome becomes inactivated early in development. This prevents the female from having twice as many *X*-chromosome gene products as the male.

OHNO and Hauschka[1] showed that in female mice one chromosome of mammary carcinoma cells and of normal diploid cells of the ovary, mammary gland and liver was heteropyknotic. They interpreted this chromosome as an *X*-chromosome and suggested that the so-called sex chromatin was composed of one heteropyknotic *X*-chromosome. They left open the question whether the heteropyknosis was shown by the paternal *X*-chromosome only, or the chromosome from either parent indifferently.

The present communication suggests that the evidence of mouse genetics indicates: (1) that the heteropyknotic *X*-chromosome can be either paternal or maternal in origin, in different cells of the same animal; (2) that it is genetically inactivated.

The evidence has two main parts. First, the normal phenotype of *XO* females in the mouse[2] shows that only one active *X*-chromosome is necessary for normal development, including sexual development. The second piece of evidence concerns the mosaic phenotype of female mice heterozygous for some sex-linked mutants. All sex-linked mutants so far known affecting coat colour cause a "mottled" or "dappled" phenotype, with patches of normal and mutant colour, in females heterozygous for them. At least six mutations to genes of this type have been reported, under the names mottled[3,4], brindled[3], tortoiseshell[5], dappled[6], and 26*K*[2]. They have been thought to be allelic with one another, but since no fertile males can be obtained from any except, in rare cases, brindled, direct tests of allelism have usually not been possible. In addition, a similar phenotype, described as "variegated", is seen in females heterozygous for coat colour mutants translocated on to the *X*-chromosome[7,8].

小鼠（小家鼠）X染色体上的基因作用

莱昂

编者按

1960 年，遗传学家大野干和豪施卡研究了各种各样的雌鼠细胞，并报道称其两条 X 染色体中的一条总是显得不一样。在本文中，英国的遗传学家玛丽·莱昂指出，在同一种动物的不同细胞中这些稠密 X 染色体来自于母本或父本，它们缺乏遗传活性。她解释道，这可能就是毛色基因杂合体雌鼠呈现斑驳毛色的原因。莱昂假说现在已被人们广泛接受，它阐述了在雌性哺乳动物发育早期一套 X 染色体会失活，这防止了雌性产生比雄性多一倍的 X 染色体基因产物。

大野和豪施卡 [1] 指出，雌鼠的乳腺癌细胞以及卵巢、乳腺和肝脏的正常二倍体细胞中都有一条染色体是异固缩的。他们认为这条染色体是一条 X 染色体，并提出所谓的性染色质是由一条异固缩的 X 染色体组成的。他们实际上留下了一个问题，即到底是只有父本的 X 染色体表现为异固缩形态，还是来源于双亲中任何一方的 X 染色体都可以表现为异固缩形态。

当下学术界的讨论认为来自小鼠遗传学的证据可以表明：(1) 同一种动物不同细胞中异固缩的 X 染色体既可能来自于父本，也可能来自于母本；(2) 异固缩染色体缺乏遗传活性。

这些证据主要包括两部分。首先是存在表型正常的 XO 型雌鼠 [2]，这表明正常发育（包括性发育）只需要一条有活性的 X 染色体。第二个证据是和杂合的性连锁突变的雌鼠具有嵌合体表型有关。至今已知所有能影响毛色的性连锁突变都能使其相应的杂合雌鼠出现“斑驳”或者“斑纹”状表型，即正常颜色和突变颜色的皮毛斑块混杂在一起。现在至少已经报道了 6 种这一类型的基因突变，被称为斑驳 [3,4]、斑点 [3]、龟甲纹 [5]、斑纹 [6] 和 26*K*[2]。人们认为它们彼此间互为等位基因，但是，除少量斑点突变外，没能够得到其他突变类型的有生育能力的雄鼠，因此通常不可能直接测定基因的等位性。此外，类似的表型（被描述为“杂色”）也可以在毛色突变能够易位到 X 染色体上 [7,8] 的杂合雌鼠中看到。

It is here suggested that this mosaic phenotype is due to the inactivation of one or other *X*-chromosome early in embryonic development. If this is true, pigment cells descended from cells in which the chromosome carrying the mutant gene was inactivated will give rise to a normal-coloured patch and those in which the chromosome carrying the normal gene was inactivated will give rise to a mutant-coloured patch. There may be patches of intermediate colour due to cell-mingling in development. The stripes of the coat of female mice heterozygous for the gene tabby, *Ta*, which affects hair structure, would have a similar type of origin. Falconer[9] reported that the black regions of the coat of heterozygotes had a hair structure resembling that of the *Ta* hemizygotes and homozygotes, while the agouti regions had a normal structure.

Thus this hypothesis predicts that for all sex-linked genes of the mouse in which the phenotype is due to localized gene action the heterozygote will have a mosaic appearance, and that there will be a similar effect when autosomal genes are translocated to the *X*-chromosome. When the phenotype is not due to localized gene action various types of result are possible. Unless the gene action is restricted to the descendants of a very small number of cells at the time of inactivation, these original cells will, except in very rare instances, include both types. Therefore, the phenotype may be intermediate between the normal and hemizygote types, or the presence of any normal cells may be enough to ensure a normal phenotype, or the observed expression may vary as the proportion of normal and mutant cells varies, leading to incomplete penetrance in heterozygotes. The gene bent-tail, *Bn*[10], may fit into this category, having 95 percent penetrance and variable expression in heterozygotes. Jimpy, *jp*, is recessive, suggesting that the presence of some normal cells is enough to ensure a normal phenotype, but Phillips[11] reported one anomalous female which showed the jimpy phenotype. Since it showed the heterozygous phenotype for *Ta* this animal cannot be interpreted as an *XO* female; it is possible that it represents an example of the rare instance when by chance all the cells responsible for the jimpy phenotype had the normal gene inactivated.

The genetic evidence does not indicate at what stage of embryonic development the inactivation of one *X*-chromosome occurs. In embryos of the cat, monkey and man sex-chromatin is first found in nuclei of the late blastocyst stage[12,13]. Inactivation of one *X* at a similar stage of the mouse embryo would be compatible with the observations. Since an *XO* female is normally fertile it is not necessary to postulate that both *X*-chromosomes remain functional until the formation of the gonads.

The sex-chromatin is thought to be formed from one *X*-chromosome also in the rat, *Rattus norvegicus*[14], and in the opossum, *Didelphis virginiana*[15]. If this should prove to be the case in all mammals, then all female mammals heterozygous for sex-linked mutant genes would be expected to show the same phenomena as those in the mouse. The coat of the tortoiseshell cat, being a mosaic of the black and yellow colours of the two homozygous types, fulfils this expectation.

(**190**, 372-373; 1961)

在此我们认为，这种嵌合体表型是胚胎发育早期一条或另一条 X 染色体失活的结果。如果确实如此，由那些携带突变基因但缺失遗传活性的染色体细胞衍生出来的色素细胞就会产生正常颜色的斑块，而由那些携带正常基因但缺乏遗传活性的染色体细胞衍生出来的色素细胞就会产生突变颜色的斑块。而发育时细胞的混合则可能产生中间颜色的斑块。斑纹基因（*Ta*，一种能够影响毛发结构的基因）杂合的雌鼠可能具有和其亲本相似类型的皮毛条纹。福尔克纳 [9] 曾报道称杂合子皮毛黑色区域的毛发结构类似于 *Ta* 半合子和纯合子黑色区域的毛发结构，而灰色区域的毛发则具有正常的结构。

因此，这一假说预示着所有性连锁基因小鼠的表型是由局部基因作用决定的，相应的杂合子都呈现嵌合体表型；并且当常染色体基因易位到 X 染色体上时，将会产生类似的效应；当表型不是由局部基因作用决定时，有可能产生各种类型的结果。除非在失活时这种基因作用被限制在具有非常少量细胞的后代中，否则除了极个别的特例外，这些原始细胞将包括两种类型。所以个体表型可能会介于正常型和半合子型之间，或者只要存在任何正常细胞就能够表现出正常的表型，或者可能由于正常细胞和突变细胞的比例不同从而该基因在不同细胞中表达水平不同而导致杂合子表现出不完全的外显率。弯尾基因 *Bn*[10] 可能就属于这种类型，其杂合子有 95% 的外显率和各种水平的基因表达。吉皮基因（*jp*）是一种隐性基因，表明只要存在一些正常细胞就能够表现出正常的表型，但是菲利普斯 [11] 曾报道有一例异常的雌性却显示出吉皮表型。由于该雌性显示出 *Ta* 杂合表型，因而这种动物就不可能是 XO 型的雌性个体；这有可能是一个极个别的特例，恰好所有决定吉皮表型的细胞中正常基因失活。

这样的遗传学证据并不能表明一条 X 染色体的失活具体发生在胚胎发育的哪个阶段。在猫、猴子和人类的胚胎中，最早能在囊胚晚期 [12,13] 的细胞核中发现性染色质。小鼠胚胎中一条 X 染色体在类似阶段失活，这与观察结果相吻合。既然 XO 型的雌性个体通常是有生育能力的，那就没必要假定直至生殖腺形成时，两条 X 染色体还都具有功能。

褐家鼠 [14] 和维儿尼亚负鼠 [15] 中的性染色质也被认为是由一条 X 染色体形成的。如果在所有哺乳动物中都是如此，那么在所有性连锁突变基因杂合的雌性哺乳动物中就都有可能出现像小鼠中一样的现象了。龟纹猫的皮毛颜色就是黑色和黄色这两种纯合子皮毛颜色的嵌合，这正好是符合这一预期的。

（荆玉祥 翻译；陈新文 陈继征 审稿）

Gene Action in the *X*-Chromosome of the Mouse (*Mus musculus* L.)

Mary F. Lyon: Medical Research Council, Radiobiological Research Unit, Harwell, Didcot.

References:

1. Ohno, S., and Hauschka, T. S., *Cancer Res.*, **20**, 541 (1960).
2. Welshons, W. J., and Russell, L. B., *Proc. U. S. Nat. Acad. Sci.*, **45**, 560 (1959).
3. Fraser, A. S., Sobey, S., and Spicer, C. C., *J. Genet.*, **51**, 217 (1953).
4. Lyon, M. F., *J. Hered.*, **51**, 116 (1960).
5. Dickie, M. M., *J. Hered.*, **45**, 158 (1954).
6. Phillips, R. J. S., *Genet. Res.* (in the press).
7. Russell, L. B., and Bangham, J. W., *Genetics*, **44**, 532 (1959).
8. Russell, L. B., and Bangham, J. W., *Genetics*, **45**, 1008 (1960).
9. Falconer, D. S., *Z. indukt. Abstamm. u. Vererblehre*, **85**, 210 (1953).
10. Garber, E. D., *Proc. U.S. Nat. Acad. Sci.*, **38**, 876 (1952).
11. Phillips, R. J. S., *Z. indukt. Abstamm. u. Vererblehre*, **86**, 322 (1954).
12. Austin, C. R., and Amoroso, E. C., *Exp. Cell Res.*, **13**, 419 (1957).
13. Park, W. W., *J. Anat.*, **91**, 369 (1957).
14. Ohno, S., Kaplan, W. D., and Kinosita, R., *Exp. Cell Res.*, **18**, 415 (1959).
15. Ohno, S., Kaplan, W. D., and Kinosita, R., *Exp. Cell Res.*, **19**, 417 (1960).

General Nature of the Genetic Code for Proteins

F. H. C. Crick *et al.*

Editor's Note

Early in the development of molecular biology, there came an urgent need to discover how the sequence of nucleotides in a molecule of DNA specifies the sequence of amino acids in a protein molecule. Francis Crick, the co-discoverer of the structure of DNA, took the lead in this endeavour. By 1965, the code had been completed: some groups of three nucleotides coded for specific amino acids, others had the property of bringing the elongation of a protein chain to a halt.

THERE is now a mass of indirect evidence which suggests that the amino-acid sequence along the polypeptide chain of a protein is determined by the sequence of the bases along some particular part of the nucleic acid of the genetic material. Since there are twenty common amino-acids found throughout Nature, but only four common bases, it has often been surmised that the sequence of the four bases is in some way a code for the sequence of the amino-acids. In this article we report genetic experiments which, together with the work of others, suggest that the genetic code is of the following general type:

(*a*) A group of three bases (or, less likely, a multiple of three bases) codes one amino-acid.

(*b*) The code is not of the overlapping type (see Fig. 1).

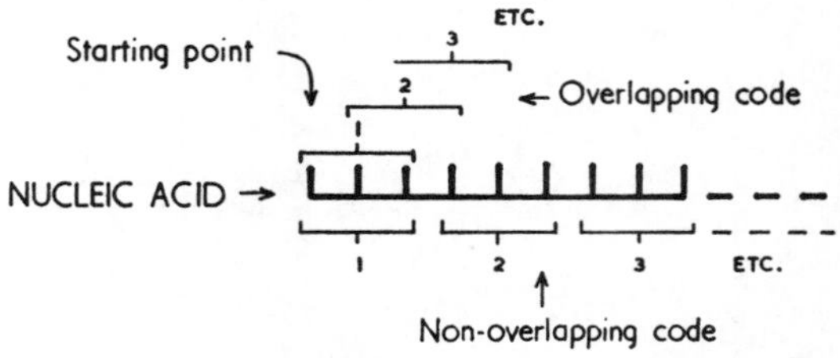

Fig. 1. To show the difference between an overlapping code and a non-overlapping code. The short vertical lines represent the bases of the nucleic acid. The case illustrated is for a triplet code

(*c*) The sequence of the bases is read from a fixed starting point. This determines how the long sequences of bases are to be correctly read off as triplets. There are no special "commas" to show how to select the right triplets. If the starting point is displaced by one base, then the reading into triplets is displaced, and thus becomes incorrect.

蛋白质遗传密码的普遍特征

克里克等

编者按

在分子生物学发展的早期，就出现了一个亟待解决的问题：一种 DNA 分子中的核苷酸序列如何特异决定一种蛋白质分子中的氨基酸序列。DNA 结构的发现者之一弗朗西斯·克里克成为了这一攻坚领域的领头人。到 1965 年，蛋白质密码的破译工作已经全部完成：一些三核苷酸组合能编码特定的氨基酸，另外一些则具有将蛋白质链的延伸过程终止的功能。

现在有大量的间接证据表明，一种蛋白质多肽链的氨基酸序列是由遗传物质核酸的某一特定部分的碱基序列所决定的。虽然自然界普遍存在 20 种常见氨基酸，但只有 4 种常见碱基，因此人们通常推测 4 种碱基的序列以某种方式编码氨基酸序列。本文中，我们将结合其他人的研究成果，报道一些遗传学实验结果，研究表明遗传密码具备以下普遍特征：

(*a*) 三个碱基（或者三的倍数个碱基，这种可能性较小）为一组编码一种氨基酸。

(*b*) 遗传密码是不重叠的（见图 1）。

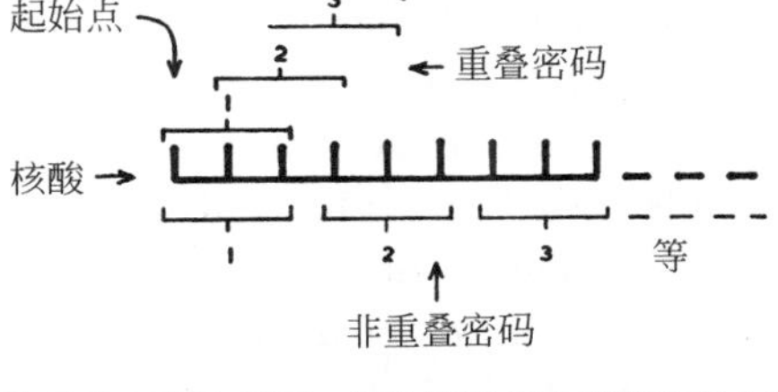

图 1. 显示重叠密码与非重叠密码的差别。短的竖线代表核酸序列中的碱基。本图是基于三联体密码概念而绘制的。

(*c*) 碱基序列是从一个固定的起始点开始被读取的。这决定着一段很长的碱基序列是如何被正确地读取为三联体的。其中并没有特别的“逗号”来提示如何选择正确的三联体。如果起始点出现了一个碱基的错位，那么读出的所有三联体密码就都将发生错位，从而导致整体读码错误。

(*d*) The code is probably "degenerate"; that is, in general, one particular amino-acid can be coded by one of several triplets of bases.

The Reading of the Code

The evidence that the genetic code is not overlapping (see Fig. 1) does not come from our work, but from that of Wittmann[1] and of Tsugita and Fraenkel-Conrat[2] on the mutants of tobacco mosaic virus produced by nitrous acid. In an overlapping triplet code, an alteration to one base will in general change three adjacent amino-acids in the polypeptide chain. Their work on the alterations produced in the protein of the virus show that usually only one amino-acid at a time is changed as a result of treating the ribonucleic acid (RNA) of the virus with nitrous acid. In the rarer cases where two amino-acids are altered (owing presumably to two separate deaminations by the nitrous acid on one piece of RNA), the altered amino-acids are not in adjacent positions in the polypeptide chain.

Brenner[3] had previously shown that, if the code were universal (that is, the same throughout Nature), then all overlapping triplet codes were impossible. Moreover, all the abnormal human haemoglobins studied in detail[4] show only single amino-acid changes. The newer experimental results essentially rule out all simple codes of the overlapping type.

If the code is not overlapping, then there must be some arrangement to show how to select the correct triplets (or quadruplets, or whatever it may be) along the continuous sequence of bases. One obvious suggestion is that, say, every fourth base is a "comma". Another idea is that certain triplets make "sense", whereas others make "nonsense", as in the comma-free codes of Crick, Griffith and Orgel[5]. Alternatively, the correct choice may be made by starting as a fixed point and working along the sequence of bases three (or four, or whatever) at a time. It is this possibility which we now favour.

Experimental Results

Our genetic experiments have been carried out on the *B* cistron of the r_{II} region of the bacteriophage *T*4, which attacks strains of *Escherichia coli*. This is the system so brilliantly exploited by Benzer[6,7]. The r_{II} region consists of two adjacent genes, or "cistrons", called cistron *A* and cistron *B*. The wild-type phage will grow on both *E. coli B* (here called *B*) and on *E. coli K*12(λ) (here called *K*), but a phage which has lost the function of either gene will not grow on *K*. Such a phage produces an *r* plaque on *B*. Many point mutations of the genes are known which behave in this way. Deletions of part of the region are also found. Other mutations, known as "leaky", show partial function; that is, they will grow on *K* but their plaque-type on *B* is not truly wild. We report here our work on the mutant *P* 13 (now re-named *FC* 0) in the *B*1 segment of the *B* cistron. This mutant was originally produced by the action of proflavin[8].

We[9] have previously argued that acridines such as proflavin act as mutagens because they (*d*) 密码可能具有“简并性”，也就是说，通常几种三联体碱基能编码同一种特定氨基酸。

读　码

遗传密码不重叠（见图 1）的证据不是来自我们的工作，而是来自维特曼[1]、次田皓和弗伦克尔–康拉特[2]对亚硝酸诱发的烟草花叶病毒突变体的研究工作。在一个重叠三联体密码中，一个碱基的改变通常将引起多肽链上三个邻近的氨基酸的改变。他们就病毒蛋白质发生改变所开展的工作表明，用亚硝酸处理病毒核糖核酸（RNA）导致的结果是，通常一次只有一种氨基酸被改变。在少数的情况下出现过两种氨基酸被改变的结果（这可能是由于亚硝酸使同一段 RNA 分子中发生了两处独立的脱氨基作用），但被改变的氨基酸并不位于多肽链上的相邻位置。

布伦纳曾指出[3]，如果这样的密码是通用的（即整个自然界都使用同一套密码），那么所有重叠三联体密码是不可能存在的。此外，所有被详细研究过的异常人血红蛋白都只显示出单个氨基酸的变化[4]。这些新近的实验结果基本上排除了重叠密码存在的可能性。

如果密码是不重叠的，那么必然存在某种规则以指示如何沿着连续的碱基序列选择出正确的三联体（或四联体，或其他任何可能的类型）。一种显而易见的设想是，每组第四个碱基都是一个“逗号”；另一种想法是某些三联体是“有义”的，而其他的则是“无义”的，就像克里克、格里菲思和奥格尔[5]提出的无逗号密码那样。或者从某个固定的位点起始沿着碱基序列以每次读取三个（或四个，或任何其他可能的数量）的方式来做出正确选择，我们现在更倾向于这种可能性。

实验结果

我们的遗传实验是在能侵染大肠杆菌菌株的 *T*4 噬菌体 r_{II} 区域的顺反子 *B* 上进行的。这是由本则尔[6,7]巧妙开发的一个的体系。r_{II} 区域由两个相邻的基因或“顺反子”组成，即顺反子 *A* 和顺反子 *B*。野生型噬菌体既可以在大肠杆菌 *B*（以下简称 *B*）上生长，也可以在大肠杆菌 *K*12（λ）（以下简称 *K*）上生长。噬菌体一旦丧失其中任何一个基因的功能就不能在 *K* 菌体上生长了，但这种噬菌体能在 *B* 菌体上产生一个 *r* 型噬菌斑。已知这两个基因的多个点突变都表现出这样的特性。也发现了这一区域的部分缺失。其他一些被称为“渗漏性的”突变则只表现出部分功能，也就是说，它们能在 *K* 菌体上生长，但它们在 *B* 菌体上所产生的噬菌斑类型并不同于真正的野生型。这里将报道我们利用顺反子 *B* 中的 *B*1 片段中的 *P*13 突变体（现被重命名为 *FC* 0）所做的研究工作。这一突变体最初是在二氨基吖啶的作用下产生的[8]。

我们[9]曾指出，二氨基吖啶等吖啶类物质之所以能作为诱变剂，是因为它们能

add or delete a base or bases. The most striking evidence in favour of this is that mutants produced by acridines are seldom "leaky"; they are almost always completely lacking in the function of the gene. Since our note was published, experimental data from two sources have been added to our previous evidence: (1) we have examined a set of 126 r_{II} mutants made with acridine yellow; of these only 6 are leaky (typically about half the mutants made with base analogues are leaky); (2) Streisinger[10] has found that whereas mutants of the lysozyme of phage *T*4 produced by base-analogues are usually leaky, all lysozyme mutants produced by proflavin are negative, that is, the function is completely lacking.

If an acridine mutant is produced by, say, adding a base, it should revert to "wild-type" by deleting a base. Our work on revertants of *FC* 0 shows that is usually reverts not by reversing the original mutation but by producing a second mutation at a nearby point on the genetic map. That is, by a "suppressor" in the same gene. In one case (or possibly two cases) it may have reverted back to true wild, but in at least 18 other cases the "wild type" produced was really a double mutant with a "wild" phenotype. Other workers[11] have found a similar phenomenon with r_{II} mutants, and Jinks[12] has made a detailed analysis of suppressors in the h_{III} gene.

The genetic map of these 18 suppressors of *FC* 0 is shown in Fig. 2, line *a*. It will be seen

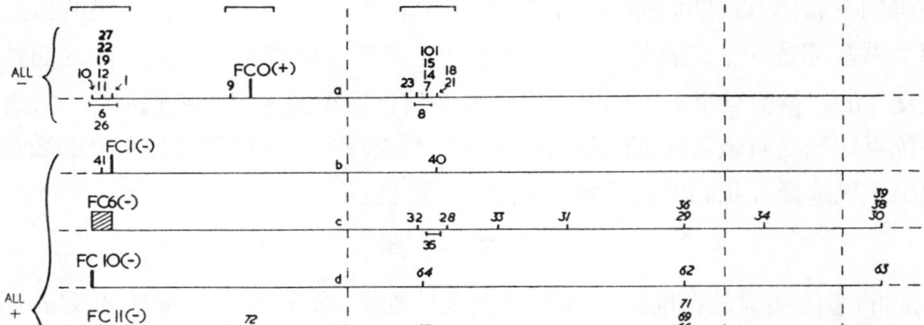

Fig. 2. A tentative map—only very roughly to scale—of the left-hand end of the *B* cistron, showing the position of the *FC* family of mutants. The order of sites within the regions covered by brackets (at the top of the figure) is not known. Mutants in italics have only been located approximately. Each line represents the suppressors picked up from one mutant, namely, that marked on the line in bold figures

增添或缺失一个或多个碱基。支持这个观点的最有力的证据是，吖啶类物质诱导的突变体很少是“渗漏性的”，它们几乎总是导致基因功能的完全丧失。在我们的实验结果发表以后，又有两项实验数据支持我们先前的证据：(1) 我们检测了一组由吖啶黄诱导的 126 种 r_{II} 突变体，其中只有 6 种是渗漏性的（一般来说，由碱基类似物诱导得到的突变体约有一半是渗漏性的）；(2) 史屈辛格[10]发现，尽管由碱基类似物诱导的 *T*4 噬菌体溶菌酶的突变通常都是渗漏性的，但所有由二氨基吖啶诱导产生的溶菌酶突变却都是阴性的，也就是其功能完全丧失了。

如果吖啶诱发的突变体，比如说，是通过增添一个碱基而产生的话，那么缺失一个碱基就应该使其回复为“野生型”。我们关于 *FC* 0 回复突变体的研究工作表明，这通常不是通过回复最初的突变来促成的，而是通过在遗传图谱上原突变位点附近的位置引入第二个突变，换句话说，是通过在同一基因中的一个“抑制子”而起作用的。实验中有一例（或者可能是两例）突变的确回复到了真正的野生型，但至少有 18 例的回复突变产生的“野生型”实际上是表现出“野生型”性状的双突变体。其他研究者[11]在 r_{II} 突变体的研究中也发现了类似的现象，金克斯[12]还对 h_{III} 基因的抑制子做了详细的分析。

这 18 个 *FC* 0 抑制子的遗传图谱如图 2 中的 *a* 行所示。从图中可以看出，虽然

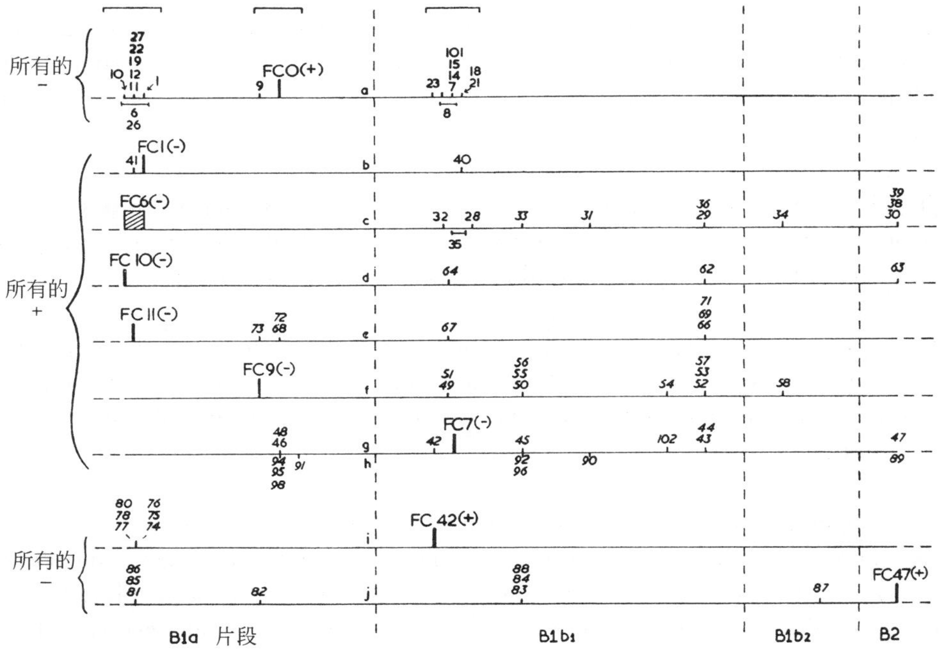

图 2. 顺反子 *B* 左端的初步图谱（只是大致的按比例），图中显示了 *FC* 家族突变的位置。括弧（在图顶部）括起来的区域内的位点的顺序目前并不清楚。斜体表示的突变只是大致的定位。每一行代表一种突变体（用加粗的线做了标记）的一系列抑制子。

that they all fall in the *B*1 segment of the gene, though not all of them are very close to *FC* 0. They scatter over a region about, say, one-tenth the size of the *B* cistron. Not all are at different sites. We have found eight sites in all, but most of them fall into or near two close clusters of sites.

In all cases the suppressor was a non-leaky *r*. That is, it gave an *r* plaque on *B* and would not grown on *K*. This is the phenotype shown by a complete deletion of the gene, and shows that the function is lacking. The only possible exception was one case where the suppressor appeared to back-mutate so fast that we could not study it.

Each suppressor, as we have said, fails to grown on *K*. Reversion of each can therefore be studied by the same procedure used for *FC* 0. In a few cases these mutants apparently revert to the original wild-type, but usually they revert by forming a double mutant. Fig. 2, lines *b-g*, shows the mutants produced as suppressor of these suppressors. Again all these new suppressors are non-leaky *r* mutants, and all map within the *B*1 segment for one site in the *B*2 segment.

Once again we have repeated the process on two of the new suppressors, with the same general results, as shown in Fig. 2, lines *i* and *j*.

All these mutants, except the original *FC* 0, occurred spontaneously. We have, however, produced one set (as suppressors of *FC* 7) using acridine yellow as a mutagen. The spectrum of suppressors we get (see Fig. 2, line *h*) is crudely similar to the spontaneous spectrum, and all the mutants are non-leaky *r*'s. We have also tested a (small) selection of all our mutants and shown that their reversion-rates are increased by acridine yellow.

Thus in all we have about eighty independent *r* mutants, all suppressors of *FC* 0, or suppressors of suppressors, or suppressors of suppressors of suppressors. They all fall within a limited region of the gene and they are all non-leaky *r* mutants.

The double mutants (which contain a mutation plus its suppressor) which plate on *K* have a variety of plaque types on *B*. Some are indistinguishable from wild, some can be distinguished from wild with difficulty, while others are easily distinguishable and produce plaques rather like *r*.

We have checked in a few cases that the phenomenon is quite distinct from "complementation", since the two mutants which separately are phenotypically *r*, and together are wild or pseudo-wild, must be put together in the same piece of genetic material. A simultaneous infection of *K* by the two mutants in separate viruses will not do.

The Explanation in Outline

Our explanation of all these facts is based on the theory set out at the beginning of this

不是所有的抑制子都非常靠近 *FC* 0，但它们都处在该基因的 *B*1 片段上。它们散布在大约为顺反子 *B* 的 1/10 大小的范围内，但并不是所有的都位于不同的位点。我们总共发现了 8 个位点，但大部分突变都处于或紧靠两个相近的位点簇。

在所有这些突变体中，抑制子都是非渗漏性的 *r* 型。这就是说，它们在 *B* 菌体上产生一个 *r* 型噬菌斑，且不能在 *K* 菌体上生长。这是基因完全缺失时的表型，表明相应的功能完全缺失了。不过，唯一可能的例外是，有一个抑制子似乎发生了快得难以对其进行研究的回复突变。

如前所述，每个抑制子都不能在 *K* 菌体上生长。因此可以用研究 *FC*0 突变体相同的步骤来对这里的抑制子的回复突变进行研究。在少数情况下，这些突变体表面上看是回复到了最初的野生型，但通常它们是通过形成双突变体来回复的。图 2 中的 *b*~*g* 行显示的突变体是作为这些抑制子的抑制子。所有这些新的抑制子都是非渗漏性的 *r* 型突变体，并且除了一个突变位点位于 *B*2 片段上之外，所有突变位点都位于 *B*1 片段上。

我们又在两个新的抑制子上重复了上述实验，得到了同样的普遍性结果，如图 2 中的 *i* 行和 *j* 行所示。

除了最初的 *FC* 0 突变体外，其余所有的突变都是自发产生的。不过，我们用吖啶黄作为诱变剂得到了一组突变体（作为 *FC* 7 突变体的抑制子）。我们获得的抑制子中突变位点的分布（见图 2, *h* 行）与自发产生的抑制子中突变位点的分布大致相似，同时所有的突变体也都是非渗漏性的 *r* 型。我们从所有突变体中选出一（小）部分并对其进行了检测，发现在吖啶黄作用下它们的回复突变率提高了。

综上所述，我们总计获得了大约 80 种独立的 *r* 型突变体，它们都是 *FC* 0 的抑制子，或者是抑制子的抑制子，或者是抑制子的抑制子的抑制子。所有的突变位点都分布在基因的某个有限区域内，而且都是非渗漏性的 *r* 型突变体。

在 *K* 菌体上生长的各种双突变体（包含一种突变加上其抑制子）在 *B* 菌体上会产生不同类型的噬菌斑。有的与野生型之间完全无法区分，有的与野生型可以区分但具有一定的难度，而其他一些则很容易区分，并长出非常类似于 *r* 型的噬菌斑。

我们检测了其中的几种回复情况，发现该现象与“互补”现象很不一样，因为两个突变体单独存在时都是 *r* 噬菌斑表型，但合在一起时却表现出野生型或假野生型表型，这里所说的合在一起是指必须被放置在遗传物质的同一片段上。而 *K* 菌株同时被位于不同病毒上的两种突变体感染却是无效的（即不能产生噬菌斑）。

解释概要

我们对于这些现象的解释都基于本文开始时所提出的理论。虽然我们没有直接

article. Although we have no direct evidence that the *B* cistron produces a polypeptide chain (probably through an RNA intermediate), in what follows we shall assume this to be so. To fix ideas, we imagine that the string of nucleotide bases is read, triplet by triplet, from a starting point on the left of the *B* cistron. We now suppose that, for example, the mutant *FC* 0 was produced by the insertion of an additional base in the wild-type sequence. Then this addition of a base at the *FC* 0 site will mean that the reading of all the triplets to the right of *FC* 0 will be shifted along one base, and will therefore be incorrect. Thus the amino-acid sequence of the protein which the *B* cistron is presumed to produce will be completely altered from that point onwards. This explains why the function of the gene is lacking. To simplify the explanation, we now postulate that a suppressor *FC* 0 (for example, *FC* 1) is formed by deleting a base. Thus when the *FC* 1 mutation is present by itself, all triplets to the right of *FC* 1 will be read incorrectly and thus the function will be absent. However, when both mutations are present in the same piece of DNA, as in the pseudo-wild double mutant *FC* (0+1), then although the reading of triplets between *FC* 0 and *FC* 1 will be altered, the original reading will be restored to the rest of the gene. This could explain why such double mutants do not always have a true wild phenotype but are often pseudo-wild, since on our theory a small length of their amino-acid sequence is different from that of the wild-type.

For convenience we have designated our original mutant *FC* 0 by the symbol + (this choice is a pure convention at this stage) which we have so far considered as the addition of a single base. The suppressors of *FC* 0 have therefore been designated −. The suppressors of these suppressors have in the same way been labelled as +, and the suppressors of these last sets have again been labelled − (see Fig. 2).

Double Mutants

We can now ask: What is the character of any double mutant we like to form by putting together in the same gene any pair of mutants from our set of about eighty? Obviously, in some cases we already know the answer, since some combinations of a + with a − were formed in order to isolate the mutants. But, by definition, no pair consisting of one + with another + has been obtained in this way, and there are many combinations of + with − not so far tested.

Now our theory clearly predicts that all combinations of the type + with + (or − with −) should give an *r* phenotype and not plate on *K*. We have put together 14 such pairs of mutants in the cases listed in Table 1 and found this prediction confirmed.

Table 1. Double Mutants having the *r* Phenotype

− With −	+ With +	
FC (1+21)	*FC* (0+58)	*FC* (40+57)
FC (23+21)	*FC* (0+38)	*FC* (40+58)
FC (1+23)	*FC* (0+40)	*FC* (40+55)
FC (1+9)	*FC* (0+55)	*FC* (40+54)
	FC (0+54)	*FC* (40+38)

证据表明顺反子 *B* 编码一条多肽链（可能通过一种 RNA 中间体），但下文中我们将假定事实就是如此。为了确定我们的想法，我们是这样设想的，核苷酸碱基串是从位于顺反子 *B* 左侧的一个起始点开始三个三个地被阅读的。比如，现在我们可以这样推测，突变体 *FC* 0 是通过在野生型序列中插入一个额外的碱基而得到的。那么这个在 *FC* 0 位点插入的额外碱基就会使得所有在 *FC* 0 突变位点右侧的三联体的读取错位一个碱基，从而导致读码错误。因此，原本由顺反子 *B* 编码的蛋白质的氨基酸序列将从这个位点开始被完全改变。这就解释了为什么这个基因突变会导致功能缺失。为了简化说明，我们现在假定 *FC* 0 的抑制子（比如 *FC* 1）是通过缺失一个碱基而产生的。那么当 *FC* 1 的突变单独出现时，所有位于 *FC* 1 突变位点右侧的三联体都将发生读码错误，从而导致基因功能丧失。然而，就像假野生型双突变体 *FC*（0+1）中的情形那样，当这两种突变存在于同一 DNA 片段上时，尽管 *FC* 0 位点和 *FC* 1 位点之间的三联体的读取被改变了，但是这个基因的其余部分的读码将会恢复到最初的正常状态。这就解释了为什么这样的双突变体通常并不是真正的野生型，而是假野生型，因为根据我们的理论，它们的氨基酸序列中有一小段与野生型是不同的。

为了方便起见，我们将最初的突变体 *FC* 0 以“+”（此标记纯属习惯）来表示，我们一直认为该突变是由增添的单个碱基造成的。因此，*FC* 0 的抑制子用“−”来表示。同样地，这些抑制子的抑制子标记为“+”，其抑制子继而又标记为“−”（见图 2）。

双突变体

现在我们可以提出这样的问题：将我们获得的约 80 种突变中的任意一对突变同时置放在同一个基因上所得到的双突变体会有什么样的特性呢？很显然我们已经知道了某些情况下的答案，为了分离得到这些突变体，我们已经得到了一些由一个“+”突变和一个“−”突变组合而成的突变。但是，根据定义，用这种方法并没有得到任何由两个“+”突变组成的双突变对，另外还有许多“+”突变和“−”突变的组合突变尚未被检测。

现在我们的理论清楚地预测到，所有“+”突变和“+”突变（或“−”突变和“−”突变）的组合都应该出现 *r* 噬菌斑表型，并且不能在 *K* 菌体上生长。我们将表 1 列出的实例中的 14 对这样的突变放在一起，结果证实了我们的预测。

表 1. 具有 *r* 噬菌斑表型的双突变体

“−”和“−”的组合	“+”和“+”的组合	
FC (1+21)	*FC* (0+58)	*FC* (40+57)
FC (23+21)	*FC* (0+38)	*FC* (40+58)
FC (1+23)	*FC* (0+40)	*FC* (40+55)
FC (1+9)	*FC* (0+55)	*FC* (40+54)
	FC (0+54)	*FC* (40+38)

At first sight one would expect that all combinations of the type (+ with −) would be wild or pseudo-wild, but the situation is a little more intricate than that, and must be considered more closely. This springs from the obvious fact that if the code is made of triplets, any long sequence of bases can be read correctly in one way, but incorrectly (by starting at the wrong point) in two different ways, depending whether the "reading frame" is shifted one place to the right or one place to the left.

If we symbolize a shift, by one place, of the reading frame in one direction by → and in the opposite direction by ←, then we can establish the convention that our + is always at the head of the arrow, and our − at the tail. This is illustrated in Fig. 3.

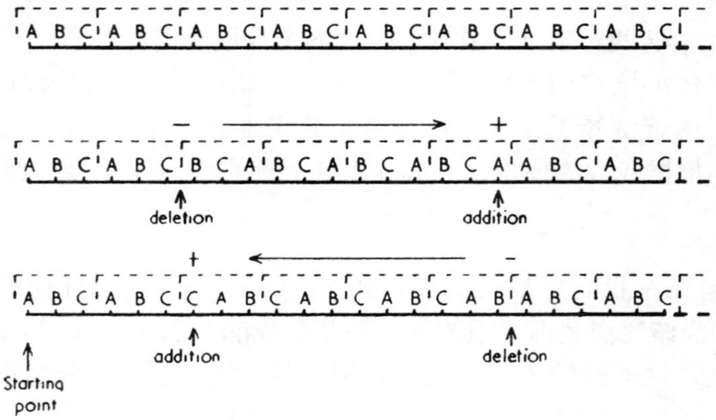

Fig. 3. To show that our convention for arrows is consistent. The letters *A*, *B* and *C* each represent a different base of the nucleic acid. For simplicity a repeating sequence of bases, *ABC*, is shown. (This would code for a polypeptide for which every amino-acid was the same.) A triplet code is assumed. The dotted lines represent the imaginary "reading frame" implying that the sequence is read in sets of three starting on the left

We must now ask: Why do our suppressors not extend over the whole of the gene? The simplest postulate to make is that the shift of the reading frame produces some triplets the reading of which is "unacceptable"; for example, they may be "nonsense", or stand for "end the chain", or be unacceptable in some other way due to the complications of protein structure. This means that a suppressor of, say, *FC* 0 must be within a region such that no "unacceptable" triplet is produced by the shift in the reading frame between *FC* 0 and its suppressor. But, clearly, since for any sequence there are *two* possible misreadings, we might expect that the "unacceptable" triplets produced by a → shift would occur in different places on the map from those produced by a ← shift.

Examination of the spectra of suppressors (in each case putting in the arrows → or ←) suggests that while the → shift is acceptable anywhere within our region (though not outside it) the shift ←, starting from points near *FC* 0, is acceptable over only a more limited stretch. This is shown in Fig. 4. Somewhere in the left part of our region, between

初看起来，人们可能会预期所有的“+”突变和“−”突变的组合都会表现为野生型或假野生型，但实际情况要比这个复杂一些，我们必须进行更加周密的考虑。这源于一个明显的事实，那就是，如果密码是三联体形式的，那么任意长度的一段碱基序列被正确读取的方式都只有一种，但被错误读取（于一个错误的起始点开始）的方式有两种，其“阅读框”或向右移动了一个碱基的位置，或向左移动了一个碱基的位置。

如果我们用“→”来表示阅读框在某处向一个方向移动了，而用“←”来表示阅读框向相反方向移动了，那么我们可以确立这样的约定，“+”总是在箭头的头端，而“−”总是在尾端，如图3所示。

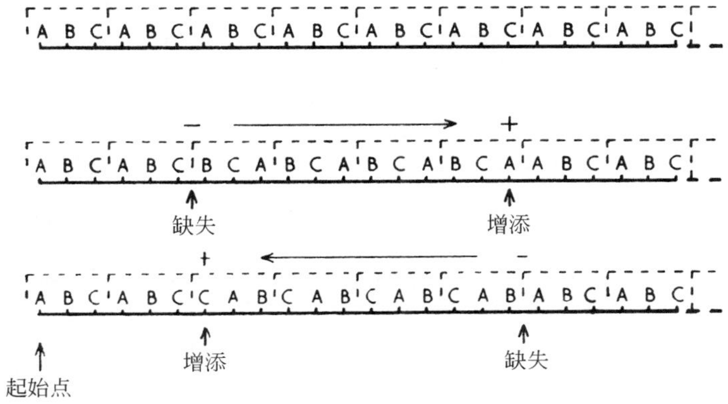

图3. 我们对于箭头意义的约定始终是一致的。字母 *A*、*B* 和 *C* 分别代表一种不同的核酸碱基。为了说明的方便，我们仅仅显示了一种 *ABC* 不断重复的碱基序列（这将编码一条只由一种氨基酸组成的多肽链）。我们假设密码是三联体形式的。虚线代表假想的从序列左端开始每三个一组进行阅读的“阅读框”。

现在我们肯定会提出这样的问题：为什么我们得到的抑制子的突变位点不是遍布在整个基因上？最简单的假设就是，阅读框的移动产生了一些读取时“不能被接受的”三联体密码。比如，它们可能是“无义”的，或者它们代表“链的结束”，再或者由于某些和蛋白质结构复杂性有关的原因而不能被接受。这意味着，一个抑制子，如 *FC* 0 抑制子，发生突变的位点必然位于一定的区域内，使得 *FC* 0 和它的抑制子之间的阅读框的移动不至于产生“不能被接受的”三联体。但很明显的是，既然任意序列都存在**两种**可能的错读，因此我们可以预期的是，由“→”方向的移动和“←”方向的移动产生的“不能被接受的”三联体将会发生在遗传图谱的不同位置上。

对抑制子（每一个实例中都用箭头“→”或“←”标示）分布情况的分析表明，尽管“→”方向的移动在我们关心的基因区域内的任意位置都是可以接受的（尽管在此之外是不行的），那么从 *FC* 0 位点附近开始的“←”方向的移动只会在一个更为有限的片段内可以被接受，如图4所示。当出现“←”方向的移动时，在我们关

FC 0 or *FC* 9 and the *FC* 1 group, there must be one or more unacceptable triplets when a ← shift is made; similarly for the region to the right of the *FC* 21 cluster. Thus we predict that a combination of a + with a − will be wild or pseudo-wild if it involves a → shift, but that such pairs involving a ← shift will be phenotypically *r* if the arrow crosses one or more of the forbidden places, since then an unacceptable triplet will be produced.

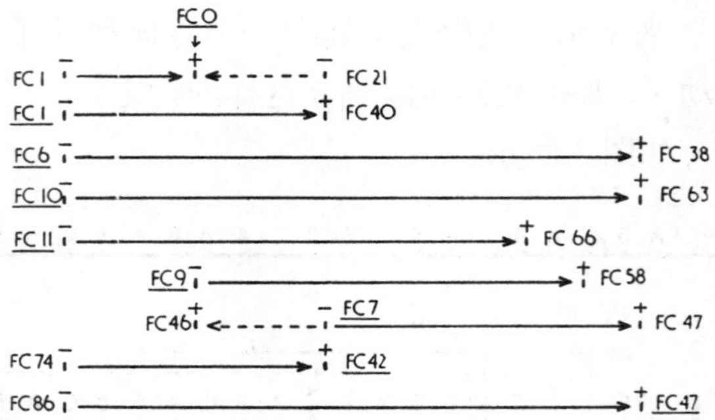

Fig. 4. A simplified version of the genetic map of Fig. 2. Each line corresponds to the suppressor from one mutant, here underlined. The arrows show the range over which suppressors have so far been found, the extreme mutants being named on the map. Arrows to the right are shown solid, arrows to the left dotted

We have tested this prediction in the 28 cases shown in Table 2. We expected 19 or these to be wild, or pseudo-wild, and 9 of them to have the *r* phenotpye. In all cases our prediction was correct. We regard this as a striking confirmation of our theory. It may be of interest that the theory was constructed before these particular experimental results were obtained.

Table 2. Double Mutants of the Type (+ with −)

+ / −	*FC* 41	*FC* 0	*FC* 40	*FC* 42	*FC* 58*	*FC* 63	*FC* 38
FC 1	*W*	*W*	*W*		W		W
FC 86		W	W	W	W	W	
FC 9	*r*	*W*	W	W	*W*		W
FC 82	*r*		W	W	W	W	
FC 21	*r*	*W*			W		W
FC 88	*r*	*r*			W	W	
FC 87	*r*	*r*	*r*	*r*			W

W, wild or pseudo-wild phenotype; *W*, wild or pseudo-wild combination used to isolate the suppressor; *r*, *r* phenotype.
* Double mutants formed with *FC* 58 (or with *FC* 34) give sharp plaques on *K*.

心区域左侧的某些位置，也就是在 *FC* 0 或 *FC* 9 位点与 *FC* 1 位点群之间，肯定会出现一个或更多个不能被接受的三联体。*FC* 21 位点簇右侧的区域也存在类似的情况。因此我们预计，如果一对“＋”突变和“－”突变的组合只涉及“→”方向的移动，就会是野生型或假野生型；而如果这种突变的组合只涉及一个“←”方向的移动并且箭头会跨过一个或更多个禁止区域的话，组合突变的结果将是 *r* 噬菌斑表型，因为那样会产生一个不能被接受的三联体。

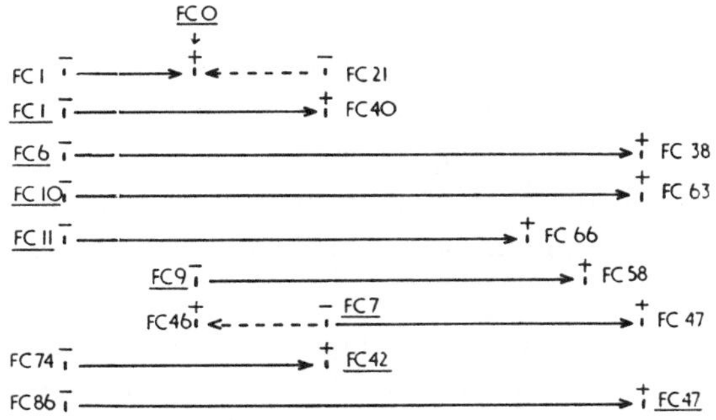

图 4. 图 2 所示遗传图谱的简化版。每一行对应由一种突变体（用下划线标记）产生的抑制子。箭头显示了到目前为止发现的抑制子的跨度范围，两端的突变体的名称在图中都有标注。向右的箭头用实线表示，向左的箭头用虚线表示。

我们在表 2 列出的 28 种情况下对这个预测进行了检验。我们预期其中 19 个会是野生型或假野生型，9 个会是 *r* 表型。结果表明，所有情况都与我们的预测完全一致。我们认为，这样的结果是对我们理论的有力验证。也许会让很多人感兴趣的是，我们的理论在这些实验结果获得之前就提出了。

表 2.“＋”和“–”组合类型的双突变体

＋ / –	*FC* 41	*FC* 0	*FC* 40	*FC* 42	*FC* 58*	*FC* 63	*FC* 38
FC 1	*W*	*W*	*W*		W		W
FC 86		W	W	W	W	W	
FC 9	*r*	*W*	W	W	*W*		W
FC 82	*r*		W	W	W	W	
FC 21	*r*	*W*			W		W
FC 88	*r*	*r*			W	W	
FC 87	*r*	*r*	*r*	*r*			W

W 代表野生型或假野生型表型；*W* 代表用于分离抑制子的野生型或假野生型组合；*r* 代表 *r* 表型。
* 由 *FC* 58（或 *FC* 34）产生的双突变在 *K* 菌体上会产生明显的噬菌斑。

Rigorous Statement of the Theory

So far we have spoken as if the evidence supported a triplet code, but this was simply for illustration. Exactly the same results would be obtained if the code operated with groups of, say, 5 bases. Moreover, our symbols + and − must not be taken to mean literally the addition or subtraction of a single base.

It is easy to see that our symbolism is more exactly as follows:

$$+ \text{ represents } + m, \text{ modulo } n$$
$$- \text{ represents } - m, \text{ modulo } n$$

where n (a positive integer) is the coding ratio (that is, the number of bases with code one amino-acid) and m is any integral number of bases, positive or negative.

It can also be seen that our choice of reading direction is arbitrary, and that the same results (to a first approximation) would be obtained in whichever direction the genetic material was read, that is, whether the starting point is on the right or the left of the gene, as conventionally drawn.

Triple Mutants and the Coding Ratio

The somewhat abstract description given above is necessary for generality, but fortunately we have convincing evidence that the coding ratio is in fact 3 or a multiple of 3.

This we have obtained by constructing triple mutants of the form (+ with + with +) or (− with − with −). One must be careful not to make shifts across the "unacceptable" regions for the ← shifts, but these we can avoid by a proper choice of mutants.

We have so far examined the six cases listed in Table 3 and in all cases the triples are wild or pseudo-wild.

Table 3. Triple Mutants having a Wild or Pseudo-wild Phenotype

FC (0 + 40 +38)
FC (0 + 40 +58)
FC (0 + 40 +57)
FC (0 + 40 +54)
FC (0 + 40 +55)
FC (1 + 21 +23)

The rather striking nature of this result can be seen by considering one of them, for example, the triple (*FC* 0 with *FC* 40 with *FC* 38). These three mutants are, by themselves, all of like type (+). We can say this not merely from the way in which they were obtained, but because each of them, when combined with our mutant *FC* 9(−),

理论的严格表述

到目前为止，我们好像是在实验证据支持三联体密码的前提下描述的，但这实际上仅仅是为了论述的方便。如果密码是其他形式的，比如说 5 个碱基一组，那么我们也将得到完全一样的结果。另外，我们的符号“+”和“−”不应该从字面上理解为一个单一碱基的增加或减少。

显然，如下表述才能更准确地表示我们的符号系统的意义：

“+”代表 $+m$，以 n 为模

“−”代表 $-m$，以 n 为模

其中，n（一个正整数）是编码比率（即编码一个氨基酸的碱基数目），而 m 代表任意整数个碱基，可正可负。

另外也可以看出，我们对阅读方向的选择带有随意性，遗传物质无论从哪一个方向被阅读，也就是说无论起始点是在基因的右边还是左边（即按照习惯所绘出的图示那样），我们得到的结果将都是相同的（大致近似的）。

三突变体和编码比率

上述略显抽象的描述对于讨论问题的普遍性是必要的，但幸运的是，我们有令人信服的证据表明编码比率确实是 3 或 3 的倍数。

我们是通过构建三个“+”组合或三个“−”组合的三突变体得到这样的结论的。实验中必须小心地避让“←”方向的移位越过“不能被接受的”区域，但是我们可以通过对突变体进行适当选择来避免这类情况。

到目前为止，我们已经检测了表 3 列出的 6 种情况，所有这些三突变体都是野生型或假野生型。

表 3. 三突变体都有野生型或假野生型表型

FC (0 + 40 +38)

FC (0 + 40 +58)

FC (0 + 40 +57)

FC (0 + 40 +54)

FC (0 + 40 +55)

FC (1 + 21 +23)

我们得到的结果十分令人振奋，下面就以其中一个三突变体（*FC* 0 和 *FC* 40 和 *FC* 38）为例来说明。这个三突变体本身都属于相似的类型（+）。我们这么说不只是基于这些突变体被获得的方式，而且是因为这三种突变中的任何一个和 *FC* 9(−) 组合在一起时都表现为野生型或假野生型。然而，这三种突变不论是单独存在还是

gives the wild, or pseudo-wild phenotype. However, either singly or together in pairs they have an *r* phenotype, and will not grow on *K*. That is, the function of the gene is absent. Nevertheless, the combination of all three in the same gene partly restores the function and produces a pseudo-wild phage which grows on *K*.

This is exactly what one would expect, in favourable cases, if the coding ratio were 3 or a multiple of 3.

Our ability to find the coding ratio thus depends on the fact that, in at least one of our composite mutants which are "wild", at least one amino-acid must have been added to or deleted from the polypeptide chain without disturbing the function of the gene-product too greatly.

This is a very fortunate situation. The fact that we can make these changes and can study so large a region probably comes about because this part of the protein is not essential for its function. That this is so has already been suggested by Champe and Benzer[18] in their work on complementation in the r_{II} region. By a special test (combined infection on *K*, followed by plating on *B*) it is possible to examine the function of the *A* cistron and the *B* cistron separately. A particular deletion, 1589 (see Fig. 5) covers the right-hand end of the *A* cistron and part of the left-hand end of the *B* cistron. Although 1589 abolished the *A* function, they showed that it allows the *B* function to be expressed to a considerable extent. The region of the *B* cistron deleted by 1589 is that into which all our *FC* mutants fall.

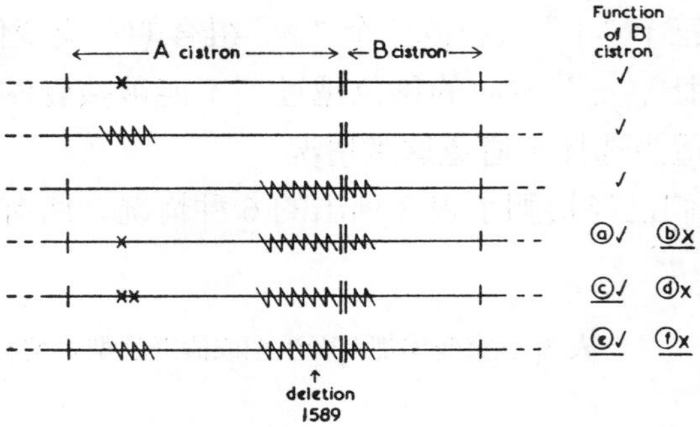

Fig. 5. Summary of the results with deletion 1589. The first two lines show that without 1589 a mutation or a deletion in the *A* cistron does not prevent the *B* cistron from functioning. Deletion 1589 (line 3) also allows the *B* cistron to function. The other cases, in some of which an alteration in the *A* cistron prevents the function of the *B* cistron (when 1589 is also present), are discussed in the text. They have been labelled (*a*), (*b*), etc., for convenience of reference, although cases (*a*) and (*d*) are not discussed in the paper. √ implies function; × implies no function

Joining two Genes Together

We have used this deletion to re-inforce our idea that the sequence is read in groups from a fixed starting point. Normally, an alteration confined to the *A* cistron (be it a deletion,

成对存在时都表现出 *r* 表型，并且不能在 *K* 菌体上生长，这就是说，基因的功能缺失了。然而，当这三种突变同时出现在同一个基因中时却能够部分地恢复该基因的功能，从而产生能在 *K* 菌体上生长的假野生型噬菌体。

这正是编码比率为 3 或 3 的倍数时，我们预期会出现的结果。

因此我们揭示编码比率的能力有赖于如下事实：至少在我们获得的一种复合“野生型”突变体中，在多肽链中增添或缺失至少一个氨基酸不会很大程度地干扰基因产物的功能。

这是一种非常幸运的情形。我们之所以能制备出这一系列的突变并研究如此大的一个基因区域，可能是因为该蛋白质的这一部分对于其功能而言是非必需的。钱普和本则尔[18]在研究 r_{II} 区域内的互补现象时就曾提出过这种观点。通过一种特别的检测方法（联合侵染 *K* 菌株后再涂布到 *B* 菌株的菌体上），顺反子 *A* 和顺反子 *B* 的功能就能够被分别检测。一种特殊的缺失突变体 1589（见图 5），它覆盖了顺反子 *A* 的右端以及顺反子 *B* 左端的部分序列。尽管 1589 突变彻底破坏了顺反子 *A* 的功能，但它却允许顺反子 *B* 的功能在一定程度上得以表达。顺反子 *B* 中因为 1589 突变而缺失的区域处于我们所获得的所有 *FC* 突变分布的位置上。

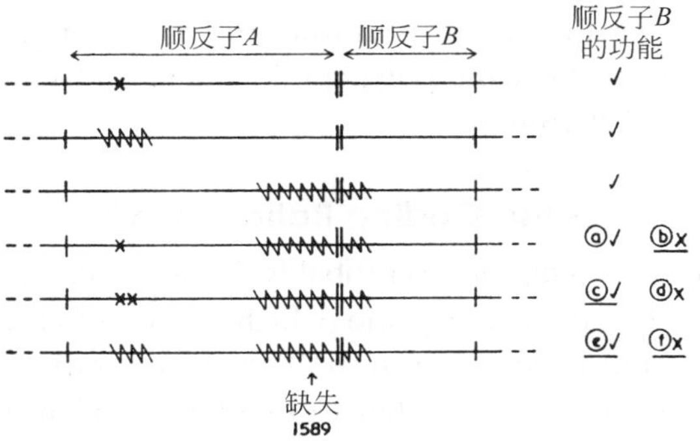

图 5. 1589 缺失实验结果的汇总。前两行显示，在没有发生 1589 缺失时顺反子 *A* 上的突变或缺失并不阻止顺反子 *B* 的功能。1589 缺失（第 3 行）发生时，顺反子 *B* 的功能仍能发挥。其他一些案例在正文中进行了讨论，在部分的这些案例中，顺反子 *A* 的变化（当 1589 缺失也存在的情况下）会阻止顺反子 *B* 的功能。为了论述中引用的方便，这些案例被标记为 (*a*)、(*b*) 等，虽然案例 (*a*) 和 (*d*) 并没有在本文中进行讨论。✓代表功能正常，× 代表功能丧失。

将两个基因连接在一起

我们使用的这一缺失突变强化了我们提出的序列是从一个固定的起始点按碱基组被读取的概念。正常情况下，一个局限于顺反子 *A* 区域内的碱基变化（可以是一

an acridine mutant, or any other mutant) does not prevent the expression of the *B* cistron. Conversely, no alteration within the *B* cistron prevents the function of the *A* cistron. This implies that there may be a region between the two cistrons which separates them and allows their functions to be expressed individually.

We argued that the deletion 1589 will have lost this separating region and that therefore the two (partly damaged) cistrons should have been joined together. Experiments show this to be the case, for now an alteration to the left-hand end of the *A* cistron, if combined with deletion 1589, can prevent the *B* function from appearing. This is shown in Fig. 5. Either the mutant *P*43 or *X*142 (both of which revert strongly with acridines) will prevent the *B* function when the two cistrons are joined, although both of these mutants are in the *A* cistron. This is also true of *X*142 *S*1, a suppressor of *X*142 (Fig. 5, case *b*). However, the double mutant (*X*142 with *X*142 *S*1), of the type (+ with −), which by itself is pseudo-wild, still has the *B* function when combined with 1589 (Fig. 5, case *c*). We have also tested in this way the 10 deletions listed by Benzer[7], which fall wholely to the left of 1589. Of these, three (386, 168 and 221) prevent the *B* function (Fig. 5, case *f*), whereas the other seven show it (Fig. 5, case *e*). We surmise that each of these seven has lost a number of bases which is a multiple of 3. There are theoretical reasons for expecting that deletions may not be random in length, but will more often have lost a number of bases equal to an integral multiple of the coding ratio.

It would not surprise us if it were eventually shown that deletion 1589 produces a protein which consists of part of the protein from the *A* cistron and part of that from the *B* cistron, joined together in the same polypeptide chain, and having to some extent the function of the undamaged *B* protein.

Is the Coding Ratio 3 or 6?

It remains to show that the coding ratio is probably 3, rather than a multiple of 3. Previous rather rough extimates[10,14] of the coding ratio (which are admittedly very unreliable) might suggest that the coding ratio is not far from 6. This would imply, on our theory, that the alteration in *FC* 0 was not to one base, but to two bases (or, more correctly, to an even number of bases).

We have some additional evidence which suggests that this is unlikely. First, in our set of 126 mutants produced by acridine yellow (referred to earlier) we have four independent mutants which fall at or close to the *FC* 9 site. By a suitable choice of partners, we have been able to show that two are + and two are −. Secondly, we have two mutants (*X*146 and *X*225), produced by hydrazine[15], which fall on or near the site *FC* 30. These we have been able to show are both of type −.

Thus unless both acridines and hydrazine usually delete (or add) an even number of bases, this evidence supports a coding ratio of 3. However, as the action of these mutagens is not

个碱基的缺失、一种吖啶引起的突变或者是其他任何突变）都不会阻止顺反子 *B* 功能的发挥。相反，在顺反子 *B* 区域内没有任何碱基变化会阻止顺反子 *A* 发挥其功能。这意味着在这两个顺反子之间可能存在一个区域，它将两个顺反子各自分开，并使两个顺反子的功能相互独立地发挥。

我们认为，1589 缺失突变会导致这个分隔区域的丢失，因此两个顺反子（部分残缺的）就应该被连在一起。实验结果表明情况确实如此，因为如果 1589 缺失和顺反子 *A* 左端的碱基变化一起发生的话，那么能够阻止顺反子 *B* 功能的出现，这一现象如图 5 所示。当两个顺反子连在一起时，无论是 *P*43 突变还是 *X*142 突变（二者都能被吖啶强烈地诱导发生回复突变）都会阻止顺反子 *B* 发挥其功能，尽管这两种突变都是发生在顺反子 *A* 区域内。同样的情况也出现在 *X*142 突变体的抑制子 *X*142 *S*1 中（见图 5 中的案例 *b*）。但是由一个“+”和“－”组合而成的双突变体（如 *X*142 和 *X*142 *S*1）本身是假野生型，与 1589 缺失一起发生时仍然能表现出顺反子 *B* 的功能（见图 5 中的案例 *c*）。我们用同样的方式也检测了本则尔列出的 10 种缺失突变体 [7]，这些突变都发生在 1589 缺失的左侧。在这些突变体中，有 3 种突变（386、168 和 221）会阻止顺反子 *B* 的功能（见图 5 中的案例 *f*），而另外 7 种突变中仍然能表现出顺反子 *B* 的功能（见图 5 中的案例 *e*）。我们猜测这 7 种突变体中每一种丢失的碱基数都是 3 的倍数。之所以预期缺失的碱基数可能不是随机的，而更经常的是丢失的碱基数等于编码比率的整数倍，是有理论依据的。

如果最终的结果表明 1589 缺失会产生一种蛋白质，其中的一部分由顺反子 *A* 编码，另一部分由顺反子 *B* 编码，它们连接在同一条多肽链上而且在某种程度上还具有未被损坏的 *B* 蛋白的功能，我们是不会吃惊的。

编码比率是 3 还是 6？

我们还需要说明为什么编码比率可能是 3，而不是 3 的倍数。以前对于编码比率的粗略估计 [10,14]（被认为是非常不可靠的）提示编码比率有可能接近 6。这就意味着，就我们的理论而言，*FC* 0 中发生变化的可能不是一个碱基，而是两个碱基（或者更确切地说是偶数个碱基）。

我们有更多的证据表明这是不太可能的。首先，在我们获得的一组由吖啶黄诱导产生的 126 个突变中，有 4 个是相互独立的突变，发生在 *FC* 9 位点或其附近的位点。通过配对检测，我们发现其中两个属于“＋”类，两个属于“－”类。其次，我们还获得了两种由肼诱导产生的突变（*X*146 和 *X*225）[15]，这两种突变发生在 *FC* 30 位点或其附近位点。我们发现它们都属于“－”类型。

因此，除非吖啶和肼通常都缺失（或增添）偶数个碱基，否则这个证据就支持编码比率为 3 结论。不过，因为我们对这些诱变剂的具体作用机理还不太清楚，因

understood in detail, we cannot be certain that the coding ratio is not 6, although 3 seems more likely.

We have preliminary results which show that other acridine mutants often revert by means of close suppressors, but it is too sketchy to report here. A tentative map of some suppressors of *P* 83, a mutant at the other end of the *B* cistron, in segment *B* 9*a*, is shown in Fig. 6. They occur within a shorter region than the suppressors of *FC* 0, covering a distance of about one-twentieth of the *B* cistron. The double mutant *WT* (2+5) has the *r* phenotype, as expected.

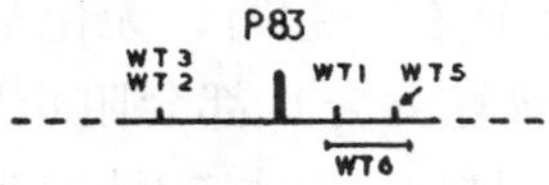

Fig. 6. Genetic map of *P* 83 and its suppressors, *WT* 1, etc. The region falls within segment *B* 9*a* near the right-hand end of the *B* cistron. It is not yet known which way round the map is in relation to the other figures

Is the Code Degenerate?

If the code is a triplet code, there are 64 (4×4×4) possible triplets. Our results suggest that it is unlikely that only 20 of these represent the 20 amino-acids and that the remaining 44 are nonsense. If this were the case, the region over which suppressors of the *FC* 0 family occur (perhaps a quarter of the *B* cistron) should be very much smaller than we observe, since a shift of frame should then, by chance, produce a nonsense reading at a much closer distance. This argument depends on the size of the protein which we have assumed the *B* cistron to produce. We do not know this, but the length of the cistron suggests that the protein may contain about 200 amino-acids. Thus the code is probably "degenerate", that is, in general more than one triplet codes for each amino-acid. It is well known that if this were so, one could also account for the major dilemma of the coding problem, namely, that while the base composition of the DNA can be very different in different micro-organisms, the amino-acid composition of their proteins only changes by a moderate amount[16]. However, exactly how many triplets code amino-acids and how many have other functions we are unable to say.

Future Developments

Our theory leads to one very clear prediction. Suppose one could examine the amino-acid sequence of the "pseudo-wild" protein produced by one of our double mutants of the (+ with −) type. Conventional theory suggests that since the gene is only altered in two places, only two amino-acids would be changed. Our theory, on the other hand, predicts that a string of amino-acids would be altered, covering the region of the polypeptide chain corresponding to the region on the gene between the two mutants. A good protein on which to test this hypothesis is the lysozyme of the phage, at present being studied chemically be Dreyer[17] and genetically by Streisinger[10].

At the recent Biochemical Congress at Moscow, the audience of Symposium I was

此我们还不能肯定地说编码比率不是 6，虽然看起来更可能是 3。

我们有一些初步的结果表明，其他由吖啶诱发的突变经常是通过邻近位点的抑制子回复的，但是这些结果还太粗略不适合在这里报道。图 6 显示了 *P* 83 突变（这一突变发生在顺反子 *B* 的另一端，*B* 9*a* 片段内）的一些抑制子分布的初步图谱。可以看出，它们分布在比 *FC* 0 的抑制子更窄的区域内，大约占顺反子 *B* 的 1/20。正如预期的那样，双突变体 *WT*（2+5）呈现出 *r* 表型。

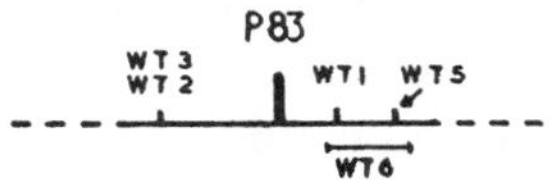

图 6. *P* 83 突变及其抑制子（*WT* 1 等）的遗传图谱。此区域位于顺反子 *B* 右端附近的 *B* 9*a* 片段中。此图谱与文中的其他各图的位置关系目前还不清楚。

密码是简并的吗？

如果遗传密码为三联体密码的话，那么就会有 64（4×4×4）种可能的三联体。我们的结果表明，不太可能只是其中 20 种三联体密码编码 20 种氨基酸，而剩余的 44 种三联体都是无义的。如果情况真是如此，那么 *FC* 0 家族的抑制子分布的区域（可能为顺反子 *B* 的 1/4）应该比我们观察到的要小得多，因为阅读框的移动可能会在更近的距离内产生一个无义读取。这个争论与我们假设的顺反子 *B* 产生的蛋白质的大小有关。但我们并不知道所产生的蛋白质的具体长度，不过顺反子 *B* 的长度表明这种蛋白质可能包含有大约 200 个氨基酸。因此，密码子可能是“简并的”，换句话说，通常而言，一种氨基酸能被不止一种的三联体所编码。众所周知，如果情况真是这样，我们也就能解释编码问题中的另一个主要难题了，即为什么不同微生物的 DNA 碱基组成差异很大，而它们的蛋白质的氨基酸组成却只有中等程度的差异 [16]。然而，具体有多少个三联体密码是编码氨基酸的，多少个具有其他功能，我们现在还无法说清楚。

未来的发展

我们的理论引出了一个非常清晰的预测。假设我们可以检测由“+”和“−”组合的双突变体中的一种产生的“假野生型”蛋白质的氨基酸序列。根据传统理论，既然该基因中只在两个位置发生了改变，那么应该只有两个氨基酸会发生改变。另一方面，我们的理论预测，两个突变位点之间的基因区域对应的多肽链区域上的一连串氨基酸都会发生改变。噬菌体的溶菌酶是验证这个假设的一种很好的蛋白质，目前德雷尔正从化学角度 [17]、史屈辛格正从遗传学角度 [10] 对此展开研究。

在最近一次于莫斯科召开的国际生物化学大会上，论坛 I 的听众都被尼伦伯格

startled by the announcement of Nirenberg that he and Matthaei[18] had produced polyphenylalanine (that is, a polypeptide all the residues of which are phenylalanine) by adding polyuridylic acid (that is, an RNA the bases of which are all uracil) to a cell-free system which can synthesize protein. This implies that a sequence of uracils codes for phenylalanine, and our work suggests that it is probably a triplet of uracils.

It is possible by various devices, either chemical or enzymatic, to synthesize polyribonucleotides with defined or partly defined sequences. If these, too, will produce specific polypeptides, the coding problem is wide open for experimental attack, and in fact many laboratories, including our own, are already working on the problem. If the coding ratio is indeed 3, as our results suggest, and if the code is the same throughout Nature, then the genetic code may well be solved within a year.

We thank Dr. Alice Orgel for certain mutants and for the use of data from her thesis, Dr. Leslie Orgel for many useful discussions, and Dr. Seymour Benzer for supplying us with certain deletions. We are particularly grateful to Prof. C. F. A. Pantin for allowing us to use a room in the Zoological Museum, Cambridge, in which the bulk of this work was done.

(**192**, 1227-1232; 1961)

F. H. C. Crick, F.R.S., Leslie Barnett, S. Brenner and R. J. Watts-Tobin: Medical Research Council Unit for Molecular Biology, Cavendish Laboratory, Cambridge.

References:

1. Wittman, H. G., Symp. 1, Fifth Intern. Cong. Biochem., 1961, for refs. (in the press).
2. Tsugita, A., and Fraenkel-Conrat, H., *Proc. U.S. Nat. Acad. Sci.*, **46**, 636 (1960); *J. Mol. Biol.* (in the press).
3. Brenner, S., *Proc. U.S. Nat. Acad. Sci.*, **43**, 687 (1957).
4. For refs. See Watson, H. C., and Kendrew, J. C., *Nature*, **190**, 670 (1961).
5. Crick, F. H. C., Griffith, J. S., and Orgel, L. E., *Proc. U.S. Nat. Acad. Sci.*, **43**, 416 (1957).
6. Benzer, S., *Proc. U.S. Nat. Acad. Sci.*, **45**, 1607 (1959), for refs. to earlier papers.
7. Benzer, S., *Proc. U.S. Nat. Acad. Sci.*, **47**, 403 (1961); see his Fig. 3.
8. Brenner, S., Benzer, S., and Barnett, L., *Nature*, **182**, 983 (1958).
9. Brenner, S., Barnett, L., Crick, F. H. C., and Orgel, A., *J. Mol. Biol.*, **3**, 121 (1961).
10. Streisinger, G. (personal communication and in the press).
11. Feynman, R. P.; Benzer, S.; Freese, E. (all personal communications).
12. Jinks, J. L., *Heredity*, **16**, 153, 241 (1961).
13. Champe, S., and Benzer, S. (personal communication and in preparation).
14. Jacob, F., and Wollman, E. L., *Sexuality and the Genetics of Bacteria* (Academic Press, New York, 1961). Levinthal, C. (personal communication).
15. Orgel, A., and Brenner, S. (in preparation).
16. Sueoka, N., *Cold Spring Harb. Symp. Quant. Biol.* (in the press).
17. Dreyer, W. J., Symp. 1, Fifth Intern. Cong. Biochem., 1961 (in the press).
18. Nirenberg, M. W., and Matthaei, J. H., *Proc. U.S. Nat. Acad. Sci.*, **47**, 1588 (1961).

的言论所震惊，他说他和马太[18]已经通过向一个能合成蛋白质的无细胞系统注入多聚尿苷酸（也就是所有碱基都是尿嘧啶的RNA）而制造出了多聚苯丙氨酸（就是说组成这种多肽链的氨基酸残基都是苯丙氨酸）。这意味着，一串尿苷酸序列编码一个苯丙氨酸，而我们的工作表明很可能是三个尿苷酸编码一个苯丙氨酸。

通过各种化学或酶学的方法，人们已经能够合成序列完全确定或部分确定的多聚核糖核苷酸。如果这些也能用于产生具有特定序列的多肽，那么编码问题就可能可以通过实验攻克了，事实上包括我们自己在内的很多实验室都已经开始研究这个问题了。如果像我们结果所表明的那样，编码比率确实是3，并且在整个自然界这一套密码都相同的话，那么遗传密码问题可能在一年内就会得到解决。

我们向艾丽斯·奥格尔博士为我们提供了某些突变体，并让我们使用她学位论文中的数据表示感谢，感谢莱斯利·奥格尔博士与我们进行了很有益的讨论，感谢西莫尔·本则尔博士为我们提供某些缺失突变。此外我们还要特别感谢潘廷教授允许我们使用位于剑桥的动物博物馆的房间，本研究的大部分工作都是在那里完成的。

（杜丽 翻译；吕增益 审稿）

Chemical Difference between Normal Human Haemoglobin and Haemoglobin-I

M. Murayama

Editor's Note

Haemoglobin's structure was, by this time, well established—the adult red-blood-cell protein contains two identical α polypeptide chains and two identical β chains. And amino-acid substitutions in the polypeptide chains had been shown to produce disease-causing variants. In particular, biologist Vernon M. Ingram had shown that that the abnormal haemoglobin I molecule differs from its normal adult counterpart because it contains the amino acid tryptophan at a particular site on its α chain. Here Makio Murayama from the National Institutes of Health, Bethesda, Maryland, refines the difference further, spelling out the chemical difference between normal human haemoglobin and haemoglobin I.

INGRAM and I have reported that a specific colour reaction on a "fingerprint" indicated that the tryptic peptide 23 of haemoglobin-I (Hb-I) contains tryptophan whereas the corresponding one in the normal haemoglobin (Hb-A) does not. Ingram reported that the peptide is in the α-chain of the molecule[2]. Hill and Konigsberg[3] found that there is only one tryptophan residue in the α-chain of Hb-A; it is in a pentapeptide with valyl as the NH_2-terminal and lysyl as the COOH-terminal residues. I wish to report that it is the lysyl residue of the pentapeptide which is exchanged with aspartyl in the genetic alteration of Hb-I. It is now known that the pentapeptide is the third tryptic peptide from the NH_2-terminal end of the α-chain[4,5] and that the interchange of lysyl for aspartyl takes place at the 16th from the NH_2-terminus.

The soluble peptides were prepared from chromatographically purified Hb-A and Hb-I as previously described[1]. One-dimensional electrophoresis was adequate for the present investigation for the examination and isolation of soluble peptides. The tryptophan-containing peptides were easily located by fluorescence under an ultra-violet lamp.

Results indicate that there were three tryptophan-positive peptides in both haemoglobins as shown in Fig. 1. The tryptophan-positive peptide which migrated the fastest at *p*H 6.4 towards the cathode in Hb-A vanished in Hb-I. (In our previous publication, Fig. 2, 4 tryptophan-positive peptides were shown for Hb-I; this is now known to be due to a trace of Hb-A present as a contaminant.) As it was previously reported the peptide 23 of Hb-I moved more rapidly towards the anode than the normal peptide. The peptide 23 of Hb-I contained tryptophan and an aspartyl residue (the latter accounted for its greater mobility towards the anode), whereas the corresponding peptide 23 of Hb-A did not.

正常的人血红蛋白和血红蛋白I之间的化学差异

村山

编者按

目前，血红蛋白的结构已经确立——成人红细胞血红蛋白包含两条相同的α多肽链和两条相同的β多肽链。已知多肽链中的氨基酸替换会产生致病的变异体。特别是生物学家弗农·英格拉姆曾指出，异常的血红蛋白I分子不同于正常成人的血红蛋白，是由于在其α链的一个特定位点上包含色氨酸。在本文中，来自于马里兰州贝塞斯达国立卫生研究院的村山氏进一步细化了两者的不同，阐释了正常的人血红蛋白和血红蛋白I之间的化学差异。

英格拉姆和我已经报道过在“指纹图谱”上的一个特异性显色反应，该结果表明：血红蛋白I经胰蛋白酶酶解后产生的第23条肽段上包含色氨酸，而在正常血红蛋白（血红蛋白A）的相应肽段上却没有。英格拉姆曾报道这条肽段来自血红蛋白分子的α链[2]。希尔和柯尼希斯贝格[3]发现，在血红蛋白A分子的α链上只有一个色氨酸残基。并且这一色氨酸残基位于一条氨基末端为缬氨酸残基而羧基端为赖氨酸残基的五肽上。这里我要报道的是，血红蛋白I的遗传改变正是由这条五肽中的赖氨酸残基被天冬氨酸残基替换引起的。现在已经知道这条五肽是血红蛋白分子被胰蛋白酶酶解后从α链[4,5]氨基末端算起的第3条肽段，而赖氨酸残基被天冬氨酸残基替换发生在从氨基端算起的第16位上。

按之前所述的方法[1]，采用层析法纯化的血红蛋白A和血红蛋白I来制备可溶性肽段。本研究中检测和分离各种可溶性肽段采用的是单向电泳的方法。采用紫外灯下观察荧光的方法可以很容易地对含色氨酸的肽段进行定位。

结果如图1所示，在两种血红蛋白中都发现了3条含色氨酸残基的肽段。在pH值为6.4时向负极迁移最快的含色氨酸的肽段只存在于血红蛋白A中，而在血红蛋白I中这条肽段消失了。（在我们以前发表的文章中，如图2所示，在血红蛋白I中有4条含色氨酸的肽段，现在知道这是由于样品中存在血红蛋白A的污染而造成的。）正如以前所报道的，血红蛋白I经酶解后的第23条肽段向正极的移动比正常肽段更快。血红蛋白I的第23条肽段含有色氨酸残基和一个天冬氨酸残基（后者的存在使血红蛋白I能更快地向正极迁移），而在血红蛋白A相应的肽段中并不存在这两种

Because the tryptic digest of the α-chain of Hb-A contained but only one tryptophan residue the peptide with which it is associated vanished in Hb-I (Fig. 1). Thus the specific chemical difference between Hb-A and Hb-I must be located in the tryptophan-containing pentapeptide.

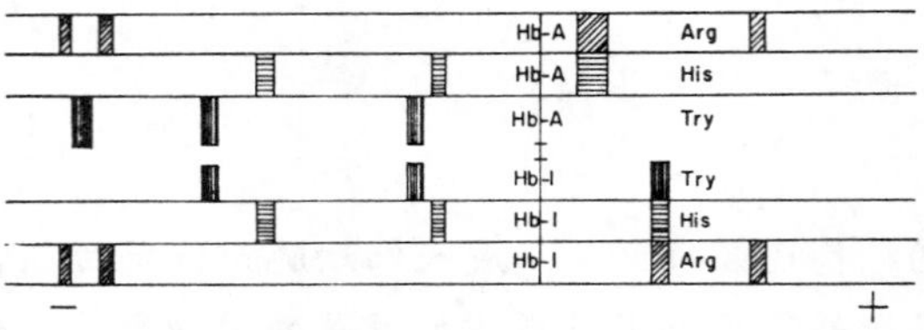

Fig. 1. Comparison by one-dimensional electrophoresis of tryptic digests of the normal and I haemoglobins at *p*H 6.4. Three peptides of both haemoglobins developed colour for tryptophan. Note that the peptide which moves the fastest toward cathode showing positive reaction for tryptophan in Hb-A is absent in Hb-I. It appears on the anode side in haemoglobin-I

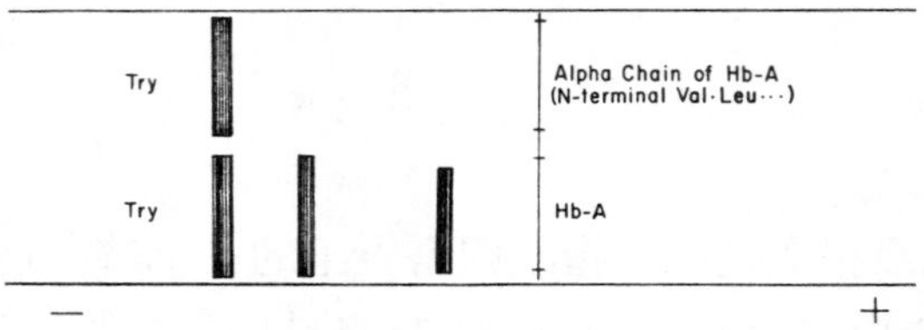

Fig. 2. Tracing of one-dimensional paper electrophoresis of tryptic digest of the normal haemoglobin (Hb-A) and the α-chain isolated from it. The α-chain contains only one tryptophan-positive peptide. It moves the fastest towards the cathode; it is this peptide which vanishes in Hb-I. The amino-acid interchange of this genetic alteration takes place in the tryptophan-positive pentapeptide of the α-chain

The specific amino-acid composition of the tryptophan-positive pentapeptide of the α-chain of Hb-A was determined by the column chromatography method of Spackman, Stein and Moore[6] and found to consist of $(Ala)_2$(Try)(Gly)(Lys); where Ala = alanyl, Try = tryptophyl, Gly = glycyl, and Lys = lysyl. In order to preserve tryptophan, leucine-aminopeptidase was used to hydrolyse the peptide which contained it. The NH_2-terminal residue of the pentapeptide was alanyl by the method of Sanger[7]. The amino-acid sequence of the pentapeptide was deduced in the following manner: the peptide was split with α-chymotrypsin and then the peptides were separated by one-dimensional paper electrophoresis; the tryptophan-positive segment behaved essentially neutral; the NH_2-terminal residue was alanyl and the amino-acid composition was $(Ala)_2$(Try); so the sequence of the tripeptide was Ala-Ala-Try. The dipeptide contained glycine and lysine. The amino-acid sequence of the pentapeptide was deduced to be Ala-Ala-Try-Gly-Lys.

The NH_2-terminal residue of peptide 23 of Hb-I was alanyl, but it was valyl for peptide 23 of Hb-A. The amino-acid composition of Hb-I peptide 23 was identical with the sum of the tryptophan-positive pentapeptide and peptide 23 of Hb-A, however, with one exception—instead of lysyl, aspartyl residue was found. Since the pentapeptide is the third

残基。由于血红蛋白 A 的 α 链经胰蛋白酶消化后的产物中只有一个色氨酸残基，所以这一残基一定和血红蛋白 I 中消失的那条肽段（图 1）有关联。因此，血红蛋白 A 和血红蛋白 I 之间特定的化学差异就一定是位于这条含色氨酸的五肽上。

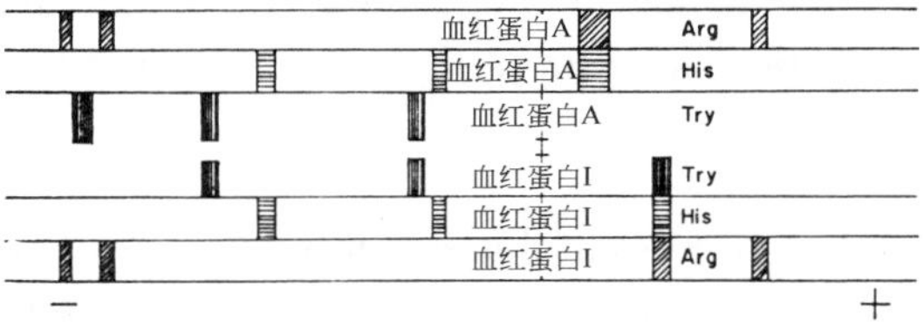

图 1. 在 pH 值为 6.4 时正常的血红蛋白 A 和血红蛋白 I 的胰蛋白酶消化产物单向电泳比较结果。通过对色氨酸显色发现这两种血红蛋白都有 3 条含色氨酸残基的肽段。需要注意的是，在血红蛋白 A 中向负极移动最快的、能呈现出色氨酸阳性反应的肽段并没有出现在血红蛋白 I 中，但血红蛋白 I 在正极一侧出现了一条含色氨酸残基的肽段。

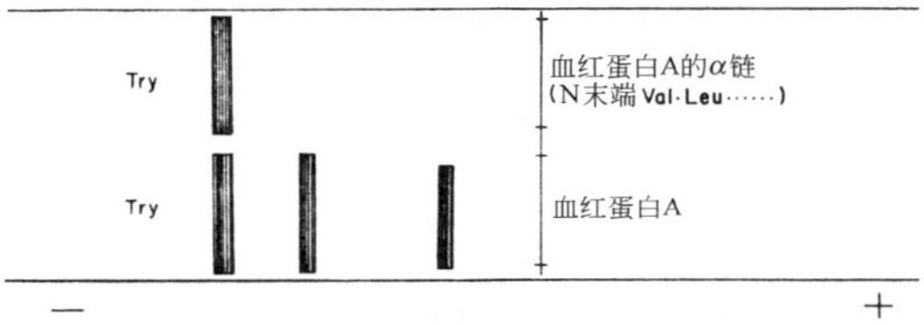

图 2. 对正常血红蛋白 A 和从中分离出来的 α 链的胰蛋白酶消化产物进行单向纸电泳后的印迹。α 链只有一条含色氨酸的肽段，它向负极移动得最快，也正是血红蛋白 I 中消失的那条肽段。因此，造成血红蛋白 A 与血红蛋白 I 的遗传改变的氨基酸替换发生在 α 链中含色氨酸的五肽上。

采用斯帕克曼、斯坦和穆尔 [6] 的柱层析方法对血红蛋白 A 的 α 链中含色氨酸的五肽的特定氨基酸组成进行测定，结果发现其氨基酸组成是 $(Ala)_2$(Try)(Gly)(Lys)。其中，Ala 代表丙氨酸残基，Try 代表色氨酸残基，Gly 代表甘氨酸残基，Lys 代表赖氨酸残基。为保护色氨酸，我们选用亮氨酸氨肽酶水解含色氨酸的肽段。采用桑格 [7] 的方法测定出该五肽的氨基端是丙氨酸残基。通过下面的方法来推断该五肽的氨基酸序列：用 α–胰凝乳蛋白酶使该五肽裂解，然后用单向纸电泳分离酶切产物，结果发现含色氨酸的片段基本呈电中性，另外也知道了这一片段的氨基酸组成是 $(Ala)_2$(Try)，而氨基末端是丙氨酸残基，所以三肽序列是 Ala-Ala-Try。剩下的二肽则是由甘氨酸和赖氨酸组成的，因此可以推断出该五肽的氨基酸序列是 Ala-Ala-Try-Gly-Lys。

血红蛋白 I 的第 23 条肽段的氨基末端是丙氨酸残基，而血红蛋白 A 的第 23 条肽段的氨基末端是缬氨酸残基。就氨基酸组成来说，血红蛋白 I 的第 23 条肽段与血红蛋白 A 的那条含色氨酸的五肽再加上其第 23 条肽段是基本一致的，但有一处不同，即血红蛋白 A 中的赖氨酸残基在血红蛋白 I 中变成了天冬氨酸残基。由于这条五肽是从

from NH_2-terminus of the α-chain, the tryptic peptide 23 must be the fourth; they are simply linked together in Hb-I through aspartyl residue.

Attempts made in this laboratory to find out whether or not other amino-acids in peptide 23 might be involved in the genetic change have not been successful; the amino-acid sequence appears to be identical with those reported by Braunitzer *et al.*[4] and by Hill and Konigsberg[5].

Schroeder *et al.*[8] reported that human haemoglobin is composed of four polypeptide chains of two different kinds, referred to as α- and β-chains. In accordance with recommendations for the nomenclature of haemoglobins[9] $\alpha_2^A\beta_2^A$ designates Hb-A and $\alpha_2^{16Asp}\beta_2^A$ could be used to define Hb-I.

I thank Dr. Robert J. Hill and Dr. William Konigsberg, of the Rockefeller Institute, who provided me with the α-chain of Hb-A; they also collaborated with me on the amino-acid analyses of the pentapeptide. I also thank T. Viswanatha and Mr. H. B. Marsh for assistance.

(**196**, 226-227; 1961)

Makio Murayama: National Institute of Arthritis and Metabolic Diseases, National Institutes of Health, Public Health Service, U.S. Department of Health, Education and Welfare, Bethesda, Maryland.

References:

1. Murayama, M., and Ingram, V. M., *Nature*, **183**, 1798 (1959).
2. Ingram, V. M., *Nature*, **183**, 1795 (1959).
3. Hill, R. J., and Konigsberg, W., *J. Biol. Chem.*, **235**, PC, 21 (1960).
4. Braunitzer, G., Gehring-Müller, R., Hilschmann, N., Hilse, K., Hobom, G., Rudloff, V., and Wittmann-Liebold, B., *Z. physiol. Chem. Hoppe-Seyler's*, **325**, 283 (1961).
5. Hill, R. J., and Konigsberg, W., *J. Biol. Chem.*, **236**, PC, 7 (1961).
6. Spackman, D. H., Stein, W. H., and Moore, S., *Anal. Chem.*, **30**, 1190 (1958).
7. Fraenkel-Conrat, H., Harris, J. I., and Levy, A. L., *Methods of Biochemical Analysis*, **2**, 359 (Interscience Pub., Inc., New York, 1955).
8. Rhinesmith, H. S., Schroeder, W. A., and Martin, N., *J. Amer. Chem. Soc.*, **80**, 3358 (1958).
9. Gerald, P. S., and Ingram, V. M., *J. Biol. Chem.*, **236**, 2155 (1961).

α 链氨基末端算起的第 3 条肽段，那么经胰蛋白酶酶解后的第 23 条肽段就一定是从 α 链氨基末端算起的第 4 条肽段，在血红蛋白 I 分子中，这两肽段是通过天冬氨酸残基连接在一起的。

本实验室曾试图寻找第 23 条肽段中是否有其他氨基酸残基可能发生了遗传改变，但没有找到。我们得到的氨基酸序列与布劳尼策尔等 [4] 以及希尔和柯尼希斯贝格 [5] 报道的序列完全一样。

施罗德等 [8] 曾报道，人血红蛋白由 4 条多肽链组成，这 4 条多肽链分属 α 链和 β 链两种类型。为了与推荐采用的人血红蛋白命名法 [9] 保持一致，可以用 $\alpha_2^A\beta_2^A$ 表示血红蛋白 A，用 $\alpha_2^{16Asp}\beta_2^A$ 表示血红蛋白 I。

我要感谢洛克菲勒研究所的罗伯特 · 希尔博士和威廉 · 柯尼希斯贝格博士，他们给我提供了血红蛋白 A 的 α 链样品，并且也和我一起对五肽的氨基酸组成进行了分析。我还要感谢维斯瓦那斯和马什先生对我的帮助。

（荆玉祥 翻译；袁峥 审稿）

Fossil Hand Bones from Olduvai Gorge

J. Napier

Editor's Note

Here British palaeontologist John Napier studies the mechanics of hand bones recovered from the same floor at Olduvai Gorge from which Louis Leakey had recently reported a new hominid skull. Napier analyses the capacity of the fossil hand for exerting the two forms of grip on external objects that modern human beings are capable of. He concludes that the creatures concerned would certainly have been capable of the power grip in which the hand is used as a clamp but that the evidence did not prove that the precision grip used by the tips of the fingers and the thumb would have been possible.

IN *Nature* of December 17, 1960, Dr. L. S. B. Leakey reported on the discovery of a number of fossil bones of the hand and the foot on a living floor some 20 ft. below the uppermost limit of Bed I, Olduvai. Later (*Nature* of February 25, 1961), Dr. Leakey reported the discovery of a mandible and two parietal fragments of a juvenile from the same site and associated with a well-defined living floor of an Oldowan culture.

Fifteen of the hand bones pertaining to at least two individuals, an adult and a juvenile, have been identified and examined, and are described here. Their allocation is given in Table 1.

Table 1

Juvenile	Uncertain Age	Adult
4 Middle phalanges *I.U.*	1 Trapezium *I.U.*	2 Proximal phalanges *C.D.*
	1 Scaphoid *I.U.*	
2 Terminal phalanges (fingers) *C.U.*	1 Capitate *C.D.*	
	1 Base of 2nd metacarpal *I.D.*	
1 Terminal phalanx (thumb) *C.U.*	2 Fragments of middle phalanges *I.D.*	

C, complete; *I*, Incomplete; *D*, damaged; *U*, undamaged.

The middle phalanges (Fig. 1, second row) from the juvenile hand, lacking only their epiphyses, constitute a series II-V from the right hand. They are robust bones, rather more so than phalanges of comparable length of juvenile *Gorilla* and adult *Homo sapiens*. They are strongly curved and, palmad, bear well-defined grooves which are situated in the distal half of the bone for the insertion of flexor digitorum superficialis.

来自奥杜威峡谷的手骨化石

内皮尔

编者按

本文中英国古生物学家约翰·内皮尔研究了在奥杜威峡谷同一生活面中发现的手骨的力学特征，最近路易斯·利基报道在那里发现了一件新的人科头骨。内皮尔分析了化石手骨是否像现代人类一样能够对外部物体施加两种形式的握力。他推断这种生物的手就像夹钳一样具有力量抓握，但不能证明化石手的拇指与其他手指的指尖能够进行精确抓握。

根据 1960 年 12 月 17 日的《自然》杂志上利基博士的报道，在奥杜威地层的第 I 层上界之下约 20 英尺的生活面中发现了大量的手、足骨化石。稍后（1961 年 2 月 25 日的《自然》），利基博士报道在同一遗址中的一个很清晰的奥杜威文化生活面中发现了一件未成年个体的下颌骨与两件顶骨破片。

经过鉴别与认定，15 块手骨至少属于两个个体，一个成年个体与一个未成年个体。这些材料的分类见表 1。

表1

未成年个体		年龄未定的个体		成年个体	
4块中节指骨	*I.U.*	1 块大多角骨 1 块手舟骨	*I.U.* *I.U.*	2 块近节指骨	*C.D.*
2 块远节指骨（手指）	*C.U.*	1 块头状骨 1 块第二掌骨的基端	*C.D.* *I.D.*		
1块远节指骨（拇指）	*C.U.*	2 块中节指骨破片	*I.D.*		

C，完整；*I*，不完整；*D*，有损；*U*，无损。

未成年个体的中节指骨（图 1，第 2 排）没有骨骺，构成了右手 II~V 指系列。与未成年大猩猩和成年智人的同等长度的指骨相比，这些骨显得更粗壮。它们强烈弯曲，掌型，骨末端一半处有很清晰的槽，以便指浅屈肌附着。

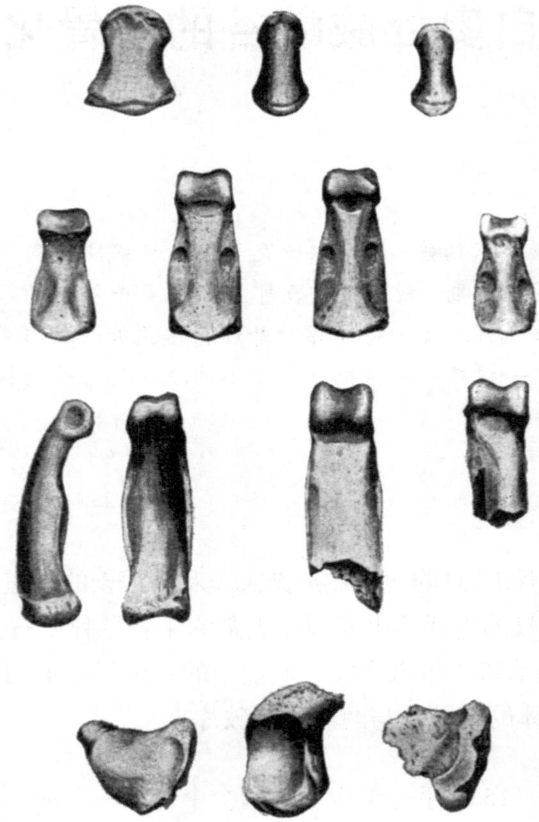

Fig. 1. Hand bone assemblage (drawings by Audrey Besterman). Top row. Juvenile. L. to R., terminal phalanx (thumb); 2 terminal phalanges (fingers). Second row. Juvenile. Middle phalanges, II-V. Third row. L. to R., proximal phalanx (adult), lateral and A.-P. views. 2 proximal phalanges (juvenile). Fourth row. Indeterminate age. L. to R. L. trapezium, L. scaphoid, L. capitate

The adult proximal phalanges (Fig. 1, third row) are also more robust than bones of comparable length in modern man; they are strongly curved both longitudinally and transversely, fusiform in shape and deeply hollowed out on the palmar aspect; sharply defined fibrous flexor sheath ridges extend from the base of the bones to their necks.

The terminal phalanges (Fig. 1, top row) which are juvenile, having incompletely fused epiphyses, are characteristically *sapiens* in form. The terminal phalanx of the thumb is of particular interest; it is stout and broad and bears a deep impression for the insertion of flexor pollicis longus.

The carpal bones (Fig. 1, 4th row) are all damaged, but sufficient of their original form remains to determine their structural and functional affinities. The lunate surface of the scaphoid has a rectangular outline; and the tubercle, which is broken off at its root, was probably somewhat elongated, though not as long as in the anthropoid apes. The

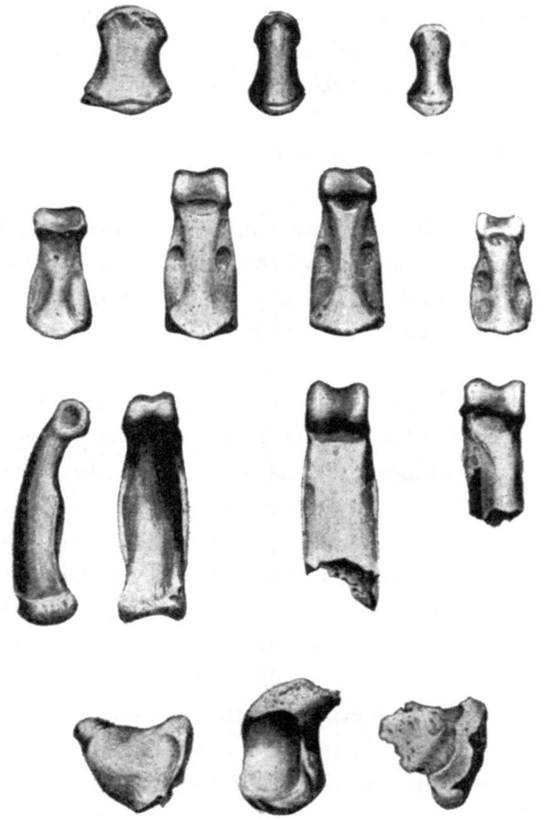

图 1. 手骨组合 (奥德丽 · 贝斯特曼绘画)。最上面一排：未成年个体，从左到右，远节指骨 (拇指)、两块远节指骨 (手指) ；第 2 排：未成年个体，中节指骨，II~V；第 3 排：从左到右，近节指骨（成年个体），侧面与掌侧视图、两块近节指骨（未成年个体）。第 4 排：年龄未确定，从左到右，大多角骨、手舟骨和头状骨。

成年个体的近节指骨（图 1，第 3 排）与现代人类的同等长度的骨相比也粗壮很多；纵横两个方向都强烈弯曲，呈纺锤形，掌面深陷；纤维状屈肌腱鞘脊非常明显，从骨基部延伸到颈部。

未成年个体的远节指骨（图 1，第 1 排）的骨骺融合不完全，形状上有智人的特征，拇指的远节指骨尤其重要，它宽大粗壮，因拇长屈肌附着而有很深的印痕。

腕骨（图 1，第 4 排）全部损坏，但凭借腕骨化石原始形状足以确定结构和功能上的亲缘关系。手舟骨的月状面轮廓呈矩形；结节根部折断，可能略被拉长，但其长度不如类人猿的结节。大多角骨表面呈清晰的马鞍状，但其他关节面提供的证

trapezium has a well-defined saddle-surface but the evidence provided by the other articular surfaces indicates that its "set" in the carpus was unlike that found in modern man and similar to the condition in *Gorilla*.

The capitate, though badly eroded, is generally more *sapiens* than ape-like.

Morphologically, the Olduvai hand bones cannot be closely matched with any known hominoid species living today. They bear, however, a greater similarity to juvenile *Gorilla* and adult *H.s. sapiens* than to adult *Gorilla*, *Pan* or *Pongo*. This is due largely to the absence in the fossil bones of any features peculiarly characteristic of brachiators. The adult gorilla hand has a number of specializations that are presumably related to its secondarily terrestrial mode of life and its great body-weight; these features, again, are absent from the fossil bone. The juvenile gorilla hand lacks the secondary specializations of the adult, and it is possibly for this reason alone that its bones have affinities with those of the fossil. The fossil bones differ from those of modern man in a number of features: (1) robustness; (2) dorsal curvature of the shafts of the phalanges; (3) distal insertion of the flexor digitorum superficialis; (4) strength of fibro-tendinous markings; (5) "set" of trapezium in the carpus; (6) the form of the scaphoid; (7) the depth of the carpal tunnel. The fossil bones resemble modern man in the following features: (1) presence of broad, stout terminal phalanges on fingers and thumb; (2) form of the distal articular surface of the capitate; (3) ellipsoidal form of metacarpo-phalangeal joint surfaces.

There seems little doubt that this assemblage of fossil hand bones all belong to the same species. The difference between the juvenile and adult hand bones are no greater than the differences between the bones of an adult and a juvenile gorilla. In view of this conclusion that the two individuals on the *F.L.K. NN* I site are co-specific, all the hand bones are taken into account in the discussion of the functional and systematic implications of the hand as a whole.

While morphologically the precise affinities of the Olduvai hand are indistinct, functionally there seems little reason to doubt that the hand is that of a hominid.

The hand of modern man is capable of two basic prehensile movements that have been termed precision grip and power grip[1]. The power grip is used by man when a secure and strong grip is required for performing an activity in which the elements of delicacy and precision are of secondary importance. In the power grip the object is held as in a clamp between the flexed fingers and the palm, reinforcement and counter-pressure being supported by the adducted thumb. The precision grip, nevertheless, is used by man where a delicate touch and a precise control of movement is required and is achieved by means of a grip between the palmar aspect of the terminal phalanx of the fully opposed thumb and the terminal phalanges of the fingers. The essential osteological correlates of the precision grip are: (1) a fully opposable thumb with a broad spatulate terminal phalanx; (2) broad terminal phalanges on the other digits; (3) a proportion in length between thumb and digits that would permit a full pulp-to-pulp contact between them when they are

据显示它在腕骨上的“接合方式”与现代人类的不一样，而类似于大猩猩的情形。

头状骨虽然侵蚀很严重，但大体能看出更像是智人的而非类似猿类的。

奥杜威手骨在形态上不与任何现存的已知人猿超科动物相一致。但它们与未成年大猩猩及成年智人的相似程度要大于它们与成年大猩猩、黑猩猩或猩猩的相似程度。这主要是由于骨化石没有呈现出任何臂行动物的独特特征。成年大猩猩的手发生了许多特化，这大概与其次生的地面生活方式及大体重有关，奥杜威手骨化石上也没有这些特征。未成年大猩猩的手没有成年个体的次生特征，原因可能是它的骨与奥杜威峡谷化石存在亲缘关系。奥杜威手骨化石与现代人类的骨相比有许多不同特点：(1) 粗壮程度；(2) 指骨骨干的背侧弯曲；(3) 指浅屈肌在远节附着；(4) 纤维–肌腱纹理的强度；(5) 腕骨上大多角骨的“接合方式”；(6) 手舟骨形状；(7) 腕管深度。手骨化石与现代人类的手骨存在下列相似特征：(1) 手指与拇指的远节指骨宽大粗壮；(2) 头状骨末端关节面的形状；(3) 掌骨与指骨间的关节面呈椭圆体形状。

毋庸置疑，这组手骨化石全都属于同一种类。未成年与成年个体手骨之间的差异不比未成年与成年大猩猩手骨之间的差异大，因此在 *F.L.K. NN* I 遗址的两个个体应该属于同一物种。在讨论手的功能与系统意义时，所有的手骨都应作为整体来考虑。

尽管奥杜威手骨在形态上还不能确定其准确的亲缘关系，但从功能上没有理由怀疑它们不是人科的手骨。

现代人类的手能够完成抓握的两种基本动作，即精确抓握和力量抓握[1]。当人类完成一个动作，对抓握的优美性与准确性要求不高，而对抓握的稳固性和力度有要求时，人类就运用力量抓握。进行力量抓握时，通过拇指的内屈反向增压，物体在弯曲的手指与手掌之间像被一把钳子夹住。然而，在要求有技巧性触摸和精确控制时，人类会采用精确抓握；这一动作依靠与其他手指完全相对的拇指的远节指骨掌面和手指的远节指骨抓握来完成。精确抓握在骨骼学上的表现特征是：(1) 与其他手指完全相对的拇指具有宽大的匙形远节指骨；(2) 其他手指的远节指骨宽大；(3) 拇指与其他手指间的长度比例可使它们在互相靠近时能完全紧密接触。虽然，毋庸置疑，奥杜威手骨化石具有精确抓握的前两个特征，但拇指掌骨的缺失使我们无法确定它是否具有最后一个特征。虽然大多角骨的马鞍状表面使人毫不怀疑拇指

approximated. While there appears to be little or no doubt that the Olduvai hand fulfils the first two requirements of the precision grip, there is no way to be certain about the last in the absence of thumb metacarpal. While the saddle-surface of the trapezium leaves no doubt that the thumb could be rotated medially about its own axis to face towards the other digits, there is no reason for supposing that the proportions between the thumb and index finger of the fossil form are exactly as in modern man; indeed, the "set" of the trapezium in the carpus suggests that this is not so. The question therefore is whether the thumb, having undergone rotation, is capable of pulp-to-pulp contact with the remaining digits. In the anthropoid apes while the thumb is opposable *per se*, pulp-to-pulp contact cannot be made owing to the marked disproportion of the length of fingers and thumb. It would seem, therefore, that the Olduvai hand was capable of power grip equal in performance, but, in view of the evidence of the attachment of the flexor tendons, comparatively greater in strength than in modern man. There is less certainty with regard to precision grip, which, while undoubtedly possible, may not have been as effective as in modern man. The overall picture presented by this assemblage is of a short powerful hand with strong, curved digits, surmounted by broad, flat nails and held in marked flexion. The thumb is strong and opposable, though possibly rather short.

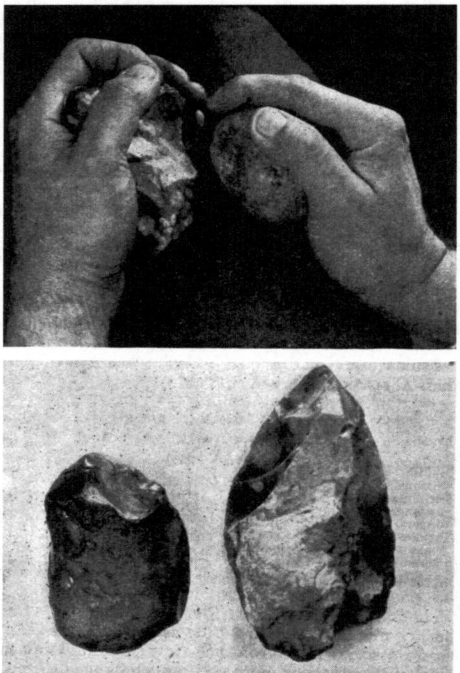

Fig. 2. Top, stone-on-stone technique of hand-axe construction using a power grip only. The flint core is being supported on the knee; bottom left, "Oldowan" pebble-tool; right, "Chellean" hand-axe made by me using the above technique

At a recent conference at Burg Wartenstein, Austria, organized by the Wenner-Gren

能绕其自身的轴向内朝其他手指的方向转动，但还没有理由推测，化石形态的拇指和食指之间的比例与现代人类的相同；腕部大多角骨的“接合方式”也表明并非如此。接下来的问题是，能经受转动的拇指能否与其余的手指紧密接触？类人猿的拇指虽然可与其他手指相对，但由于拇指与其他手指的长度明显不成比例而不能紧密接触。因此，奥杜威手骨似乎在力量抓握方式上与现代人一致，但屈肌腱附着的证据表明它的抓握力量可能比现代人类相对大些。至于精确抓握就难以确定了，虽然可能性毋庸置疑，但抓握可能不如现代人类的有效。这一组手骨呈现出来的总体特征是手短而有力，手指粗壮、抓握时明显弯曲、手指上的指甲扁而宽。拇指虽然可能相当短，但是强壮，并可与其他手指相对。

图 2. 上：仅用力量抓握石头碰石头地制造手斧，用手将燧石石核固定在膝盖上；下左：“奥杜威文化”的卵石工具；下右：笔者用上述方法制造的“阿布维利文化”的手斧。

温纳－格伦人类学研究基金会最近在奥地利瓦尔特施泰因堡组织了一次大会，

Foundation for Anthropological Research, an attempt was made to produce a diagnosis for the genus *Homo*. It was agreed that such a diagnosis could not be made unless certain characters and character complexes were present in combination. Included in these characters, which are referable to the skull, the brain and the post-cranial skeleton, was the criterion that "the hand is capable of making tools of a recognizable culture". If one assumes that the artefacts of an early Oldowan culture found on the living floor were the work of the species the remains of which are found there, then this criterion is fulfilled and, in addition, an interesting conclusion is possible: that toolmaking was established in the human lineage long before the hand had assumed its modern human form.

If, on the other hand, one bears the possibility in mind that some other, more advanced form was the toolmaker and the known incumbents of the floor were its victims, then it is in the functional morphology of the hand itself that one must look for evidence of toolmaking. On anatomical grounds there is no doubt that the Olduvai hand was sufficiently advanced in terms of the basic power and precision grips to have used naturally occurring objects as tools to good advantage. There is less certainty about toolmaking, which involves not only a peripheral but also a central intellectual factor as Oakley[2] has long insisted. The report on the Bed I juvenile skull fragments, soon to be published, may throw some light on this question by indicating the approximate cranial capacity of the juvenile skull.

Given the intellectual ability, the construction of the crude, rather small pebble-tools of the type found on the living floor, is well within the physical capacity of the Olduvai hand. Precision grip, which is imperfectly evolved in the fossil hand, is not an essential requisite at this level of craftsmanship as personal experiments in the construction of "Oldowan" pebble-tools and "Chellean" hand-axes have shown (Fig. 2).

(**196**, 409-411; 1962)

John Napler: Primatology Unit, Royal Free Hospital School of Medicine, London.

References:

1. Napier, J. R., *J. Bone and Joint Surg.*, **38**, B, 902 (1956).
2. Oakley, K. P., *Man the Toolmaker*, Fourth ed. (Brit. Mus. (N. H.) 1949).

试图确定人属的鉴定标准。大会一致认为，除非某些特征和综合特征在一起出现，否则这样的鉴定标准就无法建立。涉及头骨、脑及颅后骨骼的这些特征也是“手具有制造可识别文化特征工具的能力”的判断标准。如果假设发现在生活面上的早期奥杜威文化的器物是由在此发现遗骸的物种所创造的，那么，这个判断标准是成立的；此外，可能会得出一个有趣的结论：在人类演化的谱系上制作工具的出现远远早于现代人手雏形的出现。

从另一方面说，如果有人认为某些更高等的物种才是工具制造者，而在生活面上发现的动物只是其牺牲品，那么就必须从手的功能形态学上寻找手本身制造工具的证据。就解剖学而言，在基本的有力抓握与精确抓握方面，奥杜威手骨无疑十分高级，能够利用现成的物体作为工具来获取利益。不太确定是否能制造工具，因为这不仅涉及外部环境因素，还涉及奥克利一直坚持的大脑的智力因素[2]。地层中第I层的未成年个体头骨破片的报道即将发表，通过指出未成年个体头骨的近似颅容量可能会阐明这个问题。

倘若奥杜威人类有此智力能力，那么在生活面上发现的天然的、相当小的卵石工具就肯定在其手的制造能力范围之内。奥杜威手骨化石还没有进化形成精确抓握的能力，但这并不是技术水平高低的一个先决条件，重造“奥杜威”卵石工具和“阿布维利文化”手斧的实验都已经说明了这一点（图2）。

（田晓阳 翻译；冯兴无 审稿）

Investigation of the Radio Source 3C 273 by the Method of Lunar Occultations

C. Hazard *et al.*

Editor's Note

Radio astronomy was just getting started in the 1950s and 1960s. Before the development of the interferometer, positions of radio sources were best determined by "lunar occultations" when the Moon passed in front of the object. The position of the peculiar radio source 3C 273 is determined by such a method in this paper by Cyril Hazard and coworkers, leading to the identification of 3C 273 as the first known quasi-stellar object or quasar, a large black hole surrounded by gas.

THE observation of lunar occultations provides the most accurate method of determining the positions of the localized radio sources, being capable of yielding a positional accuracy of the order of 1 sec of arc. It has been shown by Hazard[1] that the observations also provide diameter information down to a limit of the same order. For the sources of small angular size the diameter information is obtained from the observed diffraction effects at the Moon's limb which may be considered to act as a straight diffracting edge.

The method has so far been applied only to a study of the radio source 3*C* 212 the position of which was determined to an accuracy of about 3 sec of arc[1,2]. However, 3*C* 212 is a source of comparatively small flux density and although the diffraction effects at the Moon's limb were clearly visible the signal-to-noise ratio was inadequate to study the pattern in detail and hence to realize the full potentialities of the method. Here we describe the observation of a series of occultations of the intense radio source 3*C* 273 in which detailed diffraction effects have been recorded for the first time permitting the position to be determined to an accuracy of better than 1″ and enabling a detailed examination to be made of the brightness distribution across the source.

The observations were carried out using the 210-ft. steerable telescope at Parkes, the method of observation being to direct the telescope to the position of the source and then to record the received power with the telescope in automatic motion following the source. Three occultations of the source have been observed, on April 15, at 410 Mc/s, on August 5 at 136 Mc/s and 410 Mc/s, and on October 26 at 410 Mc/s and 1,420 Mc/s, although in October and April only the immersion and emersion respectively were visible using the Parkes instrument. The 410 Mc/s receiver was a double-sided band receiver, the two channels, each of width 10 Mc/s, being centred on 400 Mc/s and 420 Mc/s, while the 136 Mc/s and 1,420 Mc/s receivers each had a single pass band 1.5 Mc/s and 10 Mc/s wide respectively.

用月掩的方法研究射电源3C 273

哈泽德等

编者按

射电天文学在20世纪50年代和60年代才刚刚起步。在干涉仪发明之前，利用月球从天体前经过时所产生的“月掩效应”是确定射电源位置的最佳方法。本文中西里尔·哈泽德及其同事们利用该方法测定了3C 273这个特殊射电源的位置，从而证认了3C 273为第一个已知的类星体——由气体包围着的一个巨大的黑洞。

对月掩的观测为确定射电源位置提供了最为准确的方法，由此能得到的位置准确度达1角秒的量级。哈泽德[1]已指出，观测提供的直径信息达到了相同量级的最低限度。对于具有小的角大小的射电源，通过从月亮的边缘处观测到的衍射效应也可获取直径的信息，其中月亮的边缘可视为一个直的衍射边缘。

这种方法目前只用于射电源3C 212的研究中，其位置测定的准确度约为3角秒[1,2]。然而，3C 212是一个流量密度相当小的射电源，虽然在月亮边缘处的衍射效应清晰可见，但其信噪比还无法满足详细研究其模式的需要，因此还无法体现出该方法的全部潜力。本文中我们描述了对强射电源3C 273一系列掩源现象的观测，之前为了使该射电源位置测量精度优于1″，已详细记录了衍射效应，并且对整个射电源的亮度分布进行了详细检测。

这次观测用的是位于帕克斯的一台210英尺的可跟踪望远镜，观测的方法是首先将望远镜对准射电源的方向，之后在望远镜自动跟踪射电源时记录所接收到的功率。目前已观测到射电源的三次掩源，其时间和频率分别为：4月15日频率为410兆周/秒，8月5日频率为136兆周/秒和410兆周/秒，以及10月26日频率为410兆周/秒和1,420兆周/秒，尽管在10月和4月用帕克斯望远镜分别只能观测到掩始和复现。其中，接收到410兆周/秒频率的是一个双边波段双通道接收器，两个通道带宽均为10兆周/秒，其中心频率分别为400兆周/秒和420兆周/秒，而接收到136兆周/秒和1,420兆周/秒频率的是两个单通道接收器，其带宽分别为1.5兆周/秒和10兆周/秒。

The record of April 15, although of interest as it represents the first observation of detailed diffraction fringes during a lunar occultation, is disturbed by a gradient in the received power and is not suitable for accurate position and diameter measurements. Therefore, attention will be confined to the occultation curves recorded in August and October and which are reproduced in Fig. 1. It is immediately obvious from these records that 3*C* 273 is a double source orientated in such a way that whereas the two components passed successively behind the Moon at both immersions, they reappeared almost simultaneously. The prominent diffraction fringes show that the angular sizes of these components must be considerably smaller than 10″, which is the order of size of a Fresnel zone at the Moon's limb.

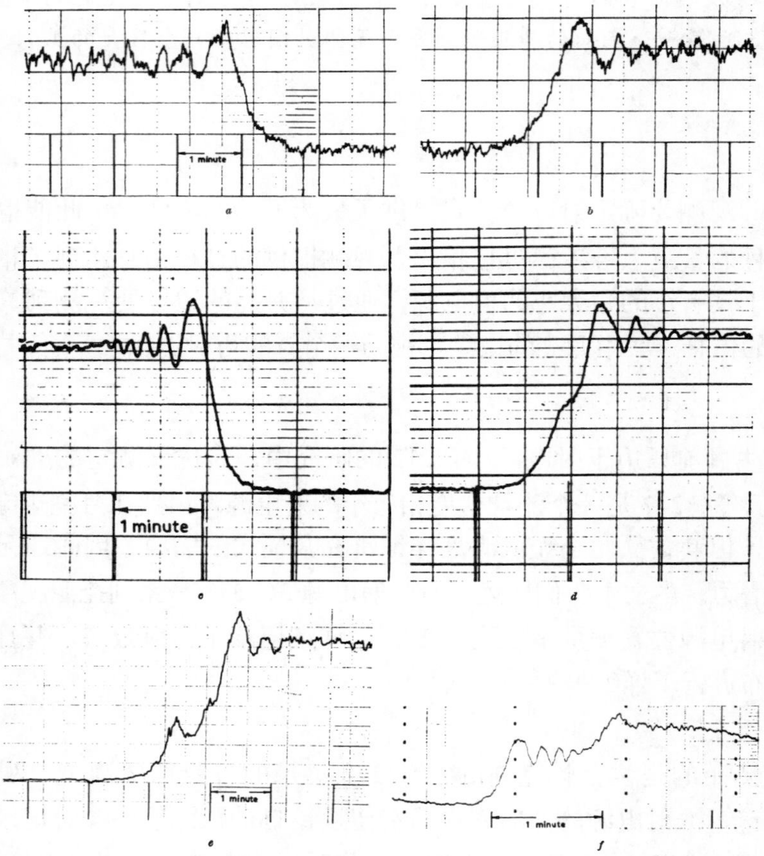

Fig. 1. Facsimiles of records showing occultations on August 5 and October 26, 1962, at different frequencies. (*a*) Emersion of August 5, 1962, at 136 Mc/s; (*b*) immersion of August 5, 1962, at 136 Mc/s; (*c*) emersion of August 5, 1962, at 410 Mc/s; (*d*) immersion of August 5, 1962, at 410 Mc/s; (*e*) immersion of October 26, 1962, at 410 Mc/s; (*f*) immersion of October 26, 1962, at 1,420 Mc/s.
Abscissae, U. T.; ordinates, flux density

尽管4月15日的记录由于展示了在月掩期间对详细的衍射条纹的首次观测而非常令人感兴趣，然而却受到了接收功率中梯度的干扰，因此并不适用于对位置和直径的准确测量。因此，注意力应集中在8月和10月所记录的掩源曲线上，如图1所示。根据这些记录可以很快发现3C 273是一组双射电源，因为它们以下列方式出现，即两个子源相继通过月亮后面两个掩始处，并几乎同时复现。这组显著的衍射条纹表明，两个子源的角大小必然远小于10″，而10″则是月球边缘处菲涅耳区大小的量级。

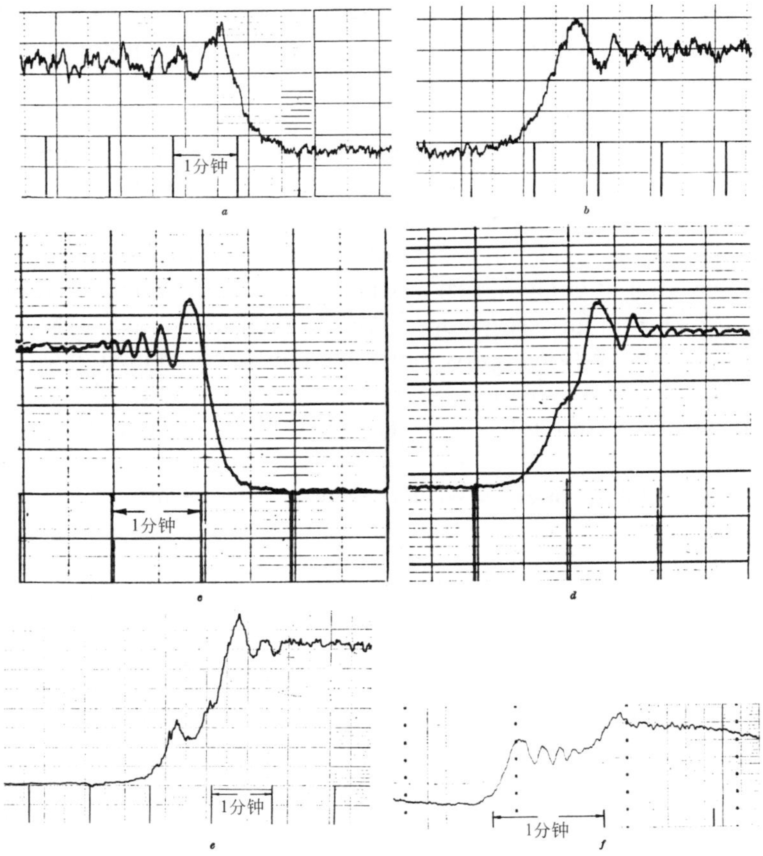

图1. 1962年8月5日和10月26日在不同频率时掩源记录的复制图。(*a*)1962年8月5日频率为136 兆周/秒时的复现；(*b*)1962年8月5日频率为136 兆周/秒时的掩始；(*c*)1962年8月5日频率为410 兆周/秒时的复现；(*d*)1962年8月5日频率为410 兆周/秒时的掩始；(*e*)1962年10月26日频率为410 兆周/秒时的掩始；(*f*)1962年10月26日频率为1,420 兆周/秒时的掩始。横坐标为世界时；纵坐标为流量密度。

The most interesting feature of Figs. 1(*e*) and 1(*f*) is the change in the ratio of the flux densities of the two components with frequency. The ratio of the flux density of the south preceding source (component *A*) to that of the north following source (component *B*) is 1:0.45 at 410 Mc/s and 1:1.4 at 1,420 Mc/s, indicating a striking difference in the spectra of the two components. If it be assumed that the flux densities[3] of 3*C* 273 at 410 Mc/s and 1,420 Mc/s are 60 and 35 Wm^{-2} $(c/s)^{-1}$ and that over this frequency-range the spectrum of each component may be represented by $S \propto f^n$, then the above ratios correspond to spectral indices for components *A* and *B* of −0.9 and 0.0 respectively. The spectral index of *A* is a representative value for a Class II radio source; but the flat spectrum of *B* is most unusual, no measurements of a comparable spectrum having yet been published. If the spectral indices were assumed constant down to 136 Mc/s then at this frequency component *A* must contribute almost 90 percent of the total emission, a conclusion which is confirmed by a comparison of the times of immersion at 136 Mc/s and 410 Mc/s on August 5.

It has been shown by Scheuer[4] that it is possible to recover the true brightness distribution across the source from the observed diffraction pattern, the resolution being subject only to limitations imposed by the receiver bandwidth and the finite signal to noise ratio and being independent of the angular scale of the diffraction pattern. However, in this preliminary investigation we have not attempted such a detailed investigation but based the analysis on the calculated curves for uniform strip sources of different widths as published by Hazard[1]. As a first step in the investigation approximate diameters were estimated from the intensity of the first diffraction lobe and the results corresponding to the three position angles defined by the occultations and indicated in Fig. 2. are given in Table 1.

Table 1. Effective Width of Equivalent Strip Source
(Sec. of arc)

Frequency Mc/s	Component *A* Position angle			Component *B* Position angle		
	106°	313°	84°	105°	314°	83°
136	6.4	6.4	—	—	—	—
410	3.1	4.2† 2(6)*	4.2	3.1	3.0†	2.7
1,420	—	—	2.9	—	—	2.1 0.5(7)*

* Estimated from an analysis of the whole diffraction pattern.
† Component *B* assumed to have width of 3″.

图 1(*e*) 和 1(*f*) 最令人感兴趣的特征是两个子源的流量密度之比随频率的变化。当频率为 410 兆周 / 秒时，南方的前导源 (子源 *A*) 与北方的后继源 (子源 *B*) 的流量密度之比为 1:0.45，而当频率为 1,420 兆周 / 秒时则为 1:1.4，这说明两个子源在光谱上的明显差异。假设当频率为 410 兆周 / 秒和 1,420 兆周 / 秒时，3*C*273 的流量密度[3]分别是 60 瓦 · 米$^{-2}$(周 / 秒)$^{-1}$ 和 35 瓦 · 米$^{-2}$(周 / 秒)$^{-1}$，并且在此频率范围内，每个子源的频谱可由 $S \propto f^n$ 表示，则上述比值相应于子源 *A* 和 *B* 的谱指数分别为 –0.9 和 0.0。*A* 的谱指数是 II 类射电源的典型值，但 *B* 的平谱是最特别的，目前尚未发表过类似的频谱的测量结果。如果假定谱指数在频率降至 136 兆周 / 秒时仍为常数，则在此频率下子源 *A* 几乎贡献总发射的 90%，通过比较 8 月 5 日当频率为 136 兆周 / 秒和 410 兆周 / 秒时的掩始时间可以证实这一结论。

朔伊尔[4]曾指出，可以通过观测到的衍射图案来重现整个射电源的实际亮度分布，分辨率的大小仅仅受到接收器带宽和有限信噪比的限制，并且和衍射图案的角尺度无关。然而，在我们这篇初步的研究中尚未进行如此详细的研究，而是建立在对哈泽德[1]发表的为具有不同宽度的均匀条带状射电源的计算曲线的分析之上。作为研究中的第一步，通过第一衍射波瓣的强度估算出近似直径，与图 2 中由月掩确定的三个位置角相对应的结果在表 1 中给出。

表 1. 等效条带源的有效宽度

(角秒)

频率 兆周 / 秒	子源 *A* 位置角			子源 *B* 位置角		
	106°	313°	84°	105°	314°	83°
136	6.4	6.4	—	—	—	—
410	3.1	4.2† 2(6)*	4.2	3.1	3.0†	2.7
1,420	—	—	2.9	—	—	2.1 0.5(7)*

* 由整个衍射图案估算得到。

† 假设子源 *B* 的宽度是 3″。

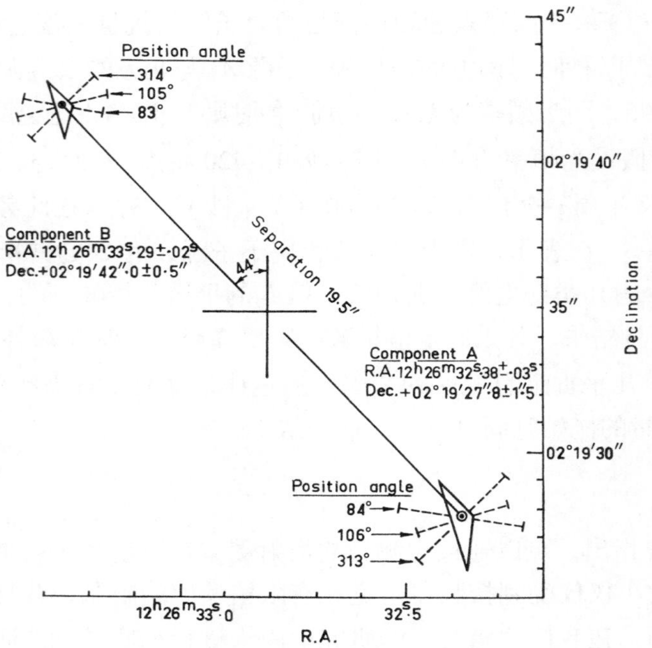

Fig. 2. Diagram of the radio source 3*C* 273. The sides of the full line triangles represent the positions of the limb of the Moon at the times of occultation. The broken lines represent the widths of the equivalent strip source as measured at 410 Mc/s for each of three position angles indicated

As already indicated here, the 136-Mc/s measurements refer only to component *A* and hence no diameter measurements are available for *B* at this frequency. The 410-Mc/s observations of the August occultation are the most difficult to interpret owing to the components having both comparable flux density and small separation relative to the angular size of the first Fresnel zone. At immersion the widths were estimated by using a process of curve fitting to reproduce Fig. 1(*d*); at emersion (position angle 313°) the diameter of component *B* was assumed to be 3″ as indicated by the estimates at position angles 105° and 83°. The individual measurements at each frequency are reasonably consistent but there is a striking variation of the angular size of component *A* with frequency and evidence of a similar variation for component *B*. As at the time of the August occultation the angular separation of the Sun and the source was about 50° and hence coronal scattering of the type observed by Slee[5] at 85 Mc/s is not likely to be significant, this variation in size suggests that the model of two uniform strip sources is inadequate.

Therefore, a more detailed analysis was made of the intensity distributions of the lobe patterns given in Figs. 1(*c*) and 1(*f*), and it was found that in neither case can the pattern be fitted to that for a uniform strip source or a source with a gaussian brightness distribution. The 1,420-Mc/s observations of component *B* can be explained, however, by assuming that this source consists of a central bright core about 0.5″ wide contributing about 80 percent of the total flux embedded in a halo of equivalent width of about

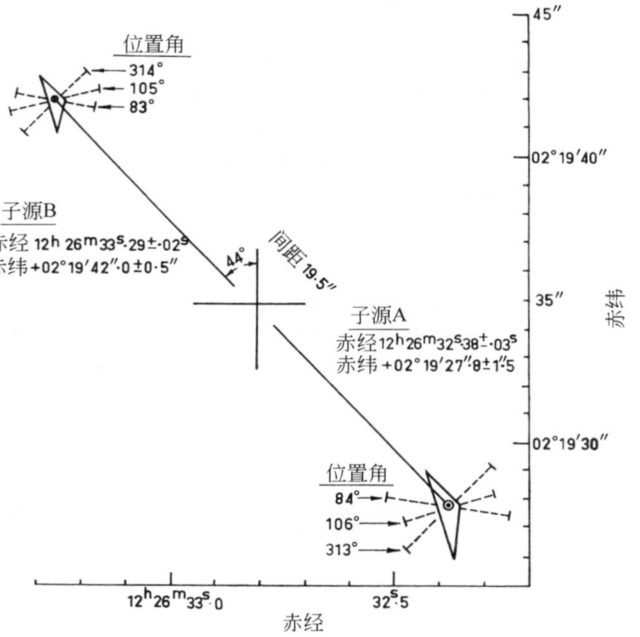

图 2. 射电源 3C 273 的示意图。实线三角形的边表示掩源时月球边缘的位置。虚线表示等效条带源的宽度，测量是频率为 410 兆周 / 秒时对三个指定位置角分别进行的。

如本文已指出的，136 兆周 / 秒的测量仅仅针对子源 *A*，因此在这个频率上并无对子源 *B* 可用的直径测量。8 月掩源的 410 兆周 / 秒的观测是最难以解释的，因为两个子源的流量密度相近，并且其间距相对于第一菲涅耳区的角大小来说很小。掩始时的宽度是用曲线拟合图 1(*d*) 来估算的；在复现时（位置角 313°），根据位置角为 105°和 83°时所估算的，子源 *B* 的直径假定为 3″。每个频率的独立测量结果是相当一致的，但子源 *A* 的角大小随频率有显著变化，有证据显示子源 *B* 也存在类似的情况。如在 8 月掩源发生期间，太阳与射电源的角间距约为 50°，因此由斯利 [5] 在频率为 85 兆周 / 秒时观测到的这种类型的日冕散射似乎并不显著，这类角大小的变化表明，用这种两个均匀条带状的模型来描述射电源是不恰当的。

因此，我们对图 1(*c*) 和图 1(*f*) 中波瓣条纹的强度分布进行了更细致的分析，发现在任何情况下，都不能将图案拟合为均匀条带源或具有高斯亮度分布的源。然而，只要假定这个源是由宽度约为 0.5″的中心亮核组成，并且贡献了相当于一个等效宽度约为 7″的晕圈所包含的总流量的 80% 左右，就可以解释子源 *B* 在频率为 1,420 兆周 / 秒

7″. Fig. 1(*b*), where component *A* predominates, suggests that this source has a similar structure but with a core of effective width about 2″ at 410 Mc/s and a halo of width 6″. It therefore seems that the overall extent of both components are comparable but that the emission is more highly concentrated to the nucleus in *B* than in *A*. The close agreement between the halo size of *A* and its effective diameter at 136 Mc/s suggests that the observed variation of effective size with frequency may be due to a difference in the spectra of the halo and central regions. This would imply that the spectrum becomes steeper in the outer regions of the sources, that is, in the regions of lower emissivity. It is of interest that the integrated spectral indices of the two components show an analogous effect. Thus the spectrum of *B*, where most of the emission arises in a source about 0.5″ wide, is markedly flatter than that of *A*, where it arises in a source about 2″ wide.

The analysis is not sufficiently accurate to reach any reliable conclusions on the ellipticity of the individual components of 3*C* 273, but allowing for the uncertainty in the estimated widths and position angle 314°, the 410-Mc/s observations indicate that both components may be elliptical with *A* elongated approximately along the axis joining the two components and *B* elongated perpendicular to this axis.

The position of each source was calculated from the observed times of disappearance and reappearance, which were estimated from the calculated flux density at the edge of the geometrical shadow and, where possible, from the positions of the diffraction lobes; these times are given in Table 2. In estimating the values of T_D^A and T_R^A from the 136-Mc/s records a small correction was applied for the effects of component *B*, this correction being estimated by comparison with the 410-Mc/s records. The corresponding times for *B* were estimated from the 410-Mc/s observations using the estimated position of component *A* and the known flux density ratio of the two components. For each component the times and associated errors given in Table 2 define three strips in each of which the source should lie; the centre lines of these strips represent the limb of the Moon at the time of observation and define in each case a triangular-shaped area. In principle, the position of the source lies in the area common to the three associated strips but it was found that for each component, and in particular for component *A*, that the size of the triangles defined by the Moon's limb was larger than would be expected from the estimated timing errors. This suggests that errors in the positions of the Moon's limb are more important than the estimated timing errors, and possibly that the effective position of the source varies slightly with frequency. The position of each source was therefore assumed to be given by the centre of the circle inscribed in the triangle defined by the Moon's limb at the relevant times. Dr. W. Nicholson of H.M. Nautical Almanac Office has kindly carried out these calculations and the estimated positions are as follows:

Component *A*	R.A.	12h 26m 32.38s ± 0.03s
(Epoch 1950)	Decl.	02° 19′ 27.8″ ± 1.5″
Component *B*	R.A.	12h 26m 33.29s ± 0.02s
(Epoch 1950)	Decl.	02° 19′ 42.0″ ± 0.5″

的观测结果。图 1(*b*) 中的子源 *A* 是占主要地位的，这表明该源具有类似的结构，但在 410 兆周 / 秒处有一个有效宽度约为 2″的核，宽度约为 6″的晕。因此两个子源的总体宽度相近，但是 *B* 的中心区的发射比 *A* 更高度集中。子源 *A* 的晕大小与它在 136 兆周 / 秒的有效直径的一致性表明，观测到的有效大小随频率的变化可能是由晕和中心区域在光谱上的差异导致的。这表明光谱在射电源的外部区域或者说在发射率较小的区域变得陡峭。非常有趣的是，两个子源的累积光谱指数显示出了一种类似的效应。子源 *B* 大部分的发射来自于一个宽度约为 0.5″的源，其光谱比大部分发射来自于宽度约为 2″的源的子源 *A* 的光谱要平缓得多。

这些分析尚未精确到足以得出任何关于 3*C* 273 各个子源椭率的可靠结论，但即便考虑到估算宽度及位置角 314°时的不确定性，410 兆周 / 秒的观测也表明两个子源可能都是椭圆状的，其中 *A* 的长轴方向大约是沿着连接两个子源的轴线，而 *B* 的长轴方向则垂直于该轴线。

每个源的位置是根据观测到的消失时间及重现时间而计算出来的，消失和重现是通过几何阴影边缘的流量密度以及可能从衍射波瓣的位置估算的；表 2 中给出了这些时间。在根据 136 兆周 / 秒的记录估算 $T_D{}^A$ 和 $T_R{}^A$ 值的过程中，对子源 *B* 的作用做了一项小的修正，这项修正是通过与 410 兆周 / 秒记录的对比估算出来的。子源 *B* 的相应时间是通过 410 兆周 / 秒观测采用子源 *A* 的估计位置及两个子源的已知流量密度比来估算的。对每个子源而言，表 2 中给出的时间和相关误差确定了源应该所在的三个条带；这些条带的中线代表了观测时月球的边缘，并且确定了在每种情况下的三角形阴影区。原则上，源的位置应位于三个相关条带共同的区域中，但发现对每个子源而言，尤其是对子源 *A*，由月球边缘所确定的三角形面积大于根据估算时间误差而预期的值。这表明月球边缘的位置误差比估算的时间误差更重要，并且源的有效位置可能随频率稍有变化。因此，每个源的位置可能是由在相关时间内月球边缘所确定的三角形中内切圆的中心所给出的。航海天文历编制局的尼克尔森博士已做过计算，估算的位置如下：

子源 *A*	赤经	12h 26m 32.38s ± 0.03s
(历元 1950)	赤纬	02° 19′ 27.8″ ± 1.5″
子源 *B*	赤经	12h 26m 33.29s ± 0.02s
(历元 1950)	赤纬	02° 19′ 42.0″ ± 0.5″

Table 2. Observed Occultation Times of the Two Components of 3*C* 273

	Component *A* (U.T.)	Component *B* (U.T.)
Time of disappearance August 5, 1962	07h 46m 00s ± 1s	07h 46m 27.2s ± 0.5s
Time of reappearance August 5, 1962	09h 05m 45.5s ± 1s	09h 05m 45.7s ± 1.5s
Time of disappearance October 26, 1962	02h 55m 09.0s ± 1s	02h 56m 01.5s ± 0.4s

The average positions of the two sources given here represent the most accurate determination yet made of the position of a radio source. The quoted errors were estimated from the size of the triangles defined by the Moon's limb at the times of disappearance and reappearance, for the method is not subject to uncertainties introduced by refraction in the Earth's ionosphere or troposphere and is also free from the effects of confusion. A comparison of the times of disappearance and reappearance at different frequencies indicates that there is also no significant source of error due to refraction in either the solar corona or a possible lunar ionosphere; any refraction appears to be less than 0.3″ even at 136 Mc/s. This may be compared with the upper limit of 2″ at 237 Mc/s and 13″ at 81 Mc/s as estimated by Hazard[1] and Elsmore[6] respectively, and allows a new limit to be set to the density of the lunar ionosphere. Thus, from his observations at 81.5 Mc/s, Elsmore has set an upper limit to the electron density of 10^3 cm^{-3}; and it follows that the present measurements set a limit of about 10^2 cm^{-3}. Similarly, Buckingham[7] has estimated that at 50 Mc/s a ray passing at 50° to the Sun would be deviated by 1″ if the electron density in the solar corona at the Earth's distance from the Sun is 100 cm^{-3}. The present observations at 136 Mc/s and 410 Mc/s on August 5 indicate that at 50 Mc/s the deviation is less than 2″ at this angle, setting an upper limit to the electron density of about 200 cm^{-3}, which may be compared with an upper limit of 120 cm^{-3}, set by Blackwell and Ingham[8] from observations of the zodiacal light.

In a preliminary examination of a print from a 200″ plate it was noted that the position of component *B* agreed closely with that of a thirteenth magnitude star. We understand that the investigations by Drs. A. Sandage and M. Schmidt of the Mount Wilson and Palomar Observatories have revealed that this star and an associated nebulosity is very probably the source of the radio emission.

We thank Mr. J. G. Bolton for his interest in this work and his assistance, with that of the staff at Parkes, in ensuring the success of these observations. We also thank Dr. W. Nicholson, who calculated the positions of the sources, for his valuable co-operation and interest in the occultation programme. One of us (C. H.) thanks Dr. E. G. Bowen for his invitation to continue occultation work at Parkes as a guest observer from the Narrabri Observatory of the School of Physics of the University of Sydney.

(**197**, 1037-1039; 1963)

表 2. 3C 273 两个子源的观测掩源的时间

	子源 A（世界时）	子源 B（世界时）
消失的时间 1962 年 8 月 5 日	07h 46m 00s ±1s	07h 46m 27.2s ± 0.5s
重现的时间 1962 年 8 月 5 日	09h 05m 45.5s ±1s	09h 05m 45.7s ± 1.5s
消失的时间 1962 年 10 月 26 日	02h 55m 09.0s ±1s	02h 56m 01.5s ± 0.4s

此处给出的两个源的平均位置是迄今对射电源位置的最准确的测定。其中误差是根据由消失和重现时月球边缘所确定的三角形的大小进行估算的，因为该方法并不受地球电离层或对流层的折射所引入的不确定性的影响，也没有干扰效应。对不同频率时消失和重现时刻的比较表明，并没有由日冕或可能的月球电离层的折射所引起的重要误差来源；即使频率为 136 兆周 / 秒时折射也小于 0.3″。这与分别由哈泽德 [1] 和埃尔斯莫尔 [6] 估算的当频率为 237 兆周 / 秒时的 2″ 和 81 兆周 / 秒时的 13″ 的上限相一致，并允许对月球电离层的密度取一个新的极限。因此，根据埃尔斯莫尔在频率为 81.5 兆周 / 秒时的观测，他取的电子密度的上限为 10^3 厘米$^{-3}$；而目前的测量取的极限约为 10^2 厘米$^{-3}$。与此类似，白金汉 [7] 假设在频率为 50 兆周 / 秒时有离开太阳 50° 的射线通过，如果在地球距离太阳的距离为 1 个天文单位那么远的地带日冕中的电子密度是 100 厘米$^{-3}$ 时，所估算射线的偏离将为 1″。8 月 5 日频率为 136 兆周 / 秒时和 410 兆周 / 秒时的观测表明，当频率为 50 兆周 / 秒时的角度偏离小于 2″，所取的电子密度的上限约为 200 厘米$^{-3}$，这与由布莱克韦尔和英厄姆 [8] 根据黄道光的观测所得的 120 厘米$^{-3}$ 的上限一致。

在对 200″ 的望远镜照相底片翻印片的初步检验中，注意到子源 B 的位置与一颗十三等的恒星的位置非常接近。我们了解到，威尔逊山天文台和帕洛玛山天文台的桑德奇博士和施密特博士的研究已揭示了这颗恒星及有关的星云状物质很可能就是该射电辐射的源。

我们特别感谢博尔顿先生对这项工作的关注以及他的帮助，并感谢帕克斯的同事为成功进行这些观测所做出的努力。我们还要感谢尼克尔森博士对月掩项目的兴趣和非常有价值的合作以及对射电源位置所进行的计算。我们其中的一员，来自悉尼大学物理学院纳拉布里天文台的哈泽德要感谢鲍恩博士的邀请，使得他能继续以客座观察员的身份在帕克斯的月掩项目中工作。

（沈乃澂 翻译；蒋世仰 审稿）

C. Hazard, M. B. Mackey and A. J. Shimmins: C.S.I.R.O. Division of Radiophysics, University Grounds, Sydney.

References:

1. Hazard, C., *Mon. Not. Roy. Astro. Soc.*, **134**, 27 (1962).
2. Hazard, C., *Nature*, **191**, 58 (1961) .
3. Bolton, J. G., Gardner, F. F., and Mackey, M. B. (unpublished results).
4. Scheuer, P. A. G., *Austral. J. Phys.*, **15**, 333 (1962).
5. Slee, O. B., *Mon. Not. Roy. Astro. Soc.*, **123**, 223 (1961).
6. Elsmore, B., *Phil. Mag.*, **2**, 1040 (1957).
7. Buckingham, M. J., *Nature*, **193**, 538 (1962).
8. Blackwell, D. E., and Ingham, M. F., *Mon. Not. Roy. Astro. Soc.*, **122**, 129 (1961).

3C 273: A Star-Like Object with Large Red-Shift

M. Schmidt

Editor's Note

Here astronomer Maarten Schmidt uses the position of the unusual radio source 3C 273 determined by Cyril Hazard and colleagues to establish that it is a star-like object with a small jet apparently emanating from it, within 1 arcsecond of the radio sources. Schmidt also reports an optical spectrum, which can be explained only if the source were at a redshift of 0.158, making it very distant. This constituted the discovery of the first quasar. We now know that quasars are massive black holes surrounded by gas. As the gas falls into the black hole it becomes very hot, and the light emitted can swamp the glow of the galaxy at whose centre the quasar lies.

THE only objects seen on a 200-in. plate near the positions of the components of the radio source *3C* 273 reported by Hazard, Mackey and Shimmins in the preceding article are a star of about thirteenth magnitude and a faint wisp or jet. The jet has a width of 1″-2″ and extends away from the star in position angle 43°. It is not visible within 11″ from the star and ends abruptly at 20″ from the star. The position of the star, kindly furnished by Dr. T. A. Matthews, is R.A.12h 26m 33.35s ±0.04s, Decl. +2° 19′42.0″+0.5″ (1950), or 1″ east of component *B* of the radio source. The end of the jet is 1″ east of component *A*. The close correlation between the radio structure and the star with the jet is suggestive and intriguing.

Spectra of the star were taken with the prime-focus spectrograph at the 200-in. telescope with dispersions of 400 and 190 Å per mm. They show a number of broad emission features on a rather blue continuum. The most prominent features, which have widths around 50 Å, are, in order of strength, at 5,632, 3,239, 5,792, 5,032 Å. These and other weaker emission bands are listed in the first column of Table 1. For three faint bands with widths of 100-200 Å the total range of wave-length is indicated.

The only explanation found for the spectrum involves a considerable red-shift. A red-shift $\Delta\lambda/\lambda_0$ of 0.158 allows identification of four emission bands as Balmer lines, as indicated in Table1. Their relative strengths are in agreement with this explanation. Other identifications based on the above red-shift involve the Mg II lines around 2,798 Å, thus far only found in emission in the solar chromosphere, and a forbidden line of [O III] at 5,007 Å. On this basis another [O III] line is expected at 4,959 Å with a strength one-third of that of the line at 5,007 Å. Its detectability in the spectrum would be marginal. A weak emission band suspected at 5,705 Å, or 4,927 Å reduced for red-shift, does not fit the wave-length. No explanation is offered for the three very wide emission bands.

3C 273：一个具有很大红移的类星体

施密特

编者按

本文中，天文学家马丁·施密特利用西里尔·哈泽德及其同事们测定的特殊射电源 3*C* 273 的位置确认了 3*C* 273 是处于该射电源 1 角秒范围内的一个看来发射着一个小喷流的类似恒星天体。他还获得了这个源的光谱，只有当该射电源处于红移 0.158 时才能解释此光谱。从而使得该源被认为是一个距离非常遥远的源，这就是第一个类星体的发现。现在我们知道，类星体其实是由气体包围着的大质量黑洞。当气体落入黑洞时它会变得非常炽热，它所发出的光线能够掩盖星系的光芒，类星体处于该星系的中心。

在之前的文章中哈泽德、麦基和西敏报道了射电源 3*C* 273 子源的位置，在 200 英寸望远镜的底片上该射电源附近唯一能看到的天体是一颗亮度约为 13 等的星和一缕暗淡的亮条或喷流。喷流的宽度为 1″~2″，从恒星沿 43° 位置角向外延伸。在从恒星开始 11″ 的范围内不可见，并在位于恒星的 20″ 处突然结束。由马修斯博士友好提供的星的位置是赤经 12h 26m 33.35s ± 0.04s，赤纬 +2° 19′ 42.0″ ± 0.5″（1950 年）或射电源子源 *B* 以东 1″。喷流末端位于子源 *A* 以东 1″。射电结构与具有喷流的恒星之间的密切关系是非常具有启发性和耐人寻味的。

恒星的光谱取自 200 英寸望远镜主焦点处的摄谱仪，其色散为每毫米 400 埃和 190 埃。它们在偏蓝色连续谱上表现出大量的宽发射特征。这些光谱宽度约 50 埃，最突出的特征是按强度排序为 5,632 埃、3,239 埃、5,792 埃、5,032 埃。表 1 第 1 列中给出了这些及其他较弱的发射带。对于宽度为 100 埃 ~ 200 埃的 3 个较暗的波段则给出了其总的波长范围。

对这种光谱仅有的解释涉及一个相当大的红移。如表 1 所示，一个红移值 $\Delta\lambda/\lambda_0$ 为 0.158 的红移可证认出 4 个发射带为巴耳末谱线。它们的相应强度与这种解释是吻合的。基于上述红移的其他证认还包括 2,798 埃附近的迄今为止仅在太阳色球的发射中发现的 MgII 线以及在 5,007 埃处的 [O III] 禁线。在此基础上可以推测在 4,959 埃处还应该有一条 [O III] 线，其强度是 5,007 埃处线的 1/3。该谱线在光谱中刚好能被检测到。一个疑似在波长 5,705 埃或是由 4,927 埃红移后的微弱的发射带与其波长并不相符。对于其中 3 个非常宽的发射带，目前还没有给出任何解释。

Table 1. Wave-lengths and identifications

λ	$\lambda/1.158$	λ_0	
3,239	2,797	2,798	Mg II
4,595	3,968	3,970	$H\varepsilon$
4,753	4,104	4,102	$H\delta$
5,032	4,345	4,340	$H\gamma$
5,200-5,415	4,490-4,675		
5,632	4,864	4,861	$H\beta$
5,792	5,002	5,007	[O III]
6,005-6,190	5,186-5,345		
6,400-6,510	5,527-5,622		

It thus appears that six emission bands with widths around 50 Å can be explained with a red-shift of 0.158. The differences between the observed and the expected wave-lengths amount to 6 Å at the most and can be entirely understood in terms of the uncertainty of the measured wave-lengths. The present explanation is supported by observations of the infra-red spectrum communicated by Oke in a following article, and by the spectrum of another star-like object associated with the radio source 3*C* 48 discussed by Greenstein and Matthews in another communication.

The unprecedented identification of the spectrum of an apparently stellar object in terms of a large red-shift suggests either of the two following explanations.

(1) The stellar object is a star with a large gravitational red-shift. Its radius would then be of the order of 10 km. Preliminary considerations show that it would be extremely difficult, if not impossible, to account for the occurrence of permitted lines and a forbidden line with the same red-shift, and with widths of only 1 or 2 percent of the wave-length.

(2) The stellar object is the nuclear region of a galaxy with a cosmological red-shift of 0.158, corresponding to an apparent velocity of 47,400 km/sec. The distance would be around 500 megaparsecs, and the diameter of the nuclear region would have to be less than 1 kiloparsec. This nuclear region would be about 100 times brighter optically than the luminous galaxies which have been identified with radio sources thus far. If the optical jet and component *A* of the radio source are associated with the galaxy, they would be at a distance of 50 kiloparsecs, implying a time-scale in excess of 10^5 years. The total energy radiated in the optical range at constant luminosity would be of the order of 10^{59} ergs.

Only the detection of an irrefutable proper motion or parallax would definitively establish 3*C* 273 as an object within our Galaxy. At the present time, however, the explanation in terms of an extragalactic origin seems most direct and least objectionable.

表 1. 波长和证认

λ	λ/1.158	λ_0	
3,239	2,797	2,798	Mg Ⅱ
4,595	3,968	3,970	Hε
4,753	4,104	4,102	Hδ
5,032	4,345	4,340	Hγ
5,200~5,415	4,490~4,675		
5,632	4,864	4,861	Hβ
5,792	5,002	5,007	[O Ⅲ]
6,005~6,190	5,186~5,345		
6,400~6,510	5,527~5,622		

因此，看起来可以用 0.158 的红移来解释宽度约为 50 埃的 6 个发射带。观测到的波长和预期的波长最大差值为 6 埃，而这完全可以认为是由波长测量的不确定度引起的。随后由奥凯发表的一篇关于红外光谱的观测结果，以及另一篇由格林斯坦和马修斯发表的旨在讨论与射电源 3*C* 48 相关的另一个类星体光谱的通讯都支持上面的这种解释。

这一史无前例的对一个具有很大红移的类星体的证认暗示了下面两种可能的解释。

(1) 该类星体是一颗具有很大引力红移的恒星，它的半径的量级约为 10 千米。初步研究结果表明，考虑到在相同红移下容许谱线和禁线的出现，并且宽度仅为波长的 1% 或 2%，这种情况即便不是不可能，其存在也是极其困难的。

(2) 类星体是宇宙学红移为 0.158 的星系的核心区域，其相应的视速度为 47,400 千米 / 秒。其距离约为 500 兆秒差距，而核心区域的直径应小于 1 千秒差距。这个核心区域的亮度在光学上是迄今为止所有通过射电源证认的亮星系的亮度的 100 倍。如果射电源的光学喷流和子源 *A* 与星系相关，那么它们的距离应为 50 千秒差距，这意味着其时间尺度超过 10^5 年。在光度恒定的情况下，其光学波段内辐射的总能量量级应为 10^{59} 尔格。

只有确定无误地检测到其自行或视差才能最终肯定 3*C* 273 为银河系中的天体。然而，目前来看，将其视为起源于河外的天体似乎是最直接、最不会引起争议的。

I thank Dr. T. A. Matthews, who directed my attention to the radio source, and Drs. Greenstein and Oke for valuable discussions.

(**197**, 1040; 1963)

M. Schmidt: Mount Wilson and Palomar Observatories, Carnegie Institution of Washington, California Institute of Technology, Pasadena.

非常感谢马修斯博士将我的注意力引向射电源，并感谢格林斯坦博士和奥凯博士与我进行了有益的讨论。

（沈乃澂 翻译；邓祖淦 审稿）

Molecular Biology, Eugenics and Euphenics*

J. Lederberg

Editor's Note

Eugenics, the deliberate improvement of the human stock by selective breeding, had been popular among scientists in Britain and the United States in the early 1930s but, with the end of the Second World War in Europe in 1945, had fallen from favour largely because of the German government's widespread use of sterilization. By the early 1960s, however, and with the prospect that the new science of molecular biology might provide better ways of improving on nature, eugenics made occasional reappearances on the scientific agenda. Joshua Lederberg was at Stanford University in California when he contributed this article to *Nature*; he had already been awarded a Nobel Prize for his work on bacteria and afterwards became the director of the Rockefeller Institute in New York.

THE risks of scientific prophecy are well known. But foresight about our scientific culture is as important for the culture to gather as it is difficult for the scientist to expound. His credentials to speak on the impact of science on human welfare are scarcely unique, but he does have a responsibility which stems from his technical judgment of the plausibility and especially the time-scale of scientific advance, which by furthering human power must impinge on policy.

Recent years have seen breath-taking advances in the molecular foundations of biology, at a pace that reminds us that the gross effort in science in one year now matches the total accumulation to the beginning of this century; as much scientific effort has been invested since 1950 as was in all previous history. These actuarial calculations cannot, of course, measure the intellectual value of the return, nor do they take account either of instrumentation multipliers or of the overloading of the communications net. The details of these advances are well told elsewhere. What must be noted here is the solution to the fundamental problems of genetics: the encoding of genetic information in the structure of DNA, and the enzymatic mechanism by which the nucleotide sequence is replicated. Intertwined with these developments have been the unification of terrestrial biology within a single biochemical genetic scheme, and the now rapid unravelling of the cellular mechanism of protein synthesis whereby the genetic information is translated into the working machinery of life.

Eugenics, the conscious betterment of man's genetic quality, has fascinated many idealistic

---

* Substance of an address to the Symposium on "The Future of Man" held at the Ciba Foundation, London, November 26-30, 1962. The full proceedings of the Symposium will be published by Messrs. J. and A. Churchill, Ltd.

分子生物学、优生学和人种改良学*

莱德伯格

编者按

20 世纪 30 年代初期，优生学曾得到英国和美国科学家的广泛关注，它是通过选育的方法对人类血统进行有意改良的一门学科。但是随着 1945 年第二次世界大战在欧洲的结束，由于德国政府大范围地推行绝育政策，使这门学科受到极大冷落。直到 20 世纪 60 年代初期，由于未来前景显示分子生物学这门新兴科学有可能为改良人类血统提供更好的途径，在此背景下优生学重新出现在科学的议事日程中。当约书亚·莱德伯格将这篇文章投到《自然》杂志的时候，他就职于加利福尼亚州斯坦福大学。此前他已经凭借在细菌研究方面的工作获得了诺贝尔奖，后来他成为了纽约洛克菲勒研究所的所长。

众所周知，提出科学预言需要承担风险。但是为我们的科学文化所做的预见对于文化的汇集非常重要，而这很难让科学家去阐述。科学家并非是唯一有资格在科学对人类的幸福所产生的影响方面发表言论的人，但他确有此责任，这种责任来源于他在专业技术上对可能性所具有的判断力，特别是对科学进展的时间尺度的判断力。而通过推进人类的力量，科学进展势必会对政策产生影响。

近年来，基础分子生物学已取得惊人的进展，其发展速度提醒我们：现在一年所取得的科学成就的分量相当于 20 世纪初研究成果的总和；同样，20 世纪 50 年代之后所投入的科研精力也相当于 50 年代之前所投入精力的总和。当然，即使不将研究设备的扩充或通信网络的超载考虑在内，这些统计估算也不能衡量这些科研投入的智力价值回报。这些研究进展的细节可以从其他渠道获知。此处值得一提的是解决遗传学基本问题的研究发现：DNA 结构中遗传信息的编码机制和核苷酸序列复制的酶学机制。以上研究进展揭示了陆上生物在生物化学水平上统一的遗传模式，以及遗传信息翻译成为生物性状的过程，也就是细胞内蛋白质合成的机制。

对人类的遗传质量进行有意改良的优生学，已经受到许多唯心主义者的关注。

* 发表于 1962 年 11 月 26 日至 30 日在伦敦汽巴基金会举行的“人类的未来”讨论会。完整的会议记录将由丘吉尔有限公司出版。

thinkers. Like other noble aims it has been perverted to justify unthinkable inhumanity; which does not help to assess its validity and feasibility by ethically proper means. The case for eugenics, ably presented by Huxley and by Muller, has one most trenchant argument against complacency: man's long pre-cultural evolution has given him a biological legacy which can be only fortuitously adapted to the physical power and technological complexity of the modern world. In a word, man, unless he grows less "human", may destroy himself.

Eugenic progress creeps within the joint constraints of our limited knowledge of human genetics and customary wisdom concerning its implementation. Even so, the eugenicists argue, some beginning must be made, to offset exigent counter-eugenic influences, perhaps to assure that some eugenic wisdom survives until the species can or must act.

The new biology is relevant here—ultimately it could diagnose, then specify, the actual DNA composition of ideal man. But clearly, this will not happen for some time ("if ever", most of my colleagues will reassure themselves, while they concentrate on more penetrating assaults on these secrets).

Having shared this view, I may record how easy and tempting it is to postpone consideration of the probable impact of biological knowledge on human affairs. It is difficult enough to make a fragmentary contribution to such knowledge, much more to be usefully concerned with its total consequences.

The emphasis on eugenics as the point of application of molecular biology overlooks the most immediate prospects for the understanding and then control of human development. To dramatize the antinomy, I propose the term "euphenics" as the counterpart of "eugenics", in the same sense that "phenotype" is opposed to "genotype".

Development is the translation of the genetic instructions of the egg, embodied in its DNA, to direct the unfolding of its substance to form the adult organism in all its aspects, which comprise its phenotype. The crucial problem of embryology is the regulation and execution of protein synthesis, how some DNA segments are made to call out their instructions, others suppressed, which underlies the orderly differentiation of cell types.

Until now, the major problems of human development—not only embryology, but also the phenomena of learning (in its neurobiological aspects), immunity (with its bearing on transplantation), neoplasia and senescence—could be approached at only the most superficial level. They are about to be transformed in the sense that genetics has been, as epiphenomena of protein and nucleic acid synthesis. The present intensity of effort suggests a span of from five to no more than twenty years for an analogous systematization.

On these premises it would be incredible if we did not have the basis of developmental engineering technique, for example, to regulate the size of the human brain by prenatal or early postnatal intervention.

像其他崇高的目标一样，优生学曾被误认为是不人道的做法，也无法通过合乎伦理的方法来评定它的有效性和可行性。赫胥黎和马勒巧妙地引用一个优生学的例子深刻驳斥了这种自满情绪：人类从长期史前进化中获得的生物学遗产很幸运地刚好能满足现代人的体能需求以及适应现代社会技术的复杂性。简单来说，如果人类长得像“现代人”，他就是自寻毁灭。

优生学受到有限的人类遗传学知识及关于其实施的传统观念的共同制约，缓慢地发展着。尽管如此，优生学家认为，为了抵消反优生学的影响，一些初步研究势在必行，这也许能够保证一些优生学的思想延续下去，直至人类能够或是必须采取行动的时候。

新兴分子生物学的价值在于，它最终可以诊断并详细说明理想人类的实际 DNA 的组成。但是，很显然，短期之内这一点是做不到的（“如果可以做到的话”，我的大部分同事们将恢复他们对研究的信心，专注于对这些未知的问题进行更深入的研究）。

分享过这些观点后，我要说暂时不考虑生物学知识对人类可能产生的影响，是多么轻松而吸引人的选择。对这些知识做一些零散的贡献已经非常困难了，更别说是对其整体的结果能够有所帮助。

对优生学是作为分子生物学一项应用的强调忽视了直接理解和调控人类的发育过程的可能。为了显示出这一矛盾，我建议将“人种改良学”与“优生学”对应起来，像“表现型”与“基因型”相对应一样。

发育是指卵细胞中 DNA 所携带的遗传信息经过翻译后，指导其自身物质演变形成完整的成熟有机体（包含它的表现型）的过程。胚胎学的关键问题是蛋白质合成的调控和执行，如何使得一些 DNA 片段表达而另外一些 DNA 片段受到抑制，这种调控机制为不同种类细胞的有序分化奠定了基础。

迄今为止，有关人类发育的主要问题不仅包括胚胎学，也包括学习现象（神经生物学方面）、免疫（移植耐受性）、肿瘤形成以及衰老，对这些问题的研究都只停留在最浅显的水平上。这些研究即将像遗传学一样产生巨变，例如遗传学不过是蛋白质和核酸合成过程的附带现象。以目前的研究力度来看，我们还需要 5 年 ~ 20 年的时间将该类问题系统化。

基于这些推测，如果我们没有发育的工程技术作为基础，例如通过产前或产后初期干预来调控人类脑的大小将令人难以置信。

The basic concept of molecular biology is the chain of information from DNA to RNA to protein. We are just now beginning to ask questions of mental mechanism from this point of view. The simplest and one of the oldest of speculations about memory is the modification of neuronal interconnexion through control of synthesis and deposition of durable proteins at the interfaces. A plausible link between electrical impulses and protein synthesis might be the accompanying shifts of potassium and sodium concentrations; these ions being also important cofactors for several enzymes involved in protein synthesis. Thus, cation balance could control the assembly of chosen polypeptide chains into a complex protein, the selective reactions of glutamine —$CONH_2$ in protein, or the imperfect specifications of degenerate RNA codes. Such speculations merely illustrate the relationship of mental science to molecular biology.

In another field of developmental engineering Medawar has already exhibited a *tour de force*, the abolition of immunity to transplants introduced in early life, which has clarified the biology of immunity and points to the solution of the transplantation problem. At present, human individuality is the bar to spare-part medicine: the organism rejects grafts from other individuals even of the same species, the alien tissue a life-extending kidney or heart notwithstanding. The solution to the homograft problem now partly resolved must be imminent, under intensive attack as an aspect of the cell biology of immunity, and of the molecular structure and cytosynthesis of antibodies and tissue antigens. The management of the problems and opportunities it raises should be a prototype for the exercise of responsible power in biological engineering. There is no evident forethought of them, perhaps just because of their cataclysmic impact on medicine.

What if surgical finesse were now the only criterion of transplantability? The direct replacement of defective, diseased or worn-out organs could pre-empt all available surgical talent for years to come. Then, many potent régimes, once restrained by the side-effects on other organs, are now available to internal medicine. These tools, like present-day drugs, will also have an indispensable role in the treatment of healthy individuals.

The most nightmarish prospects arise from indifference to technological and procedural requirements with respect to the sources of indispensable, scarce life-saving organs. The orderly evolution of transplantation technique might be facilitated if organ transplants in man (with evident trivial exceptions) were already subject to formal registration as vital statistics.

Many social problems arise from technological imbalance, or at least have possible technological antidotes which can then be properly discussed here. For example, the political stability of the world might be enhanced if the present technology of the detection matched that of the power output of nuclear explosives; likewise for the moderation of human prolificity concurrently with infant mortality. In the present case intolerable stresses arising from the economics of human organs could be averted by further advances beyond the first stage of successful homotransplantation. These might include a eugenic programme on other species to facilitate their use as sources of organs.

分子生物学的基本概念是指从 DNA 到 RNA 再到蛋白质的信息链传递。现在我们刚开始根据这种观点来提出一些关于脑机制的问题。关于记忆的一个古老而简单的推测认为记忆是神经元连接处发生修饰作用而产生的，这种作用是通过对连接处的持久性蛋白（缝隙连接蛋白）的合成与沉积进行调控来完成的。电脉冲和蛋白质合成之间的联系可能是通过钾离子和钠离子浓度的转换来实现的；这些离子也是参与蛋白质合成的几个酶的重要辅助因子。所以，阳离子平衡可能能够控制：特定多肽链如何组装成复杂的蛋白质，蛋白质中谷氨酰胺的—$CONH_2$ 基因的选择性反应，或RNA简并密码的部分特异性。以上推测只能解释脑科学和分子生物学之间的关系。

在发育工程的另一领域中，梅达沃已经展示了一个**杰作**，那就是在生命早期不会对移植体产生免疫反应，并由此阐明了免疫生物学的机理并提出了解决移植问题的方法。目前，人类个体自身对器官移植产生阻挡：生物体会排斥其他个体甚至是相同物种个体上移植而来的器官，即使是可以延续生命的外源组织的肾或心脏。通过加强对免疫细胞生物学、分子结构细胞生物学以及抗体和组织抗原细胞合成的研究，目前已经得到部分解决的同种移植问题应该很快就能被彻底攻克。对器官移植所带来的问题和机遇的处理方式，应该可以作为我们解决生物工程问题的示范。或许正是因为它们对医学的巨大冲击，我们对这些研究并没有事先预料到。

如果外科手术是目前衡量可移植性的唯一标准，那又会如何？在未来的几年，直接替换缺陷的、患病的或穿孔的器官将优先占用外科所有可用人力资源。然后，由于对其他器官有过副作用而受到限制的药物组合将应用于内科医学。这些工具就像现在的药物一样，也将在治疗正常人群中发挥不可替代的作用。

如果对那些至关重要的、来源不充足的器官的需求在技术上和程序上没有得到足够的重视，那么前景将会是非常糟糕的。如果人类器官移植（除了少数明显的例外）已经作为人口统计正式注册，那么可能会促进移植技术的有序发展。

许多社会问题是由技术不均衡引起的，尽管有少数通过技术恢复均衡的方法，随后我们会对后者进行适当的讨论。例如，如果现有的核探测技术与核爆炸技术相匹配，那么世界政治将更加稳定；同样的平衡也存在于人类适度的多育与婴儿的死亡率之间。以目前的情况看，同种移植技术已经达到初步阶段，如果在此基础上继续发展的话，那么由人类器官紧缺所引起的巨大压力将得到改善。其中一个可能的优生学方案是将其他物种作为器官来源。如果这些器官的来源在遗传上是一致的，

The more difficult problem of heterotransplantation, from other species, would be mitigated if these sources were genetically uniform and could be specifically selected for immunological and functional suitability. At present the only animals which begin to fit these criteria are inbred mice. The industrial manufacture of specific proteins (either by chemical- or cyto-synthesis) would be an invaluable adjunct. Such precious proteins, for example, hormones or enzymes, are sometimes the functional purpose of a transplant. As antibodies or tissue antigens they would play a specific part in neutralizing the homograft rejection mechanism. As structural proteins they would be valuable for the manufacture of compatible parts and connexions.

The heart probably poses the most perplexing problems of supply and allocation. Yet, of all the vital organs, this should be the first to be simulated by a mechanical analogue—machines are already available for short-term use during surgery. Should the engineering effort be accelerated to produce a practical substitute for this efficient pump? These proposals stress engineering development, partly to illustrate a prevalent gap between academic science and its useful implementation in this aspect of human welfare. There are many equally insistent candidates for the succession the military uses of industrial technology.

Man's control of his own development, "euphenics", transmutes the means, and also the ends of eugenics, as have all the precedent cultural revolutions that have shaped the species: language, agriculture, political organization, the physical technologies. Eugenics is aimed at the design of a reaction system (a DNA sequence) that, in a given context, will develop to somehow defined goal. Few insights would be worth more than the design of human value—but will culture stand still merely to validate the eugenic criteria of a past generation? For a given end, the means will have shifted: the best inborn pattern for normal development will not always react best to euphenic control.

Within the framework of formal eugenics the disruptive effects of recombination may need further investigation. Most genes segregate independently of sex, but must then work in concert with the bio-cultural dimorphism of sex. This must impede stringent selection; or conversely, does rapid eugenics not imply the convergence of the sexes to a common goal? At a considerable cost in its rate the evolutionary process might be confined to sex-limited, -linked, or -irrelevant mutations, if any, which still affect personality. Euphenics can switch the entire programme to match the sexual or other role-defining polymorphisms. Education—the whole cultural apparatus—does this now.

Euphenics will, of course, open the way for a more comprehensive eugenics, if only through the systematization of knowledge of gene action. Even now the outlook for eugenic improvement of intelligence would be improved by a biochemical assay for it.

In our inquiry on his future, the aims of human existence are inseparable from the power and responsibility for human nature. It becomes more perplexing as biological technology dissolves the barriers around individual man and intrudes on his secret, germinal

并且能通过免疫和功能适应性的特定筛选，那么从其他物种进行异种移植这个较为困难的问题就能得以缓解了。目前，动物中只有近交系小鼠符合这些标准。通过工业生产特异蛋白质（化学合成或细胞合成）将是一个非常重要的辅助手段。这些珍贵的蛋白质，例如激素或酶，有时正是能否实现器官移植的功效的关键所在。比如抗体或组织抗原在消除同种移植排异反应中起特殊作用，又如结构蛋白在兼容和连接方面起重要作用。

在器官移植中，心脏的供应和分配问题可能是最复杂的。然而，在所有重要的器官中，心脏应当是首个被机械模拟的——人工心脏已经可以在外科手术中短期使用了。我们是否应该在工程方面投入更多的精力以生产一个合适的心脏替代品呢？这项提议强调了工程技术发展的重要性，在一定程度上说明了科学理论距离为人类创造福利还有一定差距。此外，军用技术也能为工业技术的发展提供很多好的候选技术。

人类调控其自身的发育，也就是所谓的“人种改良学”，改变了优生学的方法和目的，正如先前所有的文化革命一样，它塑造了人类的语言、农业、政治组织和物理技术。优生学的目标是设计出一个在特定的环境中通过某种方式达到已定目标的反应体系（DNA 序列）。没有什么比设计人类的价值更有意义——那么，难道说文化存在的意义只是为了验证前人的优生学标准吗？因为正常发育的先天模式不会总是与人种改良的目标相适应，所以为了实现特定的改良目标，调控的具体方法要有所改变。

在正式的优生学框架内，可能需要对基因重组的副作用做进一步的研究。绝大多数基因分离与性别无关，但一定与生物文明的性别二态性有关。这一定阻止了严格的筛选；或者反过来说，快速优生学难道不正是意味着两性向一个共同目标汇聚吗？这种严格的选择和淘汰需要付出相当大的代价，进化过程可能会受到限性、伴性或无性突变的限制，如果有的话，还会对个性产生影响。人种改良学可以控制将整个方案转向为性别或其他角色分类的多态性。目前的教育体系，也就是所有的文化机构，正在发挥这样的作用。

当然，只要对基因的作用有系统化的认识，人种改良学就会开启一条通往更全面的优生学的道路，尽管现在通过生化检验已经能够进行优生学上的智力改良。

在我们对人种改良学前景的调查中发现，人类生存的目的与人的权利和责任是分不开的。以生物技术为手段的人种改良已经变得更复杂了，它可以消除围绕在个

continuity. The humanist premise of individual value must face the issue of a definition of man, taking full account of his psychosocial progeny. We now recognize genetic continuity in mechanistic terms as a nucleotide sequence—in due course this will itself be subordinate to the psychosocial machinery. While man perfects the knowledge of his own mechanism, he also vitalizes machines on to a convergent evolutionary pathway. Genetics is rapidly becoming a corollary of information theory. As he thus evolves from substance to concept, Is it the bond of genetics or of communication that qualifies "man" for the aspirations of humanistic fulfilment, apart from the other robots born of human thought?

(**198**, 428-429; 1963)

Joshua Lederberg: Kennedy Laboratories for Molecular Medicine, Department of Genetics, School of Medicine, Stanford University, Palo Alto, California.

体周围的壁垒，也可以探知个体的秘密——种质连续性。人道主义者提出，以个体价值为前提，就必须面临人的定义这个议题，也要充分考虑到他的后代的心理。现在我们认识到遗传连续性用生物学术语来说就是核苷酸序列，在适当的时候它本身将会附属于心理机制。人类在完善对自身机制认识的同时，也促使进化途径趋于一致。这些过程中，信息技术的理论为遗传学的迅速发展提供了条件。因此遗传学得以从客观存在发展到理论水平。暂且不提人类思想下诞生的其他自动机械，或许是生物学上的遗传或文化上的传承才使得“人类”得以迎来人道主义的实现？

（郭娟 翻译；金侠 审稿）

Magnetic Anomalies over Oceanic Ridges

F. J. Vine and D. H. Matthews

Editor's Note

The idea that the continents drift slowly over the surface of the Earth was first put forward by the German Geophysicist Alfred Wegener early in the twentieth century, but scientific opinion that Wegener's hypothesis might be correct swung in that direction only after the Second World War. One of the decisive pieces of evidence was that collected by Fred Vine and Drummond Matthews by means of magnetic surveys from ships crisscrossing the North Atlantic Ocean. Those data enabled Vine and Matthews to construct maps showing the presence of stripes of opposite magnetic alignment imprinted in the rocks of the ocean floor. These magnetic anomalies come about because the Earth's magnetic field reverses its direction at intervals of 100,000 years, so that rocks extruded from an active ridge, like that running from north to south in the Atlantic, will be magnetized in opposite directions according to when they were formed.

TYPICAL profiles showing bathymetry and the associated total magnetic field anomaly observed on crossing the North Atlantic and North-West Indian Oceans are shown in Fig. 1. They illustrate the essential features of magnetic anomalies over the oceanic ridges: (1) long-period anomalies over the exposed or buried foothills of the ridge; (2) shorter-period anomalies over the rugged flanks of the ridge; (3) a pronounced central anomaly associated with the median valley. This pattern has now been observed in the North Atlantic[1,2], the Antarctic[3], and the Indian Oceans[4,5]. In this article we describe an attempt to account for it.

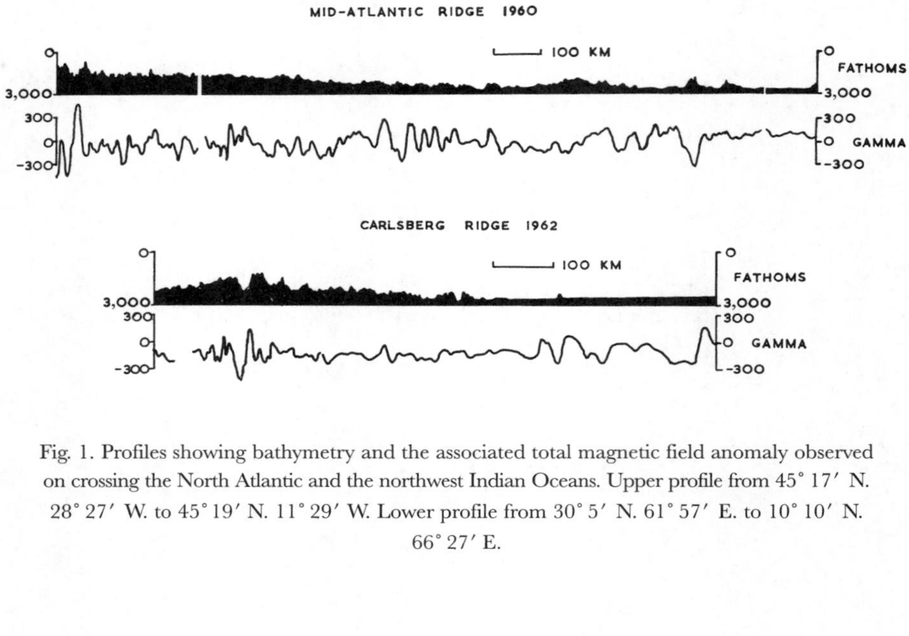

Fig. 1. Profiles showing bathymetry and the associated total magnetic field anomaly observed on crossing the North Atlantic and the northwest Indian Oceans. Upper profile from 45° 17′ N. 28° 27′ W. to 45° 19′ N. 11° 29′ W. Lower profile from 30° 5′ N. 61° 57′ E. to 10° 10′ N. 66° 27′ E.

大洋中脊上的磁异常

瓦因，马修斯

编者按

20 世纪初，德国地球物理学家阿尔弗雷德·魏格纳首次提出了大陆漂移假说，但是直到二战后，科学界才认为魏格纳的假说有可能是正确的。弗雷德·瓦因和德拉蒙德·马修斯在横跨北大西洋的考察中，通过磁力测量方法收集得到了决定性的证据之一。借助这些数据瓦因和马修斯绘制了海底岩石中正、反磁性交替排列的条状磁化带地图。之所以产生这些磁性方向反转的异常现象，是因为地球磁场每隔十万年会有一次磁性方向的反转，所以当熔融物质沿活动性洋脊（例如纵贯南北的大西洋中脊）上涌并在其两侧固化成岩的过程中，必定会受到沿当时地磁场方向的磁化。

在北大西洋与西北印度洋观测到的典型深海测量剖面以及相应的总磁场异常如图 1 所示。图中表明了大洋中脊上磁场异常的基本特征：(1) 出露或被覆盖的洋脊山麓显示出长周期异常；(2) 洋脊崎岖的两翼区域表现为短周期异常；(3) 中央裂谷显示出强烈的中心异常。目前在北大西洋 [1,2]、南极 [3] 和印度洋 [4,5] 均观测到了这种现象。本文中我们将试图对此进行解释。

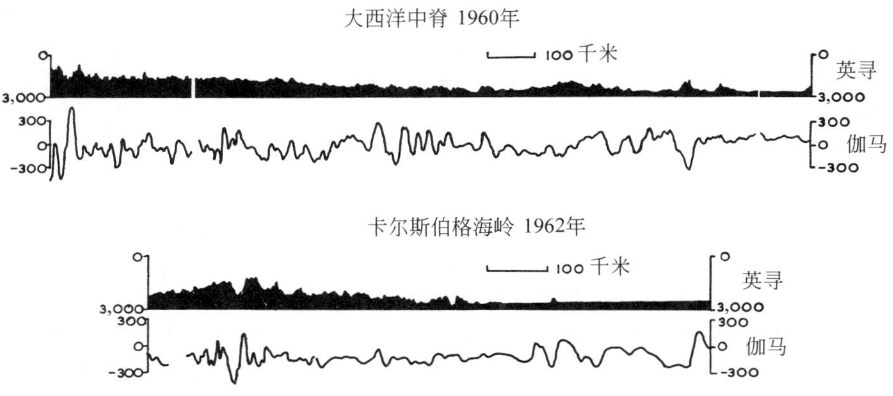

图 1. 在北大西洋和西北印度洋观测到的水深以及相关的总磁场异常图。上图位于北纬 45° 17′，西经 28° 27′ 至北纬 45° 19′，西经 11° 29′。下图位于北纬 30° 5′，东经 61° 57′ 至北纬 10° 10′，东经 66° 27′。

The general increase in wave-length of the anomalies away from the crest of the ridge is almost certainly associated with the increase in depth to the magnetic crustal material[1]. Local anomalies of short-period may often be correlated with bathymetry, and explained in terms of reasonable susceptibility contrasts and crustal configurations; but the long-period anomalies of category (1) are not so readily explained. The central anomaly can be reproduced if it is assumed that a block of material very strongly magnetized in the present direction of the Earth's field underlies the median valley and produces a positive susceptibility contrast with the adjacent crust. It is not clear, however, why this considerable susceptibility contrast should exist beneath the median valley but not elsewhere under the ridge. Recent work in this Department has suggested a new mechanism.

In November 1962, H.M.S. *Owen* made a detailed magnetic survey over a central part of the Carlsberg Ridge as part of the International Indian Ocean Expedition. The area (50×40 nautical miles; centred on 5°25′N., 61°45′E.) is predominantly mountainous, depths ranging from 900 to 2,200 fathoms, and the topographic features are generally elongated parallel to the trend of the Ridge. This elongation is more marked on the total magnetic field anomaly map where a trough of negative anomalies, flanked by steep gradients, separates two areas of positive anomalies. The trough of negative anomalies corresponds to a general depression in the bottom topography which represents the median valley of the Ridge. The Positive anomalies correspond to mountains on either side of the valley.

In this low magnetic latitude (inclination −6°) the effect of a body magnetized in the present direction of the Earth's field is to reduce the strength of the field above it, producing a negative anomaly over the body and a slight positive anomaly to the north. Here, over the centre of the Ridge, the bottom topography indicates the relief of basic extrusives such as volcanoes and fissure eruptives, and there is little sediment fill. The bathymetry, therefore, defines the upper surface of magnetic material having a considerable intensity of magnetization, potentially as high as any known igneous rock type[6], and probably higher, because it is extrusive, than the main crustal layer beneath. That the topographic features *are* capable of producing anomalies is immediately apparent on comparing the bathymetric and the anomaly charts; several have well-defined anomalies associated with them.

Two comparatively isolated volcano-like features were singled out and considered in detail. One has an associated negative anomaly as one would expect for normal magnetization, the other, completely the reverse anomaly pattern, that is, a pronounced positive anomaly suggesting reversed magnetization. Data on the topography of each feature and its associated anomaly were fed into a computer and an intensity and direction of magnetization for each obtained. Fig. 2 shows the directions of the resulting vectors plotted on a stereographic projection. Having computed the magnetic vector by a "best fit" process, the computer recalculated the anomaly over the body, assuming this vector, thus giving an indication of the accuracy of fit. The fit was good for the case of reversed magnetization but poor for that of approximately normal magnetization. The discrepancy is scarcely surprising since we have ignored the effects of adjacent topography, and the interference

远离洋脊顶部的磁异常波长几乎是随着磁性地壳物质埋深的增加而增大的[1]。短周期的局部异常通常可用水深进行修正，并且可用合理的磁化率反差和地壳结构来解释，但据此很难对类型（1）中的长周期异常做出解释。首先假设一块位于中央裂谷下的物质在当前的地磁场方向上被强烈磁化，并与相邻地壳相比产生了正的磁化率反差。如果该假设成立，这个中心异常就可以再次出现。然而，并不清楚为什么这种巨大的磁化率反差会存在于中央裂谷之下，而不是在洋脊下的其他地方。最近，剑桥大学大地测量学和地球物理学系所进行的研究给出了一种新的机制。

1962 年 11 月，作为国际印度洋考察的一部分，英国海军舰艇“欧文号”对卡尔斯伯格海岭中心部位进行了一次详细的地磁测量。该区域（50 海里 × 40 海里；中心位于北纬 5° 25′，东经 61° 45′）海底山脉显著发育，深度范围为 900 英寻 ~ 2,200 英寻，其地形特征与洋脊走向呈基本一致的平行延伸。这种延伸在总磁场异常图上更为明显，图中一个两侧梯度陡峭的负异常波谷将两个正异常区域分开。负异常波谷对应于海底地形中的一个洼陷，它代表洋脊的中央裂谷。而正异常对应于裂谷两侧的海底山脉。

在这种低磁纬度（倾角 −6°）地区，在目前的地球磁场方向上被磁化的岩体会减小其上方的磁场强度，从而导致岩体上方形成一个负异常，并且产生一个弱的向北的正异常。洋脊中心区的底部地形表示有基性岩浆喷发释放（例如火山式喷发和裂缝式喷发）并存在少量的沉积物。因此，通过水深测量确定了磁性物质的上界，它具有可观的磁化强度，其磁性有可能与其他已知火成岩的磁性一样高[6]，甚至可能比主要地壳层底部的磁性更高，这是由于它是喷出型岩石。通过水深和磁异常图的比较，明显可以看出地形特征**能够**引起异常；并且已经证实确有一些地形特征与异常有关。

我们选出两种孤立的火山型特征并对其进行了详细研究。其中一个特征因受到正向磁化作用而呈现相应的负异常，另一个则因受到反向的磁化作用而呈现明显的正异常。将每种特征及其相应的异常地形测量数据录入计算机，便可以得到其磁化作用的强度和方向。图 2 显示了球极投影上的矢量方向。计算机先对磁矢量进行“最佳拟合”并假定这个拟合结果成立，然后对地块上的异常重新进行运算，便可以得出一个拟合后的精确表示。这种拟合适用于受到反向磁化作用时的情况，但并不适用于受到近似正向磁化作用时的情况。存在这种差异并不奇怪，因为我们忽略了相邻地形的影响以及附近其他磁异常的干扰。此外，这个正向磁化作用的例子靠近区域的转角处，其边界的控制不够精确。另一个例子处于约束得较好的中心位置。在

of other anomalies in the vicinity. In addition, the example of normal magnetization is near a corner of the area where the control of contouring is less precise. The other example is central where the control is good. In both cases the intensity of magnetization deduced was about 0.005 e.m.u.; this is equivalent to an effective susceptibility of ±0.0133: (effective susceptibility=total intensity of magnetization (remanent+induced)/present total magnetic field intensity: mean value for basalts of the order of 0.01).

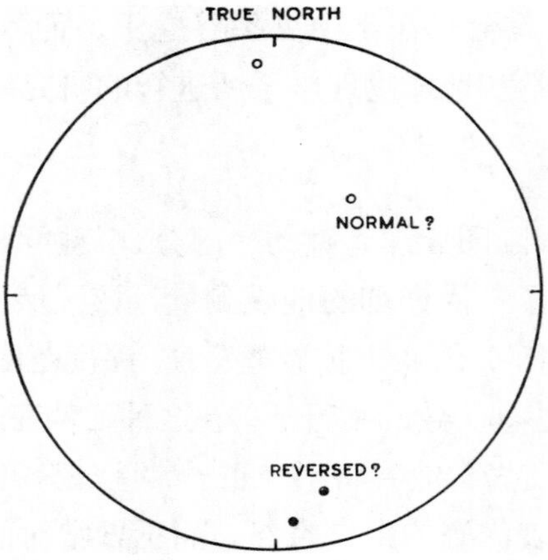

Fig. 2. Directions of the magnetic vectors obtained by the computer programme plotted on a stereographic projection, together with the present field vector and its reverse. Bearings and inclinations: present field vector 356°; −6°(up); computed vectors 038°; −40°(up);166°30′; +13°(down)

In addition, three profiles, perpendicular to the trend of the Ridge, have been considered. Computed profiles along these, assuming infinite lateral extent of the bathymetric profile, and uniform normal magnetization, bear little resemblance to the observed profiles (Fig. 3). These results suggested that whole blocks of the survey area might be reversely magnetized. The dotted curve in Fig. 3 *B* was computed for a model in which the main crustal layer and overlying volcanic terrain were divided into blocks about 20 km wide, alternately normally and reversely magnetized. The blocks were given the effective susceptibility values shown in the caption to Fig. 4 (3).

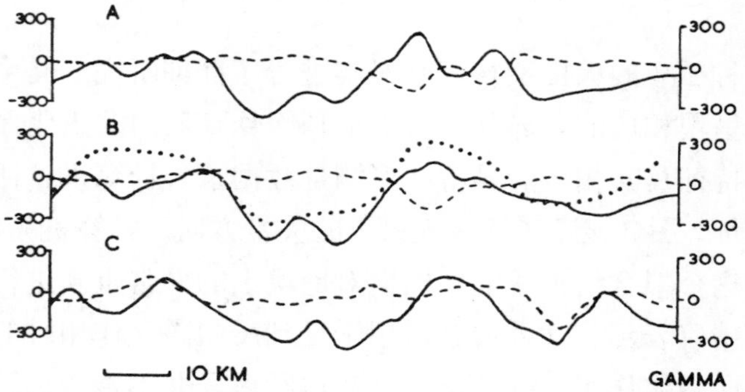

Fig. 3. Observed and computed profiles across the crest of the Carlsberg Ridge. Solid lines, observed anomaly; broken lines, computed profile assuming uniform normal magnetization and an effective susceptibility of 0.0133; dotted line, assuming reversals—see text. The computed profiles were obtained assuming infinite lateral extent of the bathymetric profiles

这两种情况下，推算出的磁化强度均约为 0.005 个电磁单位，由此可以得出有效磁化率为 ±0.0133：（有效磁化率 = 总磁化强度（剩余的 + 感应的）/ 当前总磁场强度：相当于 0.01 数量级玄武岩的平均值）。

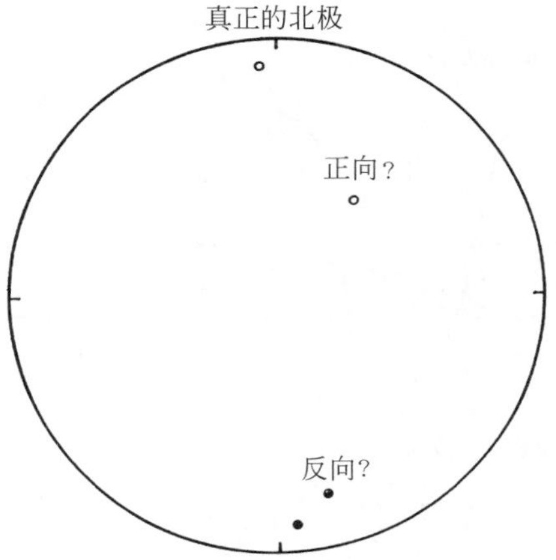

图 2. 在球极投影上由计算机程序得出的磁矢量方向，以及当前磁场矢量及其反向矢量方向。象限角和倾斜角：当前磁场矢量 356° ；–6°（向上）；计算的矢量 038° ；–40°（向上）；166° 30′ ；+13°（向下）。

此外，我们还分析了三个垂直于山脉走向的剖面。计算得到的剖面图（假定水深测量剖面横向无限延伸，并受到均匀的正向磁化作用）与观测到的剖面图非常不同（图 3）。这些结果表明研究区的岩石可能受到了反向的磁化作用。图 3*B* 中的点线为计算机绘制的一个模型，这里设定主要地壳层及其上方的火山岩层被分成了间隔约 20 千米的正、反磁化交替排列的磁化块体。图 4（3）中标出了磁化带及其有效磁化率的数值。

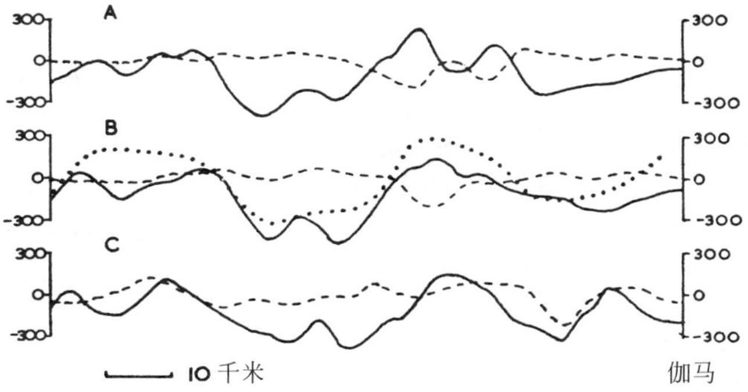

图 3. 横跨卡尔斯伯格海岭顶峰的观测图形以及计算的图形。实线为观测到的异常；虚线为假定均匀的正向磁化强度和有效磁化率为 0.0133 时计算的图形；点线为假定地磁反转情况下的图形（见正文）。计算的图形是在假定水深测量剖面可向两侧无限延伸的条件下得出的。

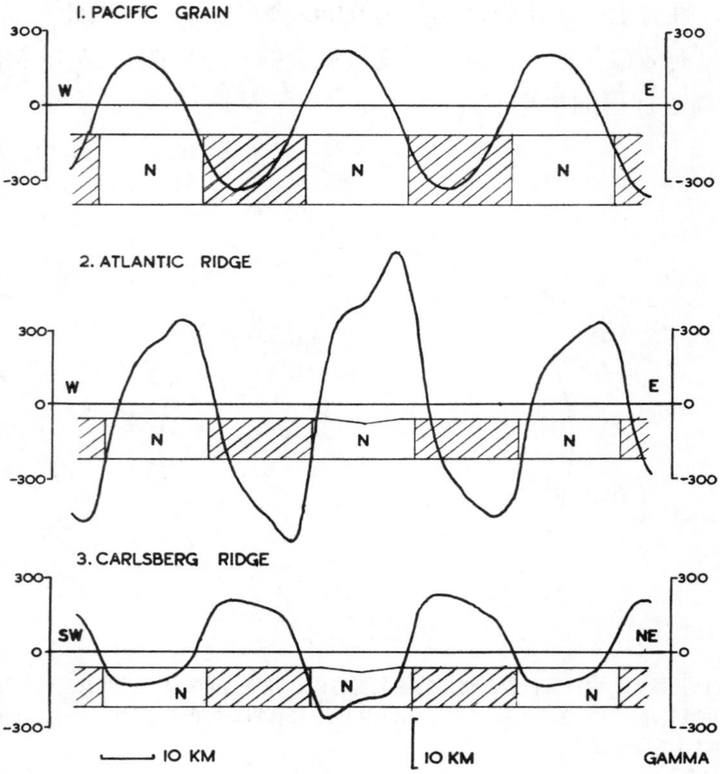

Fig. 4. Magnetic profiles computed for various crustal models. Crustal blocks marked *N*, normally magnetized; diagonally shaded blocks, reversely magnetized. Effective susceptibility of blocks, 0.0027, except for the block under the median valley in profiles 2 and 3, 0.0053 (1) Pacific Grain. Total field strength, T=0.5 oersted; inclination, I=60°; magnetic bearing of profile, θ=073°. (2) Mid-Atlantic Ridge, T=0.48 oersted; I=65°; θ=120°. (3) Carlsberg Ridge, T=0.376 oersted; $I=-6°$; θ=044°

Work on this survey led us to suggest that some 50 percent of the oceanic crust might be reversely magnetized and this in turn has suggested a new model to account for the pattern of magnetic anomalies over the ridges.

The theory is consistent with, in fact virtually a corollary of, current ideas on ocean floor spreading[7] and periodic reversals in the Earth's magnetic field[8]. If the main crustal layer (seismic layer 3) of the oceanic crust is formed over a convective up-current in the mantle at the centre of an oceanic ridge, it will be magnetized in the current direction of the Earth's field. Assuming impermanence of the ocean floor, the whole of the oceanic crust is comparatively young, probably not older than 150 million years, and the thermo-remanent component of its magnetization is therefore either essentially normal, or reversed with respect to the present field of the Earth. Thus, if spreading of the ocean floor occurs, blocks of alternately normal and reversely magnetized material would drift away from the centre of the ridge and parallel to the crest of it.

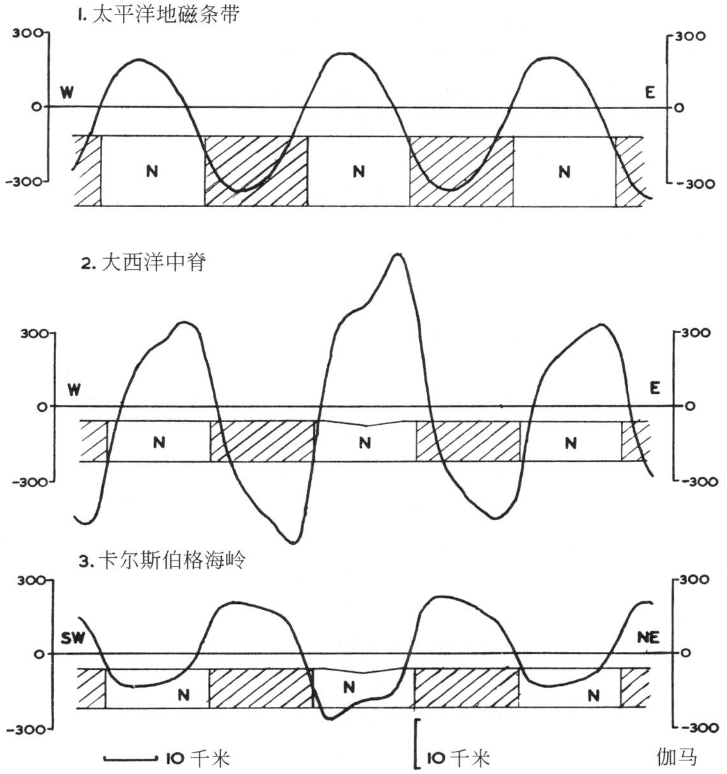

图 4. 根据不同地壳模型计算的磁剖面图。标注 N 的地壳块体，正向磁化区域；标注阴影的地壳块体，反向磁化区域。剖面 2 和 3 中，中央裂谷下的地壳块体有效磁化率为 0.0053，除此之外其他地壳块体的有效磁化率均为 0.0027。

(1) 太平洋地磁条带。总场强 $T = 0.5$ 奥斯特；倾斜角 $I = 60°$；图形的磁象限角，$\theta = 073°$。(2) 大西洋中脊，$T = 0.48$ 奥斯特；$I = 65°$；$\theta = 120°$。(3) 卡尔斯伯格海岭，$T = 0.376$ 奥斯特；$I = -6°$；$\theta = 044°$。

这项调查使我们认识到约有 50%的大洋地壳受到了反向磁化作用，反过来这个理论也为解释洋脊上的磁异常现象提供了一个新的模型。

这个理论与目前的海底扩张说[7]以及地磁场周期性反转的思想是一致的[8]，也可以说是上述思想的一个推论。假设洋脊中心的地幔物质上涌后推开两边的岩石从而形成新的岩层，而大洋地壳的主要地壳层（地震层 3）则形成于这个“传送带”式的岩层之上，那么它就会在当时的地磁场方向上受到磁化。假定海底岩层是不断更新的，那么整个大洋地壳是相对较新的，可能还不到 1.5 亿年。因此热剩磁不是受到基本正向的磁化作用，就是受到与当前地磁场反向的磁化作用。如果海底扩张确实存在，那么大量的磁性物质将会从洋脊中心涌出并平行于其顶部向两侧形成正、反交替的磁化块体。

This configuration of magnetic material could explain the lineation or "grain" of magnetic anomalies observed over the Eastern Pacific to the west of North America[6] (probably equivalent to the long-period anomalies of category(1)). Here north-south highs and lows of varying width, usually of the order of 20 km, are bounded by steep gradients. The amplitude and form of these anomalies have been reproduced by Mason[9,10], but the most plausible of the models used involved very severe restrictions on the distribution of lava flows in crustal layer 2. They are readily explained in terms of reversals assuming the model shown in Fig. 4 (1). It can be shown that this type of anomaly pattern will be produced for virtually all orientations and magnetic latitudes, the amplitude decreasing as the trend of the ridge approaches north-south or the profile approaches the magnetic equator. The pronounced central anomaly over the ridges is also readily explained in terms of reversals. The central block, being most recent, is the only one which has a uniformly directed magnetic vector. This is comparable to the area of normally magnetized late Quaternary basics in Central Iceland[11,12] on the line of the Mid-Atlantic Ridge. Adjacent and all other blocks have doubtless been subjected to subsequent vulcanism in the form of volcanoes, fissure eruptions, and lava flows, often oppositely magnetized and hence reducing the effective susceptibility of the block, whether initially normal or reversed. The effect of assuming a reduced effective susceptibility for the adjacent blocks is illustrated for the North Atlantic and Carlsberg Ridges in Fig. 4 (2, 3).

In Fig. 4, no attempt has been made to reproduce observed profiles in detail, the computations simply show that the essential form of the anomalies is readily achieved. The whole of the magnetic material of the oceanic crust is probably of basic igneous composition; however, variations in its intensity of magnetization and in the topography and direction of magnetization of surface extrusives could account for the complexity of the observed profiles. The results from the preliminary Mohole drilling[13,14] are considered to substantiate this conception. The drill penetrated 40 ft. into a basalt lava flow at the bottom of the hole, and this proved to be reversely magnetized[13]. Since the only reasonable explanation of the magnetic anomalies mapped near the site of the drilling is that the area is underlain by a block of normally magnetized crustal material[14], it appears that the drill penetrated a layer of reversely magnetized lava overlying a normally magnetized block.

In Fig. 4 it will also be noticed that the effective susceptibilities assumed are two to five times less than that derived for the isolated features in the survey area described. Although no great significance can be attached to this derived intensity it is suggested that the fine-grained extrusives (basalts) of surface features are more highly magnetized than the intrusive material of the main crustal layer which, in the absence of evidence to the contrary, we assume to be of analogous chemical composition (that is, gabbros). This would appear to be consistent with recent investigations of the magnetic properties of basic rocks[6].

The vertical extent of the magnetic crust is defined by the depth to the curie-point isotherm. In the models this has been assumed to be at 20 km below sea-level over the deep ocean but at a depth of 11 km beneath the centre of the ridges where the heat flow

这种磁化物质的构造可以解释在东太平洋至北美洲西部地区所观测到的线状或“条纹”状磁异常现象[6]（可能相当于类型（1）的长周期异常）。这里南北方向上高峰与低谷的转变以陡峭的梯度为界线，其间隔宽度通常在 20 千米上下。梅森[9,10]已经绘制出这些异常的振幅和形态，但是这些模型成立的前提是需要对地壳层 2 中的熔岩流分布做严格的限定。假设图 4（1）中所示的地磁反转理论模型成立，那么这些现象就很容易被解释了。由图可知，这种类型的异常几乎可以在任何方向及磁纬度上产生，当洋脊走势逐渐向南北方延伸时，或者剖面越靠近地磁赤道时，振幅就会随之减小。利用该地磁反转理论同样可以很容易地解释洋脊上显著的中心异常。只有这个最新形成的中心地块才具有一致的磁矢量方向。这与第四纪后期被正向磁化的一个区域非常类似，该区域位于大西洋中脊上冰岛中部地区[11,12]。而与其相邻的以及其余所有地块无疑会受到随后发生的火山喷发、裂缝喷发以及熔岩作用的影响。无论这一区域最初为正向磁化还是反向磁化，都会因受到相反的磁化作用而降低它的有效磁化率。图 4（2,3）中分别以北大西洋中脊和卡尔斯伯格海岭为例，对邻近地块有效磁化率降低所造成的影响进行了阐释。

图 4 中，我们并未试图详细地再现观测到的剖面图，这些计算仅仅是为了说明这些异常的基本形式是很容易出现的。大洋地壳的全部磁化物质可能由基性火成岩组成；然而其磁化强度的变化，以及表面喷出岩体的地形和磁化方向变化都表明了被观测剖面的复杂性。我们认为，莫霍钻探[13,14]的初步结果为这个构想提供了有力的证明。钻头进入钻井底部玄武岩熔岩流 40 英尺处，已证明这里受到了反向磁化作用[13]。地图上钻井附近出现了磁化异常，对此唯一合理的解释就是因为这个区域上方覆盖着一块被正向磁化的地壳物质[14]，这表明钻头进入的被反向磁化的熔岩层下方是一块被正向磁化的岩体。

我们还应注意到，图 4 中假设的有效磁化率是根据研究区中这些独立的特征导出的有效磁化率的$\frac{1}{2}$到$\frac{1}{5}$。尽管这种导出的强度并无太大意义，但这个现象仍可表明，与主要地壳层中的侵入岩相比，岩体表面的细纹状喷出岩体（玄武岩）受到了强度更高的磁化作用。我们认为这两类岩石具有相似的化学成分（即辉长岩），并且到目前为止尚未发现反证。上述结论与最近一项关于基性岩磁性研究的结果是一致的[6]。

磁性地壳的垂直厚度是根据居里点等温线的深度而确定的。在上述模型中，居里点等温线的位置是这样假定的，在深海区位于海平面以下 20 千米处，而在热流量

and presumably the thermal gradient are higher. These assumptions are questionable but not critical because the amplitude of the simulated anomaly depends on both the thickness of the block and its effective susceptibility, and, although the thickness is in doubt by a factor of two, the susceptibility is in doubt by a factor of ten. Present magnetic declination has been assumed throughout the calculations: it would probably have been better to have ignored this, as in palaeomagnetism, assuming that true north approximates to the mean of secular variations; but this is unimportant and in no way affects the essential features of the computations.

In order to explain the steep gradients and large amplitudes of magnetic anomalies observed over oceanic ridges all authors have been compelled to assume vertical boundaries and high-susceptibility contrasts between adjacent crustal blocks. It is appreciated that magnetic contrasts within the oceanic crust can be explained without postulating reversals of the Earth's magnetic field; for example, the crust might contain blocks of very strongly magnetized material adjacent to blocks of material weakly magnetized in the same direction. However, the model suggested in this article seems to be more plausible because high susceptibility contrasts between adjacent blocks can be explained without recourse to major inhomogeneities of rock type within the main crustal layer or to unusually strongly magnetized rocks.

We thank Dr. R. G. Mason and K. Kunaratnam of the Imperial College of Science and Technology, London, for details of the three-dimensional programme used in this work. The programme was originally devised by K. Kunaratnam for a Ferranti *Mercury* Computer. It has been rewritten for use on *Edsac* 2. We also thank the Director of the Cambridge University Mathematical Laboratory for permission to use *Edsac* 2, and Sir Edward Bullard for his advice and encouragement throughout.

This work was partly supported by a grant from the U.S. Office of Naval Research (Contract No. *N*62558-3542).

(**199**, 947-949; 1963)

F. J. Vine and D. H. Matthews: Department of Geodesy and Geophysics, University of Cambridge.

References:

1. Heezen, B. C., Ewing, M., and Miller, E. T., *Deep Sea Res.*, **1**, 25 (1953).
2. Keen, M. J., *Nature*, **197**, 888 (1963).
3. Adams, R. D., and Christoffel, D. A., *J. Geophys. Res.*, **67**, 805 (1962).
4. Heirtzler, J. R., *Tech. Rep. No.* 2, *Lamont Geol. Obs., New York* (1961).
5. Matthews, D. H., *et al.*, *Admiralty Marine Sci. Pub. No.* **4** (in the press).
6. Bullard, E. C., and Mason, R. G., *The Sea*, **3**, edit. by Hill, M. N. (in the press).
7. Dietz, R. S., *Nature*, **190**, 854 (1961).
8. Cox, A., Doell, R. R., and Dalrymple, G. B., *Nature*, **198**, 1049 (1963).
9. Mason, R. G., *Geophys. J.*, **1**, 320 (1958).

较大，温度梯度可能也更大的地方，则位于洋脊中心下方 11 千米处。虽然这些假设存在一些问题，但并不会有太大影响。因为这种模拟异常的振幅受到地块厚度及其有效磁化率的双重影响，尽管对于厚度不同的估计值相差 2 倍，对于磁化率不同的估计值相差 10 倍。整个计算过程引用了当前的磁偏角：这应该比完全忽略掉这些因素要好些，就像在古地磁学中，真正的正北向其实取自于其长周期变化的平均值；但这并不重要，也不会影响到计算的本质。

为了解释在大洋中脊上观测到的陡峭梯度和磁异常的巨大振幅，只能假设两侧相邻地壳块体之间为垂直边界和高磁化率反差。当然，最好是无需假设地球磁场反转便能解释大洋地壳中的交替磁化现象；例如，地壳在同一磁化方向上交替存在着包含强磁化物质和弱磁化物质的两种地块。然而，本文提出的模型似乎更为合理，因为它可以不必借助于主地壳层内岩石类型的强烈非均匀性或异常强的磁化岩石，便可以解释相邻地块间存在的高磁化率反差现象。

感谢伦敦帝国理工学院梅森博士和库纳拉特南博士为本文提供的三维程序。该程序是库纳拉特南博士为费兰梯水银计算机设计的，经过重新编写后用于 *Edsac* 2（电子延迟存储自动计算机）。我们还要感谢剑桥大学数学实验室主任同意我们使用 *Edsac* 2，也同样感谢爱德华 · 布拉德爵士提供的意见和一贯的支持。

美国海军研究办公室为此项研究提供了部分资金（合同号：*N*62558-3542）。

（沈乃澂 翻译；张忠杰 审稿）

10. Mason, R. G., and Raff, A. D., *Bull. Geol. Soc. Amer.*, **72**, 1259 (1961).

11. Hospers, J., *Geol. Mag.*, **91**, 352 (1954).

12. Thorarinsson, S., Einarsson, T., and Kjartansson, G., *Intern. Geog. Cong.* (*Norden*), Excursion E. I. 1 (1960).

13. Cox, A., and Doell, R. R., *J. Geophys. Res.*, **67**, 3997 (1962).

14. Raff, A. D., *J. Geophys. Res.*, **68**, 955 (1963).

A New Species of the Genus *Homo* from Olduvai Gorge

L. S. B. Leakey *et al.*

Editor's Note

In 1960, not long after Leakey found *Zinjanthropus*, fragments of an altogether different kind of hominid started turning up at Olduvai. More years of searching accumulated enough material for Leakey to be sure that this new creature was not an "ape-man", but a member of our own genus, *Homo*. The small brain of this creature necessitated a bold revision of our own genus—extending what it means, in technical terms, to be "human". The new fossils also seemed to have been associated with primitive chipped-pebble tools. Partly because of this, Leakey and colleagues called the new hominid *Homo habilis*—"handy man"—thus binding humanity forever in the public mind with technology. Leakey's message was clear: humanity began at Olduvai.

THE recent discoveries of fossil hominid remains at Olduvai Gorge have strengthened the conclusions—which each of us had reached independently through our respective investigations—that the fossil hominid remains found in 1960 at site *F.L.K.N.N.* I, Olduvai, did not represent a creature belonging to the sub-family Australopithecinae*.

We were preparing to publish the evidence for this conclusion and to give a scientific name to this new species of the genus *Homo*, when the new discoveries, which are described by L. S. B. and M. D. Leakey in the preceding article, were made.

An examination of these finds has enabled us to broaden the basis of our diagnosis of the proposed new species and has fully confirmed the presence of the genus *Homo* in the lower part of the Olduvai geological sequence, earlier than, contemporary with, as well as later than, the *Zinjanthropus* skull, which is certainly an australopithecine.

For the purpose of our description here, we have accepted the diagnosis of the family Hominidae, as it was proposed by Sir Wilfrid Le Gros Clark in his book *The Fossil Evidence for Human Evolution* (110; 1955). Within this family we accept the genus *Australopithecus* with, for the moment, three sub-genera (*Australopithecus*, *Paranthropus* and *Zinjanthropus*) and the genus *Homo*. We regard *Pithecanthropus* and possibly also *Atlanthropus* (if it is indeed distinct) as species of the genus *Homo*, although one of us (L. S. B. L.) would be prepared to accept sub-generic rank.

It has long been recognized that as more and more discoveries were made, it would

* See also *Nature* of March 7, pp. 967, 969, and preceding articles in this issue.

在奥杜威峡谷发现的一个人属新种

利基等

编者按

1960 年，在利基发现东非人后不久，他在奥杜威又发掘出一种完全不同的人科动物化石破片。多年来收集的材料足以让利基相信这个新发现的物种不是“猿人”，而是我们人类的一个新成员，一个人属新种。这个新种的脑比较小，这使得我们必须对自己的属做大胆的修正——在专业术语范畴内拓宽“人”的含义。此外，这些新化石似乎也与原始的砾石打击工具有关。一定程度上由于这个原因，利基和同事们称这种新的人科为能人——“灵巧的人”，从而在公众的脑海中将人类和技术永远地捆绑在了一起。利基传递的信息非常明确：人类始于奥杜威。

最近在奥杜威峡谷发现的人科化石使我们更加相信，1960 年在奥杜威 *F.L.K.N.N.* I 地点发现的人科化石并不属于南方古猿亚科，这是我们每个人通过自己独立的调查研究得到的一致结论 *。

当我们有了这一新发现时（正如路易斯·利基及其夫人玛丽·利基在先前文章中所描述的），就准备发表关于这一结论的证据，并且给予这个属于人属的新标本一个科学的名字。

这些发现的检验结果使我们拓宽了判断新种的基础，并充分证实了人属存在于奥杜威地层序列的下部，比确定属于南方古猿亚科的东非人头骨或者更早，或者同时代，或者更晚。

为了描述方便，本文中我们采用了威尔弗里德·勒格罗–克拉克爵士在《人类进化的化石证据》（第 110 页，1955 年）一书中提出的对于人科的判断标准。在这个科中我们暂时接受南方古猿属和人属，包括南方古猿属目前具有的三个亚属（南方古猿亚属、傍人亚属和东非人亚属）。尽管我们中的路易斯·利基准备接受亚属的分类标准，但我们还是把爪哇猿人，可能还有阿特拉猿人（如果确实有明显区别）作为人属中的种。

人们早已认识到，随着越来越多的发现，有必要对人属的判断标准进行修改。

* 参见 3 月 7 日《自然》第 967、969 页以及本期前面的文章。

become necessary to revise the diagnosis of the genus *Homo*. In particular, it has become clear that it is impossible to rely on only one or two characters, such as the cranial capacity or an erect posture, as the necessary criteria for membership of the genus. Instead, the total picture presented by the material available for investigation must be taken into account.

We have come to the conclusion that, apart from *Australopithecus* (*Zinjanthropus*), the specimens we are dealing with from Bed I and the lower part of Bed II at Olduvai represent a single species of the genus *Homo* and not an australopithecine. The species is, moreover, clearly distinct from the previously recognized species of the genus. But if we are to include the new material in the genus *Homo* (rather than set up a distinct genus for it, which we believe to be unwise), it becomes necessary to revise the diagnosis of this genus. Until now, the definition of *Homo* has usually centred about a "cerebral Rubicon" variably set at 700 c.c. (Weidenreich), 750 c.c. (Keith) and 800 c.c. (Vallois). This proposed new definition follows:

Family	hominidae	(as defined by Le Gros Clark, 1955)
Genus	*Homo*	Linnaeus

Revised diagnosis of the genus Homo. A genus of the Hominidae with the following characters: the structure of the pelvic girdle and of the hind-limb skeleton is adapted to habitual erect posture and bipedal gait; the fore-limb is shorter than the hind-limb; the pollex is well developed and fully opposable and the hand is capable not only of a power grip but of, at the least, a simple and usually well developed precision grip*; the cranial capacity is very variable but is, on the average, larger than the range of capacities of members of the genus *Australopithecus*, although the lower part of the range of capacities in the genus *Homo* overlaps with the upper part of the range in *Australopithecus*; the capacity is (on the average) large relative to body-size and ranges from about 600 c.c. in earlier forms to more than 1,600 c.c.; the muscular ridges on the cranium range from very strongly marked to virtually imperceptible, but the temporal crests or lines never reach the midline; the frontal region of the cranium is without undue post-orbital constriction (such as is common in members of the genus *Australopithecus*); the supra-orbital region of the frontal bone is very variable, ranging from a massive and very salient supra-orbital torus to a complete lack of any supra-orbital projection and a smooth brow region; the facial skeleton varies from moderately prognathous to orthognathous, but it is not concave (or dished) as is common in members of the Australopithecinae; the anterior symphyseal contour varies from a marked retreat to a forward slope, while the bony chin may be entirely lacking, or may vary from a slight to a very strongly developed mental trigone; the dental arcade is evenly rounded with no diastema in most members of the genus; the first lower premolar is clearly bicuspid with a variably developed lingual cusp; the molar teeth are variable in size, but in general are small relative to the size of these teeth in the genus *Australopithecus*; the size of the last upper molar is highly variable, but it is generally smaller than the second

* For the definition of "power grip" and "precision grip", see Napier, J. R., *J. Bone and Joint Surg.*, 38, B, 902 (1956).

尤其是现在已经清楚了不能只依赖于一个或两个特征，诸如颅容量或直立的姿势，作为是否为属中成员的必要判别条件。事实上，应该将调查中可获得材料的全部特征纳入考虑范围之中。

我们得到的结论是：除南方古猿（东非人）外，我们所讨论的在奥杜威第 I 层以及第 II 层下部发现的标本代表人属内一个单独的种，而不是南方古猿亚科的种。而且这个种明显不同于此前确认的人属内的种。但是如果我们把这个新种归入人属（而非设立一个不同的属——我们认为这样做是不明智的），则必须修正人属的判断标准。直到现在，人属的定义通常还是以“脑量的界限”为中心，而这个界限设为 700 毫升（魏登瑞）、750 毫升（基思）以及 800 毫升（瓦卢瓦），并不确定。这里建议新的定义如下：

科	人科	（1955 年由勒格罗 – 克拉克定义）
属	人属	林奈

人属的修正标准 人属具有如下的特征：骨盆带和下肢骨骼结构适应于惯常的直立姿势和两足行走的步态；上肢比下肢短；拇指发育良好，并与其他指的方向完全相反，手不仅具备有力抓握的能力，而且还至少具有简单并且通常发育良好的精确抓握的本领*；颅容量变化较大，但平均而言大于南方古猿属中成员们的颅容量范围，尽管人属颅容量范围的下限同南方古猿属颅容量范围的上限有重叠；颅容量（平均而言）相对身体尺寸要大，其范围在早期形态的 600 毫升到多于 1,600 毫升之间；颅骨肌肉附着处的粗壮程度不等，从非常强健到难以发觉均可出现，但颞脊或颞线从未达到正中线；颅骨前额部没有显著的眶后狭缩（这在南方古猿属的成员中是常见的）；额骨的眶上区变化很大，从厚大而突出的眶上圆枕到完全缺乏任何眶上突出部分和平滑的眉弓区间变化；面骨骼形态在中度的突颌到直颌间变化，但没有向内凹入（或中凹），这在南方古猿亚科的成员中也是常见的；前端联合面轮廓外形可以从显著向后倾斜到向前倾斜之间变化，而颏隆起可能完全缺乏，也可能从纤细的颏三角变化到非常发达的颏三角；属中大多数成员的齿弓是均匀的圆形并且没有齿隙；第一下前臼齿有明显的双齿尖，其中舌侧尖发育程度变异较大；臼齿的大小多变，但与南方古猿属牙齿的大小相比通常较小；最后一颗上臼齿的大小变化比较大，不过一般比第二上臼齿小，通常也比第一上臼齿小；第三下臼齿有时稍微大于第二下臼齿；从人猿超科总体上看：人属的犬齿较小，在磨耗初期后很少或没有重叠，但与南方古猿属的成员进行比较时，门齿、犬齿相对于臼齿和前臼齿不是很小；

* 对于“力量抓握”和“精确抓握”的定义参见内皮尔，《骨与关节外科杂志》，第 38 卷，B，第 902 页（1956 年）。

upper molar and commonly also smaller than the first upper molar; the lower third molar is sometimes appreciably larger than the second; in relation to the position seen in the Hominoidea as a whole, the canines are small, with little or no overlapping after the initial stages of wear, but when compared with those of members of the genus *Australopithecus*, the incisors and canines are not very small relative to the molars and premolars; the teeth in general, and particularly the molars and premolars, are not enlarged bucco-lingually as they are in the genus *Australopithecus*; the first deciduous lower molar shows a variable degree of molarization.

Genus	*Homo*	Linnaeus
Species	*habilis*	sp. nov.

(*Note*: The specific name is taken from the Latin, meaning "able, handy, mentally skilful, vigorous". We are indebted to Prof. Raymond Dart for the suggestion that *habilis* would be a suitable name for the new species.)

A species of the genus *Homo* characterized by the following features:

A mean cranial capacity greater than that of members of the genus *Australopithecus*, but smaller than that of *Homo erectus*; muscular ridges on the cranium ranging from slight to strongly marked; chin region retreating, with slight or no development of the mental trigone; maxillae and mandibles smaller than those of *Australopithecus* and within the range for *Homo erectus* and *Homo sapiens*; dentition characterized by incisors which are relatively large in comparison with those of both *Australopithecus* and *Homo erectus*; canines which are proportionately large relative to the premolars; premolars which are narrower (in bucco-lingual breadth) than those of *Australopithecus*, but which fall within the range for *Homo erectus*; molars in which the absolute dimensions range between the lower part of the range in *Australopithecus* and the upper part of the range in *Homo erectus*; a marked tendency towards bucco-lingual narrowing and mesiodistal elongation of all the teeth, which is especially evident in the lower premolars (where it expresses itself as a marked elongation of the talonid) and in the lower molars (where it is accompanied by a rearrangement of the distal cusps); the sagittal curvature of the parietal bone varies from slight (within the hominine range) to moderate (within the australopithecine range); the external sagittal curvature of the occipital bone is slighter than in *Australopithecus* or in *Homo erectus*, and lies within the range of *Homo sapiens*; in curvature as well as in some other morphological traits, the clavicle resembles, but is not identical to, that of *Homo sapiens sapiens*; the hand bones differ from those of *Homo sapiens sapiens* in robustness, in the dorsal curvature of the shafts of the phalanges, in the distal attachment of *flexor digitorum superficialis*, in the strength of fibro-tendinous markings, in the orientation of trapezium in the carpus, in the form of the scaphoid and in the marked depth of the carpal tunnel; however, the hand bones resemble those of *Homo sapiens sapiens* in the presence of broad, stout, terminal phalanges on fingers and thumb, in the form of the distal articular surface of the capitate and the ellipsoidal form of the metacarpo-phalangeal joint surfaces; in many of their characters

一般而言，牙齿，特别是臼齿和前臼齿，并不像在南方古猿属中一样在颊舌向放大；第一下乳臼齿显示出不同程度的臼化。

属	人属	林奈
种	能人	新种

（**注释**：种名来源于拉丁文，含义是“有能力的、手灵巧的、有思想的、有技术的、精力充沛的人”。我们感谢雷蒙德·达特教授的提议，对于新种而言，能人是个非常适宜的名字。）

人属新种表现出如下的特点：

平均颅容量比南方古猿属成员的颅容量大，但是比直立人的要小一些；颅部肌肉附着处粗壮程度表现不一，在微小到非常明显的范围之间；下巴后缩，颏三角轻度发育或未形成；上颌骨和下颌骨比南方古猿的小，处于直立人和智人的范围之中；就齿系特点来说，门齿比南方古猿和直立人的相对要大；犬齿相对于前臼齿成比例增大；前臼齿比南方古猿的狭小（颊舌径），但是仍处于直立人的范围之内；臼齿的绝对尺寸处于南方古猿范围下限与直立人范围上限之间；所有牙齿都具有颊舌向变窄和近中远中径向延长的显著趋势，这一趋势在下前臼齿和下臼齿尤其明显（在下前臼齿跟座显著延长，在下臼齿远侧齿尖重新排列）；顶骨矢状曲度呈现从轻微（在人亚科的变化范围之内）到中等（在南方古猿亚科的范围之内）的变化；枕骨外矢状曲度比南方古猿和直立人的轻微，在智人的范围内；在曲度及其他一些形态学特性上，锁骨类似于但不完全等同于现代智人；手骨在粗壮程度、指骨干的背脊弯曲、指浅屈肌的远节附着、纤维肌腱的强度、腕骨大多角骨的方位、手舟骨的形态和腕管显著的深度等方面不同于现代智人；但手骨也有类似于现代智人的方面，表现在手指和拇指上存在宽而短的远节指骨、头状骨末端关节面的形状和掌–指骨关节表面的椭圆体形状；足骨的很多特征在现代智人的变化范围内；大趾是短小的、内收的并且是脚掌着地行走类型；存在非常显著的纵向弧和横向弧；另一方面，第三跖骨比现代人粗壮得多，距骨滑车的中、侧剖面的曲度没有显著的差异。

the foot bones lie within the range of variation of *Homo sapiens sapiens*; the hallux is stout, adducted and plantigrade; there are well-marked longitudinal and transverse arches; on the other hand, the 3rd metatarsal is relatively more robust than it is in modern man, and there is no marked difference in the radii of curvature of the medial and lateral profiles of the trochlea of the talus.

Geological horizon. Upper Villafranchian and Lower Middle Pleistocene.

Type. The mandible with dentition and the associated upper molar, parietals and hand bones, of a single juvenile individual from site *F.L.K.N.N.* I, Olduvai, Bed I.

This is catalogued as Olduvai Hominid 7.

Paratypes. (*a*) An incomplete cranium, comprising fragments of the frontal, parts of both parietals, the greater part of the occipital, and parts of both temporals, together with an associated mandible with canines, premolars and molars complete on either side but with the crowns of the incisors damaged, parts of both maxillae, having all the cheek teeth except the upper left fourth premolar. The condition of the teeth suggests an adolescent. This specimen, from site *M.N.K.* II, Olduvai, Bed II, is catalogued as Olduvai Hominid 13.

(*b*) The associated hand bones, foot bones and probably the clavicle, of an adult individual from site *F.L.K.N.N.* I, Olduvai, Bed I. This is catalogued as Olduvai Hominid 8.

(*c*) A lower premolar, an upper molar and cranial fragments from site *F.L.K.* I, Olduvai, Bed I (the site that yielded also the *Australopithecus* (*Zinjanthropus*) skull). This is catalogued as Olduvai Hominid 6. It is possible that the tibia and fibula found at this site belong with *Homo habilis* rather than with *Australopithecus* (*Zinjanthropus*). These limb bones have been reported on by Dr. P. R. Davis (*Nature*, March 7, 1964, p. 967).

(*d*) A mandibular fragment with a molar in position and associated with a few fragments of other teeth from site *M.K.* I, Olduvai, Bed I, This specimen is catalogued as Olduvai Hominid 4.

Description of the type. Preliminary descriptions of the specimens which have now been designated the type of *Homo habilis*, for example, the parts of the juvenile found at size *F.L.K.N.N.* I in 1960, have already been published in *Nature* by one of us (**189**, 649; **191**, 417; 1961). A further detailed description and report on the parietals, the mandible and the teeth are in active preparation by one of us (P. V. T.), while his report on the cranial capacity (preceding article) as well as a preliminary note on the hand by another of us (*Nature*, **196**, 409; 1962) have been published. We do not propose, therefore, of give a more detailed description of the type here.

Description of the paratypes. A preliminary note on the clavicle and on the foot of the adult,

地质层位 维拉方期上部和中更新世下部。

正型标本 从奥杜威 *F.L.K.N.N.* I 地点第 I 层中出土的幼年个体带有齿系的下颌骨以及相关的上臼齿、顶骨和手骨。

这件标本在奥杜威人科标本中编号为 7。

副型标本 （*a*）一个不完整的颅骨，包含额骨破片和两侧顶骨部分、大部分枕骨和两侧颞骨部分，还有与之相应的下颌骨，其两侧的犬齿、前臼齿和臼齿都是完整的，但门齿齿冠破损；此外，还有部分双侧上颌骨，上附有除第四左上前臼齿外所有的颊齿。牙齿显示这件标本为青少年个体。这件出土于奥杜威 *M.N.K.* II 地点第 II 层的标本在奥杜威人科标本中编号为 13。

(*b*) 从奥杜威 *F.L.K.N.N.* I 地点第 I 层中出土的一成年个体，包括手骨、足骨以及可能的锁骨，其在奥杜威人科标本中编号为 8。

(*c*) 从奥杜威 *F.L.K.* I 地点第 I 层中（在这个位置上曾出土了南方古猿（东非人）的头骨）出土了一颗下前臼齿、一颗上臼齿和头骨破片。其在奥杜威人科标本中编号为 6。在这个地点发现的胫骨和腓骨可能属于能人而不是南方古猿（东非人）。这些肢骨由戴维斯报道在 1964 年 3 月 7 日出版的《自然》第 967 页上。

(*d*) 从奥杜威 *M.K.* I 地点的第 I 层出土了一件下颌骨破片和一颗臼齿，在原位上还有一些其他与之相联系的牙齿破片。其在奥杜威人科标本中编号为 4。

正型标本描述 关于标本（现在已定名为能人）的初步描述，例如 1960 年在奥杜威 *F.L.K.N.N.* I 地点发现的部分幼年个体的初步描述已经发表在《自然》(189 卷，第 649 页；191 卷，第 417 页，1961 年）上。我们之中的托拜厄斯在积极地准备着关于顶骨、下颌骨和牙齿进一步的详细描述和报道。托拜厄斯有关颅容量（先前的文章中）的研究和我们中另一位对于手的初步研究已经发表了（《自然》，196 卷，409 页，1962 年）。因此，我们在这里不能提供更多关于正型标本的描述。

副型标本描述 对副型标本（*b*）成年个体的锁骨和足骨的初步研究已经刊登

which represents paratype (*b*), was published in *Nature* (**188**, 1050; 1961), and a further report on the foot by Dr. M. H. Day and Dr. J. R. Napier was published in *Nature* of March 7, 1964, p. 969.

The following additional preliminary notes on the other paratypes have been prepared by one of us (P. V. T.).

Description of Paratypes

(*a*) *Olduvai Hominid* 13 *from* M.N.K. *II.* An adolescent represented by a nearly complete mandible with complete, fully-erupted lower dentition, a right maxillary fragment including palate and all teeth from P^3 to M^3, the latter in process of erupting; the corresponding left maxillary fragment with M^1 to M^3, the latter likewise erupting, the isolated left P^3; parts of the vault of a small, adult cranium, comprising much of the occipital, including part of the posterior margin of *foramen magnum*, parts of both parietals, right and left temporosphenoid fragments, each including the mandibular fossa and foramen ovale. The distal half of a humeral shaft (excluding the distal extremity) may also belong to Olduvai Hominid 13. The *corpus mandibulae* is very small, both the height and thickness at M_1 falling below the australopithecine range and within the hominine range. All the teeth are small compared with those of Australopithecinae, most of the dimensions falling at or below the lower extreme of the australopithecine ranges. On the other hand, practically all the dental dimensions can be accommodated within the range of fossil Hominінae. The Olduvai Hominid 13 teeth show the characteristic mesiodistal elongation and labiolingual narrowing, in some teeth the *L*/*B* index exceeding even those of the type Olduvai Hominid 7, and paratype Olduvai Hominid 6. The occipital bone has a relatively slight sagittal curvature, the Occipital Sagittal Index being outside the range for australopithecines and for *Homo erectus pekinensis* and within the range for *Homo sapiens*. On the other hand, the parietal sagittal curvature is more marked than in all but one australopithecine and in all the Pekin fossils, the index falling at the top of the range of population means for modern man. Both parietal and occipital bones are very small in size, being exceeded in some dimensions by one or two australopithecine crania and falling short in all dimensions of the range for *Homo erectus pekinensis*. The form of the parietal—anteroposteriorly elongated and bilaterally narrow, with a fairly abrupt lateral descent in the plane of the parietal boss—reproduces closely these features in the somewhat larger parietal of the type specimen (Olduvai Hominid 7 from *F.L.K.N.N.* I).

(*b*) *Olduvai Hominid* 6 *from* F.L.K. *I.* An unworn lower left premolar, identified as P_3, an unworn, practically complete crown and partly developed roots of an upper molar, either M^1 or M^2, as well as a number of fragments of cranial vault. These remains were found at the *Zinjanthropus* site and level, some *in situ* and some on the surface. Both teeth are small for an australopithecine, especially in buccolingual breadth, but large for *Homo erectus*. The marked tendency to elongation and narrowing imparts to both teeth an *L*/*B* index outside the range for all known australopithecine homologues and even beyond the range for *Homo erectus pekinensis*. The elongating-narrowing tendency is more marked in this molar than in

在《自然》(188 卷，第 1050 页，1961 年）上，关于足骨的进一步研究由戴博士和内皮尔博士发表在 1964 年 3 月 7 日的《自然》第 969 页上。

以下这些关于其他副型标本的初步研究是由我们之中的托拜厄斯提供的。

副型标本的描述

(*a*)**奥杜威** *M.N.K.* II **地点发现的编号为 13 的人科化石**　标本代表一个年轻个体，包括一件近乎完整的下颌骨，附有全部萌出的下齿系、保存有腭和第三上前臼齿到第三上臼齿所有牙齿在内的右侧上颌骨破片，其中第三上臼齿还在萌出中。相对应的左侧上颌骨破片附着有第一上臼齿到第三上臼齿以及脱落的第三上前臼齿，其中第三上臼齿同样处于萌出状态；一个较小的成年个体颅骨包含大部分枕骨，包括**枕骨大孔**后缘部分，部分顶骨、左右颞蝶骨破片（每个都带有下颌窝和卵圆孔）。肱骨骨干的末端半部分（排除末端部分）可能也属于奥杜威第 13 号人科化石。**下颌体**非常小，第一下臼齿在高度和厚度上小于南方古猿亚科，同时它又在人亚科变化范围之中。和南方古猿亚科相比所有牙齿均较小，大多尺寸低于南方古猿亚科变化范围的下界。一方面，几乎所有牙齿的尺寸都能够纳入人亚科化石的变化范围之内。奥杜威第 13 号人科化石的牙齿表现出近中远中向延长和颊舌向缩小的特点。在有些牙齿中，齿冠指数（长 / 宽）甚至超过了奥杜威 7 号正型标本和 6 号副型标本。枕骨矢状曲度轻微，枕骨矢状指数处于南方古猿亚科和北京直立人的变化范围之外、智人变化范围之内。另一方面，顶骨矢状曲度要比所有南方古猿亚科标本(除一例以外）和所有北京直立人标本的都要大，指数下降到现代人群变化范围的上限。顶骨和枕骨尺寸很小，某些尺寸小于一两例南方古猿亚科标本，且所有尺寸达不到北京直立人的变化范围。顶骨前后延长、两侧变窄，顶骨凸面陡然侧斜——顶骨的形态再次展现了与正型标本（从奥杜威 *F.L.K.N.N.* I 点发现的第 7 个人科）稍大的顶骨的形态接近。

(*b*) **奥杜威** *F.L.K.* I **地点发现的编号为 6 的人科化石**　该化石包括一颗尚未磨损的左下前臼齿，被鉴定为第三下前臼齿，一个没有磨损的上臼齿，不是第一上臼齿就是第二上臼齿，齿冠几乎完整，齿根部分发育。此外，还有一些头骨穹隆破片。这些化石是在发现东非人的地点和底层发现的，有些出土于原位，有些采集于地表。两颗牙齿都比南方古猿亚科的小，特别是颊舌径，但比直立人的大。两颗牙齿延长和缩小的显著趋势使得其齿冠指数超出了所有已知的南方古猿亚科的同族体的变化范围，甚至超出北京直立人的变化范围。臼齿的延长 – 缩小趋势比正型标本（从奥

the upper molar belonging to the type specimen (Olduvai Hominid 7) from *F.L.K.N.N.* I.

(*c*) *Olduvai Hominid* 8 *from* F.L.K.N.N. *I.* Remains of an adult individual found on the same horizon as the type specimen, and represented by two complete proximal phalanges, a fragment of a rather heavily worn tooth (premolar or molar), and a set of foot-bones possessing most of the specializations associated with the plantigrade propulsive feet of modern man. Probably the clavicle found at this site belongs to this adult rather than to the juvenile type-specimen; it is characterized by clear overall similarities to the clavicle of *Homo sapiens sapiens*.

(*d*) *Olduvai Hominid* 4 *from* M.K. *I.* A fragment of the posterior part of the left *corpus mandibulae*, containing a well-preserved, fully-erupted molar, either M_2 or M_3. The width of the mandible is 19.2 m level with the mesial half of the molar, but the maximum width must have been somewhat greater, The molar is 15.1 mm in mesiodistal length and 13.0 mm in buccolingual breadth; it is thus a small and narrow tooth by australopithecine standards, but large in comparison with *Homo erectus* molars. There are several other isolated dental fragments, including a moderately worn molar fragment. These are stratigraphically the oldest hominid remains yet discovered at Olduvai.

Referred Material

Olduvai Hominid 14 *from* M.W.K. *II.* (1) A juvenile represented by a fragment of the right parietal with clear, unfused sutural margins; two smaller vault fragments with sutural margins; a left and a right temporal fragment, each including the mandibular fossa.

(2) A fragmentary skull with parts of the upper and lower dentition of a young adult from site *F.L.K.* II, Maiko Gully, Olduvai, Bed II, is also provisionally referred to *Homo habilis*. This specimen is catalogued as Olduvai Hominid 16. It is represented by the complete upper right dentition, as well as some of the left maxillary teeth, together with some of the mandibular teeth. The skull fragments include parts of the frontal, with both the external orbital angles preserved, as well as the supraorbital region, except for the glabella; parts of both parietals and the occipital are also represented.

Implications for Hominid Phylogeny

In preparing our diagnosis of *Homo habilis*, we have not overlooked the fact that there are several other African (and perhaps Asian) fossil hominids whose status may now require re-examination in the light of the new discoveries and of the setting up of this new species. The specimens originally described by Broom and Robinson as *Telanthropus capensis* and which were later transferred by Robinson to *Homo erectus* may well prove, on closer comparative investigation, to belong to *Homo habilis*. The Kanam mandibular fragment, discovered by the expedition in 1932 by one of us (L. S. B. L.), and which has been shown to possess archaic features (Tobias, *Nature*, **185**, 946; 1960), may well justify further investigation along these lines. The Lake Chad craniofacial fragment, provisionally described by M. Yves Coppens in 1962, as an australopithecine, is not, we are convinced,

杜威 *F.L.K.N.N.* I 地点发现的编号为 7 的人科化石）的上臼齿更加明显。

（*c*）**奥杜威 *F.L.K.N.N.* I 地点发现的编号为 8 的人科化石** 发现的一个成年个体的化石与正型标本处于同层位中，包括两个完整的近节指骨，一件磨损得相当严重的牙齿破片（前臼齿或臼齿）和一组足骨，这组足骨有很多同现代人直立行走的脚相关的特化。在这个点发现的锁骨属于成年的可能性胜过属于幼年正型标本的可能性，并与现代智人很接近。

（*d*）**奥杜威 *M.K.* I 地点发现的编号为 4 的人科化石** 该化石为一左下颌体后部破片，其上附有一颗保存很好且完全萌出的臼齿，不是第二下臼齿就是第三下臼齿。以该臼齿的近中部分为基准，测得的下颌宽度为 19.2 米（译者注：此处原文有误，应为厘米），但实际下颌的最大宽度要更大一些。臼齿近中远中径为 15.1 毫米，颊舌径为 13.0 毫米；因此按南方古猿亚科的标准，它是一颗又小又窄的牙齿，但和直立人的臼齿相比是较大的。同时还出土了一些其他单个的牙齿破片，包括一个中度磨损的臼齿破片。这些是至今在奥杜威发现的地层时代最古老的人科动物遗骸。

参考材料

奥杜威 *M.N.K.* II 地点发现的编号为 14 的人科化石 （1）该化石属于一个幼年个体，包括一个右侧顶骨破片，有清晰且尚未愈合缝边缘；两个小的颅顶破片，有骨缝边缘；一个左侧颞骨破片和一个右侧颞骨破片，每个都带有下颌窝。

（2）从奥杜威 *F.L.K.* II 地点第 II 层中出土的年轻成年个体的头骨破片上具有部分上、下颌齿系，也临时划归能人。这件标本被编号为奥杜威人科 16，包括完整的上颌右侧齿系、部分左侧上颌骨牙齿和一些下颌骨牙齿。头骨破片包括部分额骨（保存下了两个外眶角），以及眶上区（除了眉间部分）；此外还有部分顶骨和枕骨。

人科系统演化的意义

在能人的判断标准中，我们注意到，随着许多新化石的出土和能人这一新种的建立，许多非洲（甚至是亚洲）的人科化石的地位需要重新考虑。通过进一步的比较研究，可以充分证明最初由布鲁姆和鲁滨逊记述为开普远人、后来由鲁滨逊转而归入直立人的标本属于能人。利基在 1932 年发现的卡纳姆下颌骨破片具有许多原始的特性（托拜厄斯，《自然》，第 185 卷，第 946 页，1960 年），这使得沿着这一线索进一步调查研究很必要。乍得湖发现的颅面破片由伊夫 · 柯庞在 1962 年进行过临时的描述，定为南方古猿亚科的类型，而我们确信它不属于这一亚科。我们认为发

a member of this sub-family. We understand that the discoverer himself, following his investigation of the australopithecine originals from South Africa and Tanganyika, now shares our view in this respect. We believe that it is very probably a northern representative of *Homo habilis*.

Outside Africa, the possibility will have to be considered that the teeth and cranial fragments found at Ubeidiyah on the Jordan River in Israel may also belong to *Homo habilis* rather than to *Australopithecus*.

Cultural Association

When the skull of *Australopithecus* (*Zinjanthropus*) *boisei* was found on a living floor at *F.L.K.* I, no remains of any other type of hominid were known from the early part of the Olduvai sequence. It seemed reasonable, therefore, to assume that this skull represented the makers of the Oldowan culture. The subsequent discovery of remains of *Homo habilis* in association with the Oldowan culture at three other sites has considerably altered the position. While it is possible that *Zinjanthropus* and *Homo habilis* both made stone tools, it is probable that the latter was the more advanced tool maker and that the *Zinjanthropus* skull represents an intruder (or a victim) on a *Homo habilis* living site.

The recent discovery of a rough circle of loosely piled stones on the living floor at site *D.K.* I, in the lower part of Bed I, is noteworthy. This site is geologically contemporary with *M.K.* I, less than one mile distant, where remains of *Homo habilis* have been found. It seems that the early hominids of this period were capable of making rough shelters or windbreaks and it is likely that *Homo habilis* may have been responsible.

Relationship to *Australopithecus* (*Zinjanthropus*)

The fossil human remains representing the new species *Homo habilis* have been found in Bed I and in the lower and middle part of Bed II. Two of the sites, *M.K.* I and *F.L.K. N.N.* I, are geologically older than that which yielded the skull of the australopithecine *Zinjanthropus*. One site, *F.L.K.* I, has yielded both *Australopithecus* (*Zinjanthropus*) and remains of *Homo habilis*, while two sites are later, namely *M.N.K.* II and *F.L.K.* II Maiko gully. The new mandible of *Australopithecus* (*Zinjanthropus*) type from Lake Natron, reported in the preceding article by Dr. and Mrs. Leakey, was associated with a fauna of Bed II affinities.

It thus seems clear that two different branches of the Hominidae were evolving side by side in the Olduvai region during the Upper Villafranchian and the lower part of the Middle Pleistocene.

(**202**, 7-9; 1964)

L. S. B. Leakey: Coryndon Museum, Centre for Prehistory and Palaeontology.
P. V. Tobias: University of Witwatersrand, Johannesburg.
J. R. Napier: Unit of Primatology and Human Evolution, Royal Free Hospital Medical School, University of London.

现者本人在南非和坦噶尼喀进行关于南方古猿亚科起源的调查后，如今他在这方面和我们的观点一致。我们认为它很有可能是能人的北方代表。

非洲之外，在以色列约旦河的乌贝迪亚发现的牙齿和头骨破片也可能属于能人而不是属于南方古猿。

文化联系

在 *F.L.K.* I的生活面中发现鲍氏南方古猿（鲍氏东非人）头骨的时候，在奥杜威早期层位中没有任何其他类型已知的人科动物。因此假定这个头骨代表了奥杜威文化的创造者看来是合理的。然而，在随后的三个地点发现能人遗骸与奥杜威文化并存的现象极大地改变了这一观点。东非人和能人可能都会制造石器，但是后者可能是更先进石器的制造者，这一东非人头骨代表的可能是能人生活地域的一个闯入者（或者牺牲品）。

最近在 *D.K.* I地点第I层的下部生活层发现了由石头松散堆成的类似圆圈形状，这是值得我们注意的。在地质学上这个点和 *M.K.* I地点是同一时代，就在距离它不及1英里的地方发现了能人的遗骸。看来，这一时期的早期人科具有制造粗制的掩蔽物或防风墙的能力，而这一人类很可能是能人。

与南方古猿（东非人）的关系

在第I层和第II层的中、下部发现了代表新种能人的人类化石，*M.K.* I和 *F.L.K.N.N.* I两个地点的地质学年代要比出土南方古猿亚科东非人头骨的更远。其中 *F.L.K.* I地点出土了南方古猿（东非人）和能人的遗骸，而另外两个地点——*M.N.K.* II和 *F.L.K.* II马伊科河年代稍近。路易斯·利基博士和夫人玛丽·利基在前文中报道过从纳特龙湖产出的新的南方古猿（东非人）下颌骨同第II层中的动物群是有密切联系的。

因此，我们可以清楚地了解到：在维拉方期上部和中更新世下部，人科的两个不同分支在奥杜威区域平行地演化着。

（张玉光 翻译；刘武 邢松 审稿）

Haemoglobin G_{Accra}

H. Lehmann *et al.*

Editor's Note

Here Hermann Lehmann and D. Beale from Cambridge University identify the specific amino-acid substitution responsible for haemoglobin G_{Accra}, a rare and abnormal variant of the iron-containing red-blood-cell protein. The blood sample, procured by F. S. Boi-Doku of Accra's Central Clinical Laboratory in Ghana, came from an apparently healthy individual in his sixties who had inherited two copies of the abnormal gene. All other homozygous abnormal haemoglobin variants known at that time produced disease, making haemoglobin G_{Accra} all the more enticing to study and raising the possibility that other, similarly harmless, rare haemoglobin variants might exist.

IN 1954 the major haemoglobin types, A, M, S, C, D, E and F, had been described, and the observation of a new variant, haemoglobin G (ref. 1), was the first of a series of reports on rarer human haemoglobins which is still continuing. The haemoglobin then described—and differentiated from other haemoglobins with identical or similar electrophoretic properties as haemoglobin G_{Accra}—has never been found again, except in the family in which it was originally observed. Haemoglobin G_{Accra} is abnormal in the β-chain[2]. The haemoglobins with identical electrophoretic and chromatographic properties hitherto examined were α-chain abnormal pigments. There are three: (1) haemoglobin $G_{Philadelphia}$ with which numerous other haemoglobins observed in West Africa, or in persons of West African origin, are identical[3]; (2) haemoglobin $G_{Chinese}$, which has only been found in persons of Chinese extraction[4]; (3) a haemoglobin found in a British family, haemoglobin $G_{Norfolk}$[5]. There is one other haemoglobin named G which also carries its substituted amino-acid residue in the β-chain-haemoglobin $G_{San\ José}$[6], but this pigment differs from haemoglobin G_{Accra} in its electrophoretic properties, and should perhaps have been described under a different letter.

Haemoglobin G_{Accra} is remarkable for the fact that it is the only rare haemoglobin for which an individual has been described the homozygous state of which could be established on the basis of family investigation and of laboratory findings[7]. This homozygote was found to be healthy without an enlarged spleen, without anaemia, and his red cells were morphologically indistinguishable from those containing only normal haemoglobin. This was, and still is, in contrast with what is seen in the haemoglobin S, C, D and E diseases, the only other homozygous conditions for adult haemoglobin variants so far described.

There was, therefore, a special interest in establishing the precise nature of the amino-acid substitution in haemoglobin G_{Accra}. Whatever its nature, it does not have a similar effect

血红蛋白G阿克拉

莱曼等

编者按

在本文中，剑桥大学的赫尔曼·莱曼和比尔鉴定出了血红蛋白G阿克拉中特有的氨基酸替换。血红蛋白G阿克拉是含铁红细胞蛋白质的一种稀有异常变异体。加纳阿克拉中心临床实验室的博伊–多库从一位六十多岁、看起来健康的人身上取得血液样本，此人遗传了两个拷贝的异常基因。在那个时候，已知所有其他的纯合异常血红蛋白变异体都会引起疾病，这使得血红蛋白G阿克拉更值得研究，而且增加了其他稀有的非致病血红蛋白变异体存在的可能性。

到1954年人们已经发现了血红蛋白的主要类型，包括血红蛋白A、M、S、C、D、E和F。对一种新的变异体——血红蛋白G（参考文献1）的观察研究是关于人稀有血红蛋白系列报道的第一个，这样的报道仍在继续。当时所描述的这种血红蛋白和其他与血红蛋白G阿克拉具有相同或类似的电泳性质的血红蛋白不同，除了在最初的家族观察到以外再也没有被发现过。血红蛋白G阿克拉在β链上发生异常[2]，而迄今所检测到的电泳和色谱性质相同的血红蛋白都是在α链上发生异常。这样的血红蛋白有3种：(1) 血红蛋白G费城，与在西非或西非血统的人中发现的许多其他血红蛋白都是相同的[3]；(2) 血红蛋白G中国人，只在有中国血统的人中发现过[4]；(3) 血红蛋白G诺福克[5]，在一个英国家族中发现。还有另一种命名为G的血红蛋白，其β链中携带被替换的氨基酸残基，即血红蛋白G圣何塞[6]，但是这种血红蛋白与血红蛋白G阿克拉在电泳性质上不同，也许应该用另一个字母来表示。

血红蛋白G阿克拉突出的地方在于它是唯一一个基于家族调查和实验室研究所确证的、在个体中以纯合状态存在的稀有血红蛋白[7]。这个纯合子个体是健康的，脾没有肿大，没有贫血症，并且他的红细胞在形态上与只含有正常血红蛋白的红细胞没有区别。直到今天，这都与在血红蛋白S、C、D和E疾病中所见到的情况完全不同，是迄今为止已描述的成人血红蛋白变异体中唯一一例不同的情况。

因此，科学家对血红蛋白G阿克拉中的氨基酸替换的具体情况特别感兴趣。无论如何，这种替换与血红蛋白S、C、D和E中已知的氨基酸替换对红细胞的形态也

on the morphology and, presumably, the life span of the red cell which is produced by the known substitutions in haemoglobins S, C, D and E.

Amino-acid Substitution in Haemoglobin G_{Accra}. Haemoglobin G was purified from the blood of the homozygote and a peptide-chromatogram (fingerprint) was prepared according to Ingram[8] and Baglioni[9]. It was noted that peptide 6 according to the old numbering system, or tryptic peptide β*Tp*IX according to the new nomenclature[10], was missing and another new peptide was seen instead which had moved nearer towards the cathode (Fig. 1). The new peptide gave a positive colour reaction for histidine[11], as does the β*Tp*IX of haemoglobin A (β^A*Tp*IX). This peptide contains in haemoglobin A 16 amino-acid residues[12,13] (Table 1).

Table 1. Amino-acid Sequence of Tryptic Peptide IX of the β-Chain of Haemoglobin A

Val–	leu–	gly–	ala–	phe–	ser–	asp–	gly–	leu–	ala–	his–	leu–	asp–	asn–	leu–	lys
67	68	69	70	71	72	73	74	75	76	77	78	79	80	81	82

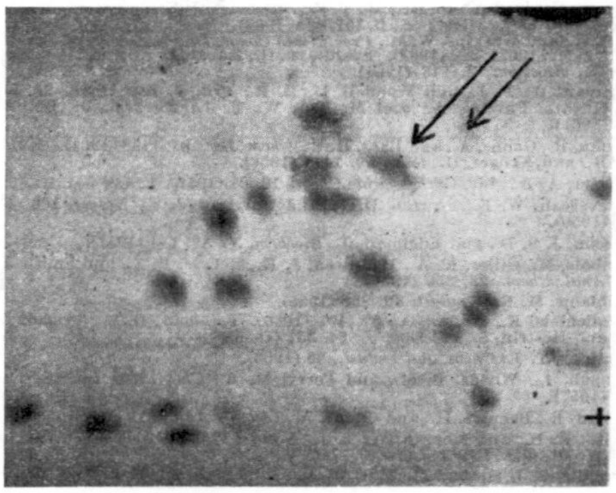

Fig. 1. Fingerprint of the tryptic digest of haemoglobin G_{Accra} . The right arrow points to the area where β^A*Tp*IX is missing, and the left arrow to the peptide which has taken its place— β^G*Tp*IX. +, Point of application

The NH_2-terminal group[14], was valyl in both peptides, and leucine amino peptidase[4] which splits off amino-acids from the NH_2-terminal part of a peptide chain released valine and leucine in both. As the peptides had arisen from tryptic digestion which implies lysyl or arginyl as the COOH-terminal, and as the colour reaction and amino-acid analysis failed to show arginine[15], lysyl had to be the COOH-terminal group.

Table 2 shows a comparison of the results of quantitative amino-acid analysis on an EEL automatic analyser[16], after the acid hydrolysis of the two peptides from haemoglobins A and G. It will be seen that the results were the same in both, although the electrophoretic mobility of the G-peptide had indicated that it had a greater positive charge than the corresponding A-peptide. The only explanation was that one of the two aspartic acid residues of β^A*Tp*IX had been replaced by an asparaginyl in β^G*Tp*IX, and that this had been converted into aspartic acid on acid hydrolysis.

可能是对红细胞的寿命产生的影响不同。

血红蛋白 G阿克拉中的氨基酸替换 从纯合子的血液中纯化出血红蛋白 G，按照英格拉姆[8]和巴廖尼[9]的方法制作肽色谱图（指纹图谱）。人们注意到 6 号肽段（根据旧的计数系统）或胰蛋白酶消化肽段 β*Tp*IX（根据新的命名法则）[10]消失了，而在更接近阴极的地方出现了另一个新的肽段（图 1）。这个新肽段与组氨酸可以发生阳性的颜色反应[11]，如同血红蛋白 A 的 β*Tp*IX（β^A*Tp*IX）一样。在血红蛋白 A 中，该肽段有 16 个氨基酸残基[12,13]（表 1）。

表1. 血红蛋白A的β链胰蛋白酶消化的肽段IX的氨基酸序列

Val–	leu–	gly–	ala–	phe–	ser–	asp–	gly–	leu–	ala–	his–	leu–	asp–	asn–	leu–	lys
67	68	69	70	71	72	73	74	75	76	77	78	79	80	81	82

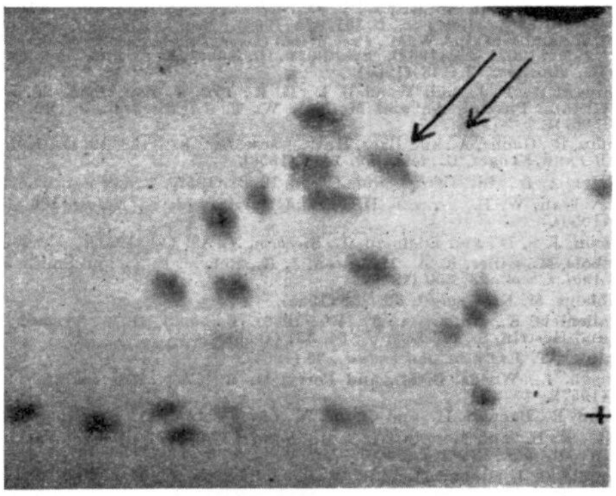

图 1. 血红蛋白 G阿克拉胰蛋白酶消化物的指纹图谱。右侧箭头指出了 β^A*Tp*IX 缺失的区域，左侧箭头指出了新出现的肽段 β^G*Tp*IX。+ 表示加样点。

两个肽段的氨基末端[14]都是缬氨酰，亮氨酸氨肽酶[4]（可以从肽链的氨基末端切下氨基酸）处理两个肽段后释放出缬氨酸和亮氨酸。由于该肽段是由胰蛋白酶消化产生，这就意味着其羧基末端只能是赖氨酰基或精氨酰基。又通过颜色反应和氨基酸分析证明其羧基末端不是精氨酸[15]，所以只能是赖氨酰基。

表 2 显示了来自血红蛋白 A 和 G 的两个肽段经酸水解后在 EEL 自动分析仪上进行氨基酸定量分析的结果比较[16]。可以看到两者的结果相同，虽然 G 肽段的电泳迁移率表明它比 A 肽段相应的多了一个正电荷。唯一的解释就是在 β^G*Tp*IX 中，原 β^A*Tp*IX 的两个天冬氨酸残基之一被天冬酰胺酰所取代，而这一残基在酸水解时转变成了天冬氨酸。

Table 2. Molar Ratio of Amino-acid Residues after Acid Hydrolysis of Tryptic Peptides IX from Haemoglobin A and Haemoglobin G_{Accra}

Residues	$\beta^{A}Tp$IX		$\beta^{G}Tp$IX	
Asp	2.8	2.7	2.6	2.6
Thr	trace	trace	trace	trace
Ser	1.0	1.2	1.1	1.3
Glu	trace	trace	trace	trace
Pro	trace	trace	trace	trace
Gly	2.1	2.0	1.9	2.2
Ala	2.5	2.4	2.3	2.1
Val	1.3	1.1	1.0	0.9
Leu	3.6	3.7	3.7	3.7
Phe	1.0	1.0	1.1	1.2
Lys	0.9	0.9	1.1	1.1
His	0.9	1.1	0.9	1.2

Although on electrophoresis at *p*H 6.4 the mobility of the A peptide is 0.0 and that of the G peptide + 0.17 (lysine = + 1.0) there seems to be no difference in amino-acid composition after acid hydrolysis.

To investigate this possibility, both peptides βTpIX were eluted with 10 percent (v/v) pyridine to prevent hydrolysis of asparaginyl, and then digested with pronase for 4 h using the same arrangement as had been used for trypsin, and the resulting smaller peptides and amino-acids were separated by high voltage electrophoresis at *p*H 6.4. Pronase attacks virtually all peptide linkages, although it is relatively inactive towards those which involve aspartic acid residues. Table 3 shows the electrophoretic mobility of these breakdown products, and their amino-acid composition found after acid hydrolysis. This latter method of course converts asparaginyl to aspartic acid. It will be seen that the number of acidic breakdown products in which aspartic acid could be demonstrated differed in the two peptides—four from haemoglobin A, and three from haemoglobin G. Three seemed to be the same in both haemoglobins. Free aspartic acid was obtained from both, and there were two peptides which had nearly the same electrophoretic mobility, and the same amino-acid composition in both. One peptide with the mobilities of −0.77 and −0.78 respectively was hydrolysed into aspartic acid and glycine with aspartyl as the NH_2-terminal residue. The other peptide with the mobilities of −0.64 and −0.62 respectively showed on hydrolysis only aspartic acid, glycine, and leucine with NH_2-terminal aspartyl and COOH-terminal leucyl[14,17]. The sequence 73-75 was therefore the same in both β^A and β^G, namely, asp-gly-leu, and the substitution of aspartyl in haemoglobin G had to be in position 79 of the β chain.

From $\beta^{A}Tp$IX one other peptide yielding aspartic acid was obtained. It had a mobility of −0.68 but produced aspartic acid only. However, aspartic acid or an asp-asp peptide would have had a mobility of −1.00, hence this peptide had to consist of aspartyl and asparaginyl, and it represented the 79-80 sequence of the β^A-chain, namely, asp-asn.

This peptide was not found in $\beta^{G}Tp$IX. However, free asparagine could be demonstrated in the neutral band before hydrolysis. No free asparagine was found in the neutral band of

表 2. 血红蛋白 A 和血红蛋白 $G_{阿克拉}$的胰蛋白酶消化的肽段 IX 酸水解后氨基酸残基的摩尔比

氨基酸残基	$\beta^{A}Tp$IX		$\beta^{G}Tp$IX	
天冬氨酸	2.8	2.7	2.6	2.6
苏氨酸	痕量	痕量	痕量	痕量
丝氨酸	1.0	1.2	1.1	1.3
谷氨酸	痕量	痕量	痕量	痕量
脯氨酸	痕量	痕量	痕量	痕量
甘氨酸	2.1	2.0	1.9	2.2
丙氨酸	2.5	2.4	2.3	2.1
缬氨酸	1.3	1.1	1.0	0.9
亮氨酸	3.6	3.7	3.7	3.7
苯丙氨酸	1.0	1.0	1.1	1.2
赖氨酸	0.9	0.9	1.1	1.1
组氨酸	0.9	1.1	0.9	1.2

虽然在 pH 为 6.4 条件下电泳时，A 肽的迁移率是 0.0，G 肽的迁移率是 +0.17(赖氨酸 =+1.0)，但是在酸水解后的氨基酸组成上看不出什么差别。

为了研究这种可能性，两种 β*Tp*IX 肽段都用 10%(v/v) 吡啶洗脱，以防止天冬酰胺酰水解，然后在与胰蛋白酶消化条件一样的情况下，用链霉蛋白酶消化 4 小时。在 pH 为 6.4 的条件下，通过高压电泳将得到的较小的肽段和氨基酸分离开。虽然链霉蛋白酶作用于含有天冬氨酸残基的肽键的活性较弱，但它几乎可以解开所有的肽键。表 3 显示了这些分解产物的电泳迁移率及其酸水解后的氨基酸组成。酸水解无疑可将天冬酰胺酰转换为天冬氨酸。可以看到在酸性水解产物中的天冬氨酸的数量在 2 个肽段中有差别——血红蛋白 A 中是 4 个，血红蛋白 G 中是 3 个。其中的 3 个在两种血红蛋白中似乎是一样的。从两种血红蛋白中都可以得到游离的天冬氨酸。还有两个肽段具有几乎相同的电泳迁移率和相同的氨基酸组成。迁移率分别是 –0.77 和 –0.78 的一种肽段可以水解成天冬氨酸和甘氨酸，氨基末端残基是天冬氨酰。而迁移率分别是 –0.64 和 –0.62 的另一种肽段水解后只生成天冬氨酸、甘氨酸和亮氨酸，其氨基末端是天冬氨酰，羧基末端是亮氨酰 [14,17]。因此在 β^{A} 和 β^{G} 中，73~75 位的序列一样，即为 asp-gly-leu，在血红蛋白 G 中天冬氨酰的替换必定发生在 β 链的第 79 位。

从 $\beta^{A}Tp$IX 中还获得了另一个产生天冬氨酸的肽，其迁移率是 –0.68，但只产生天冬氨酸。然而天冬氨酸或 asp-asp 肽的迁移率是 –1.00。因此，该肽一定是由天冬氨酰和天冬酰胺酰组成，它是 β^{A} 链的第 79~80 位序列，即为 asp-asn。

在 $\beta^{G}Tp$IX 中没有发现这种肽。但是在水解前的中性带中却发现了游离的天冬酰胺。而在 $\beta^{A}Tp$IX 的中性带中并没有发现游离的天冬酰胺。由此得出结论：与

β^{A}*Tp*IX. From this it could be concluded that the residue next to leucyl in position 79 of the β^{G}-chain was asparaginyl and haemoglobin G_{Accra} could be defined as $\alpha_2^A\beta_2^{79\ Asn}$.

Table 3. Products of Pronase Hydrolysis of β^{A}*Tp*IX and β^{G}*Tp*IX

	Mobility*	Amino acids on acid hydrolysis	NH^{2-} terminal DNP	COOH-terminal
β^{A}*Tp*IX	−1.00	Asp		
	−0.77	Asp, gly	Asp	
	−0.68	Asp		
	−0.64	Asp, gly, leu	Asp	Leu
	−0.52			
	0.00	Val, gly, leu, asp Ala, phe, ser		
	+0.53	His		
	+0.67	Leu, lys	Leu	
	+1.00	Lys		
β^{G}*Tp*IX	−1.00	Asp		
	−0.78	Asp, gly	Asp	
	−0.62	Asp, gly, leu	Asp	Leu
	−0.54			
	0.00	Val, gly, leu, asp Ala, ser, phe		
	+0.51	His		
	+0.67	Leu, lys	Leu	
	+1.00	Lys		

* Electrophoretic mobility is measured at *p*H6.4 using as markers aspartic acid (−1.00) and lysine (+1.00).

The sequence asn-asn-leu in haemoglobin G would explain why pronase digestion produced the peptide asp-asn from β^{A}*Tp*IX preferably to the free asparagine as obtained from β^{G}*Tp*IX. In β^{G}*Tp*IX due to the aspartyl → asparaginyl replacement the 79-80 linkage was more easily broken because of the absence of an acidic aspartyl residue.

Homozygote. The homozygote is now sixty-four years old, or even a little older, and is physically fit with the exception of a mild hypertension of 160/100 mm mercury. From 1923 until his retirement in 1963 he worked continually as a printer in the Accra Government Printing Department. Of his twenty children by two wives, all but one is alive and well. The age of the oldest offspring is thirty-six years and the youngest is eleven years old.

His blood shows the following values:

haemoglobin	12.6 g/100 ml
red cells	4,500,000/mm^3
packed cell volume	40 percent

β^G 链第 79 位亮氨酰相邻的残基是天冬酰胺酰，因此血红蛋白 G阿克拉还可以表示为 $\alpha_2^A\beta_2^{79\ Asn}$。

表 3. β^A*Tp*IX 和 β^G*Tp*IX 的链霉蛋白酶水解产物

	迁移率*	酸水解后得到的氨基酸	氨基末端的 DNP	羧基端
β^A*Tp*IX	–1.00	Asp		
	–0.77	Asp，gly	Asp	
	–0.68	Asp		
	–0.64	Asp，gly，leu	Asp	Leu
	–0.52			
	0.00	Val，gly，leu，asp Ala，phe，ser		
	+0.53	His		
	+0.67	Leu，lys	Leu	
	+1.00	Lys		
β^G*Tp*IX	–1.00	Asp		
	–0.78	Asp，gly	Asp	
	–0.62	Asp，gly，leu	Asp	Leu
	–0.54			
	0.00	Val，gly，leu，asp Ala，ser，phe		
	+0.51	His		
	+0.67	Leu，lys	Leu	
	+1.00	Lys		

* pH 6.4 时用天冬氨酸 (–1.00) 和赖氨酸 (+1.00) 作标记测定电泳迁移率。

血红蛋白 G 中的序列 asn-asn-leu 可以解释为什么 β^A*Tp*IX 经链霉蛋白酶消化产生了肽 asp-asn，而不是像 β^G*Tp*IX 那样产生游离的天冬酰胺。在 β^G*Tp*IX 中，由于天冬氨酰被天冬酰胺酰所替代，第 79~80 位间的肽键因为缺少了一个酸性的天冬氨酰残基而更容易断裂。

纯合子　纯合子来源于今年 64 岁的老人，也许更老一些，身体很健康，只是有些轻度的高血压（160/100 毫米汞柱）。他是一个印刷工人，从 1923 年开始一直在阿克拉政府的印刷部门工作，直到 1963 年退休。他的 20 个孩子（由两位妻子所生）除了一个之外其他的都还在世而且身体健康。这些孩子中最大的 36 岁，最小的只有 11 岁。

他的血液化验值如下：

血红蛋白	12.6 克 /100 毫升
红细胞	4,500,000/ 毫米 ^{3}
红细胞压积	40%

The mean corpuscular values are:

cell volume	89 μ^3
haemoglobin	28 $\gamma\gamma$
haemoglobin concentration	32 percent

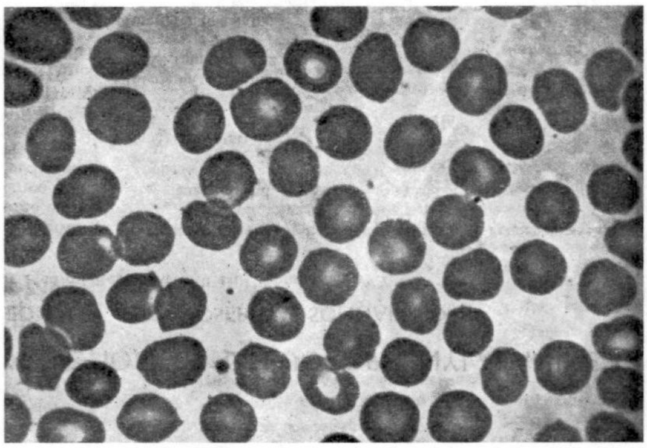

Fig. 2. Stained blood smear of the haemoglobin-G homozygote. The cells are not hypochromic and the target cells and other abnormal forms associated with the blood picture of haemoglobin S, C, D and E homozygotes are absent

The red cell fragility showed an almost normal distribution: initial haemolysis at 0.5 percent sodium chloride, 50 percent haemolysis at 0.415 and 90 percent haemolysis at 0.3 percent sodium chloride. The only unusual feature was that 10 percent of the cells were still not haemolysed at 0.3 percent sodium chloride, and that complete haemolysis was only achieved in distilled water. There was no enlarged spleen, the red cells were normal in appearance and there were no target cells. Haemoglobin A_2 was within normal limits, and on haemoglobin F was demonstrable. These findings contrast with those in haemoglobinopathies of the homozygotes for the genes controlling haemoglobins S, C, D and E. Haemoglobin $\alpha_2^A\beta_2^{79\ Asn}$ seems to cause no haemoglobinopathy and the substitution of an asparaginyl residue for an aspartyl in position 79 of the β-chain seems to have no deleterious effect.

Differences in the Morbidity of Haemoglobin Variants. Of the rarer haemoglobins only haemoglobin G_{Accra} has so far been seen in the homozygous state. It is probable that many of the other rare haemoglobins may be similarly harmless and that there is a relation between the effect a haemoglobin has on the red cell morphology in the homozygote and the advantage it confers on the heterozygote in natural selection which causes its high frequency in a population.

In the heterozygote for the genes for haemoglobin A, and for haemoglobins S, C, D and E respectively, the proportion of the abnormal variant is less than 50 percent. This has usually been interpreted as the outcome of a difference in the rate of production of normal and abnormal polypeptide chains within the cell[18]. An alternative explanation has recently been proposed by Levere, Lichtman and Levine[19]. From iron incorporation

平均红细胞体积如下：

细胞体积	89 微米 ^{3}
血红蛋白	28 $\gamma\gamma$
血红蛋白浓度	32%

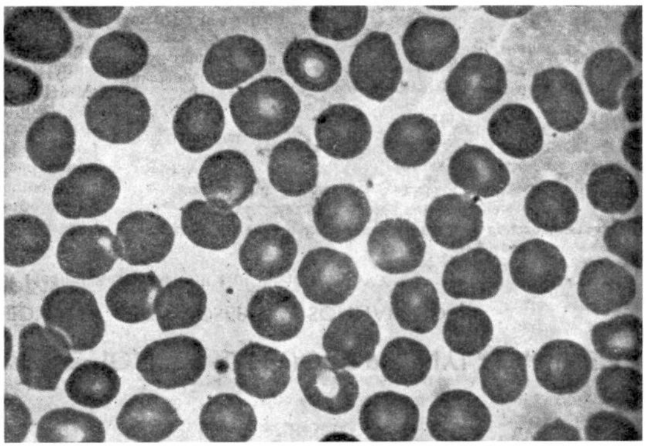

图 2. 血红蛋白 G 纯合子染色后血液涂片。细胞被充分染色，图中没有靶细胞以及其他与血红蛋白 S、C、D 和 E 纯合子血象相关联的异常形式。

红细胞的脆性实验显示出几乎正常的分布：在 0.5% 的氯化钠溶液中红细胞开始溶解，在 0.415% 的氯化钠溶液中有 50% 红细胞溶解，在 0.3% 的氯化钠溶液中有 90% 的红细胞溶解。唯一不正常的是在 0.3% 的氯化钠中仍有 10% 的红细胞没有溶解，只有在蒸馏水中才能完全溶解。脾没有肿大，红细胞外观正常，没有发现靶细胞。血红蛋白 A_2 的数量在正常范围之内，没有发现血红蛋白 F。这些结果与控制血红蛋白 S、C、D 和 E 的基因的纯合子引起的血红蛋白病的结果完全不同。血红蛋白 $\alpha_2^A\beta_2^{79\ Asn}$ 似乎不引起血红蛋白病，在 β 链 79 位上天冬酰胺酰代替了天冬氨酰似乎没有有害的作用。

血红蛋白变异体致病性的差异　在这些较稀有的血红蛋白中，迄今只发现血红蛋白 G阿克拉为纯合状态。很有可能还存在许多其他同样非致病的稀有血红蛋白。纯合子中血红蛋白对红细胞形态的作用可能与它给杂合子赋予的在自然选择过程中的优势之间存在着某种关系，这种优势使其在种群中保持有较高的频率。

在血红蛋白 A 以及血红蛋白 S、C、D 和 E 的基因杂合子中，异常变异体的比例分别小于 50%。这通常被解释为细胞内产生正常多肽链和异常多肽链的速率不同所致 [18]。近来莱维尔、利奇特曼和莱文提出了另一种解释 [19]。对具有贫血镰刀状细胞特征的（A ＋ S）携带者进行铁掺入研究，从中他们得出结论：至少在血红蛋白

studies in anaemic sickle-cell trait (A + S) carriers they concluded that, in the case of haemoglobin A + S at least, cells with a wide range of A : S proportions are produced—some with A < S and some with A > S. The first are rapidly eliminated and as a result the final over-all proportion of A : S becomes greater than 1.

In the case of haemoglobin A + G_{Accra} heterozygotes, the proportion of the two haemoglobins is exactly 1. We have established this by a number of investigations because by ordinary paper electrophoresis at alkaline *p*H the leading (A) band contains about 53 percent of the total haemoglobin. This proportion is also obtained when an artificial mixture of 50 percent A and 50 percent G is submitted to electrophoresis at alkaline *p*H. Furthermore, when open boundary electrophoresis of haemoglobin from the A + G heterozygote was performed at *p*H 6.5 (ref. 7) and the G fraction was the leading component, the G fraction then amounted to from 50 to 55 percent of the total pigment.

This equal proportion of A and G in the heterozygote would indicate that there is no elimination of cells with a higher proportion of G than A, and that the whole range of cells survives equally, those with A < G, and those with A > G.

One might predict that other haemoglobins which show an equal proportion of A and abnormal variants in the haemolysates from heterozygotes are similarly harmless as haemoglobin G_{Accra}. There would, therefore, be a series of haemoglobin types: (1) Harmless in homozygotes and heterozygotes (heterozygotes show 50 percent of the abnormal variant): example, haemoglobin G_{Accra}. (2) Harmful in homozygotes, harmless in heterzygotes (abnormal variant < 50 > 20 percent). Haemoglobins S, C, D and E would belong to this group. (3) Harmful in heterozygotes (abnormal variant < 20 percent). To this would belong the haemoglobins which are associated with haemolysis even in the heterozygote, such as haemoglobin Köln[20].

The correlation between the morbidity of a haemoglobin and its molecular structure might throw an important light on the function of haemoglobin as a whole.

We thank Mr. D. Irvine for valuable assistance, also Dr. G. Braunitzer and his colleagues of the Max Planck Institute für Biochemie, Munich, Germany, for advice and discussion.

(**203**, 363-365; 1964)

H. Lehmann and D. Beale: Medical Research Council Abnormal Haemoglobin Research Unit, University Department of Biochemistry, Cambridge.

F. S. Boi-Doku: Central Clinical Laboratory, Accra.

A + S 的情况下，机体可以产生 A : S 比例范围很广的细胞——有些是 $A < S$，有些是 $A > S$。前一种细胞被迅速清除，结果 A 与 S 的最终比例就大于 1。

在血红蛋白 A + $G_{\text{阿克拉}}$杂合子这种情况下，两种血红蛋白的比例恰好是 1。我们通过多次研究证实了这一点，因为在碱性 pH 条件下的常规纸电泳中，前带（A）大约占总血红蛋白的 53%。当 50% 的 A 和 50% 的 G 人为混合后，在碱性 pH 条件下进行电泳也得到了同样的比例。另外，当对 A + G 杂合子的血红蛋白在 pH 6.5 条件下进行开放界面电泳时 (参考文献 7)，G 部分是前沿组分，G 部分占血红蛋白总量的 50%~55%。

在杂合子中，A 和 G 的比例相等可能表明：G 的比例比 A 高的细胞并没有被清除，所有细胞，不管是 $A < G$ 还是 $A > G$，都同等地存活下来。

可以预测，在杂合子的溶血产物中 A 组分和异常变异体具有相同比例的其他血红蛋白，就像血红蛋白 $G_{\text{阿克拉}}$一样是非致病的。因此，一共可能有以下三类血红蛋白：(1) 纯合子和杂合子（杂合子有 50% 的异常变异体）均是非致病的：如血红蛋白 $G_{\text{阿克拉}}$。(2) 纯合子是致病的而杂合子（$20\% <$ 异常变异体 $< 50\%$）是非致病的。血红蛋白 S、C、D 和 E 属于这种类型。(3) 杂合子（异常变异体 $< 20\%$）是致病的。即使在杂合子中与溶血相关的血红蛋白也属于这一类，如科隆血红蛋白 [20]。

对于血红蛋白的致病性及其分子结构的相互关系的阐述也许会对血红蛋白整体功能的研究具有重要的启示。

我们感谢欧文先生的大力协助，也感谢布劳尼策尔博士和他所在的德国慕尼黑马克斯 · 普朗克生物化学研究所的同事们的建议和讨论。

（荆玉祥 翻译；杨茂君 审稿）

References:

1. Edington, G. M., and Lehmann, H., *Lancet*, ii, 173 (1954).
2. Gammack, D. B., Huehns, E. R., Lehmann, H., and Shooter, E. M., *Acta Genet. Stalist. Meà.*, **11**, 1 (1961).
3. Schwartz, I. R., Atwater, J., and Tocantins, L. M., *Blood*, **15**, 901 (1960).
4. Swenson, R. T., Hill, R. L., Lehmann, H., and Jim, R. T. S., *J. Biol. Chem.*, **237**, 1517 (1962).
5. Huntsman, R. G., Hall, M., Lehmann, H., and Sukumaran, P. K., *Brit. Med. J.*, **1**, 720 (1963).
6. Hill, R. L., Swenson, R. T., and Schwartz, H. C., *J. Biol. Chem.*, **235**, 3182 (1960).
7. Edington, G. M., Lehmann, H., and Schneider, R. G., *Nature*, **175**, 850 (1955).
8. Ingram, V. M., *Biochim. Biophys. Acta*, **28**, 539 (1958).
9. Baglioni, C., *Biochim. Biophys. Acta*, **48**, 392 (1961).
10. Gerald, P. S., and Ingram, V. M., *J. Biol. Chem.*, **236**, 2155 (1961).
11. Whitehead, J. K., and Beale, D., *Clin. Chim. Acta*, **4**, 710 (1959).
12. Braunitzer, G., and Rudloff, V., *Deut. Med. Wochschr.*, **87**, 959 (1962).
13. Goldstein, J., Konigsberg, W., and Hill, R. J., *J. Biol. Chem.*, **238**, 2016 (1963).
14. Sanger, F., *Biochem. J.*, **39**, 507 (1945).
15. Jepson, J. B., and Smith, I., *Nature*, **172**, 1100 (1953).
16. Spackman, D. H., Stein, W. H., and Moore, S., *Anal. Chem.*, **30**, 1190 (1958).
17. Ambler, R. P., *Biochem. J.*, **89**, 349 (1963).
18. Itano, H. A., in *Abnormal Haemoglobins*, edit. by Jonxis, J. H. P., and Delatresnaye, J. F., 1 (Blackwell Sci. Publ., Oxford, 1959).
19. Levere, R. D., Lichtman, H. C., and Levine, J., *Nature*, **202**, 499 (1964).
20. Pribilla, W., in *Haemoglobin Colloquium*, edit. by Lehmann, H., and Betke, K., 73 (Georg Thieme Verlag, Stuttgart, 1962).

Homo "habilis" and the Australopithecines

J. T. Robinson

Editor's Note

This trenchant critique of *Homo habilis*, the new Olduvai hominid species proposed by Leakey and colleagues in 1964, exposes many problems with Leakey's conception of "handy man" that still remain unresolved. As well as finding problems with Leakey's casual use of nomenclature—a highly technical pursuit—the author John T. Robinson suggests that *Homo habilis* from Bed I at Olduvai looked much more like *Australopithecus africanus* than *Homo*—and that the stratigraphically later finds from Bed II might be better subsumed within *Homo erectus*. The problem of inadequate definition has dogged the study of *Homo habilis* to this day. The material Leakey assigned to this species is indeed highly heterogeneous, some closely resembling australopithecine material, other specimens more akin to *Homo*.

LEAKEY, Tobias and Napier have given a preliminary account of specimens which in their opinion belong to a hitherto unknown species of the genus *Homo*[1]. They re-defined the latter genus and proposed the species name *H. habilis*, with definition, for the new taxon which includes specimens discovered between late 1960 and late 1963.

Diagnosis of the New Taxon

Two critically important functions of the original description of a new taxon are: (*a*) to demonstrate that the population sample under discussion represents a taxon which is different from all recognized taxa and is therefore indeed new and in need of a name; (*b*) to place on record the new name selected for the taxon.

In order that the first of these functions be satisfied a differential diagnosis is necessary. This brings out the points of difference between the specimens comprising the new taxon and all closely related specimens which have been referred to already existing taxa. From this point of view the original description of *H. "habilis"* by Leakey *et al.* is unsatisfactory. Doubtless the authors intend to present further evidence elsewhere at a later date, but clearly the appropriate place is in the original description (in the technical taxonomic sense) so that others may judge the validity of the proposed taxon.

The proposed new definition of the genus *Homo* depends in part on the validity of the new species proposed for it. The new species is defined briefly as though proof had previously been presented that it is a new taxon—but in fact there is no discussion of "evidence" which clearly establishes that this is the case. The definition does include a few very broad diagnostic comparisons, for example, "... premolars which are narrower (in bucco-lingual breadth) than those of *Australopithecus* ...", but no evidence is presented to support them.

“能人”和南方古猿

鲁滨逊

编者按

1964年，利基教授及其同事们提出了一种新的奥杜威原始人种——能人。对能人的尖锐批判揭露出利基的“灵巧的人”概念中存在许多问题，这些问题仍未得到解决。此外还发现利基的临时命名在更高的学术层面上存在问题，本文作者约翰·鲁滨逊认为来自奥杜威第I层的能人看起来较之于人属更像南方古猿非洲种——而将后来从第II层中发现的标本归为直立人则更合适。定义不恰当的问题至今仍伴随在对能人的研究中。被利基归为这一物种的标本确实存在不同的种类，一些标本非常类似于南方古猿亚科，其他一些标本则更类似于人属。

利基、托拜厄斯及内皮尔已经对标本进行了初步描述，依照他们的观点，这些标本属于一种迄今为止还未知的人属种类[1]。他们重新定义了这个属，并且建议将其种名命名为能人，根据定义这个新种包括了1960年末至1963年末所发现的标本。

新分类单元的鉴别分析

一个新分类单元的原始描述有两个关键的重要作用：(*a*) 论证所研究的种群样本代表的分类单元不同于所有已知的分类单元，因而确实是新的并且需要一个名称；(*b*) 将这个分类单元选用的新名称记录在案。

为了实现其中第一个作用，需要进行鉴别分析。通过鉴别分析总结出属于新分类单元的标本与所有密切相关的属于已存在的分类单元的标本之间的差异点。从这个观点来看，利基等人所给出的“能人”的原始描述并不令人满意。作者无疑打算以后在其他地方给出更进一步的证据，但是显然这个工作最应该体现在原始描述中(在分类学的专业意义上)，这样别人可以判断其所提出的分类单元的有效性。

所提出的人属的新定义在某种程度上取决于引出该定义的这一新种的有效性。这一新种定义得很简略，就好像之前已经有证据表明它是一种新的分类单元似的——但是事实上根本没有讨论出能够明确证实情况确实如此的“证据”。定义确实包括了少量而又非常宽泛的鉴别比较，例如，“……前臼齿要比南方古猿狭小（颊舌径）……”，但是没有给出证据来支持这些观点。

Furthermore, although reference is made to some previously known specimens with which the authors think their new species may be conspecific, no comparisons with the new material are actually included in their original description. In fact the following very curious statement is made: "The specimens originally described by Broom and Robinson as *Telanthropus capensis* and which were later transferred by Robinson to *Homo erectus* may well prove, on closer comparative investigation, to belong to *Homo habilis*." This statement clearly implies that the authors described a new species even though they believe that proper comparative investigation may well show that it is conspecific with specimens of which they are aware, the originals of which two of the authors have seen more than once and of which detailed descriptions exist in the literature. It is of interest also to note that the authors think that if the conspecificity be established in this case, then the material which was described more than a decade ago would belong to their new species rather than the other way about—as required by the *International Code of Zoological Nomenclature*.

One may thus conclude that: (*a*) the authors have not demonstrated that their proposed new species is in fact new; (*b*) the authors themselves are in doubt whether it is new; (*c*) since the validity of the new species has not been established, that of the new definition of *Homo* has not been established either. (In this general connexion see also the recent comment by Oakley and Campbell[2].)

Validity of the Proposed New Species

Although the authors do not present evidence in support of the few suggested differentially diagnostic features separating the proposed new species from the australopithecines, it is worth enquiring into the validity of these features.

Evidently a character which has impressed the authors as significant[1,3] is "a marked tendency toward the buccolingual narrowing and mesiodistal elongation of all the teeth, which is specially evident in the lower premolars ... and in the lower molars ... ". In particular it is held that the lower premolars are narrower than those of *Australopithecus* but fall within the range of *Homo erectus*. Through the courtesy of Dr. and Mrs. Leakey I was able to make a fairly detailed investigation, in 1961, of the mandible which has now been designated the holotype of *H.* "*habilis*". My measurements of P_3, made in the same manner as those on the South African australopithecines used for comparison, gave the following mesiodistal lengths and buccolingual breadths in millimetres: left, 9.6×9.4 and right, 9.6×9.9. These figures yield length/breadth indices $(L \times 100)/B$ of 102.2 and 98.0 respectively. Leakey[3] lists these dimensions as 11.0×9.5 in both cases and the index as 115.8. However, as comparison is being made with measurements made by me on the South African australopithecine material, my measurements on the Olduvai specimen should yield a better comparison since all the measurements involved were made by the same person using the same technique.

The table compares the mean length/breadth index and the observed range of the index for P_3 M_1 and M_2 of *Paranthropus*, *Australopithecus* and Pekin Man (*Homo erectus*) with the corresponding values for the type mandible of *H.* "*habilis*". P_3 of the latter falls within the

而且，尽管作者参考了一些之前已知的标本并由此认为他们的新种可能都属于同一物种，但是实际上在他们的原始描述中没有包括与新材料的对比。事实上他们得出了以下十分古怪的论点：“通过进一步的比较研究，可以充分证明最初由布鲁姆与鲁滨逊记述为开普远人、后来由鲁滨逊转而归入直立人的标本属于能人。”这个陈述明显暗示着作者描述了一个新种，尽管他们意识到适当的比较研究能够充分显示出它与他们知道的标本属于同一物种，而这些原始标本两位作者见过不止一次，并且在文献中也有详细的描述。同样有意思的是我们注意到作者认为，如果在此情况下确定了其同种性，那么十多年前描述的材料应该归属于他们的新种而非其他情形——遵照《国际动物命名法规》的要求。

因而可能得出下列结论：(*a*) 作者没有证明他们提出的新种确实是全新的；(*b*) 连作者他们自己都怀疑它是否是全新的；(*c*) 既然新种的有效性还不确定，人属新定义的有效性也就尚未确定。(有关这方面还可以参见奥克利与坎贝尔[2]的最近评论。)

建立新种的有效性

尽管作者没有给出证据来支持他们所提出的少量能区分新种与南方古猿亚科的不同的鉴别特征，但是这些特征的有效性仍值得探究。

很显然，给作者留下深刻印象的一个特征[1,3]是“所有牙齿都具有颊舌向变窄和近中远中向延长的显著趋势，这一趋势在下前臼齿……和下臼齿……尤其明显”。作者特别坚持其下前臼齿比南方古猿的下前臼齿窄，但是却认为其落在直立人的范围之内。承蒙利基博士与利基夫人的允许，1961 年我得以对现在被认为是“能人”正型标本的下颌骨进行了相当细致的观察研究。我测量了第三下前臼齿，测量方法与测量南非南方古猿亚科的方法一致以便用于比较，得出近中远中径与颊舌径如下（单位：毫米）：左，9.6 × 9.4；右，9.6 × 9.9。由这些数据得出：齿冠指数 $(L\times 100)/B$ 分别为 102.2 与 98.0。利基[3]列出的测量数据两边一样，均为 11.0 × 9.5，而系数为 115.8。然而，由于他在比较时用了我的南非南方古猿亚科材料测量数据，因此我对奥杜威标本测量数据应该得到更好的比较结果，因为全部测量是由同一个人用同样的方法进行的。

表 1 将傍人、南方古猿和北京人（直立人）的第三下前臼齿、第一下臼齿及第二下臼齿的齿冠指数的平均值及系数的观测范围与“能人”正型下颌骨的对应值进

observed range of that for *Paranthropus* and not far outside that for Pekin Man. The fit is slightly less close with *Australopithecus*; but the sample for this form is made up of only four specimens representing three individuals. The highest value listed for *Paranthropus* belongs to a tooth which had not yet begun to erupt and the final dimensions would possibly have been slightly higher than at present, although the length dimension already is very close to the upper limit for the sample of 12 specimens. However, since we are here concerned with proportions it is legitimate to include the value for this specimen as the crown is intact and undamaged and it is highly improbable that any slight increase in the crown dimensions that may have occurred before eruption would alter the shape so disproportionately as to change the shape index significantly.

Table 1. Length/Breadth indices

	P_3			M_1			M_2		
	N	Mean	Range	*N*	Mean	Range	*N*	Mean	Range
Australopithecus	4	83.0	77.0 - 88.5	8	107.8	100.8-117.0	9	107.7	98.0-111.3
Paranthropus	14	85.2	76.0-112.3	19	106.2	100.7-110.8	12	108.4	101.4-117.3
H. "habilis" type	2	100.1	98.0-102.2	2	117.2	117.2	2	114.3	114.3
Pekin Man	13	86.3	75.0 - 96.8	11	106.1	96.8-112.0	7	104.4	98.3-115.4

In the case of M_1, the *H. "habilis"* value falls slightly outside the ranges for *Paranthropus* and Pekin Man, but barely outside that for *Australopithecus*. Leakey[3] mistakenly quotes 114.6 as the highest observed and published value for *Australopithecus* (*sensu stricto*) and concludes that his value for the type mandible (117.0) falls outside that for *Australopithecus*. In the case of M_2 the *H. "habilis"* value falls within the observed ranges for both *Paranthropus* and Pekin Man and very slightly outside that for *Australopithecus*. In both cases the *Australopithecus* sample size is small.

In one section of the original description Tobias refers to a lower molar, of Hominid 4, which he believes to be either M_2 or M_3, and writes: "The molar is 15.1 mm in mesiodistal length and 13.0 mm in buccolingual breadth; it is thus a small and narrow tooth by australopithceine standards ...". The length/breadth index of this tooth is 116.2; the observed range for *Paranthropus* is 101.4-117.3 for M_2 and 106.6-124.1 for M_3—indeed, the "mean" index for the sample of 13 specimens for the latter tooth is 116.3. The ranges for this index for M_2 and M_3 of *Australopithecus* are 98.0-11.3 and 100.0-116.0 ($N = 10$) respectively.

The size can best be compared by using the module so that single values can be compared instead of pairs. The module for the aforementioned Olduvai tooth is 14.05. This certainly is smaller than are either M_2 or M_3 of *Paranthropus*. However, the lowest modules for the small collection of these two tooth of *Australopithecus* are, respectively, 13.75 and 13.20. These figures thus show that the Olduvai hominid 4 tooth is neither exceptionally small nor exceptionally narrow by australopithecine standards.

行比较。后者的第三下前臼齿落入傍人第三下前臼齿的观测范围，并且在北京人第三下前臼齿的范围外不远。尺寸与南方古猿不是非常吻合；但其样本仅由代表3个个体的4个标本构成。列出的傍人的最高值是还没有萌出的牙齿，其最终尺寸可能将比现在的值稍高一点，尽管其长度尺寸已经十分接近12个标本的上限。然而，既然我们在此涉及比例，那么把这个标本的值包括进来是合理的，因为牙冠完整无损，并且齿冠尺寸任何微小的增加（这在萌出之前可能已经发生）肯定不可能如此不成比例地改变其形状以至于显著地改变形状系数。

表1. 齿冠指数

	第三下前臼齿			第一下前臼齿			第二下前臼齿		
	标本数	平均值	范围	标本数	平均值	范围	标本数	平均值	范围
南方古猿	4	83.0	77.0 ~ 88.5	8	107.8	100.8~117.0	9	107.7	98.0~111.3
傍人	14	85.2	76.0~112.8	19	106.2	100.7~110.8	12	108.4	101.4~117.3
典型“能人”	2	100.1	98.0~102.2	2	117.2	117.2	2	114.3	114.3
北京人	13	86.3	75.0 ~ 96.8	11	106.1	96.8~112.0	7	104.4	98.3~115.4

就第一下臼齿而言，“能人”的值落在傍人与北京人范围外不远处，但是勉强落在南方古猿范围之外。利基[3]错误地引用114.6作为南方古猿(从狭义说)所公布的最高观测值，并得出结论认为其正型下颌骨的值(117.0)落在南方古猿之外。就第二下臼齿而言，“能人”的值落在傍人与北京人二者的观测范围之内，并且落在南方古猿第二下臼齿的值的范围外不远处。在这两种情形中，南方古猿的样本都比较小。

在一部分原始描述中，托拜厄斯提到人科4的一颗下臼齿，他认为它不是第二下臼齿就是第三下臼齿，他写道：“臼齿近中远中径为15.1毫米，颊舌径为13.0毫米；因此按南方古猿亚科的标准，它是一颗又小又窄的牙齿……”这颗牙齿的齿冠指数为116.2；傍人第二下臼齿观测值的范围是101.4~117.3，第三下臼齿为106.6~124.1——确实，对后者的牙齿，13个标本样本的系数“平均值”是116.3。对南方古猿的第二下臼齿与第三下臼齿而言，这个参数的范围分别是98.0~113.3与100.0~116.0 (N =10)。

最好用模数比较大小，以便能用单个值代替成对值来进行比较。前述奥杜威牙齿的模数为14.05。这个值一定比傍人的第二下臼齿或第三下臼齿小。然而，收集数量很少的南方古猿的这两颗牙齿的最低模数分别是13.75与13.20。因此，按南方古猿亚科的标准，这些数字表明奥杜威人科4的牙齿既不是特别小也不是特别窄。

This evidence, along with that from the type specimen, therefore does not support the contention that the shape characteristies of the *H.* "*habilis*" mandibular teeth are recognizably different from those of the australopithecines. The *H.* "*habilis*" specimens here considered have values which fall mostly toward the upper end of the ranges of variation at present available for the australopithecines. But it is very clear that in no case are adequate samples available: the ranges of variation are certainly smaller than they should be and insufficient is known about *H.* "*habilis*" to know how representative the few known specimens are of the populations from which they came.

However, a far more trenchant criticism of the use made of the dental length/breadth index by Leakey *et al.* is that analysis of the index shows that it and the features on which it is based have extremely low phyletic valence so far as hominids are concerned. This is readily apparent from the extremely wide overlap of the ranges for this index for *Australopithecus*, *Paranthropus*, *Homo erectus* and *Homo sapiens*. It is not possible to distinguish taxonomically between these groups by means of this index if anything like adequate sample sizes are used. As may be seen from Table 1 the means for *Paranthropus* and Pekin Man are 85.2 and 86.3 respectively for P_3 and (not shown in Table 1) values for samples of modern Bantu and aboriginal Australians differ from that of Pekin Man by a few tenths of a unit. Thus, populations covering so great a span of the hominids have means for this index which are very closely similar. On the other hand, various local populations of modern man have mean values for this index which actually show greater variation than the foregoing. That is to say, the intra-species variation in the mean in modern man is actually greater than the intergeneric differences in the mean for three populations of *Australopithecus*, *Paranthropus* and *Homo erectus*. Furthermore, these differences between the means are small compared with the range of variation observed within any one of the populations concerned.

The endocranial capacity of *H.* "*habilis*" appears, on the scanty and indirect evidence available[8,1], to have differed little from that of the australopithecines with a range overlapping that of the latter substantially.

The conclusion that the foot of the new form has a fairly advanced and *Homo*-like structure while the hands appear to have been relatively more primitive does not help a great deal at present since not much evidence of these parts is available for either australopithecines or *H. erectus*. However, neither conclusion should occasion astonishment. If the australopithecines were erectly bipedal in posture and locomotor habit, as much evidence suggests, then the foot was being used in an essentially human fashion and is likely to have achieved a relatively advanced structure soon after the new locomotor habit was achieved. On the other hand, neither the australopithecines, as apparent tool-users, nor *H.* "*habilis*" as an apparent primitive tool-maker, were culturally advanced and therefore one might expect that the moulding of the hand under the influence of manipulative activity of the human sort was not far advanced. Thus one might expect the foot to have had a more modern-looking structure than the hand in both the australopithecine stage and the early hominine stage. The apparently fairly advanced foot *H.* "*habilis*" does not

因而，这个证据（连同从正型标本得到的证据一起）不支持以下论点：即“能人”与南方古猿的下颌齿的形状特征存在可被识别的差异。这里所研究的“能人”标本的值大部分落在现在获得的南方古猿亚科观测值变化幅度的上限。但是很清楚的是，那绝不是充足有效的样本：其变化幅度肯定小于真实值，并且对于“能人”的认识还远远不够，仅仅凭少数几个已知标本并不可知在多大程度上可以代表其来自的群体。

然而就人科而言，对利基等人使用牙齿齿冠指数的做法的更尖锐的批判认为，系数分析显示出系数及由此而来的特点的分类价值极低。从南方古猿、傍人、直立人以及智人的这一指数范围有很大重叠来看，这是显而易见的。即使用到的样本足够大，靠系数平均值不可能在分类学上对这些种类加以区别。正如从表 1 所示，傍人与北京人的第三下前臼齿的平均值分别是 85.2 与 86.3，现代班图人与澳大利亚土著居民样本的值(表 1 中没有列出)与北京人只相差一个单位的十分之几。可见，涵盖如此大范围的人科种群的系数平均值十分接近。另一方面，现代人类不同地区种群的系数平均值实际上表现出比前述更大的变化。也就是说，现代人类种内平均值的差异实际上比南方古猿、傍人以及直立人三个种群平均值的属间差异大。而且，与任何一个种群内观测到的变化幅度相比，平均值间的差异是很小的。

根据可用的少量间接证据[8,1]，“能人”的颅容量似乎与南方古猿的颅容量差异很小，其范围与后者有很大重叠。

这种新型人科的足具有类似人属的结构，进化程度颇高，然而手似乎相对更加原始。这个结论现在没有起到太大帮助，因为对于南方古猿亚科或直立人，这部分都没有太多的证据可用。然而，这个结论也不应引起如此震惊。大量证据表明，如果南方古猿亚科在体态与运动习惯上为两足直立行走，那么它本质上以人类的方式使用足，并且有可能在养成新的运动习惯之后不久获得了进化程度相对较高的结构。另一方面，南方古猿亚科（明显的工具使用者）和“能人”（明显的原始工具制造者）在文明程度上都不够先进，因此，人们可能认为在诸如这种人类操作活动的影响下手的结构的进化程度并不很高。于是有可能认为，在南方古猿亚科阶段与早期人科阶段，足已经具有比手更加类似于现代人的结构。因此“能人”明显相当进化的足不一定表示他与人属而非南方古猿属有亲缘关系——确实，大步行走的步态似乎与

therefore necessarily indicate affinity with *Homo* rather than *Australopithecus*—indeed, the fact that a striding gait appears to be inconsistent with the morphology of the *H. "habilis"* foot[9] suggests that it is unlikely to have been significantly more advanced than that of *Australopithecus*.

In view of the foregoing it seems to me that Leakey *et al.*, in their original description of *H. "habilis"*, have by no means provided a reasonable case for establishing a new species of *Homo* to accept the recently discovered Olduvai specimens. Furthermore, some of the distinguishing criteria used do not appear to be valid for the purpose in the light of available knowledge of early hominids.

Affinities of *H. "habilis"*

In assessing the material attributed to *H. "habilis"* it must be remembered that two groups of specimens are involved: one from Bed I and the other from Bed II. On the available dating evidence these two groups are separated by a significant time gap.

The morphological characteristics of the two groups are not the same. This is well shown, for example, by comparing the type mandible from *FLKNN* I with the mandible from *MNK* II (see Leakey and Leakey[5], Fig. 3). I have elsewhere[6,7] discussed the shape of the internal mandibular contour, seen in occlusal view, and its narrow V shape in both types of australopithecine but its relatively wide U shape in "Telanthropus"and all other forms of *Homo*. The type *H. "habilis"* mandible is damaged near the symphyseal region so that the partial right side has been displaced toward the left. However, the midline can be determined within very narrow limits and the internal contour of the left half is intact and undisturbed from very near the symphysis to a point behind M_2. It is therefore simple to reflect this contour on to the right side in a graphic reconstruction in order to determine the correct original position of the displaced right half. Carrying out this procedure shows that the type mandible had a typically australopithecine internal mandibular contour with the corpus thickness in the premolar region greater than the distance between the two halves of the mandible in that region. This is actually readily apparent on visual inspection since the corpus mandibulae is relatively thick compared with the breadth of the crowns of the teeth and much of this breadth is mesial to the teeth in the premolar region. In contrast the mandible from *MNK* II does not have this narrow V-shaped contour but has the wide U-shaped contour and relatively thin corpus of the sort normal for *Homo*. The more recent, Bed II mandible thus agrees with *Homo erectus*, including "Telanthropus", in this feature as well as its generally greater gracility, while the older Bed I mandible falls within the observed range of australopithecines in both respects. It is therefore by no means clear that the Bed I and Bed II groups of specimens necessarily belong to the same species.

The teeth of the type mandible show that the australopithecine affinities of this mandible are very clearly with *Australopithecus* and not with *Paranthropus*. The latter is characterized among other things, as witnessed by the South African, East African and Indonesian evidence, by a small canine as compared with the size of the premolars, especially in the

“能人”的足的形态学不一致[9]，这个事实表明，他的足不太可能比南方古猿属的进化程度显著更高。

根据前述在我看来，似乎利基等人在对“能人”的原始描述中，对于最近发现的奥杜威标本的归属，并没有为建立一个人属新种提供一种合理的情形。而且，根据早期人科可用的知识，其采用的一些区别标准似乎并非有效。

“能人”的亲缘关系

在评价归为“能人”的材料时，一定要记得涉及两组标本：一组出自第I层，另一组出自第II层。根据现有的测年证据，这两组标本之间跨越一个很大的时间间隔。

两组标本的形态学特征是不一样的。举例来说，通过比较来自 *FLKNN* I的正型标本下颌骨与来自 *MNK* II的下颌骨(参见路易斯·利基与玛丽·利基[5]，图3)，可以充分显示这一点。我已经在其他地方[6,7]讨论过在上下齿咬合面视图中所见下颌骨内部轮廓的形状，以及它在两类南方古猿亚科中狭窄的V字形状和在“远人”及所有其他人属类型中相对较宽的U字形状。“能人”下颌骨靠近联合部的位置被损坏，所以右边的一部分错位至左边。然而，我们能在很窄的范围内确定正中线，从十分靠近下颌联合处到第二下臼齿后面的尖端左半部分的内部轮廓都完整无缺并且没有变形。因此，通过绘图重构可以很容易地反映出右边的这个轮廓，从而确定错位的右半部分正确的原始位置。这个步骤的实现显示出正型标本下颌骨具有典型的南方古猿亚科下颌骨内部轮廓，其前臼齿区的骨体厚度大于那个区下颌骨两半部分之间的距离。实际上通过目测都能发现这是相当明显的，因为与齿冠宽度相比下颌骨体相对较厚，对于前臼齿区的牙齿，这个宽度的大部分在中央。相反，来自 *MNK* II的下颌骨不具有这个窄V形轮廓，而具有宽U形轮廓，以及诸如人属正常种类的相对较薄的骨体。于是进一步而言，在这一特征及其通常更为纤细方面，第II层的下颌骨与包括“远人”在内的直立人的下颌骨一致，而较老的第I层的下颌骨在两方面都落在南方古猿亚科的观测范围之内。因此完全不能确定第I层与第II层的两组标本一定属于同一种类。

正型下颌骨的牙齿十分清楚地表明这个下颌骨与南方古猿而非傍人有亲缘关系。就如南非、东非以及印度尼西亚的证据所证实的那样，傍人的特点是犬齿与前臼齿(特别是在下颌骨中）相比，尺寸较小。确实，这个类型的下犬齿如此小，以至于它

mandible. Indeed, the lower canines of this form are so small that they fall within the observed size range for modern living man while the premolars are the largest known among fossil and modern hominids. *Australopithecus*, on the other hand, has relatively large lower canines, *Sts* 3 from Sterkfontein being one of the largest hominid mandibular canines known, but the premolars are smaller than those of *Paranthropus*. Thus the relative size of canine to P_3 in the mandible is very different in the two australopithecines and any individual mandible can be assigned to the correct genus without hesitation on visual inspection if these teeth are present. The *H.* "*habilis*" canine to P_3 ratio is like that of *Australopithecus* and quite unlike that of *Paranthropus*. This fact is further supported by greater morphological resemblance in general between the teeth of the Olduvai specimen and those of *Australopithecus* as compared with *Paranthropus*.

On the other hand, the Bed II mandible shows much greater resemblance to the "Telanthropus" mandibles, but the latter can easily be distinguished from the Bed I type mandible.

In terms of the available evidence it would seem that there is more reason for associating the Bed I group of specimens with *Australopithecus* and the Bed II group with *Homo erectus* than there is for associating the Bed I and II groups with each other. This would therefore seem a perfectly reasonable course to adopt: placing the Bed I material as advanced representatives of *Australopithecus africanus* and the Bed II group as somewhat early members of *Homo erectus*.

However, the Bed I and II groups of specimens occurred in the same geographical area, both appear to have been tool-makers and there seems no obvious morphological reasons why the earlier group could not have been ancestral to the later group. Furthermore, it seems unlikely in terms of ecology and behaviour that two morphologically similar groups, both adapting at least to a significant extent by cultural means, would develop in the same general geographic area. Clearly at least two hominid lines did in fact exist simultaneously in this region: the material under discussion and *Paranthropus* (= "Zinjanthropus"). But in this case the *Paranthropus* line consisted of forms which differed markedly in morphology and evidently also in ecology and behaviour not only from the *H.* "*habilis*" material but also all other known hominids. If the Bed I and Bed II groups represented two different lines, this would indicate not only that they would be adaptively similar but also that three different hominid lineages existed in the same area. For these reasons it seems probable that they actually do represent the same lineage at two different time levels. If this is so, then it is reasonable to place them in the same species. On the other hand, as already seen, morphological considerations favour their being placed in two different taxa which already exist, in which case they belong to two different genera. The evidence in favour of the latter course is actually the stronger.

The two interpretations do not have to be mutually exclusive: the Bed I material may represent an advanced form of *Australopithecus* and Bed II specimens an early *H. erectus* and at the same time the latter may be a lineal descendant of the former. This seems to

们落在现生人类的尺寸观测范围之内，而在化石人科与现代人科中前臼齿是已知最大的。另一方面，南方古猿的下犬齿相当大，出自斯泰克方丹的 *Sts* 3 是已知最大的人科下颌骨犬齿之一，但是其前臼齿小于傍人的前臼齿。因此，两个南方古猿的犬齿与下颌骨上的第三下前臼齿相比大小十分不同，如果展示这些牙齿，通过目测就能毫不犹豫地给任一单个下颌骨指定出正确的属。“能人”的犬齿对第三下前臼齿的比率与南方古猿的类似，而与傍人的很不相似。与傍人相比，总体来说奥杜威标本的牙齿与南方古猿标本的牙齿之间在形态学上更为相似，这也进一步支持了这个事实。

另一方面，第 II 层的下颌骨表现出与“远人”下颌骨有更多类同之处，而后者可以很轻易地与第 I 层的正型标本下颌骨区别开。

根据可用的证据，似乎更有理由把第 I 层的标本组与南方古猿联系起来，把地层 II 的标本组与直立人联系起来，而不是把第 I 层与第 II 层两组互相联系起来。因此采用以下做法似乎是完全合理的：把第 I 层的材料作为南方古猿非洲种的高等代表，第 II 层的组作为直立人稍微早期的成员。

然而，第 I 层与第 II 层的两组标本出现在相同的地理区域，两者似乎都已经能够制造工具，而且似乎没有明显的形态学的原因能够解释为什么较早的类型不能是其后类型的祖先。而且，形态学上相似的两个类型至少都通过文化群落进行了很大程度的适应性改变，根据生态学与行为学，它们似乎不可能会在同一个普通地理区域发展。事实上很明显地，在这个区域同时存在至少两种人科类型：即所讨论的材料和傍人（=“东非人”）。 但是在这种情形下，傍人种类包括与“能人”及所有其他已知的人科在形态学上明显不同，在生态学与行为学上也明显不同。如果第 I 层与第 II 层的两个组代表两个不同的种类，这将不仅表明它们有相似的适应性，而且表明三个不同的人科谱系存在于同一地区。基于这些原因，实际上它们有可能代表着不同时间层次的同一个谱系。如果真是这样，那么有理由把它们放入同一种类。另一方面，正如已经看到的，形态学上的因素有利于将它们归为已经存在的两个不同的分类单元，在这种情形下它们属于两个不同的属。实际上支持后一种做法的证据更加有力。

两种解释并不一定互斥：第 I 层的材料可能代表南方古猿的一种高等类型，而第 II 层的标本可能代表一种早期直立人，同时后者可能是前者的一直系后代。到目前为止，对我来说这似乎是最可能的解释。按照这个假说，第 I 层的标本代表了南

me to be by far the most probable interpretation. According to this hypothesis the Bed I specimens represent a transitional stage between *Australopithecus* and *H. erectus* just at that stage where the essentially tool-using stage of the former was giving way to the primarily tool-making condition of the latter. The widely held belief of recent years that *Paranthropus* at Olduvai was responsible for the stone implements found associated with it never did seem probable to me[7] in the light of the available evidence from the Sterkfontein Valley. However, it seems far more probable that the *H. "habilis"* material from Bed I represents the remains of the maker of the stone industry from that level.

If the interpretation suggested here is correct, then clearly no new species name is needed; the situation is simply one common in palaeontology when specimens are found which link two already existing taxa. Creating a new taxon here is no solution; the two taxa between which the new one falls are already so similar that insufficient morphological distance exists between them to justify the insertion of another species. As is well recognized, conventional Linnean taxonomy is not suited to dealing with a problem such as this and, if the hypothesis is correct, whatever solution is adopted must be a compromise of some sort. The more conservative approach would be simply to place the Bed I material in the specie *Australopithecus africanus* and the Bed II specimens in *H. erectus*. However, if it is a fact that the Bed I specimens were already primitive tool-makers and were ancestors of the Bed II material, the implication that the ends of a transitional sequence, which involved relatively little morphological and ecological change and did not occupy a geologically long period of time, should be in different genera seems very unsatisfactory, especially as the transition was gradual and did not involve a threshold followed by rapid re-adaptation.

A reasonable way of overcoming this difficulty would be to extend the genus *Homo* to include not only the new Olduvai material but also that at present in the genus *Australopithecus* (as distinct from *Paranthropus*). This genus would then include the whole sequence from the point where a shift to an omnivorous diet (by the inclusion of a substantial degree of carnivorousness) caused a new set of selection pressures to come into play favouring the whole complex of culture as a means of adaptation and thus caused the emergence of culture-bearing man. This suggestion comes very close to one made a long time ago by Mayr[10], but differs from it in not including *Paranthropus* since there is good evidence to indicate that the basic adaptation of the latter was quite different from that of the *Homo* lineage as defined here, a lineage which was separate from that of *Paranthropus* from at least early Pleistocene times as the evidence now clearly indicates. This difference is most conveniently indicated by a generic distinction. The known hominids would thus fall into the two genera *Paranthropus* and *Homo*.

If this were done, then it would seem to be useful to modify the species division at the same time so that the re-defined genus *Homo* includes only two species. Since these would belong to the same lineage they obviously could not be sharply defined. The first could be *H. transvaalensis* and would include the tool-using phase of the lineage involving small-brained forms which were primarily tool-using, had relatively poor communication and comparatively simple social structure. The second could be *H. sapiens*, including larger-

方古猿与直立人之间的过渡阶段，正是在那个阶段，由前者原本的使用工具阶段转变至后者最初的制造工具阶段。最近几年人们普遍认为奥杜威的傍人制造了同它一起被发现的石质工具，根据来自于斯泰克方丹峡谷的可用证据，在我看来，这似乎从未可能[7]。然而，来自第I层的“能人”的材料似乎更有可能代表着当时的石器工业制造者的遗骸。

如果这里提出的解释是正确的，那么显然并不需要新的种名：发现某标本将两个已有分类单元联系在一起的情况在古生物学上很常见。在此创立一个新分类单元不是解决办法；新种介于其间的两个已有种已经是如此相似，以至于它们之间存在的形态学差异不足以在其间插入另一种类。正如大家所普遍认可的，传统的林奈分类学不适用于处理像这样的问题，如果假设正确，无论采用哪一种解决方案，都一定是某种情况的折中。更为保守的方法是简单地将第I层的材料归为南方古猿非洲种，而把第II层标本归为直立人。然而，如果第I层的标本确实已经是原始工具制造者并且是第II层标本的祖先，那么过渡期两端的类群，其形态学与生态学的改变相对较小，且占地质时代时间不长，若放在不同的属似乎并不令人满意，尤其当过渡是渐变的且并不涉及需要快速重新适应的开端时。

要克服这个困难，一个合理的方法可能是扩展人属的范围，不仅把新的奥杜威材料包括进来，而且把南方古猿属（性质明显与傍人属不同）的现有材料包括进来。那么这个属将包括从转变到杂食(包括一定量的食肉)那一阶段之后的整个部分。这种转变使得一组新的选择压力开始起作用，并促进形成作为一种适应手段的整个文化群落综合体，于是才使得具有文明意义的人类得以出现。这个建议十分接近于很久以前迈尔[10]提出的建议，但是不同点在于它不包括傍人在内，因为有充分的证据显示后者的基本适应变化完全不同于这里所定义的人属谱系的基本适应变化，正如现在证据清楚显示的那样，人属谱系与傍人属谱系至少从更新世早期就分开了。用属的区别来表示这种差异是最为方便的。于是，已知人科将落入傍人属与人属这两个属之内。

如果做到了这些，那么对种类划分的修改将是有益的，同时重新定义的人属就仅包括两个种。既然这些将属于同一个谱系，那么很明显不能将它们定义得过于清晰。第一种可能是德兰士瓦人，包括处于工具使用阶段、脑较小的类型，它们是原始工具使用者，在信息交流方面相对较差且社会结构相对较简单。第二种可能是智人，包括脑较大的工具制造者，它们拥有的信息交流手段有了极大的提高，社会结构相

brained tool-makers who possessed greatly improved means of communication and comparatively complex social structure. These two species would clearly intergrade but by the very nature of the situation in a single lineage it is not possible to have satisfactory division points for taxonomic purposes, once enough material is available, since there is genetic continuity between successive time levels throughout the sequence. In this event the whole lineage in which culture is a very important adaptive mechanism is included in a single genus and the two species defined in terms of two major stages of cultural development.

(**205**, 121-124; 1965)

J. T. Robinson: Departments of Anthropology and Zoology, University of Wisconsin, Madison 6, Wisconsin.

References:

1. Leakey, L. S. B., Tobias, P. V., and Napier, J. R., *Nature*, **202**, 7 (1964).
2. Oakley, K. P., and Campbell, B. G., *Nature*, **202**, 732 (1964).
3. Leakey, L. S. B., *Nature*, **191**, 417 (1961).
4. Robinson, J. T., *Transvaal Mus. Mem.*, No. 9 (Pretoria, 1956).
5. Leakey, L. S. B., and Leakey, M. D., *Nature*, **202**, 5 (1964).
6. Robinson, J. T., *Amer. J. Phys, Anthrop.*, **11**, 445 (1953).
7. Robinson, J. T., *S. Afr. J. Sci.*, **57**, 3 (1961).
8. Tobias, P. V., *Nature*, **202**, 3 (1964).
9. Day, M. H., and Napier, J. R., *Nature*, **201**, 969 (1964).
10. Mayr, E., *Cold Spring Harbor Symp. Quant. Biol.*, **15**, 109 (1950).

对复杂。很明显，一旦获得足够的材料，这两个种类将逐渐合一，但是在单一谱系情况下，不可能存在符合分类学目的的令人满意的划分点，因为贯穿进化过程的连续时间层次之间具有遗传上的连续性。在这个事件中，整个谱系（其中文化是一个十分重要的适应机制）被归为一个单一属和两个种内，这两个种是根据文明演变的两个主要阶段来定义的。

（田晓阳 张立召 翻译；赵凌霞 审稿）

Dimensions and Probability of Life

H. F. Blum

Editor's Note

Harold Blum, a biologist at Princeton University, was unusual in being prepared to bring general thermodynamic considerations to bear on the seemingly intractable question of how life began. Erwin Schrödinger had already pointed out in the 1940s that life, a highly ordered system, seemed to involve the production of negative entropy or "negentropy". Here Blum attempts to explore what thermodynamics has to say about the possible course of evolution, warning that the latter may have many more "degrees of freedom" than can be easily judged from the fragmentary evolutionary record. This could lead to an underestimation of the "probability of life", tending to compel an overly teleological view of life's origin.

LIFE constitutes a very thin layer of matter on the Earth's surface, the biosphere: continuous cyclic change provides for maintenance, replication and other activities of this system; carbon dioxide is reduced by photosynthesis with concurrent formation of high-energy compounds that are then oxidized in the metabolism of living organisms, carbon dioxide being returned to the atmosphere. At present a balance is maintained with virtually no change in biosphere and atmosphere of the total amount of matter taking part in this cycle. The energy for photosynthesis is provided by continuous inflow of radiant energy from the Sun; an equal amount of energy being re-radiated from the Earth, but in the form of a larger number of quanta of lower energy than those received. The net increase in number of quanta may be regarded as a decrease in order with attendant increase in probability and entropy of a Sun-Earth system of which the biosphere system is a part[1]. Thus, increase in order may occur in the biosphere, without contradiction of the second law of thermodynamics, so long as this average increase is less than the average decrease of order in the Sun-Earth system.

If one were to think of the biosphere as an open system continuously replicated in exact quantity and pattern—the same total amount of information being maintained—one would assume that no over-all change in order occurred in this system, the only change in entropy being in the Sun-Earth system. But evolution of the biosphere has been going on for millenia, and this has certainly involved increase in orderly arrangement and decrease in entropy, which has, of course, been compensated by corresponding increase in entropy within the including Sun-Earth system.

We may represent the changes pertaining to the Sun-Earth system by:

$$\Delta S = N \, \mathrm{k} \ln \frac{W_2}{W_1} = N \, \mathrm{k} \ln \frac{P_2}{P_1} \tag{1}$$

生命的维数与可能性

布卢姆

编者按

普林斯顿大学的生物学家哈罗德·布卢姆以不同寻常的方式准备将普通热力学与生命的起源这个看来难以解决的问题联系起来。埃尔温·薛定谔在20世纪40年代就已经指出，生命这个高度有序的系统似乎包含着产生“负熵”的过程。本文中布卢姆试图去探索热力学对可能的进化过程提供了哪些解释，并且提出进化过程中可能有更多的“自由度”，而并不是仅通过零碎的进化的记载就能够轻易判断的。这可能导致对“生命的可能性”过低估价，进而对生命的起源强加一个过于目的论式的认识。

生命构成了地球表面极薄的一层，即生物圈，持续周期性的交换供给着生物圈的维持、复制和其他活动；光合作用消耗二氧化碳，进而形成高能量的化合物，这些化合物又在生物体的新陈代谢中被氧化，转化为二氧化碳释放到大气中。目前生物圈和大气圈中参加循环的物质总量事实上没有变化，使得平衡得以维持。光合作用的能量是由持续进入的太阳辐射能提供的，等量的能量再从地球辐射出去，但与接收到的相比，辐射出去的能量含有更多能量较低的量子。量子数量的净增长可以被看作有序性的下降，并伴随着日地系统的可能性及熵的增加，而生物圈正是日地系统的一部分[1]。因此，生物圈中可以出现有序性的增加，只要该平均增长小于日地系统中有序性的平均下降，就不会与热力学第二定律相矛盾。

如果把生物圈看作一个按照精确的数量及类型进行连续复制的开放系统，即该系统的信息总量保持不变，那么就会假设该系统中的有序性没有发生根本的变化，而只是日地系统中的熵发生变化。但是，生物圈的进化已经进行了千百万年，这无疑包括有序性的增加和熵的减少，而熵的减少当然被日地系统中熵的增加所相应补偿。

我们可以用下式来表示日地系统中的变化：

$$\Delta S = N \mathrm{k} \ln \frac{W_2}{W_1} = N \mathrm{k} \ln \frac{P_2}{P_1} \tag{1}$$

where S is the entropy; N is the number of molecules involved; k is the Boltzmann constant; ln indicates the natural logarithm; W is the number of arrangements of microscopic properties of the system; and P is the probability of that state. The greater the number of arrangements of microscopic properties—energy-levels of electrons, vibrations of atoms in molecules, velocities of molecules, etc.—the less the order, and the greater the probability. Thus, in accord with the second law of thermodynamics $W_2 > W_1$, and $P_2 > P_1$. We cannot hope to measure W or P, but by various means we may assess the relative change in these values for a given system in terms of ΔS, provided the system can be put into dimensions definable in terms of N and k.

In attempting to relate the increase of order in the evolving biosphere to the inverse change in the Sun-Earth system, let us first have analogy to a digital computer, to which successive questions are presented. The computer "answers" each question put to it by choosing one of two possible alternatives. If each question is postulated on the previous one, the selection of answers represents an increase in order with corresponding decrease in probability. We may describe this relationship by:

$$-\Delta s = \log_2 \frac{b_2}{b_1} \qquad (2)$$

where $-s$, the negentropy, is used to measure the increase of information; $\log_2$ indicates the logarithm to the base 2; b is the number of questions answered; and $b_2 > b_1$. The number of answers is not concerned with meaningful content—it is not a measure of the knowledge gained from the computer operation. In such an operation interest is usually focused on only the accepted answers, the rejected alternatives being disregarded.

Evolution by natural selection may be compared to computer operation by assuming that each mutation which better adapts the species to the environment is chosen from among other mutations, "unsuccessful" mutations being lost, as a rule, from the record. In cultural evolution—man being a part of the biosphere—we may think of innovations as being chosen in analogous manner, remembering, however, that the mechanisms for biological and cultural evolution are widely different[2]. In attempting to include these cases within a common mathematical framework we may write:

$$-\Delta s = q \ln \frac{f_2}{f_1} = q \ln \frac{p_1}{p_2} \qquad (3)$$

where q is a proportionality constant, f is the number of facets of orderly pattern, and p is the probability of that state: $f_2 > f_1$, $p_2 < p_1$. The term "facet" is used here in a very general sense to describe a unit of pattern which is related to the pattern as a whole; increase in number of facets indicates increase in order with corresponding decrease in probability. Nothing is specified as to the kind or properties of the facets, which might have many forms but in all cases represent choices that have been made between alternatives—successful mutations, and cultural innovations are examples. It is not meant to specify in equation (3) that each added facet of pattern depends on a choice between one of only two alternatives, as in equation (2) for the accumulation of choices.

S 为熵，N 为涉及的分子数量；k 为玻尔兹曼常数；ln 表示自然对数；W 是该系统的微观性质排列的数量；而 P 是该状态下的可能性。微观性质，即分子中电子的能量水平、分子中原子的振动和分子的速度等排列的数量越大，有序性越低，可能性越高。因此，根据热力学第二定律，$W_2>W_1$，$P_2>P_1$，我们不能去度量 W 或 P，但是在一个给定的系统中，只要该系统可表示成可以用 N 和 k 定义的维数，我们就可以用各种方法估计这些变量的相对变化，即 ΔS。

为了试着将生物圈中有序性的增加与日地系统中的相反变化联系起来，我们首先模拟一台数字计算机，并对它不断提出问题。该计算机通过从两个选项中选择一个来“回答”对它提出的每个问题。如果每个问题都以前一个问题为条件，则对答案的选择代表了有序性的增加和可能性的相应下降。我们可以用下式描述这种关系：

$$-\Delta s = \log_2 \frac{b_2}{b_1} \tag{2}$$

这里 $-s$ 表示负熵，用来度量信息的增加，$\log_2$ 表示底数为 2 的对数，b 是已回答问题的数量，且 $b_2>b_1$。回答问题的数量被认为没有实质的意义，因为它不是计算机在运算中获得知识的量度。在这种操作中，通常只关心已被选择的选项，而忽视了未被选择的选项。

自然选择下的进化可以与计算机的工作相比拟，只要假定运算规则为：每一个使物种更好地适应环境的突变均是从其他突变中选择出来的，而“不成功”的突变则从记录中去除。关于文化的进化——人类作为生物圈的一部分——我们可以类似地认为创新被选择下来，不过要记住，生物学进化与文化进化是非常不同的[2]。如果试着把这些情况囊括到一个普遍的数学框架中，我们可以写成：

$$-\Delta s = q \ln \frac{f_2}{f_1} = q \ln \frac{p_1}{p_2} \tag{1}$$

这里 q 是一个比例常数，f 是有序类型的组合的数量，p 是该状态的可能性：$f_2>f_1$，$p_2<p_1$。这里所用的概念“组合”，是一般情况中描述类型的单位，作为整体与类型相关联；组合的数量增加，表明有序性增加而可能性相应下降。对组合的特性和种类没有特指，它可能有许多形式，但在所有情况下均代表在选项中被选择的选项——例如成功的突变和文化创新。但这并不意味着，公式（3）中每个新增的类型的组合都依赖于对仅有两个选项的选择，就像公式（2）中选择的累加那样。

If we let equation (1) describe the changes of order in the Sun-Earth system, and equation (3) describe those in the included biosphere system during the same period of time, we know that $-\Delta s < \Delta S$, if we could measure these in the same dimensions. But more quantitative comparison would demand that it be possible to measure q as an N times a k, and this presents difficulties that appear insurmountable since we lack a co-ordinate frame of reference[3]. The evolutionary record retains, for the most part, only evidence of selected facets, for example, successful mutations or cultural innovations, disregarding the rejected ones that would also have to be included in the assignment of common dimensions required for drawing up a thermodynamic balance sheet. Thus, when we deal with the evolution of the biosphere, and aspects of living systems which have been determined by that evolution, we may err gravely if we view these systems too rigidly in terms of physical dimensions. Seeing only a part of the total change, we may conclude that evolution has followed a much more "direct" course than it has, losing sight of the many alternative paths which might have been possible but were not followed. In so doing we are likely to accept into our thinking an excess of determinism and may slip inadvertently into a mechanistic finalism and teleology perhaps as misleading in some aspects as vitalistic finalism and teleology.

Although number of facets, like number of choices, does not measure meaningful content, we tacitly assume that the latter runs roughly parallel in both cases—the greater the number of choices made by the computer, the greater knowledge increase is to be expected; the greater the number of successful mutations, the greater the expectation of close adaptation to the environment—but no strict quantitative relationship can be predicted. It may be noted that, similarly, number of arrangements of microscopic properties measures order, but not meaningful content—free energy change and heat of reaction are properties of specific substances not measured in terms of entropy change, although quantitatively related thereto in systems of rigidly defined dimensions. We lack knowledge of any close quantitative relationship between order and meaningful content in the evolutionary changes going on in the biosphere, so in estimating change in number of facets we must rely on subjective judgment based on what seems to us to be the meaningful content. This is done whenever numerical values are assigned in preparing curves to describe evolutionary processes[4], which thus contain an unavoidable element of uncertainty.

Similar uncertainties enter into estimations of the probability of life—here and elsewhere in the universe. Such estimates should take into account the evolution of the biosphere, which may for convenience be divided into three phases, while recognizing that the divisions must be arbitrary since we deal with a continuous process: (1) a phase of chemical evolution during which the organic components of living systems and the mechanism of replication evolved; (2) a phase of biological evolution by natural selection; (3) a phase of man's cultural evolution—from our human view this is the culmination of the evolutionary process.

About a million species of living organisms are recognized today, and we may

如果我们用公式（1）来描述日地系统中有序性的变化，用公式（3）来描述同一时间段生物圈系统中所包含的有序性的变化，则我们知道如果能在同样的维数下度量它们的话，$-\Delta s<\Delta S$。但更多定量的比较则要求能够用 N 乘以 k 来度量 q，这就出现了难以逾越的困难，因为我们缺少一个参考坐标系[3]，在绝大多数情况下，进化记录只保留被选择组合的证据，例如成功的突变或文化创新，而忽视被弃的选择，但为了保持热力学平衡，后者也应当被包括在共同维数的组成中。因此，当我们在研究生物圈的进化以及进化所选择的生命系统的状况时，如果认为这些系统在物理学维度方面极为严格，则会严重误入歧途。如果只看到整个变化的一部分，我们可能会认定进化所采取的过程比实际上“直接”得多，而看不到许多可能存在的其他途径，这些途径曾经是可能的但并未被采纳。这样做，我们可能会在头脑中接受过多的决定论，而毫不察觉地滑进机械的结局论和目的论，在某些情况下，这可能与灵活的结局论和目的论同样具有误导性。

尽管组合的数量与选择的数量一样不具有实质意义，我们假定后者在两种情况下是大致平行的——计算机所作选择的数量越多，知识增长的就越多；成功的突变越多，对环境的适应就越好——但并不能预期他们有严格的数量关系。类似地，可以注意到，微观性质的排列的数量可以度量有序性，但并无实质意义——自由能交换和反应热是特定物质的特征，且并不以熵的变化来度量，尽管它们在具有严格确定维数的系统中是定量相关的。关于生物圈内进行的有意义的进化改变和有序性之间的数量关系，我们并不了解。因此在估计组合数量的变化时，我们必须依赖主观判断，而后者是基于那些对我们来说似乎是实质内容而做出的。在指定一些数值用于制作描述进化过程的曲线时[4]，我们就会这样做，因而不可避免地包含不确定因素。

在估计地球上或宇宙中其他地方的生命可能性时，也会出现类似的不确定因素。这种估计应当考虑生物圈的进化，为了方便，可以将其划分为三个阶段，但应当认识到由于我们研究的是一个连续过程，因而这种划分是主观的：（1）化学进化阶段，包含生命系统中的有机化合物和相关复制机制；（2）自然选择下的生物进化阶段；（3）人类文化进化阶段，从我们人类的观点看这是进化过程的顶点。

目前，人们已经识别了大约一百万个物种。我们可以保守地估计，每个物种至

conservatively estimate that at least one thousand successful mutations were concerned in each one. Assuming the change in probability in the course of this process to be inversely proportional to the total number of choices of successful mutations, we estimate, in terms of equation (3) that the probability of biological evolution having arrived at its present state would be 10^{-9}. It seems again conservative to assume that a million innovations have been introduced in the course of cultural evolution, and multiplying the probability of this number of choices by the corresponding figure for biological evolution we decrease the probability of man's combined biological and cultural evolution to 10^{-15}. Presumably there were points in chemical evolution where choice of pathway also occurred, for example, where the rate of one reaction caused it to predominate over a thermodynamically more probable one[5]; but it would seem even more difficult to estimate the number. Assuming one thousand such choices, however, we reach a total figure of 10^{-18} for the probability of man having reached his present state. Conservative as this estimate seems, it approaches inversely some of those for the number of "habitable" planets in the universe that have been invoked to indicate the likelihood that man-like creatures may exist elsewhere.

Numerous uncertainties in the above estimate of man's probability must be obvious from the foregoing discussion, in which it was tacitly assumed that evolutionary choices are purely matters of chance, thus neglecting any change in meaningfulness resulting from these choices. For example, properties differ for chemical species; some of them are better fitted to be components of living systems and their environment than are others, as implied in Henderson's cogent phrase, "fitness of the envirenment"[6]; and natural selection depends on the characteristics of the environment and of the phenotype which impinge. Such things introduce "deterministic" factors which were neglected in the strictly "probabilistic" argument used in the foregoing estimates, which might be either too low or too high on this account. In any event, such estimates—open as they are to great uncertainty—may give our imagination pause in peopling the universe with living things, particularly with "intelligent" life approaching closely to the characteristics of man[7].

In general, examination of the uncertainties involved in putting living systems into the dimensions used so effectively in the study of physical systems may give us better perspective on explanations of life and of human activity, on extrapolations into space, and into past and future time.

I am greatly indebted to Dr. Roger S. Pinkham for kindly criticism throughout the development of these thoughts.

(**206**, 131-132; 1965)

H. F. Blum: National Cancer Institute, National Institutes of Health, Department of Health, Education and Welfare, Bethesda, Maryland, and Department of Biology, Princeton University.

少包含一千个成功的突变。假定该过程中可能发生的变化与选择的成功突变的总数成反比，根据公式（3），我们估计生物进化达到当前水平的可能性是 10^{-9}。假定在文化进化的过程中引入了一百万个创新（这看来也是保守的），把该选择数目的可能性乘以生物进化的相应数字，则人类生物学与文化进化的总可能性就降到了 10^{-15}。假设在化学进化的过程中也存在着一些路径选择的节点，例如，其中一个反应的比率导致它优于在热力学上更可能的另一个反应[5]；不过看来估计出这些数字更加困难。然而，假设有 1,000 个这样的选择，我们就会得出人类能够达到今天这样的进化程度的总可能性为 10^{-18}。该估计看上去是保守的，不过可以反映出宇宙中其他“适宜”星球上存在类人生物的可能性。

显而易见，上述关于进化到人类的可能性估计的讨论中存在许多不确定性，由于这里默认假定进化选择纯粹是机会性的，因而忽视了来自这些选择的任何有意义的变化。例如，化学物质的特性是不同的，其中的一些是对生物系统及其环境来说更加适合的成分，正如亨德森那个恰如其分的词汇——“环境适应性”[6]。自然选择依赖于环境和生物的显性表型，这就引入了那些“决定性”因素，而它们在之前估计中作为严格的“可能性”论据时被忽略了，这使估计也许过高或过低。任何情况下这种估计都是开放的，因为有很大的不确定性，这种估计也许会中止我们关于宇宙中存在生命的想象，特别是关于存在与人类特征非常接近的“智慧”生物的想象[7]。

总的来说，探究将生命系统转变成维数时包含的不确定性在物理学的研究中应用得非常有效，也许会为我们解释生命和人类活动以及推知空间、过去和未来提供更好的视角。

非常感谢罗杰·平卡姆博士在我进行以上思考时提出的中肯的批评意见。

（周志华 翻译；江丕栋 审稿）

References:

1. Blum, H. F., *Science*, **86**, 285 (1937).
2. Blum, H. F., *Amer. Scientist*, **51**, 32 (1963).
3. Blum, H. F., *Synthese*, **15**, 115 (1963); also in *Form and Strategy in Science* (Dordrecht, D. Reidel, 1964).
4. Cailleux, A., *C. R. Soc. Geol. France*, **20**, 222 (1950). *Bull. Soc. Prehist.*, France, **48**, 62 (1951). Hart, H., *The Technique of Social Progress* (New York, Henry Holt, 1931). *Symp. Sociological Theory*, edit. by Gross, L. (Evanston, Ill., Row Peterson, 1959). Meyer, F., *Problematique de l'Evolution* (Paris, Presses Universitaires de France, 1954). Price, J. deS., *Science Since Babylon* (New Haven, Yale Univ. Press, 1961).
5. Blum, H. F., *Amer. Scientist*, **49**, 474 (1961).
6. Henderson, L. J., *The Fitness of the Environment* (New York, Macmillan, 1917). And see Blum, H. F., *Time's Arrow and Evolution* (New York, Harpers, 1962).
7. Simpson, G. G., *Science*, 143, 769 (1964). Blum, H. F., *Science*, **144**, 613 (1964).

Possible Anti-Matter Content of the Tunguska Meteor of 1908

C. Cowan *et al.*

Editor's Note

The explosion that occurred over southern Siberia on 30 June 1908 is the most energetic meteoritic event of modern times (see also NTLRS Volume II). This paper addresses the question whether some fraction of the meteor responsible may have consisted of "anti-matter", whose annihilation by the constituents of the atmosphere would account for the large amount of energy released. A particular interest of this paper is that one of the authors was William F. Libby of the University of California at Los Angeles, who was then a member of the US Atomic Energy Commission and who had made a special study of the newly discovered radioactive isotope carbon-14: the use of carbon-14 had made it possible to use tree-rings for the more accurate determination of the age of ancient specimens of wood. The modern view is that the Tunguska event was within the limits to be expected of meteoritic phenomena.

PERHAPS the most spectacular meteor fall to be observed in modern times occurred on June 30, 1908, at $0^h\ 17^m\ 11^s$ U.T. in the basin of the Podkanemaia Tunguska River, Siberia (60°55′ N, 101°57′ E), some 500 miles to the north of Lake Baykal[1]. It was seen in a sunlit cloudless sky over an area of about 1,500 km in diameter and was described as the flight and explosion of a blindingly bright bolide which "made even the light of the Sun appear dark". The fall was accompanied by exceptionally violent radiation and shock phenomena. Although seismic, meteorological and geomagnetic field disturbances were registered at points around the world at the time, and descriptive accounts of the phenomena accompanying the fall were collected from witnesses during the years following, the first inspection of the place of fall was not made until 1927. No trace of a crater was found, though great damage of the forest was still evident due to thermal and blast effects.

Various hypotheses have been advanced to explain the massive phenomena as having been caused by a large meteor, a small comet or a nuclear explosion. All are argued cogently, for and against. Estimates of the total yield of energy, made from the records of the disturbances already mentioned and from deductions based on blast and thermal damage at the site of the fall, agree with one another quite well and place the yield at something in excess of 10^{23} ergs, probably about 10^{24} ergs. If this were the result of a nuclear explosion of some sort, then the yield of neutrons into the atmosphere with the consequent formation of carbon-14 from atmospheric nitrogen should be detectable by analysis of plant material which was growing at that time. It seemed worth while, therefore, to make such an analysis, and the growth rings of a tree were chosen for this purpose.

1908年通古斯陨石可能含有的反物质

考恩等

编者按

1908年6月30日，在西伯利亚南部上空发生了一次近代以来能量最大的陨石事件（也可参考《〈自然〉百年科学经典》第二卷）。本文主要讨论了陨石的残余部分中是否存在“反物质”成分的问题，这些成分与大气组成物质发生湮灭并释放出大量能量。特别值得注意的是，本文作者中有一位当时担任美国原子能委员会委员，美国洛杉矶加州大学的威廉·利比，他对新近发现的放射性同位素碳-14做了专门研究：碳-14的应用使得通过树木的年轮来准确测定古代树木标本的年龄成为可能。现代的观点是，通古斯陨石事件在预期的陨石现象的界限之内。

1908年6月30日世界时0点17分11秒，在距西伯利亚贝加尔湖以北500英里的石泉通古斯河流域（北纬60°55′，东经101°57′），发生了可能是现代观测到的最壮观的陨石坠落事件[1]。在晴朗天空直径约1,500千米的范围内，飞过一个能使人致盲的明亮火球并发生了爆炸，其光芒“甚至使太阳光都黯然失色”。与陨石坠落相伴而来的还有极其强烈的辐射和冲击波现象。尽管在该事件发生的同时世界各地都记录了地震、气象和地磁场方面的扰动，而且在随后几年也从目击者那里收集了对陨石下落时伴随现象的描述，但对陨石坠落地带进行的首次考察直到1927年才展开。虽然由热气流和爆炸效应对森林造成的巨大破坏依然明显，但并没有发现陨石坑的痕迹。

为了解释由大流星、小彗星或核爆炸引起的规模巨大的现象，人们已提出了各种假设。无论是支持意见还是反对意见都很有说服力。通过之前提到的扰动记录以及基于对陨石坠落地带爆炸和热破坏的推论，所得到的对产生总能量的估计是相互符合的，且产量超过10^{23}尔格，可能约为10^{24}尔格。如果这是某种核爆炸的结果，则爆炸产生的中子进入大气后，会与大气中的氮形成碳-14，能在当时生长的植物物质中分析检测得到。因此，作这种分析看来是具有价值的，并为此选择树木年轮来进行分析。

Phenomena of the Fall

Before reporting the present work it may be of interest to repeat some of the accounts of the effects of the Tunguska meteor. The general area of the fall is composed of taiga with peat bogs and forest and is (fortunately) very sparsely populated. One eye-witness, S. B. Semenov, a farmer at Vanovara some 60 km away, told L. A. Kulik, who investigated the meteor first in 1927 (ref. 2), that he was sitting on the steps outside his house around 8 a.m., facing north, when a fiery explosion occurred which emitted so much heat that he could not stand it: "My shirt was almost burnt on my body". However, the fireball did not last long. He just managed to lower his eyes. When he looked again, the fireball had disappeared. At the same time, an explosion threw him off the steps for several feet, leaving him briefly unconscious. After regaining his senses, a tremendous sound occurred, shaking all the houses, breaking the glass in the windows, and damaging his barn considerably.

Another observer[3], P. P. Kosolopov, a farmer and neighbour of S. B. Semenov, was working on the outside of his house, when suddenly he felt his ears being burnt. He covered them with his hands and ran into his house after asking Semenov if he had seen anything, on which Semenov answered that he too had been burnt. Inside the house, suddenly earth started falling from the ceiling and a piece from his large stove flew out. The Windows broke and he heard thunder disappearing to the north. Then he ran outside, but could not see anything.

A Tungus, Liuchetken, told Kulik on April 16, 1927, that his relative, Vassili Ilich, had some 500 reindeer in the area of the fall and many "storage places". With the exception of several dozen tame deer, the rest were grazing in that area. "The fire came by and destroyed the forest, the reindeer and all other animals". Then several Tungus went to investigate and found the burnt remains of several deer; the rest had completely disappeared. Everything was burnt in Vassili Ilich's storage including his clothing. His silverware and samovars (tin?) were molten. Only some large buckets were left intact.

According to Krinov[1] the dazzling fireball moved within a few seconds from the south-east to north-west leaving a trail of dust. Flames and a cloud of smoke were seen over the area of the fall. Visible phenomena were observed from a distance as great as 700 km, and loud explosions were heard after the passage of the fireball at distances up to 1,000 km.

The first inspection of the site was carried out by Kulik in 1927 (ref. 2). Trees were blown down over an area with a radius of 30-40 km. Exposed trees were uprooted with their roots pointing toward the center of the explosion in a radial manner. Additional expeditions by the Academy of Sciences of the U.S.S.R. were sent in 1928 and 1929-30. The center of the explosion area was found to have been ravaged by fire and searing could be traced to a radius of 15-18 km from the center of the explosion. Numerous holes with a diameter from several to several tens of metres had been found in the first expedition of 1927; however, subsequent work including excavations up to 34 m depth did not yield

陨石坠落现象

在陈述现阶段的工作之前，可以先来回顾一下有关通古斯陨石造成的影响的报告。陨石坠落的位置一般是泥炭沼泽地和森林，（值得庆幸的是）这里人迹罕至。住在距离陨石坠落大约 60 千米的法诺伐拉的一位目击者，名叫谢苗诺夫的农夫告诉曾在 1927 年首先研究陨石的库利克 (参考文献 2)，在上午大约 8 点他正坐在屋外的台阶上面朝北方，发生剧烈爆炸时所释放出的巨大热量使他几乎承受不了：“我的衬衫几乎在我身上着火了”。然而，火球并没有持续很久。他只是眨了下眼，当他再往前看时，火球已经消失。同时，爆炸将他从台阶上抛到几英尺外，使他陷入了短暂的昏迷。在恢复知觉后，只听一声巨响，所有的房屋都为之震动，窗上的玻璃都碎裂了，他的谷仓也遭到了严重的破坏。

另一位目击者[3]是农夫科索洛波夫，他是谢苗诺夫的邻居，当时正在屋外工作，他突然感到耳朵在燃烧。他询问谢苗诺夫是否看见了什么，谢苗诺夫说他也烧伤了，之后他便用双手捂住耳朵冲进屋里。此时屋里突然开始从天花板上掉土，炉子也有一部分碎裂飞了出去。窗户破了，接着他听见雷鸣般的声音渐渐消失在北方。然后他跑了出去，但是什么都看不见。

1927 年 4 月 16 日一位名叫柳切特坎的通古斯人告诉库利克，他的亲戚瓦西里 · 伊里奇在陨石坠落的地区大约有 500 头驯鹿和许多“贮料棚”。除几十头驯服的鹿以外，其余的正在这个区域吃草。“这场突如其来的大火烧毁了森林、驯鹿和其他动物。”然后几位通古斯人又对该地区进行了调查，发现了一些被烧死的鹿的残骸；其余的动物完全消失了。瓦西里 · 伊里奇贮料棚里的所有东西包括他的衣服也都被烧着了。他的银器和水壶(也许是马口铁做成的)也熔融了。只有几个大水桶还完好无缺地立在那儿。

根据克里诺夫[1]所说，在短短几秒的时间内耀眼的火球就从东南移动到西北方向，只留下了一些烟尘的痕迹。那些产生的火焰和烟气在整个陨石坠落地区都看得见。光学可见范围高达 700 千米，而巨大的爆炸声在火团经过的 1,000 千米距离处都听得见。

库利克在 1927 年对这片地区进行首次调查（参考文献 2)。半径 30 千米 ~ 40 千米范围内的树木被刮倒。被连根拔起的树的树根呈辐射状指向爆炸发生的中心。另外的调查是在 1928 年和 1929 年 ~ 1930 年间由苏联科学院组织进行的。他们发现爆炸的中心区域已经被大火烧得面目全非，并且距爆炸中心 15 千米 ~ 18 千米范围内也被烧焦。在 1927 年第一次调查时发现了许多直径在几米到几十米之间不等的洞，然而在后来包括深达 34 米的挖掘工作中都未再发现任何陨石类物质。库利克后来将

any meteoric material. These holes were explained later by Kulik as natural formations[4]. During 1938-39, an aerial survey was conducted over the devastated area to assess more completely the extent of the destruction.

The fall of the meteor resulted in a seismic wave recorded on the Zöllner-Repsold pendulums of the Irkutsk Magnetic and Meteorological Observatory[1]. Subsequent analyses for the epicentre of the earthquake coincide with the location of the fall and also established the accurate time of the event.

In addition, several observatories in Russia and Europe recorded the barometric waves caused in the atmosphere by the meteor. The seismic and barometric effects have been discussed in detail by Krinov[1], Fesenkov[5], and Whipple[6]. The Tunguska meteor also caused a definite disturbance of the Earth's magnetic field as registered at the Irkutsk Observatory and others around the world. The disturbances were similar to those recorded following nuclear explosions in the atmosphere.

After the fall of the meteor, the nights were exceptionally bright everywhere in Europe and Western Siberia. As far south as the Caucasus, newspapers could be read at midnight without artificial light. The brightness slowly diminished and disappeared after a duration of two months[7].

In comparison, if the fall had occurred in the United States over, say, Chicago, visible phenomena would have been noticed as far away as Pittsburgh, Pennsylvania, Nashville, Tennessee, and Kansas City, Missouri. The thunder would have been heard in Washington, D.C., Atlanta, Georgia, Tulsa, and in North Dakota.

The Meteorite Hypothesis

The results of the first investigations of the Tunguska site led to the belief that a meteorite of very large initial mass penetrated the Earth's atmosphere and hit the surface, destroying itself in a violent explosion[8]. This explanation sought to account for the absence of meteoritic debris in the fall area. Since a crater was never found, it was assumed that one might have been formed in a layer of permanently frozen soil which lost its form rapidly and could no longer be distinguished after the first summer.

In the analysis of Fesenkov[5] all evidence points to a retrograde orbit around the Sun with considerable inclination of its orbit to the ecliptic. This is atypical for meteorites derived from asteroidal disintegration. Another interpretation of the motion of the meteor is that it moved parallel to the Earth at much lower speed, in which case its relative speed had to be very low. In view of the great energy released, the explanation of a retrograde orbit associated with high relative speed is to be preferred over a slow relative speed which is difficult to reconcile with the effects of the meteor, such as burning the area, etc.

这些洞解释为天然形成[4]。在1938年~1939年间，又对被毁坏区域进行了一次空中探测，以更加全面地估计破坏程度。

伊尔库兹克地磁与气象台[1]的佐尔诺摆记录到了陨石坠落造成的地震波。对数据进行进一步分析得到的震中位置与陨石坠落的地点相一致，而且也确定了该事件发生的具体时间。

另外，在俄国和欧洲的许多台站都观测到了陨石在大气中造成的气压波。这些地震波和气压波的影响已经由克里诺夫[1]、费先科夫[5]和惠普尔[6]详细论述。正如伊尔库兹克台站及世界各地的台站记录到的，通古斯陨石也对地球的磁场造成了巨大的扰动。这种扰动与在大气中发生核爆炸后记录到的扰动类似。

陨石坠落后，欧洲和西伯利亚西部各处的多个夜晚都格外明亮。南至高加索山脉人们都可以在午夜不用人工照明就阅读报纸。这种亮光逐渐减弱，在持续了将近两个月[7]后才彻底消失。

相对而言，如果陨石坠落在美国的芝加哥，那么在远至宾夕法尼亚州匹兹堡、田纳西州纳什维尔、密苏里州堪萨斯城都可以看见光学现象。在华盛顿、亚特兰大、佐治亚州、塔尔萨和北达科他州均可以听见这种雷鸣般的声音。

陨石假设

对通古斯地区第一次调查的结果使人们相信，这是一颗原本具有巨大质量的陨石，它穿过地球大气层然后撞击地面，并且在一次剧烈的爆炸[8]中完全销毁了。这种理论试图解释在陨石坠落区域没有发现陨石残骸的原因。由于没有发现任何一个陨石坑痕迹，所以人们猜想有可能是在永久冻土层中曾经存在陨石坑，但很快就变形了，因此在第一个夏天之后就不能再辨认。

在费先科夫[5]的分析中，所有的证据都表明存在一个与黄道夹角很大、逆向围绕太阳公转的轨道。这是来源于小行星解体后的陨石的非典型轨道。关于陨石运动的另一种解释是以较低的速度相对于地球平行方向运动，但这种相对速度必须非常小。考虑到释放出的巨大能量，较高相对速度的逆行轨道的解释要优于低速轨道的解释，因为后者很难与陨石产生的一些影响相一致，比如烧焦的地区等。

The Cometary Hypothesis

This hypothesis was proposed by A. S. Astapovich and independently by F. J. W. Whipple in 1930 (ref. 6). The evidence in favour of a cometary nature of the meteor is the motion of the meteorite opposite to that of the Earth and the resulting high velocity of an estimated 60 km/sec[5] which yielded on impact the calculated 10^{23} ergs. Since F. L. Whipple's comet mode[8] consists of a conglomerate of frozen ices such as methane, water and ammonia interspersed with solid mineral matter, the meteor or small comet appears likely to have exploded above the Earth's surface without leaving significant traces of matter on the ground. Based on the observations of the Potsdam Geodetical Institute which permit the velocity determination of the shock wave propagated through the atmosphere, the speed of 318 m/sec measured corresponds to an atmospheric height of 5-6 km, which is the altitude of the main explosions of the meteor[5,6].

Further evidence favouring a small comet is the unusual luminescence of the night sky immediately after the fall over Siberia, Russia, and Western Europe, but not the United States or in the southern hemisphere[5]. Evidently the dust tail was directed away from the Sun, as expected for comets, and extended in a north-westerly direction at the moment the main body hit. The dissipation of this tail resulted in the night sky being brighter initially by about 50-100 times the normal value, but 10^4 times less than daylight.

Abbot in California found that approximately from the middle of July, or 2 weeks after the explosion, until the second half of August 1908, the coefficient of transparency of the atmosphere was noticeably depressed[9]. Fesenkov suggested that this was caused by the loss of vast amounts of material from the meteor during its flight through the atmosphere, possibly of the order of several million tons of matter[10].

It appears unusual, however, that such a comet was not observed on its collision course with the Earth, as it should have been seen unless it approached from a direction with very small angular distance from the Sun. Fesenkov estimated the size of the cometary nucleus as about several hundred metres[5], which is perhaps only one order of magnitude below that of well-known comets seen at great distances.

The Nuclear Reaction Hypothesis

In an article by F. Y. Zigel discussing the results of A. V. Zolotov's expeditions of the past three years, the events of the Tunguska fall have been re-examined[11]. The velocity of the meteor has always been required to be large in order to account for the release of 10^{23} ergs on impact. This can be determined from the ratio between the amplitudes of the ballistic wave caused by the velocity of the body in the atmosphere and the blast wave caused by the explosion of the body itself.

Zolotov selected trees which had remained standing and on which traces of the effects of both waves remained. Apparently, the ballistic wave arrived from the west and broke only very slender branches, whereas the blast wave from the north broke large tree branches.

彗星假设

1930 年阿斯塔波维奇和惠普尔独立地提出了这个假设(参考文献 6)。支持陨石是彗星的证据是，陨石是对着地球运动的，并且根据其释放出来的 10^{23} 尔格的能量可以得到其速度高达约 60 千米 / 秒 [5]。因为惠普尔的彗星模型 [8] 包含诸如甲烷、水和氨与固态矿物质混杂在一起冻结成冰状的聚合物，这种流星或小彗星可以在地球表面上方爆炸,并在地面上不留明显的物质痕迹。基于波茨坦大地测量研究所的观测，通过测定大气传播的冲击波的速度，测量的速度达 318 米 / 秒，相应地大气高度为 5 千米 ~ 6 千米，这是流星的主要爆炸高度 [5,6]。

进一步支持小彗星的证据是，在西伯利亚、俄罗斯和西欧范围内陨石坠落后，夜空立即非常明亮，但在美国或南半球并非如此 [5]。显然，正如对彗星所预期的，尘尾是背向太阳的，主体此刻在西北方向扩散。夜空中这种尘尾的耗尽产生的亮度最初约是正常值的 50~100 倍，但其是日光的万分之一。

在加州阿博特发现,大约从 7 月中旬（即在爆炸后两周）到 1908 年 8 月下半月，大气的透明度明显下降 [9]。费先科夫提出，这是由于陨石落下前在大气中飞行损失大量物质所引起的，可能有几百万吨量级的物质损失 [10]。

然而，奇怪的是，在与地球碰撞的过程并没有观察到这种彗星，这本应该被观察到的，除非这种彗星来自的方向与太阳的夹角很小。费先科夫估计，彗星核的大小约是几百米 [5]，这可能比在远距离看到的熟识的彗星仅低一个量级。

核反应假设

在席格尔讨论佐洛托夫的考察队过去三年研究结果的论文中，对通古斯陨石事件已重新做了研究 [11]。为了能在碰撞时释放 10^{23} 尔格的能量，通常要求陨石的速度很大。这可以根据在大气中由物体速度产生的弹道波振幅和物体本身爆炸产生的冲击波的比例得出。

佐洛托夫挑选了依然竖立并保留着两种波作用痕迹的树木。显然，从西方到达的弹道波只破坏了细长的树枝，而从北方来的冲击波却破坏了更大的树枝。根据这些结果，他计算出了在主要爆炸前的弹道波，事实上与冲击波相比是较小的。通

From these results he calculated that the ballistic wave before the main explosion was, in fact, of minor size as compared with the blast wave. Eye-witnesses of the Tunguska fall recalled that the flight of the meteor was dimmer than the Sun, corresponding to a velocity in the atmosphere of less than 4 km/sec. If the velocity was more than an order of magnitude lower than this, then the explosion could not have possessed the required energy for the explosion.

These considerations led to the question whether or not a massive chemical or nuclear release of energy occurred at the final break-up of the meteor. The nature of an explosion can be determined by the distribution of the energy released, one factor being the amount of radiant energy emitted.

At 17-18 km from the epicenter, Zolotov found trees which had been subjected to a thermal flash and had started to burn. A natural forest fire was ruled out for the area. In order to start a fire in a living tree, about 60-100 cal/cm^2 of incident thermal radiation is required. By calculation the radiant energy of the explosion was found to be 1.5×10^{23} ergs. Other energy-yield estimates for different locations placed the thermal energy of the explosion between 1.1 and 2.8×10^{23} ergs.

Since the estimated yield of thermal energy is so close to the estimate of the total explosive energy, Zolotov favours a nuclear rather than a chemical explosion.

The Chemical Radical Reaction Hypothesis

In an examination of the records of the fall, the radiation flash stands out among the others discussed by different authors during the past decades. Specifically, the remarks by Semenov and Kosolopov of experiencing burning sensations, and the melting of Vassili Ilich's metal ware, appear to confirm the emission of considerable amounts of thermal radiation by the explosion.

Very large chemical high-energy explosions can create sufficiently intense shock-waves in air which, in turn, will radiate thermal energy, perhaps sufficient to account for the fire-setting in the taiga. From the examination of nuclear explosions, the phenomena accompanying the release of large amounts of energy in air are well known[12]. In the case of a nuclear explosion and a fraction of a second after the detonation, a high-pressure, intensely hot and luminous shock front forms and moves outwards from the fireball.

While the dissipation of kinetic energy in the Tunguska explosion probably accounts for the major portion of energy released, the reaction with air of vast amounts of chemical high-energy species such as the radicals observed on comets can be an additional source of energy. For high meteor velocities, the relative contribution of chemical energy to the final explosive break-up will be small, but for a low-velocity body it may be significant. Theoretical considerations place the output of energy of a system using the recombination energy of chemical radicals midway between that of conventional chemical propellants and nuclear reactions in energy released/unit mass.

古斯陨石的目击者回忆起陨石的运动轨迹比太阳要模糊，相当于在大气中以小于4千米/秒的速度运动。如果速度比这个估计值大不到一个量级，则爆炸将无法拥有爆炸时所需要的能量。

这些考虑产生了一个问题：在陨石最终解体时，是否发生了大规模的化学或核能量的释放。爆炸的性质可以根据释放能量的分布来确定，其中一个因素是发射出的辐射能量。

在距震中17千米~18千米处，佐洛托夫发现了受辐射闪光影响而燃烧的树木。在此区域外的森林自然起火。为了在一棵活树上点着火，需要的热辐射约为60卡/厘米^2~100卡/厘米^2。通过计算爆炸的辐射能量，发现其值为1.5×10^{23}尔格。估计在不同位置爆炸所产生能量数值在1.1×10^{23}尔格~2.8×10^{23}尔格之间。

由于估计产生的热能与估计总的爆炸能量非常接近，因此佐洛托夫认为这是核反应，而不是化学爆炸。

自由基的化学反应假说

在陨石坠落记录的确认中，过去几十年内不同的作者对辐射闪光进行了很多讨论。尤其是谢苗诺夫和科索洛波夫感受到的烧伤感，以及瓦西里·爱里斯的金属制品的融化，似乎证明了爆炸产生的热辐射有相当大的能量。

很多化学高能爆炸可以在空气中制造出足够强的冲击波，由此而来的辐射热能也许足以使针叶树林地带着火。根据核爆炸检验，其爆炸过程会伴随着在空气中释放大量能量，这已被人所熟知[12]。在核爆炸的情况下以及爆炸声之后的几分之一秒内，会形成一团高压、强热和亮闪光的冲击波波前，并从火球向外移动。

通古斯陨石事件中耗损的动能也许是所释放能量的主要部分，在彗星上大量化学高能的与空气会发生反应的化学物质，例如在彗星上观测到的自由基可能是附加能源。对于高速陨石而言，化学能对于最终爆破能的相对贡献将是很小的，但对于低速物体而言，这可能是很重要的。利用单位质量释放能量介于传统的化学燃料和核反应能之间的化学基的重组，理论考虑了系统的能量输出。

A very large chemical radical explosion of the meteor would account for many of the observed phenomena. Our very limited knowledge of the actual concentration of radicals on comets, their exact nature and the mechanism of radical reactions make a quantitative calculation of the release of energy by such a model very difficult, especially in context with the uncertainties of the exact orbit of the Tunguska meteor[13].

The Anti-Matter Hypothesis

Discounting any but purely natural phenomena, it becomes difficult to construct a model for either a fission or fusion chain-reaction which would produce the effects observed. For the former, an almost-critical mass of fissionable material might be conceived which became tamped on entering the atmosphere. The tamping would have to be such, however, as to take material far beyond criticality in a very short time to prevent its disassembly with low yield. The multi-megaton yield observed, however, coupled with the very low efficiency known for the best of such devices, would require a large initial mass—well above the critical mass of normal density uranium or plutonium. Thus, super-criticality obtained by tamping alone could scarcely be credited as the mechanism. On the other hand, to obtain it by increasing the density of a sub-critical mass by compression seems equally unlikely, for this must be a result of the mechanical forces generated by penetration into the atmosphere.

To obtain the effects from a fusion reaction, a sufficient amount of deuterium, and possibly tritium, must be contained in a compressed state and heated to several million deg. C. It must then be maintained in that state so that self-heating can carry the reaction the explosion stage. Again, it is difficult to conceive of a model for such a mechanism which is attained merely by entry into the atmosphere of the Earth.

In searching for other natural means by which a large nuclear energy yield might be obtained, we are unable to find one other than the annihilation of charge-conjugate ("anti-") matter with the gases of the atmosphere. Several objections immediately arise to this hypothesis, all different from those raised above. No mechanical extremes are required of the model, however.

The first objection is that no evidence is known for the existence of anti-matter in the gross state. Other than as anti-particles produced by high-energy interactions of ordinary matter with itself or with electromagnetic radiation, no anti-matter has been observed. This is understandable in the environment of the Earth, and so one must look to astronomy for such evidence. The complete symmetry between the two charge-conjugate states of matter, however, makes an astronomical test of an isolated, distant object difficult.

The second problem arises in considering the flight of an "anti-rock" through the atmosphere. If the rock is approximately spherical with diameter d cm and of density ρ g/cm^3, then it might penetrate a distance of $d\rho$ g/cm^2 into an absorbing medium before being consumed. The minimum distance through the atmosphere is about 10^3 g/cm^2.

陨石的大规模化学基爆炸将会解释许多观察到的现象。我们对彗星上自由基的实际浓度及其准确的性质和自由基反应机制不够了解，使采用这种模型对释放能量作定量计算还相当困难，尤其是考虑到通古斯陨石轨道的不确定性[13]。

反物质假设

除了这些完全的自然现象之外，很难再建立出能产生已观测效果的裂变或聚变链式反应模型。对裂变反应而言，可以假定根据其中原有的已接近临界的大量裂变物质在进入大气层时被急剧填实。然而，这种填实是指在极短的时间内要使裂变物质密度急速上升到远大于临界值，以防止它爆裂飞散而导致能量释放过低。考虑人们熟知的这种情况下核爆炸效率极低，要获得所观测到的几百万吨量级的爆炸能量，对于通常的铀密度，发生这种情况将需要一个很大的初始裂变物质质量。因此，这种由填实过程获得超临界的假设不足以成为令人信服的机制。另一方面，通过在穿过大气时所产生的机械力作用使亚临界质量的裂变物质密度压缩到超临界的机制假设，似乎同样也不大可能。

要得到聚变反应效应，必须有足够量的氘和可能的氚处于压缩态，并加热到几百万摄氏度。并且还必须保持这种状态，使其自身产热足以将反应导入爆炸阶段。另外，基于这种仅仅是在其进入地球大气的机制，该模型还是很难被接受的。

在研究其他可以产生巨大核能量的自然方法中，除电荷共轭（“反”）物质与大气中气体的湮灭外，我们找不到其他方法。立刻出现了对此假说的若干反对意见，都与上述方法不同。然而，这种模型却没有设定一个呆板的限制。

第一种反对意见是，在所有领域中都没发现反物质存在的证据。除了通过普通物质之间及其与电磁辐射的高能相互作用产生反粒子之外，尚未观测到反物质。这在地球环境是可以理解的，因此人们将寻找相应证据的范围扩大到了天文学领域。然而，由于两个共轭电荷物质态之间的完全对称性，使得进行孤立的、远距离的天文实验变得很困难。

在考虑“反物质性岩石”穿过大气飞行时出现了第二个问题。如果岩石近似为球体，直径为 d 厘米，密度为 ρ 克 / 厘米^3，则其在烧毁前要穿透一段 $d\rho$ 克 / 厘米^2 的距离进入吸收介质。穿过大气层所要经过的最短距离是大约 10^3 克 / 厘米^2。因此，

Thus, if the density is of the order 10 g/cm^3, then the diameter of the rock is of the order 100 cm. The number of nucleons in such an object is approximately $\frac{1}{2}Ad^3\rho$, or about 3×10^{30}, and the yield of energy would be of the order 10^{27} ergs, rather than 10^{23} as observed. The fact that the bolide did not reach the surface of the Earth is ignored in this estimate, and is off-set by the additional distance due to the inclined trajectory of the object. The discrepancy factor is, nevertheless, quite large. In addition, the flight of the bolide would have exhibited its largest yield somewhere toward the middle of its path, rather than towards its end—it would have thinned-down and died out.

A second look at the process tempers these conclusions, however. The exceedingly strong radiation shock accompanied by heating of the air ahead of the bolide, in addition to the pressure of electrons and other particles ejected in the forward direction by the annihilation reaction of complex nuclei with other, different complex nuclei, would rarefy the atmosphere ahead and greatly increase the range. A carefully calculated model for such a process may be in order. It could be that only a small fraction of the bolide could annihilate in flight, but that it remains essentially solid until it reaches a point where it is travelling slowly deep in the atmosphere. Here, continued annihilation might heat it to the gaseous stage and dissemble it explosively, resulting in a final annihilation as the gases mixed with atmospheric gases. In any event, the process seems far too complex to dismiss on the basis of a rapid estimate.

Of the three models for a nuclear explosion, we choose the annihilation model as a basis for an estimate of the amount of carbon-14 produced. We must first estimate the number of neutrons produced/nucleon annihilated.

Annihilation of Anti-Rock in the Atmosphere

We have, of course, no information concerning the state or the chemical composition of the supposed anti-matter comprising the bolide. Assuming it to be molecular compounds similar to those of ordinary meteorites, we ignore annihilation of the electrons, for these would produce a small fraction of the yield and would form no neutrons in the process.

The simplest case of nucleon annihilation is that of $p\bar{p}$. Even in this instance, the annihilation is not limited to *S* states, and the process becomes complex due to the various possible angular momentum states in the initial system and various charge states in the final system. The final system may contain pairs of kaons and various numbers of positive, negative and neutral pions. A measure of the number of charged particles emitted in the annihilation of $p\bar{p}$ is given by Horwitz *et al.*[14] as an experimentally obtained histogram extending from zero to seven prongs/event, with a flat maximum in the region of 3–4 prongs. The high average multiplicity greatly complicates the situation because of the many possible quantum numbers in the final state. Refinements[15] in an estimate by taking into account $p\bar{n}$, $n\bar{n}$ and $n\bar{p}$ are obviated by the realization that we may be dealing here with reactions between complex nuclei and between fragments of such nuclei as they become broken by partial annihilation. Let us take four charged pions, on the average, as the basis for proceeding, two positive and two negative/nucleon pair annihilated.

如果密度为 10 克 / 厘米^3 数量级，则岩石的直径为 100 厘米数量级。在这类物体中核的数量近似为 $\frac{1}{2}Ad^3\rho$，约为 3×10^{30}，产生的能量将为 10^{27} 尔格，而不是观测到的 10^{23} 尔格。在上述估计中忽略了陨石并未到达地球表面的事实，而且用天体轨道倾斜增加的距离进一步偏置了。无论如何这两种情况的差异巨大。此外，陨石的最大状态并非是在最后出现的，而是在飞行的过程中出现的，只有这样陨石才能慢慢变小并消失。

然而，再次考虑这个过程缓解了上述结论的矛盾。除了各种复杂的核湮灭过程中在前进方向上喷出的电子及其他粒子压力外，先于陨石到达的超强的辐射冲击波及伴随着的热气团也提前使空气变得稀薄，并且很大程度上扩大了射程。在此模型下对这个过程进行精确的计算也许的确是合情合理的。可能只有一小部分陨石在飞行过程中烧毁了，但是直到其缓慢地运动到大气深层时仍然保留着一部分必要的固体形态物质。至此，进一步的燃烧会将其加热至气态，并以爆炸的形式发生，导致最后是陨石气体物质和大气气体混合后燃烧。在任何情况下，根据快速的估计，这一过程显得过于复杂而不考虑。

在核爆炸的三种模型中，我们选择湮灭模型作为估计产生碳-14 含量的基础。我们必须首先估计产生的中子 / 湮灭的核子的数量。

大气中反物质岩石的湮灭假设

当然，对于被认为是组成火球的反物质，我们还没有得到其组成或化学组分的相关信息。假设它是类似于普通陨石的分子化合物，由于电子湮灭过程中只产生一小部分物质，并且此过程中没有中子产生，所以可以忽略掉电子的湮灭。

核子湮灭的最简单情况是 $p\overline{p}$ 湮灭。即使在这种情况下，湮灭并不只限于 S 态，在初始系统中各种可能的角动量，以及在最终系统中的各种带电状态，会使过程变得复杂。最终系统可能会含有一对 K 介子以及各种数量的正、负和中性的 π 介子。在 $p\overline{p}$ 湮灭中发射出的多种带电粒子个数的测量方法是由霍维兹等人 [14] 给出的，在实验中每个事件都有 0~7 个射线径迹得到的直方图，其中在 3~4 个射线径迹时有一个平缓的极大值。由于在末态中有许多可能的量子数，因此高平均值的多重性使状态极大地复杂化了。当我们意识到我们在处理复杂原子核之间和原子核因部分湮灭而破碎成的碎片之间的反应，则这种将 $p\overline{n}$、$n\overline{n}$ 和 $n\overline{p}$ 考虑进去所进行的估算精确 [15] 就可以排除了。让我们取 4 个带电的 π 介子作为平均意义上的基础过程，每对湮灭的核子分别是 2 个正粒子和 2 个负粒子。

The positive pions will decay in the atmosphere, but the negative ones will, in general, be captured by oxygen, nitrogen and carbon nuclei. In view of the overall uncertainty in this estimate, we will assume that all of the negative pions are absorbed at rest by nuclei. A simplified picture of the process, obtained from the measurement of prongs produced in stars in nuclear emulsions from negative pion absorption, is that of the 140 MeV rest energy of the pion gained by the nucleus, 40 MeV is lost by fast neutron emission at the time of absorption and 100 MeV is then lost by boiling-off of neutrons and charged particles in an evaporative process. Taking the mean energy[16] of the prompt neutrons as 12 MeV and their binding energy as 8 MeV, the mean number of prompt neutrons is 2. Assuming that the probability for then boiling off a neutron is the same as that for a proton, and weighting the probabilities obtained from prong counts accordingly, we find that two more neutrons are produced from light nuclei. Thus, four neutrons are produced per pion absorbed, or eight neutrons per nucleon pair annihilated. In view of the great uncertainties in this estimate, we take the number to be 8±4. Thus, for a total energy yield of 10^{24} ergs by nucleon-antinucleon annihilation and a yield of about 3×10^{-3} ergs/nucleon pair, about $(2.7\pm1.4)\times10^{27}$ neutrons would be released to the atmosphere.

Effect on Atmospheric Radiocarbon Content

We may make some estimates of the effects of releasing neutrons in amounts such as this in the following way: Assume that every neutron produced is absorbed in the reaction $^{14}N(n,p)^{14}C$, and that the radiocarbon so produced is rapidly oxidized to carbon dioxide in the atmosphere. Thus $(2.7\pm1.4)\times10^{27}$ molecules of radio-CO_2 mix with the atmospheric gases. Taking the total mass of the atmosphere as 5.3×10^{21} g, and the mean carbon dioxide content of the air as 0.030 volume percent (though this varies geographically and seasonally), we readily calculate the atmospheric carbon dioxide to contain 6.6×10^{17} g carbon as carbon dioxide. Taking the decay constant of carbon-14 as 2.3×10^{-10} m^{-1}, our new radiocarbon should exhibit 9.4×10^{-1} d m^{-1} g^{-1} of atmospheric carbon. As the specific activity of atmospheric carbon is 13.56±d m^{-1} g^{-1}, this represents an increase of some 7 percent in the radiocarbon activity[17].

In making this estimate, we have taken the radiocarbon to be uniformly distributed in the atmosphere after both vertical mixing and mixing between the northern and southern hemispheres, and have neglected absorption in the ocean and biosphere. Thus the result is approximate.

An alternative basis for an estimate of the yield of radiocarbon by an anti-matter Tunguska explosion is provided by the data on the yield of this isotope by the testing of nuclear explosives in the atmosphere. By September 1961, the equivalent of 70 MT (1 MT, megaton TNT equivalent is 4×10^{22} ergs) of fission and fusion nuclear explosive was released in air bursts and about 100 MT in surface tests[18]. The specific radiocarbon-level taken up by plants at that time[19] was about 25 percent above the natural cosmic-ray level of radiocarbon. We may estimate an upper limit to the anti-matter in the Tunguska meteor in the following way:

正的π介子将在大气中衰变，但是负的π介子通常被氧核、氮核和碳核俘获。考虑到该估计中的各种不确定性，我们将假定所有的负的π介子都是在静止时被核吸收的。通过测量核乳胶负的π介子吸收产生的星状径迹，得到的简化过程是：原子核得到的π介子的140 兆电子伏静止能，在吸收时由于快中子发射损失40 兆电子伏，而蒸发中子和带电粒子损失100 兆电子伏。取瞬发中子的平均能量[16]为12 兆电子伏，其结合能为8 兆电子伏，则瞬发中子的平均数为2。假定随后蒸发放射1个中子的概率与放射1个质子的概率相同，并且通过相应的计数方式可以得到概率的加权，我们发现从轻核中会多产生2个中子。因此，每吸收1个π介子产生4个中子，或每湮灭1对核子产生8个中子。由于估计中有很大的不确定性，我们取的数为8 ± 4。因此，由核子–反核子湮灭产生的总能量是10^{24}尔格，每个中子对产生的能量约3×10^{-3}尔格，可得到约$(2.7 \pm 1.4) \times 10^{27}$个中子将在大气中被释放。

对大气中放射性碳含量的影响

我们可以用以下方法对释放中子产生的总体效果进行估计：假定产生的每个中子是被反应$^{14}N(n,p)^{14}C$吸收的，同时产生的放射性碳在大气中被氧化变成二氧化碳。因此，有$(2.7 \pm 1.4) \times 10^{27}$个放射性-$CO_2$分子与大气的气体混合。取大气的总质量为$5.3 \times 10^{21}$克，空气中二氧化碳平均含量为总体积的0.03%(虽然这随地点和季节会有些变化)，我们容易计算大气中的二氧化碳含有6.6×10^{17}克碳。取碳-14的衰变常数为每分钟2.3×10^{-10}，则新的放射性碳将以9.4×10^{-1}d 分钟$^{-1}$ · 克$^{-1}$的含量存在于大气中。当大气中碳的比放射性为$13.56 \pm$ d 分钟$^{-1}$ · 克$^{-1}$，这表示放射性碳的活度增加了7%[17]。

在进行这项估计时，我们假定在大气的垂直方向及南、北半球都很好的混合后放射性碳在大气中均匀分布，并且忽略海洋和生物对大气的吸收作用。因此这是近似值。

根据测试这次核爆炸后大气中产生的放射性碳同位素的数据，可以得到另外一种关于通古斯陨石事件的反物质估计理论基础。直至1961年9月，由核裂变和聚变在大气中爆炸反应释放出的能量相当于70 MT当量(1 MT，一百万吨TNT炸药相当于4×10^{22}尔格)，在地表内的试验中得到的结果约为100 MT[18]。当时从植物中得到的这种放射性碳水平约在自然宇宙射线水平的25%以上。我们对通古斯陨石的反物质上限可作以下的估计：

Taking the full 70 MT of air bursts and one-half of the 100 MT of surface bursts as effective for producing radiocarbon, we have $\frac{70 + 50}{25}$ or 5 MT of fission or fusion fired in the atmosphere producing a 1 percent rise in radiocarbon activity.

If, now, the known damage parameters of the Tunguska explosion are used as input data for the Nuclear Bomb Effects Computer, a value of about 30 MT (10^{24} ergs) energy yield is obtained (supplement to publication cited as ref. 12), which at 2 BeV (3×10^{-3}ergs) per nucleon pair consumed and 8±4 neutrons yield gives a total neutron yield as shown above, of $(2.7\pm1.4)\times10^{27}$ neutrons. Since the meteor disintegrated in the atmosphere, this would be expected to give $(2.7\pm1.4)\times10^{24}$ carbon-14 atoms. Therefore, if the Tunguska explosion had been due to anti-matter, it should have behaved like 35 MT of fission or fusion fired at the same latitude (say the U.S.S.R. test site at Novaya Zemlya, 74°N, 150°E) and, using our experience with bomb test carbon-14 as a basis of comparison, we can estimate the possible anti-matter content of the 1908 Siberian meteorite.

Radiocarbon Analysis

A section of a 300-year-old Douglas fir (*Pseudotsuga taxifolia*), the "Hitchcock" tree, which fell in the winter of 1951 in an unsurveyed area (35°15′N, 111°45′W) of the Santa Catalina Mountains about 30 miles from Tucson, Arizona, was provided by the Laboratory for Tree-Ring Research of the University of Arizona, Tucson. About 20 g of wood was stripped from each ring for the interval of 1870-1936, and the radiocarbon contents of the rings of each fifth year were measured, excepting for the years around 1908. Table 1 contains the results expressed as percentage deviations from the international standard reference level of 1890 (0.95 of the count-rate of the National Bureau of Standards oxalic acid). Column IV contains carbon-13 mass spectrometric corrections in per mil deviation from the Chicago PDB standard. (The mass spectrometric analyses were provided with the help of R. McIver and W. Sackett of the Jersey Production Research Co., Tulsa, Oklahoma.) The percentage deviations in carbon-14, corrected by these figures for isotopic fractionation[20], are contained in column V, according to $\left(\frac{1 + \delta^{14}C}{1 + 2\delta^{13}C} - 1\right) \times 100$. Finally, the last column contains the results corrected again for the effects of dilution of atmospheric carbon dioxide by the burning of industrial fossil fuels[20]. We have used Fergusson's[21] values for this correction (the Suess effect).

Additional tree-ring samples were measured from an oak tree (samples provided by L. Wood, Inst. Geophysics, Univ. Calif., Los Angeles) cut in 1964 near Los Angeles (in the Simi Valley, 34°12′ N, 118°48′ W). They are given as UCLA-776, 778, 779.

取空气中爆炸的全部 70 MT 和表面爆炸 100 MT 的一半作为产生放射性碳的有效值，要使放射性碳活度产生 1% 的增长，大气中裂变或聚变燃烧产生的能量约需要 (70+50)/25 或 5 MT。

如果将现已知的通古斯陨石事件的破坏参数用作为核爆炸效应计算机的输入数据，得出约产生 30 MT 能量的值 (10^{24} 尔格)(补充部分见参考文献 12)，其中每对中子消耗 2 吉电子伏（3×10^{-3} 尔格），从上文给出的 8 ± 4 个中子产量也可得到总中子产量为 $(2.7\pm1.4)\times10^{27}$ 个中子。由于陨石是在大气中解体的，所以估计给出了 $(2.7\pm1.4)\times10^{24}$ 个碳-14 原子。因此，如果通古斯陨石爆炸是由反物质引发的，那么这将等同于在相同的纬度处 (例如苏联的试验地点为新地岛，北纬 74°，东经 150°) 引发 35 MT 裂变或聚变的行为，根据核试验的经验将碳 -14 作为比较的基础，可以估计得出 1908 年西伯利亚陨石可能含有的反物质量。

放射性碳的分析

图森的亚利桑那大学树木年轮研究实验室提供了一棵 300 年树龄的道格拉斯冷杉的截面，这棵“龙爪”树是 1951 年冬在离亚利桑那的图森约 30 英里的圣卡塔利娜山未勘察区域（北纬 35°15′，西经 111°45′）倒下的。研究中选取了 1870 年～1936 年间每个年轮里约 20 克的木材，对除了 1908 年外，每隔 5 年年轮内的放射性碳含量进行了测量。表 1 列出了与 1890 年的国际标准参考基准（美国国家标准局草酸的计数速率 0.95）对比后的百分比偏差结果。第 IV 列给出了碳 -13 的质谱修正与芝加哥 PDB 标准每密耳的偏差值。（在俄克拉荷马州塔尔萨的马克依夫和萨基特的帮助下由泽西产品研究公司提供了质谱分析。）在第 V 列内给出的是根据 $\left(\frac{1+\delta^{14}C}{1+2\delta^{13}C}-1\right)\times100$ 利用同位素分馏数据计算对碳 -14 中的百分比偏差做出的修正[20]。最后一列给出了因工业矿物燃料燃烧而对大气中的二氧化碳造成稀释的修正结果[20]。我们在这项修正中采用了弗森格[21]的数值（修斯效应）。

1964年，利用在洛杉矶附近（在半山谷中，北纬34°12′，西经118°48′）取得的橡树又进行了年轮样品测量（样品由美国加州大学地球物理研究所的伍德提供）。它们分别用UCLA-776、778、779标记。

Table 1. Radiocarbon Content of Tree-Rings around 1908[22]

I	II	III	IV	V	VI
Sample No.	Year	% $\delta^{14}C$ uncorrected	Per mil $\delta^{13}C$	% $\delta^{14}C$ corrected for isotopic fractionation	% $\delta^{14}C$ corrected for Suess effect
UCLA-769	1873	0	−22.3	0	+0.05
UCLA-768	1878	−0.72	−23.0	−0.75	−0.67
UCLA-767	1883	−0.31	−22.9	−0.32	−0.22
UCLA-766	1888	−1.64	−22.2	−1.69	−1.59
UCLA-765	1893	−3.75	—	—	−3.60
UCLA-782	1894	−1.26	—	—	−1.11
UCLA-763	1898	−0.48	−22.9	−0.50	−0.30
UCLA-760	1903	−0.28	−23.1	−0.29	−0.02
UCLA-761	1908	−1.07	—	—	−0.72
UCLA-778	1908	−0.96	—	—	−0.61
UCLA-774	1909	+0.26	−22.6	+0.25	+0.60
UCLA-776	1909	+0.17	−24.8	+0.16	+0.51
UCLA-780	1910	−0.70	−22.2	−0.73	−0.38
UCLA-779	1910	−1.50	−24.5	−1.55	−1.20
UCLA-762	1913	−0.81	−22.6	−0.84	−0.45
UCLA-764	1918	−1.20	−22.4	−1.24	−0.69
UCLA-770	1923	−0.63	−23.0	−0.66	+0.04
UCLA-771	1928	−2.40	−22.4	−2.45	−1.58
UCLA-772	1933	−1.50	−22.0	−1.55	−0.27

The results of columns V and VI are plotted in Figs. 1 and 2, respectively.

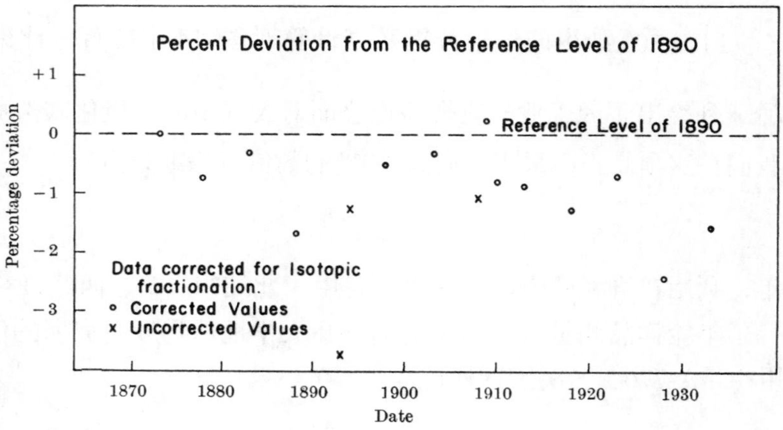

Fig. 1

表1. 1908年左右树木–年轮的放射性碳的含量[22]

I	II	III	IV	V	VI
样品号	年代	% 未修正的$\delta^{14}C$	每密耳$\delta^{13}C$	%同位素分馏修正后的$\delta^{14}C$	%修斯效应正后的$\delta^{14}C$
UCLA-769	1873	0	–22.3	0	+0.05
UCLA-768	1878	–0.72	–23.0	–0.75	–0.67
UCLA-767	1883	–0.31	–22.9	–0.32	–0.22
UCLA-766	1888	–1.64	–22.2	–1.69	–1.59
UCLA-765	1893	–3.75	—	—	–3.60
UCLA-782	1894	–1.26	—	—	–1.11
UCLA-763	1898	–0.48	–22.9	–0.50	–0.30
UCLA-760	1903	–0.28	–23.1	–0.29	–0.02
UCLA-761	1908	–1.07	—	—	–0.72
UCLA-778	1908	–0.96	—	—	–0.61
UCLA-774	1909	+0.26	–22.6	+0.25	+0.60
UCLA-776	1909	+0.17	–24.8	+0.16	+0.51
UCLA-780	1910	–0.70	–22.2	–0.73	–0.38
UCLA-779	1910	–1.50	–24.5	–1.55	–1.20
UCLA-762	1913	–0.81	–22.6	–0.84	–0.45
UCLA-764	1918	–1.20	–22.4	–1.24	–0.69
UCLA-770	1923	–0.63	–23.0	–0.66	+0.04
UCLA-771	1928	–2.40	–22.4	–2.45	–1.58
UCLA-772	1933	–1.50	–22.0	–1.55	–0.27

第 V 列和第 VI 列中的结果分别在图 1 和图 2 中绘出。

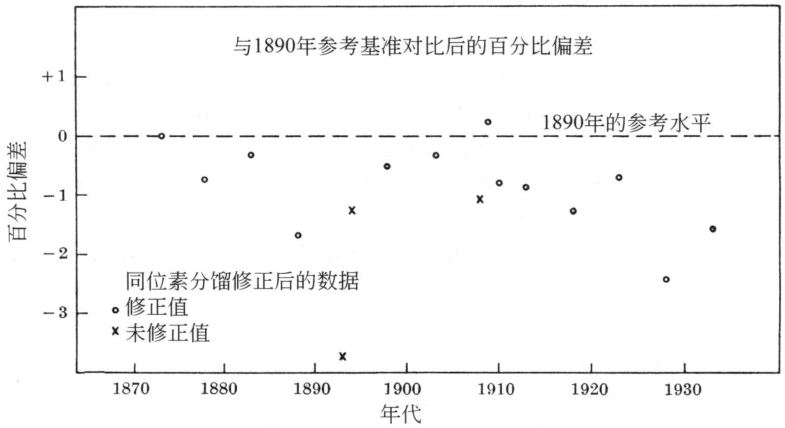

图 1

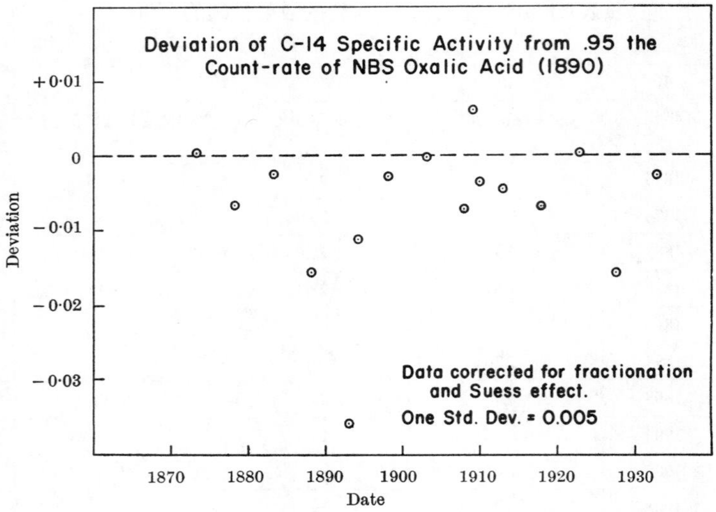

Fig. 2

As some 90,000 counts were taken on each sample, the standard deviation in each value is of the order 0.005 of that value. Experience has shown that the equipment is sufficiently stable, so the statistical uncertainty is the principal one.

Discussion

Inspection of Table 1 yields some interesting points: of all the numbers in columns III and V, only those values for the year 1909 exceed the reference-level. In column V, two others also exceed the standard, but by relatively small amounts. When a mean value is calculated for the points in a forty-year span around 1909, the latter exceeds this value by about 1 percent.

A second point to be noticed is the presence of strong fluctuations in the years around 1893 and 1928, as well as the presence of other, lesser ones at other times. These fluctuations are typical and appear to be real[23-26], though they rarely exceed 2 percent, as reported in the literature. In the results presented here, they are all negative with respect to the reference-level, though this is due to the arbitrary choice of the standard level. They are, evidently, due to variations in the carbon-14 burden of the local atmosphere. Such fluctuations tend to obscure the small effect searched for here and make its value the more uncertain.

At least three other instances are known in which strong positive deviations appear to occur[24]. They are A.D. 1687 (+2.65 percent), 1297 B.C. (+2.23 percent), and 1925 B.C. (+2.34 percent), where the deviations are taken with respect to the average values obtained from 39 oak samples ranging in age from 110 to 203 years prior to 1960. When compared with the deviation of the oxalic acid standard, however, which was +4.99±1.06 percent with respect to the oak average, these deviations are also negative.

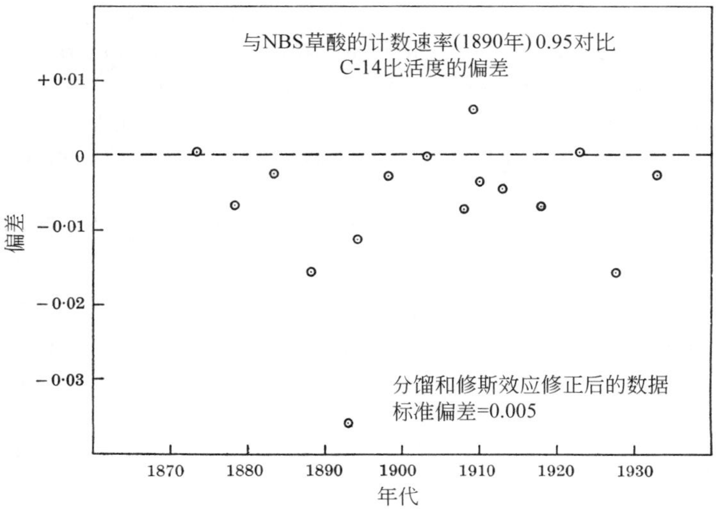

图 2

每个样品约测量 90,000 个计数，每个数值的标准偏差为该值的 0.005 量级。经验表明，仪器是足够稳定的，所以主要因素是统计数据的不确定度。

讨　论

观察表 1 数据可以发现以下有趣的特点：在第 III 和第 V 列的所有数中，仅 1909 年的数值超出参考标准水平。在第 V 列中，另两个值也超出了标准，但只超出了很小的量。当对 1909 年前后的 40 年进行平均值计算时发现，后者约超出了这个平均值 1%。

第二点值得注意的是，在 1893 年和 1928 年附近数据出现了很大的波动，在其他时段也出现了相对较小的波动情况。尽管正如在文献中提到的，这些扰动很少超出 2% 的范围，但这些的确是典型的，并且是真实存在的 [23-26]。在本文列出的结果中，由于标准水平的选择是任意的，所以此处这些值相对于参考标准水平值都是负的。显然，这些是由于局部大气中碳-14 含量的变化而引起的。这种扰动给我们研究更小尺度的作用增加了难度，并且也使其数值的不确定度更高。

至少已经知道了其他三个发生明显正偏移的例子 [24]。即公元 1687 年 (+2.65%)、公元前 1297 年 (+2.23%) 和公元前 1925 年 (+2.34%)，其中的偏移量是相对于 1960 年前在 110 年～203 年范围内的 39 个橡树样品的平均值给出的。然而，这些相对于橡树平均值的偏差为 +4.99 ± 1.06%，在与草酸标准值的偏差进行比较时，这些偏差也是负的。

Although there are uncertainties in both the estimate of the expected radiocarbon yield on the basis of the anti-matter hypothesis for the Tunguska meteor and in any extra radiocarbon burden of the atmosphere in the years following 1908 as reflected in this work, the data do yield a positive result. They appear to set an upper limit of 1/7 for the fraction of the meteorite's energy which could have been due to anti-matter.

We thank Rainer Berger, Mrs. Gera Freeman, Bette Davis and Emilio Cueto for their advice and assistance.

This work was supported in part by U.S. National Science Foundation grant *GP*-1893 to one of us (W. F. L.) and by the Walter F. Joyce Foundation to another (C. L. C.).

(**206**, 861-865; 1965)

Clyde Cowan: Department of Physics, Catholic University of America.
C. R. Atluri and W. F. Libby: Institute of Geophysics and Department of Chemistry, University of California, Los Angeles.

References:

1. Krinov, E. L., *The Solar System*, edit. by Middlehurst, B. M., and Kuiper, G. P., **4**, 208 (Univ. Chicago Press, 1963).
2. Kulik, L. A., *Akademiia Nauk S.S.S.R., Co. R. (Doklady)*, No. 23, 399 (1927).
3. Told to Kulik, L. A., on March 30, 1927. See ref. 2.
4. Kulik, L. A., *Trans. Lomonosov Inst. Akad. Sci.* (U.S.S.R.), 2, 73 (1932)
5. Fesenkov, V. G., *Astronomicheskii Zhurnal*, **38**, No. 4, 577 (1961).
6. Whipple, F. J. W., *Quart. J. Roy. Meteorol. Soc.*, **56**, 287 (1930); Astapovich is credited for putting forward this suggestion first by Krinov, E. L., in his *Principles of Meteoritics* (Pergamon Press).
7. Shenrock, A. M., *Monthly Bull. Nikolaev Main Phys., Obs.*, No. 6 (1908). Rudnev, D. D., *St. Petersburg Univ. Student Sci. Trans.*, **1**, 69 (1909). Aposlolov, L., *Mirovedenie*, No. 3, 281 (1926). Whipple, F. J. W., ref. 6.
8. Whipple, F. L., *Astrophys. J.*, **111**, 375 (1950).
9. Fesenkov, V. G., *Meteoritika*, **6** (1949).
10. Fesenkov, V. G., *Meteoritika*, **6**, 8 (1949).
11. Zigel, F. Y., *Znaniye-Sila*, No. 12, 24 (1961).
12. Glasstone, S. (edit.): *The Effect of Nuclear Weapons*, prepared by the U.S. Dept. Defense and published by the U.S. Atomic Energy Comm., Washington (1962). McMillan, W. G. (personal communication).
13. Berger, R. (personal communication).
14. Horwitz, N., Miller, D., Murray, J., and Tripp, R., *Phys. Rev.*, **115**, 474 (1959).
15. See, for example, *Nuclear Interactions*, by DeBenedetti, S. (Wiley and Sons, New York, 1964).
16. Thorndike, A. M., *Handbook of Physics*, edit. by Condon and Odishaw (McGraw-Hill, New York, 1958).
17. Karlen, I., Olsson, I., and Karlberg, P., *Arkiv Geofysik*, **4**, 465 (1964).
18. Libby, W. F., *Proc. U.S. Nat. Acad. Sci.*, **45**, 959 (1959).
19. Fergusson, G. J., *J. Geophys. Res.*, **68**, 3933 (1963).
20. Suess, H. E., *Science*, **122**, 416 (1955).
21. Fergusson, G. J., *Proc. Roy. Soc.*, A, **243**, 561 (1958).
22. Berger, R., Fergusson, G. J., and Libby, W. F., *Radiocarbon*, 7, 1975 (in the press).
23. Whitaker, W. W., Valastro, jun., S., and Williams, M., *J. Geophys. Res.*, **64**, 1023 (1959).
24. Suess, H. E., *Science*, **122**, 415 (1955).
25. Ralph, E. K., and Stuckenrath, R., *Nature*, **188**, 185 (1960).
26. Damon, P. E., Long, A., and Sigalove, J., *Radiocarbon*, **5**, 283 (1963).

虽然正如在本文中所提到的，对在通古斯陨石的反物质假设基础上的放射性碳含量估计，以及 1908 年后大气中任何额外的放射性碳的含量估计，这两个值都存在不确定度，但确实得到了一个正值的结果。这表示陨石中由反物质产生的部分能量所占比例的上限可能在 1/7。

我们感谢雷纳·伯杰、弗里曼·格拉夫人、贝特·戴维斯和埃米利奥·奎托的建议及帮助。

本工作一部分由美国国家科学基金会（基金 *GP*-1893）向我组人员（利比）提供资助，另一部分由沃尔特·乔伊斯基金会向另一组员（考恩）提供资助。

（沈乃澂 翻译；尚仁成 审稿）

Genetic Code: the "Nonsense" Triplets for Chain Termination and Their Suppression

S. Brenner *et al.*

Editor's Note

By the mid-1960s, molecular geneticists had uncovered many of the detailed processes involved in the production of RNA molecules. These transfer information from the nuclear DNA to the organelles in cells where protein synthesis takes place. The general principle is that triplets of nucleotides (codons) in DNA are represented by corresponding triplets in RNA, and that each of these codons in general specifies a particular amino acid in the respective protein. This paper by Sydney Brenner and his colleagues at Cambridge discussed the nature of the genetic code in the light of experiments carried out with the bacterium *Escherichi coli*. Brenner was awarded a Nobel Prize in 2002.

THE nucleotide sequence of messenger RNA is a code determining the amino-acid sequences of proteins. Although the biochemical apparatus which translates the code is elaborate, it is likely that the code itself is simple and consists of non-overlapping nucleotide triplets. In general, each amino-acid has more than one triplet corresponding to it, but it is not known how many of the sixty-four triplets are used to code for the twenty amino-acids. Triplets which do not correspond to amino-acids have been loosely referred to as "nonsense" triplets, but it is not known whether these triplets have an information content which is strictly null or whether they serve some special function in information transfer.

The evidence that there are nonsense triplets is mainly genetic and will be reviewed later in this article. A remarkable property of nonsense mutants in bacteria and bacteriophages is that they are suppressible; wild-type function can be restored to such mutants by certain strains of bacteria carrying suppressor genes. It was realized early that this implies an ambiguity in the genetic code in the sense that a codon which is nonsense in one strain can be recognized as sense in another. The problem of nonsense triplets has become inextricably connected with the problem of suppression and, in particular, it has proved difficult to construct a theory of suppression without knowing the function of the nonsense triplet.

In this article we report experiments which allow us to deduce the structure of two nonsense codons as UAG and UAA. We suggest that these codons are the normal recognition signals in messenger RNA for chain termination and, on this basis, propose a theory of their suppression.

遗传密码：终止翻译的“无义”三联体及其抑制机制

布伦纳等

编者按

在 20 世纪 60 年代中期，分子遗传学家已经揭示了 RNA 分子产生的具体过程。这些 RNA 分子将核 DNA 信息转运到细胞器中，在细胞器中合成蛋白质。基本原理是 DNA 中的核苷酸三联体（密码子）用 RNA 中相应的三联体表示，一般而言在各个蛋白质中，每一个密码子确定一个特定的氨基酸。本文中，剑桥大学的辛迪·布伦纳及其同事们以大肠杆菌为材料，通过实验探索了遗传密码的本质。布伦纳于 2002 年获得了诺贝尔奖。

信使 RNA 中的核苷酸序列是编码蛋白质氨基酸序列的密码。尽管翻译该密码的生化结构很复杂，但是很可能密码本身很简单并且是由不重叠的核苷酸三联体构成的。一般而言，每个氨基酸都对应着不止一种三联体，但是目前尚不清楚 64 个三联体中有多少用来编码 20 种氨基酸。“无义”三联体泛指不编码氨基酸的核苷酸三联体。但目前尚不清楚这些三联体含有的遗传信息是完全无意义的，还是在信息传递过程中发挥着某些特定的功能。

无义三联体存在的证据主要来自遗传学方面，文章在后面会进行论述。细菌和噬菌体的无义突变体的显著特性是它们是可抑制的；某些携带抑制基因的细菌菌株可以恢复这些突变体的野生型功能。这暗示着遗传密码是否有意义并不能确切的界定，这一点人们早就已经意识到。因为在一种菌株中是无义的密码子在另一菌株中可能被识别是有义的。无义三联体的问题与抑制问题是紧密联系的，特别是在不知道无义三联体功能的情况下，事实证明难以建立抑制作用的学说。

本文中，我们讲述了能让我们推出 UAG 和 UAA 这两种无义密码子结构的实验。我们认为这两种无义密码子是信使 RNA 终止翻译时的正常识别信号。并以此为基础提出了它们的抑制机制。

Nonsense mutants and their suppressors. One class of suppressible nonsense mutants which has been widely examined includes the subset I ambivalent *r*II mutants[1], the suppressible mutants of alkaline phosphatase[2], the *hd* or *sus* mutants of phage λ[3], and many of the *amber* mutants of bacteriophage *T*4 (ref. 4). These mutants have been isolated in various ways and the permissive (su^+) and non-permissive (su^-) strains used have been different. When isogenic bacterial strains, differing only in the *su* locus, are constructed, it can be shown that all these mutants respond to the same set of suppressors. They are therefore of the same class and we propose that all these mutants should be called *amber* mutants.

We may now consider the evidence that these mutants contain nonsense codons. Garen and Siddiqi[2] originally noted that *amber* mutants of the alkaline phosphatase of *E. coli* contained no protein related immunologically to the enzyme. Benzer and Champe[1] also showed that the mutants exert drastic effects and suggested that *amber* mutants of the *r*II gene interrupt the reading of the genetic message. In the *r*II genes, a deletion, *r*1589, joins part of the A cistron to part of the B cistron; complementation tests show that this mutant still possesses B activity although it lacks the A function. It may therefore be used to test the effects of mutants in the A cistron on the activity of the B. Double mutants, composed of an A *amber* mutant together with *r*1589 did not have B activity on the su^- strain; this effect is suppressed by the su^+ strain which restores B activity. This result is explained by our finding that each *amber* mutant of the head protein produces a characteristic fragment of the polypeptide chain in su^- bacteria[5]. More recently we have shown that the polarity of the fragment is such that it can only be produced by the termination of the growing polypeptide chain at the site of the mutation[6]. In su^+ strains, both the fragment and a completed chain are produced, and the efficiency of propagation depends on which of the suppressors is carried by the strain. In su^+_{I}, the efficiency of propagation is about 65 percent[7], and the completed chain contains a serine at a position occupied by a glutamine in the wild type[6] as shown in Fig. 1.

Wild Type	**Ala.Gly.(Val,Phe)Asp.Phe.Gln.Asp.Pro.Ile.Asp.Ile.Arg...**
***H* 36 on su^-**	**Ala.Gly.Val.Phe.Asp.Phe.**
***H* 36 on su^+_{I}**	**Ala.Gly.Val.Phe.Asp.Phe.**
	and
	Ala.Gly.Val.Phe.Asp.Phe.Ser.Asp.Pro.Ile.Asp.Ile.Arg...

Fig. 1. Amino-acid sequences of the relevant region of the head protein in wild-type *T4D* and in the *amber* mutant *H*36 on su^- and su^+_{I} strains

In addition to the *amber* mutants, there are other mutants, called *ochre* mutants, which are suppressed by a different set of suppressors[8]. *Ochre* mutants of the A cistron of *r*II abolish the B activity of *r*1589. This effect is not suppressed by *amber* suppressors, which shows that the *ochre* mutants are intrinsically different from the *amber* mutants.

无义突变体及其抑制基因 经大量实验证明，目前有一类可抑制的无义突变体，这类突变体包括子集 I 矛盾突变体 *r*II[1]、碱性磷酸酶可抑制突变体[2]、λ 噬菌体 *hd* 或 *sus* 突变体[3] 及 *T*4 噬菌体的许多琥珀突变体（参考文献 4）。将这些突变体用不同的方法进行分离并且在分离过程中用不同的受纳菌株（su^{+}）和非受纳菌株（su^{-}）。当构建了仅在 *su* 位点不同的等基因细菌菌株时，发现所有这些突变体都对同一套抑制基因做出应答。由此推测它们应该属于同一类突变体，我们提议将所有这些突变体统称为琥珀突变体。

现在我们来寻找这些突变体含有无义密码子的证据。加伦和西迪基[2] 首先发现了大肠杆菌的碱性磷酸酶琥珀突变体中没有碱性磷酸酶相关的免疫蛋白。本则尔和钱普[1] 也表明突变体有着明显的表型并且提出 *r*II 基因的琥珀突变体中断遗传信息的读取。*r*II 基因中 *r*1589 缺失使部分 A 顺反子与部分 B 顺反子连接在了一起，互补测验表明该突变体仍然具有 B 活性但缺少了 A 功能。因此该测验方法可用于检测 A 顺反子的突变体对 B 活性的影响。su^{-} 菌株中由 A 琥珀突变体和 *r*1589 组成的双突变体不具有 B 活性，而在 su^{+} 菌株中，由于该菌株可以恢复 B 活性，所以突变的作用被抑制。我们的发现可以解释这一结果：su^{-} 菌株中头部蛋白的每一个琥珀突变体都产生一种特征性的多肽链片段[5]。最近，我们发现该片段的极性只在正生成的多肽链终止于突变位点时才可以产生[6]。而 su^{+} 菌株中，既可以产生这种片段，也可以产生完整的多肽链，增殖效率依赖于该菌株携带了哪一个抑制基因。su^{+}_{I} 菌株的增殖效率大概为 65%[7]，完整的多肽链是将野生型中谷氨酰胺变成了丝氨酸[6]，如图 1 所示。

野生型	Ala.Gly.(Val,Phe)Asp.Phe.<u>Gln</u>.Asp.Pro.Ile.Asp.Ile.Arg······
su^{-} 菌株的 *H*36	Ala.Gly.Val.Phe.Asp.Phe.
su^{+}_{I} 菌株的 *H*36	Ala.Gly.Val.Phe.Asp.Phe.
	和
	Ala.Gly.Val.Phe.Asp.Phe.<u>Ser</u>.Asp.Pro.Ile.Asp.Ile.Arg······

图 1. 野生型 *T4D* 及 su^{-} 菌株和 su^{+}_{I} 菌株的琥珀突变体 *H*36 的头部蛋白中对应片段的氨基酸序列

除了琥珀突变体，还有一种赭石突变体，赭石突变体是受不同于琥珀突变体的另一套抑制基因所抑制的[8]。*r*II 的 A 顺反子的赭石突变体能够使 *r*1589 的 B 活性失活。而琥珀抑制基因则不能抑制这个作用，这表明赭石突变体与琥珀突变体本质上是不同的。

Thus, nonsense mutants may be divided into two types, *amber* and *ochre* mutants, depending on their pattern of suppression. In Table 1, which is abstracted from a larger set of results[8], it can be seen that strains, carrying the *amber* suppressors su^+_{I}, su^+_{II}, su^+_{III} and su^+_{IV}, suppress different but overlapping sets of *amber* mutants, but do not suppress any *ochre* mutants. This is the feature which distinguished the two classes of mutants from each other. Table 1 also shows that *ochre* mutants are suppressed by one or more of the strains carrying the *ochre* suppressors su^+_{B}, su^+_{C}, su^+_{D} and su^+_{E}. These suppressors are also active on various *amber* mutants, and we have not yet been able to isolate suppressors specific for *ochre* mutants. Table 1 also shows that the suppressor strains can be differentiated by the set of mutants they suppress.

Table 1. Suppression of *r*II Mutants by su^+ Strains of *E. coli Hfr H*(λ)

		Amber suppressors				*Ochre* suppressors			
		su^+_{I}	su^+_{II}	su^+_{III}	su^+_{IV}	su^+_{B}	su^+_{C}	su^+_{D}	su^+_{E}
Amber mutants									
*r*IIA	*HD*120	+	+	+	+	+	0	+	0
	*N*97	+	poor	+	0	poor	poor	+	0
	*S*116	0	0	+	0	0	+	+	0
	*N*19	+	poor	+	0	poor	0	+	0
	*N*34	+	+	+	+	+	+	+	0
*r*IIB	*HE*122	+	+	+	0	poor	0	+	0
	*HB*74	+	+	+	+	+	+	+	+
	*X*237	+	poor	+	0	0	+	+	0
	*HB*232	+	+	+	+	+	0	+	+
	*X*417	+	+	+	+	0	poor	+	0
Ochre mutants									
*r*IIA	*HD*147	0	0	0	0	+	+	+	+
	*N*55	0	0	0	0	+	+	+	0
	*X*20	0	0	0	0	+	0	+	0
	*N*21	0	0	0	0	+	0	0	+
*r*IIB	*UV*375	0	0	0	0	+	+	+	+
	360	0	0	0	0	+	0	+	+
	375	0	0	0	0	+	+	+	0
	*HF*208	0	0	0	0	+	0	0	+
	*N*29	0	0	0	0	0	0	+	0

Unlike some of the *amber* suppressors, all the *ochre* suppressors are weak[7,8]. This has made the isolation of *ochre* mutants of the head protein impossible. We therefore do not know the molecular consequences of *ochre* mutants, but we shall assume that, like the *amber* mutants, they too result in chain termination.

If we accept that both types of nonsense mutants result in termination of the polypeptide chain, we have to ask: at which level of information transfer is this effect exerted? We have recently shown that it is likely that chain termination occurs as part of protein synthesis,

因此，可以根据无义突变体的抑制模式将其分为两种类型：琥珀突变体和赭石突变体。表 1 是从大量实验结果中总结出来的[8]，可以看出，携带琥珀抑制基因 su^+_{I}、su^+_{II}、su^+_{III} 和 su^+_{IV} 的菌株分别能抑制一个不同的琥珀突变体组，但各组之间相互重叠，但不抑制任何赭石突变体。这一特征将这两类突变体彼此区分开来。表 1 也表明，携带赭石抑制基因 su^+_{B}、su^+_{C}、su^+_{D} 和 su^+_{E} 的一个或多个菌株均可抑制赭石突变体。而这些抑制基因在各种琥珀突变体中也有活性，我们目前还无法分离到对赭石突变体特异的抑制基因。表 1 还表明携带抑制基因的菌株可以根据它们抑制的突变体类型而区分开来。

表 1. 大肠杆菌 *Hfr H* (λ) 的 su^+ 菌株对 *r*II 突变体的抑制作用

		琥珀抑制基因				赭石抑制基因			
		su^+_{I}	su^+_{II}	su^+_{III}	su^+_{IV}	su^+_{B}	su^+_{C}	su^+_{D}	su^+_{E}
琥珀突变体									
*r*IIA	*HD*120	+	+	+	+	+	0	+	0
	*N*97	+	微弱	+	0	微弱	微弱	+	0
	*S*116	0	0	+	0	0	+	+	0
	*N*19	+	微弱	+	0	微弱	0	+	0
	*N*34	+	+	+	+	+	+	+	0
*r*IIB	*HE*122	+	+	+	0	微弱	0	+	0
	*HB*74	+	+	+	+	+	+	+	+
	*X*237	+	微弱	+	0	0	+	+	0
	*HB*232	+	+	+	+	+	0	+	+
	*X*417	+	+	+	+	0	微弱	+	0
赭石突变体									
*r*IIA	*HD*147	0	0	0	0	+	+	+	+
	*N*55	0	0	0	0	+	+	+	0
	*X*20	0	0	0	0	+	0	+	0
	*N*21	0	0	0	0	+	0	0	+
*r*IIB	*UV*375	0	0	0	0	+	+	+	+
	360	0	0	0	0	+	0	+	+
	375	0	0	0	0	+	+	+	0
	*HF*208	0	0	0	0	+	0	0	+
	*N*29	0	0	0	0	0	0	+	0

与某些琥珀抑制基因不同，所有赭石抑制基因的抑制作用都比较弱[7,8]。这令我们无法分离到头部蛋白的赭石突变体。因此我们无法知道赭石突变体的分子机理，但是我们可以假定它们与琥珀突变体一样也导致了多肽链终止。

如果这两种类型的无义突变体都导致了多肽链终止的话，那么我们不得不问这个作用是发生在信息传递的哪个阶段？最近我们发现链终止可能是在蛋白质合成的某些阶段发生的，因为当遗传信息的读取阶段发生变化时，两种类型的突变体都消

since both types of mutants vanish when the phase of reading of the genetic message is altered[9]. This leads us to conclude that *amber* and *ochre* mutants produce different triplets which have to be read in the correct phase and which are recognized as signals for chain termination.

Decoding of amber and ochre triplets. We have done two types of experiments which allow us to deduce the structures of the *amber* and *ochre* triplets. First, we studied the production and reversion of *r*II *amber* and *ochre* mutants using chemical mutagens. We show that the two triplets are connected to each other and that we can define their possible nucleotide compositions. Next, we investigated head protein *amber* mutants, to define the amino-acids connected to the *amber* triplet. Comparison of these results with known amino-acid codons allows us to deduce the structures of the *amber* and *ochre* triplets.

The experiments with *r*II mutants depend on the specificity of the mutagenic agent, hydroxylamine. This reacts only with cytosine in DNA, and although the exact structure of the product has not yet been defined, the altered base (called U′) appears to act like T with high efficiency, producing base-pair transitions of the G–C→A–T type[10]. Hence, response of any particular site of the DNA to hydroxylamine is evidence for the existence of a G–C pair at that site. Usually, phage particles are treated with hydroxylamine and, since these contain double-stranded DNA, the alteration of C occurs on only one of the strands. In any given gene, only one of the strands is transcribed into messenger RNA (ref. 11). This is the *sense* strand; it carries the genetic information proper and contains a nucleotide sequence which is the inverse complement of the sequence of the messenger RNA. The other strand, the *antisense* strand, has the same sequence as the messenger. In a phage, treated with hydroxylamine, the altered base, U′, could be on either the sense or the antisense strand of the DNA. Since the *r*II genes express their functions before the onset of DNA replication[12], only sense strand changes will register a phenotypic effect in the first cycle of growth; changes on the antisense strand, while still yielding altered DNA progeny, will go unexpressed (Fig. 2).

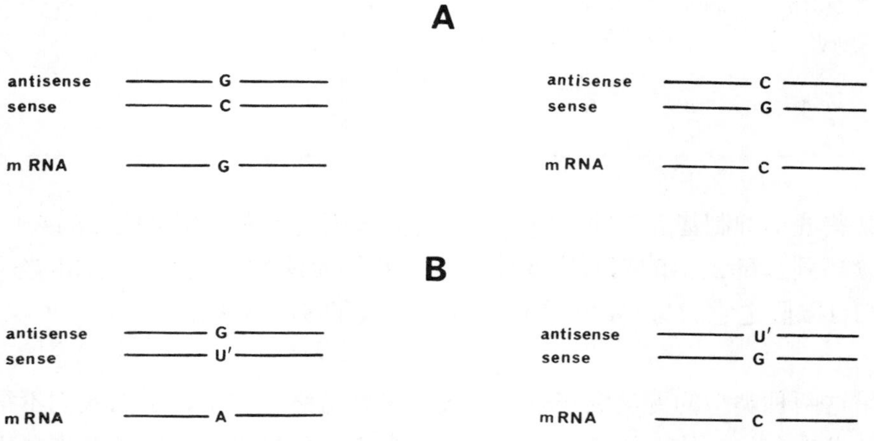

Fig. 2. Diagram illustrating the expression of the two types of G–C pairs (*A*) before and (*B*) after treatment with hydroxylamine

失了[9]。由此我们得出以下结论：琥珀突变体和赭石突变体产生了不同的三联体，这些三联体在正确的阶段必须得被读取并且它们被识别为链终止的信号。

琥珀三联体和赭石三联体的译码 为了推导琥珀三联体和赭石三联体的构成，我们进行了以下两项实验：首先，用化学诱变剂诱导产生了 *r*II 琥珀突变体和赭石突变体及它们的回复突变菌株。结果表明这两个三联体互相联系，我们可以确定出它们可能的核苷酸构成。其次，我们研究了琥珀突变体的头部蛋白来确定与琥珀三联体有关的氨基酸组成。将这些结果与已知氨基酸密码子进行比较后，我们便可以推导出琥珀三联体和赭石三联体的构成。

*r*II 突变体的实验依赖于诱变剂羟胺的特异性。羟胺只与 DNA 中的胞嘧啶作用，尽管反应产物的确切结构尚未确定，但改变后的碱基（称为 U′）表现出与碱基 T 高度相似的特点，即羟胺能够产生 G–C→A–T 类型的碱基对转换[10]。因此，DNA 中任何特定位点对羟胺的应答都可以作为该位点存在 G–C 碱基对的证据。通常，噬菌体颗粒都是用羟胺来处理的，由于噬菌体颗粒含有双链 DNA，所以碱基 C 只在其中的一条链上发生改变。任何给定的基因中，都只有一条链可以转录成信使 RNA（参考文献 11）。该链称为有义链；有义链携带有正确的遗传信息，其核苷酸序列与信使 RNA 的序列是反向互补的。另一条链称为反义链，其序列与信使 RNA 相同。经羟胺处理过的噬菌体中，改变后的碱基 U′ 既可能位于 DNA 的有义链上，也可能位于反义链上。由于 *r*II 基因在 DNA 复制开始之前表达并发挥功能[12]，所以如果有义链发生变化，表型效应在生长的第一个周期就显现出来了，而反义链上发生变化虽然也可以产生出 DNA 变异的后代，但是却不会表达，如图 2 所示。

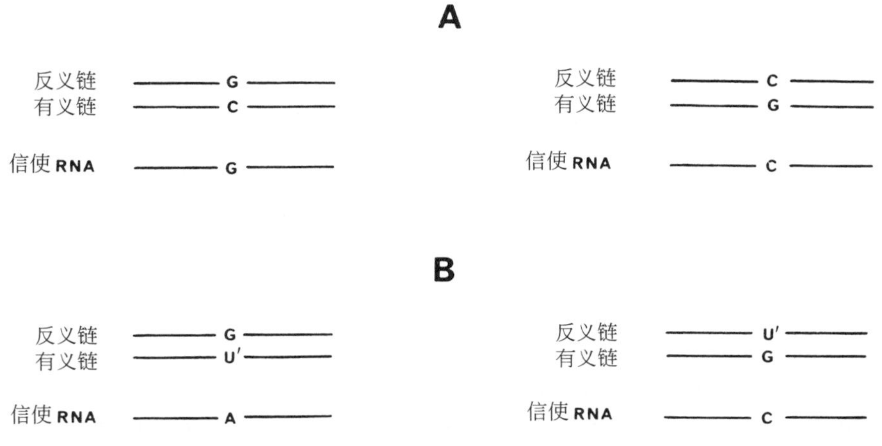

图 2. 羟胺处理前（*A*）和处理后（*B*）G–C 碱基对的两种转录形式

We can now examine the reversion properties of *amber* and *ochre* mutants. Champe and Benzer[12] studied reversion of a large number of *r*II mutants using different mutagens. They noted that no *amber* mutant was induced to revert by hydroxylamine. Some of the mutants they studied can now be identified as *ochre* mutants, and their results show that *ochre* mutants are equally insensitive to hydroxylamine. However, in their experiments, the treated mutant phages were plated directly on the bacterial strain which restricts the growth of *r*II mutants. They could therefore detect *sense* strand changes only, and any mutation on the antisense strand would not have been expressed. Strictly speaking, then, their results tell us that neither the *amber* nor the *ochre* triplet contains a C on the sense strand of the DNA, or, if any one does, it is connected by a C→U change to another nonsense codon. To extend this result and to recover all possible mutational changes, we grew the mutagenized phages in *E. coli B*, in which the *r*II functions are unnecessary, and then plated the progeny on strain *K* to measure reversion frequency. Table 2 shows that *amber* and *ochre* mutants are not induced to revert by hydroxylamine, and we conclude that in neither mutant, does the triplet in the DNA contain G–C pairs, or, if a G–C pair is present, that triplet is connected by a G–C→A–T transition to another nonsense codon. In other words, subject to the last important reservation, we can conclude that the codons on the messenger RNA contain neither G nor C.

Table 2. Reversion of *Amber* and *Ochre* Mutants after Allowing DNA Replication

		Reversion index$\times 10^{-7}$	
		Control	NH_2OH
amber mutants	*S*116	0.04	0.03
	*HD*26	0.1	0.2
	*S*24	0.4	0.9
	*S*99	0.1	0.1
	*N*19	0.15	0.13
	*HD*59	0.0	0.05
	*HB*232	0.1	0.4
ochre mutants	*UV*375	0.8	2.0
	360	0.6	0.8
	*X*27	0.3	0.5
	375	0.8	0.9
	*X*511	0.2	0.3
	*UV*256	1.0	280

Phages were incubated in a solution of M NH_2OH in 2 M NaCl and 0.05 M sodium phosphate (*p*H 7.5) for 2 h at 37°. The reaction was terminated by dilution into acetone broth. About 10^8 phage particles were used to infect a culture of *E. coli B* which was grown to lysis, and the progeny assayed on *E. coli B* and *E. coli K*12(λ). The reversion index is the *K*/*B* ratio. The control was treated in the same way except that hydroxylamine was omitted. The mutant *UV*256, which is not an *ochre* or an *amber* mutant, was used to check the efficacy of the mutagenic treatment.

However, we next discovered that *ochre* mutants can be converted into *amber* mutants by mutation. Since *ochre* mutants are not suppressed by *amber* suppressors, plating on strains carrying such suppressors selects for *amber* revertants. Wild-type revertants also grow, but the two can be distinguished by testing revertant plaques on the su^- strain. Twenty-six *r*II *ochre* mutants have been studied and, of these, 25 have been converted into *amber* mutants.

现在我们来探究琥珀突变体和赭石突变体回复突变的特点。钱普和本则尔[12]使用不同的诱变剂研究了很多 *r*II 突变体的回复突变。他们指出，琥珀突变体被羟胺诱导没有发生回复突变。同样赭石突变体也对羟胺不敏感，他们研究的琥珀突变体有些现在被鉴定为赭石突变体。但是在他们的实验中，处理过的突变噬菌体是直接涂在限制 *r*II 突变体的生长的细菌菌株上。因此他们只能检测到有义链发生的变化，而反义链发生的所有变化都没有表达出来。因此严格地说，他们的实验结果告诉我们，琥珀突变体和赭石突变体的 DNA 有义链都不含 C 碱基，或者是通过 C→U 变化而成为了另一个无义密码子。为了继续探究这一结果和回复所有可能的突变变化，我们让诱变处理过的噬菌体在大肠杆菌 *B* 菌株中生长，该条件下 *r*II 功能不是必需的，然后将其后代涂在 *K* 菌株上来测量回复突变的频率。表 2 表明羟胺不能诱导琥珀突变体和赭石突变体发生回复突变，我们推论这两种突变体 DNA 中的三联体都不包含 G–C 碱基对，或者，即使 G–C 碱基对存在的话，三联体也是通过 G–C→A–T 转换而变成了另一个无义密码子。换句话说，可以保守的估计，信使 RNA 上的密码子既不包含 G 也不包含 C。

表 2. 允许 DNA 复制后琥珀突变体和赭石突变体的回复情况

		回复指数（$\times 10^{-7}$）	
		对照	NH_2OH
琥珀突变体	*S*116	0.04	0.03
	*HD*26	0.1	0.2
	*S*24	0.4	0.9
	*S*99	0.1	0.1
	*N*19	0.15	0.13
	*HD*59	0.0	0.05
	*HB*232	0.1	0.4
赭石突变体	*UV*375	0.8	2.0
	360	0.6	0.8
	*X*27	0.3	0.5
	375	0.8	0.9
	*X*511	0.2	0.3
	*UV*256	1.0	280

噬菌体在 1 摩尔 / 升 NH_2OH 溶液（2 摩尔 / 升 NaCl，0.05 摩尔 / 升磷酸钠，pH 7.5）中于 37℃孵育。2 小时后在丙酮液体培养基中稀释来终止反应。实验中用大约 10^8 个噬菌体颗粒侵染大肠杆菌 *B* 菌株培养物，溶菌后分别对大肠杆菌 *B* 菌株和大肠杆菌 *K*12（λ）菌株上的噬菌体进行检测。回复指数用 *K*/*B* 比值来表示。对照组除了没有用羟胺处理外其余步骤均与实验组相同。选取突变体 *UV*256 作为阳性对照来检测诱变处理是否有效，该突变体不是赭石突变体或琥珀突变体。

然而，我们又发现赭石突变体可以突变为琥珀突变体。由于赭石突变体不受琥珀抑制基因所抑制，所以可以通过将突变噬菌体涂在携带琥珀抑制基因的菌株上来选择琥珀型回复突变体。野生型回复突变体也会生长，但是可以通过检测 su^- 菌株上的回复突变体噬菌斑来区分二者。我们研究了 26 个 *r*II 赭石突变体，其中 25 个被

A sample of the results is given in Table 3, which shows that the mutation is strongly induced by 2-aminopurine, as strongly as the reversion of the *ochre* mutant to wild type. Other experiments, not reported here, show that the mutations of *ochre* mutants both to the *amber* and to the wild type are also induced by 5-bromouracil, but the induction is weaker than with 2-aminopurine. These results prove that the *amber* and *ochre* triplets differ from each other by only one nucleotide base, and must have the other two bases in common. 2-Aminopurine is a base analogue mutagen inducing the transition A–T $\rightleftharpoons$ G–C in both directions[13]. This tells us that one of the triplets has a G–C pair in the DNA. The experiment reported in Table 4 shows that *ochre* mutants cannot be induced to mutate to *amber* mutants with hydroxylamine, even after the treated phages have been grown in *E. coli B*. This shows that it is the *amber* triplet which has the G–C pair and the *ochre* which contains the A–T pair.

Table 3. Mutation of *ochre* Mutants to *amber* Mutants

	Reversion index×10^{-7}		
	Spontaneous	2-Aminopurine	
*r*IIA cistron	(wild type + *ambers*)	wild type	*amber*
*N*55	0.5	830	280
*X*20	0.05	100	2,100
*X*372	0.1	300	2,100
*X*352	0.06	340	1,500
*HD*147	0.3	370	50
*r*IIB cistron			
*X*511	0.2	710	65
*N*17	0.2	610	80
*SD*160	0.6	380	390
*N*29	1.0	3,900	330
*AP*53	0.7	350	15

Cultures of *E. coli B* in minimal medium with and without 2-aminopurine (600 μg/ml.) were inoculated with about 100 phages and grown to lysis. These were plated on *E. coli B* and on *E. coli K*12(λ) su^{+}I. About 50 induced revertants were tested on *E. coli K*12(λ) su^{-} to measure the relative frequencies of *amber* revertants.

Table 4. Induction of the *ochre* → *amber* Mutation

		Reversion index×10^{-7}	
		r+	*amber*
360	Control	0.6	0.2
	Hydroxylamine	0.8	0.3
	2AP	200	1,200
*UV*375	Control	0.8	0.4
	Hydroxylamine	2.0	1.0
	2AP	660	140
*X*27	Control	0.3	<0.1
	Hydroxylamine	1.0	0.5
	2AP	7.0	73
375	Control	0.8	0.4
	Hydroxylamine	2.0	1.0
	2AP	1,400	1,700

Hydroxylamine treatment and growth of the mutagenized phages, and 2-aminopurine induction, were carried out as described in Tables 2 and 3.

转变成了琥珀突变体。表 3 给出了结果中的一个样本，表明该突变被 2– 氨基嘌呤强烈诱导而成，其突变频率与赭石突变体回复为野生型的频率相当。其他实验（本文未报道）表明 5– 溴尿嘧啶也可以诱导赭石突变体转变为琥珀突变体或者回复为野生型，但是突变频率比 2– 氨基嘌呤要低。这些结果表明琥珀三联体和赭石三联体只有一个核苷酸碱基的差异，另外两个碱基相同。2– 氨基嘌呤是一种碱基类似物诱变剂，A–T $\rightleftharpoons$ G–C 两个方向的转换都可以由它诱导发生 [13]。这告诉我们 DNA 中的一个三联体有一对 G–C 碱基对。表 4 报道的实验结果表明羟胺不能诱导赭石突变体突变为琥珀突变体，甚至羟胺处理的噬菌体已在大肠杆菌 *B* 中生长。这表明具有 G–C 碱基对的是琥珀三联体，而赭石三联体含有的是 A–T 碱基对。

表 3. 赭石突变体转变为琥珀突变体的频率

	回复指数（$\times 10^{-7}$）		
	自发突变	2–氨基嘌呤诱导突变	
*r*IIA 顺反子	野生型和琥珀突变体	野生型	琥珀突变体
*N*55	0.5	830	280
*X*20	0.05	100	2,100
*X*372	0.1	300	2,100
*X*352	0.06	340	1,500
*HD*147	0.3	370	50
*r*IIB 顺反子			
*X*511	0.2	710	65
*N*17	0.2	610	80
*SD*160	0.6	380	390
*N*29	1.0	3,900	330
*AP*53	0.7	350	15

将大肠杆菌 *B* 菌株培养在有或无 2–氨基嘌呤（600 微克 / 毫升）的基本培养基中，与约 100 个噬菌体一起孵育直至发生溶菌。溶菌后将噬菌体后代涂在大肠杆菌 *B* 菌株和大肠杆菌 *K*12（λ）su^{+}_{I} 菌株上。将以上得到的大约 50 个诱导回复突变体涂在大肠杆菌 *K*12（λ）su^{-} 菌株上以检测琥珀回复突变体所占的比例。

表 4. 赭石突变体到琥珀突变体的诱导突变

		回复指数（$\times 10^{-7}$）	
		r+	琥珀突变
360	对照	0.6	0.2
	羟胺	0.8	0.3
	2–氨基嘌呤	200	1,200
*UV*375	对照	0.8	0.4
	羟胺	2.0	1.0
	2–氨基嘌呤	660	140
*X*27	对照	0.3	<0.1
	羟胺	1.0	0.5
	2–氨基嘌呤	7.0	73
375	对照	0.8	0.4
	羟胺	2.0	1.0
	2–氨基嘌呤	1,400	1,700

上表中羟胺及 2– 氨基嘌呤诱变处理的条件和诱变噬菌体的培养条件与表 2 和表 3 的相同。

Although the insensitivity of the mutants to reversion induction by hydroxylamine might suggest that they contain A–T base pairs only, the conversion of *ochre* mutants to *amber* mutants shows that, in one position, the *amber* mutant contains a G–C pair. The other two bases must be common to both triplets, but we cannot conclude that both are A–T pairs. In fact, both could be G–C pairs and the triplets may be connected to other nonsense triplets by G–C→A–T changes. However, we know that *amber* and *ochre* mutants can be induced by hydroxylamine from wild type. This proves that both triplets have at least one common A–T pair.

We now present an experiment which shows that the *amber* triplet has two A–T base pairs, and which also establishes the orientation of the pairs with respect to the two strands of DNA. Let us suppose that the *amber* triplet in the messenger RNA contains a U. This corresponds to an A in the sense strand of DNA of the *amber* mutant, implying that the wild-type DNA contains a G in this strand and a C in the antisense strand. When the wild-type DNA is treated with hydroxylamine to alter this C the change is not effective and normal messenger is still made (Fig. 2, right). On the other hand, if the *amber* triplet in the messenger contains an A, the mutant will be induced by the action of hydroxylamine on a C in the sense strand of the wild-type phage DNA, and provided that the U′ produced acts identically to U in messenger synthesis, mutant messenger will be made. This argument has been tested by the following experiment. Wild-type $T4r^{+}$ phages were treated with hydroxylamine to induce *r* mutants to a frequency of 1 percent. In set B, the phages were then grown on *E. coli B*, in which the *r*II functions are not required, to recover all mutants. In set K, the phages were grown through *E. coli* $K12(\lambda)$ su^{-}, to eliminate from the population all phages with an immediate mutant expression. *Amber* and *ochre* mutants were then selected and mapped. Table 5 summarizes the results. About the same number of *r*I mutants were recorded in each set, and since these mutants show no difference in growth on the two bacterial strains, this shows that the results may be compared directly. It will be seen that *amber* mutants at the sites, *N*97, *S*116, *S*24, *N*34, *X*237 and *HB*232, recur many times in set B, but are absent or rarely found in set K. At other *amber* sites, such as *HB*118, *HB*129, *EM*84 and *AP*164, mutants occur with approximately equal frequency in both sets. The first class fulfils the expectation for a C→U change on the sense strand, while the second class must arise by C→U changes on the antisense strand. This shows that the *amber* triplet in the messenger contains both an A and a U. The same should be true of the *ochre* mutants. However, as shown in Table 5, *ochre* mutants are not as strongly induced by hydroxylamine as are *amber* mutants, and we cannot separate the two classes with the same degree of confidence. Nevertheless, since we have already shown that the mutants are connected, it follows that the *ochre* triplet must also contain an A and a U. We conclude that the *amber* and *ochre* triplets are, respectively, either (UAG) and (UAA), or (UAC) and (UAU). If we had a strain which suppressed *ochre* mutants only, we could specify the third base by studying the induction of the *amber*→*ochre* change with hydroxylamine.

尽管羟胺诱导的突变体回复突变灵敏度低显示出三联体中可能只含有A–T碱基对，但从赭石突变体转变成琥珀突变体的数据来看，琥珀突变体的一个位点上应该含有G–C碱基对。而另外两个碱基一定是两个三联体共有的，但是我们无法推断他们都是A–T碱基对。事实上，它们有可能都是G–C碱基对，并且可能通过G–C→A–T变化而变成了其他的无义三联体。但是我们知道野生型可由羟胺诱导成为琥珀突变体和赭石突变体，这证明两个三联体至少共有一对A–T碱基对。

我们现在通过实验证明了琥珀三联体有两对 A–T 碱基对，并且也对 DNA 双链上的碱基对进行了定位。我们假设信使 RNA 中的琥珀三联体包含一个碱基 U，则相应地，琥珀突变体的 DNA 有义链上就是一个碱基 A，这意味着野生型 DNA 该链中含有的是 G,反义链对应为 C。用羟胺处理野生型 DNA 以改变这个 C 时并没有影响，仍可转录出正常的信使 RNA，如图 2 右所示。另一方面，如果信使 RNA 中的琥珀三联体含有一个 A 的话，那么羟胺就会对野生型噬菌体 DNA 有义链上的 C 发生作用而诱导产生突变体，假设信使 RNA 合成时 U′ 产生的作用与 U 相同，就会产生突变的信使 RNA。这个假设已经通过如下的实验得到验证，用羟胺处理野生型 $T4r^{+}$ 噬菌体以诱导其产生频率为 1% 的 *r* 突变体。在 B 组中，让噬菌体在不需要 *r*II 功能的大肠杆菌 *B* 菌株上生长，以得到所有的突变体。在 K 组中，噬菌体通过侵染大肠杆菌 *K*12（λ）su^{-} 菌株而生长，以消除群体中所有具有即时突变体表达的噬菌体，然后选出琥珀突变体和赭石突变体并作图。表 5 对该结果进行了概括。每组中得到了大概同样数量的 *r*I 突变体，由于这些突变体在两种细菌菌株上的生长并无差别，表明或许可以直接比较这些结果。可以看到在 B 组中琥珀突变体在位点 *N*97、*S*116、*S*24、*N*34、*X*237 和 *HB*232 上出现许多次，但在 K 组中却完全没有或很少发现。其他的琥珀位点，例如 *HB*118、*HB*129、*EM*84 和 *AP*164，出现突变体的频率在两组中大概相同。第一类实现了在有义链上诱导 C→U 变化的期望，而第二类就必须在反义链上引起 C→U 变化。这表明信使 RNA 中的琥珀三联体既含有 A 碱基，也含有 U 碱基。赭石突变体应该也是这样。但是，正如表 5 所示，羟胺对赭石突变体的诱导效果不如对琥珀突变体的强，所以我们并不能以同样的置信度分离得到这两类突变体。但是由于我们已经表明突变体间是相关联的，因此可以认为赭石三联体也必定含有一个 A 和一个 U。从以上结果我们推论：琥珀三联体和赭石三联体分别是 UAG 和 UAA 或 UAC 和 UAU。如果我们有一种只抑制赭石突变体的菌株，那么就能够通过研究羟胺将琥珀突变体诱导成为赭石突变体这一变化而确定第三个碱基是什么。

Table 5. Hydroxylamine Induction of *amber* and *ochre* Mutants

A. No. of mutants isolated

	Set B	Set K
*r*I	2,010	1,823
Leaky or high reverting *r*II	720	508
non-suppressible *r*II	1,144	433
amber	319	121
ochre	83	82
Total	4,276	2,967

B. Recurrences found at different sites

Amber mutants			*Ochre* mutants		
	No. found at each site			No. found at each site	
Site	Set B	Set K	Site	Set B	Set K
A cistron			A cistron		
*HB*118	27	15	*HD*147	2	0
*C*204	1	0	*HF*220	1	0
*N*97	44	1	*HF*240	1	0
*S*116	31	2	*N*55	19	19
*N*11	3	3	*X*20	9	8
*S*172	9	5	*HF*219	1	0
*S*24	44	3	*HF*245	1	0
*HB*129	14	25	*N*31	3	5
*S*99	12	16	*HM*127	0	1
*N*19	15	9	*N*21	2	2
*N*34	8	0			
B cistron			B cistron		
*HE*122	1	0	360	11	10
*EM*84	29	21	*UV*375	2	0
*HB*74	16	5	*N*24	6	4
*X*237	14	2	375	2	5
*AP*164	28	12	*N*17	5	3
*HB*232	21	1	*HF*208	1	2
*X*417	1	0	*N*7	4	12
*HD*231	1	1	*N*12	5	7
			*X*234	0	2
			*X*191	1	0
			*HE*267	5	0
			*AP*53	2	2

$T4Br^+$ was treated with M hydroxylamine (see Table 2) for 2 h at 37°C. Survival was 50 percent, and the frequency of *r* and mottled plaques, 1 percent. 1.2×10^7 phage particles were adsorbed to 10^9 cells of *E. coli B* (set B) and to *E. coli K*12(λ) su^- (set K). After 8 min, the infected bacteria were diluted a thousand-fold into 2 litres of broth, incubated for 35' and lysed with $CHCl_3$. The burst sizes in both sets were 60. *r* mutants were isolated from each set using less than 2 ml. to ensure that the mutants selected had mostly arisen from independent events. These were picked and stabbed into B and K, and *r*I mutants and leaky mutants discarded. The *r*II mutants were then screened on su^+_{III} and su^+_B to select for *amber* and *ochre* mutants which were then located by genetic mapping.

表 5. 羟胺诱变分离琥珀突变体和赭石突变体

A. 分离到的突变体数

	B 组	K 组
rI 突变体	2,010	1,823
渗漏或高回复突变的 rII 突变体	720	508
不能被抑制的 rII 突变体	1,144	433
琥珀突变体	319	121
赭石突变体	83	82
总数	4,276	2,967

B. 在不同位点重复出现的突变体数

琥珀突变体			赭石突变体		
每个位点出现的次数			每个位点出现的次数		
位点	B 组	K 组	位点	B 组	K 组
A 顺反子			A 顺反子		
*HB*118	27	15	*HD*147	2	0
*C*204	1	0	*HF*220	1	0
*N*97	44	1	*HF*240	1	0
*S*116	31	2	*N*55	19	19
*N*11	3	3	*X*20	9	8
*S*172	9	5	*HF*219	1	0
*S*24	44	3	*HF*245	1	0
*HB*129	14	25	*N*31	3	5
*S*99	12	16	*HM*127	0	1
*N*19	15	9	*N*21	2	2
*N*34	8	0			
B 顺反子			B 顺反子		
*HE*122	1	0	360	11	10
*EM*84	29	21	*UV*375	2	0
*HB*74	16	5	*N*24	6	4
*X*237	14	2	375	2	5
*AP*164	28	12	*N*17	5	3
*HB*232	21	1	*HF*208	1	2
*X*417	1	0	*N*7	4	12
*HD*231	1	1	*N*12	5	7
			*X*234	0	2
			*X*191	1	0
			*HE*267	5	0
			*AP*53	2	2

将 $T4Br^+$ 用 1M 羟胺于 37℃处理 2 小时（见表 2）后存活率为 50%，*r* 和斑点状噬菌斑的频率为 1%。用 1.2×10^7 个噬菌体颗粒去侵染 10^9 个大肠杆菌 *B* 菌株（B 组）和大肠杆菌 *K*12（λ）su^- 菌株（K 组）。8 分钟后，用 2 升的培养基将上述培养物稀释 1,000 倍，再孵育 35 分钟后用三氯甲烷将其溶解。两组中的噬菌体裂解量都是 60。每组中的 *r* 突变体用少于 2 毫升来分离，保证各组中筛选的突变是彼此独立的事件。剔除 rI 突变体和渗漏突变体之后，将挑选出来的这些突变体导入 B 菌株和 K 菌株。然后在菌株 su^+_{III} 和 su^+_B 上筛选 rII 突变体作为选择出来的琥珀突变体和赭石突变体，进一步通过遗传图谱定位。

Fortunately, we can resolve the ambiguity by determining the amino-acids to which the *amber* triplet is connected by mutation. In particular, we note that it should be connected to two and only two amino-acid codons by transitions, corresponding, in fact, to the two types of origin of the mutants described here. The third codon to which it is connected by a transition is the *ochre* triplet. As mentioned earlier, the head *amber* mutant *H*36 has arisen from glutamine (Fig. 1). This mutant was induced with hydroxylamine. We have evidence that two other mutants, *E*161 and *B*278 induced by 2-aminopurine and 5-bromouracil respectively, have arisen from tryptophan. In a recent study of two *amber* mutants of the alkaline phosphatase, Garen and Weigert[14] found one mutant to arise from glutamine and the other from tryptophan; and Notani *et al.*[15] have found an *amber* mutant to arise from glutamine in the RNA phage *f*2. In addition, we have examined 2-aminopurine induced revertants of 10 different head *amber* mutants. Ten to 12 independently induced revertants of each of the mutants have been screened for tryptophan containing peptides by examining the ^{14}C-tryptophan labelled protein. Among a total of 115 revertants, 62 are to tryptophan. Determination of glutamine involves sequence analysis and takes more time. So far, among the remaining 53 revertants, glutamine has been identified in one revertant of *H*36. These results suggest that the two amino-acids connected to the *amber* triplet are glutamine and tryptophan. If the *amber* triplet is (UAC), then one of these must be (CAC) and the other (UGC); if it is (UAG), then the corresponding codons are (CAG) and (UGG). Nirenberg *et al.*[16] have shown that poly AC does not code for tryptophan, but does for glutamine. However, they find that the triplet for glutamine clearly has the composition (CAA) and is definitely not (CAC). Since this latter triplet corresponds neither to glutamine nor to tryptophan we can eliminate the first alternative. We note with satisfaction that (UGG) is the composition of a codon assigned to tryptophan[16,17] , and this assignment of (UAG) to the *amber* triplet suggests that glutamine is (CAG).

We can also make a reasonable assignment of the order of the bases in the triplet. Our original argument was based on deductions from a few known triplets and from amino-acid replacement data; it will not be given here. The order of the bases follows directly from a recent demonstration by Nirenberg *et al.*[18] that the triplet CAG does, in fact, correspond to glutamine. The *amber* triplet is therefore UAG and the *ochre* triplet UAA. This assignment is supported by the following additional evidence. We have found a tyrosine replacement in 21 independent spontaneous mutants of the head *amber* mutant, *H*36 (ref. 19). This change must be due to a transversion because we have already accounted for all the transitions of the *amber* triplet. In support of this, we find that the change is not induced by 2–aminopurine. There are six possible transversions of the *amber* triplet, namely, AAG, GAG, UUG, UCG, UAU and UAC. It has recently been shown that both UAU and UAC correspond to tyrosine[20] which confirms the order. The spontaneous revertants of the *amber* mutants to leucine, serine and glutamic acid found by Weigert and Garen[21] are further evidence for the assignment. UUG, a transversion of the *amber* triplet, does in fact code for leucine,[22] and reasonable allocations for serine and glutamic acid are UCG and GAG, respectively. Weigert and Garen[21] also find revertants of an *amber* mutant to either lysine or arginine. This may be the final transversion expected since AAG is a codeword for lysine[20].

幸运的是，我们可以通过突变来确定琥珀三联体与何种氨基酸相对应，从而解决这个问题。特别是我们注意到它应该与通过转换形成的两种（仅此两种）氨基酸密码子有关，实际上这两种密码子对应本文描述的两种突变体。通过转换与第三个密码子相关的就是赭石三联体。正如早期提到的，头部蛋白琥珀突变体 *H*36 是由羟胺诱导谷氨酰胺突变产生的（图 1）。另外，我们有证据证明，另外两个突变体 *E*161 和 *B*278 分别是由 2–氨基嘌呤和 5–溴尿嘧啶诱导色氨酸突变而产生。最近对碱性磷酸酶的两个琥珀突变体的研究中，加伦和魏格特 [14] 发现一个突变体由谷氨酰胺突变产生，另一个则由色氨酸突变产生，野谷等 [15] 则发现 RNA 噬菌体 *f*2 的一个琥珀突变体是由谷氨酰胺突变产生的。此外我们研究了 2– 氨基嘌呤诱导的 10 种不同的头部蛋白琥珀突变体的回复突变体。通过检测 ^{14}C– 色氨酸标记蛋白从每一种突变体中可筛选到 10~12 个独立诱导的包含色氨酸肽段的回复突变体。在总共的 115 个回复突变体中，有 62 个是色氨酸突变产生的回复突变体。而谷氨酰胺突变产生的回复突变体是通过序列分析进行的，所以需要花费的时间更久一些。目前为止，在其余的 53 种回复突变体中，在 *H*36 一个回复突变体已检测出是谷氨酰胺突变。以上这些结果提示我们，与琥珀三联体相关的两个氨基酸是谷氨酰胺和色氨酸。如果琥珀三联体是 UAC，则这两者之一一定是 CAC，另一个是 UGC，如果琥珀三联体是 UAG，则对应的密码子就是 CAG 和 UGG。尼伦伯格等 [16] 已经表明多聚 AC 不编码色氨酸，但是编码谷氨酰胺。并且他们发现谷氨酰胺三联体肯定含有 CAA 这种组合，而一定不含 CAC。由于 CAC 既不编码谷氨酰胺也不编码色氨酸，所以可以排除第一种情况。可喜的是，我们注意到 UGG 是编码色氨酸的一个密码子组合 [16,17]，将 UAG 确定为琥珀三联体提示编码谷氨酰胺的应该是 CAG。

现在我们也可以对三联体的碱基顺序进行合理地分配了。最初，我们的论据是根据少数已知三联体以及氨基酸替代的信息推导出来的，这里就不表述了。关于碱基顺序的确定，其直接根据是尼伦伯格等人最近的实证 [18]，即证明三联体 CAG 确实编码的是谷氨酰胺。因此琥珀三联体是 UAG，而赭石三联体是 UAA。后来的其他证据也支持这个分配顺序。我们已经在头部蛋白琥珀突变体 *H*36 的 21 个独立自发突变体中发现了酪氨酸替代的情况（参考文献 19）。这种情况一定是由颠换突变引起的，因为我们已经推算了琥珀三联体的所有转换情况。为支持这一观点，我们还发现这一变化不是由 2–氨基嘌呤诱导产生的。琥珀三联体具有六种可能的颠换，即 AAG、GAG、UUG、UCG、UAU 和 UAC。最近又有研究表明 UAU 和 UAC 都编码酪氨酸 [20]，这使得碱基顺序得以确定。魏格特和加伦 [21] 发现琥珀突变体能够自发回复突变为亮氨酸、丝氨酸和谷氨酸，这为碱基分配顺序提供了进一步的支持证据。UUG 是琥珀三联体发生一个颠换产生的，实际上确实编码的是亮氨酸 [22]，而丝氨酸和谷氨酸应分别对应 UCG 和 GAG。另外，魏格特和加伦 [21] 还发现琥珀突变体既可以回复突变成赖氨酸，也可以回复突变为精氨酸。由于 AAG 是赖氨酸的密码子 [20]，所以上述情况可能是颠换突变的最终形式。

It should be noted that in the foregoing discussion it has been tacitly assumed that the *amber* and *ochre* signals are triplets. Examination of revertants of *amber* mutants has supported this assumption, since in 41 independent revertants of *H*36 the amino-acid replaced is always at the site of mutation, and never in adjacent positions. The 21 revertants that Weigert and Garen[21] isolated reinforce this conclusion.

Function of amber and ochre triplets and the mechanism of suppression. According to present-day ideas of protein synthesis, it is expected that the termination of the growth of the polypeptide chain should involve a special mechanism. Since the terminal carboxyl group of the growing peptide chain is esterified to an *s*RNA (ref. 23), chain termination must involve not only the cessation of growth, but also the cleavage of this bond. Since the *amber* mutants have been shown to result in efficient termination of polypeptide chain synthesis, it is reasonable to suppose that this special mechanism may be provided by the *amber* and *ochre* triplets.

We postulate that the chain-terminating triplets UAA and UAG are recognized by specific *s*RNAs, just like other codons. These *s*RNAs do not carry amino-acids but a special compound which results in termination of the growing polypeptide chain. There are many possible ways of formulating the mechanism in detail, but all are speculative and will not be considered here. The essential feature of this hypothesis is to make the process of chain termination exactly congruent with that of chain extension.

In suppressing strains, a mechanism is provided for competing with chain termination; it is easy to visualize this process as being due to two ways of recognizing the nonsense codon—one by the chain-terminating *s*RNA, and the other by an *s*RNA carrying an amino-acid. Mechanisms of suppression can be classified according to which *s*RNA carries the amino-acid to the nonsense codon.

Alteration in the recognition of the chain-terminating *s*RNA might allow the attachment of an amino-acid to this *s*RNA. This could be brought about either by modifying normal activating enzymes so as to widen their specificity, or by changing the chain terminating *s*RNAs to allow them to be recognized by activating enzymes.

Another possibility is that the region of an amino-acyl *s*RNA used for triplet recognition is modified so that it can recognize the nonsense triplet. Clearly, this alteration must not affect the normal recognition of its own codon by the amino acyl *s*RNA because such a change would be lethal. Either there must be more than one gene for the given *s*RNA, or else the change must produce an ambiguity in the recognition site so that it can read both its own codon and the nonsense codon. Such ambiguity could result not only from mutation in the *s*RNA gene but also by enzymatic modification of one of the bases in the recognition site. The ambiguity, however, must be narrowly restricted to prevent the suppression from affecting codons other than the *amber* and *ochre* triplets. Moreover, the amino-acids which are inserted by the *amber* suppressors must be those the codons of which are connected to UAG. It should be noted that this condition is fulfilled by $su^{+}{}_{\text{I}}$

应该注意到，在前面的讨论中已经默认了琥珀密码子和赭石密码子是三联体。琥珀突变体的回复突变体检验实验支持该假设，因为 *H*36 的 41 个独立的回复突变体中，被取代的氨基酸总是处于突变位点，而从来没有在相邻位置出现过。魏格特和加伦 [21] 分离到的 21 个回复突变体也进一步支持了该结论。

琥珀三联体和赭石三联体的功能及其抑制机制 根据目前的蛋白质合成的观点，可以预期多肽链生长的终止应该涉及一种特定机制。*s*RNA 正确识别后使延伸的肽链的羧基末端发生酯化（参考文献 23），所以链终止不仅使翻译停止了，也使这一化学键发生了断裂。因为已经表明琥珀突变体导致了多肽链合成的有效终止，所以可以合理地认为这一特定机制是通过识别琥珀三联体和赭石三联体而实现的。

我们假定链终止三联体 UAA 和 UAG 就像其他密码子一样，由特定的 *s*RNA 识别。这些 *s*RNAs 并不携带氨基酸，而是携带一种特殊的复合物，这种复合物可以导致正在生长的多肽链的终止。关于该机制，我们可以用许多可能的方式来详细叙述，但是它们都只是推导出来的，所以在这里不赘述了。这一假说的本质特征是要使链终止的过程与链延伸的过程完全一致。

在抑制菌株中，存在着一种可与链终止竞争的机制。该过程很容易被视为识别无义密码子的两种方式，一种是通过链终止 *s*RNA，另一种是通过携带一个氨基酸的 *s*RNA。可以根据哪个 *s*RNA 将氨基酸携带至无义密码子而对抑制机制进行分类。

链终止 *s*RNA 识别的不确定性可能允许将一种氨基酸与该 *s*RNA 联系起来。而这个过程可以通过修饰正常的激活酶进而扩大酶的专一性来实现，也可以通过改变链终止 *s*RNA 以使它可以被激活酶识别来实现。

还有一种可能性即氨基酰 *s*RNA 上用来识别三联体的区域被修饰以使其能够识别无义三联体，很明显，这种修饰一定不能影响氨基酰 *s*RNA 对其自身密码子的正常识别，因为这种变化是致命的。要么该 *s*RNA 一定有多于一个基因来编码，否则这一变化一定会在识别位点产生不确定性，导致其既可以读自身的密码子也可以读无义密码子。这种不确定性可能是由于 *s*RNA 基因存在突变引起的，也可能是由于识别位点的某一碱基被酶修饰造成的。然而，这一不确定性肯定被严密限制以阻止对琥珀三联体和赭石三联体以外的其他密码子产生抑制影响。此外，被琥珀抑制基因插入突变的氨基酸的密码肯定是与 UAG 相关的。被 su^{+}_{I} 插入突变的丝氨酸密码就是这种情况，因为已经研究发现丝氨酸是琥珀突变体的一个回复突变体。这一学说

which inserts serine, since serine has been found as a reversion of an *amber* mutant. This theory does not easily explain the *ochre* suppressors. Since these recognize both *amber* and *ochre* mutants the *s*RNA must possess this ambiguity as well.

Another quite different possibility for suppression that has been considered is that the suppressors alter a component of the ribosomes to permit errors to occur in the reading of the messenger RNA (ref. 24). This is probably the explanation of streptomycin suppression[25], but suppression of *amber* and *ochre* mutants cannot be readily explained by this theory. It is scarcely likely that such a mechanism could be specific for only one or two triplets, and for this reason it might be expected to give us suppression of mutants which are not nonsense, but missense, and this has not been found[1,8]. Moreover, the efficiency of *amber* suppression argues strongly against such a mechanism. It is unlikely that a generalized error in reading nucleotides could produce the 60 percent efficiency of suppression found for $su^{+}_{\rm I}$ without seriously affecting the viability of the cell.

It is a consequence of our theory that normal chain termination could also be suppressed in these strains. Since the *amber* suppressors are efficient we have to introduce the *ad hoc* hypothesis that the UAG codon is rarely used for chain termination in *Escherichia coli* and bacteriophage *T*4 and that UAA is the common codon. This is supported by the fact that all *ochre* suppressors thus far isolated are weak[7,8]. Another possibility is that neither is the common chain terminating triplet. We cannot exclude the existence of other chain terminating triplets which are not suppressible.

To summarize: we show that the triplets of the *amber* and *ochre* mutants are UAG and UAA, respectively. We suggest that the "nonsense" codons should be more properly considered to be the codons for chain termination. In essence, this means that the number of elements to be coded for is not 20 but more likely 21. We propose that the recognition of the chain-terminating codons is carried out by two special *s*RNAs.

We thank our colleagues for their advice, and Dr. M. Nirenberg for allowing us to quote his unpublished results.

(**206**, 994-998; 1965)

S. Brenner, A. O. W. Stretton and S. Kaplan: Medical Research Council, Laboratory of Molecular Biology, Cambridge, England.

References:

1. Benzer, S., and Champe, S. P., *Proc. U.S. Nat. Acad. Sci.*, 47, 1025 (1961); **48**, 1114 (1962).
2. Garen, A., and Siddiqi, O., *Proc. U.S. Nat. Acad. Sci.*, **48**, 1121 (1962).
3. Campbell, A., *Virology*, **14**, 22 (1961).
4. Epstein, R. H., Bolle, A., Steinberg, C. M., Kellenberger, E., Boy de la Tour, E., Chevalley, R., Edgar, R. S., Susman, M., Denhardt, G. H., and Lielausis, A., *Cold Spring Harbour Symp. Quant. Biol.*, **28**, 375 (1963).

很难解释赭石抑制基因。因为它们既可以识别琥珀突变体，也能识别赭石突变体，该 *s*RNA 也一定具有上述不确定性。

关于抑制机制另一种相当不同的可能性是：抑制基因改变了核糖体组分以允许核糖体在读取信使 RNA 时出现错误（参考文献 24）。这可能是对链霉素抑制[25]的解释，但是该学说不能对琥珀突变体和赭石突变体的抑制给出很好的解释。因为这种机制不可能仅特异地针对一两种三联体，由于这个原因，所以可以预料突变体的抑制不是无义的，而是错义的，但是这种情况目前还没有报道[1,8]。此外，琥珀抑制的效率与该机制一点都不吻合。如果在读取核苷酸的过程中出现的一个普遍性错误，能在 su^{+}_{I} 菌株中产生 60% 的抑制效率却对该细胞的生活力没有严重影响，这是不可能的。

我们的理论得到的结论是正常的链终止也可以在这些菌株中被抑制。由于琥珀抑制基因很有效，所以我们在这里提出一个特别的假说，即 UAG 密码子很少被用来引发大肠杆菌和 *T*4 噬菌体中的链终止，UAA 才是通用的终止密码子。至今分离到的所有的赭石抑制子的抑制作用都很弱这一事实可以用来支持该假说[7,8]。另一种可能性是它们都不是通用的链终止三联体。我们不能排除存在其他的不可抑制的链终止三联体的可能性。

综上所述，我们的研究表明琥珀和赭石突变体的三联体分别是 UAG 和 UAA。我们认为“无义”密码子被当作终止密码子会更为恰当。从本质上说，这意味着 64 种三联体编码的氨基酸数目不是 20 而更可能是 21。我们提出链终止密码子的识别是由两种特殊的 *s*RNA 来实现的。

感谢我们的同事们提出的宝贵建议以及尼伦伯格博士允许我们引用他尚未发表的结果。

（刘皓芳 翻译；刘京国 审稿）

5. Sarabhai, A., Stretton, A. O. W., Brenner, S., and Bolle, A., *Nature*, **201**, 13(1964).
6. Stretton, A. O. W., and Brenner, S., *J. Mol. Biol.* (in the press).
7. Kaplan, S., Stretton A. O. W., and Brenner, S. (in preparation).
8. Brenner, S., and Beekwith, J. R. (in preparation).
9. Brenner, S., and Stretton, A. O. W. (in preparation).
10. Brown, D. M., and Schell, P., *J. Mol. Biol.*, **3**, 709 (1961). Freese, E., Bautz-Freese, E., and Bautz, E., *J. Mol. Biol.*, **3**, 133(1961). Schuster, H., *J. Mol. Biol.*, **3**, 447 (1961). Freese, E., Bautz, E., and Freese, E. B., *Proc. U.S. Nat. Acad. Sci.*, 47, 845 (1961).
11. Tocchini-Valentini, G. P., Stodolsky, M., Aurisicchio, A., Sarnat, M., Graziosi, F., Weiss, S. B., and Geiduschek, E. P., *Proc. U.S. Nat. Acad. Sci.*, **50**, 935 (1963). Hayashi, M., Hayashi, M. N., and Spiegelman, S., *Proc. U.S. Nat. Acad. Sci.*, **50**, 664 (1963). Marmur, J., Greenspan, C. M., Palacek, E., Kahan, F. M., Levene, J., and Mandel, M., *Cold Spring Harbor Symp. Quant. Biol.*, **28**, 191 (1963). Bautz, E. K. F., *Cold Spring Harbor Symp. Quant. Biol.*, **28**, 205 (1963). Hall, B. D., Green, M., Nygaard, A. P., and Boezi, J., *Cold Spring Harbor Symp. Quant. Biol.*, **28**, 201 (1963).
12. Champe, S. P., and Benzer, S., *Proc. U.S. Nat. Acad. Sci.*, **48**, 532 (1962). Tessman, I., Poddar, R. K., and Kumar, S., *J. Mol. Biol.*, **9**, 352 (1964).
13. Freese, E., *J. Mol. Biol.*, **1**, 87 (1959). Freese, E., *Proc. U.S. Nat. Acad. Sci.*, **45**, 622 (1959). Howard, B. D., and Tessman, I., *J. Mol. Biol.*, **9**, 372 (1964).
14. Garen, A., and Weigert, M. G., *J. Mol. Biol.* (in the press).
15. Notani, G. W., Engelhardt, D. L., Konigsberg, W., and Zinder, N., *J. Mol. Biol.* (in the press).
16. Nirenberg, M., Jones. O. W., Leder, P., Clark, B. F. C., Sly, W. S., and Pestka, S., *Cold Spring Harbor Symp. Quant., Biol.*, **28**, 549 (1963).
17. Speyer, J. F., Lengyel, P., Basilio, C., Wahba, A. J., Gardner, R. S., and Ochoa, S., *Cold Spring Harbor Symp. Quant., Biol.*, **28**, 559 (1963).
18. Nirenberg, M., Leder, P., Bernfield, M., Brimacombe, R., Trupin, J., and Rottman, F., *Proc. U.S. Nat. Acad. Sci.* (in the press).
19. Stretton, A. O. W., and Brenner, S. (in preparation).
20. Trupin, J., Rottman, F., Brimacombe, R., Leder, P., Bernfield, M., and Nirenberg, M., *Proc. U.S. Nat. Acad. Sci.* (in the press). Clark, B. F. C., presented before the French Biochemical Society, February, 1965.
21. Weigert, M. G., and Garen, A., *Nature* (preceding communication).
22. Leder, P., and Nirenberg, M. W., *Proc. U.S. Nat. Acad. Sci.*, **52**, 1521 (1964).
23. Gilbert, W., *J. Mol. Biol.*, **6**, 389 (1963). Bretscher, M. S., *J. Mol. Biol.*, 7, 446 (1963).
24. Davies, J., Gilbert, W., and Gorini, I., *Proc. U.S. Nat. Acad. Sci.*, **51**, 883 (1964).
25. Gorini, L., and Kataja, E., *Proc. U.S. Nat. Acad. Sci.*, **51**, 487 (1964).

A Radar Determination of the Rotation of the Planet Mercury

G. H. Pettengill and R. B. Dyce

Editor's Note

Remarkably, Mercury's rotation rate was determined only in 1965, in this paper by Gordon Pettengill and Rolf Dyce. Mercury had been expected to be "tidally locked" with one face pointing always to the Sun, just as the Moon is tidally locked to Earth. But it turned that its rotation rate was two-thirds of its orbital period.

DURING the recent inferior conjunction of the planet Mercury in April, 1965, radar observations were obtained by the Arecibo Ionospheric Observatory in Puerto Rico (operated by Cornell University with the support of the Advanced Research Projects Agency under a Research Contract with the Air Force Office of Scientific Research). The system operated at a frequency of 430 Mc/s, with an antenna gain of 56 dB and a transmitted power of 2 MW. The resulting sensitivity was sufficient to obtain significant echoes not only from the nearest part of the planetary disk but also from more distant regions, removed by up to 0.06 of the planet's radius. By using short transmitted pulses of 500 μsec duration, it was possible to isolate the echo power from these more distant regions, and to carry out a Fourier analysis of their spectral composition.

Since the source of the delayed echoes can quite reliably be associated with a known area of the planetary surface, the magnitude of the apparent planetary rotation can be inferred from the measured spectral dispersion through a simple geometrical relationship. The apparent rotation is the vector sum of an intrinsic rotation and a contribution arising from the relative motion of the observer and the target planet. Since the latter is quite accurately calculable from the known orbital motions of the Earth and Mercury and the known rotation of the Earth, a constraint is set on the allowable vector magnitude and position assigned to the intrinsic planetary rotation.

By carrying out observations spread over a period of time it is possible to solve for both the magnitude and direction of the planetary rotation. In the present series of observations, data have been obtained for April 6, 10, 12 and 25, 1965. On most of these days it was possible to check the results by comparing the inferred angular rotation obtained from data at various delays measured with respect to the earliest (and strongest) echo component. From this comparison a degree of confidence could be established, and an estimate obtained of the measurement error.

The data were used to compute a most likely value of intrinsic planetary rotation with

雷达测定水星的自转

佩滕吉尔，戴斯

编者按

引人注目的是直到 1965 年，戈登 · 佩滕吉尔和罗尔夫 · 戴斯才在本文中给出水星自转速率。预期中的水星是“潮汐锁定”的，有一面始终朝向太阳，就像月球是被地球潮汐锁定的一样。但实际上其自转速率是轨道周期的三分之二。

在 1965 年 4 月水星最近一次的下合期间，位于波多黎各的阿雷西博电离层天文台（它由康奈尔大学在高等研究计划局的支持下，在空军科学研究办公室的一个研究合同框架下运行）对其进行了雷达观测。该系统的工作频率为 430 兆周 / 秒，天线增益为 56 分贝，发射功率为 2 兆瓦。该系统的灵敏程度不仅可以接收到来自紧靠行星盘最近部分的显著回波信号，还能把观测区扩大到行星半径的 0.06 倍处。利用时长为 500 微秒的短发射脉冲，可以分离出更远区域的回波功率，并利用傅里叶分析研究其频谱组成。

由于延迟回波的反射源与行星表面已知区域的关系相当可靠，故行星视自转速率的大小可以通过一个简单的几何关系从测得的光谱色散中得到。视自转是行星本身的自转与观测者和目标行星间相对运动的矢量和。由于后者可以根据已知的地球和水星轨道运动情况及地球自转率很精确地计算出来，因此也就可以对行星本身的自转速率的矢量大小和方向给出一个约束值。

通过一段时期的连续观测，就有可能求解出行星自转速度的大小和方向。目前的观测数据序列是 1965 年 4 月 6 日、10 日、12 日和 25 日得到的。在大部分时间中，可以通过对比分析由测得的各种延迟数据所推算出的角自转速率与最早（同时也是最强）的回波组分来检验结果。通过这些比较可以确定置信度，并估算测量误差。

利用麻省理工学院林肯实验室欧文 · 夏皮罗博士所开发的程序，这些数据可以

a procedure developed by Dr. Irwin Shapiro of the Lincoln Laboratory, Massachusetts Institute of Technology. Fig. 1 shows the measurements together with the best fit curve. The curve for a retrograde rotation which would be permitted on the basis of the data of April 6, 10 and 12 alone is also included, as is the behaviour that would be expected on the assumption of rotation which is synchronous with the orbital period. As shown in Fig. 1, the rotation is direct with a sidereal period of 59 ± 5 days. The direction of the pole is not well-determined from these limited data, but is approximately normal to the planetary orbit.

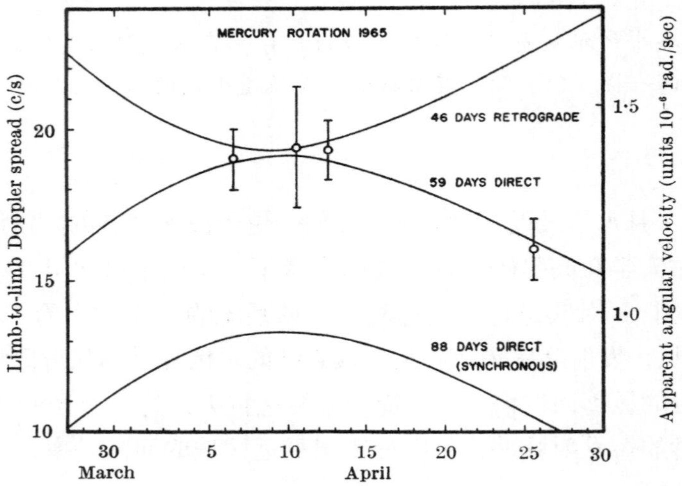

Fig. 1. Plot of the apparent rotational angular velocity of the planet Mercury versus date for several values of rotation during the inferior conjunction of April 1965. The values inferred from the measurements are shown with their estimated errors

The finding of a value for the rotational period of Mercury which differs from the orbital period is unexpected and has interesting theoretical implications. It indicates either that the planet has not been in its present orbit for the full period of geological time or that the tidal forces acting to slow the initial rotation have not been correctly treated previously, as suggested in the following communication.

We thank the staff of the Arecibo Ionospheric Observatory for their assistance in carrying out the measurements.

(**206**, 1240; 1965)

G. H. Pettengill and R. B. Dyce: Cornell-Sydney University Astronomy Center, Arecibo Ionospheric Observatory, Arecibo, Puerto Rico.

用来计算出水星本身自转速率的最大可能值。图 1 给出了观测值以及最佳拟合曲线。在假定自转与轨道周期同步的情况下，逆行自转是允许存在的，图中也包括了基于 4 月 6 日、10 日和 12 日的数据所绘制的逆行自转曲线。如图 1 所示，自转与 59±5 天的恒星周期是相一致的。尽管无法从这些有限的数据中准确测定极轴的方向，但其大致是与行星轨道面相垂直的。

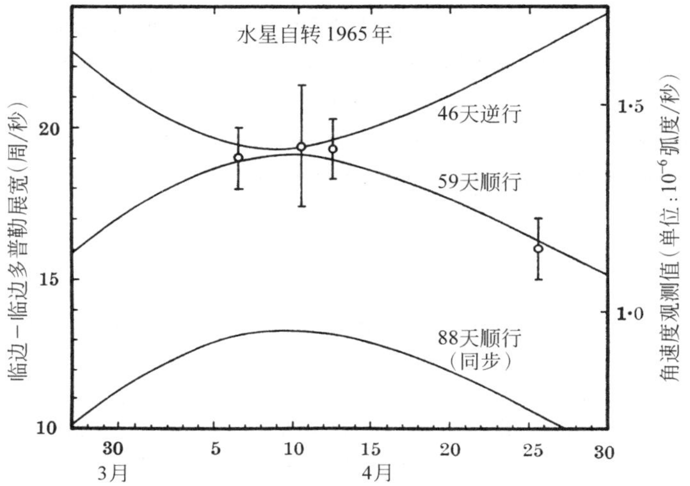

图 1. 在 1965 年 4 月下合期间，根据在不同时间所得自转值绘出了水星视自转角速度图。图中还给出了测量估计值及其误差。

对水星自转周期值和轨道周期值不一致的发现是出人意料的，这也激发了人们对其理论含义的兴趣。如在后面的报道中所指出的，它表明或者在整个地质历史时期水星并非一直处于现在的轨道上，或者之前我们并未正确对待潮汐力对减慢初始转动速率影响。

在此我们感谢阿雷西博电离层天文台的工作人员在测量过程中所给予的协助。

（钱磊 翻译；肖伟科 审稿）

Rotation of the Planet Mercury

S. J. Peale and T. Gold

Editor's Note

Here Stan Peale and Thomas Gold show that because of Mercury's large eccentricity, its rotation rate determined by Pettengill and Dyce is actually is to be expected, contrary to the previously prevailing view that the planet would be "tidally locked" with the same face always pointing sunward. They also are able to infer that Mercury is not permanently rigid, which they suggest might be partially explained by its high surface temperature. Relatively little is known about Mercury even now. The Messenger mission was launched to study the planet in 2004, and after three flybys, it will enter orbit around Mercury in March 2011.

SOLAR tidal friction must be an intense effect for Mercury, and it must be expected that the planet's spin would have relaxed from any original value to one that is under the control of this effect in a time short compared with the age of the solar system. The retarding torque exerted by the Sun on a planet is proportional to $1/r^6$ (where r is the distance Sun-planet), a factor which is some 300 times greater for Mercury than for the Earth. For a planet on a circular orbit the final condition would then be one of synchronous rotation like the motion of the Moon with respect to the Earth. Mercury's motion around the Sun takes 88 days and for synchronous rotation the sidereal period would thus be 88 days also. The observed value of 59 ± 5 days differs markedly from this (see preceding communication).

For a planet with substantial orbital eccentricity the condition is different, however, and synchronous rotation with the orbital period need not then be expected. With the $1/r^6$ dependence the tidal torque at perihelion will exceed that at other times, and the angular velocity of the planet will thus settle at a value greater than the mean orbital angular velocity, but not quite as great as the orbital angular velocity at perihelion. For Mercury, where the eccentricity is 0.2, 2π times the reciprocal of the orbital angular velocity at perihelion is 56.6 days. A spin with a sidereal period lying between 56 and 88 days thus must be expected.

A more precise calculation may be made based on the consideration that the final angular velocity of the planet will be such that the time average of the tidal torque around the orbit is zero. No further change in the planet's spin will then occur except on the much longer time scale on which other orbital elements can be influenced by tidal friction, effects which probably are unimportant in the age of the solar system. The precise calculation of the angular velocity to fit this condition can be made without a quantitative description of the dissipation properties of the planet, but involving certain assumptions. The tidal phase lag has to be assumed to be a small angle only, and one may make the

水星的自转

皮尔，戈尔德

编者按

在本文中，斯坦·皮尔和托马斯·戈尔德表明，由于水星具有较大的偏心率，佩滕吉尔和戴斯测定的水星自转速率实际上是在预料之中的，这与先前盛行的观点相反，即该行星应该是“潮汐锁定”的，有一面始终朝向太阳。他们也推断，水星不是刚性不变的，他们暗示这其中的部分原因或许是其表面的高温造成的。但即使现在我们对水星也知之甚少。用来对水星进行研究的信使号于2004年发射，在三次飞掠过水星之后它将在2011年3月进入环绕水星的轨道。

太阳的潮汐摩擦作用对水星产生强烈的影响，并且可以预期在与太阳系年龄相比更短的时间内，水星自转速率已经在潮汐作用下从某个初始值减少到了现在的数值。太阳作用于行星的黏滞力矩正比于 $1/r^6$（r 是太阳和行星间的距离），对水星来说该系数大约是地球的300倍。位于圆轨道上的行星，其最终的状态就是类似月球相对于地球的同步绕转。水星绕太阳转动一圈需要88天，并且由于同步绕转，其恒星周期也应该是88天。但观测到的 59 ± 5 天的结果与该值明显不符(见前一篇报道)。

然而对于轨道偏心率较大的行星来说情况会不一样，并且同步绕转与轨道周期并不需要一致。由于系数 $1/r^6$ 的关系，近日点的潮汐力矩将超过其他时候的值，于是行星的角速度也将出现比平均轨道角速度大的值，但也没有近日点的轨道角速度大。对于水星，其偏心率是0.2，2π 乘以近日点轨道角速度的倒数是56.6天。因此预期的自转恒星周期一定是在56天和88天之间。

更精确的计算基于以下考虑，行星的最终角速度应该满足沿轨道的潮汐力矩的时间平均等于零。这时行星的自转就不会再变化了，除非是在更长的时标上，其他轨道根数受到了潮汐摩擦的影响，但这些影响在太阳系年龄的时标下是不太重要的。在这种条件下对角速度进行精确计算并不需要对行星的耗散特性进行定量描述，但是会涉及某些特定假设。必须假设潮汐相位滞后只是一个小角度，才能利用各种依赖幅值和频率的 Q 函数方法进行计算（$1/Q$ 是比耗散函数[1]）。如果假设 Q 不依赖

calculation with Q being dependent on amplitude and frequency in a variety of ways ($1/Q$ is the specific dissipation function[1]). If Q is assumed to be independent of amplitude and inversely proportional to frequency, then the condition will yield a period of 71 days. If Q is assumed independent of amplitude and of frequency the result is 65 days. Any additional effect of amplitude dependence would go in the sense of increasing the dissipation near perihelion where the amplitudes are greatest and therefore decreasing the period still further. It thus seems likely that Mercury is indeed in its final state of spin, and that its present rotation therefore reflects very accurately certain characteristics of the dissipation process.

The condition discussed here is based on the supposition that the solar torque exerted on the tidal bulge exceeds that exerted on any permanent deformation from axial symmetry. In the converse case a period of 88 days for the rotation would indeed result. This may imply that Mercury has not much permanent rigidity. The high surface temperature may be partly responsible for this. The solar system has thus provided us with an example of each of the two final states of rotation that tidal friction can bring about: the Moon, which has locked into the synchronous rotation, and Mercury, which has come to the rotation that is enforced in the absence of any permanent asymmetry of the body.

(**206**, 1240-1241; 1965)

S. J. Peale and T. Gold: Cornell-Sydney University Astronomy Center, Cornell University, Ithaca, New York.

Reference:

1. MacDonald, G. F. J., *Rev. Geophys.*, 2, No. 3 (1964).

于幅值并且与频率成反比，那么得到的周期是 71 天。如果假设 Q 不依赖于幅值和频率，结果是 65 天。任何其他幅值相关的效应都应该是增加近日点附近（那里的幅值最大）的耗散，并进一步减小自转周期。因此很有可能水星确实是处于它的最终自转状态，它现在的自转非常准确地反映了耗散过程的某些特征。

这里讨论的条件基于以下假设：太阳作用于潮汐隆起的力矩超过任何偏离轴对称的永久形变的效果。在相反的情况下，88 天的自转周期也确实存在。这也可能暗示了水星并不能永久保持刚性。它表面的高温可能是其中的部分原因。可见太阳系为我们分别提供了由潮汐摩擦导致的两个不同的最终转动状态：月球，已经锁定到同步绕转；水星，由于其本身缺少恒定的非对称性而处于强迫性的自转状态中。

（钱磊 翻译；肖伟科 审稿）

Time's Arrow and Entropy

K. Popper

Editor's Note

Physicists since the late nineteenth century had speculated over the links between time, thermodynamics and entropy. A related question, discussed by Erwin Schrödinger, is how life on Earth seems to produce ever-increasing complexity, and therefore lower entropy. Here the philosopher Karl Popper suggests that the mystery of increasing biological order may actually have more to do with the cooling of the planet than with its perpetual warming by the Sun. Popper argues that there does not appear to be any special link between the second law of thermodynamics and either the nature of time or biological processes on Earth. Physicist Ilya Prigogine, mentioned here, went on to propose a non-thermodynamic, quantum origin for the "arrow of time".

SEVERAL years ago[1] I suggested that we should distinguish between two essentially different ways in which energy can be degraded or dissipated: "Dissipation in the form of increasing disorder (entropy increase) is one of them, and dissipation by expansion without increase of disorder is the other. For an increase of disorder, walls of some kind are essential: a sufficiently thin gas expanding in a 'vessel without walls' (that is, the universe) does not increase its disorder." Reasons for this view were given in the place cited.

In order to explain this a little more precisely, I shall here introduce, following Prigogine[2], the term "system" to denote the (energy and material) "contents of a well-defined geometrical volume of macroscopic dimensions" (so that, for example, an organism enclosed by its skin, or our solar system as enclosed by a sphere round the Sun with a radius of 10^5 light seconds, would be a "system"); and I shall speak of the "exterior" of a system X as a region of space (leaving it open whether or not this is in its turn a geometrically well-defined "system") of which X forms a part.

Following Prigogine, I shall distinguish between (materially or at least energetically) "open" and "closed" systems. (An energetically closed system is called "isolated".) Moreover, I shall call a system X "essentially open" if it is part of a system Y such that all geometrically convex systems of which Y is a part are (at least energetically) open. (This definition makes it possible even for an isolated system to be essentially open.)

I further call X "essentially open towards a cooler exterior" if X is enclosed by some convex system Y such that: (*a*) all elements of any sequence Z_i of convex systems of which Y is a part are essentially open and of a lower average temperature than Y, and that (*b*)

时间之箭和熵

波普尔

编者按

从 19 世纪末期起，物理学家们便开始思索时间、热力学和熵之间的相互联系。埃尔温·薛定谔曾讨论过一个与此相关的问题，即地球上的生命是如何不断地增加其复杂性，从而使熵值降低的。本文中，哲学家卡尔·波普尔认为生物有序性逐渐增加的奥秘实际上更多地在于地球自身的冷却，而不是由于太阳给地球的持续加温。波普尔认为热力学第二定律无论是与时间的本质还是与地球上的生物过程似乎都不存在任何特别的联系。本文还提到了物理学家伊利亚·普里高津进一步提出的“时间之箭”的非热力学的量子起源。

几年前[1]我曾指出，我们应该区分两种完全不同的使能量降低或耗散的途径：“一种是以增加无序性（熵增加）的形式进行耗散，另一种是不增加无序性，通过膨胀产生的耗散。某种形式的壁的存在对于无序性的增加是必不可少的：足够稀薄的气体在一个‘没有器壁的容器’（即宇宙）中进行膨胀并不会增加其无序性。”在前述引文中已给出了此观点的理由。

为了对此进行更为精确的解释，在本文中我将引入普里高津[2]定义的术语“系统”来表示“在宏观维度内给定几何体积之中的内含物”（能量和物质）（因此，如皮肤包被的有机体，或环绕太阳的半径为 10^5 光秒的球面之内的太阳系都属于此“系统”）；我将系统 X 的“外界”说成是一个空间区域（让它开放，无论这样反过来会不会是一个具有明确几何意义的系统），系统 X 形成了其中的一部分。

按照普里高津的观点，我将（从物质或至少从能量的角度）区分“开放”系统和“封闭”系统。（所谓的“孤立系统”就是指一个能量封闭的系统。）此外，如果系统 X 是系统 Y 的一部分，我就称系统 X 是“基本开放的”，这样包含系统 Y 的所有在几何上凸出的系统（至少在能量上）是开放的。（这个定义甚至使得一个孤立系统有可能是基本开放的。）

另外，如果系统 X 被某些凸出系统 Y 所包围并满足以下条件：(a) 包含 Y 的凸出系统的任意序列 Z_i 的所有元素都是基本开放的，并且它们的平均温度比系统 Y 的

for every such system Z_i there is a system Z_j which encloses Z_i and which is not of a higher average temperature than Z_i.

The terminology here introduced makes it possible to clarify a number of points in connexion with the second law of thermodynamics which seem in urgent need of clarification.

Again following Prigogine[3], we can split the change of entropy dS_X in any system X into two parts: dS_{Xe}, or the flow of entropy due to interaction with the exterior of X, and dS_{Xi}, the contribution to the change of entropy due to changes inside the system X. We have, of course:

$$dS_X = dS_{Xe} + dS_{Xi} \tag{1}$$

and we can express the second law by:

$$dS_{Xi} \geqslant 0 \tag{2}$$

For an energetically closed (or "isolated") system X, for which by definition $dS_{Xe} = 0$, expression (2) formulates the classical statement that entropy never decreases. But if X is open towards a cooler exterior:

$$dS_{Xe} < 0 \tag{3}$$

holds, and the question whether its total entropy increases or decreases depends, of course, on both its entropy production dS_{Xi} and its entropy loss dS_{Xe}.

The fact that entropy can decrease in an open system X does not, of course, conflict with the second law as given by expression (2). But the second law is often formulated in a different way; for example, it is said that "if we ... expand our system to include all the energy exchange, it would be found that in the larger system the entropy had increased. For example, to measure the entropy change taking place in living organisms as a whole, it would be necessary to include in our system the Sun and some additional portion of the universe, as well as the Earth itself"[4]. Thus it is suggested that for sufficiently large systems X of our universe, $dS_X \geqslant 0$, so that the entropy always increases.

Yet, so far as our knowledge of the Universe goes, the precise opposite appears to be the case. With very few and short-lived exceptions, the entropy in almost all known regions (of sufficient size) of our universe either remains constant or decreases, although energy is dissipated (by escaping from the system in question). This is so, at any rate, if we assume that the law of conservation of energy is valid; and it is also so if we assume the "steady state" theory of the expanding universe. (It is not so on the assumption of a finite and non-expanding universe with non-zero energy density.)

要低；(*b*) 对于每一个这样的系统 Z_i，都有一个包含 Z_i 在内的且温度不比 Z_i 高的系统 Z_j 存在，那么我称系统 X "对更冷的外界基本开放"。

本文中引入的术语有可能阐明与热力学第二定律有关的许多观点，该定律似乎亟待阐明。

再次按照普里高津的观点[3]，我们可将任何系统 X 熵值的变化 dS_X 分成两部分：由于与系统 X 的外界相互作用引起的熵的流动 dS_{Xe}，以及由于系统 X 内部的变化引起的熵的变化 dS_{Xi}。由此，我们可得：

$$dS_X = dS_{Xe} + dS_{Xi} \tag{1}$$

我们可用下式表示第二定律：

$$dS_{Xi} \geqslant 0 \tag{2}$$

对于能量封闭的 (或"孤立的") 系统 X，我们通过定义可知 $dS_{Xe} = 0$，式 (2) 变成了经典表述：熵永不减少。但是，如果系统 X 对更冷的外界开放，则有：

$$dS_{Xe} < 0 \tag{3}$$

那么总熵是增加还是减少便自然取决于增加的熵 dS_{Xi} 和减少的熵 dS_{Xe} 分别有多少。

事实上，开放系统 X 中熵的减少与式 (2) 所表述的第二定律并不相矛盾，但第二定律通常用另一种方式来表述。例如，它可表述为"如果我们……扩展我们的系统至其包含所有的能量交换，就会发现在更大的系统中熵增加了。又如，要测量整个生命有机体发生的熵变化时，在这个系统中有必要包含太阳以及宇宙某些其他的部分，还有地球自身"[4]。因此，如果 X 是宇宙中足够大的系统，则 $dS_X \geqslant 0$，那么熵总是增加的。

然而，就我们对宇宙的认知不断地变化而言，完全相反的情况似乎也存在。除了极少的短暂的例外，宇宙中几乎所有已知（足够大的）地区的熵都是保持不变或减少的，虽然能量（从当前系统中逃逸出）耗散了。如果我们假设能量守恒定律成立，那么无论怎样都会有上述结论；如果我们假设膨胀宇宙的"稳态"理论也成立，那么上述结论仍然成立。（但是如果假设具有非零能量密度的宇宙是有限的和非膨胀的，那上述结论则不成立。）

In order to see this, all that is needed is to be clear about the empirical fact that in our universe we know only essentially open systems, and only systems *X* which, so far as they produce entropy at all, are essentially open towards a cooler exterior. (This is true even of all so-called "closed" or "isolated" systems.) But for all such systems, one of the following cases must hold: (*a*) they are (practically) stationary, like the solar system and most stars known to us, in which case their entropy production (practically) equals their entropy loss, at least temporarily; or (*b*) they are losing temperature, and thereby entropy; or (*c*) they are producing more entropy than they lose, in which case they are in process of getting hotter, a process which, whether energy conservation is assumed or the steady state theory, can be only a comparatively rare and short-lived temporary process. (Even if the system in question should be one that collects matter from its environment until its gravitational field becomes so strong as to encapsulate and separate off the system from the rest of the universe, it would thereby presumably become stationary.) All we know about the universe points to (*a*) and (*b*) as being by far the most frequent and important cases: in almost all sufficiently large systems known to us, entropy production seems to be equalled, or even exceeded, by entropy loss through heat radiation.

This may be explained by the conjecture that every entropy-producing region is open towards some large (perhaps infinite) sinks of energy—regions the energy capacity or heat capacity of which, at least for heat in the form of radiation, is infinite (or approximately so for all practical purposes). The existence of such sinks seems to be strongly indicated by the darkness of the night sky. (We might represent this conjecture by the model of an infinite universe with zero energy density; or by that of an energy-conserving expanding—and therefore cooling and entropy-destroying—universe which tends towards zero energy density; of by that of an expanding steady-state universe with constant temperature, and entropy production equalled by entropy escape.)

So there do not seem to be theoretical or empirical reasons to attribute to expression (2) any cosmic significance or to connect "time's arrow" with that expression; especially since the equality sign in expression (2) may hold, for almost all cosmical regions (and especially for regions empty of matter). Moreover, we have good reason to interpret expression (2) as a statistical law; while the "arrow" of time, or the "flow" of time, does not seem to be of a stochastic character: nothing suggests that it is subject to statistical fluctuation, or connected with a law of large numbers.

As for the evolution of life, this seems to be connected, if at all, with a cooling rather than a heating process on Earth (or perhaps with periodic temperature fluctuations); that is, with increasing order and decreasing entropy. Yet it does not seem that "feeding on neg-entropy" has much to do with the preservation of life, as has been suggested, for example, by Schroedinger[5]. For during the incubation of birds' eggs entropy rather than neg-entropy is supplied to them, though they are in a period of increasing organization; and while in an organism dying of heat or of fever entropy may increase, if it dies of cold—say, by deep-freezing—its entropy certainly decreases.

(**207**, 233-234; 1965)

为了证明这一点，需要弄清这样一个经验事实，即在我们的宇宙中，我们只知道基本开放的系统，只知道系统 X（只要它们还能产生熵）对更冷的外界基本开放。（即使对于所谓的“封闭的”或“孤立的”系统也是成立的。）但对上述所有的系统，下列情况之一必须成立：(*a*) 它们（实际上）是定态的，像太阳系和大多数我们已知的恒星，在这种情况下，至少暂时它们的熵产生（实际上）等于其熵减少；或者 (*b*) 它们的温度正在降低，因此熵在减少；或者 (*c*) 它们正在增加的熵大于其减少的熵，在这种情况下，它们处于变热的过程中，无论我们假定能量是守恒的抑或是稳态理论，这个过程只能是一个比较罕见和短暂的瞬间过程。（尽管讨论的系统应该从外界环境中收集物质直到引力场增强到可以容纳这些物质并将系统和外部的宇宙分割开来，但是仍然可以假定这个系统是定态的。）我们对宇宙的所知显示出 (*a*) 和 (*b*) 是迄今为止最常见和最重要的两种情况：在几乎所有足够大的已知系统中，通过热辐射减少的熵可以抵消甚至超过产生的熵。

这可以用下述推测来解释，即每一个正在产生熵的区域都是在向某些大的（也许是无限大的）能量库开放的——它们的能量容量或热容量（至少对辐射形式的热容量）是无限的（或实际上就是近似于无限）。夜晚天空的黑暗似乎强有力地表明这些能量库的存在。（我们可以用能量密度为零的无限宇宙模型来表达这种推测；或用能量守恒的膨胀宇宙模型——其温度和熵都在减少——即用一种能量密度趋于零的宇宙模型表达这种推测；抑或用具有恒定温度的、熵的产生与熵的逃逸相等的膨胀稳态宇宙模型来表达这种推测。）

因此本文似乎并没有理论依据或经验依据赋予式 (2) 任何宇宙的意义，或把“时间之箭”同其联系起来；尤其因为式 (2) 的等号对几乎所有的宇宙区域（特别是对没有物质的真空）都能成立。此外，我们有很好的理由可以将式 (2) 解释为一种统计学定律；而时间之“箭”或者时间之“流”似乎并不具有随机的特性：没有证据说明它受统计性涨落支配或和大数定律相关。

至于生物进化，似乎是（如果有的话）与地球上的冷却过程而不是与升温过程有联系（或者可能同周期性的温度涨落相联系）；也就是说，其与有序性增加和熵减少的过程有联系。然而，薛定谔[5]提出似乎没有显示生命的维系与“摄入负熵”有很多联系。在鸟蛋孵化期间，尽管它们处于有机体增加的时期，但它们摄入的是正熵而不是负熵；在死于发热或高烧的有机体中熵可能增加，如果死于寒冷——比如深度冷冻——它们的熵肯定要减少。

（沈乃澂 翻译；张元仲 审稿）

Karl Popper: University of London.

References:

1. Popper, K. R., *Nature*, **178**, 381 (1956); 177, 538 (1956); **179**, 1296 (1957); **181**, 402 (1958); *Brit. J. Phil. Sci.*, **8**, 151 (1957).

2. Prigogine, I., *Introduction to Thermodynamics of Irreversible Processes*, 3 (1955).

3. Prigogine, I., *Introduction to Thermodynamics of Irreversible Processes*, 16 (1955).

4. Blum, Harold F., *Time's Arrow and Evolution*, 15 (1935). (Similar statements are to be found, for example, on pages 16, 24, 33, 201.) Compare also Planck, M., *A Survey of Physics*, 17, 27 (1925).

5. Schroedinger, E., *What is Life?* 72 (1944).

Experimental Evidence of a Twinkling Layer in the Earth's Atmosphere

C. C. Hudson

Editor's Note

The idea that stars in the sky twinkle when observed with the human eye is commonly remarked upon, but the reasons for this behaviour are far from clear. This paper from Craig C. Hudson at the Sandia Corporation (a US defence research organization) identifies a twinkling layer in the Earth's atmosphere that lies at the junction of the troposphere (the lower atmosphere) and the stratosphere (between about 10 and 50 km above the Earth's surface).

THE scintillation of stars is that part of astronomical seeing which deals with intensity fluctuations of the image, more commonly called twinkling. A large part of twinkling occurs at frequencies too high to be observable to the human eye, that is, greater than 15 c/s. For many years the cause has been thought to reside in the atmosphere, in the form of fluctuations in the index of refraction caused by air turbulence.

Other optical effects, such as blurring and dancing of the image, often accompany twinkling, but can be distinguished from it both by the method of observation and by layer of origin in the atmosphere.

Reviews of the various experiments and theories of astronomical seeing (especially twinkling) are included in Tatarski's well-known monograph[1], in the report by Keller *et al.*[2], and in the report by Wimbush[3]. The present discussion will be limited to twinkling.

The observational properties of star twinkling have been reported by many[4-7]. It is least in the zenith direction and has the broadest frequency spectrum there. For low angles of observation, the amplitude increases but the high frequency end of the spectrum fades away. The spectrum near zenith is approximately flat below 100 c/s but falls off rapidly at higher frequencies. Twinkling is enhanced by the use of a small aperture, and tends to a minimum for apertures greater than 20 in. diameter. For small apertures, the modulation (fluctuation relative to mean light level) can exceed 100 percent even at the zenith, while for large apertures 10-20 percent is more typical. Twinkling also depends on the source size; the larger planets, for example, showing very little effect. Finally, twinkling depends on meteorological conditions; in particular, there is correlation between the intensity of the effect and the speed of winds above 20,000 ft.

Contemporary theories of twinkling, according to Keller[2], can be classified into three

地球大气闪烁层存在的实验证据

赫德森

编者按

当人们用肉眼观察星空时，通常都会注意到天空中的恒星在闪烁，但是这种现象产生的原因人们却很不清楚。本文的作者，即桑迪亚公司（美国的一个防卫研究组织）的克雷格·赫德森指出，在地球大气的对流层（低层大气）和平流层（在地球表面上空约 10 千米 ~50 千米）的连接处，存在一个闪烁层。

恒星的闪光是指星像视宁度中描述图像强度起伏的那一部分，更为普遍的叫法是闪烁。大部分闪烁频率太高，即大于 15 周 / 秒，以至于人类的肉眼无法观察到。多年来，人们一直认为恒星的闪烁是由于大气扰动致使折射率发生改变造成的。

通常，伴随着闪烁会产生一些其他的光学效应，如图像的模糊与跳动，但我们可以通过观测的方法以及通过大气中的气层将其与闪烁区别开来。

在塔塔尔斯基著名的专著中[1]、凯勒等人的报告中[2]，以及温布什的报告中[3]都可以找到关于星像视宁度（特别是闪烁）的各种实验和理论综述。现在，我们的讨论仅限于闪烁。

许多文章[4-7]都报道了可被观察到的恒星闪烁的特性。其在天顶方向时幅度最小且频谱最宽。当观察角度较低时，幅度增加但频谱的高频端逐渐消失。在天顶附近，频谱低于 100 周 / 秒时近于平直，但在较高频处很快下降。用小孔径观察时闪烁增强，而用直径大于 20 英寸的孔径观察时闪烁趋于最小值。对于小孔径，在天顶的调幅（相对于平均光强级的变化）可以超过 100%。而对于大孔径，其调幅更典型的是 10%~20%。闪烁也与光源的大小有关，例如较大的行星，闪烁效应很小。最后，闪烁还依赖于气象条件，尤其是闪烁的强度与 2 万英尺以上的风速有关。

根据凯勒[2]的看法，现今的闪烁理论可以分成三类：(*a*) 闪烁是由离观察者不

groups: (*a*) those governed by the refraction of light by turbulent elements of large size not too far from the observer (also contributing to blurring and dancing); (*b*) those governed by the diffraction of light with the zeroth order predominating (thin layer); and (*c*) those governed by the diffraction of light with the higher orders predominating (thick layer). Using a theory of type (*a*), Chandrasekhar[8] deduced that twinkling could be explained on the basis of a hypothetical layer 100 m thick, of homogeneous, isotropic turbulence at 4 km altitude. Keller suggests a thinner layer at a higher altitude. Wimbush argues against a discrete layer, citing evidence of several other workers in favour of a continuous distribution of turbulence.

Keller[2], using Protheroe's autocorrelation data[9], made a parameter study on the basis of the theory of scintillation[10,11] which is of interest in what follows. The scale of turbulence is L_m; Δz is the layer thickness; and $\delta^2 n$ is the mean square fluctuation of the index of refraction. By assuming no pressure fluctuations, $\delta^2 n$ may be transformed into the mean square temperature fluctuation $\delta^2 T$. Estimates of L_m range over factors of two while Δz and $\delta^2 T$ are uncertain by orders of magnitude. The primary variables in the theory of scintillation, therefore, are the thickness of the turbulent layer and the intensity of its turbulence. Keller's parameter study is partially reproduced in Table 1. In each case, the experimental data are satisfied by a different set of parameters (assuming isotropic turbulence with a Gaussian distribution of element sizes).

Table 1

Parameters	March 1, 1954			March 16, 1954	
Altitude z (km)	6.1	9.2	15.3	9.2	15.3
L_m (cm)	6.7	5.9	5.3	6.7	6.7
Thickness Δz (km), $(\delta^2 T)^{1/2} = 0.1\,^\circ C$	0.061	0.043	0.14	0.021	0.037
Thickness Δz (km), $(\delta^2 T)^{1/2} = 0.01\,^\circ C$	6.1	4.3	14	2.1	3.7

Keller rejected the second set of thicknesses on the grounds that adiabatic mixing through such a thick layer would produce r.m.s. temperature fluctuations greatly in excess of 0.01 °C.

Light beacons suspended from balloons which drifted with the wind have been used to study scintillation by Gardiner *et al.*[12] and Mikesell[6]. The twinkling due to the lights was compared with that due to nearby stars. The amplitude twinkling in the range 1-10 c/s of the beacons was 50-75 percent less than that of stars, and in the range 147-153 c/s was more than a factor of two less than that of the stars.

They also studied scintillation as a function of the correlation of light pulses due to double stars. In the frequency range 1-10 c/s, the twinkling appeared to arise from altitudes of 100,000 ft. or higher. For higher frequencies, about 150 c/s, the twinkling appeared to be caused near 30,000 ft. To account for the high-altitude low-frequency variations, they suggest that there exist large density variations in the atmosphere at these levels, essentially

太远的大尺度扰动因素所引起的光的折射（它也引起模糊和跳动）支配的。(*b*) 闪烁主要是由光的零级衍射（薄层）支配的。(*c*) 闪烁主要是由光的高级衍射（厚层）支配的。根据理论 (*a*)，钱德拉塞卡 [8] 推断，可以以一个位于海拔 4 千米、100 米厚、均匀的、各向同性的假想扰动层为基础来解释闪烁。凯勒则建议用一个海拔更高但厚度较薄的层。温布什则引用了一些其他人支持的扰动是连续分布的证据，用以反对上述不连续层的学说。

凯勒 [2] 用普罗瑟罗的自相关数据 [9]，在闪光学说 [10,11] 的基础上作了参数化的研究，而闪光学说在后文中是非常有用的。扰动尺度为 L_m，Δz 为层的厚度，$\delta^2 n$ 为折射率的均方差。假如气压没有变化，$\delta^2 n$ 可以转变为温度的均方差 $\delta^2 T$，用 Δz 和 $\delta^2 T$ ☒个量级不确定的因子来估计 L_m 的范围。因此，在闪光学说中，主要的变量是扰动层的厚度与扰动强度。凯勒参数研究的部分数据列在表 1 中，每个案例的实验数据对应于不同的参数组（假设扰动各向同性且元素的大小符合高斯分布）。

表 1

参数	1954 年 3 月 1 日			1954 年 3 月 16 日	
海拔 z（千米）	6.1	9.2	15.3	9.2	15.3
L_m（厘米）	6.7	5.9	5.3	6.7	6.7
厚度 Δz（千米），$(\delta^2 T)^{1/2}$ =0.1℃	0.061	0.043	0.14	0.021	0.037
厚度 Δz（千米），$(\delta^2 T)^{1/2}$ =0.01℃	6.1	4.3	14	2.1	3.7

凯勒否定了第二组厚度值，因为在这样一个厚度层内，绝热混合过程将产生大大超过 0.01℃的均方根温度变化。

加德纳等 [12] 与米克塞尔 [6] 用在随风飘浮的气球下所悬挂的信标灯来研究闪光。将灯光的闪烁与附近恒星的闪烁作对比。在 1 周 / 秒 ~10 周 / 秒频率范围内信标灯的闪烁幅度比恒星的小 50%~75%，而在 147 周 / 秒 ~153 周 / 秒频率范围内其闪烁幅度则比恒星的要小 50% 以上。

他们也将闪光作为一个双星光脉冲的相关函数来研究。在 1 周 / 秒 ~10 周 / 秒频率范围内闪烁出现在海拔为 10 万英尺或更高的地方。而在更高的频率，大约 150 周 / 秒，闪烁则出现在 3 万英尺附近。为了解释这种高海拔低频率的变化，他们提出：这些高度上的大气密度变化较大，大气相对于地球而言基本上是静止的，随着地球自转，

at rest relative to the Earth, which are swept through the line of sight to the star by the Earth's rotation.

Some new experiments are now being made which may shed additional light on the structure of the atmosphere and the causes of stellar twinkling. The first of these is reported here.

The idea of the experiment was to allow a point source light beacon to fall through the twinkling region, observing it continuously with a telescope fitted with a recording photometer. The beacon was carried to 65,000 ft. as the pay-load of a 6-in. *Apache* rocket motor. To restrain the free fall somewhat, to keep the light on the bottom of the body, and to allow the beacon to sink more nearly vertically, a small parachute was deployed which caused the sink rate to be about 300 ft./sec at 30,000 ft. altitude. A 16-in. tracking telescope fitted with an RCA "7265" photomultiplier cooled with carbon dioxide was used to observe scintillations. No filters were used, so white light was observed.

The experiments were performed at the U.S. Atomic Energy Commission's rocket range at Tonopah, Nevada, at an elevation of 5,300 ft. A strong cold wind was blowing on the night of December 11, 1963, the air was dry, and visibility was nearly unlimited although a small amount of fine powder snow was being blown around at low levels. On March 10, 1964, the air was again clear, cold and dry, but the wind was calm, a front having passed the night before. Meteorological data were taken by radiosonde as often as practicable (every 2-3 h). Position of the beacon was obtained both by radar and by an optical triangulation system. Altitude accuracy is about ± 200 ft. Altitude accuracy of the radiosonde is believed to be no worse than ±300 ft.

The scintillations were recorded on magnetic tape after being telemetered from the remote telescope site. The telemetry used a 70-kc/s channel on a 220-mc carrier. The frequency response of the system was limited by the telemetry to the range DC to 10 kc. The tapes were then played back to give (*a*) a measure of the twinkling amplitude as a function of time and (*b*) a measure of the frequency spectrum.

In addition to observations of the falling beacon, scintillation measurements were also made on ground lights at various distances, on a number of stars and planets, and on the satellite *Echo I*. The purpose of these measurements was mainly to check and calibrate an untried system, but also to make available a more complete set of twinkle measurements.

The data from the beacons are shown in Fig. 1 in the form of percentage modulation of the mean light intensity. The values are weighted in favour of frequencies between 10 and 100 c/s. A sample of the frequency spectrum of the twinkling of the beacon above the layer and below the layer is shown in Fig. 2.

观察恒星的视线会扫过这些密度变化的区域。

目前正在进行一些新的实验，这些实验可能会更清楚地揭示大气的结构和恒星闪烁的原因，这里给出其中第一个实验的情况。

实验思路是让一个点光源的信标灯下落并通过闪烁区，用安装了记录用光度计的望远镜对其进行持续观测。将信标灯作为一个 6 英寸大小的“阿帕奇”火箭发动机的载荷发射到 6.5 万英尺的高空。为了在一定程度上约束自由下落使灯保持在底部并尽量垂直地下降，将会展开一个小的降落伞，使下降速度在 3 万英尺海拔处约为 300 英尺 / 秒。用来观测闪光的设备是一个 16 英寸跟踪望远镜，其上安装了使用二氧化碳冷却的 RCA“7265”光电倍增管。没有用滤光器，所以观察到的是白光。

这次实验在位于内华达州托诺帕的美国原子能委员会的火箭发射场进行，海拔为 5,300 英尺。1963 年 12 月 11 日晚，空气中刮着强冷风，虽然低空飘着少许小雪，但是空气干燥，能见度也很好。同样，在 1964 年 3 月 10 日，这一天空气清爽，干冷无风，其前夜有锋面经过。用无线电探空仪尽可能频繁地获取气象资料（每 2 小时 ~ 3 小时）。用雷达和一个光学三角测量系统测得灯的位置，海拔精度约为 ±200 英尺。无线电探空仪的高度精度一般认为要好于 ±300 英尺。

用远程望远镜遥测闪光后，闪光记录在磁带上。实验中，在 220 毫周载波上，用 70 千周 / 秒的频道进行遥测。遥测中，系统频率响应被限制在直波至 10 千周的范围内。而后回放磁带，给出（*a*）一个作为时间函数的闪烁振幅值和（*b*）频谱值。

除了观测下落的信标灯，也测量了各种距离下地面灯的闪光、许多恒星和行星的闪光以及 *Echo I* 卫星的闪光。测量这些的目的，主要是检验和校准未经实验的系统，也为了获得更完善的闪烁测量结果。

图 1 是信标灯平均光强的调制百分率数据。频率在 10 周 / 秒 ~100 周 / 秒之间的数值较好。图 2 是信标灯在闪烁层以上和以下的闪烁频谱的一个样本。

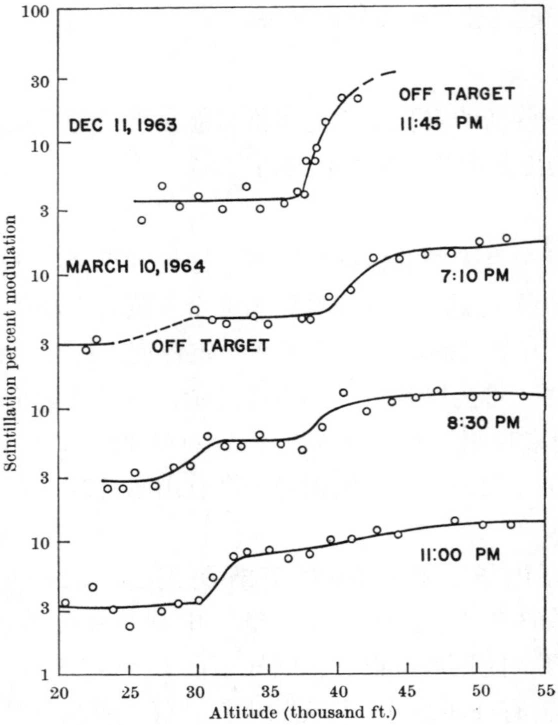

Fig. 1. Evidence of twinkling layer. Scatter in the data is partially due to hand reduction

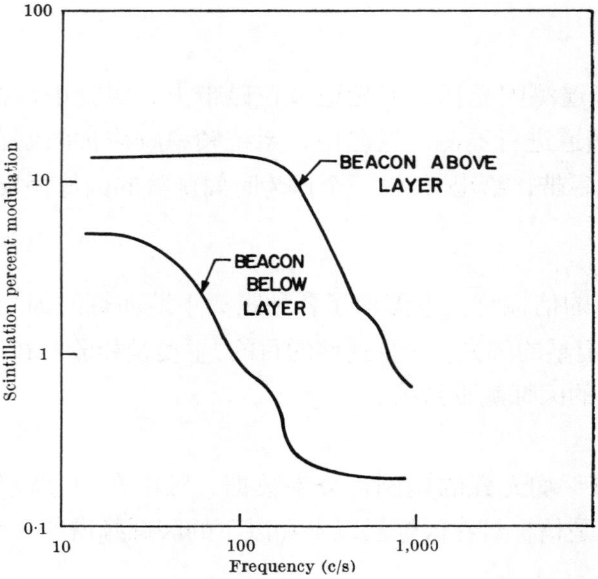

Fig. 2. Frequency spectrum of twinkling signals. System capability and data actually recorded were good to 10,000 c/s, but reduction technique was not reliable above 1,000 c/s

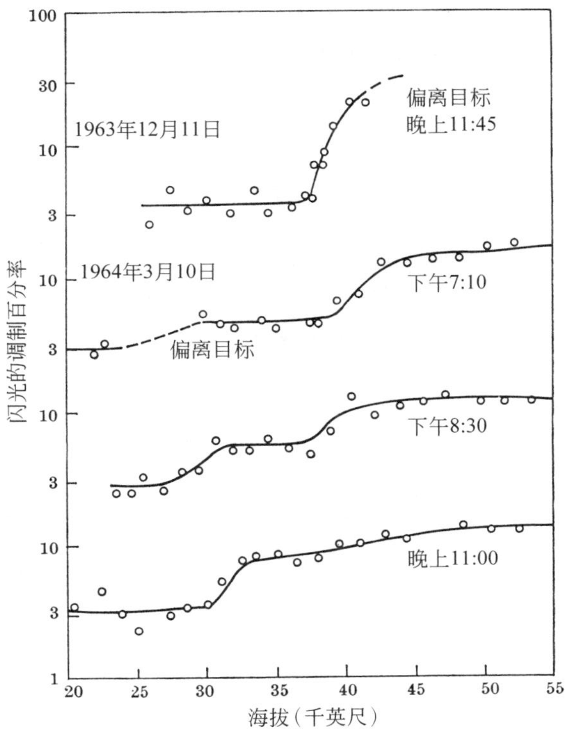

图 1. 闪烁层资料，数据的离散性部分是由于作了人工处理。

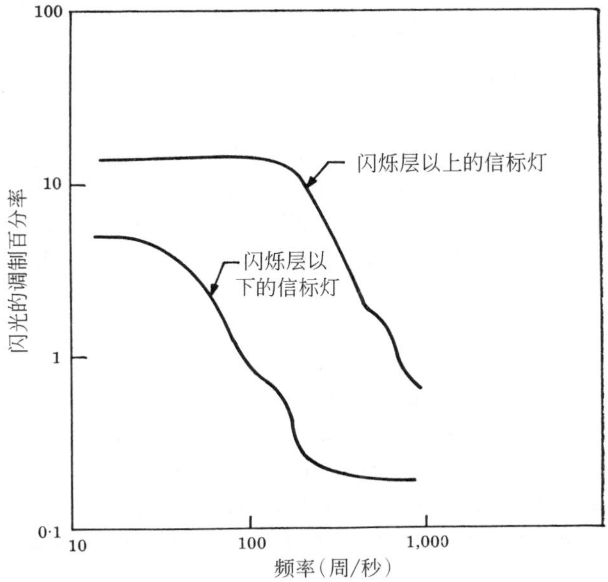

图 2. 闪烁信号的频谱。系统性能和实际记录的数据在频率直到 10,000 周 / 秒时都表现良好，但是，下降技术在频率超过 1,000 周 / 秒时则是不可靠的。

The meteorological data are shown in Fig. 3. Data points are about 400 ft. apart. A tentative assignment of the tropopause has been made. The horizontal bars indicate approximately the twinkling layers.

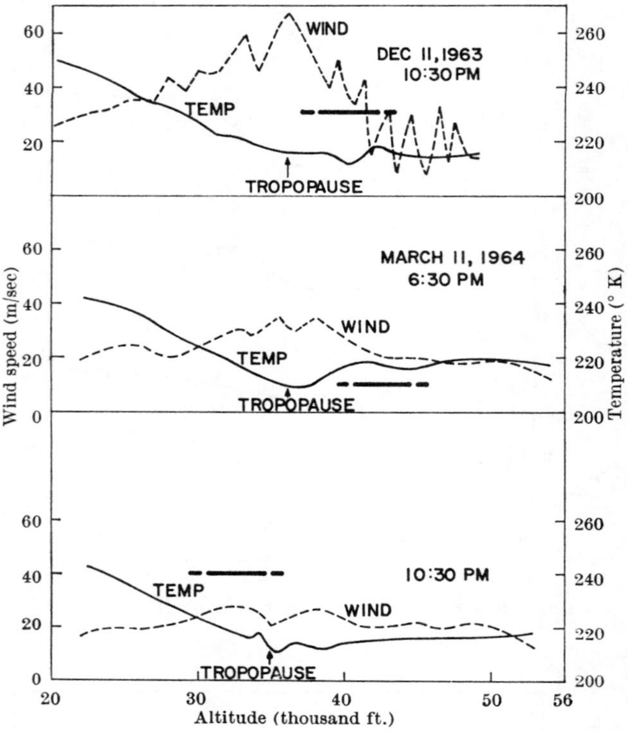

Fig. 3. Meteorological conditions. Heavy bars indicate position of principal twinkle layers

Referring to Table 1, the set of parameters which best corresponds to the present measurements comprises those of the altitude 9.2 km which imply r.m.s. temperature fluctuations of the order of 0.01 °C, appreciably smaller than the estimates typically seen. Of course, if the observed layer actually consists of several thin layers, the temperature fluctuations need not be so small.

From Fig. 3 one gets the impression that the twinkling layer is not associated either with the wind speed structure or with the tropopause; but since it seems typically to occur in that neighbourhood, a re-check of the wind vectors was made to see if strong shears or wind gradients could be found in the layer; but the shears in those regions were no greater than in nearby regions where a change in twinkling was not observed. The U.S. Weather Bureau maps for the days in question showed no jet stream in the near vicinity.

图 3 是每隔大约 400 英尺的气象数据，图中尝试确定了对流层顶，而水平线段则指示了闪烁层的大概位置。

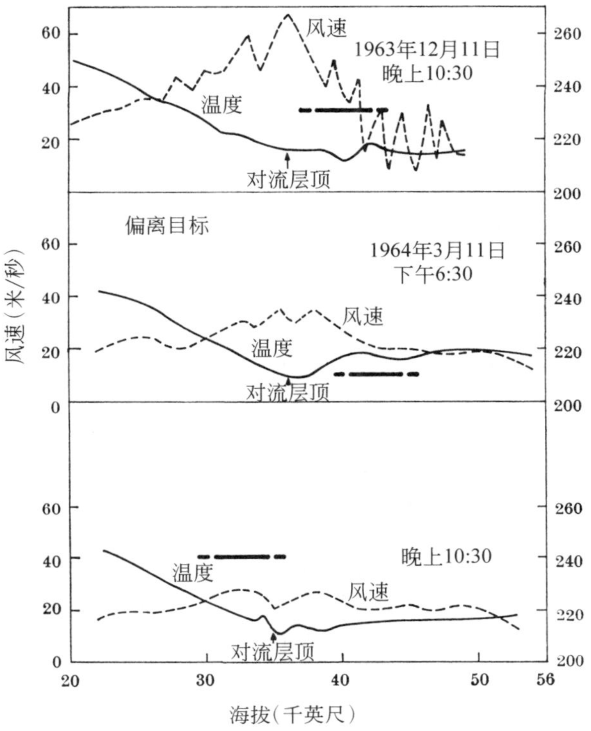

图 3. 气象条件，粗线段是主要的闪烁层的位置。

表 1 中和目前的测量最为一致的参数组是海拔为 9.2 千米的那些案例，这些案例显示出均方根温度变化处于 0.01℃的量级，略小于通常所见的估计值。当然，假如所观测的层实际上是由几个薄层组成，其温度变化就不需要那样小。

从图 3 可以看出，闪烁层似乎既不与风速结构相关，也不与对流层顶相关。但是，由于在邻近区域这种情况似乎经常发生，因此再次检查了风矢量以确定是否能在闪烁层内找到强的切变或强的风速梯度；然而，闪烁层的风向切变并不比邻近区域更大，在该区域没有观测到闪烁的变化。在美国气象局我们提到的那几天的天气图上，显示闪烁层附近并没有急流。

The peak intensity of scintillation on December 11 was probably not more than 30 percent modulation, and on March 10 scarcely more than 15 percent modulation. Unfortunately, no measurements were made on stars at the zenith, but for Capella (30° from the zenith on December 11) and Pollux (10° on March 10) the approximate intensity can be found by making a $\sec^3\varphi$ correction. The values obtained in this way were 33 percent (December 11) and 18 percent (March 10). These data indicate that only a small fraction of the total scintillation above 10 c/s occurs above the measured twinkle zone.

By the experiments already performed, the existence of a twinkle layer, long suspected, has been confirmed. The height of the layer corresponds roughly to the tropopause, although no unique relationship seems to exist between the layer and either the tropopause or wind structures. In terms of Keller's theory of twinkling, the layer thickness corresponds to temperature fluctuations of the order of 0.01°C, somewhat smaller than has been conjectured. In the higher frequency portion of the spectrum (above 10 c/s), it seems that about 80 percent of the total twinkling occurs in this layer, about 10 percent below it , and 10 percent above.

A second experiment now in progress will attempt to measure temperature fluctuations directly and to relate them to the observed twinkle layer. The mean square temperature fluctuation $\delta^2 T$ will be determined at the frequency that seems to be most prominent, and this frequency (corrected for the rocket's motion) will also establish the scale of turbulence. As a precaution, microphones will also be used to determine the level of pressure fluctuations, and the instruments are so mounted that correlations between pressure and temperature fluctuations can be made.

This work was supported by the United States Atomic Energy Commission.

(**207**, 247-249; 1965)

Craig C. Hudson: Sandia Corporation, Sandia Base, Albuquerque, New Mexico.

References:

1. Tatarski, V. I., *Wave Propagation in a Turbulent Medium* (McGraw-Hill, 1961).
2. Keller, G., Protheroe, W. M., Barnhart, P. E., and Galli, J., *Perkins Reprint, No.* 39 (1956).
3. Wimbush, M. H., *Optical Astronomical Seeing—A Review*, University of Hawaii, *UH*-2291-*SR*-1 (1961).
4. Ellison, T. H., and Seddon, H., *Mon. Not. Roy. Astro. Soc. London*, **112**, 73 (1952).
5. Mikesell, A. H., Hoag, A. A., and Hall, J. S., *J. Opt. Soc. Amer.*, **41**, 689 (1951).
6. Mikesell, A. H., *Publ. U.S. Nav. Obs. Washington*, second series **17**, 139 (1955).
7. Protheroe, W. M., *Science*, **134**, 1593 (1961).
8. Chandrasekhar, S., *Mon. Not. Roy. Astro. Soc.*, **112**, 475 (1952).
9. Protheroe, W. M., *J. Opt. Soc. Amer.*, **45**, 851 (1955).
10. Keller, G., *Astron. J.*, **58**, 113 (1953).
11. Von Isacker, J., *Inst. Roy. Meteor. de Belgique*, B, No. 8 (1953).
12. Gardiner, A. J., Gifford, jun., F., Mitchell, R. I., Gidas, H. L., Johnson, H. L., and Wilson, A. G., *Optical Studies of Atmospheric Turbulence, AFCRC-TR*-56-261, Final Report (1956).

12 月 11 日闪光强度的峰值调幅可能不超过 30%，而 3 月 10 日的几乎不超过 15%，遗憾的是没有测量到天顶的恒星，但是对于五车二（12 月 11 日离天顶 30°）和北河三（3 月 10 日离天顶 10°），其近似强度可通过 $\sec^3\varphi$ 修正而找到。用该方法得到的闪光强度的峰值调幅值在 12 月 11 日为 33%，3 月 10 日为 18%。这些数据说明，总闪光中只有一小部分超过 10 周 / 秒的闪光发生在被测量的闪烁带之上。

根据已有的实验，长期以来受到质疑的闪烁层的存在得到了确认。虽然闪烁层与对流层顶或风结构之间似乎都没有特别的联系，但是闪烁层的高度大致在对流层顶附近。用凯勒的闪烁学说定义，该层的厚度相应的温度变化应在 0.01℃这个数量级上，略小于推测值。在较高频谱部分（大于 10 周 / 秒），总闪烁中约 80% 似乎都发生在这一层，10% 发生在这一层之下，10% 发生在这一层之上。

现在正在进行的第二个实验将试图直接测量温度的变化，并将其与观测到的闪烁层相联系。我们将确定最为突出的频率下的温度变化的均方差 $\delta^2 T$，这个频率（根据火箭运行而进行修正）也将确立扰动的尺度。为防万一，也将采用扩音器来确定波动水平，并安装仪器来观测气压与温度波动间的关系。

这项工作得到了美国原子能委员会的支持。

（蔡则怡 翻译；沈志侠 审稿）

Opening Electrical Contact: Boiling Metal or High-Density Plasma?

F. Llewellyn Jones and M. J. Price

Editor's Note

The opening of an electrical contact may not appear to hide rich physics. Yet physicist Frank Llewellyn Jones and colleagues here report that the problem is more complex than usually thought. As a closed contact begins to open, the current flowing through it must follow an ever more constricted path. This will necessarily cause great heating, and perhaps even boiling of the metal. Indeed, their simple calculations suggest that small volumes of metal of the order of 10^{-12} cm^3 should be lost upon each opening, eventually damaging the contact. The researchers also show a series of high-speed photographs documenting the formation of tiny bridges of metal between contacts, which are key to understanding the process.

THE processes occurring at the opening of a low-voltage (~4 V) electrical contact have considerable fundamental physical interest as well as having practical importance in the field of electronic and communication engineering. It is well known[1] that, starting with the electrodes closely pressed together in the fully closed position, the opening process leads to a constriction of the current stream lines, which can produce intense local heating and melting of the penultimate microscopic region of contact. The maximum temperature in the contact is related to the potential difference by the ψ, θ theorem:

$$\psi = \left[2 \int_{\theta}^{\theta m} \frac{\lambda}{\kappa} \, d\theta \right]^{1/2} \tag{1}$$

where ψ = a generalized potential equal to the electrical potential in the absence of thermo-electric effects, θ = temperature, λ = thermal conductivity and κ = electrical conductivity. Thus, on gradual separation of the electrodes the constriction resistance increases and the temperature rises up to and past the melting-point of the metal. On continuing the withdrawal the molten volume thus increases and gets drawn out into a microscopic bridge of molten metal joining the solid electrodes; the contacts finally separate and the circuit opens only when this bridge is broken. The rupture process, however, can be very complicated and lead to transfer of metal from one electrode to the other, a process which, when continually repeated, can lead to the "pip" and "crater" formation which renders the contacts useless after some time. There is evidence[1,2] to show that the matter transferred per operation (~10^{-12} cm^3 in a 5-amp circuit) is related to the size of the molten metal bridge (width ~10^{-4} cm/amp), so that the stability, growth and final rupture of the bridge are a matter of importance, not only from practical

断电接触：沸腾的金属还是高密度等离子体？

卢埃林－琼斯，普赖斯

编者按

电接触的断开中似乎不会藏有高深的物理意义。然而，在本文中物理学家弗兰克·卢埃林－琼斯及其同事们指出：这个问题比人们通常想象的要复杂得多。在一个闭合电路的接触即将断开的时候，通过它的电流一定会经过一个更加狭窄的路径。这种情况必然会产生大量的热，甚至导致金属的沸腾。确实，他们通过简单的计算表明在每次断开电路时都会有体积为 10^{-12} 厘米^3 数量级的小块金属消失，最终使这个电接触毁坏。研究者们也展示了一系列电接触间形成的微小金属桥的高速照相图片，这是理解此过程的关键。

低压下（约为 4 伏特）电接触断开的过程有重要的基础物理学意义，同时对电子工程学和通信工程领域也有重要的实用价值。众所周知[1]，初始状态是两个电极紧压在一起处于完全导通的状态，断开过程中会导致电流线的收缩，这会导致在最后的微观接触区域产生很强的局部加热和熔化。在接触区的最高温度与电势差有关，可以通过 ψ，θ 定理表示，如下式：

$$\psi = \left[2\int_{\theta}^{\theta m}\frac{\lambda}{\kappa}\,d\theta\right]^{1/2} \tag{1}$$

式中 ψ 为广义势（在没有热电效应情况下就等于电势），θ 为温度，λ 为热导率，κ 为电导率。因此，随着电极的逐渐分离，收缩电阻增大，温度升高并超过了金属的熔点。继续分离，熔化的体积随之增加，这种熔融金属逐渐被拉成连接着两个固体电极的微观桥；电接触最终会断开，但只有这个微观的桥断开时整个电路才会断开。然而，这个断裂过程可能是非常复杂的并且会导致金属从一个电极转移到另一个电极上，当不断重复这个过程时，便会产生“点”和“坑”状形态，以致过一段时间后触点失效。有证据[1,2]表明，每次操作过程中物质的转移量（在电流为 5 安培的电路中约 10^{-12} 厘米^3）与熔融金属桥的尺寸（宽度约为 10^{-4} 厘米 / 安培）有关，因此桥的稳定性、增长性以及最终的断裂都是具有重要意义的，这不仅是对实际应用而言，而且对研究熔融状态和高温状态下金属的一些物理性质也有重要意义。

considerations, but also from the point of view of the physical properties of metals in the molten state and at high temperatures.

In the first place, an important condition of equilibrium, at least in the earlier stages, is that which depends on the application of surface tension forces. The shapes of the bridges would then be surfaces of revolution satisfying the equation:

$$\Delta p = T\left(\frac{1}{R_1} + \frac{1}{R_2}\right) \tag{2}$$

and these are unduloids, catenoids or nodoids according as Δp is positive, zero or negative respectively[3]. Photographs of static microscopic bridges have indeed confirmed that these stable shapes can be attained[1]. In the later stages of opening Δp will be negative, and experiment has established that the final stable shape is usually the nodoid. The ψ, θ theorem shows that the hottest region of the microscopic molten metal bridge between like electrodes will probably be the narrow neck and, at first sight, it might appear that this is the region at which the bridge is most likely to break. However, detailed investigation of this final process raises some important problems in the physics of metals at high temperatures, and, in particular, near their boiling points.

Mechanisms of Break

It can be seen at once from the ψ, θ theorem that the mechanism of rupture of the molten metal bridge involves the physical properties of the metal, not at any one temperature, but over a wide range of temperatures up to boiling-point, and a number of different processes of rupture are possible.

In the first place, continued separation of the electrodes and the drawing out of the bridge increases the contact resistance R_c; consequently, the contact voltage V_c ($=R_c I_c$) for a given circuit current I_c continually rises. Inspection of the ψ, θ theorem shows that the maximum temperature θ_m correspondingly increases; in fact, it is readily seen by using the Wiedermann-Franz law that, when V_c exceeds about 1.5 V, the corresponding value of θ_m from (1) exceeds the boiling-point of any known metal. Thus, this process of rise of maximum temperature may well continue until θ_m reaches the boiling-point θ_b so breaking the molten metal bridge. The voltage V_b at which this occurs is called the boiling voltage, and is related to θ_b by equation (1). Further analysis[4] of the ψ, θ theorem shows that, since the relationship between ψ and θ depends on the variation of λ/κ with θ, thermal instability can occur for certain functional relationships of λ/κ with θ, in which case a sudden rise of θ_m up to the boiling point can, in certain circumstances, take place. Measurements of the contact current, potential difference and maximum temperature, and its location, enable a determination to be made of the transport properties of metals such as their thermal and electrical conductivities and Thomson coefficients and their dependence on temperature to be determined for the molten state at high temperatures[1].

首先，至少是在较早期阶段，达到平衡的一个重要条件取决于表面张力的应用。桥的形状将由满足式（2）的旋转曲面构成：

$$\Delta p = T\left(\frac{1}{R_1} + \frac{1}{R_2}\right) \tag{2}$$

当 Δp 分别为正值、零或负值[3]时，形态依次是类波状、类链状或类结节状。静态微观桥的照片的确已证实这些稳定形态是可以达到的[1]。在断开的较后期阶段，Δp 将是负值，实验已证实最终的稳定形态通常是类结节状。ψ，θ 定理表明，相同电极间的微观熔融金属桥中最热的区域可能位于窄口处，初看之下，这里非常有可能就是金属桥即将断裂的地方。然而，有关这个最终过程的详细研究引发出了一系列高温下金属物理的重要问题，尤其在接近沸点时。

断裂的机制

从 ψ，θ 定理可以一目了然地看出，熔融金属桥的断裂机制涉及许多金属的物理性质，但断裂并不是发生在某一特定温度下，而是在逼近沸点的较大温度范围内都会发生，许多不同的断裂过程都是有可能的。

首先，电极的连续分离和桥的拉长增大了接触电阻 R_c；结果，对于给定的回路电流 I_c，其接触电压 V_c $(=R_cI_c)$ 连续增高。对 ψ，θ 定理的分析表明，最高温度 θ_m 相应地增高；实际上，用威德曼–弗朗兹定律很容易看出，当接触电压 V_c 超过约 1.5 伏特时，由式（1）得出的 θ_m 对应值超出了任何已知金属的沸点。因此使最高温度上升的过程会持续下去直至 θ_m 达到沸点 θ_b，从而使熔融金属桥断裂。此时的电压 V_b 称为沸点电压，它通过式（1）与 θ_b 相关。对 ψ，θ 定理做进一步分析[4]可知，由于 ψ 和 θ 的关系取决于 λ/κ 随 θ 的变化，因此 λ/κ 和 θ 之间具有特定的函数关系时可以产生热的不稳定性，在这种情况下，θ_m 在特定的环境中可能突然上升至沸点。通过测量接触电流、电势差和最高温度及其位置，便能得出金属的输运性质，例如，金属的热导率、电导率和汤姆孙系数以及这些性质在高温熔融态下与温度之间的关系[1]。

These thermal effects, however, are not the only processes which may sever the bridge. For example, the electromagnetic pinch effect might well, with large currents, so constrict the bridge at the narrowest, hottest and therefore weakest point as to rupture it there. Again, the known variation of surface tension with temperature is an important factor influencing the stability of the bridge, and the consequences of this can only be neutralized by the influence of surface impurities or compensating internal viscous motions in the bridge. Restriction due to the size and geometry of the actual electrodes in a given practical contact might well prevent the continued formation of the stable nodoid form, and instability could result.

The shape and volume of the final bridge and its mechanism of rupture are very important from the practical point of view on account of their relation to the rate of matter transfer on rupture. For example, suppose that a thermo-electric effect displaced the hottest section of the molten metal bridge towards one electrode, then it follows that the rupture at that particular section could have the effect of producing net transfer from one electrode to the other. The amount transferred may then only be that of the hottest region in the neck. On the other hand, if, in a different process of rupture, the molten metal bridge disintegrated as a whole and was transferred to one or other electrode (say, by mechanical splashing of minute droplets), then in this case the matter transfer could be relatively high and this, of course, could have serious practical effects.

Thus, the precise processes of the actual opening of the circuit are a matter of considerable practical and theoretical importance, and these phenomena have been under investigation at Swansea for some time. The relationships of the size of the molten metal bridge to the current and to the matter transferred per operation and the local self-inductance have been investigated[1,5-10].

Accurate measurement of the amount of metal of a given electrode ($\sim 10^{-12}$ g) actually transferred on the rupture of the molten metal bridge was found possible using the radioactive tracer technique, and a very rapid variation with local inductance, particularly in the range 10^{-6} to 10^{-8} H, was found for a number of metals and, particularly so, for platinum[1,6-9]. Further, optical examination of the crater formed on bridge rupture indicated that in some metals the whole volume of the molten metal bridge took part in the transfer. The shape and volume of the microscopic bridge were determined from the geometry of the melting isothermals in each electrode after rupture.

Facts such as these are difficult to reconcile with the picture of matter transfer occurring as the result of a mechanical splashing of small droplets formed from the disintegrating molten metal bridge. On the contrary, they are more consistent with the view that the transfer may well be ionic, the motions of the ions being determined by the oscillatory electric field between the electrodes after the bridge has broken. For reasons such as these an alternative view was put forward based on the production of a micro-plasma, possibly initially formed at the broken neck of the molten metal bridge[11]. Consequently, in recent years effort has been directed to finding direct evidence for the existence of

然而，这些热效应并不是导致桥断裂的唯一过程。例如，电磁箍缩效应可产生很大的电流，因此在最窄、最热因而最薄弱的点使桥收缩，并导致其断裂。此外，已知的表面张力随温度而变化也是影响桥稳定性的一个重要因素，这些结果只能被表面杂质的影响或对桥内部黏滞运动的补偿所抵消。在特定的实际电接触中，由于真实电极尺寸和几何形状的限制会有效地阻止稳定类结节状桥的连续形成，从而使其具有了不稳定性。

从实际的观点看，考虑到最终桥的形态和尺寸及其断裂机制与桥断裂时物质转移的速率有关，所以它们都是非常重要的。例如，假定热电效应会将熔融金属桥的最热部分移向某个电极，则将引起在某个特定位置上发生断裂并导致从一个电极净转移到另一个电极的效果。那么传递的量只是颈部最热区域的量。另一方面，在另一不同断裂过程中，熔融金属桥作为整体分解，并转移到一个或另一个电极（譬如说，通过微滴的机械喷溅），那么在这种情况下，物质转移量可以相当高，当然，这也可能具有重大的实际影响。

因此，电路实际断开的详细过程是一个具有重要的应用性和理论性的课题，我们在斯旺西大学已对此现象做了一段时间的研究。研究人员也对熔融金属桥的尺寸与电流、每次操作中转移的物质以及局部自感之间的关系开展了研究[1,5-10]。

采用放射性示踪技术，能够精确测量出在熔态金属桥断裂时实际转移到给定电极的金属量(约为 10^{-12} 克)。人们已发现在许多金属中，特别是铂[1,6-9]中，局部电感(尤其是在 10^{-6} 亨 ~ 10^{-8} 亨之间）有很快的变化。并且，通过对由桥断裂形成的坑状结构进行的光学检测发现，在一些金属中，整个熔融金属桥的体积都参与了转移。这个微观桥的形态和大小取决于各个电极断裂后熔融等温线的几何形状。

这些情况很难与由熔融金属桥分解时产生的微滴机械喷溅而导致的物质转移图像相吻合。相反，这些情况与如下观点更为一致，即这种物质的转移是呈离子态的，而这种离子的运动取决于熔融金属桥断裂后在电极间振荡的电场。由于上述原因，人们提出了另一种基于微等离子体产物的观点，这一微等离子体很有可能最初形成于熔融金属桥的断裂颈上[11]。因此，近年来我们努力寻找这类等离子体存在的直接证据。可喜的是，由于熔融金属桥发展的最后一步的变化速度，使得等离子体扩张

such a plasma. It will be appreciated that, owing to the speed of events in the final stages of the development of the molten metal bridge, extensive expansion of the plasma to a size which can readily be seen may not take place. In fact, particularly in the presence of a high-pressure ambient atmosphere, a plasma of metal vapour might well be severely restricted in size throughout its short life.

Photography of the Microscopic Molten Metal Bridge

Early attempts to photograph the development of the exploding bridge were confined to cases in which it would be expected that surface tension would be the dominant controlling force and large stable bridges obtainable. Such photographs have been previously obtained for large iron bridges in air[1]. In appropriate circumstances the oxide film on the surface would enable a constant surface tension to be set up over the whole surface, and thus produce stability in accordance with (2).

A number of standard ciné films (25 f.p.s.) were taken of the formation, development and final rupture of the bridge, and many thousands of frames were examined in the hope of finding an illustration of the actual rupture. One or two frames were found which showed that the actual rupture process might not be a simple parting of the nodoid, and this indicated that it was necessary to use high-speed photography if rupture was to be examined in more detail. There were considerable difficulties in the high-speed photography of the molten bridge mainly on account of the small area to be photographed ($\leqslant 10^{-4}$ cm^2), the low luminosity for metals other than platinum and tungsten, and the difficulty associated with the synchronization of the camera and the phenomenon to be photographed. A certain degree of elusiveness of the bridge at all stages of its life also made photography difficult. However, an optical system incorporating a high-speed camera was designed and constructed to examine the development of a molten metal bridge for time-intervals down to about 10 μsec. In this way a large number of metals were investigated under varying conditions of ambient atmosphere and pressure. Some preliminary photographs thus obtained were shown at conferences at Oklahoma[5], at Graz[9] and at Berlin[10]. Sets of later photographs giving a succession of frames extending over a total time of a few milliseconds covering in some detail various phases of the rupture of the microscopic molten metal bridge are given here. The results for iron are of particular interest in that they illustrate the three different aspects of the rupture process discussed here, and these are given in Figs. 1, 2 and 3.

Fig. 1 shows a series of photographs at a rate of 10^4 frames per sec and deals with iron in air. Doubtless on account of consequent oxidation affecting the surface tension, well-shaped stable bridges were formed after a number of operations, and these are in accordance with the theoretical prediction of the stable nodoid. Stability could be controlled by surface tension forces, and the fact that the bridge ruptured when the hottest section boiled is clearly indicated by the photographs, which show the two white-hot separate parts of the bridge after rupture.

到能易于看到的尺寸的情况并没有发生。实际上，尤其是在高压环境的气氛下，在金属蒸气等离子体的短寿命内，它的大小受到了严格的限制。

微观熔融金属桥的拍摄

早期对于拍摄桥断裂过程的尝试受到一些条件的限制，因为人们认为表面张力会成为首要的控制力，从而能获得大而稳定的桥。这样的照片最先是在空气[1]中对大的铁金属桥拍摄而得。在适宜的环境下，表面上的氧化膜将在整个表面范围内产生恒定的表面张力，因此得到如式（2）中的稳定性。

我们采用许多标准的电影胶卷（25 帧 / 秒）对桥的形成、发展和最终的断裂过程进行拍摄，我们对成千上万个镜头进行分析，希望能够发现桥实际断裂时的景象，最终找到了一两个镜头，显示出实际的断裂过程可能不是一个简单的类结节体的分开，并且这也表明如果想对断裂进行更细致地分析，就必须使用高速照相机。利用高速照相机拍摄熔融金属桥面临相当多困难，这主要是因为拍摄的目标范围非常小（小于等于 10^{-4} 厘米^2），除铂金属和钨金属外，其他金属的亮度都很低，控制好现象发生与拍摄的同步也很困难。此外桥在寿命中不同阶段持续的时间不好把握，这同样为拍摄带来了困难。尽管如此，还是设计和制造了一个结合了高速照相机的光学系统，它能够以约为 10 微秒的时间间隔对熔融金属桥的断裂过程进行拍摄。利用这种方法，我们在不同的气氛和气压下对大量的金属进行了研究。通过这种方式获得的一些初步的照片，在俄克拉荷马州[5]、格拉茨[9]和柏林[10]的会议上进行了展示。这里给出几组后来得到的照片，照片拍摄到一段连续的镜头，覆盖了几毫秒内微观熔融金属桥断裂时不同阶段的一些细节。铁金属的结果格外有趣，因为它们说明了本文中讨论的在不同条件下断裂过程的三种状态，结果如图 1、图 2 和图 3 中所示。

图 1 示出了以每秒 10^4 帧拍摄到的一系列照片，其中金属铁是在空气中处理的。毫无疑问的是随后的氧化反应会影响到表面张力，在经过多次操作后才最终形成形状完好的稳定桥，并且这与稳定的类结节型桥的理论预测是相一致的。稳定性受到表面张力的控制，事实上照片清楚显示出，桥是在最热部分沸腾时断裂的，并且在断裂后形成两个白热分离的部分。

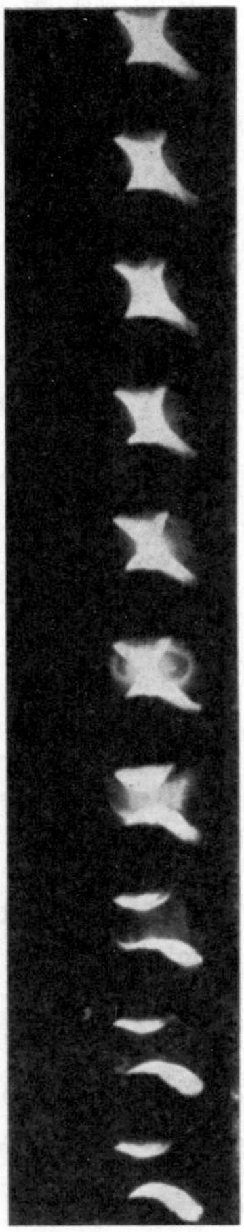

Fig. 1

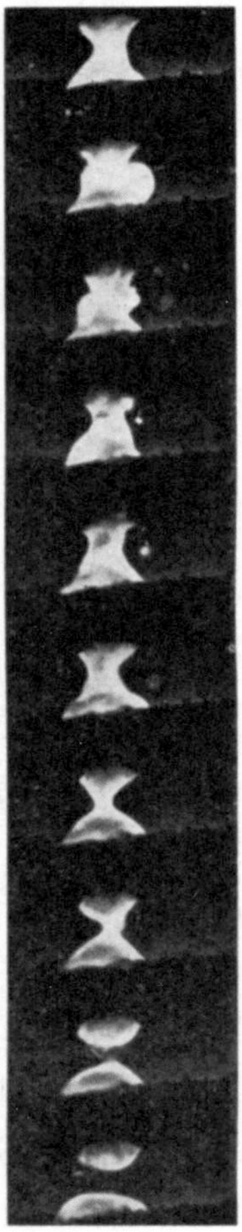

Fig. 2

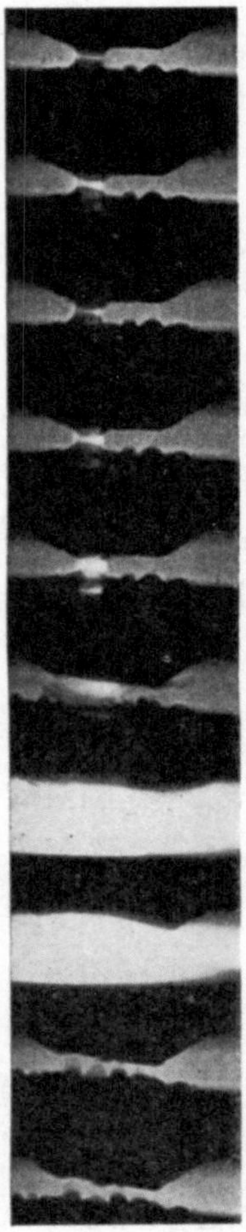

Fig. 3

Fig. 1. Material, iron; atmosphere, air; current, 30 amp; circuit E.M.F., 6 V; polarity, top electrode negative; magnification, ×6; framing rate, 5,000 f.p.s.

Fig. 2. Material, iron; atmosphere, air; current, 30 amp; circuit E.M.F., 6 V; polarity, top electrode negative; magnification, ×6; framing rate, 2,000 f.p.s.

Fig. 3. Material, iron; atmosphere, vacuum; current, 60 amp; circuit E.M.F., 6 V; polarity, top electrode positive; magnification, ×19.5; framing rate, 7,000 f.p.s.

Fig. 2 illustrates a less stable condition in which the degree of oxidation was such that the surface tension could not be maintained constant over the surface. In such cases stability can only be produced by internal viscous motion, and this is consistent with the effect illustrated by the rapid change from frame to frame in the location of the hottest region of the bridge surface.

In order to minimize the effect of surface tension forces in establishing stability, the iron surfaces were cleaned by a glow-discharge treatment in hydrogen and the contact was also operated in a vacuum in order to avoid further oxidation. The development of the

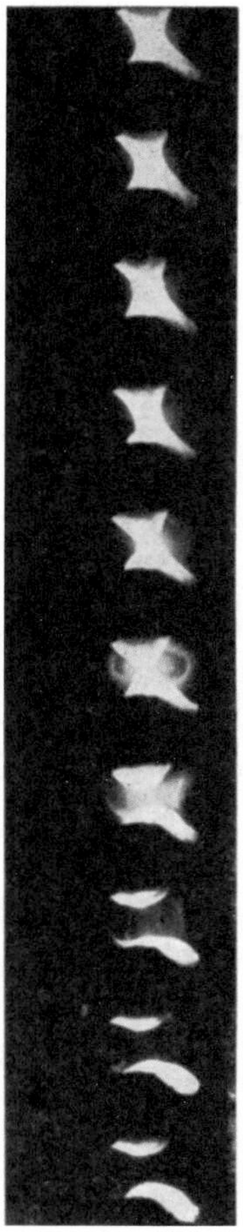

图 1

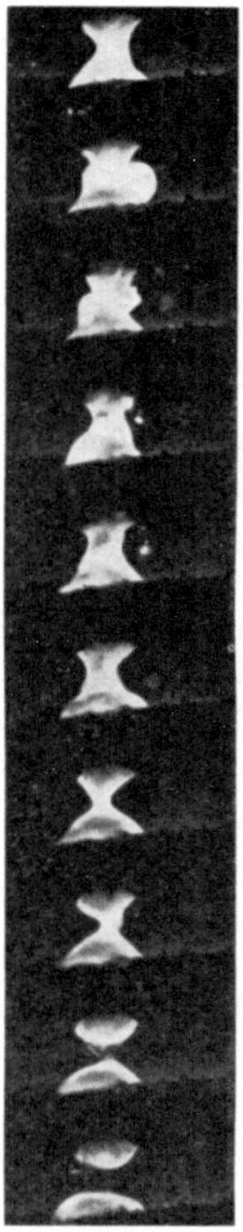

图 2

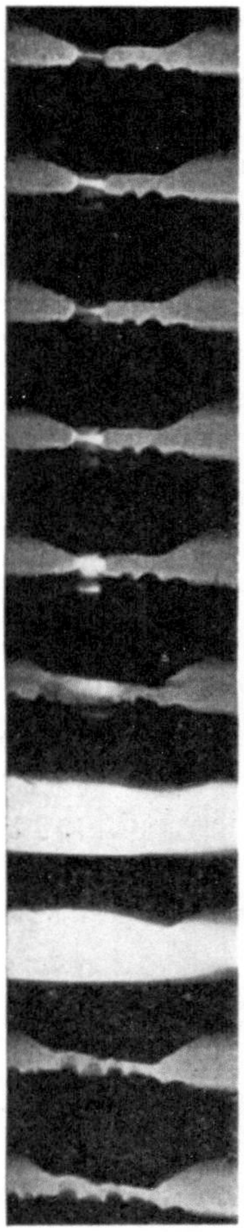

图 3

图 1. 材料：铁；气氛：空气；电流：30 安培；回路电动势：6 伏特；极性：顶部电极为负极；放大倍数：×6；帧速率：5,000 帧 / 秒。

图 2. 材料：铁；气氛：空气；电流：30 安培；回路电动势：6 伏特；极性：顶部电极为负极；放大倍数：×6；帧速率：2,000 帧 / 秒。

图 3. 材料：铁；气氛：真空；电流：60 安培；回路电动势：6 伏特；极性：顶部电极为正极；放大倍数：×19.5；帧速率：7,000 帧 / 秒。

图 2 示出一个稍不稳定的条件，该条件下氧化的程度使表面张力不能在表面保持不变。这种情况下，稳定性仅靠内部的黏滞运动产生，并且这与用桥表面最热区域处帧－帧之间的快速变化说明的效应是一致的。

在稳定性的建立过程中为了使表面张力的效应最小，我们利用在氢中辉光放电处理法对铁的表面进行了清洗，而且为了避免进一步的氧化，接触在真空中进行。

bridge in this case is illustrated by the series in Fig. 3. This is dramatically different from the two series in Figs. 1 and 2 in that the molten metal bridge no longer severs over a very small section while the bridge remains in the liquid form. On the contrary, in this case an electric micro-discharge appears to have been formed from the completely exploded bridge, producing a high-density plasma of great brightness the duration of which is less than 100 μsec and probably less than 10 μsec. On account of the inability to expand appreciably in these conditions, the particle density in the micro-plasma must be extremely high.

Similar effects have been found for other metals, and the radio-tracer technique enables the directions of the metallic transfer occurring during this short existence of the plasma to be measured.

We thank Mr. Ieuan Maddock of the Atomic Weapons Research Establishment, U.K. Atomic Energy Authority, Aldermaston, for the loan of a high-speed camera and for advice. One of us (M. J. P.) is also grateful for the award of a Department of Scientific and Industrial Research postgraduate research studentship. Thanks are also due to the Royal Society for a grant for the purchase of precious metals.

(**207**, 255-257; 1965)

F. Llewellyn Jones and M. J. Price: Department of Physics, University College of Swansea, University of Wales.

References:

1. Llewellyn Jones, F., *Physics of Electrical Contacts* (Clarendon Press, 1957).
2. Llewellyn Jones, F., *Proc. Intern. Res. Symp. Electric Contact Phenomena*, University of Maine (1961).
3. Davidson, P. M., *Brit. J. App. Phys.*, **5**, 189 (1954).
4. Greenwood, J. A., and Williamson, J. B. P., *Proc. Roy. Soc.*, A, **240**, 13 (1958).
5. Llewellyn Jones, F., *Proc. Twelfth Intern. Conf. Electromagnetic Relays*, Oklahoma State Univ. (1964).
6. Price, M. J., *Proc. Thirteenth Intern. Conf. Electromagnetic Relays*, Oklahoma State Univ. (1965).
7. Jones, C. R., Hopkins, M. R., and Llewellyn Jones, F., *Brit. J. App. Phys.*, **12**, 485 (1961).
8. Jones, C. H., and Hopkins, M. R., *Brit. J. App. Phys.*, **14**, 137 (1963).
9. Llewellyn Jones, F., *Proc. Intern. Symp. Electrical Contacts*, Technische Hochschule, Graz, Austria (1964).
10. Hopkins, M. R., *Proc. Intern. Symp. Electrical Contacts*, Technische Hochschule, Graz, Austria (1964).
11. Llewellyn Jones, F., *Proc. Third Intern. Conf. Ionization Phenomena in Gases*, Venice, **2**, 620 (1958).
12. Llewellyn Jones, F., *Proc. Intern. Conf. Electrical Contacts*, Deutsche Akademie der Wissenschaften zu Berlin (1964); also *Elektrie*, **3**, 129 (1965).

在这种情况下建立的桥通过图 3 中的系列照片进行了说明。这与图 1 和图 2 的两个系列照片有很大差别，图 3 中当熔融金属桥以液体的形式存在时，其不会以很小的截面分离。相反，在这种情况下，在完全分解的桥上已出现电的微放电，在小于 100 微秒或可能小于 10 微秒的时间内产生了高亮度的高密度等离子体。由于在这些情况下无法明显地扩展，因此微等离子体中的粒子密度必然是极高的。

在其他金属中已发现了类似效应，放射性示踪技术使在存在等离子体的这段极短时间内对金属转移方向进行测定成为可能。

我们感谢位于奥尔德马斯顿的英国原子能管理局原子武器研究中心的爱恩·马多克先生借给我们一台高速照相机并提供了一些建议；感谢科学及工业研究署颁发给我们之间的一员（普赖斯）的研究生研究奖学金，也同样感谢皇家学会同意为给我们购买一些贵金属。

（沈乃澂 翻译；赵见高 审稿）

Abnormal Haemoglobins and the Genetic Code

D. Beale and H. Lehmann

Editor's Note

Here biologists D. Beale and Hermann Lehman from Cambridge University describe how the degenerate genetic code influences different types of human haemoglobin, and settle an ongoing debate between themselves and Nobel laureate Francis Crick. Crick, best known for his work deciphering the structure of DNA, had pointed out that haemoglobin I, an abnormal type of the oxygen-binding protein, cannot be the outcome of a single mutation. But Beale and Lehman show that it can, identifying a single amino-acid substitution on the alpha polypeptide chain.

DR. F. H. C. CRICK has directed our attention to the latest work of Nirenberg *et al.*[1] which has considerably advanced the definition of the code whereby messenger RNA determines which amino-acid is incorporated into a protein. The code is "degenerate" and more than one arrangement of three bases or a codon can spell the same amino-acid. The first two bases are, however, somewhat more specific than the third. For example, for glutamic acid (Glu) they are guanine adenine (GA), but the third can be either A or G. However, the first two bases in the codon spelling aspartic acid (Asp) are also GA, but the third may be cytosine or uracil (C or U). Thus the coding for Glu is **GA**A or **GA**G. Some amino-acids are coded by any of the four possible bases in the third place of the codon. For example, the coding for threonine (Thr) is **AC**A or G or C or U. For a few amino-acids only, alternatives have also been found for the first two bases of the codon: leucine (Leu), for example, may be coded **UU**A or G or as **CU**G or C or U. From the considerable evidence for A being an alternative third part of the codon when G is one, one might write the second coding for leucine as **CU***A* or G or C or U. Table 1 gives the codons for amino-acids involved in substitutions of human haemoglobin; those surmised because A and G, and C and U, respectively, are alternatives in the third position, are in italics. Table 2 summarizes the amino-acid substitutions which have been reported in human haemoglobin. They include the abnormal haemoglobins fully described and those for which an amino-acid substitution is known but has not yet been finally allocated to a definite part in one of the polypeptide chains. Furthermore, as the β- and δ-polypeptide chains differ in only a very few amino-acid residues, likely to be point mutations, differences between these two chains have also been listed.

异常的血红蛋白及其遗传密码

比尔，莱曼

编者按

本文中，剑桥大学的生物学家比尔和赫尔曼·莱曼阐述了简并的遗传密码是如何影响不同类型的人血红蛋白的，并由此结束了他们与诺贝尔奖获得者弗朗西斯·克里克之间的不休争论。以提出 DNA 双螺旋结构而闻名的克里克曾经指出，血红蛋白 I（一种氧结合蛋白质的异常类型）不可能是单点突变的结果。但是比尔和莱曼指出那是可以的，并鉴定了发生在 α 多肽链上的单个氨基酸替换。

克里克博士已使我们的注意力集中到尼伦伯格等人最近的工作上[1]，他们的工作极大地促进了遗传密码的确定，而信使 RNA 正是通过遗传密码来决定用哪种氨基酸合成蛋白质的。遗传密码具有“简并性”，不止一组三碱基序列或者说不止一个密码子能够编码相同的氨基酸。然而，前两个碱基的特异性比第三个碱基稍强。例如，对于谷氨酸（Glu）来说，前两个碱基是鸟嘌呤（G）和腺嘌呤（A），但是第三个碱基可以是 A 或 G。不过编码天冬氨酸（Asp）的密码子前两个碱基也是 GA，但是第三个碱基可以是胞嘧啶或尿嘧啶（C 或 U）。因此，编码 Glu 的密码子是 **GA**A 或 **GA**G。有些氨基酸密码子的第三个碱基可以是四种碱基中的任何一个。比如，编码苏氨酸（Thr）的密码子可以是 **AC**A、**AC**G、**AC**C 或 **AC**U。只有少数一些氨基酸，编码它的密码子的前两个碱基也具有可替换性：如亮氨酸（Leu），可以被 **UU**A 或 **UU**G 编码，也可以被 **CU**G、**CU**C 或 **CU**U 编码。大量的证据表明当密码子的第三个碱基是 G 时就可以用 A 替换，于是编码亮氨酸的第二类密码子可以记为 **CU***A*、**CU**G、**CU**C 或 **CU**U。表 1 给出了编码人血红蛋白中可能发生替换的氨基酸的密码子；由于密码子的第三个碱基可能分别被 A、G、C 或 U 中的一种碱基替换，所以这些猜测的碱基用斜体标注。表 2 总结了已经报道的人血红蛋白中发生的氨基酸替换。其中包括详细记述的异常血红蛋白，以及一些已知发生氨基酸替换但还未最终定位在某条多肽链的特定位置上的情况。另外，由于 β 多肽链和 δ 多肽链只有很少的几个氨基酸残基不一致，很可能是点突变，我们也列出了这两条链之间的差异。

Table 1. Messenger Ribonucleic-acid Codons for Amino-acids involved in Substitutions in Human Haemoglobin

Lysine	**AA** A or G	Proline	**CC** A or *G* or C or U
Asparagine	**AA** C or U	Leucine	**CU** *A* or G or C or U **UU** A or G
Threonine	**AC** A or G or C or U	Glutamic acid	**GA** A or G
Arginine	**AG** A or *G* **CG** A or *G* or C or *U*	Aspartic acid	**GA** C or U
Serine	**AG** C or U **UC** A or G or C or U	Alanine	**GC** *A* or G or *C* or U
Methionine	**AU** *A* or G	Glycine	**GG** *A* or G or *C* or U
Glutamine	**CA** A or G	Valine	**GU** *A* or G or C or U
Histidine	**CA** C or U	Tyrosine	**UA** C or U

(Surmised bases in italics.)

A, Adenine; C, cytosine; G, guanine; U, uracil

Table 2. Amino-acid Substitutions in Human Haemoglobins

Substitution	Examples	Substitution	Examples
Lys → Asn	β61, Hikari[2]	Val → Glu	β67, M Milwaukee[23]
Lys → Asp	α16, I[3]	Gly → Asp	α15, J Oxford[24] (also described as "I" Interlaken[25]); α22 J Medellin[26]; α57 Norfolk[27]; β16, Baltimore[28]
Lys → Glu	β95, N[4]	Asp → Gly	α47, L Ferrara[29]
Thr → Lys	β87, D Ibadan[5]	Asp → Asn	β79, G Accra[30]
Asn → Lys	α68, G Philadelphia[6]	His → Tyr	α58, M Boston[23], α87 M Iwate[31], β2, Tokuchi[32]; β63 M Saskatoon[33]
Glu → Lys	α116, O Indonesia[7]; β6, C[8]; β7, Siriraj[9]; β26, E[10]; β121 O Arab[7]; γ6, F Galveston[11]	His → Asp	β143, Kenwood (or His-Glu)[32]
Glu → Gln	α30, G Chinese[12]	His → Asn	δ117, A_2[19,20]
Gln → Glu	α54, Mexico[13]	His → Arg	β63, Zurich[34]; δ117, A_2[19,20]
Gln → Arg	α54, Shimonoseki[14]	Leu → Arg	δ14, A'_2 (or B_2)[35]
Glu → Gly	β7, San Jose[15]	Ser → Thr	δ9, A_2[19,20]
Gly → Glu	β46 or β56, K Ibadan[16]	Thr → Asn	δ12, A_2[19,20]
Glu → Ala	β22 or β26, G Coushatta[17]; β43, G Galveston[18]; δ220, A_2[19,20]	Thr → Ser	δ50, A_2[19,20]
Ala → Glu	β70 or β76, Seattle[21]	Pro → Gln	δ126, A_2[19,20]
Glu → Val	β6, S[22]		

Fig. 1 illustrates the possible one-step mutations for the amino-acids listed in Table 2. This scheme covers all substitutions with one exception. As Dr. Crick has pointed out to us, haemoglobin I α16 Lys → Asp cannot have been the outcome of a single mutation but requires two mutations within one codon. As this is a point of considerable theoretical interest we have re-investigated haemoglobin I and have found that, in fact, the substitution is α16 Lys → Glu. Thus, at present, all amino-acid substitutions in human haemoglobin can be the outcome of single mutations. Degeneracy of the code must be assumed because the last base in the codon for glycine cannot be the same for the mutations Glu → Gly[15] and Gly → Asp[24-28]; similarly, it cannot be the same for arginine in His → Arg[34] and Gln → Arg[14]. The exclusion of the step Lys → Asp or Asp → Lys as a single mutation strongly supports the formula involving α116 Glu → Lys for haemoglobin O Indonesia[7]. The electrophoretic mobility suggests a double charge change from an acidic to a basic residue. The peptide involved (α*Tp*XII) contains both, one Glu (α116) and one Asp (α126), but as Glu → Arg, Asp → Arg, and Asp → Lys would require a double

表 1. 编码人血红蛋白可能发生替换的氨基酸的信使核糖核酸密码子

赖氨酸 (Lys)	**AA** A 或 G	脯氨酸 (Pro)	**CC** A 或 *G* 或 C 或 U
天冬酰胺 (Asn)	**AA** C 或 U	亮氨酸 (Leu)	**CU** *A* 或 G 或 C 或 U **UU** A 或 G
苏氨酸 (Thr)	**AC** A 或 G 或 C 或 U	谷氨酸 (Glu)	**GA** A 或 G
精氨酸 (Arg)	**AG** A 或 *G* **CG** A 或 *G* 或 C 或 *U*	天冬氨酸 (Asp)	**GA** C 或 U
丝氨酸 (Ser)	**AG** C 或 U **UC** A 或 G 或 C 或 U	丙氨酸 (Ala)	**GC** *A* 或 G 或 *C* 或 U
甲硫氨酸 (Met)	**AU** *A* 或 G	甘氨酸 (Gly)	**GG** *A* 或 G 或 *C* 或 U
谷氨酰胺 (Gln)	**CA** A 或 G	缬氨酸 (Val)	**GU** *A* 或 G 或 C 或 U
组氨酸 (His)	**CA** C 或 U	酪氨酸 (Tyr)	**UA** C 或 U

（猜测的碱基用斜体标注。）

A，腺嘌呤；C，胞嘧啶；G，鸟嘌呤；U，尿嘧啶

表 2. 人血红蛋白中的氨基酸替换

替换	例子	替换	例子
Lys → Asn	β61, 光市 [2]	Val → Glu	β67, M 密尔沃基 [23]
Lys → Asp	α16, I[3]	Gly → Asp	α15, J 牛津 [24]（也可以表示为“I”因特拉肯 [25]）；α22 J 麦德林 [26]; α57 诺福克郡 [27]; β16, 巴尔的摩 [28]
Lys → Glu	β95, N[4]	Asp → Gly	α47, L 费拉拉 [29]
Thr → Lys	β87, D 伊巴丹 [5]	Asp → Asn	β79, G 阿克拉 [30]
Asn → Lys	α68, G 费城 [6]	His → Tyr	α58, M 波士顿 [23], α87, M 岩手 [31], β2, 德地 [32]; β63, M 萨斯卡通 [33]
Glu → Lys	α116, O 印尼 [7]; β6, C[8]; β7, 诗里拉吉 [9]; β26, E[10]; β121, O 阿拉伯 [7]; γ6, F 加尔维斯顿 [11]	His → Asp	β143, 肯伍德（或 His-Glu）[32]
Glu → Gln	α30, G 中国人 [12]	His → Asn	δ117, A_2[19,20]
Gln → Glu	α54, 墨西哥 [13]	His → Arg	β63, 苏黎世 [34]; δ117, A_2[19,20]
Gln → Arg	α54, 下关市 [14]	Leu → Arg	δ14, A'_2（或 B_2）[35]
Glu → Gly	β7, 圣何塞 [15]	Ser → Thr	δ9，A_2[19,20]
Gly → Glu	β46 或 β56, K 伊巴丹 [16]	Thr → Asn	δ12, A_2[19,20]
Glu → Ala	β22 或 β26, G 考沙塔 [17]; β43, G 加尔维斯顿 [18]; δ220, A_2[19, 20]	Thr → Ser	δ50, A_2[19,20]
Ala → Glu	β70 或 β76, 西雅图 [21]	Pro → Gln	δ126, A_2[19,20]
Glu → Val	β6, S[22]		

图 1 说明了表 2 列出的氨基酸中可能发生的一步突变。除了一个例外，这个图涵盖了所有可能发生的替换。正如克里克博士指出，血红蛋白 I α16 处 Lys → Asp 不是单点突变的结果，而是需要某一密码子内双突变。鉴于这一点具有相当重要的理论意义，我们再一次对血红蛋白 I 展开研究，发现实际上 α16 处的替换是 Lys → Glu。因此，目前发现的人血红蛋白中所有的氨基酸替换都是单点突变的结果。我们必须假设密码子具有简并性，因为编码甘氨酸的密码子的最后一个碱基与突变 Glu → Gly[15] 和 Gly → Asp[24-28] 不可能相同；类似地，编码精氨酸的密码子的最后一个碱基与突变 His → Arg[34] 和 Gln → Arg[14] 也不可能相同。排除 Lys → Asp 或 Asp → Lys 为单点突变，这强有力地支持了印尼氧合血红蛋白中 α116 Glu → Lys 突变 [7] 的规则。电泳迁移率显示残基从酸性转变为碱性，发生了两次电荷改变。涉及的多肽（α*Tp*XII）有两处存在这种情况：一个 Glu（α116）和一个 Asp（α126），但是由于 Glu → Arg、 mutation the likely formula is $\alpha_2^{116Glu \rightarrow Lys}\beta_2$. By similar reasoning one can assume that haemoglobin Kenwood[32], for which two alternative formulae involving β143 His → Glu and β143 His → Asp have been proposed, is likely to be $\alpha_2\beta_2^{143His \rightarrow Asp}$.

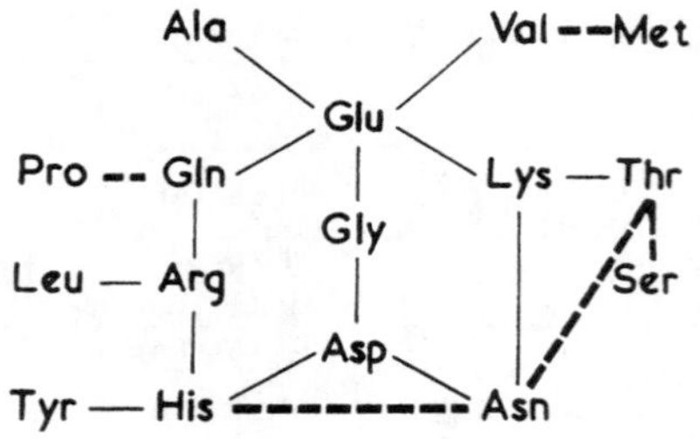

Fig. 1. Possible one-step mutations for amino-acids involved in substitutions in human haemoglobin. The dotted lines indicate differences between β- and δ-chains

So far as human haemoglobin is concerned, there are four possible charge changes detectable by electrophoresis at *p*H 8.6 (that is, a *p*H at which charge changes do not include the influence of histidine) (Fig. 2). A loss of a negative charge can arise from the replacement of Glu or Asp by a neutral residue, or from replacing a neutral residue by Lys or Arg. The variant of haemoglobin A will then move in the position of haemoglobins S or G. A positive charge can be lost by substitution of a Lys or Arg by a neutral residue or of a neutral residue by Glu or Asp. The resulting variants will then have the mobility of haemoglobins J or K. A double charge change involving either the replacement of a negative by a positive or of a positive by a negative charge can arise by a single mutation only when Glu is substituted by Lys, or Lys by Glu. Thus the haemoglobins C, E, O are all Glu → Lys mutations, and the haemoglobins of the I and N type must be expected to involve a change of Lys → Glu.

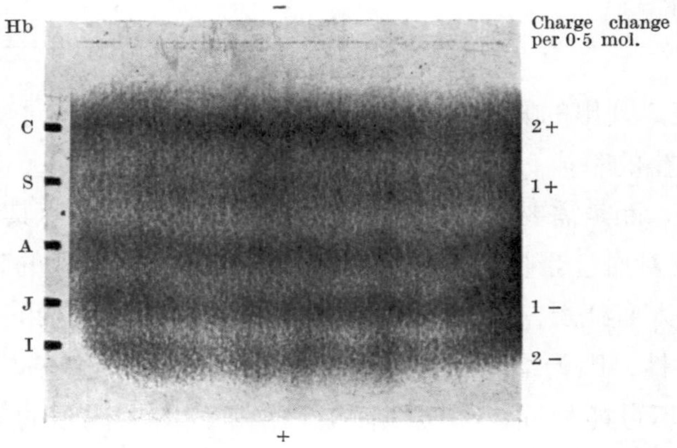

Fig. 2. Paper electrophoresis at *p*H 8.6 of haemoglobin A, and four variants showing respectively one and two additional positive or negative charges per half molecule

It seems remarkable that of eleven glutamic acid residues, nine and possibly ten have been

Asp → Arg 及 Asp → Lys 可能需要双重突变，可能的形式是 $\alpha_2{}^{116Glu\rightarrow Lys}\beta_2$。根据类似的原因可以推测，肯伍德血红蛋白[32] 中提出的包括 β143 His → Glu 和 β143 His → Asp 的两种可变形式可能是 $\alpha_2\beta_2{}^{143His\rightarrow Asp}$。

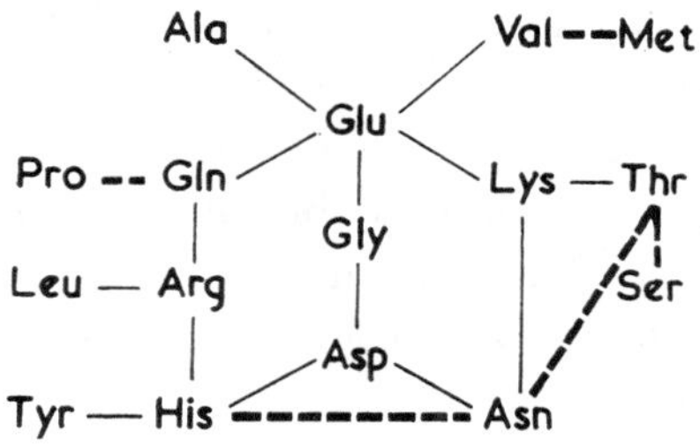

图 1. 人血红蛋白中发生替换的氨基酸可能的一步突变。虚线代表 β 链和 δ 链间的差异。

就人血红蛋白而言，在 pH 8.6 的条件下（也就是说，在这个 pH 值下不包括组氨酸影响的电荷变化）进行电泳，可检测到 4 种可能的电荷变化（图 2）。Glu 或 Asp 被一个中性残基替换，或者一个中性残基被 Lys 或 Arg 替换，会导致损失一个负电荷。然后变异的血红蛋白 A 将移动到血红蛋白 S 或血红蛋白 G 的位置。Lys 或 Arg 被一个中性残基替换，或者一个中性残基被 Glu 或 Asp 替换，会导致损失一个正电荷。产生的变异体将具有血红蛋白 J 或血红蛋白 K 的迁移率。只有 Glu 被 Lys 替换或者 Lys 被 Glu 替换时，一个单点突变才能引起双电荷改变（包括负电荷被正电荷替换或者正电荷被负电荷替换）。因此，血红蛋白 C、E、O 都是 Glu → Lys 突变，预计 I 型和 N 型的血红蛋白必然涉及 Lys → Glu 的突变。

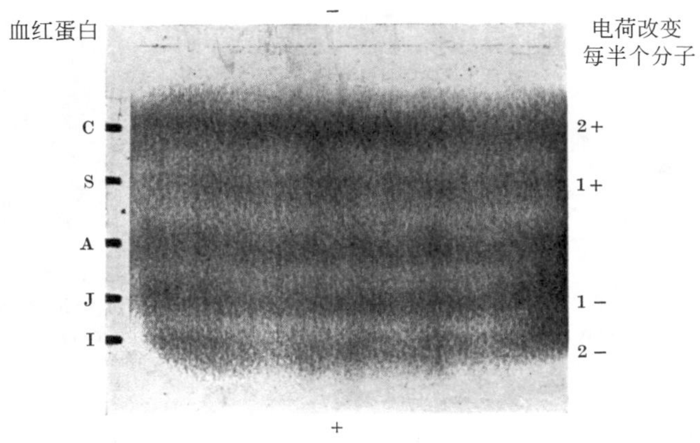

图 2. 在 pH 8.6 的条件下进行纸电泳，血红蛋白 A 及 4 种变异体分别显示出每半个分子增加 1~2 个正电荷或负电荷。

似乎比较显著的是，11 个谷氨酸残基中有 9 个（也可能是 10 个）发生了突变，

involved in mutations, three of them twice, yet of seventeen aspartic acid residues only one[30], or possibly two[29], have been subject to substitutions. On the other hand, changes to Asp and Glu occur with similar frequency, six and five times respectively. The genetic code would permit Glu and Asp to mutate equally well to Val, Ala, or Gly. In addition, whereas Glu can mutate to Lys and Gln, Asp can mutate to Asn, His or Tyr. All such mutations would involve charge changes in the molecule which would be detected by electrophoresis. The frequency of mutations from Glu to other residues and the rarity of replacements of Asp could suggest that Asp may be more important for the structure and function of the haemoglobin A molecule ($\alpha_2\beta_2$). This is not necessarily so for the haemoglobins A_2 ($\alpha_2\delta_2$) and F ($\alpha_2\gamma_2$) because only two Asp and two Glu respectively are common to all four polypeptide chains, α, β, γ and δ.

Analysis of haemoglobin I. Haemoglobin I[36] was isolated from a specimen kindly given to us by Miss J. Atwater, Philadelphia. The purified haemoglobin was "fingerprinted" by the usual methods (all relevant methods have recently been summarized[5]) and the fingerprints showed that α*Tp*III and α*Tp*IV were missing and a new peptide moving towards the anode was observed (Fig. 3). It will be seen that the electrophoretic (horizontal) mobility of the new peptide is the same as that of β*Tp*V and β*Tp*V (oxidized). β*Tp*V yields on hydrolysis three aspartic acid residues. Prolonged chromatography is required to remove traces of β*Tp*V and particularly of β*Tp*V (oxidized) from the abnormal peptide in haemoglobin I.

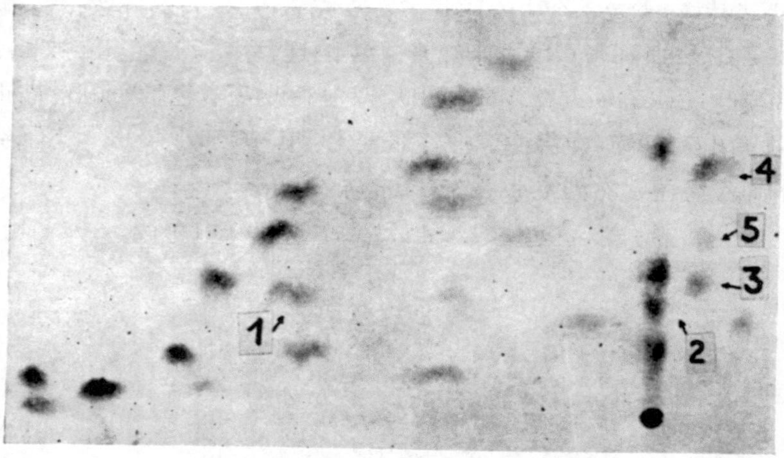

Fig. 3. The "fingerprint" of haemoglobin I. 1, α^{A}*Tp*III missing; 2, α^{A}*Tp*IV missing; 3, new peptide (α^{I}*Tp*IIIIV); 4, β*Tp*V; 5, β*Tp*V (oxidized). Note that the β*Tp*V peptides have the same electrophoretic mobility (horizontal) as the abnormal peptides from haemoglobin I, but they are well separated by chromatography (vertical)

The new peptide was purified by electrophoresis at *p*H 6.4 followed by chromatography in isoamyl alcohol:pyridine:water (30:30:35) and its amino-acid composition determined on an automatic analyser. This analysis (Table 3), when compared with a similar analysis for α*Tp*III and α*Tp*IV, showed that a lysine residue, presumably at position 16 of the α-chain, had been replaced by one of glutamic acid or of glutamine (glutamine would have been converted to glutamic acid during hydrolysis).

其中的 3 个是 2 次突变，而 17 个天冬氨酸残基中只有 1 个[30]或 2 个[29]发生了替换。另一方面，突变为 Asp 和 Glu 的频率相似，分别为 6 次和 5 次。遗传密码可能允许 Glu 和 Asp 机会均等地突变为 Val、Ala 或 Gly。另外，Glu 可以突变为 Lys 和 Gln，Asp 可以突变为 Asn、His 或 Tyr。所有的这些突变都可能涉及分子中电荷的改变，因而可以通过电泳进行检测。Glu 突变为其他残基的突变频率和 Asp 很少发生替换都表明，Asp 对于血红蛋白 A 分子（$\alpha_2\beta_2$）的结构和功能可能具有更重要的作用。对于血红蛋白 A_2（$\alpha_2\delta_2$）和 F（$\alpha_2\gamma_2$）来说则并非如此，因为对于所有的 4 条多肽链 α、β、γ 和 δ，各自仅有 2 个 Asp 和 2 个 Glu 是共有的。

血红蛋白 I 的分析 血红蛋白 I 是从费城的阿特沃特小姐惠赠给我们的样品中分离出来的[36]。采用通常的方法（最近已经对所有相关的方法进行了总结[5]）对纯化的血红蛋白进行“指纹测定”，指纹图谱显示 α*Tp*III 和 α*Tp*IV 缺失，并且观察到一个新的多肽朝正极移动（图 3）。由此可知新肽链的电泳（水平方向上）迁移率与 β*Tp*V 和 β*Tp*V（被氧化的）相同。β*Tp*V 水解产生 3 个天冬氨酸残基。需用长效色谱技术从血红蛋白 I 的异常多肽中分离出微量的 β*Tp*V，特别是氧化的 β*Tp*V。

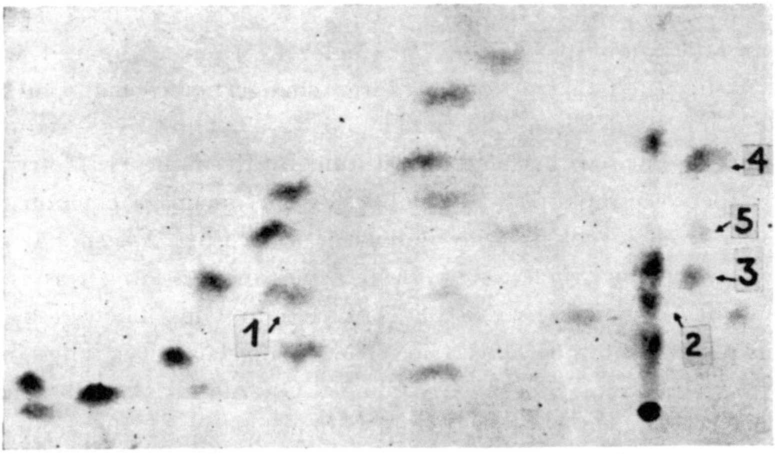

图 3. 血红蛋白 I 的“指纹测定”。1, α^A*Tp*III 缺失；2, α^A*Tp*IV 缺失；3, 新的多肽（α^I*Tp*III-IV）；4, β*Tp*V；5, β*Tp*V（被氧化的）。注意 β*Tp*V 多肽与来自血红蛋白 I 的异常多肽的电泳迁移率（水平方向上）相同，但色谱法（垂直方向上）可以将它们很好地分离。

在 pH 6.4 的条件下进行电泳，随后用流动相为异戊醇：吡啶：水（30:30:35）的色谱进行分离，从而使这个新的多肽得到纯化，并用氨基酸自动分析仪分析其氨基酸组成。与 α*Tp*III 和 α*Tp*IV 的类似分析相比较，这一分析结果（表 3）显示可能在 α 链的第 16 个氨基酸的位置上，一个赖氨酸残基被一个谷氨酸或者谷氨酰胺取代（在水解过程中谷氨酰胺可以转变为谷氨酸）。

Table 3. Amino-acid Analysis of Abnormal Peptide from Hb-I and the Peptides αTpIII and αTpIV from Hb-A

Amino-acid	α[I]TpIII-IV		α[A]TpIII		α[A]TpIV	
	μ Mole	Molar ratio	μ Mole	Molar ratio	μ Mole	Molar ratio
Asp	0.005	0.07	0.003	0.05	0.004	0.06
Thr	0.003	0.04	0.005	0.08	0.002	0.03
Ser	0.003	0.04	0.002	0.03	0.003	0.04
Glu	0.285	4.07	0.006	0.10	0.222	3.09
Pro	0.002	0.03	0.003	0.05	0.002	0.03
Gly	0.283	4.04	0.062	1.09	0.208	2.90
Ala	0.401	5.73	0.110	1.93	0.273	3.79
Val	0.082	1.17	0.004	0.07	0.075	1.04
Met	0.001	0.01	0.001	0.02	0.002	0.03
Leu	0.078	1.11	0.008	0.05	0.069	0.96
Tyr	0.068	0.97	0.001	0.02	0.062	0.86
Phe	0.004	0.06	0.003	0.05	0.002	0.03
Try*	+	(1.0)	+	(1.0)	–	(0.0)
Lys	0.004	0.06	0.057	1.00	0.005	0.07
His	0.065	0.93	0.005	0.08	0.058	0.80
Arg	0.070	1.00	0.001	0.02	0.072	1.00

* Detected in peptide by the Ehrlich reagent. A positive reaction was assumed to be due to one residue of tryptophan.

The electrophoretic mobility of the haemoglobin when compared with that of haemoglobin A suggested that a double charge change per α-chain had taken place, thus favouring a mutation Lys → Glu rather than Lys → Gln. To substantiate this, the new peptide was digested with chymotrypsin and the resulting chymotryptic peptides separated by paper electrophoresis at *p*H 6.4. By this means a chymotryptic peptide giving a transient yellow colour with ninhydrin (indicating *N*-terminal glycine) and giving a positive reaction when tested for tyrosine and histidine was isolated. Acid hydrolysis (by which any Gln would be converted to Glu) followed by amino-acid analysis of this peptide showed 3Gly, 2Glu, 2Ala, 1Val, 1His, 1Tyr. These results would correspond with a peptide, α15-24: Gly-Glu-Val-Gly-Ala-His-Ala-Gly-Glu-Tyr which would have been produced by the chymotryptic cleavage of the tryptophanyl and tyrosyl bonds of the original peptide (Table 4). To prove that the second residue of the chymotryptic peptide was the expected glutamyl rather than glutaminyl, the peptide was treated with leucine amino peptidase whereby glycine, glutamic acid and valine, but no glutamine, were quickly released.

This biochemical finding arising from a suggestion made by Dr. F. H. C. Crick is of interest because it is probably the first time that the genetic code has been used as an aid in the analysis of a protein, rather than that the analysis of a protein has been used for the unravelling of the genetic code.

表 3. 来自血红蛋白 I 的异常多肽与来自血红蛋白 A 的 α*Tp*III 和 α*Tp*IV 多肽的氨基酸分析

氨基酸	α^{I}*Tp*III-IV		α^{A}*Tp*III		α^{A}*Tp*IV	
	微摩尔	摩尔比	微摩尔	摩尔比	微摩尔	摩尔比
Asp	0.005	0.07	0.003	0.05	0.004	0.06
Thr	0.003	0.04	0.005	0.08	0.002	0.03
Ser	0.003	0.04	0.002	0.03	0.003	0.04
Glu	0.285	4.07	0.006	0.10	0.222	3.09
Pro	0.002	0.03	0.003	0.05	0.002	0.03
Gly	0.283	4.04	0.062	1.09	0.208	2.90
Ala	0.401	5.73	0.110	1.93	0.273	3.79
Val	0.082	1.17	0.004	0.07	0.075	1.04
Met	0.001	0.01	0.001	0.02	0.002	0.03
Leu	0.078	1.11	0.008	0.05	0.069	0.96
Tyr	0.068	0.97	0.001	0.02	0.062	0.86
Phe	0.004	0.06	0.003	0.05	0.002	0.03
Try*	+	(1.0)	+	(1.0)	–	(0.0)
Lys	0.004	0.06	0.057	1.00	0.005	0.07
His	0.065	0.93	0.005	0.08	0.058	0.80
Arg	0.070	1.00	0.001	0.02	0.072	1.00

* 借助埃利希试剂进行多肽的测定。推测阳性反应可能是由于存在一个色氨酸残基。

与血红蛋白 A 相比，血红蛋白的电泳迁移率显示每条 α 链都发生了双电荷改变，从而支持是 Lys → Glu 而不是 Lys → Gln。为了证实这一点，用胰凝乳蛋白酶消化新肽，将酶解后的多肽片段在 pH 6.4 的条件下通过纸电泳分离。用这种方法分离出胰蛋白酶酶解后的多肽：茚三酮染色显示出短暂的黄色（表明氮末端为甘氨酸），游离酪氨酸和组氨酸检测呈阳性。对这个肽链进行酸解（这样 Gln 可以完全转化为 Glu），随后对多肽氨基酸分析，结果显示为 3Gly、2Glu、2Ala、1Val、1His、1Tyr。这些结果可能对应多肽 α15~24：Gly-Glu-Val-Gly-Ala-His-Ala-Gly-Glu-Tyr，它应由胰蛋白酶切断原来多肽的色氨酰与酪胺酰之间的肽键而得到（表 4）。为了证明胰蛋白酶酶解肽段的第二个残基是预期的谷氨酰而非谷氨酰胺酰，将这个多肽用亮氨酸氨肽酶进行处理，结果快速释放出甘氨酸、谷氨酸和缬氨酸，而不释放谷氨酰胺。

由克里克博士提出的建议而引出的这一生化发现是很吸引人的，因为它可能是第一次将遗传密码用于辅助蛋白质分析，而不是像之前那样通过分析蛋白质来揭示遗传密码。

Table 4. The Chymotryptic Digestion of the Abnormal Tryptic Peptide in Haemoglorin I

Note that peptide 4 just separated from 5 under the conditions of this experiment

Proposed peptide $\alpha^{A}Tp$III-IV based on the known amino-acid sequence of $\alpha^{A}Tp$III and $\alpha^{A}Tp$IV		α 12 13 14 15 16 17 18 19 20 21 22 23 24 25 26 27 28 29 30 31 Ala-Ala-Try-Gly-Glu-Val-Gly-Ala-His-Ala-Gly-Glu-Tyr-Gly-Ala-Glu-Ala-Leu-Glu-Arg ↑ (after Try 14) ↑ (after Tyr 24) ↑ (after Leu 29)
Chymotryptic* peptides from the abnormal peptide in Hb I	Amino-acids found on hydrolysis	
1	Gly, Ala Glu, Leu	Gly Ala Glu Ala Leu
2	Gly, Glu, Val Ala, His, Tyr Leu	Gly Glu Val Gly Ala His Ala Gly Glu Tyr Gly Ala Glu Ala Leu
3	3 Gly, 2 Glu, 1 Val 2 Ala, 1 His, 1 Tyr	Gly Glu Val Gly Ala His Ala Gly Glu Tyr
4	Glu, Arg	Glu Arg
5	Ala, Try	Ala Ala Try

* The composition was found in all cases by paper electrophoresis, but in peptide 3 the amino-acids were also determined on the amino-acid analyzer; molar ratio (±0.2) is, therefore, also given.

We thank Dr. A. J. Munro for advice concerning the genetic code.

(**207**, 259-261; 1965)

D. Beale and H. Lehmann: Medical Research Council Abnormal Haemoglobin Research Unit, Department of Biochemistry, University of Cambridge.

References:

1. Nirenberg, M., Leder, P., Bernfield, M., Brimacombe, R., Trupin, J., Rottman, F., and O'Neal, C., *Proc. U.S. Nat. Acad. Sci.*, **53**, 1161 (1965).
2. Shibata, S., Miyaji, T., Iuchi, I., Ueda, S., and Takeda, I., *Clin. Chim. Acta*, **10**, 101 (1964).
3. Murayama, M., *Nature*, **196**, 276 (1962).
4. Kraus, L. (personal communication).
5. Watson-Williams, E. J., Beale, D., Irvine, D., and Lehmann, H., *Nature*, **205**, 1273 (1965).
6. Baglioni, C., and Ingram, V. M., *Nature*, **189**, 465 (1961).
7. Baglioni, C., and Lehmann, H., *Nature*, **196**, 229 (1962).
8. Hunt, J. A., and Ingram, V. M., *Biochim. Biophys. Acta*, **42**, 409 (1960).
9. Tuchinda, S., Beale, D., and Lehmann, H., *Brit. Med. J.*, **1**, 1583 (1965).
10. Hunt, J. A., and Ingram, V. M., *Biochim, Biophys. Acta*, **49**, 520 (1961).
11. Schneider, R. G., and Jones, R. T., *Science*, **148**, 240 (1965).
12. Swenson, R. T., Hill, R. L., Lehmann, H., and Jim, R. T. S., *J. Biol. Chem.*, **237**, 1517 (1962).
13. Jones, R. T., Koler, R. D., and Lister, R., *Clin, Res.*, **11**, 105 (1963).
14. Miyaji, T., Iuchi, I., Takeda, I., and Shibata, S., *Acta Haemat. Jap.*, **26**, 531 (1963).
15. Hill, R. L., Swenson, R. T., and Schwartz, H. C., *J. Biol. Chem.*, **235**, 3182 (1960).
16. Allan, N., Beale, D., Irvine, D., and Lehmann, H. (in preparation).
17. Schneider, R. G., Haggard, M. E., McNutt, C. W., Johnson, J. E., Bowman, B. H., and Barnett, D. R., *Science*, **143**, 687 (1964).
18. Bowman, B. H., Oliver, C. P., Barnett, D. R., Cunningham, J. E., and Schneider, R. G., *Blood*, **23**, 193 (1964).
19. Ingram, V. M., and Stretton, A. O. W., *Biochim. Biophys. Acta*, **62**, 456 (1962).
20. Ingram, V. M., and Stretton, A. O. W., *Biochim. Biophys. Acta*, **63**, 20 (1962).
21. Huehns, E. R., and Shooter, E. M., *J. Med. Genet.*, **2**, 48 (1965).

表 4. 对血红蛋白 I 中的异常胰蛋白酶多肽进行胰凝乳蛋白酶酶解后的酶解产物

注意肽段 4 仅能在此实验条件下从肽段 5 中分离出来

根据已知的 α^{A}*Tp*III 和 α^{A}*Tp*IV 氨基酸序列提出的 α^{A}*Tp*III-IV 多肽序列		α 12 13 14 15 16 17 18 19 20 21 22 23 24 25 26 27 28 29 30 31 Ala-Ala-Try-Gly-Glu-Val-Gly-Ala-His-Ala-Gly-Glu-Tyr-Gly-Ala-Glu-Ala-Leu-Glu-Arg ↑ ↑ ↑
血红蛋白 I 中异常多肽的胰凝乳蛋白酶酶解肽段 *	水解得到的氨基酸	
1	Gly, Ala Glu, Leu	Gly Ala Glu Ala Leu
2	Gly, Glu, Val Ala, His, Tyr Leu	Gly Glu Val Gly Ala His Ala Gly Glu Tyr Gly Ala Glu Ala Leu
3	3Gly, 2Glu, 1Val 2Ala, 1His, 1Tyr	Gly Glu Val Gly Ala His Ala Gly Glu Tyr
4	Glu, Arg	Glu Arg
5	Ala, Try	Ala Ala Try

* 通过纸电泳检测所有情况的构成组分，但是在氨基酸分析仪中也对肽段 3 的氨基酸进行了分析；因此也给出了摩尔比（±0.2）。

我们对芒罗博士在遗传密码方面给予的建议表示感谢。

（郑建全 翻译；崔巍 审稿）

22. Ingram, V. M., *Biochim. Biophys. Acta*, **36**, 402 (1959).
23. Gerald, P. S., and Efron, M. L., *Proc. U.S. Nat. Acad. Sci.*, **47**, 1758 (1961).
24. Liddell, J., Brown, D., Beale, D., Lehamnn, H., and Huntsman, R. G., *Nature*, **204**, 269 (1964).
25. Marti, H. R., Pik, C., and Mosimann, P., *Acta Haemat.*, **32**, 9 (1964).
26. Gottlieb, A. J., Restrepa, A., and Itano, H. A., *Fed. Proc.*, **23**, 172 (1964).
27. Baglioni, C., *J. Biol. Chem.*, **237**, 69 (1962).
28. Baglioni, C., and Weatherall, D. J., *Biochim. Biophys. Acta*, **78**, 637 (1963).
29. Baglioni, C. (personal communication).
30. Lehamann, H., Beale, D., and Boi Doku, F. S., *Nature*, **203**, 363 (1964).
31. Miyaji, T., Iuchi, I., Shibata, S., Takeda, I., and Tamura, A., *Acta Haemat. Jap.*, **26**, 538 (1963).
32. Shibata, S., Iuchi, I., Miyaji, T., and Takeda, I., *Bull. Yamaguchi Med. Sch.*, **10**, 1 (1963).
33. Bayrakel, C., Josephson, A., Singer, L., Heller, P., and Coleman, R. D., *Proc. Soc. Haemat. Tenth Congr., Stockholm L*, **6** (1964).
34. Muller, C. J., and Kingma, S., *Biochim. Biophys. Acta*, **50**, 595 (1961).
35. Stretton, A. O. W. (personal communication).
36. Schwartz, I. R., Atwater, J., Repplinger, E., and Tocantins, L. M., *Fed. Proc.*, **16**, 115 (1957).

A New Class of Faults and Their Bearing on Continental Drift

J. T. Wilson

Editor's Note

John Tuzo Wilson was a Canadian geologist who greeted the hypothesis of sea-floor spreading and consequent continental drift by seeking to apply classical geology to the structure of the ocean floor. This paper summarized his reasons for expecting there to be "transform faults" roughly at right angles to mid-ocean ridges, which are thought to be the lines along which new crust is created on the ocean floor.

TRANSFORMS and half-shears. Many geologists[1] have maintained that movements of the Earth's crust are concentrated in mobile belts, which may take the form of mountains, mid-ocean ridges or major faults with large horizontal movements. These features and the seismic activity along them often appear to end abruptly, which is puzzling. The problem has been difficult to investigate because most terminations lie in ocean basins.

This article suggests that these features are not isolated, that few come to dead ends, but that they are connected into a continuous network of mobile belts about the Earth which divide the surface into several large rigid plates (Fig. 1). Any feature at its apparent termination may be transformed into another feature of one of the other two types. For example, a fault may be transformed into a mid-ocean ridge as illustrated in Fig. 2*a*. At the point of transformation the horizontal shear motion along the fault ends abruptly by being changed into an expanding tensional motion across the ridge or rift with a change in seismicity.

A junction where one feature changes into another is here called a transform.This type and two others illustrated in Figs. 2*b* and *c* may also be termed half-shears (a name suggested in conversation by Prof. J. D. Bernal). Twice as many types of half-shears involve mountains as ridges, because mountains are asymmetrical whereas ridges have bilateral symmetry. This way of abruptly ending large horizontal shear motions is offered as an explanation of what has long been recognized as a puzzling feature of large faults like the San Andreas.

一类新断层及其与大陆漂移的关系

威尔逊

编者按

加拿大地质学家约翰·图佐·威尔逊设法应用传统的地质学解释海底构造，从而接受了海底扩张和大陆漂移假说。该文对他预测的“转换断层”的存在依据进行了总结。“转换断层”大致垂直于大洋中脊，而洋底新的地壳通常被认为沿大洋中脊而形成。

转换与半剪切 许多地质学家[1]都认为地壳运动集中在活动带上；这些活动带一般表现为山脉、大洋中脊或具有大规模水平运动的主断层。令人迷惑的是，这些构造及其内部的地震活动通常会在末端突然消失。然而，由于绝大多数末端都位于大洋盆地内部，因此很难对这一问题展开研究。

本文提出，这些构造并不是孤立存在的，其末端极少完全停止活动。事实上，这些构造在地球表面相互联结成一个连续的活动带网，并将地球表面分隔成几个大的刚性板块（图 1）。某一构造在其貌似终止的地方可能转换成其他两种构造之一。如图 2*a* 所示，一个断层可能会转换为大洋中脊。在发生转换的地方，沿断层发生的水平剪切运动会突然终止，并转变为洋脊或裂谷的扩张运动，地震活动也随之发生变化。

一种构造转变为另一种构造的交汇处在这里被称为转换。上述这种类型以及图 2 中的 *b* 和 *c* 所示的其他两种类型也可以称为半剪切（这一名称由贝尔纳教授在一次交谈中提出）。因为山脉是不对称的，而洋脊是两边对称的，所以山脉半剪切类型是洋脊半剪切类型的两倍。这种大规模水平剪切运动的突然终止方式可以用来解释大型断层的一些长期令人费解的现象，如圣安德烈亚斯断层。

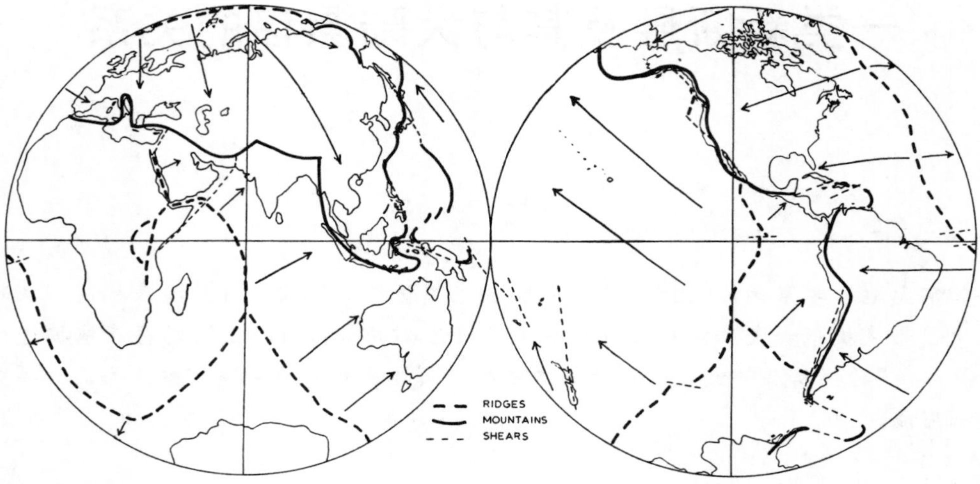

Fig. 1. Sketch map illustrating the present network of mobile belts, comprising the active primary mountains and island arcs in compression (solid lines), active transform faults in horizontal shear (light dashed lines) and active mid-ocean ridges in tension (heavy dashed lines)

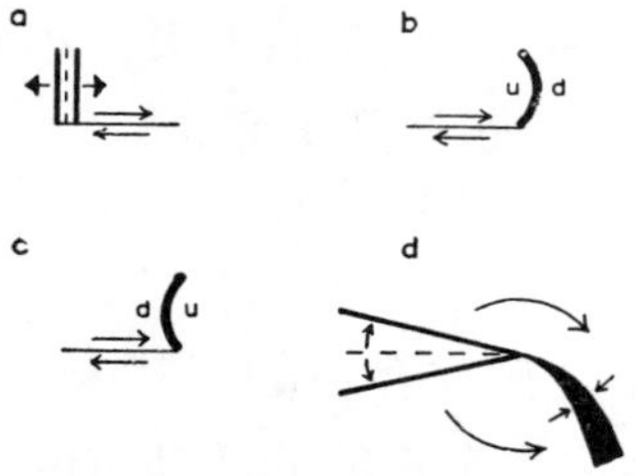

Fig. 2. Diagram illustrating the four possible right-hand transforms. *a*, Ridge to dextral half-shear; *b*, dextral half-shear to concave arc; *c*, dextral half-shear to convex arc; *d*, ridge to right-hand arc

Another type of transform whereby a mountain is transformed into a mid-ocean ridge was suggested by S. W. Carey[2] when he proposed that the Pyrenees Mountains were compressed because of the rifting open of the Bay of Biscay (presumably by the formation of a mid-ocean ridge along its axis). The types illustrated are all dextral, but equivalent sinistral types exist.

In this article the term "ridge" will be used to mean mid-ocean ridge and also rise (where that term has been used meaning mid-ocean ridge, as by Menard[3] in the Pacific basin). The terms mountains and mountain system may include island arcs. An arc is described as being convex or concave depending on which face is first reached when proceeding in the direction indicated by an arrow depicting relative motion (Figs. 2 and 3). The word fault may mean a system of several closely related faults.

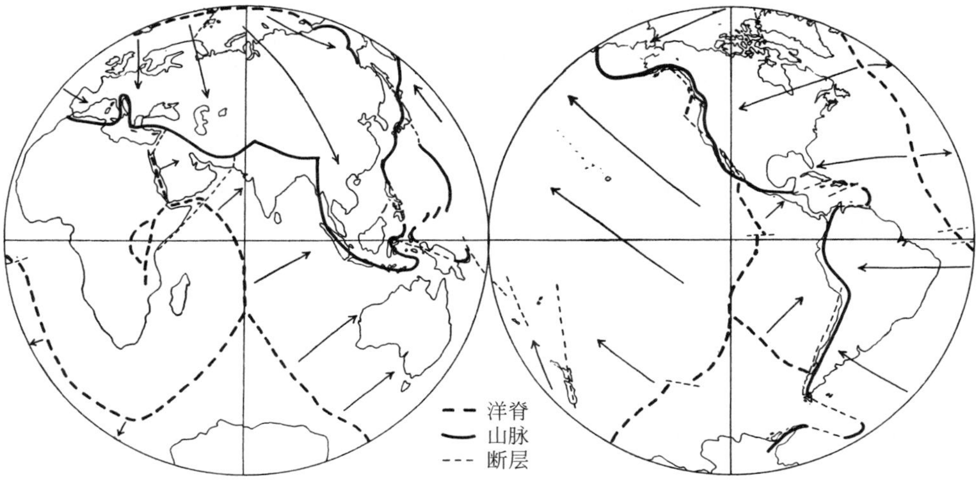

图 1. 现今地球活动带网的示意图，包括处于挤压状态的主要活动山脉和岛弧（实线）、处于水平剪切作用下的活动转换断层（细虚线）以及处于拉张环境的活动大洋中脊（粗虚线）。

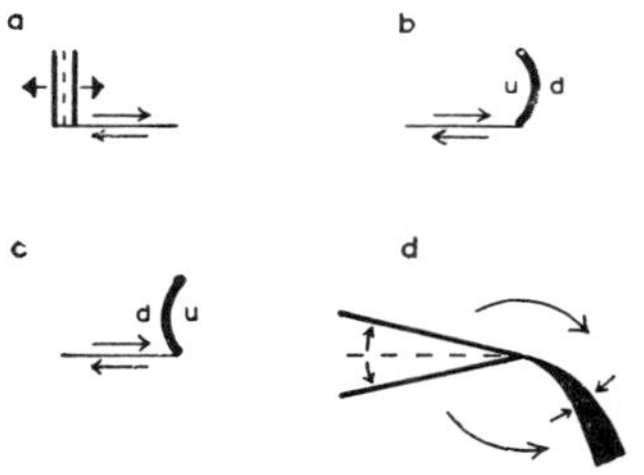

图 2. 4 种可能的右旋转换示意图。*a*，洋脊转换为右旋剪切；*b*，右旋剪切转换为凹形岛弧；*c*，右旋剪切转换为凸形岛弧；*d*，洋脊转换为右旋岛弧。

凯里[2]曾提出，比利牛斯山脉的挤压是比斯开湾的裂开（可能与大洋中脊沿其轴线的形成有关）所造成的，这便提出了一种新的转换类型用以解释山脉向大洋中脊的转换。上述列举的类型都是右旋型，但左旋型也同样存在。

在本文中“脊”和“隆”这两个名词都是指大洋中脊（梅纳德[3]曾经在太平洋海盆中用了“隆”这一名词来表示大洋中脊）。山脉和山系则可能包含岛弧。岛弧可呈凸出或凹入的形态，它是凸出还是凹入取决于当它沿着表示相对运动的箭头所指方向前进时首先到达的是哪一个面（图 2 和图 3）。断层一词则表示由几个密切相关的断层所构成的一个体系。

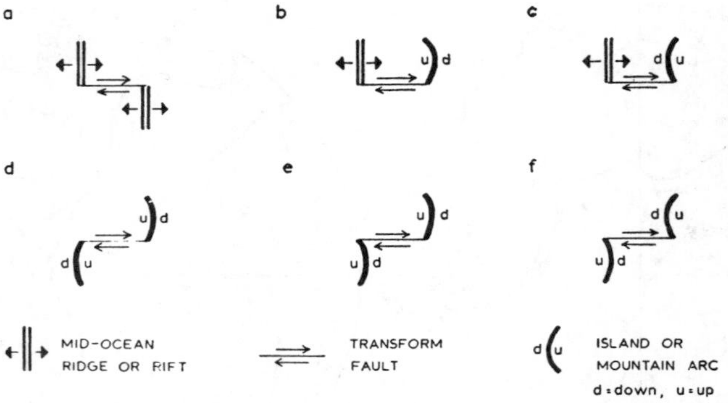

Fig. 3. Diagram illustrating the six possible types of dextral transform faults. *a*, Ridge to ridge type; *b*, ridge to concave arc; *c*, ridge to convex arc; *d*, concave arc to concave arc; *e*, concave arc to convex arc; *f*, convex arc to convex arc. Note that the direction of motion in *a* is the reverse of that required to offset the ridge

Transform faults. Faults in which the displacement suddenly stops or changes form and direction are not true transcurrent faults. It is proposed that a separate class of horizontal shear faults exists which terminate abruptly at both ends, but which nevertheless may show great displacements. Each may be thought of as a pair of half-shears joined end to end. Any combination of pairs of the three dextral half-shears may be joined giving rise to the six types illustrated in Fig. 3. Another six sinistral forms can also exist. The name transform fault is proposed for the class, and members may be described in terms of the features which they connect (for example, dextral transform fault, ridge-convex arc type).

The distinctions between types might appear trivial until the variation in the habits of growth of the different types is considered as is shown in Fig. 4. These distinctions are that ridges expand to produce new crust, thus leaving residual inactive traces in the topography of their former positions. On the other hand oceanic crust moves down under island arcs absorbing old crust so that they leave no traces of past positions. The convex sides of arcs thus advance. For these reasons transform faults of types *a*, *b* and *d* in Fig. 4 grow in total width, type *f* diminishes and the behaviour of types *c* and *e* is indeterminate. It is significant that the direction of motion on transform faults of the type shown in Fig. 3*a* is the reverse of that required to offset the ridge. This is a fundamental difference between transform and transcurrent faulting.

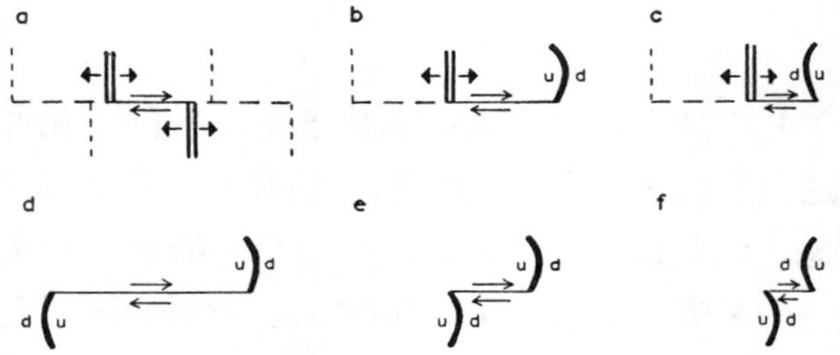

Fig. 4. Diagram illustrating the appearance of the six types of dextral transform faults shown in Fig. 3 after a period of growth. Traces of former positions now inactive, but still expressed in the topography, are shown by dashed lines

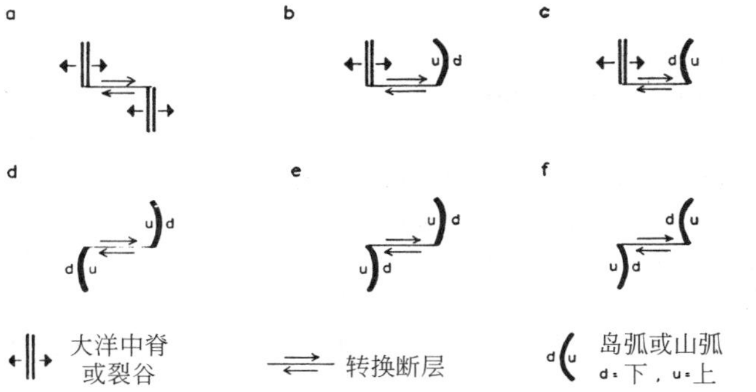

图 3. 6 种可能的右旋转换断层类型的示意图。*a*，脊–脊型；*b*，洋脊–凹形岛弧型；*c*，洋脊–凸形岛弧型；*d*，凹弧–凹弧型；*e*，凹弧–凸弧型；*f*，凸弧–凸弧型。注意：*a* 图中断层运动方向与洋脊错开的方向相反。

转换断层　表现为位移突然停止或者改变其形态和方向，但它们不是真正的平移断层。我认为存在另一类水平剪切断层，其两端突然终止，但仍表现出巨大的断距。每个转换断层都可以看成是一对尾与尾相连的半剪切构造。3 个右旋半剪切的任意两个组合可以形成如图 3 所示的 6 种类型。同样也存在 6 种左旋类型。转换断层是这类半剪切构造的统称，并且可以根据它们的连接特征来描述不同类型的断层（例如，右旋转换断层，洋脊–凸形岛弧型）。

如果忽略不同类型转换断层的形成特点的差别（如图 4 所示），类型之间的区别是微不足道的。这些区别是，洋脊扩张形成新的地壳，从而在其原来的位置上遗留下了不活跃的地貌痕迹。另外，洋壳向岛弧之下俯冲，因而老的地壳消失，没有留下任何先前位置的痕迹。因此，凸面岛弧是向前运动的。鉴于这些原因，图 4 中 *a*、*b* 和 *d* 三种类型的转换断层的总宽度会变大，而 *f* 型则变小，*c* 型和 *e* 型则不确定。值得注意的是，图 3*a* 所示转换断层的运动方向与洋脊错开的方向相反。这是转换断层与平移断层的根本区别。

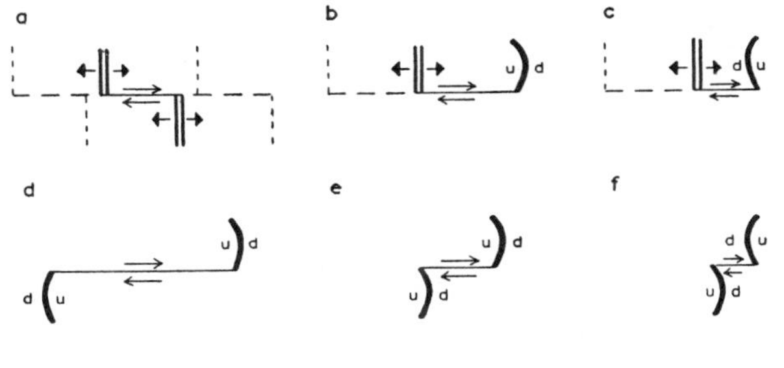

图 4. 图 3 所示的 6 种类型右旋转换断层经过一个时期发展之后的形状。之前所处位置的遗迹目前已经不活动了，不过在地貌上仍有显现，如虚线所示。

Many examples of these faults have been reported and their properties are known and will be shown to fit those required by the constructions above. If the class as a whole has not heretofore been recognized and defined, it is because all discussions of faulting, such as those of E. M. Anderson, have tacitly assumed that the faulted medium is continuous and conserved. If continents drift this assumption is not true. Large areas of crust must be swallowed up in front of an advancing continent and re-created in its wake. Transform faults cannot exist unless there is crustal displacement, and their existence would provide a powerful argument in favour of continental drift and a guide to the nature of the displacements involved. These proposals owe much to the ideas of S. W. Carey, but differ in that I suggest that the plates between mobile belts are not readily deformed except at their edges.

The data on which the ensuing accounts are based have largely been taken from papers in two recent symposia[4,5] and in several recent books[3,6,7] in which many additional references may be found.

North Atlantic ridge termination. If Europe and North America have moved apart, an explanation is required of how so large a rift as the Atlantic Ocean can come to a relatively abrupt and complete end in the cul-de-sac of the Arctic Sea. Fig. 5 illustrates one possible explanation.

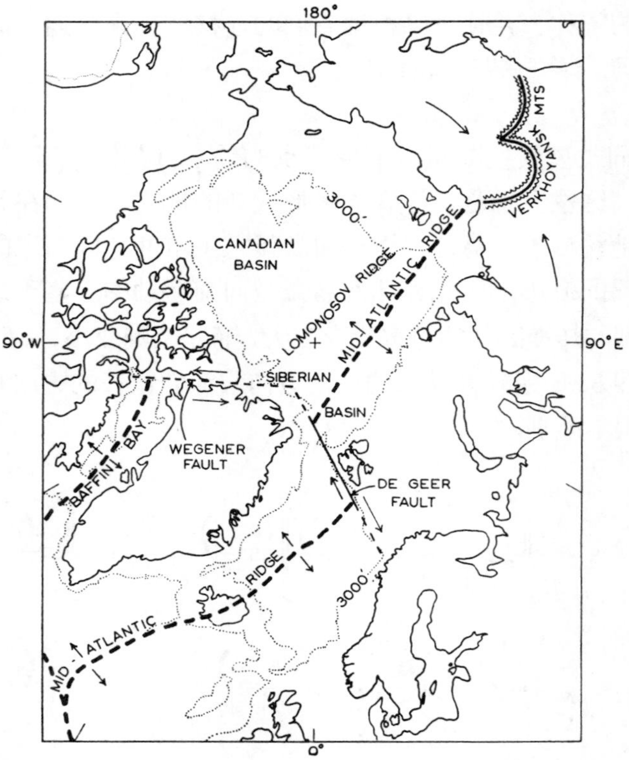

Fig. 5. Sketch map of the termination of the Mid-Atlantic ridge by two large transform faults (Wegener and De Geer faults) and by transformation into the Verkhoyansk Mountains

已有许多该类断层的实例报道，其特征也被大家所认识，并且将被证明与上述特征相吻合。如果说这类断层作为一个整体迄今为止还没有被认识和定义的话，那是因为所有关于断裂作用的讨论，例如安德森等人的讨论，一致都是假定断裂介质是连续的并且可以被保存下来。但如果大陆是漂移的，这一假设就不成立。前进大陆的前缘会有大面积的地壳被吞没，而在其后端又形成新地壳。只有在地壳发生位移的情况下才会存在转换断层。转换断层的存在为大陆漂移提供了强有力的证据，同时也为了解位移的性质提供了某些指导。上述看法的提出主要归功于凯里的观点，但与之不同的是，我认为活动带之间的板块在除边缘外的其他地方是不易发生变形的。

下面的示例所依据的数据大部分来自于最近的两本会议论文集[4,5]和几本新书[3,6,7]中的论文，许多附加的参考文献也可在其中找到。

北大西洋洋脊的终端 如果欧洲和北美洲是相互分离开的，那么就需要解释大西洋这样一个如此巨大的裂谷是如何在北冰洋的绝路里相对突然而又完全地终止。图 5 给出了一种可能的解释。

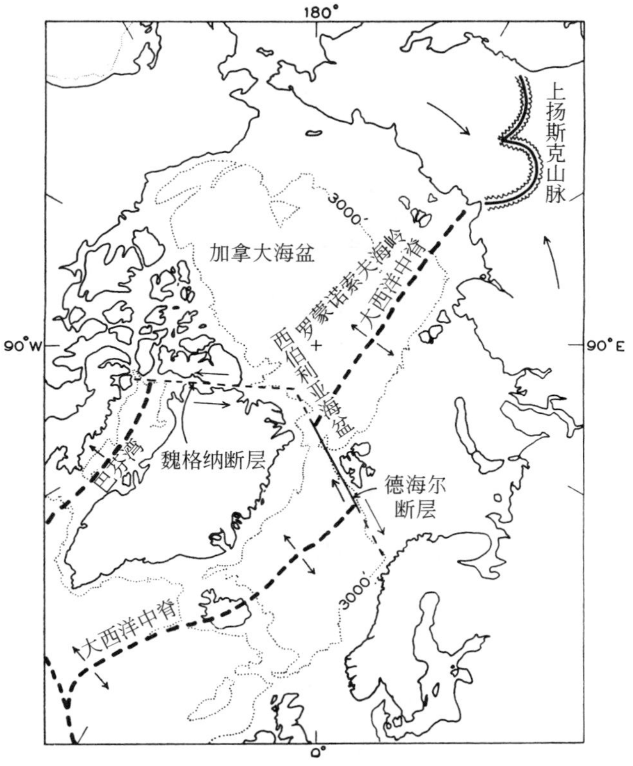

图 5. 大西洋中脊通过两个大型转换断层（魏格纳断层和德海尔断层）而终止，并转换为上扬斯克山脉。

Wegener[8] suggested that the strait between Greenland and Ellesmere Island was formed by a fault, here postulated to be a sinistral transform fault (ridge-ridge type). Wegmann[9] named another between Norway, Spitsbergen and Greenland, the De Geer line, which is here regarded as a dextral transform fault (ridge-ridge type). The extension of the Mid-Atlantic ridge across the Siberian basin was traced by Heezen and Ewing[10], while Wilson[11] proposed its transform into the Verkhoyansk Mountains by rotation about a fulcrum in the New Siberian Islands. In accordance with the expectations from Fig. 4*a* earthquakes have been reported along the full line of the De Geer fault in Fig. 5, but not along the dashed older traces between Norway and Bear Island and to the north of Greenland. The Baffin Bay ridge and Wegener fault are at present quiescent. W. B. Harland[10] and Canadian geologists have commented on the similarities of Spitsbergen and Ellesmere Island.

Equatorial Atlantic fracture zones. If a continent in which there exist faults or lines of weakness splits into two parts (Fig. 6), the new tension fractures may trail and be affected by the existing faults.

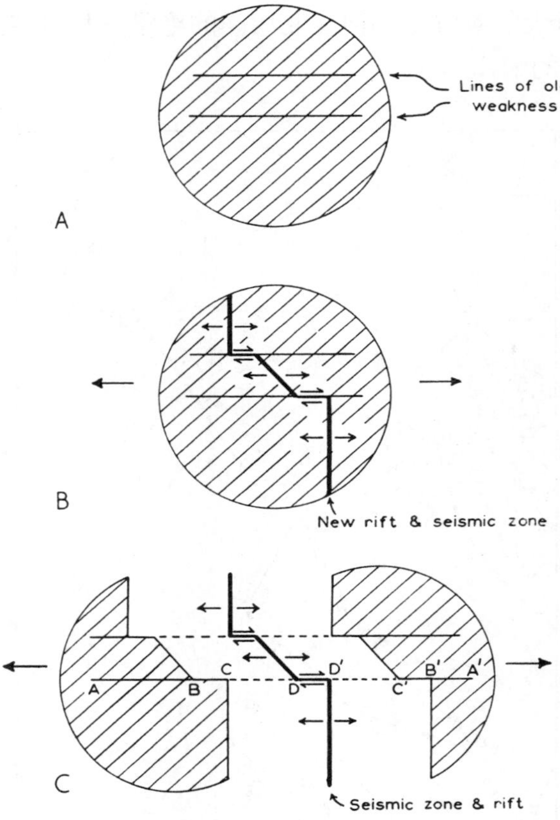

Fig. 6. Diagram illustrating three stages in the rifting of a continent into two parts (for example, South America and Africa). There will be seismic activity along the heavy lines only

魏格纳[8]认为，格陵兰和埃尔斯米尔岛之间的海峡是由一个断层形成的，这里将其假设为一个左旋转换断层（脊–脊型）。韦格曼[9]将另一个位于挪威斯匹次卑尔根岛和格陵兰之间的海峡称为德海尔线，这里将其看作一个右旋转换断层（脊–脊型）。希森和尤因[10]认为大西洋中脊向西伯利亚海盆方向延伸，而威尔逊[11]则提出大西洋中脊以新西伯利亚群岛为支点发生了旋转，并转换为上扬斯克山脉。与图 4*a* 所预测的一致，如图 5 所示，地震沿整个德海尔断层线分布，而沿虚线所示的挪威、熊岛和格陵兰岛北部之间的老痕迹则没有地震发生。巴芬湾中脊和魏格纳断层如今都是静止的。哈兰德[10]与加拿大地质学家就斯匹次卑尔根岛和埃尔斯米尔岛的相似性曾做过评论。

赤道大西洋破碎带 如果一个内部存在断层或薄弱带的大陆分裂为两部分（图 6），那么新的伸展断裂就会沿着已经存在的断层发育，并受其影响。

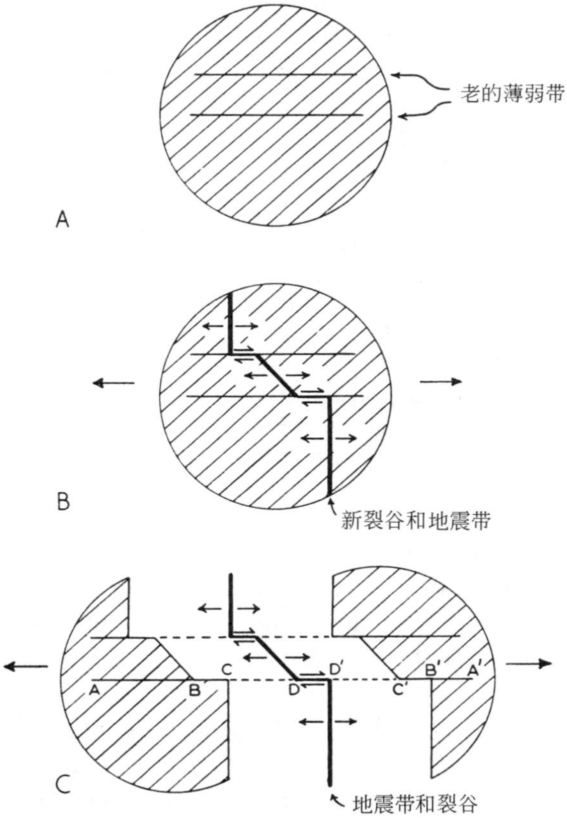

图 6. 大陆分裂为两部分所经历的三个阶段（例如，南美洲与非洲）。仅仅沿粗线部分会有地震活动。

The dextral transform faults (ridge-ridge type) such as *AA′* which would result from such a period of rifting can be seen to have peculiar features. The parts *AB* and *B′A′* are older than the rifting. *DD′* is young and is the only part now active. The offset of the ridge which it represents is not an ordinary faulted displacement such as a transcurrent fault would produce. It is independent of the distance through which the continents have moved. It is confusing, but true, that the direction of motion along *DD′* is in the reverse direction to that required to produce the apparent offset. The offset is merely a reflexion of the shape of the initial break between the continental blocks. The sections *BD* and *D′B′* of the fault are not now active, but are intermediate in age and are represented by fracture zones showing the path of former faulting.

Fig. 7 shows that the Mid-Atlantic ridge and the facture zones in the equatorial Atlantic may well be a more complex example of this kind. If so the apparent offsets on the ridge are not faulted offsets, but inherited from the shape of the break that first formed between the coasts of Africa and the Americas. Fig. 7 is traced from Heezen, Bunce, Hersey and Tharp[12] with additions to the north from Krause[13]. The fracture zones are here held to be right-hand transform faults and not left-hand transcurrent faults as previously stated. If the fracture zones can be traced across the Atlantic and are of the type postulated, then the points where they intersect the opposite coasts are conjugate points which would have been together before rifting.

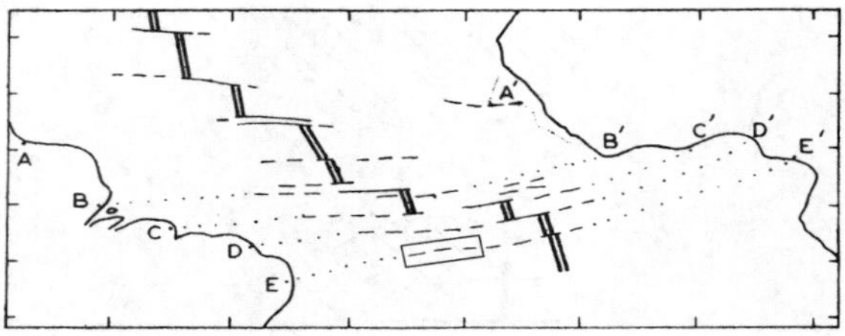

Fig. 7. Sketch (after Krause and Heezen *et al.*) showing how the Mid-Atlantic ridge is offset to the left by active transform faults which have dextral motions if the rift is expanding (see Fig. 4*a*). ||, Mid-ocean ridge; —, active fault; - - -, inactive fault trace; ···, hypothetical extension of fault

It seems possible that the old fault in Pennsylvania and the offset of the Atlantic Coast described by Drake and Woodward[14] are of the same nature, although it is suggested that it is not usual for a fracture zone to follow a line of seamounts, and that the fracture zone may extend eastward, not south-east.

A possible explanation of the termination of the Carlsberg ridge. Another type of transform fault is found in the Indian Ocean (Fig. 8). If the Indian Ocean and Arabian Gulf opened during the Mesozoic and Cenozoic eras by the northward movement of India, new ocean floor must have been generated by spreading of the Carlsberg ridge. This ends abruptly in a transcurrent fault postulated by Gregory[15] off the east coast of Africa. A parallel fault has been found by Matthews[16] as an offset across the Carlsberg ridge and traced by him to the coast immediately west of Karachi. Here it joins the Ornach-Nal and other faults[17] which

像 AA' 这样的右旋转换断层（脊–脊型）可能就经历了这样一个裂解过程，并具有一些特殊性质。AB 段及 $B'A'$ 段在断裂作用之前就已存在。DD' 比较年轻，并且是唯一正在活动的部分。它所代表的洋脊错距并不像平移断层所产生的普通断距。它与大陆运动的距离无关。这一点让人感到有些迷惑，但事实的确如此。也就是说，沿着 DD' 的运动方向与造成洋脊明显的错位所要求的方向相反。错距仅仅是陆块之间最初破裂形状的映像。断层中的 BD 段和 $D'B'$ 段现在已停止活动，其年龄处于中期，并且表现出早期断裂带的特征。

图 7 表明，赤道大西洋的大洋中脊和破碎带可能恰好是这种类型中一个较为复杂的例子。如果真是这样的话，那么洋脊的错距并不是断距，它仅反映非洲和美洲海岸之间最初断裂的形状。图 7 是根据希森、邦斯、赫西以及撒普 [12] 等人的研究成果绘制而成，并根据克劳斯 [13] 的成果增加了北侧的部分。这些破碎带都是右旋转换断层，而不是之前所认为的左旋平移断层。如果可以证实这些破碎带穿过大西洋并且与我们所推测的类型一致，那么便可以得出它们与对岸的相交点是共轭的，它们在裂开前应该是连在一起的。

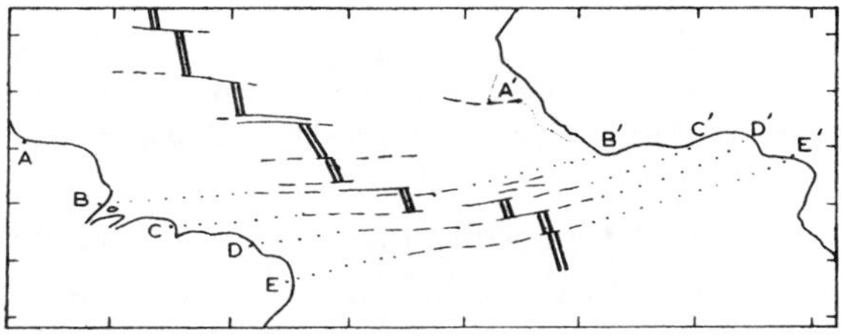

图 7. 该图（据克劳斯和希森等）展示了裂谷在扩张时，活动的右旋转换断层如何使大西洋中脊发生向左的位移（见图 4*a*）。|| 表示大洋中脊；—表示活动断层；- - - 表示非活动断层的轨迹；…表示断层的可能延伸方向。

位于宾夕法尼亚州的古老断层与德雷克和伍德沃德 [14] 所描述的大西洋海岸的错位似乎具有相同的特征，尽管人们认为破碎带沿海山走向延伸的情况并不常见，而且破碎带可能是向东而不是向东南延伸的。

关于卡尔斯伯格海岭终止的一种可能的解释　在印度洋中发现了另一种转换断层类型（图 8）。若印度洋和阿拉伯湾是由于中生代和新生代时期印度板块向北运动而分开的，那么卡尔斯伯格海岭的扩张一定会导致新洋壳的产生。格雷戈里 [15] 推测卡尔斯伯格海岭在非洲东海岸外突然终止于一个平移断层。马修斯 [16] 曾经发现一个平行断层，认为它错开了卡尔斯伯格海岭并一直延伸到紧临卡拉奇西侧的海岸。该断层与奥尔纳杰–纳尔断层以及与其他一些延伸到阿富汗内部的断层 [17] 在此处相连，

extend into Afghanistan and, according to such descriptions as I can find, probably merge with the western end of the Hindu Kush. This whole fault is thus an example of a sinistral transform fault (ridge-convex arc type).

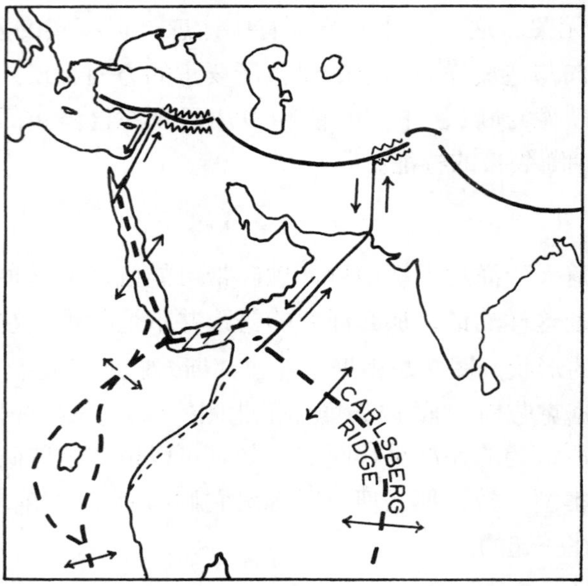

Fig. 8. Sketch illustrating the end of the Carlsberg mid-ocean ridge by a large transform fault (ridge-convex arc type) extending to the Hindu Kush, the end of the rift up the Red Sea by a similar transform fault extending into Turkey and the still younger East African rifts

At a later date, probably about Oligocene time according to papers quoted by Drake and Girdler[18], the ridge was extended up the Red Sea and again terminated in a sinistral transform fault (ridge-convex arc type) that forms the Jordan Valley[19] and terminates by joining a large thrust fault in south-eastern Turkey (Z. Ternek, private communication). The East African rift valleys are a still later extension formed in Upper Miocene time according to B. H. Baker (private communication).

The many offsets in the Gulf of Aden described by Laughton[20] provide another example of transform faults adjusting a rift to the shape of the adjacent coasts.

Possible relationships between active faults off the west coast of North America. This tendency of mid-ocean ridges to be offset parallel to adjacent coasts is thought to be evident again in the termination of the East Pacific ridge illustrated in Fig. 9. The San Andreas fault is here postulated to be a dextral transform fault (ridge-ridge type) and not a transcurrent fault. It connects the termination of the East Pacific ridge proper with another short length of ridge for which Menard[3] has found evidence off Vancouver Island. His explanation of the connexion—that the mid-ocean ridge connects across western United States—does not seem to be compatible with the view that the African rift valleys are also incipient mid-ocean ridges. The other end of the ridge off Vancouver Island appears to end in a

根据目前所掌握的这些描述，这些断层可能与兴都库什山脉的西端相接。因此，整个断层是一个左旋转换断层的实例（洋脊–凸形弧型）。

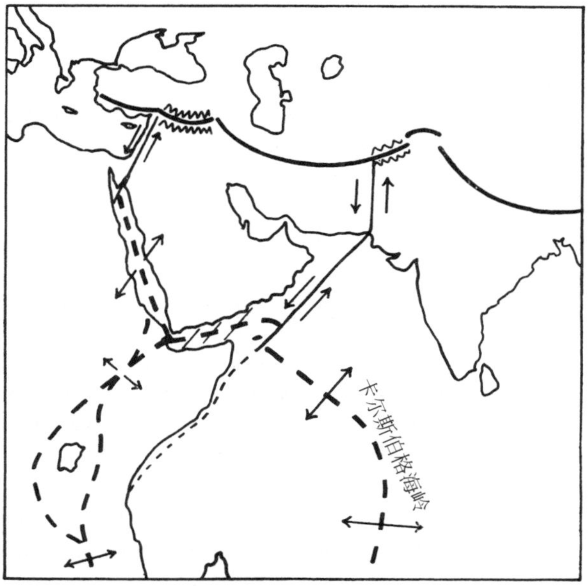

图 8. 本图显示卡尔斯伯格海岭终止于一个向兴都库什山脉延伸的大型转换断层（洋脊–凸弧型），红海北侧裂谷的末端终止于一个向土耳其方向延伸的类似的转换断层及年轻的东非大裂谷。

在随后一个时期，根据德雷克和格德勒 [18] 所引用的文章来看，可能是在渐新世，该洋脊扩张到了红海，并再次终止于一个左旋断层（洋脊–凸形弧型），该断层形成了约旦河谷 [19] 并与土耳其东南部的一个大型逆冲断层相连而终止（泰尔内克，私人交流）。根据贝克的说法，东非大裂谷在中新世晚期才形成（私人交流）。

劳顿 [20] 所描述的亚丁湾中的许多位移是转换断层的另一种实例，它们使裂谷与其相邻的海岸的形状相一致。

北美洲西海岸外活动断层之间可能存在的相互关系　在图 9 所示的东太平洋海隆的末端，大洋中脊与邻接海岸相互平行的趋势表现得非常明显。在这里圣安德烈亚斯断层被假定为一个右旋转换断层（脊–脊型），而不是一个平移断层。它正好将东太平洋海隆的末端与另一个较短的洋脊连接起来。对此，梅纳德 [3] 在温哥华岛外发现了相关的证据。他将这一联结解释为大洋中脊穿过美国西部而相连，而这一解释似乎与东非大裂谷是初期大洋中脊的观点不一致。温哥华岛外的洋脊的另一端终止于不列颠哥伦比亚岸外的第二大海底断层，贝尼奥夫 [7] 认为该断层

second great submarine fault off British Columbia described by Benioff[7] as having dextral horizontal motion.

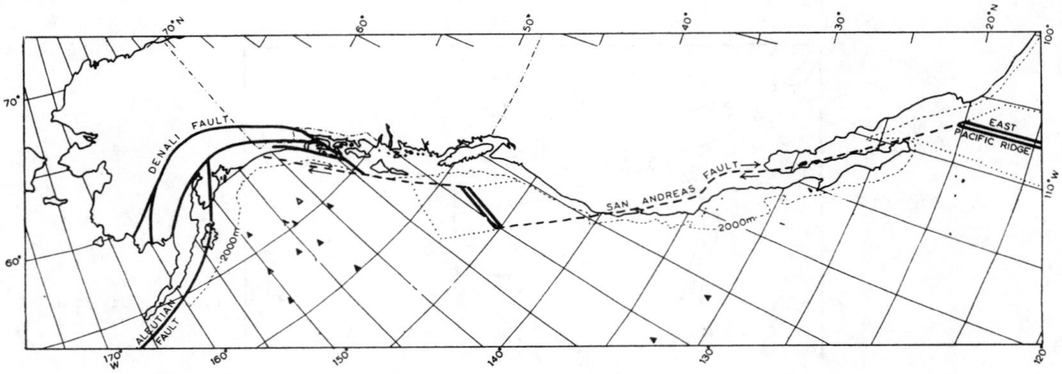

Fig. 9. Sketch map of the west coast of North America showing the approximate location of a submarine thrust fault along the Aleutian trench, the Denali faults (after St. Amand), the San Andreas and another large transform fault (after Benioff) and part of the East Pacific ridge and another mid-ocean ride (after Menard)

In Alaska are several large faults described by St. Amand[21]. Of the relations between them and those off the coast he writes: "If the two systems represent one consistent system, some interesting possibilities arise. One that the San Andreas and Alaska Complex is a gigantic tear fault, along which the Pacific Basin is being slid, relatively speaking under the Alaska Mainland, and the Bering Sea. On the other hand, if the whole system is a strike-slip fault having consistent right-lateral offset, then the whole of the western north Pacific Basin must be undergoing rotation".

St. Amand was uncertain, but preferred the latter alternative, whereas this interpretation would favour the former one. Thus the Denali system is considered to be predominantly a thrust, while the fault off British Columbia is a dextral transform fault.

At a first glance at Fig. 9 it might be held that the transform fault off British Columbia was of ridge-concave arc type and that it connects with the Denali system of thrust faults, but if the Pacific floor is sliding under Alaska, the submarine fault along the Aleutian arc that extends to Anchorage is more significant. In that case the Denali faults are part of a secondary arc system and the main fault is of ridge-convex arc type.

Further examples from the Eastern Pacific. If the examples given from the North and Equatorial Atlantic Ocean, Arabian Sea, Gulf of Aden and North-west Pacific are any guide, offsets of mid-ocean ridges along fracture zones are not faulted displacements, but are an inheritance from the shape of the original fracture. The fracture zones that cross the East Pacific ridge[22] are similar in that their seismicity is confined to the offset parts between ridges. An extension of this suggests that the offsets in the magnetic displacements observed in the aseismic facture zones off California may not be fault displacements as has

为右旋水平运动。

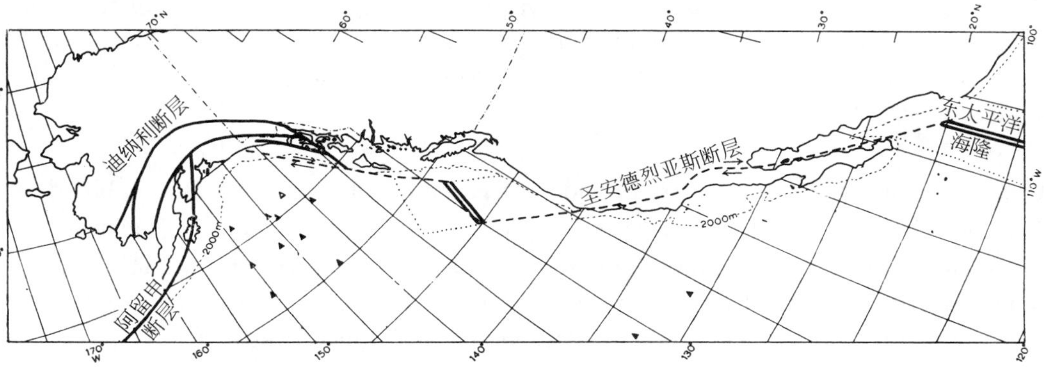

图 9. 北美洲西海岸简图，图中示出了沿阿留申海沟的一个海底逆冲断层、迪纳利断层（据圣阿芒）、圣安德烈亚斯断层以及另一个大型转换断层（据贝尼奥夫）、部分东太平洋海隆和另外一个大洋中脊（据梅纳德）的大概位置。

圣阿芒[21]描述了几个位于阿拉斯加的大断层。关于它们与岸外断层之间的关系，他写道："如果两个体系代表的是一个统一的体系，那么将会出现一些有趣的可能性。一种可能性是，圣安德烈亚斯断层和阿拉斯加的复合体是一个巨大的横推断层，太平洋海盆沿该断层滑动，或者更确切地说，是在阿拉斯加大陆和白令海之下滑动。另一种可能性是，如果整个体系是具有右行错位的走滑断层，那么，整个北太平洋海盆的西部肯定正在发生旋转。"

圣阿芒对此并不确定，但他更倾向于后者，而这种解释又支持了前者。因此，迪纳利体系被认为主要是一个逆冲断层，而不列颠哥伦比亚岸外的断层则是一个右旋转换断层。

初看图 9，可能会认为不列颠哥伦比亚岸外的转换断层属于洋脊–凹弧型，并且与迪纳利逆冲断层体系相连。然而，如果太平洋板块滑到阿拉斯加之下，那么沿着伸向安克雷奇群岛的阿留申岛弧的海底断层将更加明显。在这种情况下，迪纳利断层将只是一个次级弧体系的一部分，主断层属于洋脊–凸弧类型。

来自东太平洋的更多例证　如果来自北大西洋和赤道大西洋、阿拉伯海、亚丁湾以及西北太平洋的这些例子能够提供某些指示的话，那么大洋中脊沿破裂带的错位并不代表断层的断距，而是早期破裂形状的遗迹。穿过东太平洋海隆的破碎带[22]都非常类似，因为它们的地震活动都仅限于洋脊之间的错位部分。我们进一步推论，在加利福尼亚岸外的无震破碎带中所观测到的磁条带错位可能并不是通常所认为的

usually been supposed, but that they reflect the shape of a contemporary rift in the Pacific Ocean. More complex variants of the kind postulated here seem to offer a better chance of explaining the different offsets noted by Vacquier[7] along different lengths of the Murray fracture zone than does transcurrent faulting. If the California fracture zones are of this character and are related to the Darwin rise as postulated by Hess, then the Darwin rise should be offset in a similar pattern.

The southern Andes appear to provide an example of compression combined with shearing. The compressional features are obvious. The existence of dextral shearing is also well known[23]. It is suggested that the latter may be due to the transformation of the West Chile ridge into a dextral transform fault (ridge-convex arc type) along the Andes which terminates at the northern end by thrusting under the Peruvian Andes (Fig. 10).

The observation that there is little seismicity and hence little movement south of the point where the West Chile ridge intersects the Andes can be explained if it is realized that the ridge system forms an almost complete ring about Antarctica, from which expansion must everywhere be directed northwards. This may explain the absence of an isthmus across Drake Passage.

It would also appear that the faults at the two ends of the South Antilles and West Indies arcs are examples of dextral and sinistral pairs of transform faults (concave-concave arc types). According to Fig. 4 both these arcs should be advancing into the Atlantic and inactive east-west faults should not be found beyond the arcs.

This article began by suggesting that some aspects of faulting well known to be anomalous according to traditional concepts of transcurrent faults could be explained by defining a new class of transform faults of which twelve varieties were shown to be possible.

The demonstration by a few examples that at least six of the twelve types do appear to exist with the properties predicted justifies investigating the validity of this concept further.

It is particularly important to do this because transform faults can only exist if there is crustal displacement and proof of their existence would go far towards establishing the reality of continental drift and showing the nature of the displacements involved.

I thank the Departments of Geodesy and Geophysics and of Geology and Churchill College, University of Cambridge, for the opportunity to write this article, those whose data I have used, and colleagues—especially Sir Edward Bullard, W. B. Harland, H. H. Hess, D. H. Matthews and F. J. Vine—for advice; and Sue Chappell and Sue Vine for assistance.

断层断距，而是太平洋现代裂谷形状的一种反应。和平移断层相比，这里所提出的这类断层更为复杂的变种似乎能更好地解释瓦基耶[7]所指出的沿默里断裂带不同地段的差异错位。如果加利福尼亚断裂带具有这种特征并且正如赫斯所推测的那样与达尔文隆起有关，那么达尔文隆起应该以相似的方式被错位。

南安第斯山似乎提供了一个伴随剪切的挤压作用的实例。它的挤压特点非常明显。这里的右旋剪切作用也早已被人们所了解[23]。我们认为，右旋剪切作用可能是由于西智利洋脊沿安第斯山转换为右旋转换断层（洋脊−凸弧型）而造成的，该转换断层的北端终止于秘鲁安第斯山之下的逆冲断层（图 10)。

如果意识到环绕南极洲的洋脊体系是一个几乎完整的环形，并且所有地方都应该从这里起向北扩张，那么我们就可以解释为什么在西智利洋脊与安第斯山相交处以南几乎没有地震活动和板块运动的现象。这也可以解释为什么穿过德雷克海峡没有出现地峡。

南安的列斯群岛和西印度群岛两端的那些断层应该是一个右旋和左旋转换断层对（凹弧−凹弧型）的实例。如图 4 所示，这两个岛弧应该向大西洋方向运动，并且在岛弧以外不存在静止的东西向断层。

本文在开篇时提出，根据传统的平移断层概念，一些著名断层的异常可以通过转换断层这一新的断层类型来解释，并且转换断层可能存在 12 种类型。

通过对几个实例的论证，可以看出 12 种转换断层中至少有 6 种确实存在，并且具有所推测的各种特征。因此，有必要进一步研究转换断层概念的正确性。

这项研究是非常重要的，因为只有当地壳发生位移时转换断层才能产生，并且证明转换断层的存在可进一步确立大陆漂移的真实性，同时也可以说明所涉及的地壳位移的性质。

感谢剑桥大学大地测量学和地球物理学系、地质学系以及丘吉尔学院为我提供了撰写该论文的机会，感谢为我提供所需数据的人，感谢我的同事，特别是爱德华·布拉德、哈兰德、赫斯、马修斯以及瓦因提出的建议；感谢休·查普尔和休·瓦

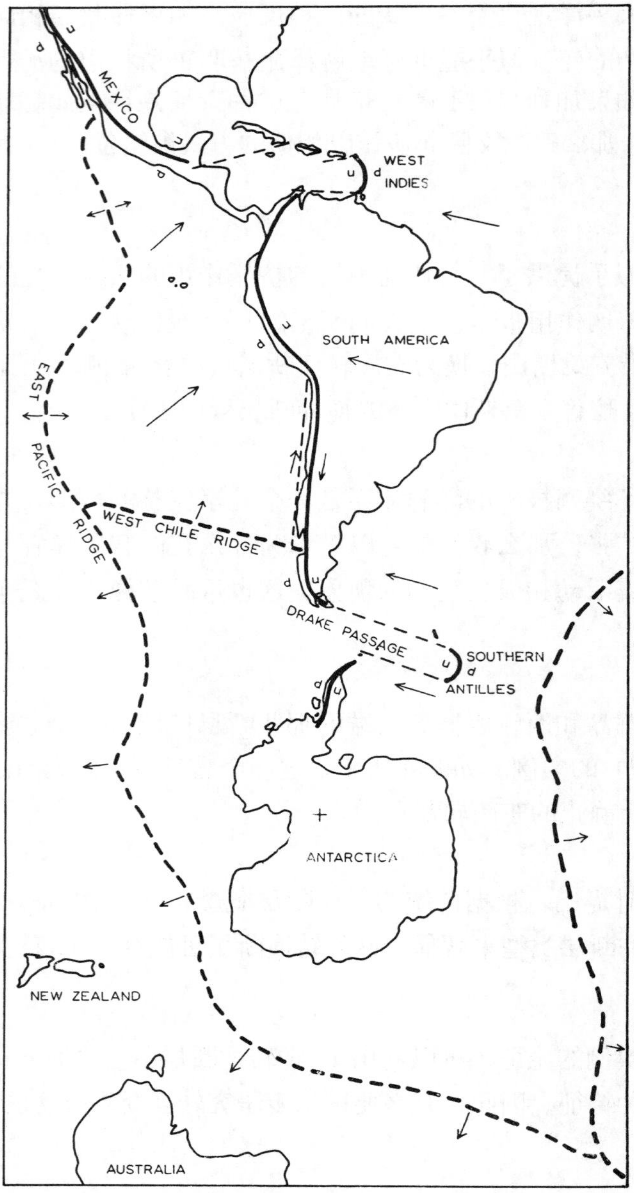

Fig. 10. Sketch map of Mexico, South America, Antarctica and part of the mid-ocean ridge system (heavy dashed lines) illustrating that the great loop of the ridge about Antarctica can only grow by increasing in diameter. Transform faults are shown by light dashed lines

This is a contribution to the Vela Uniform programme and to the Canadian Upper Mantle Project.

(**207**, 343-347; 1965)

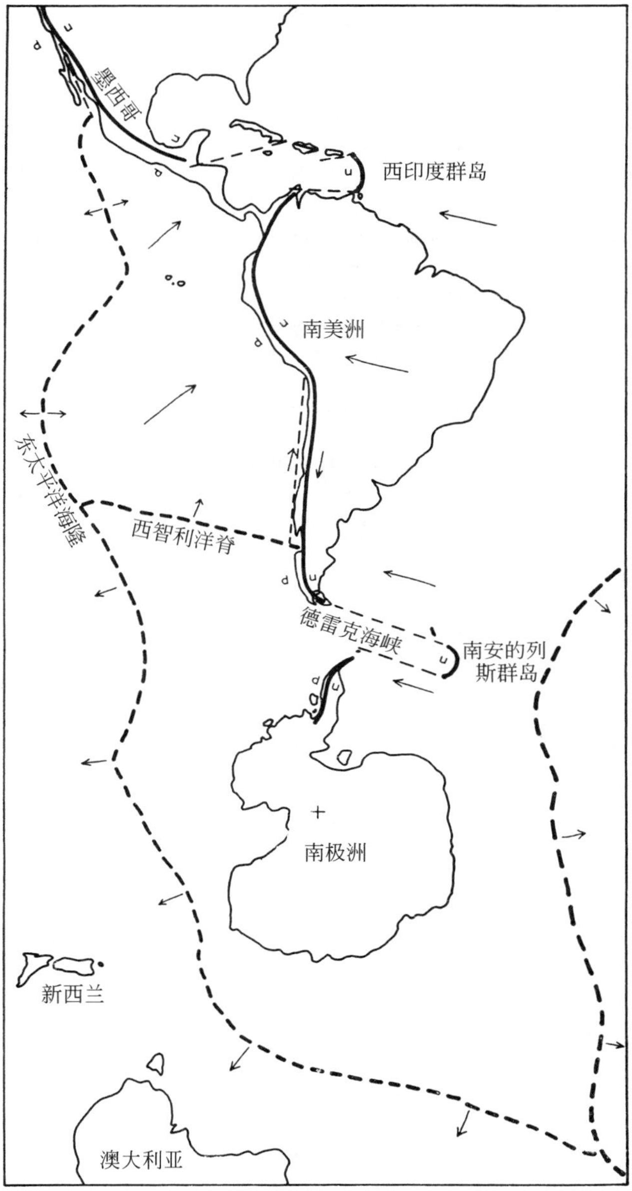

图 10. 墨西哥、南美洲、南极洲以及部分大洋中脊体系（粗虚线）简图，表明环绕南极洲的大型洋脊环只能随直径的增加而增长。细虚线表示转换断层。

因给予的帮助。本研究得到了维拉均一项目和加拿大上地幔计划项目的支持。

（齐红艳 翻译；孟庆任 审稿）

J. Tuzo Wilson: Institute of Earth Sciences, University of Toronto.

References:

1. Bucher, W. H., *The Reformation of the Earth's Crust* (Princeton Univ. Press, 1933).
2. Carey, S. W., *Proc. Roy. Soc. Tasmania*, **89**, 255 (1955).
3. Menard, H. W., *Marine Geology of the Pacific* (McGraw-Hill Book Co., 1964).
4. *Symp. on Continental Drift, Phil. Trans. Roy. Soc.*, edit. by Blackett, P. M. S., Bullard, E. C., and Runcorn, S. K. (in the press).
5. *Symp. Earth Sciences, Mass. Inst. Tech.*, edit. by Townes, C. H. (in the press).
6. *The Sea*, edit. by Hill, M. N., **3** (Interscience Pubs., New York and London, 1963).
7. In *Continental Drift*, edit. by Runcorn, S. K. (Academic Press, New York and London, 1963).
8. Wegener, A., *The Origin of Continents and Oceans* (E. P. Dutton and Co., New York, 1924).
9. Wegmann, C. E., *Med. om Gronland*, **144**, No. 7 (1948).
10. In *Geology of the Arctic*, edit. by Raasch, O., **1** (University of Toronto Press, 1961).
11. Wilson, J. T., *Nature*, **198**, 925 (1963).
12. Heezen, B. C., Bunce, E. T., Hersey, J. B., and Tharp, M., *Deep-Sea Res.*, **11**, 11 (1964).
13. Krause, D. C., *Science*, **146**, 57 (1964).
14. Drake, C. L., and Woodward, H. P., *Trans. N.Y. Acad. Sci.*, Ser. II, **26**, 48 (1963).
15. Gregory, J. W., *Geog. J.*, **56**, 13 (1920).
16. Matthews, D. H., *Nature*, **198**, 950 (1963).
17. *Hunting Survey Corp., Recon. Geol. of Part of West Pakistan*, 365 (Toronto, 1960).
18. Drake, C. L., and Girdler, R. W., *Geophys. J.*, **8**, 473 (1964).
19. Quesnell, A. M., *Quart. J. Geol. Soc. Lond.*, **114**, 1 (1958).
20. Laughton, A. S., *Proc. Roy. Soc.* (in the press).
21. St. Amand, P., *Bull. Geol. Soc. Amer.*, **68**, 1343 (1957).
22. Sykes, L. B., *J. Geophys. Res.*, **68**, 5999 (1963).
23. St. Amand, P., *Los Terremotos de Mayo, Chile* 1960 (Michelson Lab., U.S. Naval Ordnance Test Stations *NOTS* TP2701, China Lake, California, 1961).

A Physical Basis for Life Detection Experiments

J. E. Lovelock

Editor's Note

James Lovelock is best known for his Gaia hypothesis, which postulates that the Earth regulates its climate with feedback processes much like the homeostatic mechanisms that maintain constant conditions in living organisms. Lovelock developed these ideas as an independent scientist, funded from the proceeds of inventions such as instruments for detecting small amounts of trace gases in the atmosphere. In the mid-1960s Lovelock was engaged in discussions at NASA about experiments to search for life on the surface of Mars, to be conducted by lander spacecraft. Here Lovelock sidesteps difficult questions about the unknown chemical basis of extraterrestrial life by proposing a general physical argument rooted in the way life will create a departure from thermodynamic equilibrium in its environment.

THE design of an efficient and unequivocal experiment in extra-terrestrial life detection should take into account: (1) A definition of life stated in terms favourable for its recognition. (2) A description of the past and present environment of the planet to be sampled.

As yet, there is no formal physical statement to describe life from which an exclusive definition for experimental purposes could be drawn. Moreover no comprehensive description is available of the atmospheric as well as the surface physical and chemical environment of any of the planetary bodies.

It is not surprising, in view of the vast expense of space-probe experiments and of the formidable uncertainties already stated here, that the proposed experiments in life detection all ask the cautious geocentric question: "Is there life as we know it?" Most certainly it is difficult to envisage in detail an alien biochemistry; it would seem pointless and very uneconomic to send a space probe to detect a speculative life-form.

It is the object of this article to show that we are not necessarily limited to experiments based on the recognition of a specific life-form, either Earth-like or alien. Also, that it is possible, by accepting a limited phenomenological definition of life, to design simple experiments from the general recognition of life phenomena, including that with which we are familiar. The application of this approach to experiments in life detection is the basis of the discussion which follows.

Recognition of Life

It is a relatively simple matter to distinguish between living and inorganic matter on

生命探测实验的物理基础

洛夫洛克

编者按

令詹姆斯·洛夫洛克最为出名的是他提出的盖亚假说，它假设地球通过反馈过程对其气候进行调节，这非常类似于生物有机体内保持恒定状态的稳态机制。洛夫洛克是作为一名独立科学家提出以上想法的，他的经费来自于他发明诸如检测大气中痕量气体的仪器获得的收入。20 世纪 60 年代中期，洛夫洛克曾参与过美国国家航空航天局关于利用登陆航天器在火星表面进行生命搜索实验的讨论。本文中洛夫洛克以生命会在其生存环境中使热力学平衡发生偏离为基础提出一个普遍的物理论据，绕开了由于对地外生命的化学基础未知而产生的一系列难题。

为了对地球外的生命进行有效而明确的检测，实验设计应考虑以下两点：(1) 从便于识别生命出发确定生命的定义；(2) 对被调查行星的过去和现在环境的描述。

到目前为止，尚无正式的物理表述可以给出生命唯一可用的定义。此外，对任何行星的大气、表面物理和化学环境都还没有一个全面的描述可供使用。

考虑到航天探测器实验的巨大花费以及本文已经阐述过的巨大的不确定性，人们就不会奇怪，为何对所有提出的生命探测实验都会谨慎地问一个以地球为中心的问题："那里的生命和我们所知的相同吗？" 详细地设想一种外星生物化学绝对是困难的；因此发射航天探测器去寻找一种推测的生命形式没有意义，也不划算。

本文的目的就是要说明，我们不必将实验的基础局限于识别某种特别生命形式，无论其是类似地球上的生命形式，还是外星球的生命形式。此外，我们也可以接受对生命有限的唯象定义，并根据普遍承认的，包括一些我们所熟知的生命现象设计一些简单的实验，这是可能的。将这种方法应用到生命探测的实验中是下面讨论的基础。

生命的识别

尽管还没有用生化术语对生命做出的正式定义，但用生化实验来区分地球上

Earth by biochemical experiments even though no formal definition of life in biochemical terms exists. Experience suggests, for example, that a system capable of converting water, atmospheric nitrogen and carbon dioxide into protein, using light as a source of energy, is unlikely to be inorganic. This approach for recognition of life by phenomenology is the basis of the experiments in detection of life so far proposed. Its weakness lies not in the lack of a formal definition but in the assumption that all life has a common biochemical ancestry.

It is also possible to distinguish living from inorganic matter by physical experiments. For example, an examination of the motion of a salmon swimming upstream suggests a degree of purpose inconsistent with a random inorganic process. The physical approach to recognition of life is no more rigorous, at this stage, than is the biochemical one; it is, however, universal in application and not subject to the local constraints which may have set the biochemical pattern of life on Earth.

Past discussions of the physical basis of life[1-3] reach an agreed classification as follows: "Life is one member of the class of phenomena which are open or continuous reaction systems able to decrease their entropy at the expense of substances or energy taken in from the environment and subsequently rejected in a degraded form". This classification is broad and includes also phenomena such as flames, vortex motion and many others. Life differs from the other phenomena so classified in its singularity, persistence, and in the size of the entropy decrease associated with it. Vortices appear spontaneously but soon vanish; the entropy decrease associated with the formation of a vortex is small compared with energy flux. Life does not easily form, but persists indefinitely and vastly modifies its environment. The spontaneous generation of life, according to recent calculations from quantum mechanics[4,5], is extremely improbable. This is relevant to the present discussion through the implication that wherever life exists its biochemical form will be strongly determined by the initiating event. This in turn could vary with the planetary environment at the time of initiation.

On the basis of the physical phenomenology already mentioned, a planet bearing life is distinguishable from a sterile one as follows: (1) The omnipresence of intense orderliness and of structures and of events utterly improbable on a basis of thermodynamic equilibrium. (2) Extreme departures from an inorganic steady-state equilibrium of chemical potential.

This orderliness and chemical disequilibrium would to a diminished but still recognizable extent be expected to penetrate into the planetary surface and its past history as fossils and as rocks of biological origin.

Experiments for Detection of Life

The distinguishing features of a life-bearing planet, described here, suggest the following simple experiments in detection of life:

生命体和无机物质相对来讲是比较简单的事情。例如经验表明，一个能够利用光作为能源，将水、大气中的氮和二氧化碳转换成蛋白质的系统，就不太可能是无机的。这种通过现象表征来识别生命的方法是至今为止提出的探测生命实验的基础。它的缺陷并不在于缺乏正式的定义，而在于假定所有生命的生物化学源头都相同。

也可以用物理实验来区分有生命的和无机的物质。例如，对鲑鱼逆流而上的游动的调查显示出一定程度的目的性，与随机的无机过程并不一致。现阶段识别生命的物理研究方法与生化研究方法相比并不是很严格；然而，它在应用中是普适的，并不受局部条件的限制，这种限制可能已经限定了地球上生命的生化模式。

过去对生命的物理基础[1-3]的讨论达成了如下普遍认同的分类："生命是一类开放的或连续反应系统中的一员，它可以消耗从外界环境中摄取的物质或能量来使自己的熵减少，随后以降解后的形式排出"。这个分类覆盖面很广，也包括了诸如火焰、涡旋运动及其他许多现象。生命与上述分类中其他现象不同还表现为它的奇特性、持久性以及伴随生命过程的熵的减少程度。涡旋自发形成，但很快就会消失；与能流相比涡旋形成时伴随的熵的减少是很小的。生命不容易形成，但一旦形成存在期限就无限定，并在很大程度上改变其环境。近来根据量子力学的计算结果表明[4,5]，生命的自发产生几乎是不可能的。与此相关的是现今的讨论暗示了无论生命在哪里存在，它的生化形式很大程度上受初始事件所决定。并且这又可能因初始时行星的环境条件的不同而变化。

在已经提到的物理现象学的基础上，一个存在生命的行星与一个不毛之地的区别在于：(1）高度有序性及基于热力学平衡几近不可能的结构和事件的普遍存在。(2）完全偏离无机物化学势的稳态平衡。

这种有序性和化学不平衡虽然微小，但仍有希望以能被识别的程度穿透到行星的表面，并成为生物起源的历史化石和基础。

生命探测的实验

基于上述维持有生命的行星所具有的显著特性，我们提出了下列简单的探测生命的实验：

(*A*) *Search for order*. (1) Order in chemical structures and sequences of structure. A simple gas chromatograph or a combined gas chromatograph-mass spectrometer instrument would seek ordered molecular sequences as well as chemical identities.

(2) Order in molecular weight distributions. Polymers of biological origin have sharply defined molecular weights, polymers of inorganic origin do not. A simple apparatus to seek ordered molecular weight distributions in soil has not yet been proposed but seems worthy of consideration.

(3) Looking and listening for order. A simple microphone is already proposed for other (meteorological) purposes on future planetary probes; this could also listen for ordered sequences of sound the presence of which would be strongly indicative of life. At the present stage of technical development a visual search is probably too complex; it is nevertheless the most rapid and effective method of life recognition in terms of orderliness outside the bounds of random assembly.

(*B*) *Search for non-equilibrium*. (1) Chemical disequilibrium sought by a differential thermal analysis (DTA) apparatus. Two equal samples of the planetary surface would be heated in a DTA apparatus: one sample in the atmosphere of the planet, the other in an inert gas, such as argon. An exotherm on the differential signal between the two samples would indicate a reaction between the surface and its atmosphere, a condition most unlikely to be encountered where there is chemical equilibrium as in the absence of life. It should be noted that this method would recognize reoxidizing life on a planet with a reducing atmosphere. This experiment could with advantage and economy be combined with, for example, the gas chromatography mass spectrometry experiment (*A*1) where it is necessary to heat the sample for vaporization and pyrolysis.

(2) Atmospheric analysis. Search for the presence of compounds in the planet's atmosphere which are incompatible on a long-term basis. For example, oxygen and hydrocarbons co-exist in the Earth's atmosphere.

(3) Physical non-equilibrium. A simplified visual search apparatus programmed to recognize objects in non-random motion. A more complex assembly could recognize objects in metastable equilibrium with the gravitational field of the planet. Much of the plant life on Earth falls into this category.

Experiments *A*1, *B*1 and *B*2 are the most promising for the development of practical instruments. Indeed, the gas chromatography-mass spectrometry combination experiment and the DTA experiment already proposed for planetary probes[7] are, with minor modifications, capable of recognizing the ordered sequences and chemical disequilibrium discussed earlier. Experiment *B*2, atmospheric analysis, is simple and practical as well as important in the general problem of detection of life. A detailed and accurate knowledge of the composition of the planetary atmosphere can directly indicate the presence of life in terms of chemical disequilibrium; such knowledge also is complementary to the

(*A*) **搜寻有序性** (1) 化学结构和结构序列的有序性。一台简单的气相色谱仪或气相色谱–质谱联用仪就能检测出有序的分子序列和其化学对应物。

(2) 分子量分布的有序性。生物学来源的聚合物具有明确的分子量，而无机物起源的聚合物并非如此。尚未提出在土壤中探测分子量分布有序性的简便设备，但似乎值得考虑。

(3) 对有序性的“看”和“听”。已经有人提出将用于其他目的（气象学）的简单话筒应用在未来的行星探测器上。我们也可以用其听取能够强烈显示出生命存在的有序序列的声音。对于现阶段的技术发展水平，可视化搜索可能太复杂了；而从无序组织中依据有序性来识别生命却是最快和最有效的方法。

(*B*) **搜寻非平衡性** (1) 用差热分析（DTA）装置搜寻化学的不平衡性。在DTA装置中对行星表面上两份相同的样品加热，一份样品在行星大气中，另一份样品置于惰性气体中（例如在氩气中）。两份样品放热曲线的不同信号即可说明地表和大气之间发生反应。在没有生命的情况下是存在化学平衡的，这时不会产生上述的差异。值得注意的是这种方法还可以用来识别存在于还原性行星大气中的再氧化生命。本实验还可以和气相色谱质谱联用实验结合起来（*A*1），使得分析更加有效和经济，但这时需要加热样品使其汽化并产生热分解。

(2) 大气分析。在行星的大气中寻找是否有从长期看来不相容的化合物共存。比如在地球大气中氧和碳氢化合物的共存。

(3) 物理不平衡。一种简化过的可视化搜索设备，经设计可识别出非随机运动的物体。更加复杂的组装仪器可以识别出在行星重力场下处于亚稳平衡态的物体。地球上的大部分植物都属于这一类。

由于发展了实用的仪器，实验*A*1、*B*1和*B*2是最有希望的。实际上，对行星探测器已提出的气相色谱–质谱联用实验和DTA实验[7]只需较小的改动便可识别出有序序列和前面提到的化学不平衡。大气分析实验*B*2简单实用，在解决生命探测的一般问题中很重要。依据化学不平衡，对行星大气组分详细和准确的了解能够直接证明生命的存在；这些了解对其他生命探测实验的理解以及后续实验的规划也都是有帮助的。即使在生物很丰富的地球上，也存在很多区域，诸如被新雪所覆盖的区域，

understanding of other life detection experiments and to the planning of subsequent experiments. Even on Earth where life is abundant there are many regions, such as those covered by fresh snow, where a surface sample might be unrewarding in the search for life. The atmospheric composition is largely independent of the site of sampling and provides an averaged value representative of the steady state of chemical potential for the whole planetary surface.

Fig. 1 shows the abundance of hydrocarbons of carbon number between 11 and 33 for abiotic hydrocarbons of the Fischer-Tropsch process[8] and hydrocarbons of biological origin, wool wax[9]. Poisson distributions around the predominant hydrocarbon numbers are shown as solid lines. The inorganic hydrocarbons fit closely the expected Poisson distribution for a state of chemical equilibrium. By contrast the biological hydrocarbons show large departures in the distribution of their abundance from this equilibrium state; also, especially for the higher molecular weight alkanes, a two-carbon ordered sequence is well established.

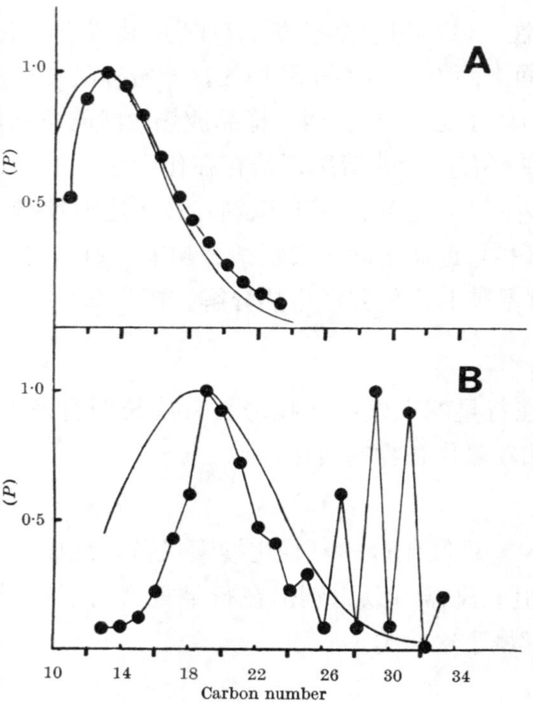

Fig. 1. The abundance of *n*-alkanes from an inorganic source (*A*), Fischer-Tropsch hydrocarbons, and from a biological source (*B*), wool wax. The observed abundances (●——●) are compared with normalized Poisson distributions (——) around the preponderant alkanes

In a similar manner with experiment *B*1 the disequilibrium associated with life can be demonstrated. A few mg of soil heated in a DTA apparatus in air shows a large exotherm when compared with a similar reference sample heated in argon. The combustion of even

取自其中的表面样品可能找不到生命存在的迹象。大气组分与取样的地点大体无关，并且可以提供一个可以代表整个行星表面的化学势稳恒态的平均值。

图 1 分别显示了来自费–托合成过程的非生物源的烃[8] 和来自生物源羊毛蜡的烃[9] 中碳原子数目在 11 到 33 之间的烃的丰度。实线表示的是在含量最多的烃周围的泊松分布。无机烃和化学平衡态所预期的泊松分布很好地吻合了。相反，生物源的烃丰度分布却和这个平衡态有较大的偏离；尤其对于具有较高分子量的烷烃，建立了双碳的有序序列。

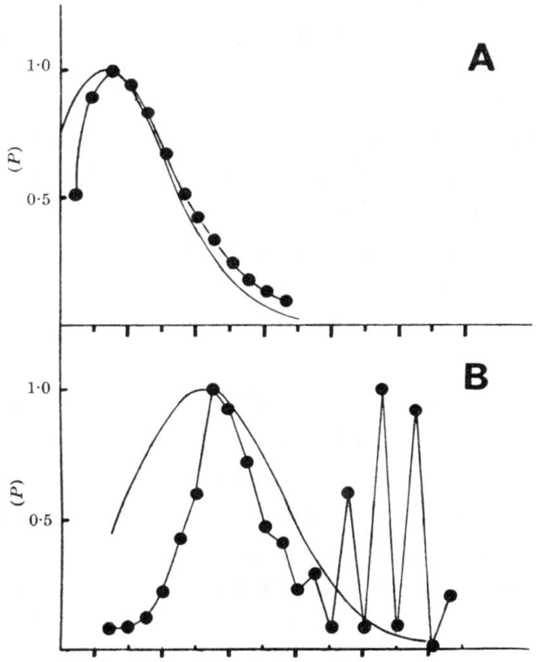

图 1. 来自于费–托烃的无机源（*A*）以及来自于生物源羊毛蜡（*B*）的 *n*- 烷烃的丰度。在主要烷烃附近，观察到的丰度（●——●）与标准泊松分布（——）的比较。

通过与实验 *B*1 类似的方法，还可以证明与生命有关的不平衡。加热放置在空气中的 DTA 装置中的几毫克土壤，当与在氩中加热的类似的参考样品相比时，有更

a few micrograms of organic matter in these circumstances is capable of generating a detectable signal.

Detection of Life on Mars

Ordinarily one does not look for fish in a desert, nor for cacti on an ice cap. Should we, therefore, look for microorganisms of Earth-like habits on Mars, or should we rather ask one or more of the general questions discussed here? The answer to this must depend on the history of Mars, past and present.

The following is the only sure information so far available on Mars. It is dry. The atmosphere is thin and contains no more than a trace of oxygen. The flux of solar radiation at the surface, although less than on Earth, is also less filtered and may include an appreciable content of energetic radiation; in particular, short wave-length ultra-violet. The temperature range includes periods above zero centigrade. Finally, but less certain, is the possibility[6] that oxides of nitrogen are present in appreciable amounts.

If these conditions are representative of Mars in the past as well as now, there seems no reason to assume that life, if present at all, can resemble that on Earth. However, it is possible that Mars was once Earth-like (primeval non-living Earth) and has changed physically to its present state; or less likely that the present state of Mars, like that of the Earth, is a consequence of biological change. For success a geocentric biochemical experiment must assume that Mars was once Earth-like and that life is still surviving in a highly adapted form yet still recognizable to the experiment.

If Mars is as it always was or has been changed to its present state by biological action, then life, if there now, would be very different from that we know. Could we conceive of living systems in liquid N_2O_4 as an ionizing solvent? Could they use hard ultra-violet as a source of energy? Is cellular life necessary in a dry environment, or did cell membranes evolve on Earth to offset the overwhelming effects of dilution in the primeval seas? What sort of Martian biochemistry could have generated the present atmosphere?

Answers to these questions are important in the design of experiments to detect particular life-forms; thus, with a growth experiment, or a biochemical experiment, the strength, composition and conditions of incubation of the medium are of vital importance. This information, however, is not needed in the general detection of life. In view of what is not known of conditions on Mars, the physicochemical experiments in life recognition such as experiments *A*1 and *B*1 and *B*2 seem more worth considering for early probe experiments. These simple experiments do not require a prior knowledge of the planetary environment and are not limited to Earth biochemistry.

大的放热。在这种环境下即便有几微克的有机物燃烧，也可以检测到信号。

探测在火星上的生命

通常，人们不会在沙漠中寻找鱼，也不会在冰盖上寻找仙人掌。那么我们应该在火星上寻找具有类似地球上习性的微生物吗？或者我们更应该问一些在本文中提到的一个或多个一般性的问题？这些问题的答案必然取决于火星的历史，包括过去和现在。

以下是至今所能获得的关于火星的有限确切信息。它很干燥，大气稀薄，仅含有痕量的氧气。火星表面的太阳辐射量虽然要比地球表面的低，但相对来讲被过滤掉的量也较少，因此可能含有相当的高能辐射（尤其是短波紫外线辐射）。温度范围有一部分时间在零摄氏度以上。最后还有一点不太确定的是火星上可能[6]存在相当数量的氮的氧化物。

如果上述信息可以代表火星的过去和现在，那么似乎没有理由假设火星上的生命（如果存在的话）和地球上的是类似的。但有可能火星曾经是类似地球的（原初无生命的地球），只是后来才按照自然规律演变成了现在的状态。或者还有一种比较小的可能性是火星现在的状态，正如地球一样，是由于生物演变的结果。为了成功进行一个以地球为中心的生化实验，必须先要假设火星曾经是类似地球的，并且现在生命仍以一种高度适应的形式存活下来，而且这种形式仍可以为我们的实验所识别。

如果火星一直以来就是现在的模样，或者通过生物活动而变成了现在的样子，那么火星上的生命（如果现在还有的话）将与我们所知道的生命非常不同。我们可以构想以液态 N_2O_4 为离子化溶剂的生命系统吗？它们能否将硬紫外线作为能量的来源呢？细胞生物是否必须要在干燥环境下生存，或者是否在地球上细胞膜得到了进化以防止被远古时期的海水过度的稀释？什么样的火星生化反应才能产生现在的火星大气呢？

以上问题的解答对于我们在设计检测某种特别形式的生命存在的实验时具有很重要的意义。因而，对于发育实验或生化实验，孵化环境的强度、成分和条件是至关重要的。但这些信息对于一般的生命检测是不必要的。鉴于火星上还有一些我们不知道的情况，生命识别的 *A*1、*B*1 和 *B*2 这三个物理化学实验作为早期的探测器上的实验更值得我们优先予以考虑。这些简单的实验并不要求我们对行星环境有预先的了解，并且也不局限于地球上的生物化学。

I thank A. Zlatkis and P. G. Simmonds of the University of Houston for their advice and for conducting and providing me with the results of the differential thermal analysis experiments suggested in the discussion here. I also thank G. Hobby and G. Mamikunian of the Jet Propulsion Laboratory, California Institute of Technology, Pasadena, California, for their advice.

This work was supported by a grant from the National Aeronautics and Space Administration (*NSG* 199-62, J. E. Lovelock).

(**207**, 568-570; 1965)

J. E. Lovelock: Bowerchalke, Nr. Salisbury, Wiltshire.

References:

1. Schrödinger, E., *What is Life?* (Camb. Univ. Press, 1944).
2. Bernal, J. D., *The Physical Basis of Life* (Routledge and Kegan Paul, London, 1951).
3. Denbigh, K. G., *The Thermodynamics of the Steady State* (Methuen and Co., London, 1951).
4. Wigner, E. P., *The Logic of Personal Knowledge* (Routledge and Kegan Paul, London, 1961).
5. Landsberg, P. T., *Nature*, **203**, 928(1964).
6. Kiess, C. C., Karrer, S., and Kiess, H. K., *Publ. Astro. Soc. Pacific*, **72**, 256 (1960).
7. Lipsky, S. R., and Lovelock, J. E., *Recommendations report.* Submitted to Donald Easter, Planetary Atmospheres Section, NASA Headquarters, Washington, D.C. (April 1964).
8. Meinschein, W. G., *Space Sci. Revs.*, **2**, 665 (1963).
9. Mold, J. D., *et al., Biochemistry*, **3**, 1293 (1964).

我要感谢休斯敦大学的兹拉特基斯和西蒙兹对本文中的差热分析实验给出建议、进行操作并将结果提供给我。我还要感谢来自加利福尼亚州帕萨迪纳市的加州理工学院喷气推进实验室的霍比和马米库尼安的建议。

本项工作受来自于美国国家航空航天局的基金（*NSG*199-62，洛夫洛克）支持。

（沈乃澂 翻译；邓祖淦 审稿）

Spectral Data from the Cosmic X-Ray Sources in Scorpius and near the Galactic Centre

R. Giacconi *et al.*

Editor's Note

Riccardo Giacconi was an Italian working at the Massachusetts Institute of Technology (MIT) when he developed the X-ray telescope—a device based on the formation of images of extraterrestrial X-ray sources involving the scattering of X-rays incident on the shaped mirror at glancing angles. Using such a telescope launched by a rocket, Giacconi discovered the existence of X-ray sources in 1962. In this paper, Giacconi and his colleagues described the discovery of further X-ray sources, many of them near the centre of our Galaxy. The culmination of this work was the launch of the Einstein satellite by the United States in 1978. Giacconi left MIT to become director of the European Southern Observatory in Chile (with an administrative and research base in Munich, Germany).

DURING two rocket flights conducted from White Sands Missile Range on August 28,1964 (flight I), and October 26, 1964 (flight II), we have obtained information regarding the spectral composition of the X-ray source in Scorpius (*ScoX*-1) and those along the Galactic equator in the vicinity of the Galactic centre. The results were obtained from two separate detectors and extend over the spectral region 1-25 keV. We find that the radiation from *ScoX*-1 extends from 15 keV to at least 2.5 keV, and that the spectral distribution is not consistent with black-body radiation. The radiation from the region along the Galactic centre extends to about 25 keV. The latter region apparently contains several distinct X-ray sources as reported by Giacconi *et al.*[1], Bowyer *et al.*[2] and Fisher *et al.*[3].

Since the discovery of cosmic X-ray sources by Giacconi *et al.*[4] in 1962, only gross information regarding the spectral composition of the radiation has been reported. In the same paper an effective wave-length near 3 Å was reported based on atmospheric attenuation and the difference in counting rate in two separate Geiger counters. Giacconi *et al.*[5] afterwards reported that the spectrum was consistent with a black-body temperature of about 10^7 °K. Bowyer *et al.*[6] attempted to measure the spectral composition of radiation from the Crab Nebula between 1 and 10 keV by making observations in two independent Geiger counters. Later, they published[2] a critical evaluation of their experiment which showed that one of the counters did not function as expected. In the same paper they presented results on the atmospheric attenuation of X-radiation from the Scorpius source which was consistent with a black-body temperature of $2\text{-}3\times10^6$ °K. In another experiment

天蝎座和银河系中心附近的宇宙 X 射线源光谱数据

贾科尼等

编者按

里卡尔多·贾科尼是一位在麻省理工学院工作的意大利人，期间，他研制了 X 射线望远镜，这是基于地球外 X 射线源在按不同掠射角入射到特定形状的镜面上时所产生的散射成像的一种装置。1962 年，用这种由火箭发射到太空的望远镜，贾科尼发现了 X 射线源。本文中，贾科尼及其同事们描述了发现更多 X 射线源的过程，其中很多射线源靠近我们银河系的中心。1978 年，美国爱因斯坦号人造卫星的发射标志着这项工作达到了顶峰。贾科尼离开麻省理工学院后，成为位于智利的欧洲南方天文台的主管（在德国慕尼黑拥有行政部门和科研基地）。

白沙导弹靶场分别于 1964 年 8 月 28 日（第一次飞行）和 1964 年 10 月 26 日（第二次飞行）进行了两次火箭飞行实验，对天蝎座（*ScoX*-1）和银道面上银河系中心附近的 X 射线源进行了探测，获得了大量光谱信息。这些结果由两个独立的探测器获取，能谱范围为 1 千电子伏 ~ 25 千电子伏。结果表明，天蝎座 *X*-1 的辐射能谱范围为 2.5 千电子伏 ~ 15 千电子伏，但其光谱分布与黑体辐射谱并不一致；来自银河系中心区域的辐射能谱延伸到大约 25 千电子伏，这一区域明显包括若干不同的 X 射线源，相关报道可以参见贾科尼等人 [1]、鲍耶等人 [2] 和费希尔等人 [3] 的研究。

自从贾科尼等人于 1962 年发现宇宙 X 射线源以来 [4]，关于该辐射谱组成的报道均较为粗略。贾科尼的小组在同一篇文章中还基于大气衰减和两个单独的盖革计数器的计数率差异而报道了有效波长位于 3 埃附近的辐射。随后，他们进一步报道 [5]，该辐射谱与温度约为 10^7 K 的黑体相符。鲍耶等人 [6] 则尝试使用两个独立盖革计数器，在 1 千电子伏 ~ 10 千电子伏范围内观察蟹状星云的辐射谱组成。不久，他们在发表的论文中 [2] 对自己的实验进行了关键性的评估，发现其中的一个计数器并没有按照预期进行工作；在同一篇文章中他们给出了天蝎座射电源 X 射线辐射的大气衰减数据，其与温度为 2×10^6 K~3×10^6 K 的黑体相符。在另一项实验中，克拉克 [7] 则使用气球搭载设备，在 20 千电子伏 ~ 60 千电子伏范围内，对蟹状星云的 X 射线

X-radiation from the Crab has been observed between 20 and 60 keV by Clark[7] using balloon-borne instrumentation.

Discussions of the source mechanism for the generation of the observed X-rays has centred on three possibilities: (1) black-body radiation from a neutron star; (2) radiation from an optically thin hot plasma; (3) synchrotron radiation from high-energy electrons in a weak magnetic field. Specific literature citations appear in refs. 5 and 7 cited here and in a review article by Giacconi and Gursky[8].

We are reporting here spectral data obtained by placing absorbers in front of the Geiger counters during flight I and by performing a pulse height analysis of the output of a sodium iodide (NaI) scintillation counter during flight II. The several sources along the Galactic equator could not be resolved with these counters and all contribute to the spectral data from that region. Other results from these rocket flights have been reported by Giacconi *et al.*[9], which demonstrated the separation between *ScoX*-1 and the sources near the Galactic centre, and by Oda *et al.*[10], which presented the results of the measurement of the angular diameter of *ScoX*-1.

The Geiger counter detector used during flight I of this experiment was a bank of twelve individual argon-filled counters with beryllium windows of 9.0 mg/cm^2 thickness and a total sensitive area of about 70 cm^2. The efficiency, calculated as the product of the absorption in the gas filling and the transmission of the window, lies above 10 percent between 17 keV and 1.2 keV and peaks at between 3 and 4 keV. This computed efficiency was checked experimentally by exposing counters to the beam from a tungsten target, windowless X-ray tube operated from 1.8 to 10 kV. The observed counting rates were in agreement over the entire range of voltage with those predicted using thick target yield curves and the computed counter efficiency.

The Geiger counters were equipped with rectangular collimators which limited the field of view to 15° full width at half maximum (FWHM) in the direction of rotation of the rocket and 20° FWHM in the direction of the rocket long axis. The counter bank was mounted so that its axis of maximum sensitivity made an angle of 80° with respect to the long axis. Two filters, *F*1 of 7.04 mg/cm^2 of beryllium and *F*2 of 1.72 mg/cm^2 of mylar, were placed in front of the detector and were sequentially removed during the flight to allow measurements for approximately equal time-intervals of the X-ray fluxes with *F*1 and *F*2 in place, *F*1 alone in place, and no filter.

The motion of the rocket during this flight (flight I) consisted of a rapid rotation with a period of 0.55 sec about the long axis plus a slow precession of the rotation axis with a period of 83 sec along a cone of a small opening angle. The X-ray source regions were observed during each rotation but, because of the low counting rates, data from successive rotations were added in order to obtain sufficient statistical precision.

辐射进行了观测。

目前，围绕着所观察到的X射线源的产生机制主要存在三种可能性：(1) 中子星产生的黑体辐射；(2) 光学薄热等离子体产生的辐射；(3) 弱磁场中高能电子引起的同步辐射。这方面具体的相关文献可见本文中引用的参考文献5和参考文献7，以及贾科尼与古尔斯基的综述文章[8]。

在第一次飞行中，我们将吸收体放置在盖革计数器前；在第二次飞行中，我们对碘化钠闪烁计数器的输出进行了脉冲高度分析，并将在本文报道这两次探测的光谱数据。根据这些计数器并不能分辨出银道附近的各个辐射源，但是这些辐射源对该区域的光谱数据都有贡献。关于这两次火箭飞行探测，贾科尼等人[9]先前也曾报道过一些其他结果，验证了天蝎座*X*-1与银河系中心附近的辐射源是分离的；同时小田稔等人[10]给出了天蝎座*X*-1角直径的测量结果。

第一次飞行实验所使用的盖革计数器包括一组12个单独的充氩计数器，其窗口材料为铍，厚度为9.0毫克/厘米^2，总传感面积约为70厘米^2。计数器的效率用氩气的吸收率乘以窗口的透射率计算，在1.2千电子伏~17千电子伏之间一般高于10%，而且峰值在3千电子伏~4千电子伏之间。这种计数器的理论计算效率可以通过实验进行检验，方法是将计数器暴露在钨靶的射线中，无窗X射线管工作电压为1.8千伏~10千伏。在整个电压范围内，观测到的计数率与使用厚靶产额曲线和计数效率计算值所得到的预测值相符。

实验中使用的盖革计数器配备了矩形准直器，从而可以限制其视场，在火箭的旋转方向上，半高全宽为15°；在火箭的长轴方向上，半高全宽为20°。氩气计数器采用最大灵敏度方向与火箭长轴方向呈80°夹角的方式安装。探测器前面安装有两个滤光片*F*1和*F*2，*F*1的窗口材料为7.04毫克/厘米^{2}厚的铍，*F*2的窗口材料为1.72毫克/厘米^{2}厚的聚酯薄膜。在飞行过程中，两滤光片先后被去掉，这样就可以分别测量同时存在*F*1和*F*2、只有*F*1以及没有滤光片三种条件下的X射线流量，三次测量的持续时间间隔大体相同。

在第一次飞行中，火箭的运动包括周期为0.55秒绕长轴的快速转动，以及周期为83秒的沿小孔径角圆锥面的缓慢进动。在每次转动过程中，X射线源区域都会被观测一次；但是，由于计数率较低，所以我们将连续转动获取的数据叠加在一起，以便获得足够的统计精确度。

During each rotation the detector swept out a band on the celestial sphere the width of which, 20°, equalled that of the collimator. The precession results in an approximately sinusoidal variation of the angle of closest approach of a given celestial object to the centre of this band. During each precession cycle the centre of the band came within 2° of *ScoX*-1 and moved along the Galactic equator between $l_{II} = 2°$ to $l_{II} = 27°$.

Three full precession cycles were recorded during the rocket flight, and since a filter change occurred almost in phase with the precession we have essentially a complete precession cycle of data for each of the three filter conditions. The data from the precession cycle with no filter in place have been the subject of a previous paper[9]. The counting rates with background subtracted observed with the three filter conditions when the detector crossed *ScoX*-1 and crossed the region along the Galactic equator are listed in Table 1. The counting rates represent an average over the same fraction of the precession cycle for the three cases. Listed also is the attenuation, defined as the ratio of the counting rates for the two filter combinations compared with no filter.

Table 1. Counting Rate observed in the Two-source Regions with and without Filters

Filter condition	Source region	Counting rate measured c.p.m	Attenuation relative to no filter
No filter	*ScoX*-1	620±20	1
*F*1	*ScoX*-1	440±18	0.71±0.04
*F*1+*F*2	*ScoX*-1	350±17	0.56±0.03
No filter	Gal cen	350±18	1
*F*1	Gal cen	240±18	0.70±0.06
*F*1+*F*2	Gal cen	210±15	0.62±0.05
Typical background rate		30 c.p.m	

The significance of the attenuation factor can be partially understood from the following arguments. Photons at 2.5 keV will give the observed attenuation of about 0.7 per filter. In order to obtain the same attenuation factor in the case of a distribution of energies, the number of lower energy photons present, which are absorbed more strongly, must be compensated for by high-energy photons which are absorbed less strongly. Thus, there must be comparable numbers of photons above and below 2.5 keV. The magnitude of the attenuation depends on the true spectral distribution and can be calculated from the relation:

$$\text{Attenuation} = \int \varphi(\lambda) e^{-\mu(\lambda)x} \varepsilon(\lambda) d\lambda \Big/ \int \varphi(\lambda) \varepsilon(\lambda) d\lambda \qquad (1)$$

where $\varphi(\lambda)$ is an assumed spectrum in terms of number of photons per unit wave-length interval, $\varepsilon(\lambda)$ is the counter efficiency, $\mu(\lambda)$ is the linear absorption coefficient of the filter and x is the thickness of the filter. We performed this calculation for three assumed spectra, namely, (1) a power law spectrum of the form:

$$\varphi(\lambda) = A\lambda^{-(\alpha+1)} \qquad (2)$$

对于每一次转动，探测器在天球上都扫过 20° 的区域，这与矩形准直器角宽度一致。指定天体与扫描带中心最接近点的角度近似成正弦变化，这是由进动引起的。在每个进动周期内，扫描带中心都会进入与天蝎座 X-1 呈 2° 的范围内，同时在 $l_{II} = 2°$ 到 $l_{II} = 27°$ 之间沿银道移动。

本次火箭飞行中，我们记录了三个完整的进动周期，并且由于滤光片的转换几乎与进动同相，所以基本上对于三种滤光片情况下的每一种我们都得到了完整的进动周期数据。对于没有滤光片的情况，我们在先前的一篇文章中已经分析过这方面的进动周期数据 [9]。当探测器扫过天蝎座 X-1 和银道区域，在以上三种滤光片情况下观测到的计数率参见表 1，该计数率已经减去了背景计数率。这里的计数率是指在三种情况下进动周期某一小段相同时间内的平均值。表 1 也给出了滤光片的衰减，定义为两滤光片条件下的计数率与无滤光片条件下的计数率的比值。

表 1. 不同滤光片条件下两个辐射源区域的计数率

滤光片条件	辐射源区域	测量计数率（每分钟计数）	相对没有滤光片的衰减
无滤光片	天蝎座 X-1	620 ± 20	1
$F1$	天蝎座 X-1	440 ± 18	0.71 ± 0.04
$F1$+$F2$	天蝎座 X-1	350 ± 17	0.56 ± 0.03
无滤光片	银河系中心	350 ± 18	1
$F1$	银河系中心	240 ± 18	0.70 ± 0.06
$F1$+$F2$	银河系中心	210 ± 15	0.62 ± 0.05
典型背景计数率	30（每分钟计数）		

衰减因子的重要性可以由以下分析看出。能量为 2.5 千电子伏的光子穿过每个滤光片的衰减大约为 0.7。滤光片对低能光子的吸收较强，对高能光子的吸收较弱，因此就能量分布而言，为了获得相同的衰减因子，需要对前者进行补偿。所以，在高于和低于 2.5 千电子伏的范围内，必然存在数目相近的光子数目。衰减的具体数值取决于实际的光谱分布，并可以通过以下关系计算：

$$\text{衰减} = \int \varphi(\lambda) e^{-\mu(\lambda)x} \varepsilon(\lambda) d\lambda \Big/ \int \varphi(\lambda) \varepsilon(\lambda) d\lambda \tag{1}$$

其中 $\varphi(\lambda)$ 是给定的光谱分布，为单位波长间隔内的光子数，$\varepsilon(\lambda)$ 为计数器效率，$\mu(\lambda)$ 为滤光片的线性吸收系数，x 为滤光片的厚度。下面对以下三种给定的光谱分布进行计算。也就是，（1）幂律谱形式：

$$\varphi(\lambda) = A\lambda^{-(\alpha+1)} \tag{2}$$

Equation (2) is equivalent to a distribution of the form $\nu^{-\alpha}$ (ν = frequency) when the spectrum is expressed in terms of power per unit frequency interval.

(2) An exponential spectrum of the form:

$$\varphi(\lambda) = (A/\lambda)\exp(-hc/\lambda kT) \qquad (3)$$

Except for the weak energy dependence of the Gaunt factor this spectral distribution describes free-free emission by electrons having a Maxwellian distribution of energy.

(3) A thermal spectrum of the form:

$$\varphi(\lambda) = A\lambda^{-4}[\exp(hc/\lambda kT)-1] \qquad (4)$$

The quantity A that appears in these three distribution laws is a constant that can be determined from the relation:

$$A = N/\int\varphi(\lambda)\varepsilon(\lambda)d\lambda \qquad (5)$$

where N is the observed counting rate.

For each of the distribution laws and for each filter condition, equation (1) was evaluated by numerical integration for a series of values of α in the case of the power law spectrum and of T in the case of exponential and thermal spectra. The observed attenuations for *ScoX*-1 are obtained with $\alpha = -1.1 \pm 0.3$ for a power law spectrum, with $T = (3.8 \pm 1.8) \times 10^7$ °K for an exponential spectrum, and $T = (9.1 \pm 0.9) \times 10^6$ °K for a blackbody spectrum. The listed uncertainties result from the statistical fluctuations expected from the total accumulated counts. Within the precision of the measurement, the spectrum from the two-source regions is the same over the interval of wave-lengths to which the Geiger counter is sensitive. Furthermore, it is not possible to decide between the three spectral types from these data alone.

Additional spectral results come from the observation during flight II of the same two-source regions by an NaI(T1) crystal with area of 38.5 cm^2 and a thickness of 1 mm covered by 6.9 mg/cm^2 of aluminium. The crystal was viewed by a 7188 CBS photomultipler and the combination had a measured resolution of 48 percent FWHM at 22 keV. The detector field of view was limited to 5°×25° FWHM and the detector was mounted with its axis at 60° from the long axis of the rocket. During the flight this detector scanned substantially the same source regions in the sky as did the Geiger counters in flight I, and the rocket motion was comparable with that of flight I.

事实上，如果光谱分布表达为每单位频率间隔功率的形式，式(2)就等价于 $\nu^{-\alpha}$（ν 表示频率）分布。

（2）指数谱形式：

$$\varphi(\lambda) = (A/\lambda)\exp(-hc/\lambda kT) \tag{3}$$

除了冈特因子的弱能量依存性之外，这种光谱分布描述了具有麦克斯韦能量分布的电子的自由–自由发射。

（3）热辐射谱形式：

$$\varphi(\lambda) = A\lambda^{-4}[\exp(hc/\lambda kT)-1] \tag{4}$$

以上三种分布律中的系数 A 为一常数，其大小可以由下式决定：

$$A = N/\int\varphi(\lambda)\varepsilon(\lambda)\mathrm{d}\lambda \tag{5}$$

其中 N 为观测到的计数率。

对于每一种分布律和每一种滤光片条件，在幂律谱情况下取不同 α 值，以及在指数谱和热辐射谱情况下取不同 T 值，从而对式(1)中进行数值积分求解。观测到的天蝎座 X-1 的衰减，对于幂律谱，对应的 $\alpha = -1.1 \pm 0.3$；对于指数谱，对应的温度 $T =（3.8 \pm 1.8）\times 10^7$ K；对于黑体辐射谱，对应的温度为 $T =（9.1 \pm 0.9）\times 10^6$ K。以上给出的不确定度是由累积计数中的统计涨落造成的。在测量精度范围内，两个 X 射线源区域的辐射谱在盖革计数器敏感的波长区间上是相同的。此外，仅仅通过这些数据不太可能决定光谱分布的具体形式。

另外，在第二次飞行实验中，我们也对以上两个辐射源区域进行了观测并获取了光谱数据。这次探测中的探测器使用了面积为 38.5 厘米^2 的碘化钠（Tl）晶体，其厚度为 1 毫米，镀有 6.9 毫克 / 厘米^2 的铝。该晶体由一个 7188 CBS 光电倍增管观测，该组合的分辨率在 22 千电子伏处为半高全宽的 48%。探测器的半高全宽视场为 5° ×25°，探测器的固定轴与火箭长轴方向夹角为 60°。在飞行过程中，探测器基本上是持续地扫描天空中相同的辐射源区域，这和第一次飞行中的盖革计数器扫描的类似，而且火箭的运动也和第一次飞行类似。

The results from this detector consisted of those photomultiplier pulses above a threshold equivalent to about 8 keV. These were stretched to 1 ms with their pulse height preserved and telemetered in real time from the rocket. Pulses from successive spins of the rocket were summed as a function of both pulse height and rocket azimuth. The azimuthal distribution of all telemetered pulses is shown in Fig. 1. Sources are apparent at azimuths of 2° and 26° which correspond respectively to traversal of the regions containing *ScoX*-1 and the Galactic equator. We have assumed that the same X-ray sources are responsible for the radiation detected in the NaI and Geiger counter detection systems.

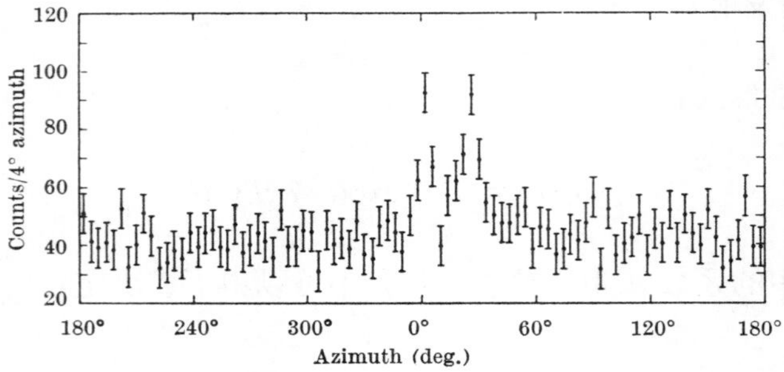

Fig. 1. Azimuthal distribution of counts observed in NaI detector

The differential pulse height distributions of the data within the source regions are shown with background subtracted in Fig. 2, as well as the background spectrum itself. The data below 10 keV show the cut-off resulting from the electronic threshold. Above 10 keV the distribution of pulse heights observed in the two-source region is markedly different from the background distribution. The distribution observed from *ScoX*-1 is consistent with a cut-off in the spectrum at about 15 keV, whereas the radiation from the Galactic equator region extends to higher energies and there is evidence for a possible peak at 20 keV from the same region. The observation of this peak must be regarded as only tentative because of the low statistical precision of the results; however, this feature cannot be an instrumental effect since it does not appear in either of the other two spectra.

The ambiguity in the choice of spectral distribution law that arises from the Geiger counter data alone can be partially resolved by considering the NaI data as well. The counting rates observed for the two-source regions by the two detectors are listed in Table 2. The ratio of counting rates for *ScoX*-1 is (14±3):1, which can be obtained for either a power law or exponential spectral distribution with the parameters determined from the Geiger counter data. To fit a black-body distribution, however, requires a temperature of $(17\pm1)\times10^6$ °K which cannot be reconciled with the Geiger counter data. The black-body temperature consistent with the Geiger counter data predicts a ratio of about 200:1. This analysis applied to the ratio of counting rates observed in the Galactic counter region yields the same general results; namely, that the ratio can be fitted with either an exponential or power law spectrum but that a black-body spectrum yields an insignificant

探测器的数据与那些能量强度均大于阈值约为 8 千电子伏的光电倍增管脉冲相等。在 1 毫秒的时间长度上保持这些脉冲的高度不变，并实时地从火箭传回地面。然后将火箭连续旋转过程中探测到的脉冲进行加和，最后结果可以作为脉冲高度和火箭方位角的函数。图 1 给出了所有遥测脉冲的方位角分布。显然辐射源位于 2° 和 26° 方位角，分别对应天蝎座 *X*-1 和银道区域。事实上，在以上分析中，我们已经假设碘化钠和盖革计数器探测系统探测到的辐射来自相同的 X 射线源。

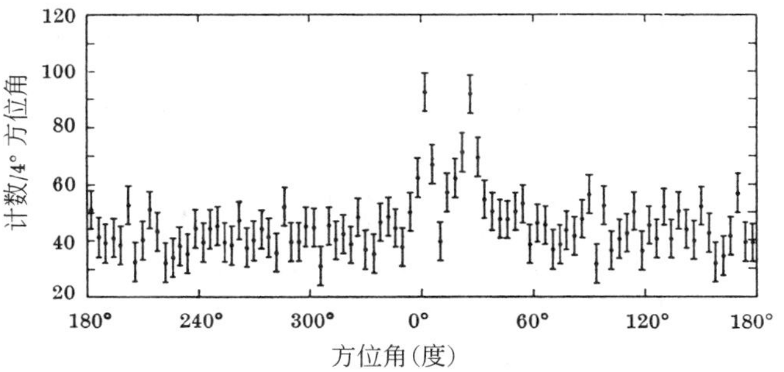

图 1. 碘化钠探测器计数的方位角分布

图 2 给出了辐射源区域内不同的脉冲高度分布和背景辐射谱，前者已经扣除了背景计数。由图可知，10 千电子伏之下的数据存在能谱的截止现象，该现象是由电子的阈值引起的。在高于 10 千电子伏范围内，观测到的两个辐射源的脉冲高度分布与背景分布非常不同。所观测到的天蝎座 *X*-1 的分布与在 15 千电子伏左右存在截止的光谱一致，而银道区域的辐射则延伸到更高的能量范围，但同样在该区域 20 千电子伏附近可能存在另一个峰值。由于结果统计精度较低，20 千电子伏附近的峰尚属于推测；但该峰不可能是仪器引起的，因为它并没有在另外两个能谱中出现。

仅使用盖革计数器数据而难以确定采用何种光谱分布律的问题，可以通过同时参考碘化钠数据得到部分解决。两探测器对两个辐射源观测得到的计数率如表 2 所示。天蝎座 *X*-1 的计数率的比值为 $(14\pm3):1$，该结果由幂律或指数谱分布得到，两种分布的具体参数可以由盖革计数器数据确定。为了拟合黑体辐射分布，需要满足特征温度为 $(17\pm1)\times10^6$ K，然而，该值与盖革计数器数据不符。另一方面，与盖革计数器数据相符的黑体温度给出的计数率比值约为 200:1。将以上分析应用于银河系区域计数率比值也会得到相似的结果，即指数谱或幂律谱均可以拟合计数率比值，但是黑体辐射谱给出的碘化钠探测器流量与实际观测值相比几乎可以忽略。

flux in the NaI detector compared with what is observed. It is possible that a series of black-body sources gives rise to the observed radiation which, however, implies that one of the sources has a temperature of several times 10^7 °K.

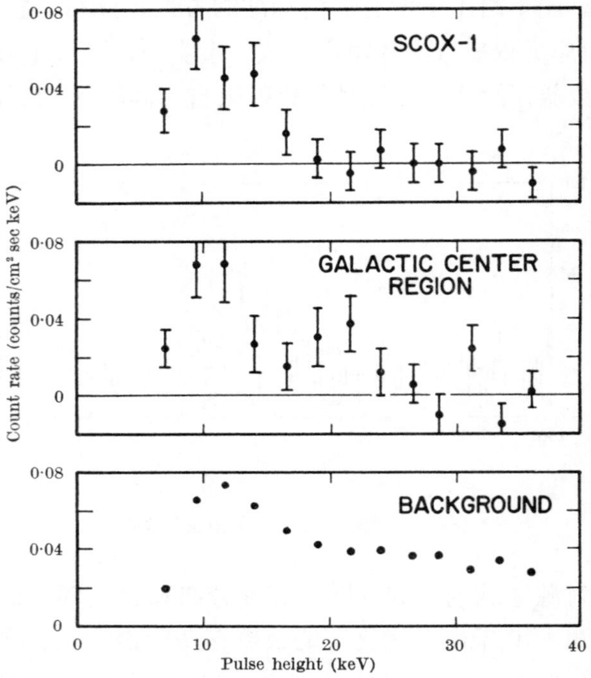

Fig. 2. Pulse height distribution of counting rates observed in NaI detector

Table 2. Counting Rates and Absolute Fluxes Observed for the Two-Source Regions

	Counting rate counts/cm^2 · sec	Integrated power ergs/cm^2 · sec	Integrated flux photons/cm^2 · sec
ScoX-1			
1-10 keV	16.8±0.6	$(1.61\pm0.4)\times10^{-7}$	32±6
> 8 keV	1.2±0.3	$(3.3\pm0.8)\times10^{-8}$	1.8±0.4
Galactic equator			
1-10 keV	4.3±0.2	$(0.4\pm0.1)\times10^{-7}$	8±2
> 8 keV	0.67±0.15	$(1.9\pm0.4)\times10^{-8}$	0.8±0.2

Numbers listed for 1-10 keV are derived from Geiger counters and those listed for >8 keV are derived from the NaI detector. The listed errors are based on the count statistics and in the case of the integrated power and flux in the 1-10 keV range include the effect of the uncertainty of the spectral index

In the case of *ScoX*-1, if one wishes to fit a thermal spectrum of the order of 10^7 °K as is consistent with the Geiger counter data alone plus a high-energy tail to account for the NaI results, the power in the tail must be the order of 25 percent of that in the thermal portion of the spectrum and to fit a lower temperature requires an even more substantial non-thermal tail. Thus, if a neutron star is postulated as the X-ray source, a large fraction of the observed flux cannot arise from the black-body radiation from that object.

原因可能是，若干黑体辐射源都对观测值有贡献，但是其中一个具有数倍于 10^7 K 的温度。

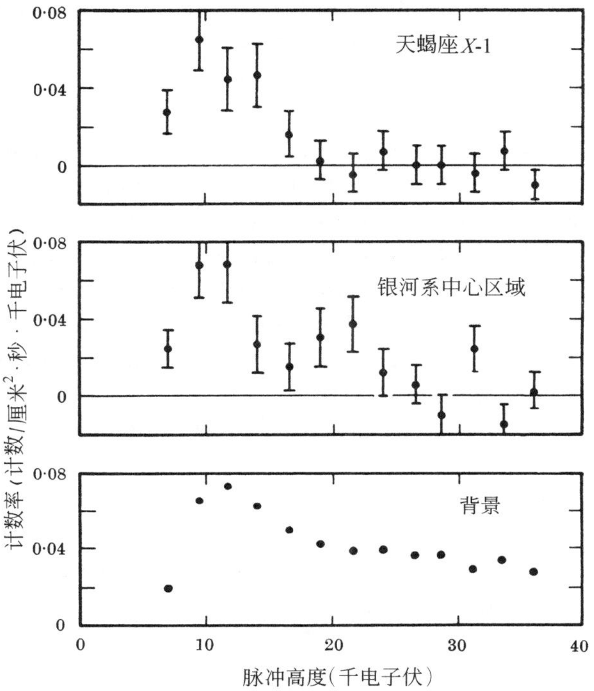

图 2. 碘化钠探测器观测到的计数率的脉冲高度分布

表 2. 对于两个辐射源区域观测得到计数率和绝对流量

	计数率 个 / 厘米²·秒	积分功率 尔格 / 厘米²·秒	积分流量 个光子 / 厘米²·秒
天蝎座 *X*-1			
1 千电子伏 ~10 千电子伏	16.8 ± 0.6	$(1.61 \pm 0.4) \times 10^{-7}$	32 ± 6
> 8 千电子伏	1.2 ± 0.3	$(3.3 \pm 0.8) \times 10^{-8}$	1.8 ± 0.4
银道			
1 千电子伏 ~10 千电子伏	4.3 ± 0.2	$(0.4 \pm 0.1) \times 10^{-7}$	8 ± 2
> 8 千电子伏	0.67 ± 0.15	$(1.9 \pm 0.4) \times 10^{-8}$	0.8 ± 0.2

表中给出的1千电子伏~10千电子伏能量范围内的数据由盖革计数器获得，大于8千电子伏的数据来自碘化钠探测器。表中给出的误差来源于计数统计；对于积分功率和流量两栏，1 千电子伏 ~10 千电子伏范围内的误差也考虑了光谱指数的不确定度。

对于天蝎座 *X*-1，如果希望拟合量级为 10^7 K 的热辐射谱，使其与盖革计数器数据一致，并符合碘化钠探测结果中的高能拖尾，那么拖尾部分的能量必须大约是光谱热辐射部分的 25%。如果希望以较低的温度拟合，则要求存在一个更大的非热辐射拖尾。因此，如果假定 X 射线源是中子星的话，那么观测流量中的大部分不可能来自中子星的黑体辐射。

More generally the absence of a substantial thermal contribution to the spectrum indicates that the observed X-rays are being generated in regions that are optically thin. Whether the X-rays are generated in a hot plasma or by the synchrotron process cannot be determined on the basis of these data except for noting that, in a hot plasma line, emission and edge discontinuities can arise, either of which could account for the peak at 20 keV for which there is some evidence from the NaI detector. The synchrotron process cannot give rise to such features.

Table 2 lists the counting rate, the integrated power and photon flux observed in the two-source regions by the two detectors. For *ScoX*-1 the counting rates are corrected for the shadowing of the collimators and result from the fact that the detector axis comes only within 2° of the source. No such correction was made in the case of the sources near the Galactic centre. In the 1-10 keV region the integrated power and photon flux were obtained by assuming a power law distribution with the spectral index obtained from the filter attenuation of the Geiger counter results. The uncertainty in the spectral index yields the uncertainties in the integral quantity. In the >8 keV region the integrated power and photon fluxes were obtained by summing over the NaI pulse-height distribution.

In summary, the results presented here indicate the following:

(1) The ratio of the counting rate in the Geiger counters to that in the NaI detector is not consistent with a single thermal spectrum.

(2) The NaI detector does not detect significant radiation from *ScoX*-1 beyond about 15 keV, whereas radiation is observed from the Galactic centre region to beyond 20 keV. The minimum detectable flux density at 20 keV (defined as equivalent to 1σ above background) is about 3×10^{-27} ergs/cm^2·sec(c/s). Clark[7] measures a flux of $(2.4\pm0.6)\times10^{-27}$ ergs/cm^2·sec (c/s) over the range of 20-40 keV from the Crab Nebula. The power from *ScoX*-1 at these high energies is thus considerably below what is emanating from the Crab even though at lower energies (1-10 keV) *ScoX*-1 is the brighter object as reported by Friedman[2].

(3) For both source regions the attenuation of the counting rate in the Geiger counters by the filters indicates that the X-ray flux below 2.5 keV is comparable with that above 2.5 keV. This result does not agree with that reported by Fisher[3] that little or no radiation is present below 4 keV from these sources.

The work reported here was sponsored by the U.S. National Aeronautics and Space Administration, Office of Space Sciences, under contract *NASw*-898.

(**207**, 572-575; 1965)

一般而言，辐射谱中缺乏大量的热辐射表明观测到的X射线源是产生自光学薄区域的。并不能仅仅根据以上数据来判断X射线源究竟是产生于热等离子体还是同步辐射过程，我们需要注意到：热等离子体谱线存在的发射和边缘非连续性均可能引起20千电子伏峰（碘化钠探测器显示出的一些证据）的形成，而同步辐射过程并不能解释这一峰值。

表2给出了两探测器探测到的两个辐射源区域的计数率、积分功率和光子通量。对于天蝎座*X*-1，根据计数率仅来自探测器轴与辐射源呈2°夹角的范围内，对准直器的遮蔽效应进行了校准。但对于银河系中心附近的辐射源并没有进行这样的校准。通过假定幂律分布，可以求得1千电子伏~10千电子伏范围内的积分功率与光子通量，其中光谱指数可以由盖革计数器的滤光片衰减推出。但是，光谱指数的不确定性会引起积分数值的不确定性。在大于8千电子伏的范围内，通过在碘化钠脉冲高度分布上进行加和，可以求得积分功率和光子通量。

综上所述，通过本文给出的结果可以得出以下推论：

（1）盖革计数器与碘化钠探测器二者计数率的比值与单一热辐射谱并不符合。

（2）对于天蝎座*X*-1，碘化钠探测器并没有探测到超过15千电子伏的显著辐射；而观测到的银河系中心区域的辐射延伸范围超过20千电子伏。位于20千电子伏的最小可探测流量密度(其值定义为比背景高1σ)大约为3×10^{-27}尔格/厘米^2·秒(周/秒)。克拉克[7]对于蟹状星云在20千电子伏~40千电子伏范围内测量，得到的流量为$(2.4\pm0.6)\times10^{-27}$尔格/厘米^2·秒（周/秒）。在这么高的能量范围内，天蝎座*X*-1的辐射功率明显低于蟹状星云的辐射功率。但是，弗里德曼[2]曾报道过天蝎座*X*-1在较低能谱范围内（1千电子伏~10千电子伏）是相对较亮的天体。

(3)对于本文中的两个辐射区域，由滤光片引起的盖革计数器计数率的衰减表明，低于2.5千电子伏的X射线流量与高于2.5千电子伏的X射线流量相当。这一结果与费希尔[3]的报道并不一致，后者认为这些辐射源在低于4千电子伏的区域几乎没有辐射。

本研究得到了美国国家航空航天局空间科学办公室的资助，项目合同号为*NASw*-898。

（金世超 翻译；蒋世仰 审稿）

R. Giacconi, H. Gursky and J. R. Waters: American Science and Engineering, Inc., Cambridge, Massachusetts.

References:

1. Clark, G., Garmire, G., Oda, M., Wada, M., Giacconi, R., Gursky, H., and Waters, J., *Nature* (this issue, p.584). Reported also by Giacconi, E., *et al.*, at Sec. Conf. Relativistic Astrophysics, Austin, Texas (December 1964).
2. Bowyer, S., Byram, E. T., Chubb, T. A., and Friedman, H., *Science*, **147**, 394 (1965). Reported also by Friedman, H., at Sec. Conf. Relativistic Astrophysics, Austin, Texas (December 1964).
3. Fisher, P. C., Johnson, H. M., Jordan, W. C., Meyerott, A. J., and Acton, L. W. (submitted to *Astrophys. J.*).
4. Giacconi, R., Gursky, H., Paolini, F. R., and Rossi, B., *Phys. Rev. Letters*, **9**, 439 (1962).
5. Giacconi, R., Gursky, H., Paolini, F. R., and Rossi, B., *Proc. Fifth Intern. Space Sci. Symp.* (to be published).
6. Bowyer, S., Byram, E. T., Chubb, T. A., and Friedman, H., *Science*, **146**, 912 (1964).
7. Clark, G., *Phys. Rev. Letters*, **14**, 91 (1965).
8. Giacconi, R., and Gursky, H., *Space Sci. Rev.*, **4**, 151 (1965).
9. Giacconi, R., Gursky, H., Waters, J., Clark, G., and Rossi, B., *Nature*, **204**, 981 (1964).
10. Oda, M., Clark, G., Garmire, G., Wada, M., Giacconi, R., Gursky, H., and Waters, J., *Nature*, **205**, 554 (1965).

Positions of Three Cosmic X-Ray Sources in Scorpio and Sagittarius

G. Clark *et al.*

Editor's Note

The 1960s saw the opening up of a new part of the electromagnetic spectrum in which signals from star-like objects could be detected. Riccardo Giacconi, an Italian national working at the Massachusetts Institute of Technology, played a crucial part in the development of what is now called X-ray astronomy by developing the mirrors by means of which X-rays can be focused as if they were radiation from optically visible stars. (The technique is to reflect the X-rays from glass or metal surfaces at very small angles.) In this paper, Giacconi and his colleagues described the detection of three previously unknown X-rays stars based on evidence collected during a rocket flight from White Sands in New Mexico. In the remainder of the decade, Giacconi and his colleagues built satellites able to monitor the whole sky for X-ray sources. It is interesting that two of Giacconi's collaborators in this study, M. Oda and M. Wada, both returned to Japan to important positions in Japanese science—Oda as director of the national space research enterprise and Wada as a molecular biologist using techniques borrowed from physics.

WE have determined the positions of three cosmic X-ray sources in the constellations of Scorpio and Sagittarius within uncertainty areas of 1.2-3 square degrees. Positions for these sources were reported earlier by us at the Austin Conference on Relativistic Astrophysics on the basis of a preliminary analysis of the same data[1]. One of these sources is *ScoX*-1, which was first detected by Giacconi *et al.* in 1962 (ref. 2). (Our designations specify the constellation and the order of discovery, for example, *ScoX*-2 for second X-ray source in Scorpio.) The other two, *SgrX*-1 and *ScoX*-2, lie near the galactic plane in the complex of sources the existence of which was reported in a previous publication[3]. We have also located a probable fourth source to within 1° of a segment of a great circle that is almost parallel to and about 4° below the galactic equator. The Kepler supernova remnant *SN*1604 was scanned and no evidence of an X-ray source at its position was found.

Table 1. Positions (Epoch 1950.0) of Three X-ray Sources

Source	Right ascension		Declination	
ScoX-1	16h 12m		−15.6°	
	or 16h 19m		−14.0°	
ScoX-2	16h 50m	(16h 50m)	−39.6°	(−41°)
SgrX-1	17h 44m	(17h 37m)	−23.2°	(−24°)

The preliminary values of the position co-ordinates given earlier in ref. 1 are shown in parentheses

We obtained the data with a rocket that was launched from White Sands, New Mexico,

天蝎座和人马座中三个 X 射线源的位置

克拉克等

编者按

从 20 世纪 60 年代开始，电磁波谱增加了一个新的作用即能检测到类星体的信号。在现今称为 X 射线天文学的开创中，在麻省理工学院工作的意大利人里卡尔多·贾科尼扮演了重要角色，他开发了可聚焦 X 射线的镜面，就好像这些 X 射线来自于光学可见星体的辐射一样。(这项技术是在玻璃或者金属表面，以非常小的角度反射 X 射线。) 在本文中，贾科尼和他的同事们基于在新墨西哥州的白沙导弹靶场发射的火箭在飞行过程中收集的资料，描述了探测到的三颗以前未知的 X 射线星体。在这十年贾科尼和他的同事们还建造了能够监测整个天空 X 射线源的卫星。有趣的是，在这次研究中贾科尼的两位合作者小田稔和和田后来都回到了日本，并在日本科学界担任重要职务——小田稔担任国家空间研究院的主任，和田成为了一名借鉴物理学技术做研究的分子生物学家。

我们已经确定了位于天蝎座和人马座中的三个宇宙 X 射线源的位置，面积不确定度为 1.2 平方度～3 平方度范围。早前在奥斯汀的相对论天体物理学会议上，我们也曾基于相同数据的初步分析报道过这些射线源的位置 [1]。其中一个射线源是天蝎座 *X*-1（*ScoX*-1），由贾科尼等人于 1962 年首先探测到（参考文献 2）。（我们主要根据星座和发现顺序对射线源进行命名，比如，天蝎座 *X*-2（*ScoX*-2）表示在天蝎座中发现的第二个 X 射线源。）另外两个射线源人马座 *X*-1（*SgrX*-1）和天蝎座 *X*-2 位于银道面附近，先前的一篇论文曾报道过该区域具有一系列的辐射源 [3]。同时我们也找出了可能的第四个 X 射线源，它位于近似平行于银道但比银道低约 4° 的大圆中的一段（1° 之内）。此外，对开普勒超新星遗迹 *SN*1604 也进行了扫描，但没有发现存在 X 射线源的证据。

表 1. 三个 X 射线源的位置（历年 1950.0）

辐射源	赤经	赤纬
天蝎座 *X*-1	16h 12m 或者 16h 19m	–15.6° –14.0°
天蝎座 *X*-2	16h 50m (16h 50m)	–39.6° (–41°)
人马座 *X*-1	17h 44m (17h 37m)	–23.2° (–24°)

先前参考文献 1 给出的位置坐标的初步值标示在括号里。

1964 年 10 月 26 日在恒星时 20h 20m 的时候，一枚用于探测 X 射线源的火箭

on October 26, 1964, at a sidereal time of 20h 20m, and reached an apogee of 224 km. Above the atmosphere the rocket spun around its long axis with an almost constant angular velocity of approximately 806 deg/sec. The spin axis precessed with an angular velocity of 5.51 deg/sec around a circular cone the apex angle and spatial orientation of which did not vary by more than 0.3° during the 260 sec when useful X-ray data were obtained.

The effects of the rocket motion on the observations are most easily visualized in the rocket frame of reference which we define to be a co-ordinate system fixed in the rocket with its z-axis parallel to the spin axis. During each spin any given point on the celestial sphere moved through 360° of azimuth in the rocket frame at an almost constant angle of elevation with respect to the rocket equator. In addition, the precession caused the elevation angle of an object to vary periodically with an amplitude equal to one-half of the apex angle of the precession cone. Thus an object was observed repeatedly in successive spins whenever it moved within the elevation range of a given detector's field of view.

In describing our analysis, we shall refer to the precession frame of reference which we define to be a co-ordinate system the z-axis of which is parallel to the axis of the precession cone, and the x-axis of which is in the direction of the vector product $\hat{z}_C \times \hat{z}_P$, where $\hat{z}_C$ and $\hat{z}_P$ are unit vectors parallel to the z-axes of the celestial and precession co-ordinate systems, respectively. We define the spin azimuth of a direction to be its azimuthal angle measured around the spin axis from the direction of $\hat{z}_P \times \hat{z}_S$, where $\hat{z}_S$ is a unit vector in the direction of the spin axis. We define the bearing of a direction to be the sum of its spin azimuth and the precession azimuth of the spin axis. During one complete precession cycle the spin azimuth of a given direction fixed in space decreases non-uniformly by 360°. In the same period the precession azimuth of the spin axis increases uniformly by 360°. Therefore, the bearing of a fixed direction varies about a mean value which, as one can easily see, differs by 90° from the azimuth of the fixed direction in the precession frame. The amplitude of this variation is determined by the angle of the precession cone and the elevation of the direction with respect to the precession equator.

The rocket carried a variety of instruments, among which were several X-ray detectors and two star sensors. The data consisted essentially of the occurrence times of pulses from these detectors and sensors. Four of the X-ray detectors were banks of Geiger tubes, each having sensitive areas of 70 cm^2, beryllium windows 9 mg cm^{-2} thick, and argon fillings giving a gas thickness of 5.4 mg cm^{-2}. Three of the banks had slat collimators that gave rectangular fields of view with full widths of 3.0° in the narrow dimension, and 30° (detectors *GH*0 and *GH*20) or 40° (detector *GV*10) in the wide dimension. The narrow dimensions of detectors *GH*0 and *GH*20 were perpendicular to the rocket equator, while that of detector *GV*10 was parallel. The fourth bank, detector *GMC*0, had a modulation collimator[4] the response function of which, in the direction perpendicular to the rocket equator, was a saw-tooth function with maxima at rocket elevation angles given by the formula $1.4° \pm \arctan(0.0417n)$, where n is an integer. In the direction parallel to the rocket equator the

在新墨西哥州的白沙导弹靶场发射升空，火箭到达 224 千米的远地点，我们由此火箭获得了数据。穿过大气层之后，火箭以大约 806 度 / 秒的固定角速度围绕其长轴旋转，同时该旋转轴以 5.51 度 / 秒的角速度围绕圆锥进动；其中在采集 X 射线有用数据的 260 秒内，该圆锥顶角和空间方向变化不超过 0.3°。

我们将火箭参考系定义为固定于火箭之上且 z 轴平行于火箭旋转轴的坐标系；那么，火箭运动对于观测的影响就可以很容易在该参考系中观测到。对于每一次旋转，天球上的任意给定点在火箭坐标系中都会移动 360° 方位角，但该点与火箭赤道面的仰角几乎不变。此外，火箭的进动可以使得天体的仰角周期性变化，其幅度等于进动圆锥顶角的一半。因此，在连续旋转过程中，无论它何时进入探测器视场的仰角范围内，都可以重复的观测到同一天体。

为了便于分析，下面我们定义进动参考系，该坐标系的 z 轴平行于进动圆锥的轴，x 轴方向与 $\hat{z}_C \times \hat{z}_P$ 矢量积的方向一致，其中 $\hat{z}_C$、$\hat{z}_P$ 分别表示平行于天球坐标系的 z 轴和进动坐标系 z 轴的单位矢量。我们将自旋方位定义为自旋轴相对 $\hat{z}_P \times \hat{z}_S$ 矢量积方向的方位角，其中 $\hat{z}_S$ 代表自旋轴方向的单位矢量。我们将特定的方位定义为自旋方位与自旋轴进动方位之和。在一个完整的进动周期内，在给定的空间方向的固定的自旋方位将非均匀的减小 360°；同样在这个周期中，自旋轴的进动方位将均匀增加 360°。因此，特定的方位会围绕某一平均值变化，显然，该平均值与进动参考系中固定方向的方位相差 90°。围绕平均值变化的幅度取决于进动圆锥的角度和该方向相对进动赤道面的仰角。

在这次飞行试验中，火箭携带了各种仪器，其中包括若干 X 射线探测器与两个星敏感器。需要采集的数据主要包括这些探测器和敏感器记录下的脉冲发生次数。四个 X 射线探测器各由一组盖革管组成，每个管子的灵敏面积为 70 厘米^2，铍窗的厚度为 9 毫克 · 厘米$^{-2}$，氩气的厚度为 5.4 毫克 · 厘米$^{-2}$。其中三组盖革管含有狭缝准直器，准直器矩形视场的窄方向全宽为 3.0°，宽方向上全宽为 30°（探测器 *GH*0 和 *GH*20）或 40°（探测器 *GV*10）。探测器 *GH*0 与 *GH*20 的窄方向是与火箭赤道平面相垂直的，而探测器 *GV*10 的窄方向平行于该平面。第四组盖革管，即探测器 *GMC*0，包括一个调制式准直器 [4]，其响应函数在垂直于火箭赤道平面的方向上是锯齿函数；当火箭仰角为 $1.4° \pm \arctan(0.0417n)$，$n$ 为整数，该函数取值最大。在平

response function of detector *GMC*0 was triangular with a base width of 15°. The star sensors, *SS*0 and *SS*30, had effective fields of view of 1.0°×5.2°, with their long dimensions perpendicular to the rocket equator. In our detector designations the number following the letter code specifies the nominal elevation in degrees of the centre of its field of view above the rocket equator. We determined the actual orientations of the detectors and star sensors in the rocket frame of reference to accuracies of ±0.3° in elevation and azimuth by optical measurements on the ground before and after the flight.

We solved the problem of determining the orientation of the rocket in the celestial frame of reference at any given instant in the following way. We first made use of the fact that *ScoX*-1 was within the elevation range of the modulation collimator throughout the precession cycle. We could therefore determine the amplitude of its variation in elevation from the observed modulation caused by the motion of *ScoX*-1 back and forth over the saw-tooth response function. This amplitude, which is equal to the full apex angle of the precession cone, was found to be 5.1±0.1°. (This angle could also be determined from the star sensor data, though not with as high accuracy as from the modulation collimator data.) From the relative times of the signals from the star sensor *SS*0, we identified seven stars between the second and fourth magnitude as the sources of the signals. We then determined the orientation of the precession cone axis and the phase of the precession motion which minimized the mean square difference between the predicted and observed times when these seven stars entered and left the elevation range of the star sensor during the precession cycle. We found that the precession axis lay in the direction with right ascension 302.2°±0.5° and declination 38.2°±0.3°. From these data we could calculate the celestial orientation of the spin axis at any given instant. Analysis of the nearly periodic pulses from *SS*0 produced by various stars repeatedly crossing the field of view showed that the spin frequency increased approximately linearly with time by about 0.2 percent during the useful period of the flight. Thus the bearing of the axis of any given detector, which for constant precession and spin frequencies would be a linear function of time, could be expressed by a quadratic function of time. The average deviation between the computed and the actual bearing was less than ±0.5° over the useful observation period.

To determine the relative bearings of the X-ray sources and reference stars, we plotted the numbers of counts per bearing interval from each of the detectors as a function of the bearing of the detector's axis, reduced modulo 360°. The data accumulated over four precession periods are shown in Fig. 1. The main peak of the distribution for detector *GV*10 in Fig. 1*a* is due to *ScoX*-1. The difference between its average bearing and that of the star β-Cetus, observed by the star sensor *SS*0, is 239.8°±0.3°. A segment of the great circle through the precession axis direction with this azimuth relative to β-Cetus is marked *A* in Fig. 3. We conclude that *ScoX*-1 lies within 0.3° of this segment.

行于火箭赤道平面的方向上，探测器 *GMC*0 的响应函数是三角函数，其底宽为 15°。星敏感器 *SS*0 和 *SS*30 的有效视场为 1.0° × 5.2°，其长轴方向垂直于火箭赤道平面。在我们的探测器命名中，字母代码后面紧跟数字，这个数字表示视场中心相对火箭赤道的标定仰角，以度为单位。通过火箭飞行前后的地面光学测量，我们可以确定在火箭参考系中，探测器与星敏感器的仰角和方位角实际指向的准确度为 ±0.3°。

我们将用下面的方法阐述如何在任意时刻确定天球参考系中的火箭方向。我们首先注意到以下事实：在整个进动周期内，天蝎座 *X*-1 始终位于调制式准直器的仰角范围内。而天蝎座 *X*-1 伴随锯齿响应函数的往返运动会造成调制现象，这样，我们就可以通过观测调制确定仰角变化的幅度。这一幅度等于进动圆锥的整个顶角大小，具体大小为 5.1±0.1°。（这一角度也可以由星敏感器数据得到，但不如调制式准直器数据得出的结果准确度高。）根据星敏感器 *SS*0 捕获信号的相对次数，我们可以识别出信号源为七颗恒星，星等位于 2 等和 4 等之间。然后，我们可以确定进动圆锥轴的指向和进动运动的相位，这需要满足在进动周期内，以上七颗恒星进入和离开星敏感器仰角范围的预计次数和观测次数的均方差最小。这样我们发现，进动轴方向位于赤经 302.2° ±0.5°，赤纬 38.2° ±0.3°。通过这些数据，我们可以计算出任意时刻自旋轴的天球方向。反复穿越视场的各个恒星在敏感器 *SS*0 中都会产生近似周期性脉冲，对这些脉冲分析可知，在整个有效的飞行期间，自旋频率大约随时间线性增加了 0.2%。因此，任意给定的探测器轴的方位可以表达为时间的二次函数，因为对于恒定进动和自旋频率它是时间的线性函数。在有效观测时间内，方位计算值和实际值之间的平均差值小于 ±0.5°。

为了确定 X 射线源和参考星的相对方位，我们需要绘制出探测器分布函数曲线，如图 1 所示，纵轴为探测器每方位间隔内计数，横轴为探测器轴对 360° 取模后的方位角，需要注意的是图 1 中数据是由四个进动周期累积得到的。图 1*a* 中是探测器 *GV*10 的分布，其中主要的峰值是由天蝎座 *X*-1 引起的。通过星敏感器 *SS*0 观测，其平均方位角与恒星 β−鲸鱼座相差 239.8° ±0.3°。图 3 中标记出了通过进动轴方向的大圆周上的一段，用 *A* 表示，相对 β−鲸鱼座的方位也为 239.8° ±0.3°。我们可以得出结论，天蝎座 *X*-1 位于该段上 0.3° 以内。

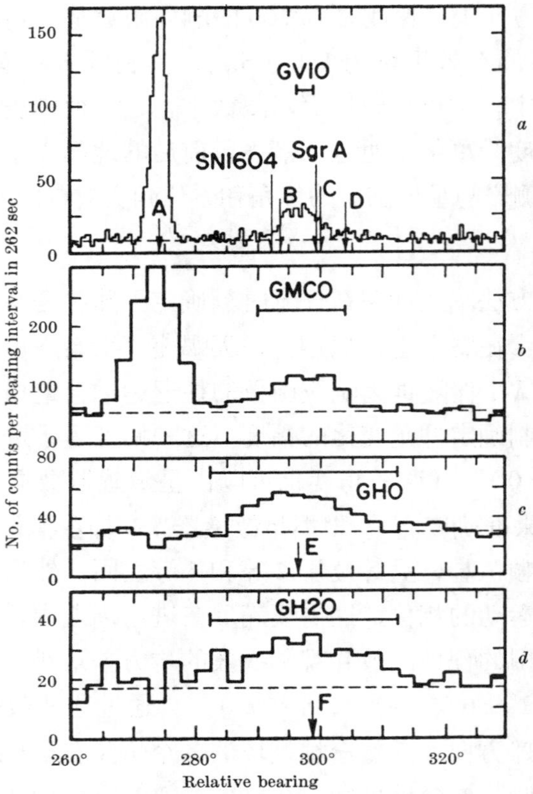

Fig. 1. Bearing distributions of the counts from the four detectors in the vicinity of *ScoX*-1 and the galactic centre complex. The full widths of the fields of view are indicated under the label of each detector. The background levels are indicated by the dashed lines

The second, broader peak in Fig. 1*a* is due to the complex of sources near the galactic centre. From the fact that the ratio of the amplitude to the area of the peak is less than one-half times that of the *ScoX*-1 peak we conclude that it contains more than two sources. Arcs *B* and *C* in Fig. 3 are loci of positions the average bearings of which are equal to the values marked *B* and *C* in Fig. 1*a*. They are segments of great circles drawn through the precession axis, and they bound the region within which these sources lie. The Kepler's supernova remnant *SN*1604 lies 2° outside this region, and the radio source *SgrA* at the galactic centre is just barely within it. The separate peak, the average bearing of which is marked *D* in Fig. 1*a*, is 3.5σ above the background. It is probably caused by a separate source that lies somewhere along the great circle segment marked *D* in Fig. 3.

The bearing distribution for the *GMC*0 detector is shown in Fig. 1*b*. It has separate peaks due to *ScoX*-1 and the galactic centre complex, but it has a low angular resolution and does not improve the bearing determinations already make with the *GV*10 data.

Figs. 1*c* and 1*d* show the bearing distributions for the two detectors *GH*0 and *GH*20 the fields of view of which were narrow slits parallel to the rocket equator. Both show the

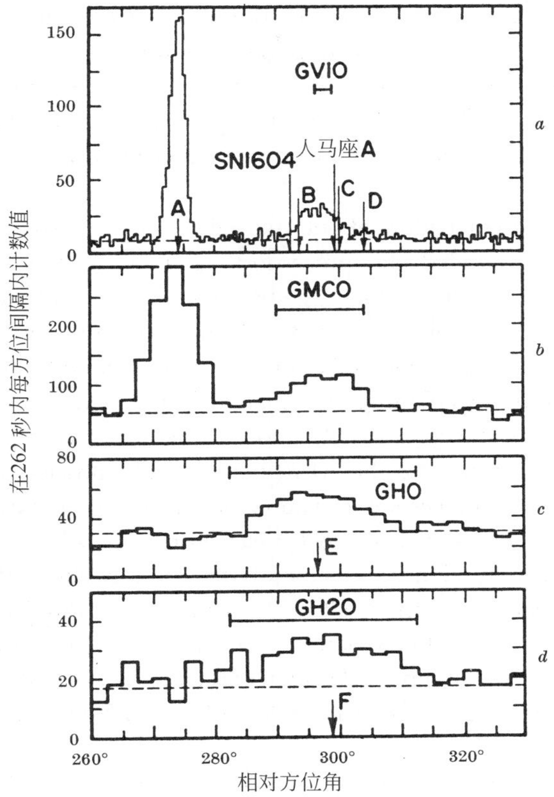

图 1. 四个探测器对天蝎座 *X*-1 附近和银心复合辐射源探测计数的方位分布。其中，探测器命名中的数字代表视场的全宽，图中虚线表示本底水平。

图 1*a* 中第二个较宽的峰是由银河系中心附近的若干辐射源形成的。基于振幅与峰面积的比值小于天蝎座 *X*-1 峰一半的事实，因此我们可以得出结论：宽峰对应的辐射源不止两个。图 3 中的 *B* 弧、*C* 弧表示位置轨迹，平均方位角分别等于图 1*a* 中的 *B*、*C* 标记值，它们都是经过进动轴的大圆周上的一段，所围绕的区域正好是辐射源所在的区域。开普勒超新星遗迹 *SN*1604 位于该区域外 2°，而位于银河系中心的射电源人马座 *A* 正好位于这一区域。图 1*a* 中另一个平均方位角的独立峰用 *D* 标记出，比背景高 3.5σ。该峰可能由另外一个独立辐射源引起，该源位于图 3 中 *D* 段上的某处。

图 1*b* 给出了探测器 *GMC*0 的方位分布。该图中的两个独立峰分别源自天蝎座 *X*-1 和银河系中心复合辐射源，但是角分辨率较低，且并不能进一步提高由 *GV*10 数据给出的方位精度。

图 1*c* 和图 1*d* 分别给出了探测器 *GH*0 和 *GH*20 的方位分布，二者的视场均是平

presence of sources which are a part of the complex between circles *B* and *C*, and which lie within the two 8-degree wide elevation bands scanned by the detectors during the precession cycle. These bands are bounded by the small circles marked *GH*0 and *GH*20 in Fig. 3. It is apparent from the absence of a peak at the bearing of *ScoX*-1 in either distribution that *ScoX*-1 does not lie within either of these bands.

To obtain more precise information about the elevation of a source with respect to the precession equator we examined the precession variation in the rates of counts in an appropriate bearing interval round the average bearing of the source. At any fixed bearing the precession elevation of a detector axis varied with an amplitude equal to one-half the apex angle of the precession cone. If a source lay in the region scanned, this variation in elevation caused a variation in the X-ray counting rates that could be fitted to the known response curve of the detector by a proper choice of the elevation of the source with respect to the precession equator. Fig. 2*a* shows the results for the *GV*10 detector. The abscissa is the relative elevation which we define to be the precession elevation of the detector axis at the centre of the indicated bearing interval minus its fixed rocket elevation. The fact that the counting rate was a maximum at the maximum relative elevation of the spin axis shows that *ScoX*-1 is above the maximum precession elevation of the *GMC*0 axis, which limit is indicated by the dashed line that crosses the bearing circle *A*. On the other hand, *ScoX*-1 cannot lie above the band bounded by the *GH*20 lines because the observed elevation variation is too small. Therefore, *ScoX*-1 must lie between the dashed line and the lower boundary of the *GH*20 band.

To refine the elevation determination of *ScoX*-1 we used the *GMC*0 data the elevation variation of which is shown in Fig. 2*b*. From the completeness of the modulation, as well as that of the modulation observed in a previous experiment with a similar but higher resolution collimator, it was possible to conclude that the angular diameter of *ScoX*-1 is less than 7 arc min (ref. 5). One sees here that *ScoX*-1 lines on one of the maxima of the response function when the precession elevation of the *GMC*0 axis is $-2.3°$, $-0.2°$ or $+1.8°$. The solid lines crossing the bearing circle *A* show the positions of the two maxima which fall between the limits previously determined. We are not able to choose between the two intersections on the basis of the data from this experiment. The boxes around each of the two intersections are $0.6°$ wide by $1.0°$ long, and they indicate the estimated errors in the bearing and elevation determinations, respectively.

Figs. 2*c* and 2*d* show the elevation variation of the counts from the sources observed by the *GH*0 and *GH*20 detectors. In both cases the sources appear to lie about $0.3°$ below the midpoint of the elevation scan as indicated by the line crossing the bearing circles *D* and *E*. We determined these latter bearing circles using only the data from the parts of the precession cycle when the sources gave the highest counting rates. As before, the boxes around each intersection indicate the estimated errors in the position determinations.

The two alternative positions we find for *ScoX*-1 are both within the uncertainty circle of $2°$ radius around the position published by the *NRL* group[6]. The lower of the two is within $0.5°$ of the position given by Fisher *et al.*[7].

行于火箭赤道平面的狭缝。两个探测器都表明，存在的辐射源是圆周 *B* 和 *C* 之间复合源的一部分，且在一进动周期内分别位于两个 8 度宽的仰角扫描带内。同时这两个带区位于用 *GH*0 和 *GH*20 标记的小圆周之间，如图 3 所示。显然，图 1*c* 和图 1*d* 中并未出现天蝎座 *X*-1 对应的峰，因此天蝎座 *X*-1 并不位于以上两个扫描带内。

为了使辐射源相对进动赤道平面的仰角信息更加精确，我们在辐射源平均方位附近提取合适的方位区间，然后在该区间检查了进动过程中的计数率变化。对于任意给定的方位，探测器轴的进动仰角的变化幅度等于进动圆锥顶角的一半。如果某个辐射源位于扫描区域内，仰角变化会引起 X 射线计数率的变化；通过合理选取辐射源相对于进动赤道平面的仰角，X 射线计数速率可以用已知的探测器响应曲线进行拟合。图 2*a* 给出了探测器 *GV*10 的探测结果。图中横坐标是相对仰角，我们将其定义为指定方位区间中心的探测器轴的进动仰角减去固定的火箭仰角。当自旋轴相对仰角最大时，计数率达到最大。这一事实表明天蝎座 *X*-1 位于 *GMC*0 轴最大进动仰角之上，这一限制对应于图 3 中与方位圆周 *A* 交叉的虚线。另一方面，天蝎座 *X*-1 不可能位于 *GH*20 线包围的带上，因为观测到的仰角变化过小。因此，天蝎座 *X*-1 一定位于虚线和 *GH*20 扫描带下边界之间。

为了进一步改善天蝎座 *X*-1 的仰角精度，我们采用 *GMC*0 的数据，图 2*b* 给出了这些数据的仰角变化。根据本次实验以及以前一次实验（使用了一个相似的但分辨率更高的准直器）观测到的完整调制，也许可以得出结论：天蝎座 *X*-1 的角直径小于 7 角分（参考文献 5)。这样，我们可以发现，当 *GMC*0 轴的进动仰角为 – 2.3°、– 0.2° 或 + 1.8° 的时候，天蝎座 *X*-1 位于响应函数某个极大值上。与方位圆周 *A* 交叉的实线给出了两个极大值的位置，正好落在以前确定的极限之间。但根据实验数据，我们尚不能确定究竟是哪个点。位于两个交叉点附近的方框，长宽分别为 1.0° 、0.6° ，分别表示仰角和方向角的估计误差。

图 2*c* 和图 2*d* 给出了探测器 *GH*0 和 *GH*20 对辐射源观测计数随仰角的变化。在这两种情况下，辐射源看起来大概都位于仰角中点以下 0.3°，其中仰角可以由与方位圆周 *D*、*E* 交叉线得到。当辐射源产生最大的计数率时，我们可以只采用进动周期的部分数据，确定该方位圆。如前所述，每个交叉点附近的方框代表位置的估计误差。

我们发现，天蝎座 *X*-1 存在两个可以选择的位置，均位于美国海军研究实验室研究小组确定的位置附近半径为 2° 的不确定圆内 [6]。两个位置中较低的那个距离费希尔等人 [7] 确定的位置小于 0.5°。

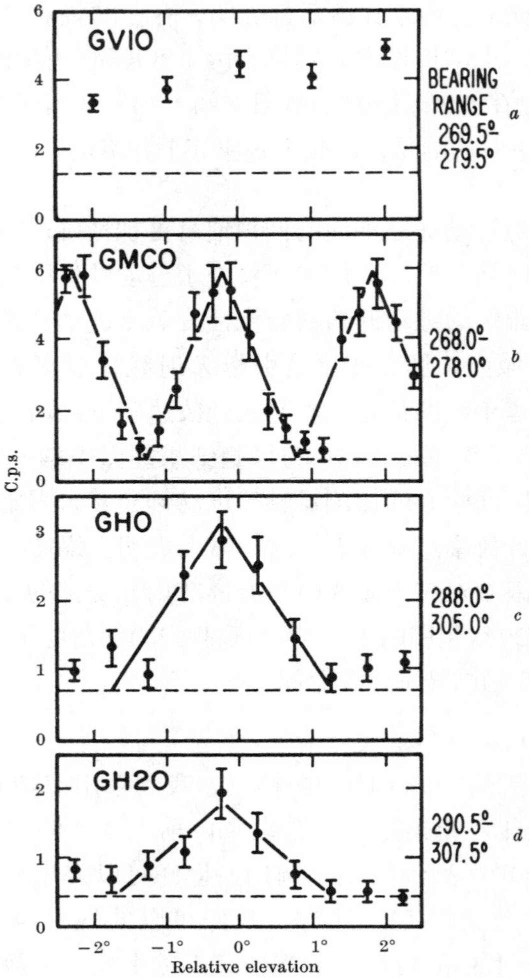

Fig. 2. Variation of the counting rates with the relative elevation of the detector axis at the midpoint of the indicated bearing interval. The background levels are indicated by the dashed lines

SgrX-1 is 5° away from the Kepler supernova remnant *SN*1604. The absence of a significant peak at the average bearing of *SN*1604 in the *GV*10 data in Fig. 1*a* shows that any X-ray emission from this remnant must be several times smaller than that of the nearby sources. Therefore, our observations do not support the identification of an X-ray source with *SN*1604, as suggested by the *NRL* group[6] on the basis of data obtained with an instrument of lesser angular resolution.

ScoX-2 lies more than 5° away from the position of the nearest source reported by the *NRL* group[6].

Two of the circular arcs along which Fisher *et al.*[7] have located sources pass within 1° of our locations for *SgrX*-1 and *ScoX*-2, respectively.

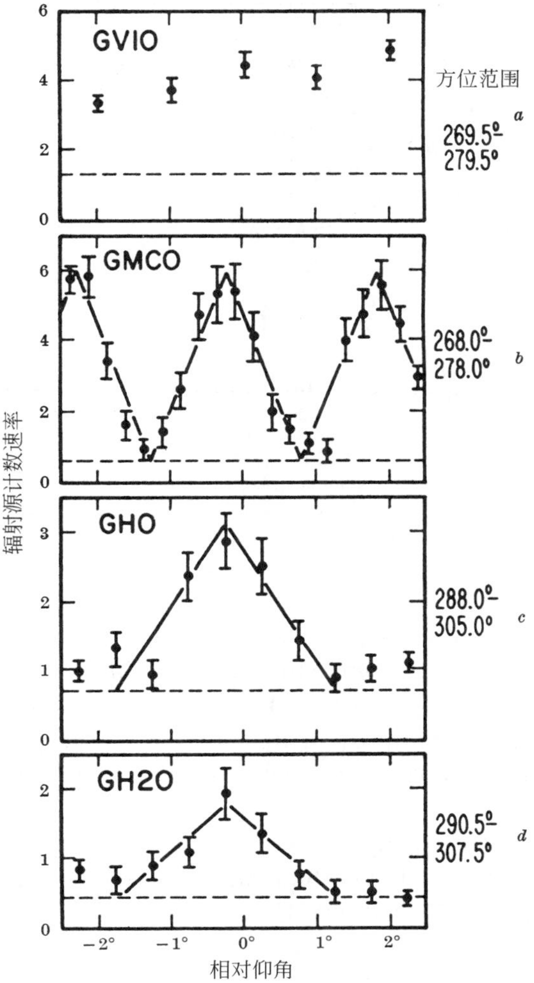

图 2. 计数率随探测器轴相对仰角的变化，其中仰角是方位间隔中心点对应的值，图中虚线表示本底。

人马座 X-1 与开普勒超新星遗迹 SN1604 的距离为 5°。如图 1a 给出了探测器 GV10 的数据，在 SN1604 平均方位附近缺乏明显的峰值；由此图可知来自遗迹的 X 射线辐射比附近的辐射源小若干倍。因此，我们的观测并不能确认是否在 SN1604 中存在 X 射线源；基于使用角分辨率较低的仪器获得的数据，美国海军研究实验室研究小组也表明了这一点[6]。

天蝎座 X-2 与美国海军研究实验室研究小组报道的最近辐射源位置相差 5°[6]。

费希尔等[7] 定位辐射源的两条圆弧位于我们对人马座 X-1、天蝎座 X-2 定位的距离小于 1° 范围内。

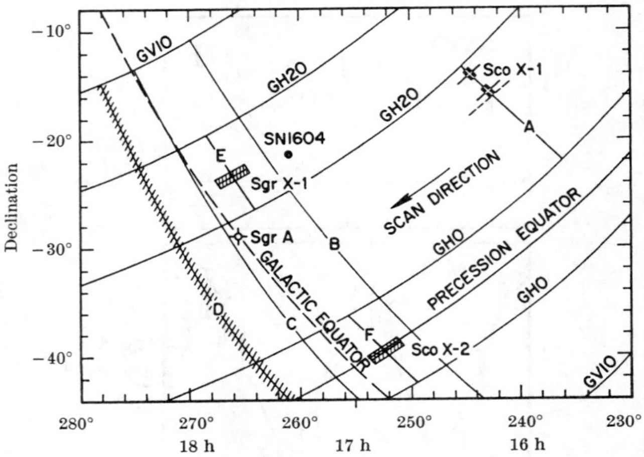

Fig. 3. Mercator projection of the celestial sphere in the region of the galactic centre. The cross-hatched areas show the locations of the sources as determined in this experiment. The small circles labelled *GV*10, *GH*0, etc., are the extreme boundaries of the regions scanned by the corresponding detectors.

Finally, we note that there is a striking lack of symmetry with respect to the galactic centre in the distribution of the general X-ray emission from this region. The centre line of the emission region between lines *B* and *C* in Fig. 3 passes the galactic centre at a galactic latitude of $b^{II} = +2.5$. It is also apparent that the radio centre of the galaxy, *SgrA*, is at most a weak X-ray source compared with the other sources nearby.

This work was supported in part by the National Aeronautics and Space Administration under contracts *NASw*-898 and *NsG*-386 and in part by the U.S. Atomic Energy Commission under contract *AT* (30-1) 2098.

(**207**, 584-587; 1965)

G. Clark, G. Garmire, M. Oda and M. Wada: Laboratory for Nuclear Science and Department of Physics, Massachusetts Institute of Technology.

R. Giacconi, H. Gursky and J. R. Waters: American Science and Engineering, Inc.

References:

1. Giacconi, R., *Proc. Austin Conf. Relativistic Astrophysics*, Dec. 1964 (to be published).
2. Giacconi, R., Gursky, H., Paolini, F., and Rossi, B., *Phys. Rev. Letters*, **9**, 439 (1962).
3. Giacconi, R., Gursky, H., Waters, J. R., Clark, G., and Rossi, B., *Nature*, **204**, 981 (1964).
4. Oda, M., *App. Optics*, **4**, 143 (1965).
5. Oda, M., Clark, G., Garmire, G., Wada, M., Giacconi, R., Gursky, H., and Waters, J., *Nature*, **205**, 554 (1965).
6. Bowyer, S., Byram, E. T., Chubb, T. A., and Friedman, H., *Science*, **147**, 394 (1965).
7. Fisher, P. C., Johnson, H. M., Jordan, W. C., Meyerott, A. J., and Acton, L. W. (preprint).

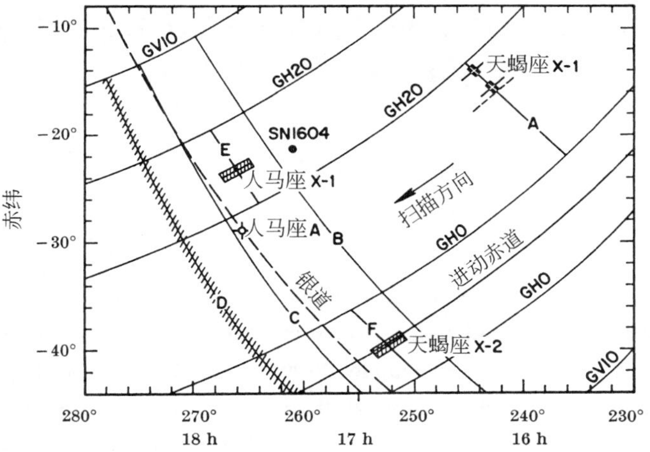

图 3. 在银河系中心区域天球的墨卡托投影。交叉影线区域给出了实验中确定的辐射源的位置。标记为 *GV*10、*GH*0 等的小圆，表示相应探测器扫描区域的极限边界。

最后，需要指出的是，银河系中心区域一般 X 射线辐射分布相对银河系中心明显缺乏对称性。如图 3 所示，辐射区域的中心线位于 *B*、*C* 两线之间，以银纬 $b^{\mathrm{II}} = +2.5$ 穿过银河系中心。另一点值得注意的是，与附近其他辐射源相比，银河系中心的人马座 *A* 是一个比较弱的 X 射线源。

本工作部分由美国国家航空航天局资助，合约序号为 *NASw*-898 和 *NsG*-386；同时也受到美国原子能委员会的部分资助，合约序号为 *AT*(30-1)2098。

（金世超 翻译；尚仁成 审稿）

A Model of the Quasi-Stellar Radio Variable *CTA* 102

M. J. Rees and D. W. Sciama

Editor's Note

In 1965 quasars were still newly discovered, and people were struggling to understand how to generate both the brightness and periodic variation of their emission. Here Martin Rees and Denis Sciama report an early interpretation applied to the quasar *CTA* 102, which crucially contains the idea of a rotating disk of material. Although their specific model was soon superseded, it served to outline the size scale and energy mechanisms needed for a better understanding.

ACCORDING to Sholomitsky[1], the quasi-stellar[2] radio source *CTA* 102 (ref. 3) has a variable flux density at 32.5 cm, the period being about 100 days. Sholomitsky takes this to mean that the source cannot be larger than ~0.1 parsec, which is the distance light travels in one period. Since its angular diameter is not less than about 0.01 sec[4,5], he concludes that it must be closer than 2 Mpc, and is possibly inside our own Galaxy. However, Schmidt[6] has recently announced that the optical object identified with *CTA* 102 has a red shift $z=\delta\lambda/\lambda$ of 1.037, and so is probably at a distance comparable with the radius of the universe (~3,000 Mpc).

Although it is by no means certain that the observed variations originate in the source itself, we wish to propose a model which assumes this, and is consistent with the red shift observations.

The model is illustrated in Fig. 1. The radio emission is produced in a spheroidal shell the axis of symmetry of which is approximately along the line of sight. (Shell models for radio sources have been discussed by several authors[7], and spheroidal shells in particular by Layzer[8].) The main part of the emission comes from the region *ADB*, and its spectrum is taken to have a peak at about 300 Mc/s (Fig. 2). The variable part is assumed to come from the disk-like region *ACB*, which is pulsating (perhaps as a result of an explosion occurring at O, the effect of which may reach all parts of the disk at about the same time). When this region is compressed, the magnetic field strength will rise, the individual electrons will be accelerated by the betatron mechanism, and the radiated power will be greatly enhanced. When radiating at its maximum, it is required to emit ~ 25 percent of the total flux observed at 1,000 Mc/s in order to account for the observed variations (that is, its flux density must be $\sim 2\times 10^{-26}$ W/m^2/(c/s)). Its spectrum is taken to be as shown in Fig. 2. The total spectrum then agrees with the observed spectrum of *CTA* 102 (ref. 9).

类星体射电变星 *CTA* 102 模型

瑞斯，夏玛

编者按

1965 年类星体才刚刚被发现，在当时人们致力于对其同时产生的亮度及周期性变化的辐射机制进行研究。本文中马丁·瑞斯和丹尼斯·夏玛给出了适用于类星体 *CTA* 102 的早期解释，他们的观点中最关键的就是提出了存在旋转的盘状物质。尽管他们给出的具体模型很快就被更合适的模型取代了，但是他们的工作有助于给出类星体的大致尺寸并且进一步帮助人们更好地理解能源机制。

根据肖洛米斯基的论文[1]，类星体[2]射电源 *CTA* 102（参考文献 3）在波长 32.5 厘米附近存在流量密度变化，周期大约为 100 天。因此，肖洛米斯基认为，该辐射源的尺寸不可能大于 ~0.1 秒差距，而这恰好是光在一个周期内传播的距离。由于该射电源的角直径不小于 0.01 角秒[4,5]，所以他得出以下结论：*CTA* 102 的距离要小于 2 兆秒差距，很可能就位于银河系内。然而施密特最近的研究表明[6]，认证出的 *CTA* 102 的光学天体存在 $z=\delta\lambda/\lambda=1.037$ 的红移，所以该辐射源的距离可能相当于宇宙半径（~3,000 兆秒差距）。

尽管不能确定上述观测到的变化是否源于辐射源本身，但在我们提出的模型中将仍然假设这种变化源自辐射源，并尽量使模型符合红移观测。

图 1 给出了该模型的示意图。射电辐射产生于图中球状壳，球状壳的对称轴基本上是沿着视线方向的。（一些研究者已经讨论过射电源的壳模型[7]，而雷泽尔也特别提到了球状壳[8]。）大部分辐射主要来自 *ADB* 区域，其光谱在约 300 兆周 / 秒附近有一个峰（如图 2）。假设辐射变化源自 *ACB* 盘状区域，该区域处于脉动状态（这也许是因为 O 点发生爆炸，其影响可以在大致相同的时间到达盘状区域的各部分）。当该区域被压缩时，磁场强度就会增加，单个的电子基于电子回旋加速机制被加速，这样辐射功率就会大大增强。当辐射达到最大时，辐射源在 1,000 兆周 / 秒的辐射需要达到总流量的 25%，这才能够解释观测到的变化（即其流量密度必须为 $\sim 2\times10^{-26}$ 瓦 / 米^2/（周 / 秒））。辐射源模型的光谱如图 2 所示，该总光谱与观测到的 *CTA* 102 光谱较符合（参考文献 9）。

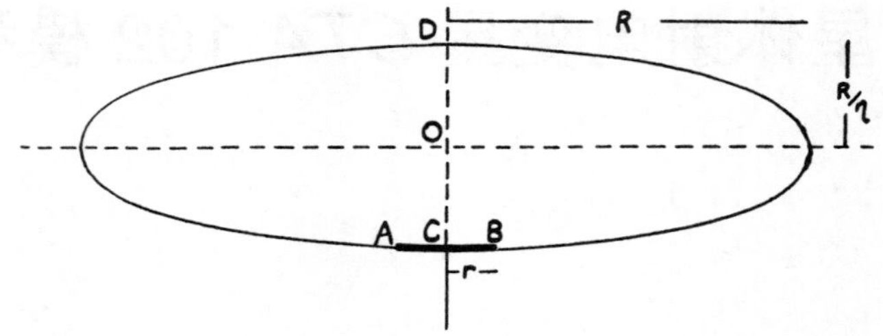

Fig. 1. Proposed model of *CTA* 102

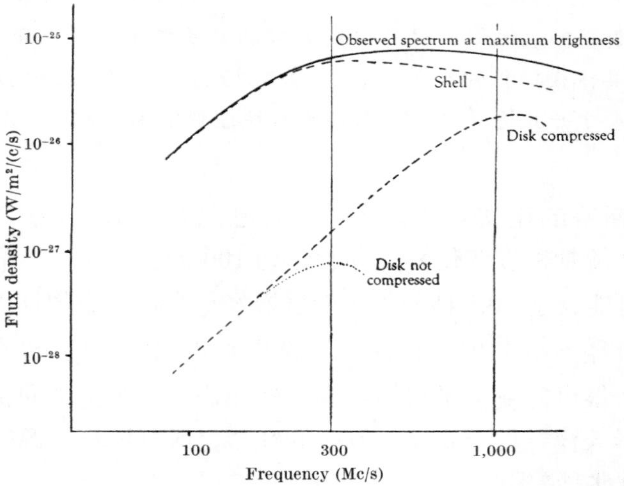

Fig. 2

The disk will have its minimum size consistent with the required flux if it is opaque at (proper) frequencies up to ~1,000(1+z) Mc/s when compressed. Furthermore, if its emission is to vary with a (proper) period of 100/(1+z) days, its thickness cannot exceed $3\times10^{17}/(1+z)$ cm. The electrons which radiate at frequencies around 1,000(1+z) Mc/s have energies of $\sim2\times10^{-5}(1+z)^{\frac{1}{2}}H^{-\frac{1}{2}}$ ergs, each electron producing $\sim2.16\times10^{-22}H$ ergs/sec/(c/s) (where H is in gauss). If synchrotron self-absorption is occurring, the power radiated from the surface of the disk at this frequency is $\sim3\times10^{-8}(1+z)^{\frac{5}{2}}H^{-\frac{1}{2}}$ ergs/sec/(c/s)/cm². The number density of these electrons is therefore $\sim5\times10^{-4}(1+z)^{\frac{7}{2}}H^{-\frac{3}{2}}$ per c.c., and their energy density $\sim10^{-8}(1+z)^{4}H^{-2}$ ergs/c.c. Allowing for the fact that they only contribute a few percent of the particle energy density, and assuming that the total particle energy is comparable with the magnetic energy, we conclude that the magnetic field when the disk is compressed is $\sim5\times10^{-2}(1+z)$ gauss. A threefold increase in the field strength will probably be sufficient to produce the required increase of about 20 in luminosity at 1,000(1+z) Mc/s (though the exact factor depends on the energy spectrum of the electrons). The pulsations will be sufficiently rapid if the Alfvén speed ~c, and this will be true if the particle density of the ambient gas does not exceed ~1 per c.c.

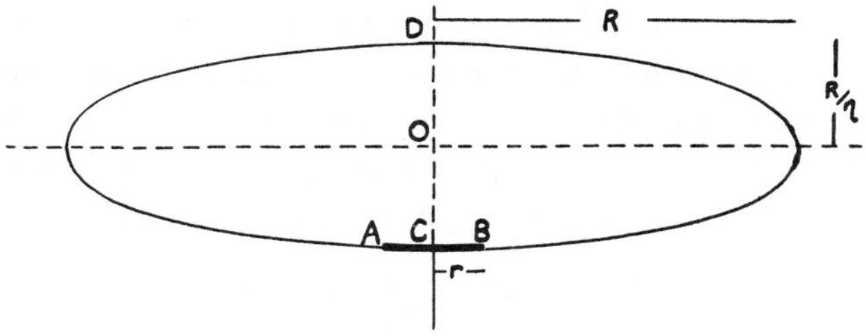

图 1. 提出的 *CTA* 102 模型

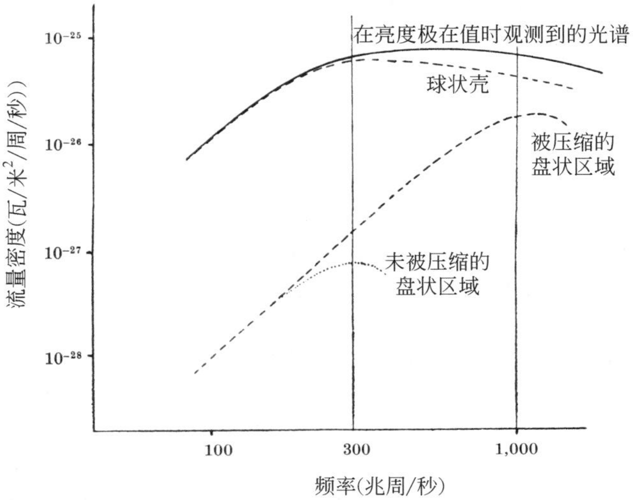

图 2

如果压缩过程中在直到 ~1,000(1+z) 兆周 / 秒的（固有）频率范围内，盘状区域都是不透明的，那么该区域不但具有最小尺寸，而且也符合流量的要求。此外，如果其辐射变化的（固有）周期为 100/(1+z) 天，那么它的厚度不可能超过 $3 \times 10^{17}/(1+z)$ 厘米。辐射频率约为 1,000(1+z) 兆周 / 秒附近的电子，能量为 $\sim 2 \times 10^{-5}\ (1+z)^{\frac{1}{2}}H^{-\frac{1}{2}}$ 尔格，其中每个电子产生的功率为 $\sim 2.16 \times 10^{-22}H$ 尔格 / 秒 /（周 / 秒）（H 单位为高斯）。如果发生了同步加速自吸收现象，则盘状区域表面在该频率的辐射功率为 $\sim 3 \times 10^{-8}(1+z)^{\frac{5}{2}}H^{-\frac{1}{2}}$ 尔格 / 秒 /（周 / 秒）/ 厘米^2。因此，这些电子数密度是 $\sim 5 \times 10^{-4}(1+z)^{\frac{7}{2}}H^{-\frac{3}{2}}$ 个 / 厘米^3，电子的能量密度为 $\sim 10^{-8}(1+z)^4H^{-2}$ 尔格 / 厘米^3。考虑到电子只贡献了一部分粒子能量密度，并假设粒子总能量可与磁能相比的事实，我们就可以得出结论：在盘状区域压缩的情况下，磁场为 $\sim 5 \times 10^{-2}(1+z)$ 高斯。场强增加到 3 倍将可能足以使频率 1,000(1+z) 兆周 / 秒的光度增加到大约 20 倍（尽管准确的因数取决于电子的能量谱）。如果阿尔文速度接近于 c，则这种脉动变化就会足够的迅速；然而，这只在周围气体粒子密度不超过 ~1 个 / 厘米^3 的条件下成立。

The angular diameter of the disk when the magnetic field has the foregoing value is[4,5] $\sim 3\times 10^{-3}(1+z)^{\frac{1}{2}}$ sec. (This assumes that the electrons are radiating incoherently. If they were coherent the angular diameter of the source could be much smaller, which might permit its linear diameter to be ~0.1 parsec, consistently with a large red shift.) It follows that:

$$r \simeq 22.5\frac{z}{(1+z)^{\frac{1}{2}}} \text{ parsecs}$$

in the steady state cosmology. (In the Einstein-de Sitter model this value must be decreased by a factor ~2 if $z \sim 1$.) Estimating the average magnetic field over the whole shell as 10^{-2} $(1+z)$ gauss, we deduce from the occurrence of self-absorption below 300 Mc/s that, in the steady state model:

$$R \simeq 225\frac{z}{(1+z)^{\frac{1}{2}}} \text{ parsecs}$$

This estimate of R enables the parameter η to be determined, for since the disk must not deviate from the tangent plane at C by more than $\sim 0.1/(1+z)$ parsec, it follows from the geometry that $R \simeq 2{,}500z^2/\eta$ and so $\eta \simeq 11z(1+z)^{\frac{1}{2}}$.

If $z \sim 1$ the dimensions are: $R \sim 160$ parsecs, $r \sim 16$ parsecs, and $\eta \sim 15$. The lifetime of the electrons is 50-100 years in the fluctuating region, and rather longer in the rest of the source. The total energy of the source is at least $\sim 10^{57}$ ergs, of which $\sim 10^{54}$ ergs is in the disk. The probability that the shell should be oriented so that the disk points towards us is about 3×10^{-5}, which implies that very few radio sources can conform to our model. This model enables us to make the following predictions:

(1) The amplitude of the variations depends on the frequency ν of observation as follows:

$$\begin{array}{ll} \sim 0 & 0 < \nu < 300 \\ \sim 0.013 \left\{\left(\frac{\nu}{300}\right)^{2.5} - 1\right\} & 300 < \nu < 1{,}000 \\ \sim 0.25 & \nu > 1{,}000 \end{array}$$

where ν is in megacycles. Thus the observations of Caswell and Wills[10], who found no variations at 178 Mc/s, are not necessarily inconsistent with Sholomitsky's observations.

(2) For $300 < \nu < 1{,}000$ the intensity reaches a maximum in a time t (ν) days, say, ($t < 50$), and then remains constant for a time $(100 - 2t)$ days (that is, while the disk is opaque to frequencies between ν and 1,000 Mc/s). The rise-time t (ν) is an increasing function of ν, as illustrated in Fig. 3.

当磁场达到上述值的时候，盘状区域的角直径为 ~$3 \times 10^{-3}(1+z)^{\frac{1}{2}}$ 角秒[4,5]。(这里假设电子进行非相干辐射。如果电子是相干的话，辐射源的角直径会小很多，对应于较大的红移量线直径可能为 ~0.1 秒差距。) 基于稳恒态宇宙学理论，角直径可以由以下公式求得：

$$r \doteq 22.5 \frac{z}{(1+z)^{\frac{1}{2}}} \text{秒差距}$$

(在爱因斯坦－德西特模型中，如果 z~1，则上式需要除以因数 ~2。) 在整个壳上，以平均磁场 $10^{-2}(1+z)$ 高斯为估计值，从 300 兆周 / 秒以下自吸收的发生率可以推导出以下适用于稳恒态模型的公式：

$$R \doteq 225 \frac{z}{(1+z)^{\frac{1}{2}}} \text{秒差距}$$

既然盘状区域偏离 C 点切面不会超出 ~0.1/(1+z) 秒差距，那么该区域几何结构满足 $R \doteq 2{,}500z^2/\eta$，对比公式可以由 R 确定参数 $\eta \approx 11z(1+z)^{\frac{1}{2}}$。

如果 z~1，则代入上式可得，R~160 秒差距，r~16 秒差距，η~15。电子在辐射脉动区域的寿命为 50 年 ~ 100 年，在该辐射源的其他区域会更长一些。辐射源的总能量至少为 ~10^{57} 尔格，其中盘状区域的能量为 ~10^{54} 尔格。球状壳的盘状区域具有方向性且指向我们的概率大约为 3×10^{-5}，这意味着符合我们模型的辐射源很少。我们根据该模型进行如下预测：

(1) 流量幅度变化取决于观测频率 v，规律如下：

$$\begin{array}{ll} \sim 0 & 0 < v < 300 \\ \sim 0.013 \left\{ \left(\frac{v}{300} \right)^{2.5} - 1 \right\} & 300 < v < 1{,}000 \\ \sim 0.25 & v > 1{,}000 \end{array}$$

其中 v 的单位为兆周。因此，尽管卡斯韦尔与威尔斯[10] 在 178 兆周 / 秒观测不到变化，但这并不一定与肖洛米斯基的观测结果相矛盾。

(2) 在 $300 < v < 1{,}000$ 频率范围内，流量强度在第 $t(v)$ 天 ($t < 50$) 达到最大，然后在 ($100 - 2t$) 天内该强度保持不变 (换言之，此时盘状区域频率在 v 到 1,000 兆周 / 秒范围内不再透明)。如图 3 所示，强度上升时间 $t(v)$ 是关于 v 的增函数。

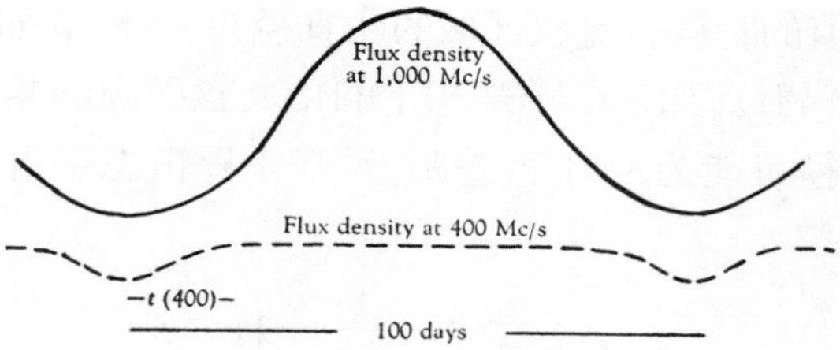

Fig. 3. Time variation of flux density

(3) The times at which the intensity is a minimum should be the same at all frequencies $\nu > 300$ Mc/s, unless there is appreciable dispersion.

However, as regards (3), even if there is negligible dispersion in the source, there may be appreciable dispersion produced by ionized intergalactic gas[11]. At 400 Mc/s, for example, the resulting delay may be as large as 2 h. At this frequency our model predicts an increase in flux of more than 1 percent in about 10 days following the minimum, so that an intergalactic delay might be detectable. Moreover, there may be, superposed on the main variation, an additional small amplitude variation of much shorter time-scale than 50 days, which might then be detectable when the main variation is at a minimum. It would therefore appear to be worth while to develop the sophisticated techniques necessary to detect the possible dispersion, and so to test the hypothesis that there is a significant ionized gas in intergalactic space, and perhaps even to determine the scale-factor of the universe if other radio variables are discovered[11].

We thank Profs. F. T. Haddock, A. Sandage and M. Schmidt for their advice. This work was begun while one of us (D. W. S.) was visiting the Department of Physics and Astronomy, University of Maryland, under National Aeronautics and Space Administration grant *NsG* 5860. He is grateful to Profs. H. Laster and G. Westerhout for their hospitality.

Note added in proof. It has been reported by W. A. Dent (*Science*, **148**, 1458; 1965) that the quasi-stellar source *3C* 273 (and possibly *3C* 279 and *3C* 345 as well) is variable at 8,000 Mc/s, and that again there is a discrepancy between light-size, red shift and angular diameter. However, the discrepancy is much less than for *CTA* 102, and a special geometry of the type considered here might be a possible explanation without leading to such an unfavourable probability factor.

(**207**, 738-740; 1965)

M. J. Rees and D. W. Sciama: Department of Applied Mathematics and Theoretical Physics, University of Cambridge.

References:

1. Sholomitsky, G. B., *I. A. U. Information Bulletin on Variable Stars*, No. 83 (Feb. 27, 1965).

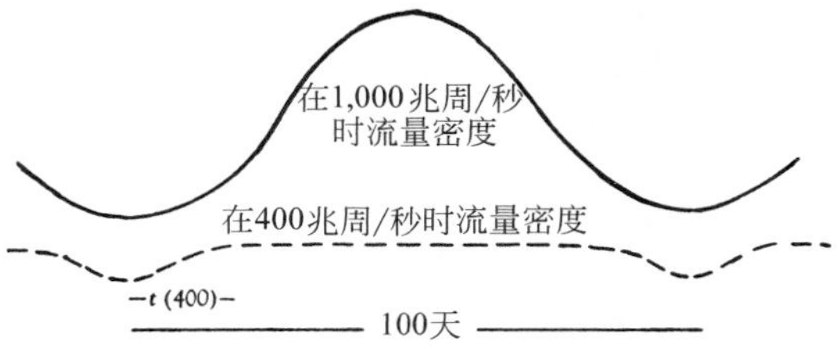

图 3. 流量密度的时间变化

（3）除非存在明显的色散，否则对于 $v > 300$ 兆周 / 秒的频率，辐射强度达到最小的时间是一致的。

针对上面第（3）点，即使辐射源中的色散可以忽略，电离的星系际气体也可能产生明显的色散[11]。比如，在频率为 400 兆周 / 秒时，造成的延时大约为 2 小时。在该频率下，我们的模型预测到当流量达到最小值后约 10 天其增加值超过了 1%，因此星系际间的延时是可以探测到的。此外，在主要变化之上也可能叠加有小幅度变化，其时间尺度小于 50 天；这样，当主要变化达到最小时，就可以探测到这种小幅度变化。基于以上分析，看起来有必要发展更加精密的技术，用于探测可能存在的色散，并且可以验证星系间存在电离气体的假设；如果可以发现其他射电变星的话[11]，甚至也许可以确定宇宙的尺度因子。

我们非常感谢哈多克教授、桑德奇教授、施密特教授提供有益的建议。这项工作起始于本文作者之一夏玛访问马里兰大学天文物理系期间，得到了美国国家航空航天局资助，合约序号为 *NsG* 5860。最后也非常感谢拉斯特教授和韦斯特豪特教授的盛情接待。

附加说明 登特（《科学》，第 148 卷，第 1458 页；1965 年）曾报道过，类星体射电源 3*C* 273（可能也包括 3*C* 279 和 3*C* 345）在 8,000 兆周 / 秒是变化的，并且与 *CTA* 102 类似，其光学尺度、红移以及角直径之间并不一致。然而，这一差异远小于 *CTA* 102 的差异，在不引起这种不利因素的条件下，本文中所指出的这种特殊几何模型将成为一种可能的解释。

（金世超 翻译；于涌 审稿）

2. Sandage, A., and Wyndham, J. B., *Astrophys. J.*, **141**, 328 (1965).

3. Harris, D. E., and Roberts, J. A., *Publ. Astro. Soc. Pacific*, **72**, 237 (1960).

4. Slish, V. I., *Nature*, **199**, 682 (1963).

5. Williams, P. J. S., *Nature*, **200**, 56 (1963).

6. Schmidt, M., *Astrophys. J.*, **141**, 1295 (1965).

7. Menon, T. K., *Nature*, **206**, 810 (1965).

8. Layzer, D., *Astrophys. J.*, **141**, 837 (1965).

9. Conway, R. G., Kellermann, K. I., and Long, R. J., *Mon. Not. Roy. Astro. Soc.*, **125**, 261 (1963).

10. Caswell, J. L., and Wills, D., *Nature*, **206**, 1241 (1965).

11. Haddock, F. T., and Sciama, D. W., *Phys. Rev. Letters*, **14**, 1007 (1965).

Haemoglobin J and E in a Thai Kindred

R. Q. Blackwell *et al.*

Editor's Note

By 1965, many abnormal variants of haemoglobin had been described, including haemoglobin J, which was originally discovered in an "American Negro woman" and subsequently identified in several other ethnic groups. Here R. Quentin Blackwell and colleagues from the U.S. Naval Medical Research Unit in Taiwan, and Chamras Thephusdin from the Royal Thai Army's Institute of Pathology in Bangkok, report the discovery of haemoglobin J in a Thai family. It was the first time this variant had been found in people from Thailand, and was surprising because there it is often associated with another abnormal haemoglobin variant, haemoglobin E.

SINCE its discovery in 1956 by Thorup *et al.*[1] in an American Negro woman, haemoglobin J has been identified in other ethnio groups including Gujerati Indians[2,3], Indonesians[4,5], French-Canadian[6] and Swedish-American[7] Caucasians, Algerians[8], Chinese in Singapore[9], Hakkanese Chinese in Taiwan[10], and Hawaiian-Chinese-Caucasians[11]. This communication concerns the occurrence of haemoglobin J in a Thai family; the family is of special interest because it has haemoglobin E in addition to J.

The presence of an electrophoretically fast-moving haemoglobin in addition to normal haemoglobin A was detected in one subject among 676 presumably healthy Thai soldiers stationed at Nakhornratchsima (Korat), Thailand. Results of the haptoglobin distribution[12,13] and haemoglobin E distribution[13] in that group of subjects were reported previously. Subsequent studies indicated that the electrophoretic mobilities of the haemoglobin under various *p*H conditions appeared to be identical to those of a fast haemoglobin found in members of a Hakkanese Chinese family in Taiwan[10]. Furthermore, both the Thai and the Chinese fast-moving haemoglobins appeared to have mobilities identical with that of a sample of haemoglobin J provided by Dr. Oscar Thorup from his original patient[1]. In addition, a sample of the Hakkanese Chinese haemoglobin was studied electrophoretically by Dr. H. Lehmann, who identified it as J. Pending completion of structure studies on the Thai haemoglobin it can be identified as J_{Korat}.

Subsequent investigations on blood samples from 16 other members of the Thai family by Smithies's vertical starch-gel electrophoresis procedure[14] at *p*H 9.0, with the *tris*-EDTA-borate buffer system[15] as used by Goldberg[16], disclosed the family to comprise a mixture of individuals possessing E, A+J, A+E and E+J type haemoglobin combinations. The distribution of the haemoglobin phenotypes in the kindred is shown in Fig. 1 and

一个泰国家族中的血红蛋白 J 和 E

布莱克韦尔等

编者按

截止到 1965 年，已经描述了许多异常的血红蛋白变异体，其中包括血红蛋白 J，这一蛋白最初是在一名“美国黑人妇女”体内发现的，随后在其他一些种族中得到鉴定。在本文中，来自位于中国台湾的美国海军第二医学研究所的昆廷·布莱克韦尔及其同事们和来自曼谷泰国皇家军队病理学研究所的占叻·泰普丁报道了在一个泰国家族中发现了血红蛋白 J。这是第一次在泰国人中发现该变异体，并且令人吃惊的是，此处的血红蛋白 J 常和另一个异常血红蛋白的变异体——血红蛋白 E 相关联。

自从 1956 年索普等人在一名美国黑人妇女体内发现了血红蛋白 J 以来 [1]，人们已在其他种族中发现了这种血红蛋白，包括古吉拉特印度人 [2,3]、印度尼西亚人 [4,5]、法裔加拿大 [6] 和瑞典裔美国 [7] 白种人、阿尔及利亚人 [8]、新加坡华人 [9]、中国台湾的客家人 [10] 和有华人血统的夏威夷白种人 [11]。本篇通讯报道了在一个泰国家族中发现的血红蛋白 J，该家族有特殊的意义，因为它除了含有血红蛋白 J 外，还有血红蛋白 E。

对 676 名驻扎在泰国那空叻差是玛（呵叻）的可能健康的泰籍士兵进行研究，发现在其中一名士兵的血样中除了有正常的血红蛋白 A，还能检测到一种电泳时快速移动的血红蛋白。此前曾报道过在这一群体中结合珠蛋白的分布 [12,13] 和血红蛋白 E[13] 的分布。随后的研究表明，该血红蛋白在多种不同的 pH 条件下的电泳迁移率与在一中国台湾客家人家族中发现的一种快速移动的血红蛋白相同 [10]。此外，在泰国人以及中国人中发现的快速移动的血红蛋白似乎与奥斯卡·索普博士提供的来自其最初病人 [1] 的一份血红蛋白 J 的样品具有相同的电泳迁移率。另外，莱曼博士还对一份中国客家人的血红蛋白样品进行了电泳研究，鉴定它为血红蛋白 J。在弄清楚这种泰国人中发现的血红蛋白的结构之前，我们可将其称为血红蛋白 $J_{\text{呵叻}}$以作区别。

随后我们用史密西斯提出的垂直淀粉凝胶电泳方法 [14] 研究了该泰国家族中其他 16 名成员的血液样品，实验在 pH 9.0 下进行，并选用戈德堡 [16] 采用的三羟甲基氨基甲烷–乙二胺四乙酸–硼酸盐缓冲系统 [15]，研究发现该家族的成员中存在 E、A+J、A+E 和 E+J 几种类型的血红蛋白组合。该家族血红蛋白表型的分布如图 1 所

representative electrophoretic patterns of the haemoglobins are illustrated in Fig. 2. The E type haemoglobin components in the present subjects were identified by comparison of their electrophoretic mobilities with those of numerous other haemoglobin E and A+E samples found in the earlier studies on the 676 Thai blood samples. In those investigations an authentic Thai blood sample with haemoglobins A+E, provided by Dr. Prawase Wasi, Siriraj Hospital, Bangkok, was used for comparison. Numerous studies have reported the presence of haemoglobin E in South-east Asia since its occurrence in Thais[17] was initially recognized. Our work[13] among the 676 Thai subjects, for example, disclosed that 39, or 5.8 percent, of the individuals were homozygous for the haemoglobin E gene and that 246, 36.4 percent, had haemoglobins A and E. The combined incidence in the Thai sample of 42.2 percent for the E and A+E genotypes, which is higher than those reported previously, has been confirmed in recent studies among North-eastern Thais by Wasi and NaNakorn[18].

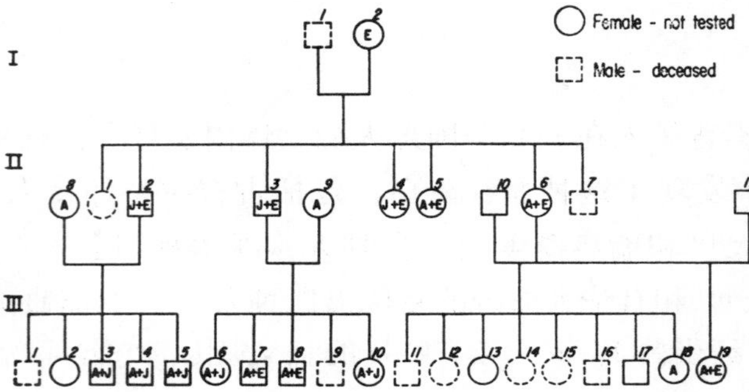

Fig. 1. Distributions of haemoglobin types E, A+E, A+J, and J+E among 3 generations of Thai kindred. Subject III-3 is the propositus

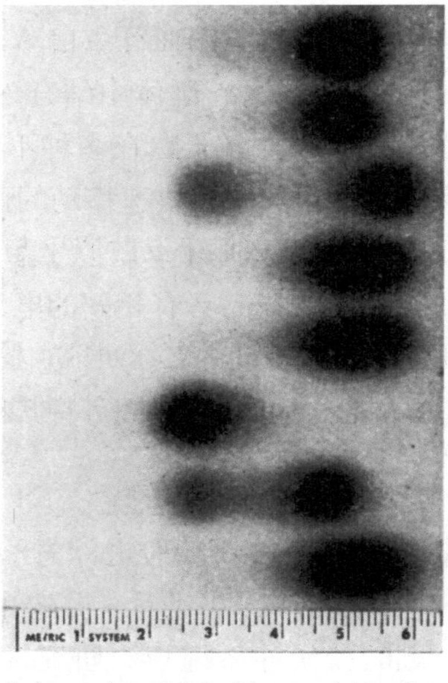

Fig. 2. Results of starch-gel electrophoresis[14-16] of haemoglobins from Thai kindred. From top downward the subjects and haemoglobin types are: 1, normal control, A; 2, II-8, A; 3, II-2, J+E; 4, III-4, A+J; 5, III-5, A+J; 6, I-2, E; 7, II-6, A+E; 8, III-3, propositus, A+J

示，图 2 显示了有代表性的血红蛋白的电泳图谱。通过与此前对 676 名泰国人血样研究时发现的众多其他血红蛋白 E 和 A+E 样品的电泳迁移率相比较，我们在目前的研究对象中鉴定出了 E 型血红蛋白组分。在这些研究中，由曼谷诗里拉吉医院的普拉瓦设·瓦西博士提供的一份确定含有血红蛋白 A+E 的泰国人血液样品用于对比参照。自从在泰国人中发现了血红蛋白 E[17] 以来，已经有大量的研究报道称其存在于东南亚。例如，在我们对 676 名泰国士兵进行的研究中 [13]，发现有 39 名士兵(占 5.8%)是血红蛋白 E 基因的纯合子，有 246 名士兵（占 36.4%）同时有血红蛋白 A 和 E。这样，我们研究的泰国人血样中血红蛋白 E 和 A+E 基因型的总量就达到了 42.2%，这一数值高于此前报道的数据，而最近瓦西和纳那空 [18] 关于泰国东北部人群的研究已经证实了我们的这一结果。

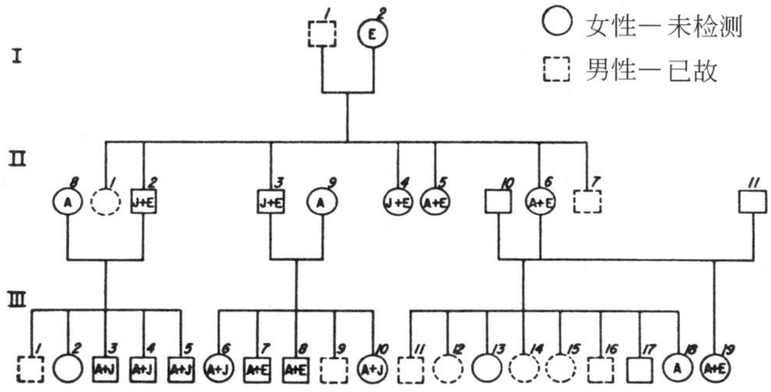

图 1. 某泰国家族的三代人中 E 型、A+E 型、A+J 型和 J+E 型血红蛋白的分布情况。编号为 III-3 的研究对象是在该家族中发现的先证者。

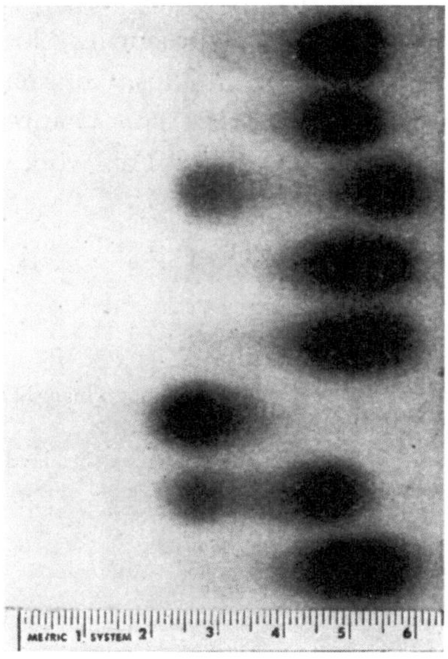

图 2. 该泰国家族成员的血红蛋白淀粉凝胶电泳 [14-16] 结果。从上到下，研究对象和血红蛋白类型依次是：1. 正常对照，A；2. II-8，A；3. II-2，J+E；4. III-4，A+J；5. III-5，A+J；6. I-2，E；7. II-6，A+E；8. III-3，先证者，A+J。

Subject III-3 was the original case with type A+J haemoglobins found in our study of Thai subjects; his 2 brothers also had the same combination. Their mother, II-8, possessed only normal A-type haemoglobin; their father, II-2, possessed genes for both J and E haemoglobins, and the J haemoglobin genes in the sons were apparently inherited from him. Subject II-3, the brother of subject II-2, also had types J and E haemoglobins; his wife, subject II-9, had normal haemoglobin A. Among the children of subjects II-3 and II-9, one daughter, III-6, had types A and J haemoglobins and 2 sons, III-7 and III-8, had types A and E.

All 5 of the living siblings in the second generation of the kindred had E haemoglobins in combination either with A or J haemoglobin. Their mother, I-2, was homozygous for the E haemoglobin gene as illustrated in Fig. 2. Their father is presumed to have had A and J haemoglobins.

The present family provides the first reported examples of haemoglobin J in Thais and also of an association within a kindred of haemoglobins E and J. Due to the high density of the gene for haemoglobin E in the Thai race as described here, it is obvious that any other abnormal haemoglobin occurring in Thais would occur rather frequently in the same kindred with haemoglobin E. Among those members of the family studied thus far, subjects II-2, II-3 and II-4 are the only examples of the E+J haemoglobin combination in one individual. In future work this family will be examined clinically and haematologically.

We thank Dr. H. Lehmann for his help in identifying one of our haemoglobin J samples, and Drs. Prawase Wasi and Oscar Thorup for their generous contributions of abnormal haemoglobin samples. We also thank the medical officers and technicians of the Royal Thai Army Medical Corps for their aid in procuring blood specimens from the Thai family. Likewise the support of Capt. R. A. Phillips, Commanding Officer of NAMRU-2, and Col. James L. Hansen, director of the U.S. Army Component of the SEATO Medical Research Laboratory, Bangkok, is acknowledged. This work was supported in part by U.S. Public Law 480, Section 104(*c*).

(**207**, 767-768; 1965)

R. Quentin Blackwell, Boon-Nam Blackwell and Jeanette Tung-Hsiang Huang: Department of Biochemistry, U.S. Naval Medical Research Unit No. 2, Taipei, Taiwan, China.

Chamras Thephusdin: Royal Thai Army, Institute of Pathology, Bangkok, Thailand.

References:

1. Thorup, O. A., Itano, H. A., Wheby, M., and Leavell, B. S., *Science*, **123**, 889 (1956).
2. Raper, A. B., *Brit. Med. J.*, i, 1285 (1957).
3. Sanghvi, L. D., Sukumaran, P. K., and Lehmann, H., *Brit. Med. J.*, ii, 828 (1958).
4. Huisman, T. H. J., Noordhoek, K., and Da Costa, G. J., *Nature*, **179**, 322 (1957).

在我们这项对泰国人的研究中，编号为III-3的研究对象是我们最先发现的A+J型血红蛋白的案例；他的两个兄弟也有同样的组合。他们的母亲II-8只有正常的A型血红蛋白；他们的父亲II-2则同时有血红蛋白J和E的基因，因此其儿子的血红蛋白J基因显然是遗传自父亲。II-2的兄弟II-3也有血红蛋白J和E，II-3的妻子II-9则只有正常的血红蛋白A，在II-3和II-9的孩子中，一份女儿III-6有血红蛋白A和J，两个儿子III-7和III-8有血红蛋白A和E。

这个家族的第二代中健在的5人都有血红蛋白E，它或与血红蛋白A结合，或与血红蛋白J组合。如图2所示，他们的母亲I-2是血红蛋白E基因的纯合子。因此可以推断他们的父亲同时带有血红蛋白A和J。

所示家族是首次报道的泰国人中含有血红蛋白J的案例，也是在一个家族内同时存在血红蛋白E和J的案例。鉴于泰国人中血红蛋白E基因的密度较高（如本文所述），很明显，在泰国含有血红蛋白E的同一家族中，任何其他异常血红蛋白出现的频率会相当高。在已研究的该家族成员中，同一个体中存在血红蛋白E+J组合的例子只有编号为II-2、II-3和II-4的研究对象。今后我们还将对该家族进行临床学和血液学的研究。

我们感谢莱曼博士帮助我们鉴定了其中一份血红蛋白J样品，也感谢普拉瓦设·瓦西博士和奥斯卡·索普博士慷慨地给我们提供异常血红蛋白样品。我们还要感谢泰国皇家军队医疗团的医疗官员和技术人员帮助我们取得了该泰国家庭的血样。同时，我们也要感谢美国海军第二医学研究所指挥官菲利普斯上尉和泰国曼谷东南亚条约组织医疗研究实验室美国军队组主任詹姆斯·汉森上校对我们工作的支持。我们的部分研究工作得到美国480号公法第104（*c*）节的支持。

（周志华 翻译；崔巍 审稿）

5. Lie-Injo, L. E., *Acta Haemat.*, **19**, 126 (1958).
6. McCabe, M. E., Lange, R. D., and Crosby, W. H., *Amer. J. Med.*, **23**, 329 (1957).
7. Wasi, P., Githens, J., and Hathaway, W., *Blood*, **16**, 1795 (1960).
8. Boulard, C., Cabannes, R., Duzer, A., and Scotto, J. -Cl., *Bull. Mem. Soc. Med. Hopit.* (Paris), **76**, 41 (1960).
9. Ager, J. A. M., Lehmann, H., and Vella, F., *Brit. Med. J.*, ii, 539 (1958).
10. Blackwell, R. Q., and Huang, J. T. -H. (in preparation).
11. Jim, R. T. S., and Yarbro, M. T., *Blood*, **15**, 285 (1960).
12. Blackwell, R. Q., and Thephusdin, C., *Nature*, **197**, 503 (1963).
13. Thephusdin, C., Blackwell, B. -N., Huang, J. T. -H., and Blackwell, R. Q., *Proc. Third Congr. Asian Pac. Soc. Haem. Jerusalem*, August 17-23, 1964 (in the press).
14. Smithies, O., *Biochem. J.*, **71**, 585 (1959).
15. Aronsson, T., and Grönwall, A., *Scand. J. Clin. Lab. Invest.*, **9**, 338 (1957).
16. Goldberg, C. A. J., *Clin. Chem.*, **4**, 484 (1958).
17. Chernoff, A. I., Minnich, V., and Chongchareonsuk, S., *Science*, **120**, 605 (1954).
18. Wasi, P., and Na-Nakorn, S. (personal communication).

Haemoglobin E in Vietnamese

R. Q. Blackwell *et al.*

Editor's Note

In his continuing search for abnormal haemoglobin variants in different ethnic groups, R. Quentin Blackwell and colleagues from the US Naval Medical Research Unit in Taiwan, China, screened 482 Vietnamese hospital inpatients for the presence of haemoglobin E. Here they report the presence of haemoglobin E in 17 patients, always expressed alongside haemoglobin A, the most common and normal adult version of the protein. Their results add to the catalogue of haemoglobin E-expressing ethnic groups, which most notably included groups from the Middle East and Asia.

SINCE its simultaneous discovery a decade ago in an American family of mixed Spanish, Guatemalan, and Indian ancestry[1] and in Thais[2], haemoglobin E has been found in a variety of ethnic groups a majority of which are located in the Middle East and Asia. It is particularly common among the peoples of south-east Asia where it had been found in relatively high incidence in Burmese[3], Thais[4-7] and Cambodians[8], and in lower incidences in Vietnamese[9], Malayans[10,11], Indonesians[12], Chinese[13,14] and Filipinos[15]. The results in this communication confirm the occurrence of haemoglobin E among Vietnamese.

Subjects for this investigation were residents of Saigon and environs. At the time of the work, during February and March 1964, they were patients in the Cho Quan Hospital, Saigon, where they had been admitted with diarrhoea during the cholera epidemic and were under treatment for dehydration. Red cells were obtained from residual heparinized blood samples collected for other diagnostic purposes and were preserved with merthiolate and by refrigeration prior to their transfer by air to the Biochemistry Department Laboratory of this Unit for analysis.

On receipt in the laboratory the red cells were washed with saline, mixed with equal volumes of distilled water, and frozen until used for electrophoretic analysis. After thawing, the samples were centrifuged and the supernatant haemolysates examined by Smithies's vertical starch-gel electrophoresis procedure[16]. The gel buffer employed was the *tris*-EDTA-borate buffer, *p*H 9.0, at the concentrations recommended by Goldberg[17].

Results of the study indicate that 17, or 3.53 percent, of the 482 subjects had A+E haemoglobins. No other abnormal haemoglobins were detected. Although no quantitative determinations were made of the relative amounts of haemoglobins A and E in the samples, haemoglobin E was always the minor component. By inspection the E component

越南人中的血红蛋白 E

布莱克韦尔等

编者按

来自位于中国台湾的美国海军第二医学研究所的昆廷·布莱克韦尔及其同事们，一直在寻找不同种族人群中的异常血红蛋白变异体。他们从越南医院 482 名住院患者中筛选含有血红蛋白 E 的患者。在本文中，布莱克韦尔等人报道了 17 名患者存在血红蛋白 E 并且总是伴随着血红蛋白 A 的表达，血红蛋白 A 是最普遍和常见的成人血红蛋白。他们的研究结果增加了表达血红蛋白 E 的种族人群数，其中来自中东和亚洲地区的人群血红蛋白 E 表达最显著。

自从十年前在一个具有西班牙、危地马拉和印度混合血统的美国家庭 [1] 及泰国人 [2] 中同时发现血红蛋白 E 后，人们又在许多种族中发现了血红蛋白 E，这些种族大多分布在中东和亚洲地区。血红蛋白 E 在东南亚人群中特别常见，其中缅甸人 [3]、泰国人 [4-7] 和柬埔寨人 [8] 呈现相对较高的发生率，而在越南人 [9]、马来人 [10,11]、印度尼西亚人 [12]、中国人 [13,14] 和菲律宾人 [15] 中发生率相对较低。本篇文章的研究结果证实了血红蛋白 E 存在越南人中。

本研究的对象是西贡市及近郊的居民。在我们进行研究时，即 1964 年 2 月至 3 月间，他们是霍乱流行期因患痢疾而在西贡赵泉医院住院的患者，当时正在接受脱水症状的治疗。从剩余的肝素化血液样本（原本供其他诊断用）中获得红细胞，用硫柳汞保存红细胞，冷冻后通过航空转运到美国海军第二医学研究所的生物化学实验室进行分析。

当实验室收到样品后，首先用生理盐水洗涤红细胞，然后将红细胞与等体积的蒸馏水混合并冷冻保存以供电泳分析。实验时，先将样品解冻，然后离心，按照史密西斯的垂直淀粉凝胶电泳方法 [16] 对上层溶血液进行检测。凝胶缓冲液是参照戈德堡推荐的浓度配制的 pH 为 9.0 的三羟甲基氨基甲烷–乙二胺四乙酸–硼酸盐缓冲液 [17]。

研究结果表明，在 482 名研究对象中，17 人（占 3.53%）有血红蛋白 A+E。实验中没有检测到其他的异常血红蛋白。尽管没有对样品中血红蛋白 A 和 E 的相对含量进行定量测定，但是血红蛋白 E 总是相对较少的成分。经检验，血红蛋白 E 大概占血红蛋白总量的 1/5 到 1/3。在所有样本中，血红蛋白 E 的含量都超过了血红蛋白 A_2

was estimated to comprise from one-fifth to one-third of the total; in all cases it exceeded the levels to be expected for A_2 haemoglobin, which has the same electrophoretic mobility as E in the buffer employed.

Three cases of haemoglobin E, 2.7 percent, were reported by Albahary *et al.*[9] among their 113 Vietnamese subjects. Based on the results of both investigations the incidence of the gene for haemoglobin E in the Vietnamese appears to be lower than those in Thais, Cambodians, Burmese and Malayans, similar to those of some of the Indonesians, and higher than those of Chinese and Filipinos.

Although our results with respect to haemoglobin E in Vietnamese agree with those of Albahary *et al.*[9], we were unable to confirm their finding of a slow-moving component which they called haemoglobin "Sud-Vietnam". No slow component other than E or A_2 was found among our 482 subjects.

We thank James W. Fresh, Charles Neave, Donald L. Pankratz and other members of the Cholera Treatment Team of this Research Unit, for collection and transport of the blood samples. This work was supported in part by a fund provided under U.S. Public Law 480, Section 104 (*c*).

(**207**, 768; 1965)

R.Quentin Blackwell, Jeanette Tung-Hsiang Huang, Li-Chin Chien: Department of Biochemistry, U.S. Naval Medical Research Unit No. 2, Taipei, Taiwan, China.

References:

1. Itano, H. A., Bergren, W. R., and Sturgeon, P., *J. Amer. Chem. Soc.*, **76**, 2278 (1954).
2. Chernoff, A. I., Minnich, V., and Chongchareonsuk, S., *Science*, **120**, 605 (1954).
3. Lehmann, H., Story, P., and Thein, H., *Brit. Med. J.*, i, 544 (1956).
4. Na-Nakorn, S., Minnich, V., and Chernoff, A. I., *J. Lab. Clin. Med.*, **47**, 490 (1956).
5. Wasi, P., and Na-Nakorn, S. (personal communication).
6. Flatz, G., Pik, C., and Sundharagiati, B., *Lancet*, ii, 385 (1964).
7. Thephusdin, C., Blackwell, B.-N., Huang, J. T.-H., and Blackwell, R. Q., *Proc. Third Congr. Asian Pac. Soc. Haem.* (In the press).
8. Brumpt, L., Brumpt, V., Coquelet, M. L., and De Traverse, D. M., *Rev. Hemat.* (Paris), **13**, 21 (1958).
9. Albahary, C., Dreyfus, J. C., Labie, D., Schapira, G., and Tram, L., *Rev. Hemat.* (Paris), **13**, 163 (1958).
10. Lehmann, H., and Singh, R. B., *Nature*, **178**, 695 (1956).
11. Vella, F., *Lancet*, i, 268 (1963).
12. Lie-Injo, L. E., and Oey, H. G., *Lancet*, i, 20 (1957).
13. Vella, F., *Acta Haemat.*, **23**, 393 (1960).
14. Blackwell, R. Q., Huang, J. T. -H., and Chien, L. -C., *Proc. Third Congr. Asian Pac. Soc. Haem. Jerusalem*, August 17-23, 1964 (in the press).
15. De La Fuente, V., Florentino, R. F., Alejo, L. G., Huang, J. T. -H., Chien, L. -G., and Blackwell, R. Q., *J. Philipp. Med. Assoc.* (in the press).
16. Smithies, O., *Biochem. J.*, **71**, 585 (1959).
17. Goldberg, C. A. J., *Clin. Chem.*, **4**, 484 (1958).

的预期水平，在我们所用的缓冲液中血红蛋白 A_2 与 E 具有相同的电泳迁移率。

在此之前，阿尔巴阿里等人[9]曾报道，他们研究的 113 个越南人中，3 人（占 2.7%）含有血红蛋白 E。基于这两项研究结果可以看出，血红蛋白 E 基因在越南人中的出现频率似乎比在泰国人、柬埔寨人、缅甸人和马来人中出现的频率低，与印度尼西亚人类似，比在中国人和菲律宾人中出现的频率高。

尽管我们关于越南人中血红蛋白 E 的研究结果与阿尔巴阿里等人的结果[9]一致，但是我们未能证实此前他们发现的一种迁移较慢的被称为血红蛋白“南越”的组分。在所有 482 名研究对象中，没有发现比血红蛋白 E 或 A_2 迁移更慢的组分。

我们感谢詹姆斯·弗雷什、查尔斯·尼夫、唐纳德·潘克拉茨和本研究所霍乱医疗组的其他成员在血样采集及转运中所做的工作。这项工作部分由美国 480 号公法第 104（*c*）节设立的一项基金资助。

（郑建全 翻译；崔巍 审稿）

New Model for the Tropocollagen Macromolecule and Its Mode of Aggregation

R. A. Grant *et al.*

Editor's Note

Collagen is the main component of connective tissue, present in ligament and tendon, blood vessels, skin and bone. This makes it one of the key structural proteins, which act as materials rather than enzymes. Like many biomaterials, it has a hierarchical structure: the protein strands are woven into triple helices and then bundled together in fibrils. Early electron-microscope studies showed the fibrils have periodic light and dark bands about 64 nanometres apart. Here researchers at the UK's Agricultural Research Council suggest an explanation, based on the notion that the protein strands have regularly spaced regions that can and cannot form crosslinks. The idea was on the right lines: the bands in fact come from a staggered arrangement of polypeptide chains.

THE molecular architecture of collagen has been intensively studied by a variety of physical and chemical techniques. According to current views collagen fibres are composed of fibrils which are themselves built up from a basic structural unit termed the tropocollagen macromolecule. Each tropocollagen unit is believed to have a three-stranded coiled-coil structure in which the most probable arrangement of the polypeptide chains would appear to be the collagen II model proposed by Rich and Crick[1]. The tropocollagen unit has been described as a rigid rod-like structure for which Boedtker and Doty[2], using physico-chemical methods, originally found a diameter of 13.6 Å, an average length of 3,000 Å and an average molecular weight of 345,000. Recently, Rice, Casassa, Kerwin and Maser[3] have suggested a length of 2,800 Å and a molecular weight not greater than 310,000.

One of the earliest observations made on biological material with the electron microscope was that native collagen fibres exhibited a conspicuous transverse banding with a repeat distance of approximately 640 Å (Schmitt, Hall and Jakus[4]; Wolpers[5]). There have since been many reports on the structure of collagen using shadowing, thin sections and positive staining. These have been reviewed in detail by Harrington and Von Hippel[6], Gross[7], Fitton Jackson[8] and Veis[9]. Much research has been devoted to clarifying the relationship of the basic tropocollagen unit to the native collagen fibre.

An important aspect of the problem is to explain how the observed periodicity of 640 Å of native collagen results from the combination of tropocollagen units of length 2,800 Å.

It is well known that native-type collagen fibres may be reconstituted from acetic acid

原胶原大分子及其聚集模式的新模型

格兰特等

编者按

胶原蛋白是结缔组织的主要组成部分，分布在韧带、肌腱、血管、皮肤和骨骼中。这使得胶原蛋白成为一种重要的结构蛋白，它主要充当组成材料，而不是酶。和许多生物材料一样，它具有多级结构：蛋白质链被编织成三股螺旋后捆绑在一起形成纤维。早期的电子显微镜研究表明蛋白纤维含有以 64 nm 为间隔周期的明暗带。本文中，英国农业研究委员会的研究者基于以下这一概念给出了一种解释，即蛋白质链有规则的间隔区，这些区域之间可以形成或不可以形成交联。这一想法大体正确：事实上，这种结合来自多肽链之间的交错排列。

人们通过多种物理和化学技术已经深入地研究了胶原蛋白的分子结构。根据现在的观点，胶原蛋白纤维是由以原胶原大分子为基本结构单元构成的纤维组成的。通常认为每个原胶原单位都有一个三链卷曲螺旋结构，这种结构中多肽链最可能的排列方式可能符合里奇和克里克[1]所提出的胶原蛋白 II 模型。原胶原单位被描述成一个刚性的棒状结构，起初，博德克和多蒂[2]利用物理化学方法发现其直径为 13.6 Å，平均长度为 3,000 Å，平均分子量为 345,000。最近，赖斯、卡萨萨、克尔温和马泽尔[3]认为其长度为 2,800 Å，分子量不超过 310,000。

利用电子显微镜对生物材料最早的观察结果之一表明，天然胶原纤维显示出一个明显的重复距离约为 640 Å 的横向带（施米特，霍尔和亚库斯[4]；沃尔佩斯[5]）。自此以后，有了许多使用投影、超薄切片和正染技术研究胶原蛋白结构的报道。哈林顿和冯 · 希佩尔[6]、格罗斯[7]、菲顿 · 杰克逊[8]和维斯[9]对此进行了详细的论述。许多研究都致力于阐明基本原胶原单位与天然胶原蛋白纤维之间的关系。

这一问题的一个重要的方面是解释长度为 2,800 Å 的原胶原单位是怎样形成了天然胶原蛋白中所观察到的 640 Å 周期性的。

众所周知，通过调节胶原蛋白乙酸溶液的 pH 和离子强度可以使天然胶原蛋白

solutions of collagen by adjustment of *p*H and ionic strength. It is also possible to reconstitute collagen in a number of forms differing characteristically from the native fibre. A particularly interesting form is the segment long spacing (SLS) crystallites (Gross, Highberger and Schmitt[10]) produced by the addition of adenosine triphosphate (ATP) to an acetic acid solution of collagen. The SLS crystallites appear to consist of tropocollagen units aggregated side by side with the ends of the molecules in register. A large number of bands, arranged at right angles to the long axes of the tropocollagen units, may be seen with the electron microscope using either positive- or negative-staining techniques. The fact that these bands are distributed asymmetrically is strong evidence that the structure of the tropocollagen macromolecule is polarized.

Another type of collagen fibril, produced by dialysing an acetic acid solution of collagen (tropocollagen) containing acid glycoprotein or chondroitin sulphate (Highberger, Gross and Schmitt[11]; Schmitt, Gross and Highberger[12]) has been termed the fibrous long spacing (FLS) form. The repeat distance of this form has been found to vary with the method of preparation and the different varieties produced have been further designated FLS—I, II, etc., depending on the spacing observed. In the case of the FLS form of collagen a maximum repeat distance of about 2,500 Å has been found. It has been suggested (Schmitt and Hodge[13]) that in the FLS form of fibre the tropocollagen units are aggregated end to end. The direction of polarization of the macromolecules was considered to be alternated in view of the symmetrical pattern obtained in the electron microscope after positive staining with phosphotungstic acid.

Application of the negative staining technique (Brenner and Horne[14]) to high-resolution studies of collagen with the electron microscope showed that it was possible to visualize, directly, tropocollagen macromolecules occurring in native collagen fibrils (Tromans *et al.*[15]; Olsen[16,17]). In their negatively stained preparations of collagen fibrils the most striking feature seen was the arrangement of slender, somewhat crooked filaments running roughly parallel to each other along the long axis of the fibril. These filaments, 15-20 Å across, were interpreted as being the tropocollagen macromolecules.

In a detailed study of negatively stained collagen specimens, Tromans[18] suggested that the light and dark bands resulted from differences in the density of the protein and in the penetration of the negative stain between the macromolecules. It was not found possible to demonstrate the precise positions of the ends of the macromolecules within the fibrils, nor was there any evidence in favour of a "quarter staggered" arrangement as suggested by the model of Hodge and Schmitt[19]. The recent descriptions of native and FLS-type collagen by Olsen[16,17] and Kuhn and Zimmer[20] have indicated that the macromolecules are aggregated by end overlap. This view is not in agreement with the model proposed by Schmitt and Hodge[13], in which it is suggested that end-to-end aggregation takes place by a coiling around each other of polypeptide chains projecting from each end of the tropocollagen macromolecule (Hodge and Petruska[21]).

This report is based on an electron microscope investigation on native, SLS and FLS

纤维重组。也可以使天然纤维重组为具有大量不同形态特征的胶原蛋白。通过向胶原蛋白的乙酸溶液中加入三磷酸腺苷（ATP）可以产生片段长间距微晶（SLS）（格罗斯，海贝格和施米特[10]），这是一个非常有趣的形态。片段长间距微晶可能是由原胶原分子末端并排聚集而成的。使用正染或负染技术，在电子显微镜下可能看到与原胶原单位长轴呈直角排列起来的大量的条带。这些条带的不对称分布可以有力地证明原胶原大分子结构是极性的。

通过透析含有酸性糖蛋白或硫酸软骨素的胶原蛋白（原胶原）的乙酸溶液而产生的另一种形态的胶原蛋白纤维（海贝格，格罗斯和施米特[11]；施米特，格罗斯和海贝格[12]）已经被定义为纤维长间距型（FLS）。人们发现这种形态的重复距离随着制备的方法不同而改变，根据观察到的间隔，将这些不同的产物种类进一步定义为纤维长间距 I 型、II 型等。在胶原蛋白的纤维长间距形态中，已发现的最大的重复距离约为 2,500 Å。有人认为（施米特和霍奇[13]）纤维长间距型纤维是由原胶原单位首尾相连聚集而成的。根据磷钨酸正染后在电子显微镜下所得到的对称构型可以认为，大分子的极化方向是交替变化的。

应用负染技术（布伦纳和霍恩[14]）在电子显微镜下对胶原蛋白的高分辨率研究表明，直接观察天然胶原纤维中的原胶原大分子是有可能的（特罗芒等[15]；奥尔森[16,17]）。在经过负染处理的胶原蛋白纤维制品中可以看到的最明显的特征是，稍弯曲的细丝大致平行地排列在纤维的长轴上。这些跨度大约为 15 Å~20 Å 的细丝被认为是原胶原大分子。

在对经过负染的胶原蛋白样本的详细研究中，特罗芒[18]认为明暗带是蛋白质密度和大分子间负染渗透不同导致的。人们发现要证明纤维中大分子末端的准确位置是不可能的，也没有任何证据可以支持霍奇和施米特[19]的模型所提出的“四分之一交错”排列。最近在对天然胶原蛋白和纤维长间距型胶原蛋白的描述中，奥尔森[16,17]、库恩和齐默[20]指出，大分子是通过末端重叠聚集形成的。这种观点与施米特和霍奇[13]所提出的模型不一致，后者认为原胶原大分子首尾相连聚集的发生是通过其各末端伸展出的多肽链彼此缠绕实现的（霍奇和彼特鲁斯卡[21]）。

这篇报道是以电子显微镜下观察天然胶原蛋白、片段长间距型胶原蛋白和纤维

forms of collagen, and on these same forms modified by treatment with various cross-linking agents. Our experiments have also included observations on the mode of aggregation of tropocollagen to the above forms. The effect of collagenase on native fibres was also investigated, in experiments which will be reported in greater detail elsewhere. Acetic acid solutions of rat-tail tendon and guinea-pig skin collagen were used as sources of tropocollagen. From these investigations, a model has been developed which explains, in a relatively simple manner, the production of the majority of collagen forms. Their characteristic spacings can be considered to be determined by a basically random process of aggregation of tropocollagen units.

It was considered important to elucidate the mechanism whereby the light and dark bands, seen in negatively stained preparations of collagen, are produced. Treatment with a cross-linking agent, such as glutaraldehyde, resulted in an increase in the size of the light bands (*A* bands), Fig. 1, *b* and *c*; a well-defined light band also appeared in the dark or *B* bands. It was obvious from marked changes in the chemical and physical properties of the treated fibres (for example, no longer being soluble when autoclaved with water) that a number of strong cross-links had been introduced. Since the introduction of intermolecular cross-links by mild chemical means resulted in an increase in the size of the light or electron-transparent bands we may infer that the light bands, seen in native unaltered collagen, also

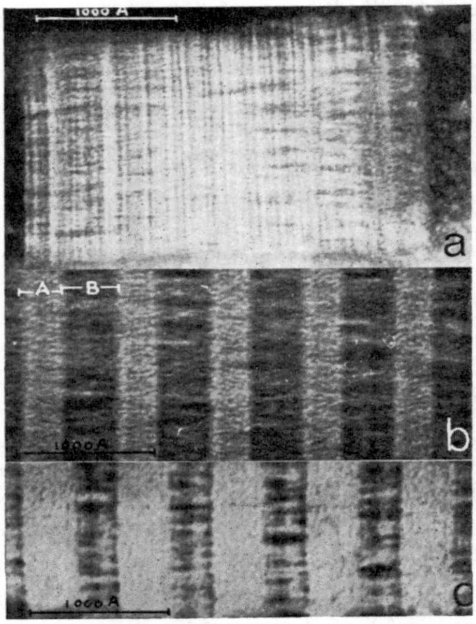

Fig. 1. *a*, Electron micrograph of negatively stained SLS crystallite. The length of the crystallite spans five *A* bands of the native fibril, shown in *b* at the same magnification. *b*, Negatively stained collagen fibril showing regions of light *A* bands and dark *B* bands. The rather flexible tropocollagen macromolecules are seen arranged roughly parallel to the fibril long axis. *c*, Negatively stained collagen fibril following treatment with glutaraldehyde. The increase in both size and density of the *A* bands is demonstrated. A well-defined light band within the *B* zone is also apparent

长间距型胶原蛋白以及具有上述三种相同形态的改性胶原蛋白为基础的，其中改性胶原蛋白是用各种交联剂处理获得的。同时我们的实验也包括观察上述形态中原胶原的聚集模式。同时也对胶原酶对天然纤维的作用进行了研究并将在其他地方给出实验较详细的报道。大鼠尾部肌腱和豚鼠皮肤胶原蛋白的乙酸溶液被用来作为原胶原的来源。我们通过这些研究建立了一个模型，以一个相对简单的方式解释了多数胶原蛋白形态的形成。它们的特征间距被认为是由原胶原单位聚集的基本随机过程决定的。

人们认为阐明经过负染处理的胶原质制品的明暗带的产生机制是非常重要的。利用交联剂（如戊二醛）进行处理导致了明带（*A* 带）大小的增加（图 1，*b* 和 *c*）；一个很清晰的明带也出现在暗带或 *B* 带中。从处理过的纤维的物理化学性质的显著变化（比如，当用蒸汽高压处理时不再可溶）明显可以看出纤维中产生了大量强有力的交联键。由于通过温和的化学方法产生的分子间交联键导致了明带或是电子透过带大小的增加，因此我们可以推断在天然的未作改变的胶原蛋白中所看到的明带也是由相邻大分子的结合区形成的。在天然胶原蛋白中这种分子间的结合可能是由

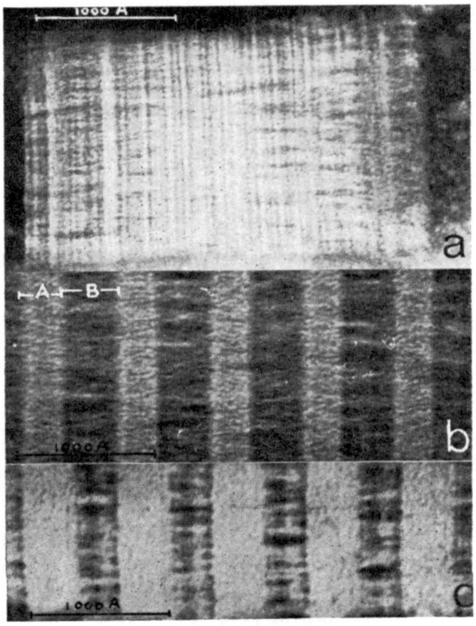

图 1. *a*，负染的片段长间距微晶的电子显微图片。微晶的长度横跨相同放大倍数下，示于图 *b* 的天然纤维的 5 条 *A* 带。*b*，负染的胶原蛋白纤维表现出 *A* 带明区和 *B* 带暗区。可以看到颇为柔韧的原胶原大分子沿着纤维长轴大致平行排列。*c*，经过戊二醛处理后的负染的胶原蛋白纤维。*A* 带增宽且密度增大。在 *B* 区也出现了一条清晰的明带。

result from regions of bonding between adjacent macromolecules. In native collagen this intermolecular bonding probably consists of polar and hydrogen bonds arising from polar amino acid side-chains arranged in a structurally complementary manner. It thus appears that the tropocollagen units, forming the fibril, are not laterally bonded uniformly throughout their length. Such a concept is in conformity with the finding that the primary structure of collagen consists of inhomogeneous amino-acid sequences (Grassman *et al.*[22]).

In order to deduce a simple rational explanation of the relationship of the length of the tropocollagen macromolecule (*c.* 2,800 Å) to the normal repeat distance (*D*) of 640 Å, use may be made of the observation that the length of an SLS crystallite spans 5 *A* bands of a native fibril when electron micrographs at the same magnification are compared (see Fig. 1, *a* and *b*). On average, the length of an *A* band (light) is about 0.4 *D*; hence the length of the tropocollagen unit equals the total distance spanned by 5 *A* bands plus the intervening *B* bands (=4.4 *D*). Careful examination of the electron micrographs gives no evidence of end-to-end junctions, all the macromolecules appearing to be aggregated together by lateral association with a good deal of cross-over in both *A* and *B* bands. The precise positions of the ends of tropocollagen macromolecules within the fibrils were difficult to determine. However, on careful inspection of the electron micrographs instances were noted of tropocollagen filaments appearing to end at the edge of an *A* band after passing through the band.

We suggest, on the basis of this evidence, that the tropocollagen macromolecule consists of alternating bonding and non-bonding regions, the bonding regions containing polar amino-acids which are arranged in a structurally specific manner. When two such bonding regions approach one another closely in proper alignment a strong lateral attraction results from the formation of many intermolecular polar and hydrogen bonds. All the 5 bonding regions may not be exactly equivalent and there is some evidence that the terminal bonding zones differ from the intermediate ones. Examination of the SLS form, by positive or negative staining, indicates that the tropocollagen macromolecule is polarized, and this is supported by the fact that in native fibres the band structure is asymmetrical. Tromans *et al.*[15] have suggested that the light bands be regarded as regions of crystallographic disorder. In view of the evidence from the cross-linking experiments we feel that this interpretation may be abandoned in favour of the more definitive explanation that the light bands correspond to regions of bonding between adjacent macromolecules.

The proposed model for tropocollagen (Fig. 2, 1) consists of a somewhat flexible filament of length *c.* 2,800 Å, divided into 9 zones consisting of 5 bonding zones of length about 0.4 *D* (265 Å) separated by 4 non-bonding zones of length about 0.6 *D* (375 Å). It should be appreciated that the measurements quoted in this report represent approximate values drawn from our own experiments and other results cited in the literature.

以结构互补方式排列的极性氨基酸侧链所形成的极性键和氢键所组成的。因此，组成纤维的原胶原单位似乎并不是自始至终均一地横向结合。这种观念与胶原蛋白的一级结构是由不均一氨基酸序列组成的这一发现（格拉斯曼等[22]）是一致的。

对于原胶原大分子的长度（*c* 为 2,800 Å）和 640 Å 的正常重复距离（*D*）之间的关系，我们为了给出一个简单合理的解释，对相同放大倍数下的电子显微图片进行了比较，发现片段长间距微晶的长度跨越了天然纤维的 5 条 *A* 带（图 1，*a* 和 *b*）。平均来说，1 条 *A* 带（明带）的长度约为 0.4 *D*，因此原胶原单位的长度就等于 5 条 *A* 带的跨度加上其间的 *B* 带跨度（=4.4 *D*）。通过对电子显微图片的仔细观察并没找到有关首尾相连的证据，所有大分子似乎都是以横向结合的方式与 *A* 带和 *B* 带中的大量横向线条聚集而成。很难确定纤维中原胶原分子末端的准确位置。然而通过对电子显微图片的仔细观察发现，原胶原细丝经过整条带后似乎停止在 *A* 带边缘。

在这一证据的基础上，我们认为原胶原大分子是由结合区域和非结合区域交替组成的，结合区域包括以结构特异性方式排列的极性氨基酸。当两个结合区域适当地以排列整齐的方式彼此紧密靠近时，许多分子间极性键和氢键的形成导致一个强有力的横向吸引力的产生。所有的 5 个结合区都不是严格相同的，有证据表明结合区的末端与中间部分是有区别的。利用正染或负染技术对片段长间距型胶原蛋白的检测表明原胶原大分子具有极性，天然纤维中带结构的不对称性也支持这一观点。特罗芒等人[15]认为可以把明带看作微晶的无序区域。然而根据交联实验得到的证据，我们感觉这种解释可以被否定，而明带对应的是相邻大分子间的结合区域这一明确的解释更具有说服力。

提出的原胶原模型（图 2，1）是由长度（*c*）为 2,800 Å，有一定韧性的细丝组成的，分为 9 个区域，包括 5 个长度约为 0.4 *D*（265 Å）的结合区域以及将它们分开的 4 个长度约为 0.6 *D*（375 Å）的非结合区域。值得一提的是，本文提供的测量结果代表着我们自己从实验得到的近似值和从文献中所引用的其他结果。

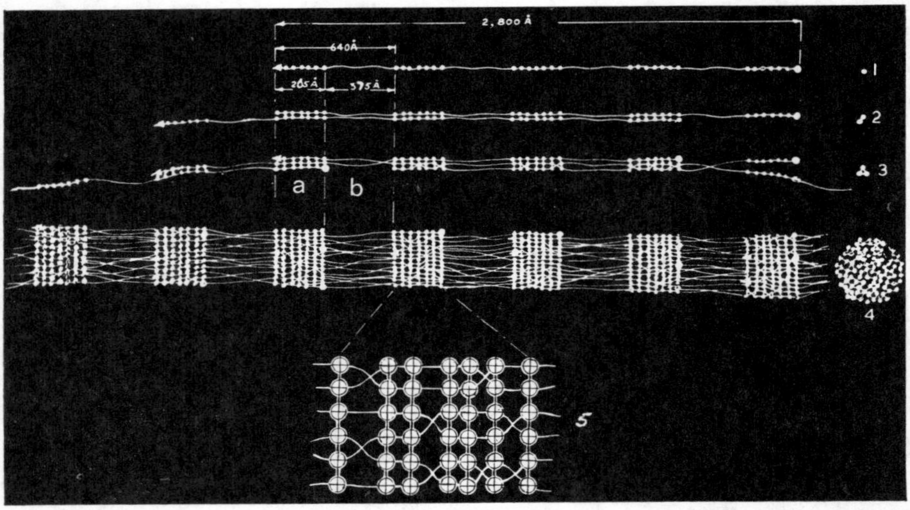

Fig. 2. 1, The diagram illustrates the proposed model for tropocollagen, consisting of a rather flexible filament divided into 9 zones. Five of these are bonding zones and four are considered as non-bonding zones. 1, 2, 3; Association of tropocollagen by random aggregation through bonding zones is illustrated. The overlap between two adjacent macromolecules can cover one to five bonding zones. The direction of the macromolecules, indicated by arrows, determines the polarization of the collagen fibril. 4, The establishment of a repeat pattern of 640 Å results in the formation of light (*a*) bands as bonding zones and dark (*b*) bands as non-bonding zones. 5, For diagrammatic purposes, the linking with an (*a*) band is shown to illustrate the possible flexibility of the macromolecules

It need not necessarily be assumed that the non-bonding regions are completely devoid of polar amino-acids. Indeed it appears from the cross-linking experiments that there is some lysine in these parts of the macromolecule. Nevertheless, it seems that in the native fibre only a few intermolecular bonds are formed between the non-bonding zones.

When tropocollagen units, conforming to the above model, are aggregated together so that there is an initial random choice as to which bonding region on one molecule cross-links in a structurally complementary manner with a bonding region on a different molecule, a fibre with 640 Å periodicity results (Fig. 2). A model of a collagen fibril constructed in this way shows a close resemblance to the structure of native collagen revealed by negative staining. Moreover, aggregation of tropocollagen macromolecules in an apparently random manner to form collagen fibrils has been observed by us in the electron microscope. There is no need to postulate a two-stage process in which tropocollagen macromolecules are first polymerized by end-to-end linkage through the interaction of terminal peptide chains to form protofibrils, which are then displaced relatively to one another by 0.25 of the molecular length (Schmitt and Hodge[13]; Hodge and Petruska[21]). Nor is it necessary to suggest an initial polymerization of tropocollagen units by overlapping which is limited to the ends of the molecules, to be followed by "quarter staggering" of the protofibrils (Olsen[17]).

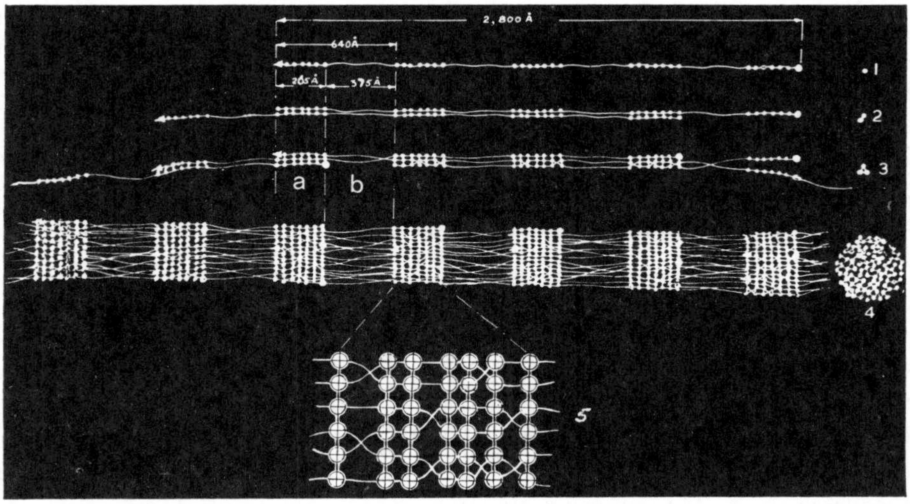

图 2. 1，图示说明提出的原胶原模型，由 1 条被分成 9 个区的颇为柔韧的细丝组成。其中 5 个是结合区，另外 4 个被认为是非结合区。1、2、3 表示通过结合区随机聚合在一起的原胶原联合体。相邻两个大分子间的重叠可以覆盖 1 至 5 个结合区。大分子的方向(箭头所示)决定了胶原蛋白纤维的极性。4，一个 640 Å 重复模式的建立导致结合区明带（*a*）和非结合区暗带（*b*）的形成。5，图中 (*a*) 带之间的耦联说明了大分子可能的柔韧性。

没有必要去假设在非结合区间完全不存在极性氨基酸。实际上从交联实验可以知道，在大分子的非结合区有一些赖氨酸的存在。然而在天然纤维中，只有少数分子间的键在非结合区间形成。

当原胶原单位按上述模型聚集在一起时，就为一个分子的结合区以结构互补的方式与另一不同分子的结合区交联提供了最初的随机选择，产生了一条以 640 Å 为周期性的纤维（图 2）。按这种方式建立起来的胶原纤维模型与通过负染所表现出的天然胶原蛋白的结构非常相似。而且，在电子显微镜下我们已经观察到原胶原大分子是以一种非常明显的随机方式聚集起来从而形成胶原纤维的。没必要去假设以下包含两个阶段的过程：首先原胶原大分子通过末端肽链的相互作用首尾相连聚合在一起形成原纤维，然后由原纤维互相取代掉其分子长度的 0.25 倍（施米特和霍奇 [13]；霍奇和彼特鲁斯卡 [21]）。也没有必要去考虑原胶原单位仅限于分子末端重叠的最初聚合以及随后的原纤维的“四分之一交错”（奥尔森 [17]）。

It also follows from the model for native collagen that all the tropocollagen units in one fibril will face in the same direction. The direction of polarization of a fibril, as determined from the band pattern, will depend on the direction of polarization of the first tropocollagen macromolecule. If, therefore, the tropocollagen macromolecules are not initially all pointing in the same direction, the resulting collagen fibrils will also be polarized in different directions. This is of interest in view of the recent finding of Braun-Falco and Rupec[24] that in human dermis the collagen fibrils have an "antiparallel arrangement".

More direct evidence that the tropocollagen macromolecule consists of nine segments comes from experiments on the FLS form. In Fig 3*a* is shown an electron micrograph of FLS Type 1, made by dialysing an acetic acid solution of collagen containing serum glycoprotein; the repeat distance is about 2,500 Å while the distance measured between the outer edges of the light bands corresponds to the length of an SLS crystallite (*c.* 2800 Å) or tropocollagen unit. This indicates that the FLS-1 structure is formed by overlap of the terminal bonding zones of tropocollagen as suggested by Olsen. However, the reason for the formation of this type of fibre may be that adsorption of negatively charged glycoprotein on to the tropocollagen units prevents the establishment of intermolecular bonds by the intermediate bonding zones, thus producing the wide spacing (Fig. 4; 1, 2). Moreover, when such an FLS-1 preparation was treated with glutaraldehyde the 640 Å repeat period was re-established (Fig. 3*b*). Presumably the glutaraldehyde was able to bridge between amino-groups in the blocked bonding zones to re-establish the native period. These experiments appear to provide clear evidence of the existence of 5 similar zones in the tropocollagen molecule separated by regions having different properties. The three intermediate bonding zones in tropocollagen can thus be suppressed with glycoprotein but revealed by subsequent treatment with glutaraldehyde (Fig. 4; 2, 3).

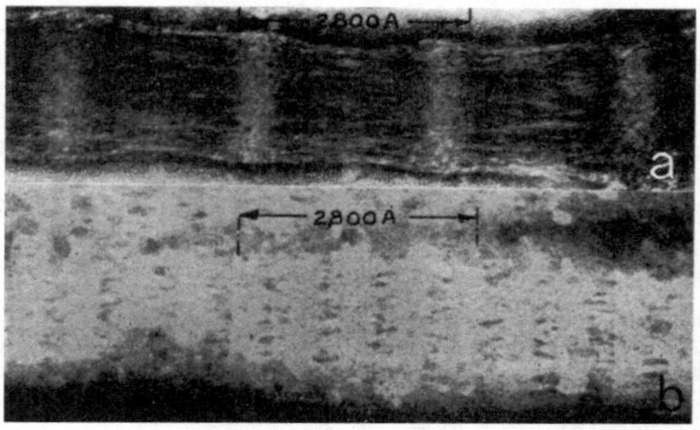

Fig. 3. *a*, FLS type 1, showing repeat period of about 2,500 Å. *b*, FLS Type 1, following treatment with glutaraldehyde. The re-establishment of the 640-Å period is clearly visible. Both preparations were negatively stained

In the case of the SLS crystallite, negative staining has revealed a marked asymmetry of the band structure. On the other hand, although Olsen[17] has attempted to deduce, by photographic methods, a relationship between SLS and the native fibril, a number

根据这一模型，天然胶原蛋白中所有的原胶原单位都将朝同一方向排列。一条由带的类型决定的纤维的极性方向，将依赖于第一个原胶原大分子的极性方向。因此，如果原胶原大分子最初并不全都指向同一方向，就会导致胶原纤维也会在不同方向产生极性。有意思的是，最近布朗–法尔科和鲁佩克[24]发现人类皮肤的胶原纤维中存在“反向平行排列”。

更多支持原胶原大分子是由9个部分组成的直接证据来源于纤维长间距型胶原质实验。图3*a*显示的是纤维长间距I型胶原蛋白的电子显微图片，它是通过透析含有血清糖蛋白的胶原蛋白乙酸溶液得到的；重复距离约为2,500 Å，而明带外边缘间的实测距离则与一个片段长间距微晶（*c*为2,800 Å）或原胶原单位的长度一致。正如奥尔森所提出的，这表明纤维长间距I型结构是通过原胶原末端结合区重叠而形成的。然而，之所以形成这种类型的纤维可能是由于原胶原单位吸附了带负电荷的糖蛋白，阻止了中间结合区分子间键的形成，从而产生了宽间距（图4，1、2）。而且当这种纤维长间距I型胶原蛋白经过戊二醛处理后，640 Å的重复周期又会重新出现（图3*b*）。据推测戊二醛可以使在被阻碍的结合区内的氨基群之间关联，并重建天然周期。这些实验似乎能够提供明显的证据来证明原胶原分子中存在被不同性质区域分开的5个相似区域。原胶原中间的3个结合区能够被糖蛋白抑制，也可以通过随后的戊二醛处理而暴露出来（图4，2、3）。

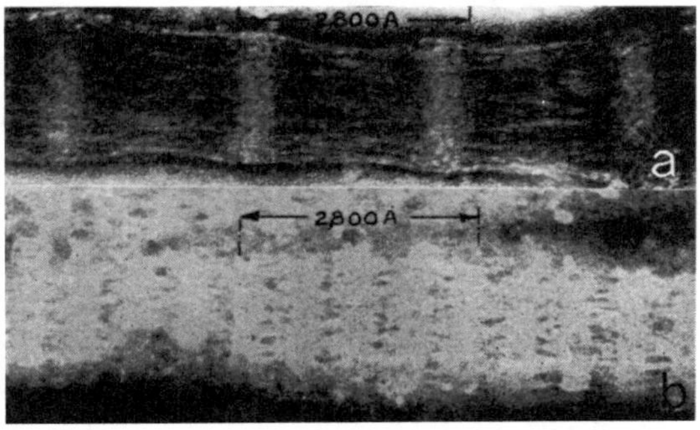

图3. *a*，纤维长间距I型胶原蛋白，显示了约为2,500 Å的重复周期。*b*，戊二醛处理后的纤维长间距I型胶原蛋白。640 Å的周期重新出现，清晰可见。制品经过负染处理。

在片段长间距微晶中，负染样品表明带结构具有明显的不对称性。另一方面，尽管奥尔森[17]曾尝试利用照相的方法来推断片段长间距和天然纤维之间的关系，但还是有很多地方是模糊不清的。在片段长间距型胶原蛋白中观察到的带状图案可能

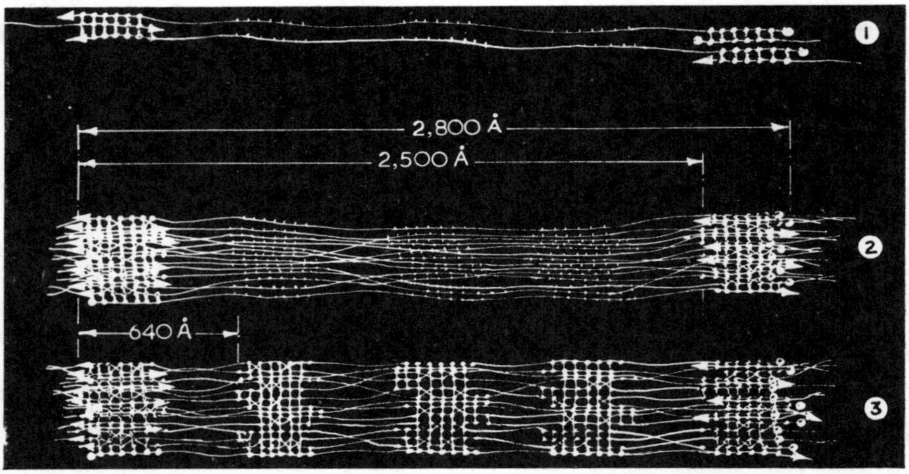

Fig. 4. 1 and 2, The establishment of a repeat period of 2,500 Å by tropocollagen macromolecules aggregated in the presence of glycoprotein. Linking between intermediate bonding zones is suppressed by glycoprotein, resulting in the observed long spacing. 2 and 3, FLS 1, showing re-establishment of 640- Å period by treatment with glutaraldehyde

of points remain obscure. The band pattern observed in the SLS form may in part be due to the presence of negatively charged ATP molecules interacting with positively charged groups in tropocollagen, outside as well as within the bonding regions. If this interpretation is correct, the SLS pattern could be regarded, in part at least, as an artefact with a band structure (by negative staining) not directly related to the native fibre. Furthermore, in the case of positively stained SLS form, the staining with phosphotungstic acid or uranyl acetate undoubtedly reveals the position of basic and acidic groups in the macromolecule. Positive staining, however, does not seem to indicate whether or not these groups are involved in the formation of bonds between adjacent macromolecules.

The fundamental difference between the model proposed here and other interpretations lies in the division of the tropocollagen filament into five more or less equal bonding zones separated by four regions apparently capable of forming few intermolecular links. It should be emphasized that the bonding zones mentioned in this report have no connexion with the subunits of Petruska and Hodge[23]. Collagen fibres have also been observed with a repeat period of only 210-220 Å (Gross[7]). By assuming that, under the conditions of *p*H and ionic strength necessary to precipitate this form, only a portion of each bonding zone is able to interact with another, it is possible to derive this repeat period from the new model (Fig. 5). It may be noted that the short period of 210-220 Å is less than the length of a bonding zone (A band) and also one-third of the native period as would be expected if this model is correct.

This investigation has been restricted to the longitudinal and transverse structure of collagen fibres in a two-dimensional sense. Work is at present in progress to include three-dimensional (cross-sectional) aspects of the problem and a three-dimensional model

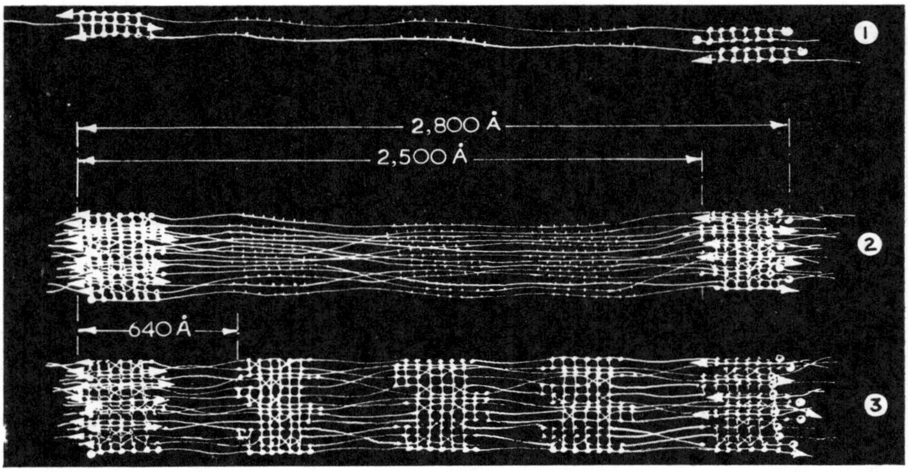

图4. 1和2，在存在糖蛋白的情况下，原胶原大分子聚集产生2,500 Å的重复周期。中间结合区的连接受糖蛋白的抑制，导致长间距的产生。2和3，纤维长间距 I 型胶原蛋白经戊二醛处理后，640 Å的周期重新出现。

在一定程度上是由于在结合区内外存在与原胶原中正电基团相互作用的带负电荷的三磷酸腺苷分子。如果这种解释是正确的，那么至少在一定程度上片段长间距模式可以被认为是与天然纤维没有直接关系的具有带结构（通过负染反应得到的）的一种人为产物。而且，在正染的片段长间距型胶原蛋白中，利用磷钨酸或醋酸双氧铀染色确实显示出了大分子中碱性基团和酸性基团的位置，然而正染似乎并不能说明这些基团是否参与了相邻大分子间键的形成。

本文所提出的模型与其他说法之间的根本区别在于，认为原胶原细丝被 4 个有可能形成少数分子间连接的区域分为 5 个几乎相同的结合区。需要强调的是，这篇报道中所提到的结合区与彼特鲁斯卡和霍奇 [23] 所说的亚单位无关。人们还观察到了仅有 210 Å~220 Å 重复周期的胶原蛋白纤维（格罗斯 [7]）。在能够沉淀这一胶原蛋白的酸碱度和离子强度的条件下，如果假设每个结合区只有一部分可能与其他区域发生相互作用，那么就有可能从新模型中导出这种重复周期（图 5）。值得注意的是，如果这个模型正确的话，210 Å~220 Å 的短周期要比一个结合区（*A* 带）的长度短，并且是预期的天然周期的三分之一。

这项研究局限于由胶原蛋白纤维的纵向和横向结构所构成的二维空间上。当前正在进行的工作包括将这一问题扩展到三维空间（截面）上并建立一个三维模型。

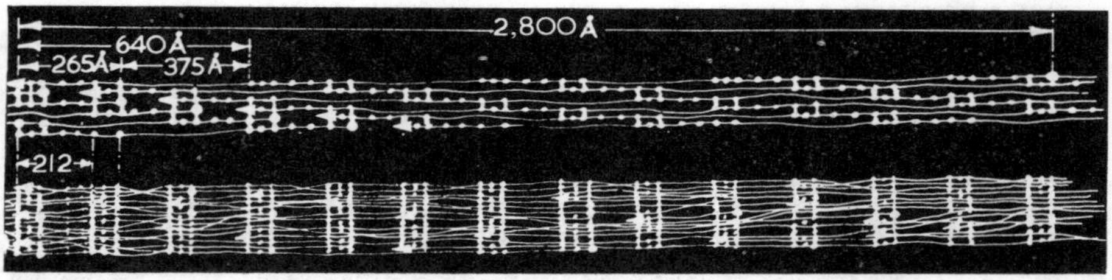

Fig. 5. The establishment of the observed short (210-220 Å) period is illustrated in the diagram. This can be considered to occur under conditions where each macromolecule is capable of interacting only with neighbours over a portion of the bonding zone

is being developed. Notwithstanding that this is only a two-dimensional model, since aggregation takes place in an essentially random fashion the criteria of Smith[25] appear to be satisfied.

We thank the Wellcome Trust for a grant for the purchase of an electron microscope and ancillary apparatus.

(**207**, 822-826; 1965)

R. A. Grant, R. W. Horne and R. W. Cox: Agricultural Research Council, Institute of Animal Physiology, Babraham, Cambridge.

References:

1. Rich, A., and Crick, F. H. C., *J. Mol. Biol.*, **3**, 483 (1961).
2. Boedtker, H., and Doty, P., *J. Amer. Chem. Soc.*, **78**, 4267 (1956).
3. Rice, R. V., Casassa , E. F., Kerwin, R. E., and Maser, M. D., *Arch. Biochem. Biophys.*, **105**, 409 (1964).
4. Schmitt, F. O., Hall, C. E., and Jakus, M. A., *J. Cell. Comp. Physiol.*, **20**, 11 (1942).
5. Wolpers, C., *Klin. Wschr.*, **22**, 624 (1943).
6. Harrington, W. F., and Von Hippel, P. H., *Adv. Protein Chem.*, **16**, 1 (1961).
7. Gross, J., in *Comparative Biochemistry*, edit. by Florkin, M., and Mason, H. S., **5**, 307 (Academic Press, New York and London, 1963).
8. Fitton, Jackson, S., in *The Cell*, edit. by Brachet, J., and Mirsky, A. P., **6**, 387 (Academic Press, New York and London, 1964).
9. Veis, A., *The Macromolecular Chemistry of Gelatin* (Academic Press, New York and London, 1964).
10. Gross, J., Highberger, J. H., and Schmitt, F. O., *Proc. U.S. Nat. Acad. Sci.*, **40**, 679 (1954).
11. Highberger, J. H., Gross, J., and Schmitt, F. O., *Proc. U.S. Nat. Acad. Sci.*, **37**, 286 (1951).
12. Schmitt, F. O., Gross, J., and Highberger, J. H., *Symposia Soc. Exp. Biol.*, **9**, 148 (1955).
13. Schmitt, F. O., and Hodge, A. J., *J. Soc. Leather Trades Chem.*, **44**, 217 (1960).
14. Brenner, S., and Horne, R. W., *Biochim. Biophys. Acta.*, **34**, 103 (1959).
15. Tromans, W. J., Horne, R. W., Gresham, G. A., and Bailey, A. J., *Z. Zellforsch.*, **58**, 798 (1963).
16. Olsen, B. R., *Z. Zellforsch.*, **59**, 184 (1963).
17. Olsen, B. R., *Z. Zellforsch.*, **59**, 199 (1963).
18. Tromans, W. J., Ph. D. thesis, Cambridge University (1963).
19. Hodge, A. J., and Schmitt, F. O., *Proc. U.S. Nat. Acad. Sci.*, **46**, 186 (1960).
20. Kuhn, K., and Zimmer, E., *Naturwiss.*, **48**, 219 (1961).
21. Hodge, A. J., and Petruska, J. A., *Fifth Intern. Cong. Electron Microscopy, Philadelphia*, **2**, QQ-1 (Academic Press, New York and London, 1962).
22. Grassman, W., Hannig, K., and Nordwig A., *Z. Physiol. Chem.*, **333**,154 (1963).
23. Petruska, J. A., and Hodge, A. J., *Proc. U.S. Nat. Acad. Sci.*, **51**, 871 (1964).
24. Braun-Falco, O., and Rupec, M., *J. Invest. Dermatol.*, **42**, 15 (1964).
25. Smith, J. W., *Nature*, **205**, 356 (1965).

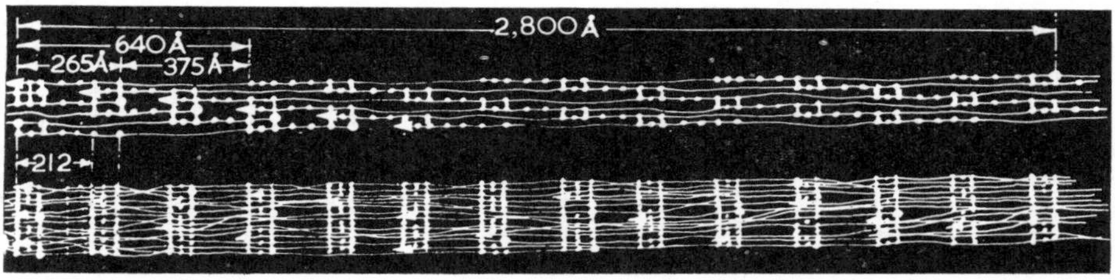

图 5. 图中所示的是观测到的短周期（210 Å~220 Å）的形成。只有当每个大分子都仅能与相邻大分子的部分结合区相互作用的情况下，才可能产生这样的条带。

尽管这只是一个二维空间模型，但聚集是以本质上符合史密斯[25]标准的随机方式发生的。

我们感谢维康基金会为购置电子显微镜和辅助设备提供资金。

（郭娟 翻译；周筠梅 审稿）

Formation of Oceanic Ridges

M. H. P. Bott

Editor's Note

The twentieth-century picture of the Earth's crust, developed by Fred Vine and Drummond Matthews, is one in which the continental plates "float" on the more dense, very sluggish mantle beneath and in which they move relative to each other by convective circulation of material in the mantle. At the submarine structures called mid-ocean ridges, hot rock from the mantle wells up to form new ocean crust. Here the British geophysicist Martin Bott ontlines a possible mechanism for their formation.

OCEANIC ridges form an interconnected system of underwater mountain ranges about 80,000 km in total length (Fig. 1). They stand 2-4 km above the average depth of the oceans and vary in width from a few hundred to four thousand kilometres. They form the largest uplifted surface feature of the Earth. This article suggests a mechanism for their uplift.

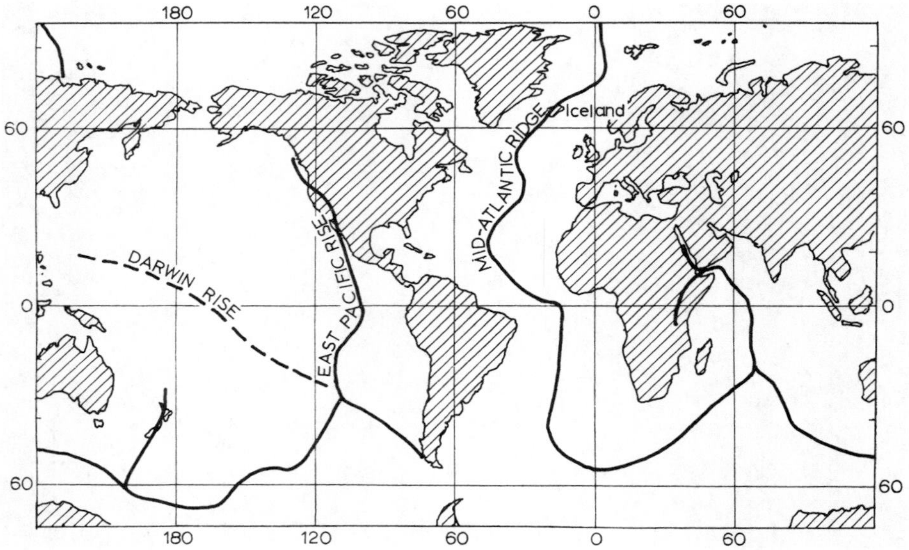

Fig. 1. System of oceanic ridges

It has recently been shown that the East Pacific Rise was formed by uplift of the sea-bed from normal oceanic depths during the Tertiary[1]. The Mid-Atlantic Ridge was also probably formed during the Tertiary[2], Menard[3] has shown that the atolls and guyots scattered over a substantial area of the north-west Pacific were originally volcanoes reaching sea-level on the crest and flanks of a Mesozoic ocean rise (the Darwin Rise)

大洋中脊的形成

博特

编者按

20 世纪人们对地壳的认知是由弗雷德·瓦因和德拉蒙德·马修斯发展起来的，他们认为大陆板块“漂移”在密度更大且移动缓慢的地幔之上，并且板块之间通过地幔内部物质的对流循环发生相对运动。在被称为大洋中脊的海底构造处，地幔内部的热熔岩不断上涌，从而形成新的洋壳。在这里，英国地球物理学家马丁·博特概括性地描述了形成大洋中脊的一种可能机制。

地球上所有大洋中脊构成了一个互联的水下山脉系统，总长度约 80,000 千米（图 1）。它们高出大洋平均深度 2 千米 ~ 4 千米，宽度从几百千米至 4,000 千米不等，形成了地球表面最大的隆起。本文提出了大洋中脊隆起的一种可能机制。

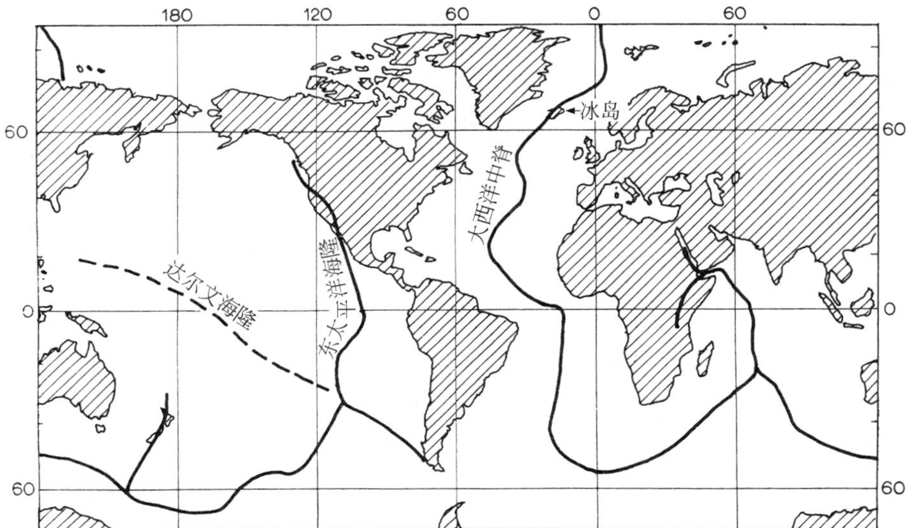

图 1. 大洋中脊系统

最近的研究表明，东太平洋海隆是在第三纪由海床从正常大洋深度向上隆升而形成的 [1]，大西洋中脊很可能也形成于第三纪 [2]。梅纳德 [3] 曾指出，散布在西北太平洋广大地区的环礁和平顶山最初都是位于一个中生代洋隆（达尔文海隆）顶部和

which has since subsided to normal ocean depths.

A similar type of uplift has affected some continental regions. Much of the western United States has been uplifted nearly 2 km since the Eocene[4], forming a continental extension of the uplift which formed the East Pacific Rise[5,1]. This uplift is particularly well displayed in the Colorado Plateau, which remained close to sea-level from before the Cambrian until the early Tertiary and was afterwards uplifted without folding. A similar situation appears to exist where the Indian Ocean Ridge passes into the part of Africa and Arabia which shows evidence of strong epeirogenic uplift.

Thus vertical movements of 2-km amplitude have affected vast areas of ocean floor and more restricted (but still quite substantial) areas of continent in extension of the ocean ridges. It has been widely suggested that mantle convection currents upwelling beneath the ocean ridges may indirectly provide a mechanism for the formation of the ridges and for their elevation. I support this hypothesis and further suggest that dilatation accompanying partial fusion in the rising convection current provides a direct explanation of the uplift. The evidence and arguments favouring this hypothesis are stated here.

It is inconceivable that vertical movements of 2-km amplitude can have affected regions of large areal extent without a change in density in the underlying rocks adequate to maintain approximate isostatic equilibrium. Otherwise these regions would have isostatic anomalies of more than 200-mgal magnitude either now or before the uplift occurred. Nowhere are widespread isostatic anomalies of this magnitude known: in particular the western United States[6] and the oceanic ridges[7,3] are in approximate isostatic equilibrium despite small local departures. It also seems out of the question that regions such as the Colorado Plateau were out of isostatic equilibrium by −250 mgal from the Cambrian until the Eocene unless the mantle was very much stronger then. Thus uplift and subsidence have occurred in isostatic response to substantial changes in the density of the underlying rocks.

Seismic refraction profiles show that changes in crustal thickness are inadequate to explain the uplift of the East Pacific Rise[1] (Fig. 2), or the subsidence of the Darwin Rise[3], or the present elevation of the Mid-Atlantic Ridge[8]. The region of anomalously low density causing the elevation is therefore within the upper mantle beneath. Support for this conclusion comes from the relatively low-compression wave velocities in the topmost mantle beneath the Mid-Atlantic Ridge[2,8], part of the East Pacific Rise[3], Iceland[9] and the western United States[10], since low seismic velocities normally correspond to low densities.

A region of relatively low density in the upper mantle could be attributed either to chemical inhomogeneity or to changed physical conditions causing dilatation of otherwise normal upper mantle rocks. Chemical inhomogeneity could result from a crust-mantle mix[11] or from variation in the proportion of minerals such as plagioclase[12]. Possible explanations depending on changed physical conditions include thermal expansion, silicate mineral phase changes, partial fusion and serpentinization of olivine[13]. Thermal expansion

两侧的火山，它们原来在海平面附近，后来才下沉至正常大洋深度。

类似的隆升也影响到了某些大陆地区。始新世[4]以来，美国西部很多地方隆升了近2千米，是东太平洋海隆[5,1]的隆升在大陆的延伸。科罗拉多高原表现出的隆升作用尤为显著，从寒武纪以前到早第三纪，其高度一直与海平面相近，随后开始了未经挤压褶皱作用的隆升。在印度洋中脊逐渐转入非洲和阿拉伯半岛的位置似乎也存在类似的情形，而这正是强烈造陆上升的证据。

这种幅度达2千米的垂直运动，影响了广阔的大洋底部和大洋中脊延伸到的部分大陆地区（面积也相当大）。一般认为，大洋中脊之下地幔物质的对流上涌是洋脊形成和隆升的间接原因。我支持该假说，并进一步认为，上升对流中部分熔融所伴随的膨胀扩张作用是隆升的直接原因。下文将阐明支持该假说的证据和论点。

很难想象，幅度为2千米的垂直运动，影响了大范围的地区，却没有改变其下伏岩石的密度，而且还保持了均衡（即等压平衡）状态。如果不是这样，那么现在或隆升之前，这些地区应有大于200毫伽的均衡异常。但事实并非如此，特别是美国西部[6]和大洋中脊[7,3]地区，除一些小的局部异常外，都接近于均衡状态。几乎可以确定，诸如科罗拉多高原等地区，从寒武纪到始新世，都应该存在–250毫伽的均衡异常，除非当时的地幔异常坚固。因此，曾经发生过的隆升和下沉是对于下伏岩层密度发生巨大变化的均衡响应。

地震波折射剖面图说明，地壳厚度的变化不足以解释东太平洋海隆的隆升[1]（图2)、达尔文海隆[3]的下沉以及大西洋中脊[8]正在进行的抬升。因此，这种抬升是由洋脊之下上地幔的异常低密度区引起的。大西洋中脊[2,8]、部分东太平洋海隆[3]、冰岛[9]和美国西部[10]等地区地幔顶部的地震波速相对较低，即可以作为支持该结论的证据，因为低地震波速通常对应着低密度。

上地幔中的相对低密度区，可能是由于化学的非均一性所致，或是由于物理条件的改变而引起正常的上地幔岩石膨胀所致。前者的成因可能是地壳–地幔的混合[11]或矿物（如斜长石[12]）组成比例的变化。后者的成因则可能包括：热膨胀，硅酸盐矿物的相变，部分熔融以及橄榄石[13]的蛇纹石化等。热膨胀似乎不大可能产生足够大

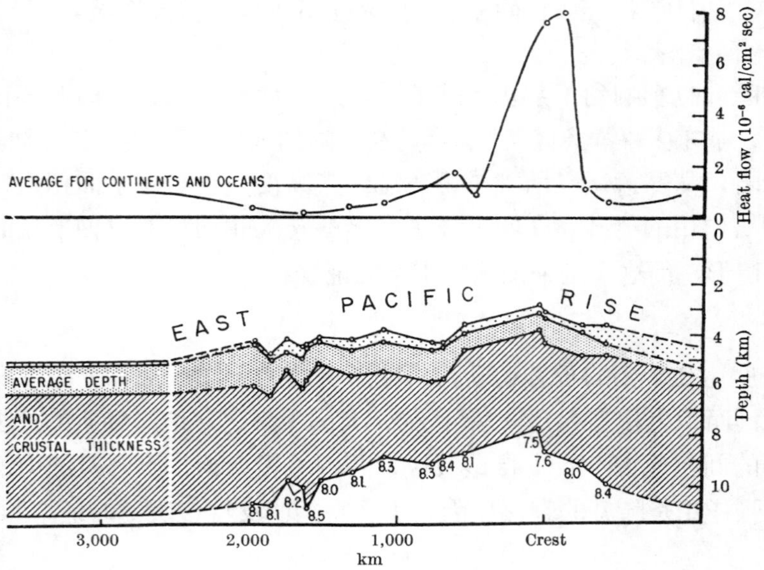

Fig. 2. Topographic and crustal structure profile across the East Pacific Rise showing also the heat flow and the sub-Moho seismic *P*-velocity. Reproduced from an article by H. W. Menard[1] in *Science*, **132**, 1741(December 9, 1960), with permission

seems to be inadequate to produce sufficiently large changes in density[10,14]. If it is assumed that a single process is of dominant importance, four disconnected pieces of evidence enable a tentative choice to be made between the remaining hypotheses. These are: (1) the gravimetry and seismology of Iceland[14]; (2) the epeirogenic and reversible character of the uplift; (3)-(4) the inadequacy of silicate phase changes and reactions to produce a sufficiently large density contrast. These are discussed in turn as follows:

(1) Iceland lies on the Mid-Atlantic Ridge. The average Bouguer anomaly is about +15 mgal[15]. If the upper mantle beneath were normal, this would mean that the crust is continental (30-35 km thick). However, seismic studies in Iceland[16,9] suggest that the crust is only about 17 km thick and has a high average *P* velocity. Combining these observations, we conclude that the upper mantle beneath Iceland possesses an anomalously low density which contributes a gravity anomaly of about −250 mgal. This could be caused by a reduction in density of 0.03 g/cm^3 extending over a vertical thickness of at least 225 km, or 0.3 g/cm^3 over at least 23 km. Further evidence of critical importance comes from Tryggvason's[9] discovery that compression wave arrivals from distant earthquakes arrive about 1.3 sec late at Reykjavik. Tryggvason interprets this delay as caused by an anomalously low compression wave velocity of 7.4 km/s extending to a depth of 200 km below Iceland. Most common rocks show an empirical relation between compression wave (*P*) velocity and density, such that reduction in *P* velocity from the normal upper mantle value of 8.2 km/s to 7.4 km/s would correspond to a reduction in density of more than 0.1 g/cm^3. Spread over a vertical extent of 200 km, this would cause a mass deficiency more than three times as large as the observed value. This suggests that the region of low

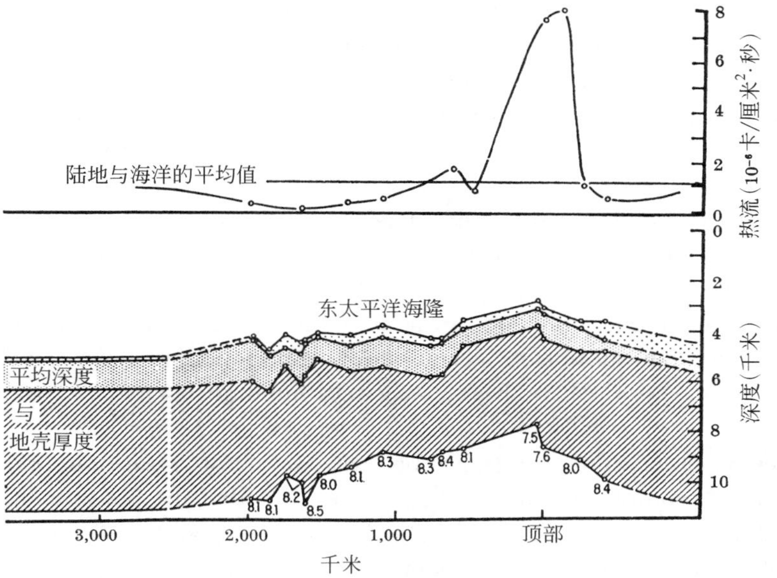

图 2. 穿过东太平洋海隆的地形和地壳结构剖面图，同时说明了热流和莫霍面下的地震P波速度。已得作者允许，引自《科学》，第132卷，第1741页，梅纳德[1]（1960年12月9日）。

的密度变化[10,14]。如果低密度异常是由单一过程所主导的，那么以下四个独立的过程可以用来判断上述两种假设哪一个是正确的：(1) 冰岛的重力测量和地震学研究[14]；(2) 隆升的造陆作用及其可逆性；(3) ~ (4) 硅酸盐相变或反应不足以产生足够大的密度差。现依次讨论如下：

（1）冰岛位于大西洋中脊上，平均布格异常约为 +15 毫伽[15]。如果下方的上地幔为正常状态，则该值意味着它属于大陆型地壳（厚度为 30 千米 ~ 35 千米）。然而地震学研究[16,9]显示，冰岛的地壳厚度只有 17 千米，且P波平均波速较低（译者注：此处原文为“高”有误，应为“低”）。综合上述观测结果，我们可以得出结论，冰岛地区上地幔的密度异常低，并由此导致了 –250 毫伽的重力异常。这样的重力异常需要在至少 225 千米的垂直厚度内密度降低 0.03 克 / 厘米^3，或者在 23 千米内密度降低 0.3 克 / 厘米^3。进一步的重要证据来自特里格瓦松[9]的发现：远震的压缩波从震中传输到雷克雅未克比预期晚了约 1.3 秒，他认为该延时是由于 7.4 千米 / 秒的异常低的压缩波波速一直延伸到了冰岛下部 200 千米处。对于大多数常见岩石来说，压缩波（P波）波速与密度间存在一个经验关系，因此，上地幔P波波速由正常的 8.2 千米 / 秒降到 7.4 千米 / 秒时，密度随之降低的幅度将超过 0.1 克 / 厘米^3。那么在 200 千米的垂直厚度内，将会产生至少 3 倍于观测值的质量亏损。这说明，该低密度区

density is not caused by common rock types with relatively low density. This rules out a crust-mantle mix, serpentine and phase changes in common silicate minerals, although it is possible that an unusual chemical composition could explain the discrepancy. The simplest explanation is that partial fusion causes the mass deficiency, since this would reduce the *P* velocity relatively more strongly than the density as the rigidity modulus vanishes on fusion.

(2) Menard[3] has suggested that the uplift of oceanic rises is reversible. Furthermore, there is no evidence to suggest that equal vertical movements in the opposite sense affect the adjacent belts of ocean floor during the uplift or subsidence of an oceanic rise. These considerations suggest that uplift occurs as a result of dilatation within the underlying upper mantle and that subsidence accompanies contraction to normal volume; this is difficult to reconcile with the hypothesis of chemical inhomogeneity.

(3) Experimental observations on solid-solid silicate phase transitions likely to be of importance in the topmost 200 km of the mantle show that the phase boundaries follow gradients within the range 17-35°C/km (ref. 17). Yoder and Tilley show the basalt-eclogite transition with a gradient of about 50°C/km (ref. 18). Suppose the temperature of the upper mantle were raised by 100°C. The phase boundaries would move to greater depths by 2-6 km. If the aggregate change in density caused by all such phase changes were 0.3 g/cm^3, this would cause a negative gravity anomaly within the range −25 to −75 mgal, which would only be capable of causing an uplift of 0.7 km at most. Thus solid-solid silicate phase transitions appear to be inadequate as a complete explanation of the cause of uplift, unless the upper mantle temperatures are raised excessively.

(4) Another possibility is that olivine is hydrated to give low-density serpentine. This reaction cannot occur much above 500°C. The geothermal gradient of Iceland[19] is such that temperatures of 500°C almost certainly occur at a shallower depth than 10 km. Similar considerations apply to regions of anomalously high flow of heat on the East Pacific Rise and the Mid-Atlantic Ridge. This raises a serious difficulty for the serpentinization hypothesis.

The foregoing considerations (1)-(4) together suggest that partial fusion is probably the dominant cause of the low-density region in the upper mantle beneath oceanic ridges and their continental extensions. It remains to demonstrate the feasibility of this hypothesis.

Experiments by Daly[20] show that basalt undergoes a reduction in density of about 10 percent, or 0.3 g/cm^3, on fusion. The fused fraction of an ultrabasic parent rock would almost certainly undergo a similar reduction in density. Suppose 10 percent of the parent rock undergoes fusion, then the overall reduction in density is 0.03 g/cm^3. Thus 10 percent partial fusion extending over a vertical range of 150 km would explain the uplift of an oceanic ridge 2 km high, or a continental uplift of about 1.4 km. Partial fusion causes reduction in density by dilatation, causing uplift without the necessity of contemporaneous subsidence nearby. We now require a mechanism for causing partial fusion on this scale.

不是由常见的密度较低的岩石类型引起的。由此排除了地壳–地幔的混合，或者常见硅酸盐矿物的蛇纹石化和相变等因素，但是还有可能用不同寻常的化学组成来解释这种差异。而最简单的解释则是，熔融过程中，随硬度系数的消失产生的压缩波波速的降低比由密度变化引起的波速降低的幅度更大，因此质量的亏损更主要是由部分熔融引起的。

（2）梅纳德[3]指出，洋隆的隆升是可逆的。而且没有证据表明，当洋隆发生隆升或沉降时，在洋底的邻近区域出现了等量的反方向垂直运动。这说明，当洋脊下的上地幔膨胀时，洋脊发生隆升，反之，当体积向正常状态收缩时，洋脊发生沉降，这很难用化学不均一性假说来解释。

（3）在地幔最上部的200千米内，固–固硅酸盐相变具有重要意义，实验观察显示，其相边界的梯度为17℃/千米～35℃/千米（参考文献17）。约德和蒂利证明玄武岩–榴辉岩的相变梯度约为50℃/千米（参考文献18）。因此，如果假定上地幔温度升高100℃，相边界便会加深2千米～6千米。如果相变引起的总密度变化为0.3克/厘米^3，则将引起–25毫伽～–75毫伽的重力异常，而这最多也只能形成0.7千米的隆升。因此，固–固硅酸盐相变不能充分解释隆升的原因，除非上地幔的温度极大地升高。

（4）另一种可能性是橄榄石水化而形成低密度的蛇纹石，但这种反应不可能发生在500℃以上。而冰岛的地热梯度[19]表明，低于500℃的温度只出现在距地表10千米内的浅层中。同样，热流量异常高的东太平洋海隆和大西洋洋中脊地区的情况与此类似。因此，蛇纹石化假说也很难成立。

综合（1）～（4）可见，对于大洋中脊及其大陆延伸区下部的上地幔，部分熔融很可能是其低密度产生的主要原因。下文将证明该假说的可行性。

戴利的实验[20]说明，在熔融时，玄武岩的密度降低约10%，即约0.3克/厘米^3。同样，超基性母岩的熔融部分，密度也会有相同幅度的降低。假定有10%的母岩熔融，则总体的密度将降低0.03克/厘米^3。在150千米的垂直范围内，10%的母岩部分熔融，就可以使大洋中脊隆升2千米或大陆隆升1.4千米。因此，部分熔融产生的膨胀使密度减小，从而引起隆升，并且不需要相邻地区的沉降补偿。现在我们需要了解在这个尺度上引发熔融的机制。

Partial fusion of the upper mantle can be caused by reduction in the confining pressure provided the initial temperature is near to the melting point. Reduction in pressure can occur by: (1) stress release in a static mantle; or (2) progressive reduction of confining pressure in an uprising mantle convection current. Both processes depend critically on the fusion gradient, which is about 6.5-10°C/kbar or 2-3°C/km. This is an order of magnitude higher than the adiabatic gradient and an order of magnitude lower than the conduction temperature gradient observed at the Earth's surface.

I make the simplifying assumption that a two-phase boundary separates a liquid phase and a single solid phase (Fig. 3 shows a fusion zone). During reduction of pressure p, material initially on the phase boundary is constrained to remain on the boundary until fusion is complete. Consequently the temperature (T) is reduced by $(\mathrm{d}T/\mathrm{d}p)_t \cdot \Delta p$, where Δp is the reduction of confining pressure. Under adiabatic conditions in the field of the solid or liquid phase the reduction in temperature is given by $(\mathrm{d}T/\mathrm{d}p)_a \cdot \Delta p$, where the suffix refers to the adiabatic gradient. The excess cooling resulting from the steeper fusion gradient provides the latent heat of fusion, L_p. If the appropriate specific heat is c, assumed the same for both phases, the fractional amount of fusion, f, is given approximately by:

$$f = \left\{ \left(\frac{\mathrm{d}T}{\mathrm{d}p}\right)_t - \left(\frac{\mathrm{d}T}{\mathrm{d}p}\right)_a \right\} \cdot c \cdot \Delta p / L_p$$

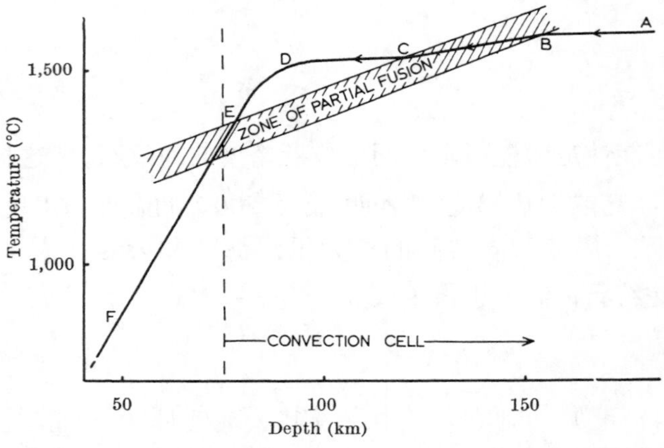

Fig. 3. Mechanism of partial fusion in a rising convection current. *AB* represents a temperature gradient slightly in excess of the adiabatic gradient. Partial fusion commences as the upwelling current passes *B*, and continues until *C* with a steeper temperature gradient. No further partial fusion occurs in the topmost section of the convection cell *CDE*. Cooling by thermal conduction affects *DEF*. A fusion zone is shown, since this is more realistic than a simple two-phase boundary

In a static mantle the vertical principal pressure is the weight of the overburden, which is fixed in value at a given depth. Release of confining pressure can only come about through reduction of horizontal pressure. The amount of pressure reduction is limited by the strength of the upper mantle which probably does not exceed 200 bars. If both

当初始温度接近熔点时，围压的下降可导致上地幔部分熔融。而围压的下降可能有两种原因：(1) 静态地幔的应力释放，(2) 地幔对流上升过程中，围压的逐渐减小。这两种过程都与熔融梯度密切相关，该熔融梯度约为6.5℃ / 千巴~10℃ / 千巴，即约为2℃ / 千米 ~3℃ / 千米。该数值比地表观测到的绝热梯度高出一个数量级，而比地表观测到的传导温度梯度低一个数量级。

作一个简化的假设：存在某二相边界将液相和固相分开（图3给出了一个熔融带）。当压力（p）减小时，处于相边界状态的物质一直保持该状态，直到完全熔融。温度（T）降低了 $(dT/dp)_t \cdot \Delta p$，其中 Δp 是围压的下降值。在绝热条件下，固相或液相区域内温度的降低值为 $(dT/dp)_a \cdot \Delta p$，其中下标表示绝热梯度。较大的熔融梯度产生的过冷却效应为熔融提供了潜热（L_p）。假如液态和固态的比热相等且均为 c，则熔融量 f 可由下式近似给出：

$$f = \left\{\left(\frac{dT}{dp}\right)_t - \left(\frac{dT}{dp}\right)_a\right\} \cdot c \cdot \Delta p / L_p$$

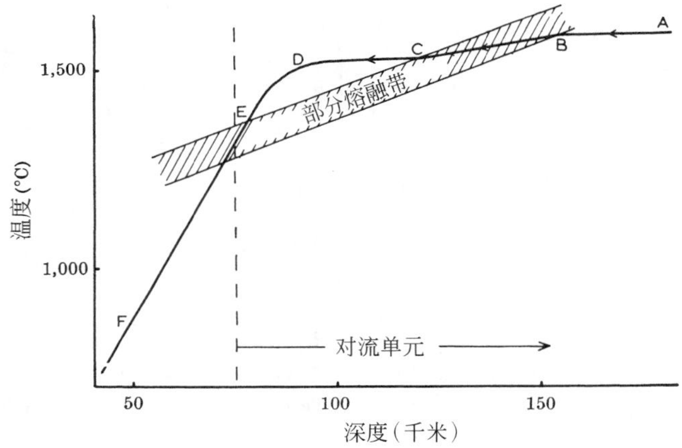

图3. 在上升对流中部分熔融的机制。AB 表示温度梯度稍大于绝热梯度。在上升流通过 B 点时，开始部分熔融，以较大的温度梯度持续到 C 点。在对流单元 CDE 的顶部不再发生部分熔融。DEF 由于热传导而冷却。由此所示的熔融带比简单的二相边界更符合实际。

在静态的地幔内部，垂向压力主要来自覆盖层的重量，当深度一定时该值是确定的。围压的释放只能通过水平压力的下降来实现。压力下降幅度受上地幔强度的限制，一般不超过200巴。如果两侧水平压力都下降200巴，围压下降133巴，这

horizontal principal pressures are reduced by 200 bars, the confining pressure is reduced by 133 bars. This would cause a lowering of temperature of less than 1.5 °C. Taking the latent heat of fusion as 400 J/g and the specific heat as 1.2 J/g, the amount of fusion possible is only 0.45 percent. This is inadequate to provide magma on the scale required to explain the uplift of the ocean ridges.

The alternative mechanism is that an upwelling mantle convection current causes fusion in its upper reaches (Fig. 4). Since the fusion gradient is steeper than the adiabatic gradient, fusion is restricted to the topmost section of the rising current. As material is carried upwards in the convection current, it follows a temperature gradient slightly in excess of the adiabatic gradient (Fig. 3, *AB*) until it reaches the fusion boundary. It is then constrained to follow this boundary (or zone) until fusion (or partial fusion) is complete (Fig. 3, *BC*). Taking the difference between the fusion and adiabatic gradient to be 1°C/km and latent and specific heats as above, the amount of fusion is 10 percent in a 33 km rise. Here we have a powerful mechanism for producing magma on a very large scale in a rising convection current. The existence of more than one solid phase complicates the argument but does not alter the conclusion. In reality, it is likely that the olivine present cannot fuse completely, and thus that there is a limit to the degree of partial fusion possible.

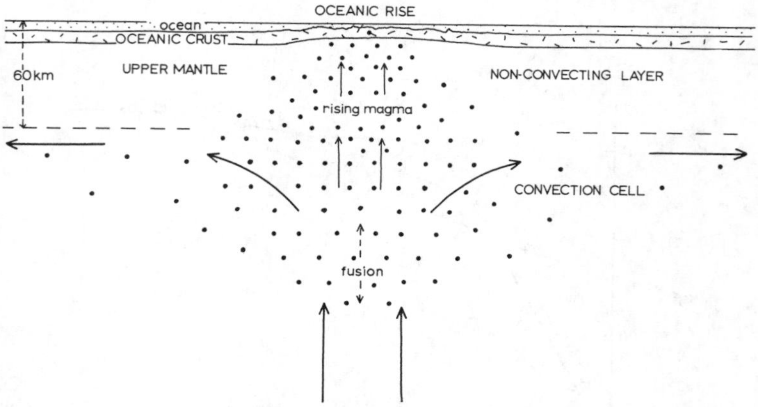

Fig. 4. Mechanism suggested for the uplift of oceanic ridges in isostatic response to a mass deficiency caused by dilatation on partial fusion. Partial fusion occurs in an upwelling mantle convection current

The magma produced in this way would tend to rise towards the Earth's surface owing to its relatively low density. It is likely to form a network of dykes and magma chambers in the layer overlying the convection cell. In this way, the mass deficiency causing the uplift is probably partly within the topmost part of the upwelling current and partly in the overlying layer, where it may build up to a substantial fraction locally.

Subsidence of an ocean ridge would occur when the underlying low-density rocks increased in density to the normal value appropriate to their depth. On the convection hypothesis, this would start happening when the convection current died out, causing the

将会使得温度下降不足 1.5℃。取熔融潜热为 400 焦 / 克，比热为 1.2 焦 / 克，则熔融量则可能只有 0.45%，所产生的少量岩浆不足以解释大洋中脊的隆升。

另一种机制是，上涌的地幔对流环上升处发生部分熔融（图 4）。由于熔融梯度要比绝热梯度大，熔融就被限制在上升物质的顶部。由于在对流中物质向上输送，所以其温度梯度稍大于绝热梯度（图 3，*AB*），直到状态达到熔融边界。然后沿着这个边界（或带），直到完全熔融（或部分熔融）（图 3，*BC*）。如取熔融梯度和绝热梯度的差为 1℃ / 千米，潜热和比热同上文，则隆升 33 千米即对应 10% 的熔融量。由此我们得到了一个地幔对流上升过程中形成大规模岩浆的强有力的机制。虽然不止一种固态物质存在时论证将更为复杂，但不会影响结论。实际上，橄榄岩很可能不会全部熔融，因此使得部分熔融的程度有一个上限。

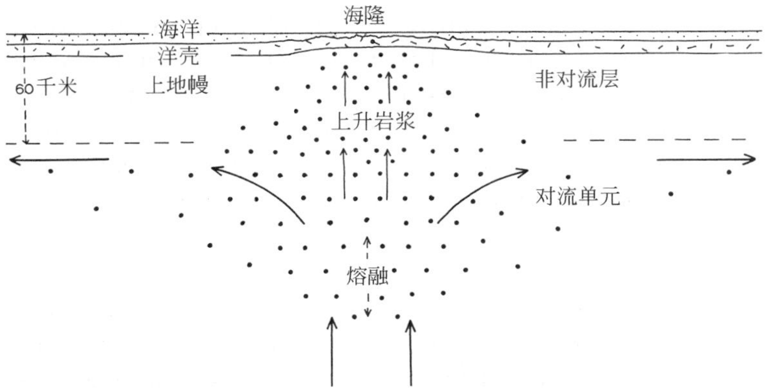

图 4. 大洋中脊隆升的机制。大洋中脊隆升为了均衡响应部分熔融膨胀引起的质量亏损。部分熔融发生于上升的地幔对流中。

由于密度相对较低，通过上述机制产生的岩浆会持续向地表方向上升。这很可能会在上覆对流物质层形成一个岩脉和岩浆房网络。这样，引起隆升的质量亏损可能一部分存在于上涌物质的最顶部，一部分存在于上覆层中，并在其中占相当大的比例。

当下伏岩层的密度增加到该深度的正常值时，大洋中脊会发生沉降。根据对流假说，当对流消失时，新的岩浆源也随之消失，这种情况就会发生。残余岩浆一部

source of fresh magma to disappear. The residual magma would partly rise towards the Earth's surface to solidify rapidly, forming lava flows and near-surface intrusions: part of the magma would probably remain trapped in the upper mantle where it would solidify more slowly by cooling through the geothermal gradient. Calculations show that magma distributed uniformly between depths of about 60 km and 200 km would probably solidify in a period of about 80 my. at the most.

The uplift and subsidence of oceanic ridges have important implications for the stratigrapher, as recognized by Hallam[21] and Menard[3]. Uplift of an oceanic ridge would cause eustatic rise in sea-level of the order of 100 m, and subsidence of a ridge would cause a regression of similar magnitude. In general, this mechanism explains transgressions and regressions of world-wide incidence. In particular, it may explain the extraordinarily widespread and deep transgression at the base of the chalk and the similar regression when the chalk seas withdrew.

Conclusions

The low-density underlying rocks causing the uplift of the oceanic ridges and the western United States lie in the upper mantle, and substantially result from partial fusion, although other causes such as serpentinization may contribute. The evidence leading to this conclusion comes from a combination of geological, geophysical and geochemical discoveries of recent years, and particularly the present burst of oceanographical research. When pieced together, this evidence suggests rejection of other hypotheses such as crust-mantle mix and solid-solid phase changes as the major cause on the assumption that a single mechanism is of prime importance throughout the whole system of ocean ridges. The hypothesis of partial fusion, however, seems to be consistent with all the lines of evidence.

The only mechanism known for causing magma generation on such a large scale depends on the reduction of confining pressure in an upwelling convection current in the mantle. Such convection currents appear to rise beneath the oceanic ridges, causing their volcanism and uplift.

The hypothesis is equally applicable to uplifts such as the East Pacific Rise which have taken place without associated horizontal movements, and to the Mid-Atlantic Ridge where in addition to the vertical uplift new oceanic crust may be in the process of formation.

(**207**, 840-843; 1965)

M. H. P. Bott: Department of Geology, University of Durham.

分向地表涌升迅速凝固，形成熔岩流和近地表的侵入体，另一部分可能仍留在上地幔，以地热梯度缓慢固化。计算表明，均匀分布在 60 千米 ~ 200 千米深度之间的岩浆，最多需要 8 千万年便能固化。

正如哈勒姆[21]和梅纳德[3]所指出，大洋中脊的隆升和沉降在地层学中具有重要意义。大洋中脊的隆升可使海平面发生 100 米尺度的上升，而大洋中脊的沉降也可引起同样规模的海退。总之，这一机制可用来解释世界范围内的海侵和海退，尤其是可用来解释分布异常广泛和深入的白垩纪早期海侵，以及白垩纪海水后退形成的类似海退。

结　论

上地幔中低密度的岩石引起了上覆的大洋中脊和美国西部的隆升，且本质上来说是部分熔融的结果，尽管蛇纹石化等其他过程也可能起作用。该结论综合了近年来地质、地球物理和地球化学各方面的成果，特别是海洋学研究的突破。总而言之，如果假设在大洋中脊系统中只有一个单一机制为主要影响因素，那么事实上便否定了其他假说作为主要的原因，如地壳–地幔混合说及固–固相变说；然而，从各方面证据看，部分熔融假说始终与事实一致。

目前已知，地幔对流上涌过程中围压的降低是能够在如此大的尺度上产生岩浆的唯一机制。这种对流发生于大洋中脊之下，并造成了火山作用和洋脊隆升。

该假说同样也适用于东太平洋海隆和大西洋中脊的隆升，只是前者不存在水平运动，而后者除了垂直隆升外，新的洋壳也正在形成。

（孙惠南 翻译；李三忠 审稿）

References:

1. Menard, H. W., *Science*, **132**, 1737 (1960).
2. Heezen, B. C., in *Continental Drift*, edit. by Runcorn, S. K., 235 (Academic Press, 1962).
3. Menard, H. W., *Marine Geology of the Pacific*, **117** (McGraw-Hill, 1964).
4. King, P. B., *The Evolution of North America* (Princeton University Press, 1959).
5. Hess, H. H., *J. Marine Res.*, **14**, 423 (1955).
6. Heiskanen, W. A., and Vening-Meinesz, F. A., *The Earth and its Gravity Field*, **187** (McGraw-Hill, 1958).
7. Talwani, M., Le Pichon, X., and Ewing, M., *J. Geophys. Res.*, **70**, 341 (1965).
8. Le Pichon, X., Houtz, R. E., Drake, C. L., and Nafe, J. E., *J. Geophys. Res.*, **70**, 319 (1965).
9. Tryggvason, E., *Bull. Seismol. Soc. Amer.*, **54**, 727 (1964).
10. Pakiser, L. C., *J. Geophys. Res.*, **68**, 5747 (1963).
11. Cook, K. L., *Adv. Geophys.*, **9**, 295 (1962).
12. Ringwood, A. E., *J. Geophys, Res.*, **67**, 857 (1962).
13. Hess, H. H., *Geol. Soc. Amer. Spec. Paper*, **62**, 391 (1955).
14. Bott, M. H. P., *Geophys. J.*, **9**, 275 (1965).
15. Einarsson, T., *Soc. Sci. Islandica*, publication **30**, 1 (1954).
16. Báth, M., *J. Geophys. Res.*, **65**, 1793 (1960).
17. Wyllie, P. J., in *High Pressure Physics and Chemistry*, edit. by Bradley, R. S., **2**, 1 (Academic Press, 1963).
18. Yoder, H. S., and Tilley, C. E., *J. Petrol.*, **3**, 342 (1962).
19. Bodvarsson, G., and Walker, G. P. L., *Geophys. J.*, **8**, 285 (1964).
20. Daly, R. A., *Bull. Geol. Soc. Amer.*, **55**, 1363 (1944).
21. Hallam, A., *Amer. J. Sci.*, **261**, 397 (1963).

Submarine Fracture Zones, Aseismic Ridges and the International Council of Scientific Unions Line: Proposed Western Margin of the East Pacific Ridge

J. T. Wilson

Editor's Note

The Canadian geophysicist John Tuzo Wilson made pivotal contributions to the theory of plate tectonics. In a series of papers of which this is the fourth, he described a hitherto unrecognized type of geological fault (where tectonic plates move relative to one another at their boundary). At mid-ocean ridges such as that in the mid-Atlantic, new ocean crust is formed on the sea bed as two plates move apart from one another and hot rock wells up along the boundary. Here Wilson explains that these fault lines may be divided into a series of staggered segments by cracks perpendicular to the plate boundaries. Along these cracks, called transform faults, the two plates slide past one another horizontally.

THIS is the fourth of a series of articles advancing the hypothesis that another class of strike-slip faults can exist besides transcurrent faults[1-3]. Transform faults, as the class has been called, can only exist, and must be expected, if areas of the Earth's crust are being absorbed into the interior in some places and freshly formed elsewhere. If they have not attracted much attention heretofore, it is because they are largely a feature of the ocean floors and most examples are partly or wholly submarine. The fracture zones which B. C. Heezen, E. T. Bunce, J. B. Hersey and M. Tharp[4] have recently described in the equatorial Atlantic have been cited as examples of dextral, ridge-ridge, transform faults related to the growth of the Atlantic Ocean, and it has been suggested that these fracture zones join points on opposite coasts which were once in contact. Such points may be called conjugate.

Three Guides to Reconstructing Continents

If this is so, three different guides have been proposed for fitting together the opposite sides of the Atlantic Ocean. The first method is well known and was used by A. Wegener, A. L. Du Toit and E. C. Bullard, J. E. Everett and A. G. Smith[5]. It depends on fitting the topography and matching the geology of opposite coasts. In Figs. 1 and 2 this is illustrated diagrammatically by the fit in shape of regions A and A'.

A second proposal[6] pointed out that, where a pair of aseismic ridges lead from an active volcanic island on the mid-ocean ridge to opposite coasts, the ridges join the coasts at

海底破碎带、无震海岭和国际科联划线：东太平洋海隆西部边缘的推测

威尔逊

编者按

加拿大地球物理学家约翰·图佐·威尔逊为板块构造理论做出了关键性的贡献。在他的一系列文章中（本文是第四篇），他描述了一种迄今尚未被人们所认识的地质断层（在其边界处板块发生相对运动）。在大洋中脊上，如大西洋中脊，新的洋壳在海底形成，两个板块之间彼此分离，热熔岩沿着洋脊边界不断涌出。威尔逊在这里解释道，这些断层线可能被垂直于板块边界的裂缝切割成一系列交错排列的片段。板块之间会沿着这些被称为转换断层的裂缝而进行水平滑动。

除横推断层外，还可能存在另一类走向滑动断层[1-3]，本文是关于这一假说的一系列论文中的第四篇。只有当地壳在某些地方被地球内部吸收，并在其他地方重新生成时，所谓的转换断层才能够存在，并且这是可以预测的。此前，转换断层并未引起人们的广泛关注，原因在于它们大多被作为洋底的特征，且多数实例部分或全部位于海底。希森、邦斯、赫西和撒普[4]最近在赤道大西洋所描述的破碎带已经被引为与大西洋生长相关的右旋型洋脊–洋脊转换断层的典型实例，并被认为这些破碎带连接着海岸两侧曾经相接触的点。这些点可以被称为共轭点。

重建大陆的三种途径

假使如此，人们提出了三种不同的途径将大西洋两岸合并到一起。第一种方法已广为人知，由魏格纳、迪图瓦和布拉德、埃弗里特和史密斯所采用[5]。它依赖于两岸的地形拟合以及地质学特征的匹配。图 1 和图 2 图示说明了 A 和 A' 区形态的拟合。

第二种建议[6]指出，在一对无震海岭从大洋中脊上的一个活火山岛通向对岸的地方，在共轭点处无震海岭可将两岸连接起来。例如，沃尔维斯和里奥格兰德无震

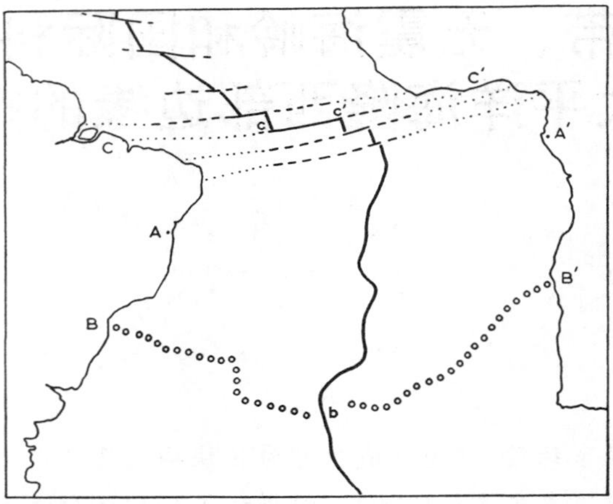

Fig. 1. Sketch map of the South Atlantic. *A* and *A′* are conjugate points which fit together. *Bb* and *bB′* are the Rio Grande and Walvis ridges and *Ccc′C′* is a fracture zone

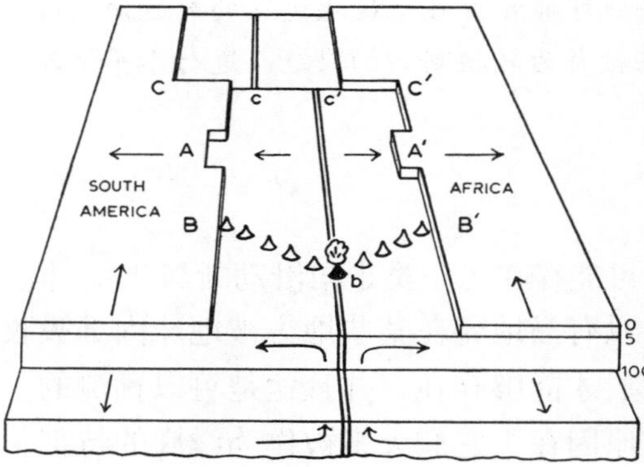

Fig. 2. Three-dimensional diagram illustrating how the two crustal plates on either side of the South Atlantic may be moving relative to each other and to a layer 100 km or more deep within the mantle

conjugate points. For example, the Walvis and Rio Grande aseismic ridges join Tristan da Cunha Island to conjugate points on the coasts of Africa and South America. The ridges from Iceland to Greenland and Europe are another example. In Figs. 1 and 2 this case is illustrated by the lines *Bb* and *bB′*.

The third method suggested that at least some great submarine fracture zones are transform faults and that their ends join conjugate points[1]. In Figs. 1 and 2 this is illustrated by the transform fault and fracture zone *Ccc′C′*.

In the South Atlantic all three methods lead to the same result, but at first sight one aspect is puzzling. Both the aseismic ridges and the fracture zones are the loci of past motions of the crust, but they are not parallel. Since a crustal plate cannot move in two directions at once, this seems to imply a contradiction.

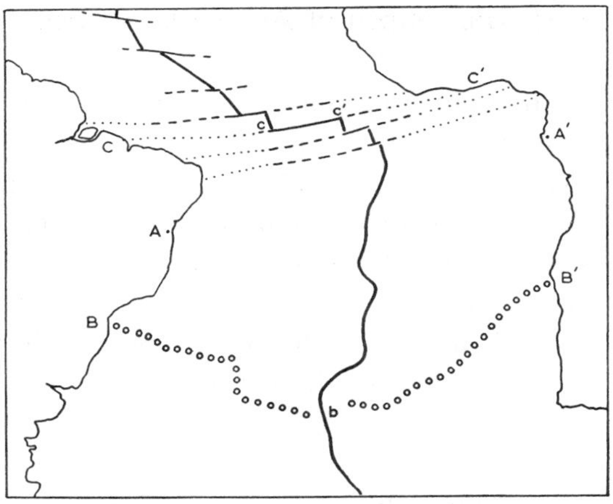

图1. 南大西洋简图，*A*和*A′*为可以合并在一起的共轭点。*Bb*和*bB′*为里奥格兰德和沃尔维斯海岭，*Ccc′C′*为一个破碎带。

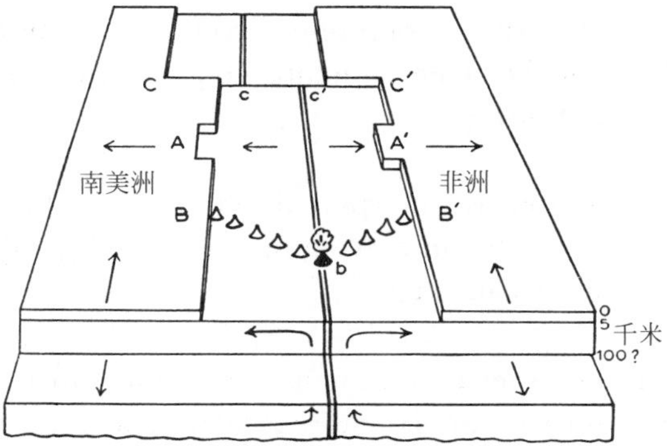

图2. 表示南大西洋两侧两个地壳板块彼此间如何相对运动以及相对于地幔中100千米或更深层如何运动的三维图。

海岭可以把特里斯坦–达库尼亚岛连接到非洲和南美洲海岸上的共轭点。从冰岛至格陵兰和欧洲的海岭则是另一个例子。在图 1 和图 2 中用 *Bb* 和 *bB′* 线表示。

第三种方法认为，至少一些大的海底破碎带就是转换断层，它们的末端连接共轭点 [1]。在图 1 和图 2 中此种情况如转换断层和破碎带 *Ccc′C′* 所示。

在南大西洋，这三种方法均得到了相同的结果，但初看起来仍有一个问题令人困惑。无震海岭和破碎带都是地壳曾经移动的轨迹，但它们并不平行。既然一个地壳板块不能同时向两个方向移动，这似乎存在着矛盾。

Possible Origin of Aseismic Ridges

One possible explanation is that different motions have been recorded. The fracture zones represent the motion of the plates in the crust relative to one another with no reference to the deeper mantle. It has been suggested elsewhere[6,7] that the pairs of aseismic ridges perhaps represent the movements of two crustal plates relative to a source in the mantle. Thus the aseismic ridges are chains of volcanoes, now inactive, which grew at a single place on the mid-ocean ridge and were then carried away, some to one side, some to the other, by streaming motion. Their creation has been presumably due to unusually large and continuing source of lava in the mantle beneath the mid-ocean ridge (for example, Iceland and Tristan).

This pushing away of older volcanoes from a continuing source on a central rift zone was essentially the explanation for the geology of Iceland arrived at by G. Bodvarsson and G. P. L. Walker[8] as a result of field mapping. This explanation may also be extended to include the pair of ridges from Iceland to Greenland and Europe. These ridges lie in the same line, although they get older in opposite directions, are normal to the mid-ocean ridge and are parallel to the De Geer fracture zone, a transform fault lying between Greenland, Spitzbergen and Norway[1].

This arrangement of features may be interpreted to mean that the directions of motion of two crustal plates and of flow in the underlying mantle are all parallel with each other and normal to the axis of the mid-ocean ridge.

In the South Atlantic, on the other hand, the aseismic ridges form a chevron and are not parallel with the fracture zones of the equatorial Atlantic as Figs. 1 and 2 show. This has been interpreted to mean that the crustal plates are not moving in the same direction as that part of the mantle in which the source of the volcano lies. Since no method is known for measuring the direction of flow in the mantle directly, this interpretation is hypothetical, but, as will be shown towards the end of this article, it is an interpretation capable of further development.

In Figs. 1 and 2 the fracture zone *Ccc′C′* is considered to represent the loci of relative motion of two crustal plates, whereas the two aseismic ridges *Bb* and *bB′* each represent the loci of motion of one of the plates relative to the mantle beneath. The crustal plates are not considered to be bounded by the Mohorovičić discontinuity, but by a zone of mobility in the upper mantle.

Relationships between Aseismic Ridges and Fracture Zones

This led me to speculate on what might be expected to happen if, during their growth, a pair of aseismic ridges came to intersect a fracture zone. This is hard to visualize, and indeed most of us are unaccustomed to thinking of geology in terms of growing oceans and continental drift so that this introduces new and difficult ideas. Simple paper and

无震海岭可能的成因

一种可能的解释是，无震海岭和破碎带记录的是不同的运动。破碎带代表地壳中板块彼此间的运动，而并未考虑深部的地幔。但已经有人提出，成对的无震海岭可能代表两个地壳板块相对一个地幔源的运动[6,7]。因此，无震海岭是现在不活动的火山链，它们在大洋中脊的一个位置生长，之后由于板块漂移发生了分向两侧的分离。它们的产生可能是由于在大洋中脊（例如冰岛和特里斯坦）下部的地幔中存在异常大且持续的熔岩源。

在一个中央裂谷带上将老的火山从连续的源头处推开，这种说法便是博德瓦尔松和沃克根据野外制图而对冰岛地质学所做的实质性解释[8]。这种解释也可以扩展到从冰岛到格陵兰及欧洲的成对海岭。虽然这些海岭在相反的方向上逐渐变老，但它们位于同一条线上，与大洋中脊垂直，并平行于德海尔破碎带——位于格陵兰、斯匹兹卑尔根群岛和挪威之间的一条转换断层[1]。

这种排列特征意味着两个地壳板块的运动方向和下伏地幔流动的方向彼此都是平行的，并且与大洋中脊的轴向垂直。

另一方面，在南大西洋，无震海岭呈 V 字形，如图 1 和图 2 所示，它们与赤道大西洋破碎带并不平行。这表明地壳板块运动与火山源所处的那部分地幔的运动不在同一个方向上。因为无法直接测量地幔的流动方向，所以此处解释具有推测性，但是正如本文结尾将要指出的，这种解释还有进一步发展的空间。

图 1 和图 2 中破碎带 *Ccc′C′* 被认为是代表两个地壳板块相对运动的轨迹，而两个无震海岭 *Bb* 和 *bB′* 则分别代表一个板块相对其下的地幔的运动轨迹。地壳板块并不受莫霍不连续面的限制，而是受限于上地幔的一个活动带。

无震海岭和破碎带之间的关系

这让我对一个问题产生了思索，即如果一对无震海岭在生长时与一个破碎带相交，那么将会发生什么现象呢？这种状况是难以想象的，而我们中大多数人也确实不习惯用成长中的海洋和大陆漂移去思考地质学，因此这就要引进新的且困难的思

cardboard models help, and the construction of one which enables the properties of ridge-ridge transform faults to be studied is shown in Fig. 3.

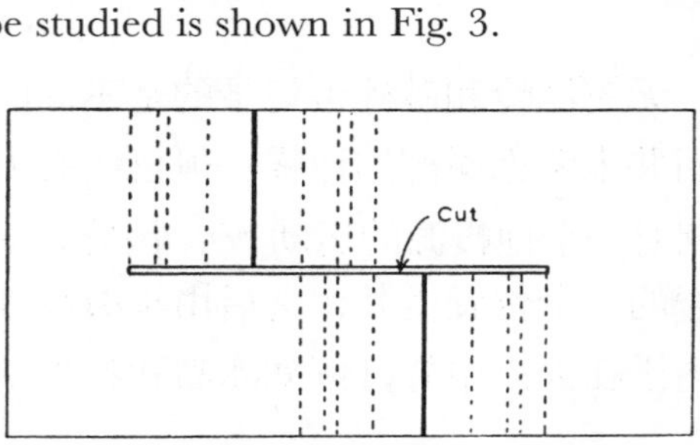

Fig. 3. Diagram showing how to cut and fold a cardboard and paper model to illustrate a fracture zone intersecting two lengths of mid-ocean ridge which are separating with the formation of new crust. ——, Hinge to fold sides up; ---, hinge to fold sides down

With the aid of such a model and that of Fig. 4 it can be appreciated that on intersecting a transform fault one of a pair of aseismic ridges (that one which intersects the active part of the fault) is immediately cut off and removed laterally away from the source. That aseismic ridge must therefore come to an abrupt end against the fault. The other aseismic ridge of any pair is not moved laterally, but the central rift in the mid-ocean ridge is moved away from it. It is therefore uncertain whether this aseismic ridge will end on the fault or continue. If it continues it will no longer touch the mid-ocean rift but it will seem to start at a random point. Only this member of each pair should still be active.

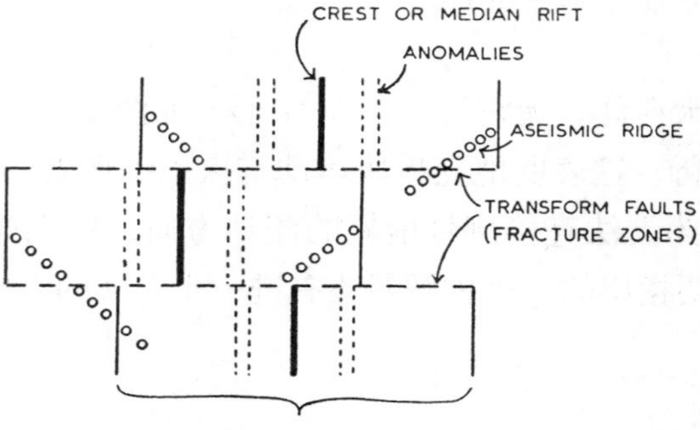

Fig. 4. Diagram showing the relationship of aseismic ridges to fracture zones which they intersect. Note that of each pair one has to terminate at a fracture zone

Some of the chains of islands in the Pacific Ocean seem to meet well the patterns predicted for pairs of aseismic ridges intersected by fracture zones as is shown in Fig. 5. In part, this is copied from Figs. 5.7 and 6.6 in H. W. Menard's book[9], which shows three straight and parallel chains of volcanic islands (the Nasca, Cocos and Tehuantepec Ridges) each intersecting and apparently terminating against a fracture zone. It is particularly significant that on the other side of the East Pacific Rise in an approximately mirror-image position to the Nasca Ridge lie the Austral, Society and Tuamotu-Gambior ridges. This suggests that many chains of islands in the Eastern Pacific which are parallel either with the Nasca aseismic ridge or the Tuamotu aseismic ridge are associated in origin with

想。简单的纸片和硬纸板模型会有帮助。一个能研究洋脊–洋脊转换断层性质的纸片模型如图 3 所示。

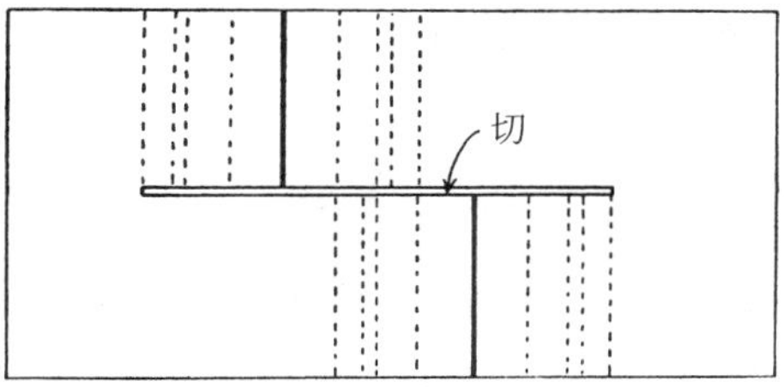

图 3. 该图显示如何切割和折叠一个硬纸板模型来表示一个破碎带与被新生地壳分开的两段大洋中脊相交的情形。——，是两边向上折的对接线；---, 是两边向下折的对接线。

借助这样的模型和图 4 我们会意识到，在与一个转换断层相交时，成对无震海岭中的一支（与断层活动部分相交）会被立即切断，并从源头处横向移开。因此，那支无震海岭必定突然终止于该断层处。成对无震海岭中另一支并不横向移动，但是大洋中脊处的中央裂谷会向远离它的方向移动。因此，我们并不能确定这支无震海岭将在断层处终止还是延伸。假如它继续延伸，它将不再与大洋中脊裂谷接触，而可能会在某处突然出现。成对无震海岭中仅仅这一支会继续活动。

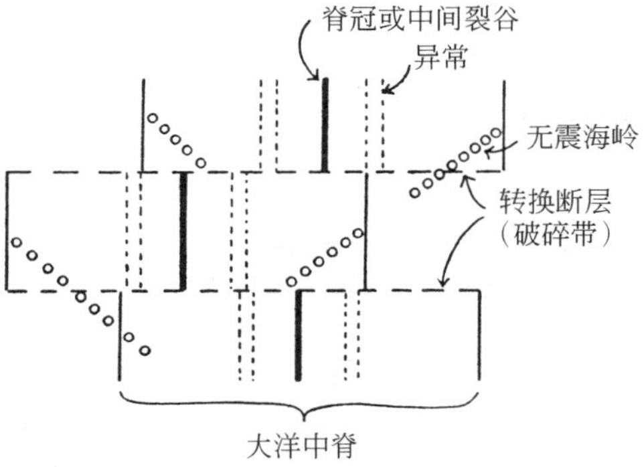

图 4. 图示为无震海岭和与它们相交的破碎带的关系。注意：每对无震海岭中必定有一支在破碎带处终结。

太平洋中某些岛链似乎能很好地满足与破碎带相交的成对无震海岭的模型（如图 5 所示）。这部分是从梅纳德书中图 5.7 和图 6.6 复制而来的[9]。它表示了三条直的平行火山岛链（即纳斯卡海岭、科科斯海岭和特万特佩克海岭），每条都与一个破碎带相交，并明显地在此破碎带终结。特别有意义的是，在东太平洋海隆的另一侧，与纳斯卡海岭大致成镜像的位置分布有南部海岭、社会海岭和土阿莫土–甘比尔海岭。因此可以说明，东太平洋许多岛链与纳斯卡无震海岭或土阿莫土无震海岭平行，并

the East Pacific mid-ocean ridge and that the great east-west fracture zones are too. If this is so and if the theory of transform faults is correct, then some very specific relationships can be predicted that should hold between the East Pacific Ridge, fracture zones, aseismic ridges and the patterns of magnetic anomalies.

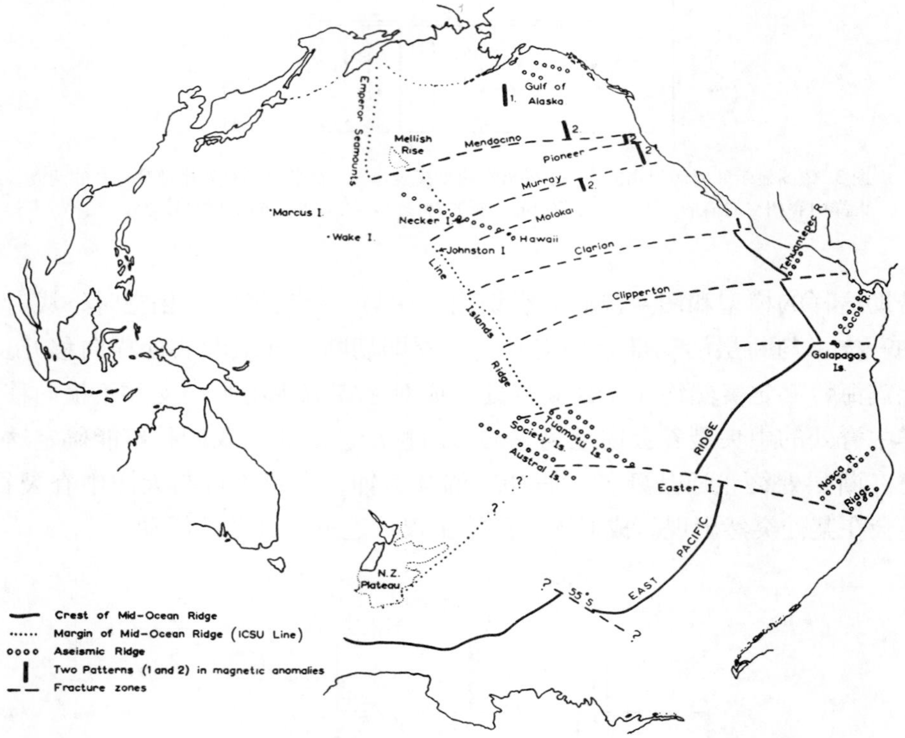

Fig. 5. Sketch map of the Pacific Ocean showing the location of the ICSU Line which is the margin of the East Pacific Ridge

The East Pacific Ridge has been well described by H. W. Menard[9] and the following account owes much to him and especially to his Fig. 6.12. This has been redrawn and modified in Fig. 5, which shows the general shape of the ridge. The eastern margin and northern crest have been overridden by the Americas. H. H. Hess has given me much advice, especially about the western Pacific. It would be interesting to identify the remaining, western margin of this ridge and important for the present discussion.

The ICSU Line, Possible Margin of the East Pacific Ridge

Menard shows the western margin of the East Pacific Ridge crossing the Pacific Basin. This margin should surely be discernible and, in seeking to identify it, other known rift margins provide the best possible guide. Heezen and Ewing[10] have implied that the Lomonosov Ridge is such a submarine margin. It may be partly volcanic according to Gakkel and partly sedimentary according to Ostenso. Elsewhere the Atlantic is bordered

在成因上都与东太平洋洋中脊相关，还预示着那些巨大的东–西向破碎带也与东太平洋洋中脊相关。假如真是这样，并假设转换断层的理论是正确的，在东太平洋海隆、破碎带、无震海岭和磁异常之间所存在的一些非常特殊的关系就能够得到预测。

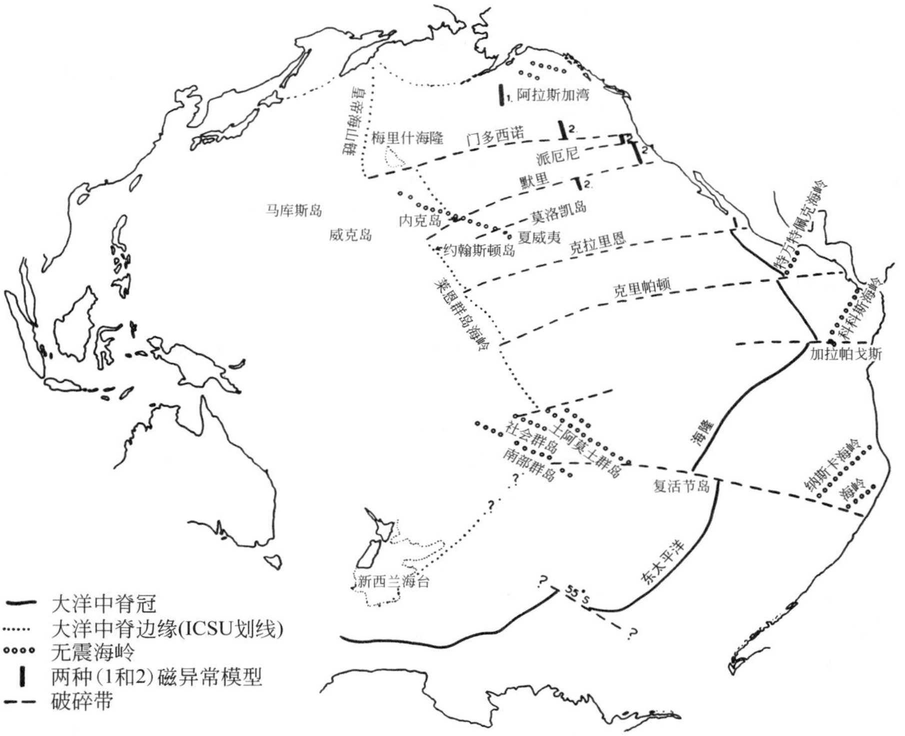

图 5. 太平洋简图，该图显示东太平洋海隆边缘的 ICSU 划线的位置。

梅纳德对东太平洋海隆进行了很好的描述[9]，下面的许多内容都归功于他，尤其是他的图 6.12。图 5 对此进行了重画，并做了改进，它显示了东太平洋海隆总的形态。美洲覆盖了其东缘和北部的脊峰。赫斯给予我许多建议，特别是关于西太平洋方面。鉴别该洋中脊的西缘将非常有趣，并且对现在的讨论亦非常重要。

ICSU 划线，东太平洋海隆可能的边缘

梅纳德指出东太平洋海隆的西缘跨越了太平洋盆地。洋中脊的西缘确实能够辨别出来，要鉴定它，其他已知的裂谷边缘可能提供了最佳的标识。希森和尤因已经暗示罗蒙诺索夫海岭就是这样一条海底的边缘[10]。该洋中脊在加克部分以火山作用为主，在厄斯滕索部分则以沉积为主。大西洋的边界为大陆地块，沿岸是零星的大

by continental blocks. Along the coasts are sporadic, large outpourings of basalt as in Greenland[11]. The only features which lie in the expected location in the Pacific Basin and which appear to have the required properties are, from north to south, the Emperor Seamounts, the group of very large seamounts at the north-western end of the Hawaiian chain, part of the western end of the Hawaiian Islands, part of the Mid-Pacific Mountains, the Line Islands Ridge and the eastern edge of the New Zealand submarine plateau. Between the last two features charting is inadequate, but a few elevations recorded as seamounts may represent crossings of a marginal ridge. No other group of features crossing the Pacific is so prominent.

Because many nations have contributed to knowledge of this feature and because great progress in oceanography resulted from the International Geophysical Year, it is proposed to call this feature the ICSU Line after the International Council of Scientific Unions which sponsored the International Geophysical Year.

Relationships of Ridges to Other Features

There has already been considerable debate about whether the fracture zones are genetically related to the East Pacific Ridge[9] or to the Darwin Rise[12]. On one hand, palaeontologists[13] find rates of sedimentation of as much as a few tens of metres in the 1 or 1.5 million years since the Pliocene-Pleistocene boundary, only Pliocene fossils over the crest of the East Pacific Ridge, progressively older Tertiary rocks away from the crest and Cretaceous fossils in the western Pacific only. This is all compatible with extensive continental movement and growth of the East Pacific Ridge during the Tertiary beside an older floor to the west.

On the other hand, those who do not accept drift are embarrassed by the paucity of sediments in the Pacific. To explain this they have proposed either that older sediments have been consolidated to form Layer 2 on the ocean floor[14], a view incompatible with Vine and Wilson's interpretation[3], or they propose drastically to reduce the rate of sedimentation by a factor of as much as 100 (ref. 15). This leads them to the conclusion that the few hundred metres of sediments formed on the East Pacific Ridge must be old and undisturbed. Hence they conclude that the East Pacific Ridge has just formed, is not yet rifted and that the fracture zones are related to the Darwin Rise. The direct evidence for this is not certain.

In view of this difference of opinion it seems reasonable to test the alternatives in relation to the theory of transform faults and to see whether the ICSU Line has any of the properties required for the margin of a mid-ocean ridge.

Some of these tests and the way in which they apply follow.

(*a*) Transform faults should only be moving and active seismically between intercepts with their related mid-ocean ridge. This is the case for all the great fracture zones of the south-

型溢流玄武岩，如同在格陵兰一样[11]。在太平洋盆地中位于预期的位置上、并具有相关属性的构造从北向南依次是皇帝海山链——位于夏威夷链西北端的一组巨型海山，夏威夷岛的西端，部分中太平洋山脉，莱恩群岛海岭及新西兰海台东缘。在后两个构造之间没有合适的海图，但是作为海山记录的一些高地可以代表边缘海岭的交叉处。目前还没有其他穿越太平洋的构造形貌群是如此明显的。

因为许多国家都对该构造的认识做出了贡献，也因为国际地球物理年促使海洋学取得重大进展，我们提议按资助了国际地球物理年的国际科联的名称把该项构造称为 ICSU 划线。

海岭与其他构造的关系

关于破碎带在成因上是与东太平洋海隆[9]还是与达尔文海隆[12]有关，已经有相当多的争论。一方面，古生物学家发现[13]，从上新世–更新世界限以来的 100 或 150 万年内沉积厚度高达数十米，在东太平洋海隆脊冠上仅仅有上新世的化石，并且随着到洋脊脊冠距离的增加第三纪岩石逐渐变老，而白垩纪的化石仅在西太平洋出现。这与第三纪中发生在西部更古老的地层之上的大范围大陆运动和东太平洋海隆生长是完全一致的。

另一方面，不接受漂移的人们遭受到了太平洋沉积物缺乏的困扰。为了解释此种现象，有人假设更老的沉积物已经固结，形成了太平洋洋底的第二层[14]，这是一种与瓦因和威尔逊的解释相矛盾的观点[3]。有人则提出沉积速率最多可急剧降到原来的百分之一（参考文献 15）。由此得出结论，在东太平洋海隆上所形成的几百米厚的沉积物必然是古老且未遭受扰动的。因此，他们的结论是，东太平洋海隆刚刚形成，尚未裂开，并且破碎带与达尔文海隆相关。但是这缺乏直接的证据。

鉴于观点的分歧，合理的做法是检验与转换断层理论相关的两种观点，看 ICSU 划线是否具有作为一个大洋中脊边缘所需要的属性。

他们所进行的某些检验及所利用的方法如下：

(*a*) 转换断层应当仅在与相关大洋中脊相截处之间发生运动，并且地震活跃。

eastern and southern Pacific. It is generally considered that these fracture zones are related to those in the north-eastern Pacific Basin, so it can be tentatively concluded that all these great Pacific fracture zones (but not those in the eastern Pacific) are transform faults connected with the East Pacific Ridge.

(*b*) The offsets in the crest and in the pattern of magnetic anomalies should be reflected at the margins. According to A. D. Raff and R. G. Mason[16] there are sinistral 900 and 210 km offsets in anomaly patterns across the Mendocino and Pioneer fracture zones. All authorities indicate the Mendocino zone to strike towards the south side of the large Mellish Bank at 180° long. and the south end of the Emperor Seamounts. A sinistral offset of 1,100 km would relate the Emperor Seamounts to an area of shallower water and seamounts which extend south to western and central parts of the Hawaiian Islands near Necker Island.

The Murray fracture zone which offsets anomalies by 560 km dextrally[17] strikes towards the Necker Ridge which has a notably linear topography[18]. A dextral displacement of rather more than 560 km (nearly 700 km) along the Necker Ridge seems to be needed to align the south end of the ridge discussed in the last paragraph (near Necker Island) with the north end of the Line Island ridge (near Johnston Island), but the distance cannot be precisely measured. According to this interpretation the Hawaiian Islands have a composite structure.

H. H. Hess assures me that there are offsets at the places where the Clarion and Clipperton fracture zones probably reach the Line Island ridge. They seem to have appropriate directions and lengths. The charting is too uncertain to draw any conclusions about fracture zones farther south. Again the displacements of the margin appear to agree well with theory.

(*c*) Transform faults should terminate against margins. The fracture zones become harder to trace beyond the ICSU Line, but the data are insufficient to make this a good test.

(*d*) All the aseismic ridges in the same crustal plate and on one side of a mid-ocean ridge should be parallel. On the east side of the East Pacific Ridge this is true of the Tehuantepec, Cocos and Nasca ridges and of the small companion ridge to the East (Nasca Two). On the west side it is true of the Gulf of Alaska Seamounts, the Hawaiian, Tuamotu-Gambier, Society and Austral Islands[7].

(*e*) All the aseismic ridges should get younger from the margin towards the mid-ocean ridge with which they are connected, and so far as is known this is true of the East Pacific Ridge.

(*f*) Aseismic ridges should generally begin at a margin. The Hawaiian Taumotu-Gambier, Society and Austral Islands all seem to start on or near the ICSU Line; the Marquesas do not and the older ends of others have been over-ridden.

这正是东南太平洋和南太平洋所有大破碎带的情形。一般认为这些破碎带与东北太平洋盆地的破碎带相关，因此可暂时得出结论，即所有这些太平洋大破碎带（东太平洋的除外）都是与东太平洋海隆相联系的转换断层。

（*b*）在洋脊脊冠和磁异常模式上的偏移应当在边缘处有所反映，按照拉夫和梅森的研究 [16]，在横跨门多西诺和派厄尼破碎带的磁异常模式上分别存在 900 千米和 210 千米的左旋偏移。所有相关学者都指出，门多西诺带的走向指向了经度 180°处巨大的梅里什滩南侧和皇帝海山链的南端。1,100 千米左旋偏移将会使皇帝海山与一个较浅水的区域和海山相关联，后者往南可以延伸到内克岛附近夏威夷群岛的西部和中部。

以 560 千米右旋 [17] 的方式使磁异常偏移的默里破碎带朝向内克海岭，该海岭明显呈线性形态 [18]。沿内克海岭 560 千米以上（将近 700 千米）的右旋位移可能需要将上节提到的海岭南端（靠近内克岛）与莱恩群岛海岭（靠近约翰斯顿岛）对齐，但是不能精确地测量其距离。按照这种解释，夏威夷群岛将具有一种复合构造。

赫斯使我确信在克拉里恩和克里帕顿破碎带可能与莱恩岛海岭相遇的地方存在着偏移。它们似乎还具有合适的方向和长度。由于海图不清楚，我们无法得出关于再往南的破碎带的任何结论。那么该边缘的位移似乎也与理论相一致。

（*c*）转换断层应当终止于紧靠边缘处。破碎带在 ICSU 划线之外更难追踪，而且资料不足以使其成为一个好的验证方法。

（*d*）在同一地壳板块内，所有的无震海岭和大洋中脊的一侧都应当是平行的。在东太平洋海隆东侧的特万特佩克海岭、科科斯海岭和纳斯卡海岭，以及东侧的小伴生海岭（纳斯卡二号）都是如此。在其西侧的阿拉斯加湾海山、夏威夷群岛、土阿莫土–甘比尔群岛、社会群岛及南部群岛亦是如此 [7]。

（*e*）所有无震海岭的年龄从边缘到与其相连的大洋中脊应当越来越年轻，迄今为止这在东太平洋海隆也是成立的。

（*f*）无震海岭一般从一个边缘开始。夏威夷群岛、土阿莫土–甘比尔群岛、社会群岛和南部群岛等似乎都从沿着或靠近 ICSU 划线处开始，而马克萨斯群岛并非如此，并且其他群岛的较老一端已被覆盖。

(*g*) One should expect to find pairs of aseismic ridges symmetrically arranged in chevron pattern about the crest. The Tuamotu-Gambier, Society and Austral chains are so arranged relative to the Nasca and Nasca Two ridges (to the extent that they have not been over-ridden).

(*h*) The theory predicts that in the Pacific aseismic ridges should terminate against the eastern end of dextral transform faults (that is, those which paradoxically show apparent sinistral offsets) and against the western end of sinistral faults. Aseismic ridges may cross and be active at the other ends of fracture zones. According to Menard[9], the Mendocino, Pioneer, Molokai, Clipperton and Easter fracture zones show apparent sinistral offsets. As predicted the Tehuantepec, Nasca and Nasca Two ridges all stop against their eastern ends, and according to Hess[19] the Hawaiian Islands cross the western end of the Molokai fracture zone and are still active while the Austral Islands cross the Easter fracture zone.

For the other fracture zones the relationships should be the reverse, and it is true that the Galapagos Islands are still active, even if they scarcely cross the Galapagos zone. The Hawaiian Islands should not cross the Murray zone but appear to do so. This is the only exception, but may be due to a greater complexity in the structure of the Hawaiian chain than has heretofore been suspected.

The conclusion is that the fracture zones and aseismic ridges are associated with the East Pacific Ridge. The oldest rocks reported are Eocene in cores[13] and from Makatea Island in the Tuamotu group near the western margin[20]. Rapid spreading and rapid rates of sedimentation are indicated. The orientation of the aseismic ridges suggests that the floor of the Pacific is moving northwards like that of the Atlantic Ocean and several southern continents.

Possible Causes of Northward Spreading and Orientation of Aseismic Ridges

An explanation can readily be offered in terms of the possible sub-crustal currents mentioned earlier. On an infinite body they might flow as in Fig. 6 (left), but on a sphere they might be constrained to flow as in Fig. 6 (right). This pattern, like a J folded about the Earth, can be taken to be a diagrammatic simplification of the real mid-ocean ridge system and can be compared with Fig. 10 in my previous article[1]. The stem represents the Mid-Atlantic Ridge, the loop the mid-ocean ridge system through the Southern Ocean to the West Chile Ridge. Antarctica would be in the centre of the loop.

Because there is no sink within the looped source the diameter of the loop itself increases and the surface currents move outwards with twice the velocity of the deeper counter-currents. If the sources of volcanoes lie in the counter currents (if the convecting system is shallow), or within the stagnant cores of convection cells (if the system is deep), then the differential in rates of flow will produce chevron patterns in the aseismic ridges.

The northward motion is absorbed in the Alpine Himalayan and Circum-Pacific Mountains and hence has not affected the Icelandic ridges.

(*g*) 人们应希望发现成对的无震海岭以 V 字形方式在脊冠周围对称排列。土阿莫土–甘比尔群岛、社会群岛和南部群岛链相对于纳斯卡和纳斯卡二号海岭就是这样排列的（某种程度上，在它们并无重叠的地方）。

(*h*) 根据转换断层理论预测，太平洋中的无震海岭应当终止于右旋转换断层的东端（即那些看似左旋偏移的断层）和左旋的断层的西端位置。无震海岭可能会跨越到破碎带的另一端并保持活动。按照梅纳德的看法 [9]，门多西诺、派厄尼、莫洛凯、克里帕顿和复活节岛破碎带明显为左旋偏移。正如所预测的，特万特佩克海岭、纳斯卡和纳斯卡二号海岭都在它们的东端停止。并且，按照赫斯的看法 [19]，夏威夷群岛与莫洛凯岛破碎带西端相交，并还在活动，而南部群岛则与复活节岛破碎带相交。

对于其他破碎带，上述关系则应相反。加拉帕戈斯群岛虽然与加拉帕戈斯破碎带几乎不相交，但它们确实仍在活动。夏威夷群岛不应当与默里破碎带相交，但是看起来却是相交的。这是唯一的例外，可能是由于夏威夷岛链构造的复杂性远超出了此前的预测。

综上所述，破碎带和无震海岭均与东太平洋海隆有关。从钻孔岩芯 [13] 以及西部边缘附近的土阿莫土群岛中的马卡泰阿岛 [20] 上得到的最古老的岩石都是始新世的。这意味着那里曾经历了快速的扩张和沉积。无震海岭的走向表明，太平洋底如同大西洋和若干南部大陆一样正在向北运动。

无震海岭向北扩张和取向的可能原因

根据此前所叙述的地壳下可能存在流动的理论，我们能够很容易地对太平洋向北扩张给予解释。在一个无限的物体上面，它们以如图 6（左）的方式流动；但是在一个球体上，如同图 6（右），它们流动会受到限制。该模式就像一个包绕地球的 J 字形，能够作为真正大洋中脊系统的简化图，并能与我过去论文中的图 10 进行对比 [1]。图 6（右）中的杆代表大西洋洋中脊，环代表从南大洋到西智利海岭的大洋中脊系统。南极洲位于环的中心。

因为环形的来源中并无沉陷，因此环本身的直径会增加，而且表层流以两倍于深部逆向流动的速度向外进行。若火山源存在于逆向流动中（假如该对流系统较浅），或者位于对流单元的滞留核中（假如该系统较深），那么流速差将导致无震海岭形成 V 字形的样式。

向北的运动在阿尔卑斯–喜马拉雅和环太平洋山脉中被吸收，因而并不影响冰岛的海岭。

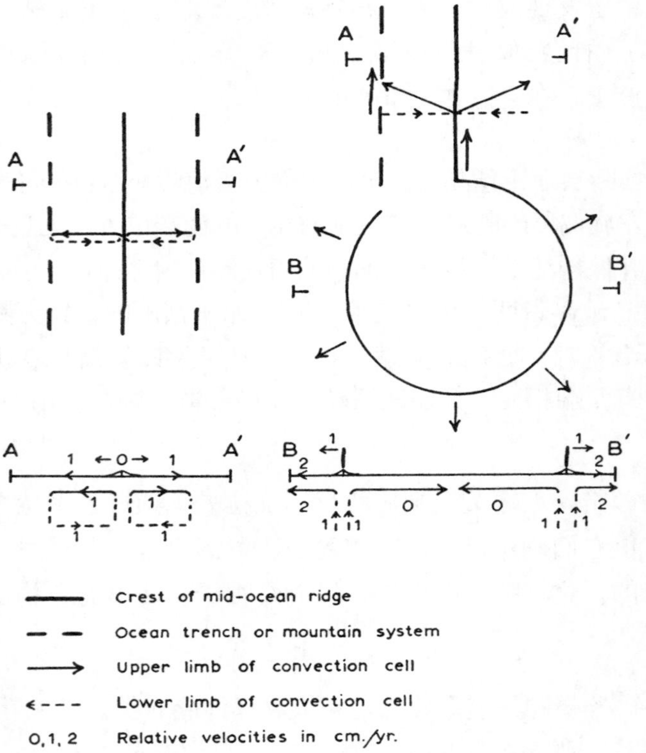

Fig. 6. Left, diagrammatic sketch of an unconstrained pattern of possible crustal and sub-crustal flow; right, the same for a pattern representing in simplified fashion the Earth's mid-ocean ridges, showing how the loop of ridge in the southern oceans could explain the directions of aseismic ridges, if the sources of their volcanoes lay below the crustal motions

Besides Antarctica, another continent, Africa, is ringed by mid-ocean ridges on all but the northern side and corresponding effects can be detected in the Indian Ocean ridges.

I should like to acknowledge that this article could not have been written if the oceans had not been so well charted by others. I have particularly used maps by H. W. Menard[9] and H. H. Hess[21], and a globe showing bathymetry[22], but I first noticed the ICSU Line on a large new Soviet chart[23] which shows it clearly.

This article was written while I was a guest in the Departments of Geodesy and Geophysics and of Geology and in Churchill College, University of Cambridge; I thank them and particularly B. C. Browne, Sir Edward Bullard, H. H. Hess, M. N. Hill, R. G. Mason, D. H. Matthews and F. J. Vine for discussions which have been invaluable in arriving at these conclusions, though they may not agree with all of them; and I also thank Sue Chappell and Sue Vine for their assistance.

(**207**, 907-911; 1965)

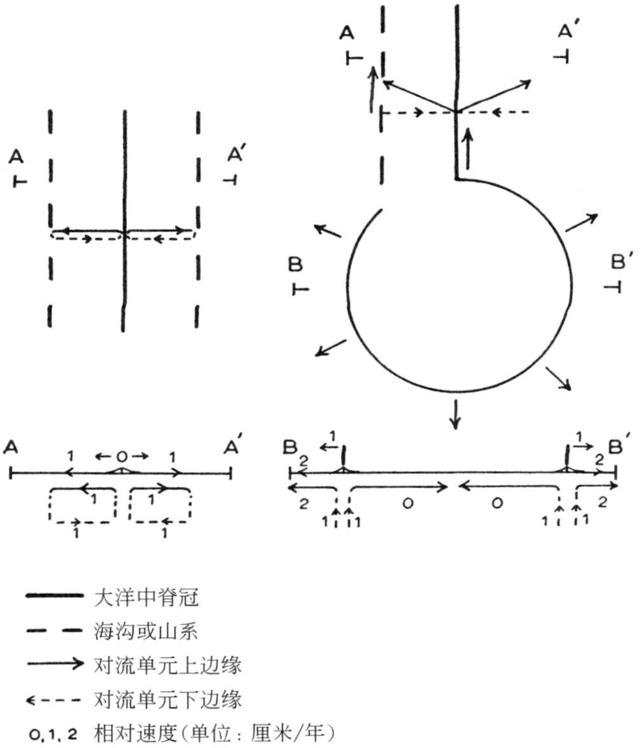

图 6. 左图表示一个无约束的地壳和（地）壳下可能有的流动模式；右图同样是一种模式图，其以简化的方式代表地球的大洋中脊，假如火山源位于地壳运动之下，图中显示了南部大洋中的洋脊环如何能解释无震海岭的方向。

除南极洲外，另一个大陆——非洲大陆也全被大洋中脊所包围（北侧除外），相应的效果能够在印度洋洋脊中看到。

必须承认，假如没有其他人绘出如此好的海图，我不可能写出此文。我特别使用了梅纳德 [9] 和赫斯的地图 [21]，以及显示海洋测深的地球仪 [22]；而我第一次注意到 ICSU 划线是在一张苏联的大型新海图上 [23]，该图清晰地显示了此划线。

本文写于我在剑桥大学大地测量学和地球物理学系、地质学系和丘吉尔学院作客之际；在此对他们表示感谢，特别要感谢与布朗、爱德华 · 布拉德爵士、赫斯、希尔、梅森、马修斯以及瓦因所进行的讨论，这对本文能取得这些结论是非常宝贵的，尽管他们并不完全同意这些结论；同时也感谢休 · 查普尔和休 · 瓦因的帮助。

（李任伟 翻译；李三忠 审稿）

J. Tuzo Wilson: Department of Physics, University of Toronto.

References:

1. Wilson, J. T., *Nature*, **207**, 343 (1965).
2. Wilson, J. T., *Science* (in the press).
3. Vine, F. J., and Wilson, J. T., *Science* (in the press).
4. Heezen, B. C., Bunce, E. T., Hersey, J. B., and Tharp, M., *Deep-Sea Research*, **11**, 11 (1964).
5. Bullard, E. C., Everett, J. E., and Smith, A. G., *Phil. Trans. Roy. Soc.*, A (in the press).
6. Wilson, J. T., *Nature*, **198**, 925 (1963).
7. Wilson, J. T., *Canad. J. Phys.*, **41**, 863 (1963).
8. Bodvarsson, G., and Walker, G. P. L., *Geophys. J.*, **8**, 285 (1964).
9. Menard, H. W., *Marine Geology of the Pacific* (McGraw-Hill Book Co., New York, 1964).
10. Heezen, B. C., and Ewing, M., in *Geology of the Arctic*, **1**, 622 (Univ. Toronto Press, 1961).
11. Wager, L. R., and Deer, W. A., *Meddr. Gronland*, **105**, 1 (1939).
12. Hess, H. H., in *Colston Symp. Marine Geology* (Univ. Bristol; in the press).
13. Riedel, W. R., and Funnell, B. M., *Quart. J. Geol. Soc. Lond.*, **120**, 305 (1964).
14. Hamilton, E. L., *J. Sed. Petrol.*, **30**, 370 (1960).
15. Goldberg, E. D., and Koide, M., *Geochim. Cosmochim. Acta*, **26**, 417 (1962).
16. Raff, A. D., and Mason, R. G., *Bull. Geol. Soc. Amer.*, **72**, 1267 (1961).
17. Raff, A. D., *J. Geophys. Res.*, **67**, 417 (1962).
18. Hamilton, E. L., *Geol. Soc. Amer. Mem.*, **64** (1956).
19. Hess, H. H., *Nature*, **203**, 629 (1964).
20. Repelin, J., *C.R. Acad. Sci., Paris*, **168**, 237 (1919).
21. Hess, H. H., *Chart of the Pacific* (unpublished results).
22. Darley, J. M., *National Geographic Globe* (Nat. Geog. Soc., 1962).
23. Soviet Institute of Oceanology, Moscow, *Chart of the Pacific Ocean*, scale 1 to 10,000,000 (1964).

An Improved Method for the Characterization of Human Haemoglobin Mutants: Identification of $\alpha_2\beta_2^{95GLU}$, Haemoglobin N(Baltimore)

J. B. Clegg *et al.*

Editor's Note

In this paper, researchers from the Johns Hopkins University School of Medicine, Baltimore, describe an improved method for analysing abnormal haemoglobin proteins. Previous methods failed to fully digest these complex proteins and struggled to effectively separate α and β polypeptide chains from the small quantities of starting material. The new technique, devised by John Clegg, Mike Naughton and David Weatherall, relied on high-resolution chromatography to separate the chains, and a chemical step to convert them to a fully digestible form. The method was quick, sensitive and enabled the team to separate normal and abnormal chains, as demonstrated by their analysis of the abnormal haemoglobin N (Baltimore) protein.

ONE of the problems during investigation of human haemoglobin mutants has been the difficulty of separating the α and β chains in a pure form from small quantities of starting material. While chain separation is not a pre-requisite for all chemical investigations, such work can be carried out more easily on the isolated α and β chains. The method for the separation of the peptide chains of human haemoglobin described in this communication is relatively easy to use and has an advantage over those previously reported in that it will not only give separation of the α and β chains, but is also capable of resolving a charged mutant chain from the normal, thus enabling the globin of a heterozygous charged mutant to be fractionated into all its component chains.

A second difficulty usually encountered is the familiar one of incomplete digestion of proteins by proteolytic enzymes. Digestion of human α and β haemoglobin chains with trypsin normally leaves a trypsin-resistant "core" with the result that a region consisting of about 30 percent of the molecule cannot easily be examined by fingerprinting. However, conversion of the cysteine residues of the α and β chains to aminoethyl-cysteine by reaction with ethyleneimine[1] has been shown by Jones[2] to give derivatives which no longer contain the trypsin-resistant region. Thus, fingerprints of aminoethylated α and β chains show all the expected trypsin peptides plus additional ones due to splits at aminoethyl-cysteine.

The combination of a high-resolution chromatographic separation of the α and β chains and the conversion of the separated chains into aminoethyl derivatives susceptible to trypsin[2] affords a procedure considerably more rapid and more sensitive than any previously available for studying haemoglobin mutants. With the technique described

一种改进的研究人类血红蛋白突变体的方法：$\alpha_2\beta_2^{95GLU}$ 血红蛋白N（巴尔的摩）的鉴定

克莱格等

编者按

在这篇论文中，来自巴尔的摩约翰斯·霍普金斯大学医学院的研究者们描述了一种改进的分析异常血红蛋白的方法。此前的方法不能使这些复杂的蛋白质完全酶解，且很难高效地从少量原始材料中分离出 α 多肽链和 β 多肽链。由约翰·克莱格、迈克·诺顿以及戴维·韦瑟罗尔设计的新技术采用高分辨色谱法分离多肽链，通过化学步骤将它们转化为可以完全酶解的形式。这种方法快速、灵敏并且可以使研究团队将正常多肽链和异常多肽链分离，就像他们在对异常血红蛋白 N(巴尔的摩)的分析中所展示的那样。

在研究人类血红蛋白突变体的过程中，长久以来困扰人们的一个难题是从少量的原始材料中分离出纯的 α 链和 β 链。虽然链的分离并不是所有化学研究的必要条件，但分离的 α 链和 β 链可使这类研究实施起来更容易。本文中描述的人类血红蛋白多肽链的分离方法比较容易操作，与此前报道的那些方法相比，它具有一个优点，因为它不仅可以分离 α 链和 β 链，而且也能从正常的链中分离出带电突变链，进而使得杂合的带电突变体的珠蛋白的全部组成链都得以分离。

经常遇到的第二类难题是，较为常见的蛋白水解酶不完全消化蛋白质。用胰蛋白酶消化人类血红蛋白的 α 链和 β 链，通常会留下一个胰蛋白酶耐受的“核心”，结果导致指纹图谱不能容易地检测这个约占整个分子 30% 的区域。然而琼斯[2] 指出，通过与吖丙啶[1] 反应将 α 链和 β 链的半胱氨酸残基转化为氨乙基－半胱氨酸，得到的衍生物中就不包含胰蛋白酶耐受区域。因而，氨基乙基化的 α 链和 β 链的指纹图谱可以显示所有预期的胰蛋白酶多肽段以及在氨乙基－半胱氨酸处进行切割而得到的肽段。

α 链和 β 链的高分辨色谱分离产物与将分离链转化为对胰蛋白酶敏感[2] 的氨乙基衍生物相结合，为研究血红蛋白突变体提供了一个比以前更为快速和更为灵敏的方法。通过本文描述的技术，从少至 10 毫克的原珠蛋白中可回收到相当数量的分离

here, recoveries of the separated α and β chains are quantitative and sufficient material for aminoethylation and subsequent fingerprinting can be obtained from as little as 10 mg of starting globin. In addition, quantitative amino-acid analyses of peptides eluted from fingerprints of 2 mg of the digested chains have been routinely achieved.

Isolation and characterization of the β chain of haemoglobin N (Baltimore). An 8-month-old Negro female was found to have two haemoglobins by routine electrophoretic screening. Apart from a mild iron deficiency there were no significant haematological abnormalities either in the child or in the mother, who also carried the abnormal variant. The relevant haematological values and the proportions of normal and abnormal haemoglobins are summarized in Table 1. On starch-gel electrophoresis at *p*H 8.6 (Fig. 1) the abnormal haemoglobin migrated faster than haemoglobin J (Baltimore)[3] but slower than haemoglobin H. These electrophoretic characteristics are similar to those previously described for haemoglobin N[4] and the variant has therefore been designated as haemoglobin N (Baltimore). Comparative gel-electrophoresis experiments with other known haemoglobin mutants suggested that at *p*H 8.6 haemoglobin N (Baltimore) possesses four more negative charges per 68,000 molecular weight than does haemoglobin A. Hybridization with canine haemoglobin indicated that the abnormality in haemoglobin N (Baltimore) was in the β chain. Fingerprints of tryptic digests of whole haemoglobin N (Baltimore) or of isolated $\beta^{N(Baltimore)}$ chain showed no detectable differences from those of haemoglobin A or normal β chain.

Table 1. Haematological and Electrophoretic Data

Family member		Propositus	Mother
Age		8 months	24 years
Haemoglobin (g/100 ml.)		10.2	13.8
Red cell count (millions/mm^3)		4.06	4.13
Reticulocytes (%)		5.1	1.1
MCV (μ^3)		81	102
MCH ($\mu\mu$g)		28	33
MCHC (%)		31	33
Haemoglobin constitution		A+N	A+N
Haemoglobin fractionation	HbA(%)	46.3	48.6
	HbN(%)	44.3	49.6
	HbA$_2$(%)	1.0	1.4
Alkaliresistant haemoglobin (%)		8.4	0.4

20 mg of the child's globin, prepared by 2 percent acid-acetone precipitation of a whole red-cell lysate, was dissolved in 2 ml. of a buffer consisting of 8 M urea, 0.05 M 2-mercaptoethanol, and 0.005 M Na_2HPO_4 , adjusted to *p*H 6.7 with phosphoric acid. The solution was dialysed at room temperature against three changes of a 50-fold excess of the same buffer for a total of 2.5 h and then applied to a 1 cm × 10 cm column of carboxymethyl-cellulose (0.7 m.equiv.g) equilibrated against the same buffer. After the column had been washed to remove any unretarded material the peptide chains were

的α链和β链，足以进行氨基乙基化和随后的指纹图谱分析。另外，对2毫克酶解后的肽链进行指纹图谱，洗脱下的肽段通常能进行定量氨基酸分析。

血红蛋白N（巴尔的摩）β链的分离与鉴定 通过常规的电泳分析，发现在一个8月龄的黑人女性体内存在两种血红蛋白。除了轻微的缺铁，无论孩子还是母亲体内（她也携带异常变异体）都没有发现明显的血液学上的异常。表1列出了相关的血液学值、正常的和异常的血红蛋白的比例。在pH 8.6的条件下进行淀粉凝胶电泳（图1），发现异常的血红蛋白的迁移速率大于血红蛋白J（巴尔的摩）[3]，但是小于血红蛋白H。这些电泳特征与之前描述的血红蛋白N[4]相似，因此这种变异体被确定为血红蛋白N（巴尔的摩）。将凝胶电泳的实验结果与其他已知的血红蛋白突变体进行比较发现，在pH 8.6的条件下每68,000分子量的血红蛋白N(巴尔的摩)比血红蛋白A多4个负电荷。与犬科血红蛋白杂交结果显示，血红蛋白N(巴尔的摩）的β链存在异常。胰蛋白酶消化整个血红蛋白N（巴尔的摩）所得产物的指纹图谱，或者分离出的$\beta^{N（巴尔的摩）}$链的指纹图谱表明，与血红蛋白A或者正常的β链相比没有可检测的差别。

表1. 血液学和电泳数据

家庭成员		先证者	母亲
年龄		8个月	24岁
血红蛋白（克/100毫升）		10.2	13.8
红细胞量（百万/毫米^3）		4.06	4.13
网状细胞（%）		5.1	1.1
红细胞平均容量（微米^3）		81	102
红细胞平均血红蛋白量（皮克）		28	33
红细胞平均血红蛋白浓度（%）		31	33
血红蛋白组成		A+N	A+N
血红蛋白组分	HbA（%）	46.3	48.6
	HbN（%）	44.3	49.6
	HbA_2（%）	1.0	1.4
耐碱血红蛋白（%）		8.4	0.4

用2%的丙酮酸沉淀一个完整红细胞的溶出物，得到20毫克儿童的珠蛋白，将其溶解于2毫升缓冲液中（缓冲液成分：8摩尔/升尿素，0.05摩尔/升2–巯基乙醇和0.005摩尔/升Na_2HPO_4，用磷酸调pH为6.7）。在室温下透析溶液，将透析袋放入50倍过量的相同缓冲液中，其间更换缓冲液3次，共透析2.5小时，然后将透析后的溶液上样到用同样的缓冲液平衡过的1厘米×10厘米羧甲基纤维素柱里(0.7 m.equiv.g)，洗脱去除所有未挂柱的物质后，通过线性钠离子梯度的方法

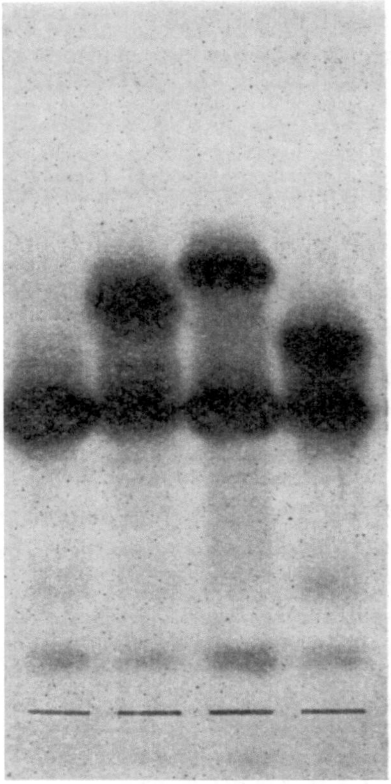

Fig. 1. Starch-gel electrophoresis (*tris*-EDTA-borate, *p*H 8.6) of haemolysates containing (left to right): haemoglobin A, haemoglobins A and N, haemoglobins A and H, and haemoglobins A and J

eluted at a flow rate of 1 ml./min by means of a linear Na^+-ion gradient made by mixing 100 ml. of starting buffer with 100 ml. of a buffer consisting of 8 M urea, 0.05 M 2-mercaptoethanol, and 0.03 M Na_2HPO_4, adjusted to *p*H 6.7 with phosphoric acid. The column effluent was monitored continuously at 280 mμ and the resulting chromatogram is shown in Fig. 2. Of the three peaks obtained, two were found at the expected elution volumes of normal α and β chains, while the third peak emerged much earlier than normal β chain, indicating the presence of a more acidic β chain. This confirmed the findings of the hybridization experiments.

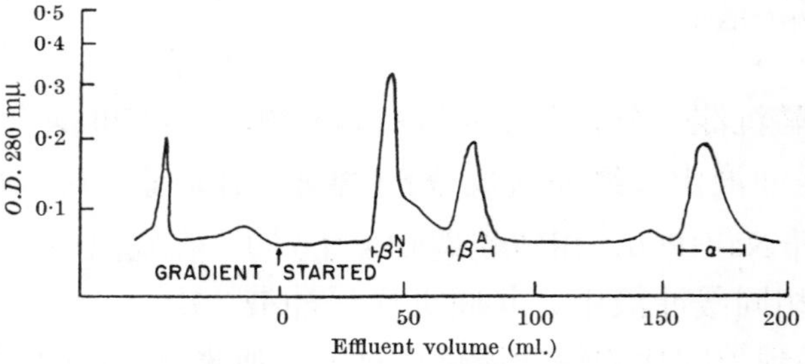

Fig. 2. Gradient elution chromatography on carboxymethyl-cellulose of globin from haemoglobin N heterozygote

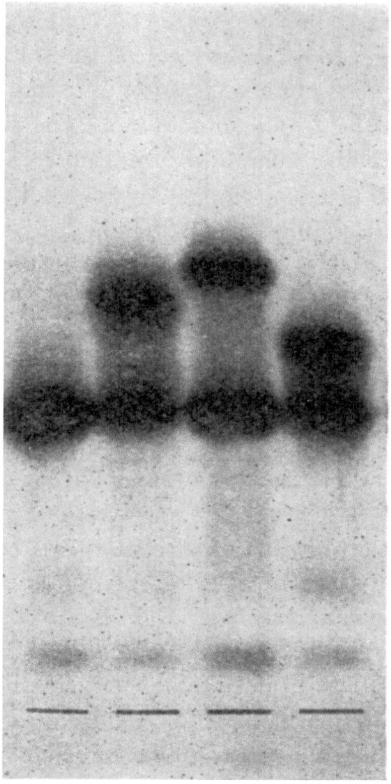

图1. 红细胞溶解物的淀粉凝胶电泳（三羟甲基氨基甲烷–乙二胺四乙酸–硼酸盐缓冲系统，pH 8.6），从左向右依次为血红蛋白A、血红蛋白A和N、血红蛋白A和H、血红蛋白A和J。

（将100毫升起始缓冲液与100毫升组分为8摩尔/升尿素、0.05摩尔/升2–巯基乙醇和0.03 摩尔/升Na_2HPO_4且用磷酸调pH为6.7的缓冲液进行混合而制得），以1毫升/分钟的速率洗脱多肽链。在280纳米下连续监测柱子洗脱液，得到的色谱图见图2。在获得的三个峰中，两个出现在预期的正常α链和β链的洗脱体积处，然而第三个峰出现的时间早于正常的β链，表明存在一个酸性更强的β链。这证实了杂交实验的结果。

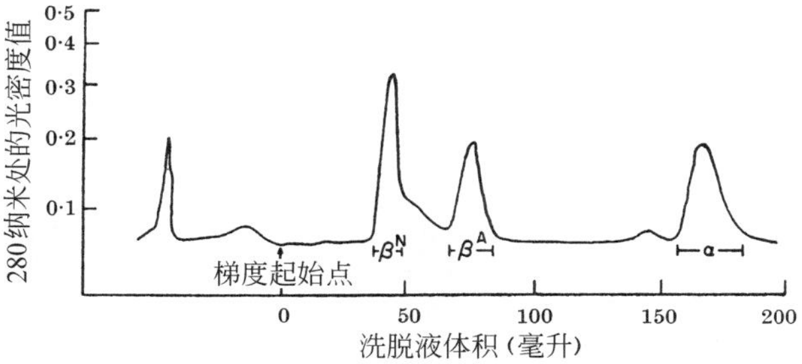

图2. 血红蛋白N杂合体的珠蛋白在羧甲基纤维素层析柱上梯度洗脱的色谱图

The fractions corresponding to the two β chains were collected and solid *tris* added to each solution to give a concentration of 1 M. After the *p*H of the solutions had been adjusted to 9.2 with concentrated HCl, ethyleneimine was added to a final concentration of 0.5 M (that is, a 10-fold molar excess over the 2-mercaptoethanol). The aminoethylation reactions were then allowed to proceed at room temperature until no free sulphydryl groups were detectable by the nitroprusside test[5] (usually after about 2.5 h). The *p*H was then adjusted to 3 with concentrated HCl and the solutions passed through a "Sephadex *G*-25" column equilibrated with 0.5 percent formic acid, in order to remove urea, salts, etc. Finally, the recovered protein fractions were freeze dried.

Tryptic digests of amounts of protein greater than 10 mg were carried out at *p*H 9.0 for 2 h at room temperature in a radiometer *p*H-stat. Digestion was terminated by adjusting the *p*H to 4.7 and freeze-drying the solution. It was preferable to digest smaller amounts of protein in 1 percent NH_4HCO_3, *p*H 8.2 (the amounts of salt introduced by the automatic procedure being sufficient to cause smearing of peptide spots when it was necessary to apply all the digest to a single fingerprint). After digestion was complete, the NH_4HCO_3 was removed by repeated freeze-drying. For all the digestions the trypsin/protein weight ratio was 1/100. The dried digests were dissolved in *p*H 4.7 buffer (1.25 percent pyridine, 1.25 percent acetic acid) and aliquots corresponding to 2 mg of the original proteins were subjected to electrophoresis in this buffer on 108 cm × 57 cm sheets of Whatman No. 3 MM paper for 3.25 h at 33 V/cm in a "Varsol"-cooled tank. After drying, the papers were chromatographed overnight in *n*-butanol, acetic acid, water, pyridine (15 : 3 : 12 : 10)

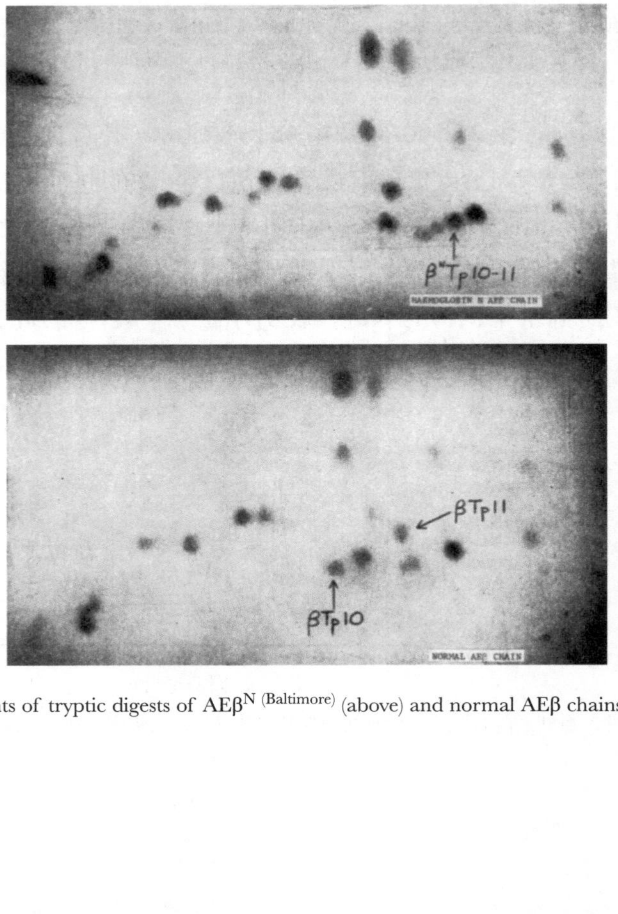

Fig. 3. Fingerprints of tryptic digests of $AE\beta^{N\ (Baltimore)}$ (above) and normal AEβ chains (below)

收集两个 β 链对应的分离组分，在每一收集液中加入固体三羟甲基氨基甲烷使浓度为 1 摩尔 / 升。用浓盐酸将收集液的 pH 调到 9.2 后，加入吖丙啶使其终浓度为 0.5 摩尔 / 升（即摩尔数超过 2– 巯基乙醇 10 倍）。在室温条件下进行氨基乙基化反应，直至用硝普盐试验检测不到游离的巯基为止 [5]（通常为 2.5 小时后）。然后用浓盐酸将 pH 调为 3，再使溶液通过一个用 0.5% 的甲酸平衡过的“葡聚糖凝胶 *G*-25”柱，以便除掉尿素、盐等。最后将收集到的蛋白质组分冷冻干燥保存。

在雷迪美特 pH 恒定仪中将 pH 调为 9，用胰蛋白酶消化总量大于 10 毫克的蛋白质，室温条件下反应 2 个小时。然后将 pH 调为 4.7 以终止反应，并且冷冻干燥反应液。在 1% 的 NH_4HCO_3、pH 为 8.2 的条件下消化少量蛋白质效果会更好（当必须对所有消化物进行单一指纹图谱时，自动化程序引入的盐的量足以引起肽点的拖尾效应）。消化完成后，再通过一次冷冻干燥将 NH_4HCO_3 除去。对于所有消化物，胰蛋白酶与蛋白质的重量比是 1/100。消化物干粉溶于 pH 为 4.7 的缓冲液（1.25% 嘧啶，1.25% 醋酸）中，剩余的 2 毫克原始蛋白质在相同缓冲液中进行电泳，选用规格为 108 厘米 × 57 厘米的沃特曼 No.3 MM 纸，在“瓦索尔”冷却系统中于 33 伏特 / 厘米条件下电泳 3.25 小时。烘干后，在正丁醇 : 醋酸 : 水 : 吡啶（15 : 3 : 12 : 10）的条件下，

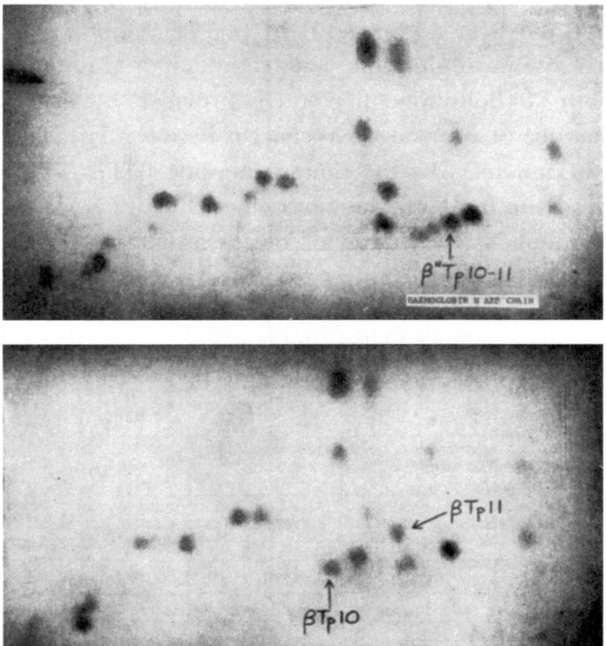

图 3. 用胰蛋白酶消化 $AE\beta^{N(巴尔的摩)}$（上图）和正常的 AEβ 链（下图）的指纹图谱

(ref. 6). The resulting fingerprints were stained by dipping in 0.02 percent ninhydrin-acetone and developing at 60°. Photographs of the two fingerprints are shown in Fig. 3 and the significant differences between the mutant and the normal patterns are indicated by arrows. The other slight differences are due to the varying amounts of partially split peptides.

The fingerprint of the mutant β chain is characterized by the absence of peptides βTp10 and βTp11 and by the appearance of a new peptide which has a distinctive yellow colour. Since βTp10 also gives a yellow colour with ninhydrin, these observations suggest that the mutant peptide is a combination of βTp10 and βTp11. (No tryptic cleavage at the aminoethyl-cysteine residue in βTp10 has been found, presumably because aspartic acid is the adjacent amino-acid, the sequence in this region being AECys (aminoethyl-cysteine)^{93}-Asp^{94}-Lys^{95} (ref. 7).This absence of a split at AECys^{93} was previously reported by Jones[2].) The peptides to be analysed were cut from the fingerprints and eluted with 6 N HCl into 100 μl. capillary disposable pipettes by the method described by Sanger and Tuppy[8]. Collection of 30-40 μl. was sufficient to ensure complete removal of the peptide from the paper. The tubes were then sealed, and heated at 105° for 18 h. After hydrolysis, the contents of the tubes were washed into 0.5 ml. of distilled water and applied directly to a "Technicon" 5-column amino-acid analyser. This made it unnecessary to dry down the hydrolysates, a procedure which has been shown to reduce the yield of amino-acids, possibly because of further reaction with ninhydrin[9]. Table 2 gives the amino-acid analysis and composition of the mutant peptide. From this it is apparent that the lysine residue (95) of βTp10 has been replaced by glutamic acid (or glutamine), with the result that a conjugate peptide, β^{N}Tp10-11, is formed by tryptic digestion of the mutant $\beta^{N(Baltimore)}$ chain. The evidence for a lysine to glutamic acid (rather than glutamine) change at position 95 in the haemoglobin N (Baltimore) β chain is provided by the starch-gel electrophoresis findings of a difference of four negative charges between haemoglobin N (Baltimore) and haemoglobin A. It explains why the mutant peptide β^{N}Tp10-11, occurring as it does in the "core" region of the β chain, was not detected on the original fingerprints of tryptic digests of haemoglobin N (Baltimore) or of the isolated $\beta^{N(Baltimore)}$ chain which had not been reacted with ethyleneimine.

Table 2. Amino-Acid Analysis and Compositions of AEβ Chain Peptides

Amino-acid	AE$\beta^{N(Baltimore)}$			AEβ^{A} (ref. 7)		
	$\beta^{N(Baltimore)}$ Tp10-11			β^{A}Tp10	β^{A}Tp11	β^{A}Tp10+β^{A}Tp11
	Found (μmoles)	Residues	Nearest whole residue	Expected	Expected	Expected
Lys	-	-	-	1	-	1
His	0.043	1.6	2	1	1	2
Arg	0.028	1.0	1	-	1	1
Asp	0.078	2.8	3	1	2	3
Thr	0.051	1.8	2	2	-	2
Ser	0.033	1.2	1	1	-	1
Glu	0.085	3.0	3	1	1	2

连夜进行色谱分离（参考文献 6）。产生的指纹图谱浸泡在 0.02% 的水合茚三酮溶液中染色并在 60℃下显影。图 3 列出了两种指纹图谱的照片，用箭头标注突变体和正常样品之间的显著差异。其他微小的差异是由于不完全酶切多肽量的不同造成的。

突变 β 链的指纹图谱的特征是缺失肽段 βTp10 和 βTp11 并且出现了一条呈特殊黄色的新肽段。加入茚三酮后，βTp10 也显黄色，因此这些结果表明突变多肽是 βTp10 和 βTp11 的结合。（在 βTp10 中，未发现胰蛋白酶在氨乙基 – 半胱氨酸残基处的酶切位点，据推测因为邻近的氨基酸是天冬氨酸，这段区域的序列是 AECys（氨乙基 – 半胱氨酸）^{93}-Asp（天冬氨酸）^{94}-Lys（赖氨酸）^{95}（参考文献 7)。之前琼斯也曾报道过在 AECys^{93} 处酶切位点的缺失 [2]。）利用桑格和塔皮 [8] 描述的方法将多肽从指纹图谱上切下来，在 100 微升一次性毛细管中用 6 摩尔 / 升的盐酸洗脱，对得到的多肽进行分析。收集 30 微升 ~ 40 微升就能确保从纸上分离出全部多肽。将管密封，在 105℃下加热 18 小时。水解后，在 0.5 毫升蒸馏水中洗涤管内物质，然后直接利用“泰克尼康”5– 柱氨基酸分析仪进行分析。这样就不必干燥水解产物，已证明这个过程可以减少氨基酸的生成，可能是因为与水合茚三酮进一步反应 [9]。表 2 给出了氨基酸的分析结果和突变多肽的组成。从这里可以明显看出，βTp10 的赖氨酸残基（95）被谷氨酸（或者谷氨酰胺）代替，结果形成一个结合肽 β^NTp10-11，它是通过胰蛋白酶消化突变的 $\beta^{N(巴尔的摩)}$ 多肽链形成的。通过淀粉凝胶电泳发现血红蛋白 N(巴尔的摩）和血红蛋白 A 之间相差 4 个负电荷，因此为血红蛋白 N（巴尔的摩）β 链的 95 位上的赖氨酸突变为谷氨酸（而非谷氨酰胺）提供了证据。这解释了为什么突变多肽 β^NTp10-11 在血红蛋白 N（巴尔的摩）的胰蛋白酶消化产物的原始指纹图谱或在未与吖丙啶发生反应的分离的 $\beta^{N(巴尔的摩)}$ 链的原始指纹图谱中都没有检测到，看起来它确实存在于 β 链的“核心”区域。

表 2. 氨基酸分析结果和 AEβ 链多肽的组成

氨基酸	$AE\beta^{N(巴尔的摩)}$			$AE\beta^A$（参考文献 7）		
	$\beta^{N(巴尔的摩)}$ Tp10-11			β^ATp10	β^ATp11	β^ATp10 + β^ATp11
	结果（微摩尔）	残基	最接近的残基整数	预期	预期	预期
Lys	-	-	-	1	-	1
His	0.043	1.6	2	1	1	2
Arg	0.028	1.0	1	-	1	1
Asp	0.078	2.8	3	1	2	3
Thr	0.051	1.8	2	2	-	2
Ser	0.033	1.2	1	1	-	1
Glu	0.085	3.0	3	1	1	2

Continued

Amino-acid	$AE\beta^{N(Baltimore)}$			$AE\beta^{A}$ (ref. 7)		
	$\beta^{N(Baltimore)}$ Tp10-11			β^{A}Tp10	β^{A}Tp11	β^{A}Tp10+β^{A}Tp11
	Found (μmoles)	Residues	Nearest whole residue	Expected	Expected	Expected
Pro	0.026	0.9	1	-	1	1
Gly	0.026	0.9	1	1	-	1
Ala	0.030	1.1	1	1	-	1
Val	0.028	1.0	1	-	1	1
AE-Cys	0.032	1.1	1	1	-	1
Met	-	-	-	-	-	-
Lieu	-	-	-	-	-	-
Leu	0.076	2.7	3	2	1	3
Tyr	-	-	-	-	-	-
Phe	0.047	1.7	2	1	1	2
Tryp	-	-	-	-	-	-

Overall recovery of $AE\beta^{N(Baltimore)}$ Tp10-11 was 24 percent of amount originally applied to the fingerprint.

In accordance with the recommended nomenclature[10], haemoglobin N (Baltimore) is designated as $\alpha_2\beta_2^{95Glu}$.

The procedure outlined in this article has the following advantages over those previously described:

(1) The chromatographic system enables globin from a heterozygous charged mutant to be resolved quantitatively into all its component chains, thus simplifying subsequent chemical investigations. In addition, the high resolution achieved during chromatography eliminates the need for hybridization experiments to determine in which chain an amino-acid substitution is located. (It should be mentioned that the *p*H of the chromatographic system is not critical and can be varied from at least *p*H 6.5 to 7.2, the actual choice depending largely on the nature of the mutant globin to be fractionated and the degree of resolution required. As an example of this flexibility, Fig. 4 shows a separation of 11 mg of sickletrait globin into β^A, β^S and α components at *p*H 7.2.)

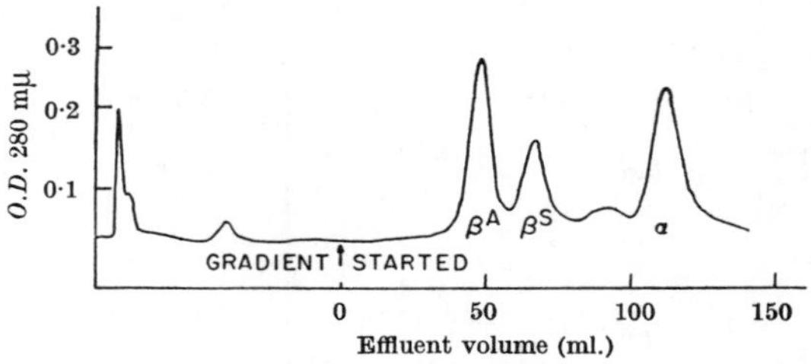

Fig. 4. Chromatography at *p*H 7.2 of globin from haemoglobin S heterozygote

(2) All the tryptic peptides of the amino-ethylated α and β chains can be resolved by fingerprinting.

续表

氨基酸	AEβN(巴尔的摩)			AEβA（参考文献 7）		
	βN(巴尔的摩) Tp10-11			βATp10	βATp11	βATp10 + βATp11
	结果（微摩尔）	残基	最接近的残基整数	预期	预期	预期
Pro	0.026	0.9	1	-	1	1
Gly	0.026	0.9	1	1	-	1
Ala	0.030	1.1	1	1	-	1
Val	0.028	1.0	1	-	1	1
AE-Cys	0.032	1.1	1	1	-	1
Met	-	-	-	-	-	-
Lieu	-	-	-	-	-	-
Leu	0.076	2.7	3	2	1	3
Tyr	-	-	-	-	-	-
Phe	0.047	1.7	2	1	1	2
Tryp	-	-	-	-	-	-

全部回收的AEβN(巴尔的摩) Tp10-11占最初应用于指纹图谱量的24%。

根据有人提议的命名法[10]，血红蛋白 N（巴尔的摩）被确定为 $\alpha_2\beta_2^{95Glu}$。

本文中描述的流程与之前提到的那些相比具有以下优点：

（1）色谱系统能定量地分离来自杂合带电突变体的珠蛋白的所有肽链组分，因而简化了后续的化学研究。另外，色谱实现的高分辨率使通过杂交实验检测氨基酸替换位于哪条链上变得不必要。（值得一提的是色谱系统的 pH 不是至关重要的，至少可以在 pH 6.5~7.2 之间变化，实际选择的 pH 值主要取决于需要分离的突变珠蛋白的性质和需要的分辨率。作为实际应用的一个例子，图 4 显示了在 pH 7.2 的条件下将 11 毫克镰刀型珠蛋白分离为 β^A、β^S 和 α 三个组分的结果。）

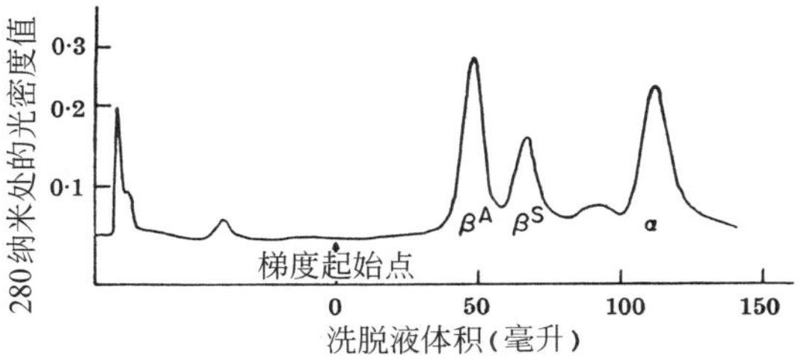

图 4. 血红蛋白 S 杂合体的珠蛋白在 pH 7.2 的条件下的色谱图

（2）可以通过指纹图谱分离氨乙基化的 α 链和 β 链的所有胰蛋白酶分解形成的片段。

(3) Quantitative amino-acid analysis of theses peptides can be determined on samples obtained by elution from a ninhydrin-stained fingerprint of as little as 2 mg of digested chain.

One of us (J. B. C.) thanks the Wellcome Foundation for a travel grant. This work was supported by U.S. National Institutes of Health grant *AM*-06006-03, U.S. National Science Foundation grant *CB*-2630, a continuation of *G*-24214, and U.S. Public Health Service grants *HE*-02799 and *TI-AM*-5260.

(**207**, 945-947; 1965)

J. B. Clegg and M. A. Naughton: Department of Biophysics.

D. J. Weatherall: Department of Medicine, Johns Hopkins University School of Medicine, Baltimore 5, Maryland.

References:

1. Raftery, M. A., and Cole, R. D., *Biochem. Biophys. Res. Comm.*, **10**, 467 (1963).
2. Jones, R. T., *Cold Spring Harbour Symp.*, **29**, 297 (1964).
3. Weatherall, D. J., *Bull. Johns Hopkins Hosp.*, **114**, 1 (1964).
4. Ager, J. A. M., and Lekmann, H., *Brit. Med. J.*, i, 929 (1958).
5. Katchalski, E., Benjamin, G. S., and Gross, V., *J. Amer. Chem. Soc.*, **79**, 4096 (1957).
6. Hill, R. L., Swenson, R. T., and Schwartz, H. C., *Blood*, **19**, 573 (1962).
7. Hill, R. J., Konigsberg, W., Guidotti, G., and Craig, L. C., *J. Biol, Chem.*, **237**, 1549 (1962).
8. Sanger, F., and Tuppy, H., *Biochem. J.*, **49**, 463 (1951).
9. Reider, R., and Naughton, M. A., *Bull. Johns Hopkins Hosp.*, **116**, 17 (1965).
10. "Recommendations of the International Society of Haematology on the Nomenclature of Abnormal Haemoglobins" (*Brit. J. Haemat.*, **11**, 121; 1965).

（3）仅需用从低至2毫克的酶解肽链的茚三酮染色指纹图谱洗脱获得的样本，便可对这些多肽进行定量的氨基酸分析。

我们中的一位研究者（克莱格）对威康基金会的旅费补助表示感谢。本研究由美国国立卫生研究院（基金 *AM*-06006-03）、美国国家科学基金会（基金 *CB*-2630 以及后续的 *G*-24214）和美国公共卫生署（基金 *HE*-02799 和 *TI-AM*-5260）资助。

（郑建全 翻译；刘京国 审稿）

The Bath-Tub Vortex in the Southern Hemisphere

L. M. Trefethen *et al.*

Editor's Note

Because of the rotation of the Earth (and the Coriolis forces thereby established), rotating structures are differently affected in the Northern and Southern Hemispheres. The most familiar example is that cyclones rotate anti-clockwise in the Northern Hemisphere and clockwise in the Southern Hemisphere. In the same spirit, it has been speculated that the familiar case of water emptying at the exit of a bath-tub would move counter-clockwise in the Northern Hemisphere and oppositely in the Southern Hemisphere. This paper apparently confirms that prediction. In practice, the direction of rotation of the water may be affected by irregularities in the exit hole and may not correspond with the prediction.

IT has long been thought that water draining from a tank would rotate counter-clockwise in the northern hemisphere and clockwise in the southern hemisphere, provided other influences were kept small compared with the influence of the rotation of the Earth. This idea has only recently been tested, by Shapiro in Watertown, Massachusetts, as part of a film on vorticity[2-4], and later by Binnie in Cambridge, England[1]. Shapiro and Binnie both acquired confidence, after surmounting difficulties in their early experiments, that the counter-clockwise rotations observed in their later experiments were due to the rotation of the Earth.

The experiment has now been performed in Sydney, Australia. For this we should like to express appreciation for assistance from the University of Sydney, Tufts University, and the U.S. National Science Foundation.

The apparatus was modelled on Shapiro's. It was a tank, 6 ft. in diameter and 9 in. high, with a central drain pipe 0.375 in. in diameter connected to a draining hose. The tank differed from Shapiro's in ways suggested by early difficulties Shapiro and Binnie experienced. It was made of ply-wood instead of metal, to reduce thermal convection. The drain pipe projected up 1 in. from the bottom, and was tapered to a sharp-edged opening; and the tank was located in a small, cement-walled basement room which had an overhead louvre but no windows, and in which both room temperature and inlet-water temperature remained within a degree of 20°C during the tests. As in Shapiro's experiments, the tank was filled by hose to a depth of about 6 in. above the orifice. The hose was directed so as to leave water swirling counter-clockwise in the tank.

Initially, the apparatus did not work as expected. In the first test, after a 60-h settling period, dust particles on the water surface showed no discernible rotation at any time

南半球的浴盆涡旋

特雷费森等

编者按

由于地球的自转（以及由此形成的科里奥利力），在地球的南北半球，物体旋转的方式会受到不同的影响。最常见的例子是，气旋在北半球为逆时针方向旋转，而在南半球则是顺时针方向。同样的道理，有人推测在北半球，浴盆排水口处的水流是逆时针运动的，而在南半球则方向相反。本文似乎证实了这种预测。实际上，由于排水口不规则性的影响，水流的旋转方向可能与预期的并不一致。

长期以来，人们一直认为，假设与地球自转的影响相比，其他因素的影响都微乎其微的话，那么从水箱内排出的水在北半球将呈逆时针旋转，而在南半球则顺时针旋转。最近，作为一个关于涡度的影片的一部分，美国马萨诸塞州沃特顿的谢皮罗对此观点[2-4]进行了检验。随后，英国剑桥的比尼也进行了实验[1]。在克服了早期实验的困难后，谢皮罗和比尼都确信，他们在后期实验中观测到的逆时针旋转是由地球的自转引起的。

现在，在澳大利亚的悉尼也已完成这项实验。为此，我们对悉尼大学、塔夫斯大学和美国国家科学基金会的协助表示感谢。

实验仪器以谢皮罗的仪器为模板。装置是一个直径为 6 英尺、高 9 英寸的圆形水箱，中心排水管的直径为 0.375 英寸，与排水软管相连。受谢皮罗和比尼早期实验所遇到的困难的启发，水箱的设置与谢皮罗的实验有所不同：为了减小热对流，水箱是用胶合板制成的，而非金属。排水管离底部 1 英寸，且呈锥形渐变为一个边缘尖锐的开口；水箱置于一间水泥构筑的小地下室内，天花板上设有散热孔，但是没有窗户，实验期间室内温度和注入的水温均保持在 20℃左右。与谢皮罗的实验相同，用软管向水箱注水，注水深度为高于排水孔约 6 英寸的位置。软管是定向的，以使水的旋涡在水箱内为逆时针方向。

最初，这种装置并没有按照预期的那样工作。首次实验中，经过了 60 个小时的静置时间后，在 80 分钟的排水期间内，水表面的尘粒没有呈现任何可辨别的旋转。

during an 80-min draining period. This apparently meant that the water was moving to the centre so slowly that the viscous damping effect of the bottom was cancelling the water's angular momentum to the point where no angular momentum was perceptible in the draining fluid. To speed draining, the tank was raised to 30 in. above the floor. From then on, with the increased drop of the draining hose, drainage took about 22 min, and some form of rotation was always observed above the orifice.

Clockwise rotation was observed in all five of the later tests that had settling times of 18 h or more. During the first 10 or 12 min of drainage, no rotation was apparent. Rotation then developed as drainage progressed. In three of these tests a float 0.625 in. in diameter, a slice from a wine cork, was used to indicate rotation. It reached speeds of about one revolution in 8 sec for the runs with settling times of 18 and 20 h, and one revolution in 3 sec in the one run with a settling time of 70 h. One revolution in 3 sec is what one would expect of a ring of particles rotating with the surface of the Earth at the latitude of Sydney, and then brought in from a diameter of 6 ft. to a diameter of 0.375 in., provided the ring conserves its angular momentum.

To provide a comparison with Shapiro's work, a floating cross made of two matchstick segments 1 in. long was alternated in one test with the cork float. Both cross and float rotated at approximately the same speed. Shapiro used a comparable cross. He reported[3] and filmed[4] rotation speeds of one revolution in about 3-4 sec. His drainage time was also comparable, that is, 20-24 min, and he also reports rotation only after about 10-12 min of drainage.

One early test did not fit the pattern of settling-time influence that emerged later from the tests. The tank, after a settling time of only 4 h 40 min, performed as if it had had 20 h of settling time. Near the end of the drainage period, a 0.5-in. patch of dust particles that had accumulated at the centre was rotating one revolution in 8 sec, clockwise. This was the only test in which the tank had not been mostly or wholly covered during the settling period. It was an unusually windy day outside, and just before drainage dust specks on different areas of the water surface were moving in several directions at large speeds of about 1 cm/min. The test may therefore have been significantly influenced by air currents. For subsequent tests, the louvre in the ceiling, which had been blocked off, though not completely, by ply-wood sheets, was additionally covered outside with "Pliofilm". The door was kept closed, except briefly to allow entry, and the tank was kept mostly covered by two ply-wood sheets resting on two angle irons placed diametrically across the tank. The angle irons were usually spaced about 3 in. apart, so that surface motions could be observed between them, and the direction of these supporting beams in relation to the room was varied from test to test in an attempt to detect any remaining influence of air currents. Air currents did not appear to be a significant influence in the later tests, but it is our opinion that they are likely to have been the largest of the disturbing influences.

In one early test, after a settling period of only 13 h, the no-rotation period was followed by a period of counter-clockwise rotation, which changed to clockwise near the end of

这显然意味着水移动到水箱中心时的速度太慢，以致底部的黏滞阻尼效应抵消了水的角动量，从而在排放的水流中观测不到明显的角动量。为了使排放速度加快，将水箱上升到离地面 30 英寸的位置。此后，随着软管排水量的增加，排放进行了大约 22 分钟，在孔口上方始终能观测到某种形式的旋转。

在随后的五次实验中，静置时间均在 18 小时以上，均观测到了顺时针旋转。在排水的最初 10 到 12 分钟内，没有明显的旋转。然后，随着排水的进行开始产生旋转。在其中的三次实验中，一片漂浮着的直径为 0.625 英寸的紫红色软木被用来指示旋转。经过 18 小时和 20 小时的静置时间后，旋转达到了约 8 秒 / 圈的速度，在一次 70 小时的静置时间后则达到 3 秒 / 圈的速度。我们可以推测，3 秒 / 圈的速度就是在悉尼所处纬度的地球表面上，一个旋转粒子环由 6 英尺直径被带入 0.375 英寸的直径时，假设该环仍要保持它的角动量所形成的速度。

为了与谢皮罗的研究结果进行比较，在一次实验中，一个用两段 1 英寸长的火柴棍做的十字形浮标和一个软木浮标被交替用来进行实验。结果显示，这两种浮标以大致相同的速度进行旋转。谢皮罗使用了一个类似的十字形浮标，他报道[3]并拍摄了[4]约 3 秒 / 圈 ~4 秒 / 圈的旋转速度。他的排水时间也是类似的，即 20 分钟 ~24 分钟，此外他还报道了排水约 10~12 分钟后的旋转情况。

在一次早期的实验中，静置时间对实验结果产生影响的模式与后来几次实验中出现的情况并不相同。水箱在经历了仅 4 小时 40 分钟的静置时间后的实验结果，与静置时间为 20 小时的实验结果相同。在排水快要结束时，水箱中心积累的一个 0.5 英寸大小的尘埃斑块沿顺时针方向以 8 秒 / 圈的速度旋转。这是仅有的一次水箱在静置时间内没有被大面积或全部覆盖的实验。进行这次实验时，室外是一个不寻常的大风天气。就在排水前，水表面上不同区域的尘粒正在不同方向上以约 1 厘米 / 分钟的速度作高速运动，因此这项实验受到了气流的严重影响。尽管天花板上的散热孔已经被胶合板塞住，但是不太完全，因此在接下来的各次实验中，又用“胶膜”将散热孔覆盖了一遍。除了短时间的进入外，门也保持关闭，水箱用两层胶合板覆盖，胶合板放在直接跨过水箱的角铁上。角铁间距通常为 3 英寸，因此可以在它们之间观测水的表面运动。在不同的实验中，房间支柱的方向也各不相同，目的是检测气流所带来的任何影响。在后面的实验中，气流并没有对实验结果造成严重影响，但我们认为，它们很可能已经是最大的扰动因素了。

在早期的一次实验中，仅经过 13 小时的静置后，排出的水流先经过一段没有旋转的时间，紧接着是逆时针旋转，而在排水即将结束时又变为顺时针旋转（在这

the draining period. (In this particular test it is not known how the tank had been filled.) Shapiro reports one similar test, experienced after a settling time of 4-5 h, attributed to undamped initial angular velocity residing in the upper water, while the water nearer the bottom was rotating in the direction of the Earth's rotation. In another of our tests, with a deliberately short settling time of 3 h, water drained out counter-clockwise during all but an initial 2 min of no rotation. Shapiro reports a similar result. In fact, it would seem that the results of these experiments at Sydney are quite similar to those obtained by Shapiro in the northern hemisphere, with one exception. After suitable settling periods, Shapiro observed counter-clockwise rotation. We, in Australia, observed the opposite.

These tests posed for us an unusual problem in experimental work. Normally, one does experiments in which there is some uncertainty in the expected outcome. In these experiments, however, our confidence in the idea that the Earth rotates, and in the applicability of conservation of angular momentum to masses of fluid, was probably so strong that experimental denial would have been almost inadmissible. We should have gone to unusual lengths to get the apparatus to work as expected. Realizing this, we found ourselves reluctant to accept as conclusive the results we were getting, results which apparently confirmed our ideas. One can never prove, for example, that it was not some small air current which persistently maintained a circulation that gave the results we observed, and that a quantitatively comparable, but oppositely directed, air current caused Shapiro's results, There is, in principle, an infinite number of hypotheses that can explain any set of observations. This difficulty in validation of scientific theories is not a new one and, in this instance, as in all instances, it cannot be proved that any one hypothesis is correct. Nevertheless, we have acquired confidence in the hypothesis that carefully performed experiments on liquid drainage from a tank will show clockwise rotation, if done in the southern hemisphere.

(**207**, 1084-1085; 1965)

Lloyd M. Trefethen, R. W. Bilger, P. T. Fink, R. E. Luxton and R. I. Tanner: University of Sydney, New South Wales, Australia.

References:

1. Binnie, A. M., *J. Mech. Eng. Sci.*, **6**, 256 (1964).
2. Shapiro, A. H., Film, *Vorticity* (Educational Services Inc., Watertown, Mass., 1961).
3. Shapiro, A. H., *Nature*, **196**, 1080 (1962).
4. Shapiro, A. H., Four-min film loop No. *FM*-15, *The Bathtub Vortex* (Educational Services Inc., Watertown, Mass., 1963).

次特殊的实验中，水箱充满的方式未知）。谢皮罗报道了一个类似的实验，是经过4小时~5小时的静置后进行的，其原因被解释为无阻尼的初始角速度保留在水的上部，而接近底部的水则按地球的自转方向旋转。在我们的一次实验中，特地做了静置时间仅为3小时的实验，排水时水流除最初的2分钟没有旋转，此后都以逆时针旋转排出，谢皮罗也报道了一个类似的结果。实际上，除了一个例外，在悉尼的实验结果完全类似于谢皮罗在北半球得到的结果。经过适当的静置时间后，谢皮罗观测到逆时针旋转，我们在澳大利亚则得到了相反的结果。

这些测试为我们的实验工作提出了一个不同寻常的问题。通常，在做实验时，预期的结果中会存在某些不确定性。然而在这些实验中，我们过于认同地球旋转的观点及流体角动量守恒的适用性，以致几乎不可能接受否定的实验结果。我们本应该用不同长度的实验使装置如预期的工作。意识到这一点，我们发现自己很难对实验所得到的，看起来支持我们观点的结果下定论。例如，我们永远不能证明，在我们的实验中，并不是一些一贯存在的小气流的作用使得我们看到漩涡，而与此同时，也存在数量相似但方向相反的气流导致了谢皮罗的结果。原则上讲，任何一组观测都可以用无数个假设来解释。这种在证实科学理论时所遇到的困难并不是一个新问题。与所有的例子相同，在这次实验中，并不能证明任何一个假设是正确的。然而我们已经确信一个假设，那就是，如果在南半球仔细完成实验，水箱内液体排放时将显示顺时针旋转。

（沈乃澂 翻译；高守亭 审稿）

The Temperature Scale

Editor's Note

Mechanical engineer John Georgian had recently proposed a new temperature scale based on the MKS (meter-kilogram-second) system of units. Its advantages, he had suggested, lay in eliminating the various gas constants as conversion factors, and in fitting temperature naturally into the MKS system. In the first paper here, R. A. Laws objects to certain points in Georgian's definitions. In the new system, he suggests, quantities such as specific heats or enthalpies would be closely tied to the properties of water, which is unsatisfactory. Laws also notes that he had earlier made a similar proposal to eliminate conversion factors from the basic equations by re-scaling the number of temperature degrees between freezing and boiling points.

In the second paper, Georgian responds to Laws' criticisms. He points out that several well-known scientists, including Richard Tolman and George Porter, had made various suggestions along these lines. Moreover, he says Laws is wholly incorrect to say that certain quantities in Georgian's system would be tied to the properties of water. Rather, he says, they can rely on the recently adopted standard of mass, based on a platinum-iridium cylinder kept in France. His system naturally eliminates the various gas constants from the basic equations. Georgian's system today remains in wide use, especially in engineering.

MOST of the points raised by Prof. J. C. Georgian on the subject of the temperature scale[1] are discussed in Chapter 23 of *A Textbook of Heat* by Allen and Maxwell (1948). The authors refer to a paper by Lewis and Adams[2] making the very point about the dimensions of temperature, specific heat and enthalpy made by Prof. Georgian and proposing a temperature scale that would make $PV = n\theta$, where n = Avogadro's number. They also discuss a proposal by Planck which seems to have been essentially that now made by Prof. Georgian.

There are, however, certain objections to these proposals. Unlike, for example, the Reynolds number, specific heat and enthalpy are dimensionless only so long as we bear in mind their relationship to water, for they rely for the invariance of their nominal numerical values on the retention of liquid water as the nominal datum. A change of a temperature scale from Kelvin to Georgian would therefore result merely in a change of the value of J that had to be used in equations relating temperature and heat, unless we were prepared to re-calculate all our specific heat in terms of the relationship of the material to a perfect gas rather than to water. Furthermore, the unit of energy is nominally based on the properties of water (via the definition of the unit of mass), and to proceed to define temperature by invoking another substance altogether (perfect gas) is, I submit, unnecessary and undesirable.

温标

编者按

最近，机械工程师约翰·杰奥尔吉安根据MKS（米·千克·秒）单位制得出了一套新温标。他认为这套温标的优势在于可以消除作为换算因子的各种不同的气体常数，并且将温度自然地适用于MKS单位制。在本文的第一篇文章中，劳斯反对杰奥尔吉安定义中的部分论点。他指出，在这套新的系统中，诸如对比热或者焓的量化是与水的性质紧密联系在一起的，这并不能令人满意。劳斯也提到，在此之前他曾提出过一个类似的提议，即通过重新标定冰点和沸点之间的温度数来消除基本方程式中的换算因子。

在第二篇文章中，杰奥尔吉安针对劳斯的批评做出了回复。他指出，包括理查德·托尔曼和乔治·波特在内的几位著名科学家都在这些问题上给出了各种各样的建议。此外，他提到，劳斯认为的杰奥尔吉安系统中有些量与水的性质紧密联系是完全错误的。正好相反，他说这些量有赖于最近被接受的质量标准，这一标准基于一个存放在法国的铂–铱合金圆柱体。他的系统能够从基本方程式中自然地消除各种气体常数。现在，杰奥尔吉安系统仍然被广泛使用，尤其在工程领域。

艾伦和麦克斯韦在1948年主编的《热学教程》第23章中讨论了由杰奥尔吉安教授对温标[1]这一论题提出的大部分论点。作者们参考了刘易斯和亚当斯[2]的一篇论文，其内容着重强调了杰奥尔吉安教授提出的温度量纲、比热和焓，同时还提出了一套能使 $PV = n\theta$ 成立的温标，式中 n 是阿伏伽德罗常数。他们还讨论了普朗克提出的十分重要的建议，实质上就是现在杰奥尔吉安教授提出的理论。

然而，我对这些建议有一些异议。例如，与雷诺数不同，比热和焓是无量纲量，因此，我们只需要关注这些量与水的关系，因为作为名义基准，它们可依靠液体水的阻滞保持它们的名义数值不变。除非我们准备依据材料与理想气体而不是与水的关系来重新计算我们的比热，否则从开尔文温标到杰奥尔吉安温标的变化将只是引起 J 值的变化，其中 J 是在温度与热相关的方程式中必须使用的值。此外，能量的单位名义上是基于水的性质（通过质量单位的定义），并引用另一种物质（理想气体）一起来定义温度，而我认为这是不必要的，并且是多此一举。

I have already proposed[3] that the calorie and the factor J could be eliminated simply from temperature equations by the replacement of the Kelvin scale by one having $100 \times J$ degrees between the ice point and the steam point. I suggested[3] that such a degree should be called the degree Joule. I think that the adoption of such a scale would be easier and more satisfactory than would the adoption of Prof. Georgian's scale, as it would not require any properties to be re-calculated, and I think it would commend itself more readily to practical users.

R. A. Laws

(**207**, 1285; 1965)

* * *

I wish to thank Mr. Laws for refs. 2 and 3.

I was aware of ref. 2 and, in addition, Tolman[4] has an interesting discussion of the dimensions of temperature. Only Tolman wishes to give temperature the units of ML^2/T^2, that is, allow the molecular mass number (molecular weight) to take on the dimension of mass. However, Porter[5] in his book *Method of Dimensions* explains clearly that the dimension of temperature is indeed L^2/T^2.

I cannot accept the objection by Mr. Laws to my temperature scale, as in using the MKS system any relationship to water is now irrelevant, because the kilogram mass is defined as a platinum-iridium cylinder deposited at the International Bureau of Weights and Measurements at Sèvres, France. The unit of energy is not based on the properties of water but is defined as one Newton-meter equals one Joule. Hence, all forms of energy will have the same unit, be it heat, mechanical, electrical, chemical, or atomic energy.

The purpose of my temperature scale is to base the scale on the MKS system and, thereby, eliminate the conversion factor R, in the same manner as the conversion factors J and g_c have been eliminated in the MKS system.

The proposal of Mr. Laws of adopting a temperature scale in order to preserve the tabulated numbers of c_p is unnecessary as these values can be readily converted to the MKS system from presently tabulated values in absolute molal units. For example, the National Bureau of Standards has tabulated thermal properties of gases in its *Circular* 564 (ref. 6) in dimensionless molal values. Using the MKS temperature scale, it can easily be seen that the ideal gas relation between specific heat at constant pressure and volume becomes:

$$c_p - c_v = \frac{1}{M} \tag{1}$$

我曾提出[3]，通过利用一种介于冰点和沸点间且具有 $100 \times J$ 度的温标来代替开尔文温标，就能够轻松地将卡路里和因子J从温度方程式中消除。我认为[3]这里的度应被命名为“焦耳度”。我认为接受这种温标比接受杰奥尔吉安教授的温标更加容易和令人满意，因为此温标不需要进行任何性质的重新计算并且更加适合于实际用户。

劳斯

* * *

我感谢劳斯先生提供参考文献 2 和参考文献 3。

我知道参考文献 2，并且除此之外，托尔曼[4]对于讨论温度的量纲有很大的兴趣。只不过托尔曼希望用 ML^2/T^2 作为温度的单位，也就是说，允许将分子质量数（分子量）作为质量的量纲。然而，波特[5]在他的《量纲的方法》一书中清晰地解释了温度的量纲实际上是 L^2/T^2。

我不能接受劳斯先生对我的温标理论所提出的异议，当使用 MKS 单位制时，任何物理量与水的关系此时都不相关，因为千克质量是通过采用位于法国塞夫尔的国际计量局的铂–铱合金圆柱体来定义的。能量单位也不是基于水的性质，而是定义为：1 牛顿 · 米等于 1 焦耳。因此，无论是热能、机械能、电能、化学能还是原子能，所有形式的能量都具有相同的单位。

我的温标理论的目的是将温标系统建立在 MKS 单位制上，由此将换算因子 R 消除，并以相同的方式将换算因子J以及 g_c 从 MKS 单位制中消除。

劳斯先生认为采用一套温标以保留恒压比热 c_p 的列表值的提议是没有必要的，因为这些列表数值能够被轻而易举地从现有的绝对摩尔单位转化到 MKS 单位制。例如，美国国家标准局在它的 564 号通报（参考文献 6）中，以无量纲摩尔值的形式列出了气体热性质的表。我们用 MKS 单位制温标可以很容易地看到，在恒压条件下理想气体的比热与体积之间的关系变为：

$$c_p - c_v = \frac{1}{M} \tag{1}$$

where the usual gas constant R is replaced by $1/M$. The specific heat at constant pressure then becomes:

$$c_p = \left(\frac{\gamma}{\gamma - 1}\right)\frac{1}{M} \tag{2}$$

and at constant volume:

$$c_v = \left(\frac{\gamma}{\gamma - 1}\right)\frac{1}{M} \tag{3}$$

The specific heats of gases can be readily determined by dividing the molal values by the molecular mass number M (molecular weight). I submit the following short table of specific heats at constant pressure for use with the MKS system of units and temperature scale.

Gas	Specific heat c_p at 1 atmosphere and 241.11×10^4 J/kmole temperature (290°K)
Air	0.1210
Argon	0.0627
Hydrogen	1.717
Nitrogen	0.1252
Oxygen	0.1105
Steam	0.2405(γ=1.3)
Carbon dioxide	0.1014
Carbon monoxide	0.1253

If other properties of fluids are required it is possible to re-calculate the properties of fluids very rapidly with the digital computer by substituting the proper coefficients in the appropriate equations.

I have, since writing the original proposal[1], had a series of thermometers manufactured using Joules per kilomole as a scale; and I am now using them in the laboratory and requiring students to become familiar with them. There was only a nominal surcharge for making these thermometers, and with wide adoption of the scale the price of the thermometers would be the same as present centigrade or Fahrenheit thermometers.

John C. Georgian

(**207**, 1285-1286; 1965)

R. A. Laws: 39 Park Road, Watford, Hertfordshire.

J. C. Georgian: Washington University, Saint Louis, Missouri.

式中，通常的气体常数 R 被 $1/M$ 代替。恒压条件下的比热则变为：

$$c_p = \left(\frac{\gamma}{\gamma - 1}\right)\frac{1}{M} \tag{2}$$

并且在恒定体积下：

$$c_v = \left(\frac{\gamma}{\gamma - 1}\right)\frac{1}{M} \tag{3}$$

气体的比热可以很容易地用摩尔值除以分子质量数 M（分子量）来确定。下表中我简短列出了采用 MKS 单位制和温标时，恒压条件下的气体比热。

气体	在一个大气压和 241.11×10^4 焦耳 / 千摩尔温度（290K）下的比热 c_p
空气	0.1210
氩	0.0627
氢	1.717
氮	0.1252
氧	0.1105
蒸汽	0.2405 (γ=1.3)
二氧化碳	0.1014
一氧化碳	0.1253

如果需要液体的其他性质，通过在适当的方程中代入正确的系数，利用数字计算机可以迅速地重新计算出液体的性质。

自从写了第一篇文章 [1] 以来，我已有了一系列以焦耳每千摩尔为标度的温度计；我现在在实验室使用这些温度计，并要求学生们熟悉它们。制造这些温度计只需要很少的附加费，随着这种标度被人们广泛地接受，这种温度计的价格将与目前的摄氏或华氏温度计的价格相同。

约翰·杰奥尔吉安

（沈乃澂 翻译；赵见高 审稿）

References:

1. *Nature,* **201**, 695 (1964).
2. *Phys. Rev.*, **3**, 92 (1914).
3. *New Scientist,* No. 269, 100; No. 277, 585; No. 286, 309 (1962).
4. *Phys. Rev.*, **4**, 244 (1914).
5. Porter, A. W., *The Method of Dimensions,* 50, 62 (Methuen and Co., London, 1933).
6. Hilsenrath, J., *et al., Tables of the Thermal Properties of Gases,* National Bureau of Standards Circ. 564 (United States Government Printing Office, Washington, D. C., 1955).

A Biological Retrospect*

P. Medawar

Editor's Note

Peter Medawar had already won a Nobel Prize for his work on the limits to the compatibility of tissues taken from different individuals when he delivered this address on the state of biological research to the Zoological Section of the British Association for the Advancement of Science. The address deals only peripherally with molecular genetics, which had by 1965 transformed the pattern of biological research in Britain. Medawar suffered a severe stroke in 1969 when he was 54. Although he was physically handicapped, he remained mentally active until he died in 1987.

THE title of my presidential address, you will have discerned, is "A Biological Retrospect", and on the whole it has not been well received. "Why a biological *retrospect*?", I have been asked; would it not be more in keeping with the spirit of the occasion if I were to speak of the future of biology rather than of its past? It would indeed be, if only it were possible, but unfortunately it is not. What we want to know about the science of the future is the content and character of new scientific theories and ideas. Unfortunately, it is impossible to predict new ideas—the ideas people are going to have in ten years' or in ten minutes' time—and we are caught in a logical paradox the moment we try to do so. For to predict an idea is to have an idea, and if we have an idea it can no longer be the subject of a prediction. Try completing the sentence "I predict that at the next meeting of the British Association someone will propound the following new theory of the relationships of elementary particles, *namely* ...". If I complete the sentence, the theory will not be new next year; if I fail, then I am not making a prediction.

Most people feel more confident in denying that certain things will come to pass than in declaring that they can or will do so. Many a golden opportunity to remain silent has been squandered by anti-prophets who do not realize that the grounds for declaring something impossible or inconceivable may be undermined by new ideas which cannot be foreseen. Here is an instructive passage from the philosophic writings of a great British physiologist, J. S. Haldane (father of J. B. S.). It comes from *The Philosophy of a Biologist* of 1931, and its subject is the nature of memory in a very general sense that includes "genetic memory", for example, the faculty or endowment which ensures that a frog's egg develops into a frog and, indeed, into a particular kind of frog.

---

* Presidential address delivered to Section D (Zoology) on September 2, 1965, at the Cambridge Meeting of the British Association for the Advancement of Science.

生物学回顾*

梅达沃

编者按

彼得·梅达沃向英国科学促进会动物学分会发表该篇关于生物学研究状况的演讲之时，就已经因对不同个体之间组织不相容性的研究工作而获诺贝尔奖了。这篇演讲只是粗浅地论及了分子遗传学，自1965年以来分子遗传学已经改变了英国的生物学研究模式。1969年，54岁的梅达沃得了严重的中风，尽管他身体残疾了，但思维依然活跃，直至1987年去世。

大家可能已经注意到了，我演讲的题目是“生物学回顾”，但总的来说这个题目不是很受欢迎。有人曾问我，“为什么要**回顾**生物学？”讲生物学的发展趋势而不是生物学回顾，岂不是更适合这一场合？如果可以预测未来的话，这的确可以，但遗憾的是不能。对于未来的科学，我们想知道的是新科学理论和新科学思想的内容和特征。但遗憾的是，十年后甚至十分钟后人们的新思想都是无法预知的，人们一旦试图去预测未来，就会让自己陷入自相矛盾的境地。因为预测一种思想也就等于接受了这种思想，如果我们接受了这种思想，它就不再是预测的产物。让我们试图将下面这句话补充完整：“我推测，下一届英国科学促进会会议上将有人提出基本粒子间相互关系的新理论，**叫做**……”如果我现在将这句话补充完整的话，那么下次会议时这个理论就不是新理论，而如果我无法说出这是一个什么样的理论，那么我就没有完成这次预测。

与推测将来可能或肯定会发生某事相比，大部分人在否定将来会发生某些事上更有把握。伪预言者们已经浪费了无数次保持缄默的宝贵机会，他们没有意识到不可预见的新理论可能会推翻用于宣称某事不可能或难以想象的依据。在这个问题上，英国伟大的生理学家约翰·斯科特·霍尔丹（约翰·伯登·桑德森·霍尔丹之父）1931年在其哲学著作《生物学家的哲学》中的一段话非常具有启发性，这段话的主旨是在广义上说（包括“遗传记忆”在内）记忆的本质，例如先天因素，使一枚蛙卵发育成一只青蛙，确切地说是一只特定种类的青蛙。

* 本文系作者1965年9月2日在英国科学促进会剑桥会议上对D分部（动物学）发表的就职演说。

Haldane is very critical of the theories of memory propounded by Ewald Hering and Richard Semon, who "assume that memory in general is dependent on protoplasmic 'engrams', and that germ-cells are furnished with a system of engrams, functioning as guide-posts to all the normal stages of development". ("Engrams", I should explain, are more or less permanent physical memory traces or memory imprints that act as directive agencies in development[1].) "This theory", Haldane goes on to say, "has quite evidently all the defects of other attempts at mechanistic explanations of development. How such an amazingly complicated system of signposts could function by any physico-chemical process or reproduce itself indefinitely often is inconceivable[2]."

What Haldane found himself unable even to conceive is today a commonplace. Only twelve years after the publication of the passage I quote, Avery and his colleagues had determined the class of chemical compound to which genetic engrams belong. In the meantime our entire conception of "the gene" has undergone a revolution. Genes are not, as at one time or another people have thought them, samples or models; they are not enzymes or hormones or prosthetic groups or catalysts or, in the ordinary sense, agents of any kind. Genes are messages. I think Kalmus[3] was the first to use this form of words, but the idea that a chromosome is a molecular code script containing a specification of development is Schrödinger's[4].

My purpose in this address is to identify some of the great conceptual advances that have taken place during the past twenty-five or thirty years on four different planes of biological analysis. As I have pointed out elsewhere[5], working biologists tend nowadays to classify themselves less by "subjects" than by the analytical levels at which they work—a horizontal classification where the older was vertical. So we have molecular biologists, whose ambition is to interpret biological performances explicitly in terms of molecular structure; we have cellular biologists, biologists who work at the level of whole organisms (the domain of classical physiology), and biologists who study communities or societies of organisms. We can discern each of these four strata within each "subject" of the traditional, that is, the vertical, classification. There are molecular and cellular geneticists, geneticists in Mendel's sense, and population geneticists. So also in endocrinology or immunology: each is now studied at the molecular and cellular level as well as at the level of whole organisms. They abut into the population level, too: we study the effects of crowding and fighting on the adrenals and so indirectly on reproductive performance, and we study the epidemiological consequences of natural or artificial immunization and the evolutionary consequences of epidemics. I have noticed that a biologist's interests and understanding, and also, in a curious way, his loyalties, tend to spread horizontally, along strata; rather than up and down. Our instinct is to try to master what belongs to our chosen plane of analysis and to leave to others the research that belongs above that level or below. An ecologist in the modern style, a man working to understand the agencies that govern the structure of natural populations in space and time, needs much more than a knowledge of natural history and a map. He must have a good understanding of population genetics and population dynamics generally, and certainly of animal behaviour; more than that, he must grasp climatic physiology and have a feeling for whatever may concern him among

埃瓦尔德·赫林和理查德·西蒙"认为总体来说，记忆源于原生质的'印痕'，生殖细胞内存储着一个印痕系统，用以指挥细胞各个时期的正常发育"。（需要指出的是，"印痕"在一定程度上是指永恒的物理记忆痕迹或者用以指挥发育的记忆印记[1]。）霍尔丹对他们提出的记忆理论很不赞成，他接着说："该理论很明显具有其他发育机理假说的所有缺点。这个如此复杂的痕迹系统竟然能通过任何物理–化学过程起作用或者无限复制自我，这简直难以置信[2]。"

上述令霍尔丹难以相信的关于记忆痕迹的说法在今天已经是一个共识了。事实上，在我引用的这段文字发表仅 12 年后，埃弗里和他的同事们就确定了遗传痕迹物质所归属的化合物种类。同时，"基因"的整个概念也发生了一次变革。基因不是我们一度认为或其他人现在所认为的某种样本或者模型，也不再是普通意义上的酶、激素、辅基或者催化剂之类的成分。基因是信息。我认为这个概念是由卡尔马斯[3]首次提出的，而关于染色体是包含发育信息的分子编码图的说法则是由薛定谔[4]首次提出的。

我这次演讲的目的是阐述在过去 25 年 ~30 年内，生物学研究四个不同水平内所发生的一些重要概念演变。就像我在其他地方[5]指出过的，如今生物学研究人员趋向于根据分析水平的不同，而不是根据"学科"来自我分类，这是一种水平分类法，传统的则是垂直分类。按照这种分类，生物学家被划分成了四类，产生了致力于从分子结构的角度来解释生物学现象的分子生物学家，细胞生物学家，以整个生物体（传统生理学领域）为研究对象的生物学家以及以群体或生物体群落为研究对象的生物学家。我们可以在传统的，即垂直分类的各个"学科"中识别这 4 个层次，例如遗传家包括分子遗传学家、细胞遗传学家、孟德尔意义上的遗传学家以及种群遗传学家。这在内分泌学或免疫学中也同样如此：现在这些学科既在分子和细胞水平上研究，又在整个生物体水平上研究。此外，还有在群体水平上研究。我们研究集群行为和打斗行为对肾上腺素分泌的影响，以及随后对生殖行为的间接影响；我们研究自然免疫或人工免疫的流行病学结果以及流行病的进化结果。我注意到这样一个现象，在求知方面而言，生物学家对一门学科的兴趣和思维倾向往往在同一学科的不同水平之间横向发展，而不会在不同学科之间纵向移动。我们凭直觉试着去区分哪些是属于我们研究领域的内容，并把这个研究领域之外的那些内容留给其他研究者研究。一名研究生物种群时空结构的现代生态学家所应当掌握的不只是博物学知识和一张地图而已，他还应该精通种群遗传学、种群动态学、动物行为学，更为重要的是，他应该掌握气候生理学以及其他许许多多的相关生物学知识（包括我所提

the other conventional disciplines in biology (I have already mentioned immunology and endocrinology). There is no compelling reason why he should be able to talk with relaxed fluency about messenger-RNA, and it is not essential that he should ever have heard of it—though an unreasonable feeling that he "ought" to know something about it is more likely to be found in a good ecologist than in an indifferent one.

I shall now take one example from each of these four planes of biological analysis and try to show how our ideas have changed since the last Cambridge meeting of the British Association in 1938—a period that corresponds roughly with my own professional lifetime.

Population Genetics and Evolution Theory

Biologists of my generation were still brought up in what I call the "dynastic" concept of evolution. The course of evolution was unfolded to us in the form of pedigrees or family trees, and we used the old language of universals in speaking of the evolution of *the* dogfish, *the* horse, *the* elephant and, needless to say, of Man.

The dynastic conception coloured our thoughts long after the revival of Darwinism had made it altogether inappropriate. By the "revival of Darwinism" I mean the reformulation of Darwinism in the language of Mendelian genetics—the work, as we all so very well know, of Fisher, J. B. S. Haldane, Wright, Norton and, in a rather qualified sense, of Lotka and Volterra. The subject of evolutionary change, we now learned, was a population, not a lineage or pedigree: evolution was a systematic secular change in the genetical structure of a population, and natural selection was overwhelmingly its most important agent. But to those brought up in the dynastic style of thinking about evolution it seemed only natural to suppose that the outcome of an evolutionary episode was the devising of a new genotype—of that new genetical formula which conferred the greatest degree of adaptedness in the prevailing circumstances. This improved genetic formula, a new solution of the problem of remaining alive in a hostile environment, would be shared by the great majority of the members of the population, and would be stable except in so far as it might be modified by further evolution. The members of the population were predominantly uniform and homozygous in genetic makeup, and, to whatever degree they were so, would necessarily breed true. Genetic diversity was maintained by an undercurrent of mutation, but most mutants upset the hard-won formula for adaptedness and natural selection forced them into recessive expression, where they could do little harm. When evolution was not in progress natural selection made on the whole for uniformity. Polymorphism, the occurrence of a stable pattern of genetic inequality, was recognized as an interesting but somewhat unusual phenomenon, each example of which required a special explanation, that is, an explanation peculiar to itself.

These ideas have now been superseded, mainly through the empirical discovery that natural populations are highly diverse. Chemical polymorphism (allotypy[6]) is found wherever it is looked for intently enough by methods competent to reveal it. The molecular

到过的免疫学和内分泌学）。但是，我们不必强求他能够流利地阐述信使 RNA 的相关知识，甚至于他有没有听说过信使 RNA 都并不重要——尽管我们可能会不合理地将“应该”知道某些知识作为区分生态学家优劣的指标。

自 1938 年英国科学促进会剑桥会议召开以来（这一时期与我的研究生涯基本一致），生物学的理论发生了很大变化，下面，我将在四个生物学研究水平内各举一个例子来说明这种巨大变化。

种群遗传学和进化理论

我同时代的生物学家还是在进化的“王朝”概念下成长的。进化理论是通过家系或家谱的形式展开的，我们用传统的民间用语来描述角鲨、马、大象的进化，不用说，还有我们人类的进化。

在达尔文主义复兴后的很长一段时间内，王朝这一概念丰富了我们的思想，但它已经完全不合适了。我所说的“达尔文主义复兴”是指通过孟德尔遗传学的方式再现达尔文主义，如我们非常熟知的费希尔、霍尔丹、赖特、诺顿所做的工作以及一定程度上洛特卡和沃尔泰拉所做的工作。现在我们知道进化是发生在种群水平上的，而不是沿着世系或家系发生的：进化是一个种群在遗传结构上所发生的长期而系统的变化，其中自然选择起着至关重要的作用。但是，对于以王朝形式考虑进化的人来说，进化的结果是产生了一个新的基因型。新基因型的产生为种群在恶劣环境下的生存提供了一条解决途径，并且能够在种群内绝大多数个体之间共享，还能在未来的进化中保持稳定。一个种群内的绝大多数个体在遗传结构上大体是一致的或者是同源的，无论这种一致或同源性是何种程度，都能使种群的性状稳定地遗传。遗传多样性通过隐性突变的方式保留下来，但是大部分突变会破坏来之不易的适应性，因此它们在自然选择中被迫隐性表达，这样便能减小发生突变所引起的危害。在进化没有发生时，自然选择就保持一个群体上的同一性。多样性是稳定型遗传不均等的结果，它是一种有趣却不常见的现象，每一种多样性都需要有一个独特的解释，即自身特有的解释。

如今，研究结果发现自然种群是高度多样化的，从而取代了上述观点。只要留意并使用恰当的方法，处处可以发现化学多样性（同种异型性[6]）。仅人类血液中已

variants known in human blood alone provide combinations that far outnumber the human race—variants of haemoglobin, non-haemoglobin proteins, and red-cell enzymes; of red-cell antigens and white-cell antigens; and of haptoglobins, transferrins and gamma globulins. Today it is no longer possible to think of the evolutionary process as the formulation of a new genotype or the inauguration of a new type of organism enjoying the possession of that formula. The "product" of evolution is itself a population—a population with a certain newly devised and well adapted pattern of genetic *in*equality. This pattern of genetic differentiation is determined and actively maintained by selective forces: it is the population as a whole that breeds true, not its individual members. We can no longer draw a distinction between an active process of evolution and a more or less stationary end-product: evolution is constantly in progress, and the genetical structure of a population is actively, that is dynamically, sustained.

These newer ideas have important practical consequences. The older outlook was embodied in that older, almost immemorial ambition of the livestock breeder, to produce by artificial selection a true breeding stock with uniform, and uniformly desirable characteristics; and this was also the ambition—sometimes kindly, but always mistaken—of old-fashioned "positive" eugenics. It now seems doubtful if, with free-living and naturally out-breeding organisms, such a goal can ever be achieved. Modern stockbreeders tend to adopt a very nicely calculated regimen of cross-breeding which, abandoning the goal of a single self-perpetuating stock, achieves a uniform marketable product of hybrid composition. The genetical theory underlying this scheme of breeding embodies, and was indeed partly responsible for, the newer ideas of population structure I have just outlined.

I cannot predict what new ideas will illuminate the theory of evolution in future, but it is not difficult to guess the contexts of thought in which they are likely to appear. The main weakness of modern evolutionary theory is its lack of a fully worked out theory of variation, that is, of *candidature* for evolution, of the forms in which genetic variants are proffered for selection. We have therefore no convincing account of evolutionary progress—of the otherwise inexplicable tendency of organisms to adopt ever more complicated solutions of the problems of remaining alive. This is a "molecular" problem, in the newer biological usage of that word, because its working out depends on a deeper understanding of how the physicochemical properties and behaviour of chromosomes and nucleoproteins generally qualify them to enrich the candidature for evolution; and this reflection is my cue to turn to conceptual advances in biology at the molecular level.

Physical Basis of Life

In the early 1930's no one knew what to make of the nucleic acids. Bawden and Pirie had not yet shown that nucleic acid was an integral part of the structure of tobacco mosaic virus, and we were still a decade from the astonishing discovery by Avery and his colleagues, in the Rockefeller Institute, that the agent responsible for pneumococcal transformations was a deoxyribonucleic acid.

知的分子变异体的组合，就远远超过人类种族的数量，如血红蛋白变异体、非血红蛋白变异体和红细胞酶系变异体；红细胞抗原变异体和白细胞抗原变异体；结合珠蛋白变异体、转铁蛋白变异体以及伽马球蛋白变异体。如今，我们不再认为进化只是产生了一个新基因型或者含有这种新基因的新生物体。种群进化的“产物”就是种群本身——该种群具有一种新的、适应性良好的遗传**不**均等性模式。选择力决定和维持这种遗传分化的模式，这是一种保持遗传稳定性的群体行为，而不是个体的行为。我们不能再区分进化的动态过程和一个多少算作稳定的终产物：因为进化是一个持续的过程，并且种群遗传结构处在连续的、动态的变化之中。

这些新理论具有重要的现实意义。以前的家畜饲养者根据旧的进化理论去人工筛选纯种的优良牲畜，可是结果往往不能如愿，这被认为是传统的“积极”优生学。如今看来，在野外放养和自然地异系繁殖条件下，家畜饲养者的育种目标是很难实现的。现代饲养者们抛弃了传统的筛选方法，采用杂交手段获得了适应市场需求的杂种牲畜。遗传理论奠定了这种育种方法的基础，上面我所提到的关于种群结构的新理论也在一定程度上促进了这种新型育种方法的产生。

我无法预测到以后的进化论将会有什么样的新思想，不过不难猜测它可能包含的内容。现代进化论的一大局限就是缺少完整的变异理论，即进化的**备选物**，也就是为选择提供遗传突变的形式。因此，对于进化过程（另一令人费解的趋势是面对继续生存的难题，生物体趋于采用更复杂的解决方案），我们没有令人信服的解释。用现代生物学术语来说，变异是“分子”水平上的问题，因为它的解决依赖于更深地理解个体的生化特性、染色体的行为以及核蛋白是如何使它们有资格丰富进化的备选物的，我的思路是将这一思考转向生物学在分子水平上的概念演变。

生命的物质基础

在 20 世纪 30 年代早期，没有人知道核酸是由什么构成的。鲍登和皮里尚未发现核酸是烟草花叶病毒的组成部分，距离埃弗里及其同事们在洛克菲勒研究所的惊人发现——脱氧核糖核酸是肺炎球菌的转化因子——也还有十年之久。

Since there was nothing very much to say about nucleic acids you may well wonder what everybody *did* talk about. One topic of conversation was the crystallization of enzymes. Sumner had crystallized urease in 1926 and Northrop pepsin in 1930; soon Stanley would crystallize tobacco mosaic virus, at that time still thought to be a pure protein. But the most exciting and, as it seemed to us, portentous discoveries were those of W. T. Astbury, whose X-ray diffraction pictures of silk fibroin and hair and feather keratins had revealed an essentially crystalline orderliness in ordinary biological structures. For some purposes, however, X-ray analysis was too powerful. The occasion called for resolving powers between those of the optical microscope and the X-ray tube, and this need was fulfilled by electron microscopy. I saw my first electron-photomicrograph in *Nature* in 1933; its resolving power was then one micron.

Electron microscopy has shown that cells contain sheets, tubes, bags and, indeed, micro-organs—real anatomical structures in the sense that they have firm and definite shapes and look as if only their size prevented our picking them up and handling them. Moreover, there is no dividing line between structures in the molecular and in the anatomical sense: macromolecules have structures in a sense intelligible to the anatomist and small anatomical structures are molecular in a sense intelligible to the chemist. (Intelligible *now*, I should add: as Pirie[7] has told us, the idea that molecules have literally, that is, spatially, a structure was resisted by orthodox chemists, and the credentials of molecules with weights above 5,000 were long in doubt.) In short, the orderliness of cells is a structural or crystalline orderliness—a "solid" orderliness, indeed, for "the so-called amorphous solids are either not really amorphous or not really solid"[4].

This newer conception represents a genuine upheaval of biological thought, and it marks the disappearance of what may be called the *colloidal* conception of vital organization, itself a sophisticated variant of the older doctrine of "protoplasm". The idea of protoplasm as a fragile colloidal slime, a sort of biological ether permeating otherwise inanimate structures, was already obsolete in the 'thirties; even then no one could profess to be studying "protoplasm" without being thought facetious or slightly mad. But we still clung to the colloidal conception in its more sophisticated versions, which allowed for heterogeneity and for the existence of liquid crystalline states, and it was still possible to applaud Hopkins's famous aphorism from the British Association meeting of 1913, that the life of the cell is "the expression of a particular dynamic equilibrium in a polyphasic system". For inadequate though the colloidal conception was seen to be, there was nothing to take its place. Peters's idea of the existence of a "cytoskeleton" to account for the orderly unfolding of cellular metabolism in time and place now seems wonderfully prescient, but there was precious little direct evidence for the existence of anything of the kind, and much that seemed incompatible with it.

The substitution of the structural for the colloidal conception of "the physical basis of life" was one of the great revolutions of modern biology; but it was a quiet revolution, for no one opposed it, and for that reason, I suppose, no one thought to read a funeral oration over protoplasm itself.

因为人们对核酸尚无甚了解，所以无话可说，你可能想知道大家**究竟**都在谈论些什么呢？话题之一就是酶的晶体结构。萨姆纳在 1926 年结晶了脲酶，诺斯罗普在 1930 年结晶了胃蛋白酶；随后不久，斯坦利获得了烟草花叶病毒的结晶，但当时还认为该病毒是单纯的蛋白质。但是最令人兴奋和具有预见性的是阿斯特伯里的发现，他通过 X 射线衍射的方法分析蚕丝蛋白、头发和羽毛的角蛋白后在一般生物结构中发现了重要的晶体秩序。然而，对于某些实验分析而言，X 射线分析技术显得过于强大了，它的分辨率远远超过了普通的光学显微镜，因而需要用分辨率介于两者之间的电子显微镜来填补分辨率中间的空白。我见到的第一幅电子显微图谱出现在 1933 年的《自然》上，那时的分辨率是 1 微米。

用电子显微镜观察发现，细胞的结构组成包括片层结构、管状结构、袋状结构以及微小的“细胞器”——从解剖学角度看，它们拥有固定而精确的形状，似乎只是因为个体太小，我们才无法将它们拿在手上进行操作。另外，分子结构和解剖结构之间没有明确的界限：大分子在解剖学家眼中是有结构的，而小的解剖学结构在化学家眼中是分子。（我需要补充的是，**现在**可以理解，正如同皮里[7]告诉我们的，传统化学家们不认为分子真的具有所谓的空间结构，并且长期以来怀疑分子量在 5,000 以上的大分子是否存在。）总而言之，细胞秩序是一种结构或晶体秩序，即一个“固体”秩序，而实际上，“这种所谓无定形固体既不是真的没有固定形状也不是纯粹的固体”[4]。

这个新概念是生物学史上的一次巨大变革，它标志着旧有的认为生命机体是**胶质**的说法的消失，胶质学说是一个由古老的“原生质体”学说衍生而来的复杂概念。原生质学说认为原生质是一种易碎的胶状物，是一种生物醚渗透结构或者是无生命的结构，这早在 30 年代就已经过时，那时如果有人声称自己在研究“原生质”，那么他肯定会被嘲笑或被认为是疯子。然而我们对较高深的胶质学说仍然深信不疑，此理论认为细胞内存在异质性和液态晶体秩序。同时，我们也赞成霍普金斯于 1913 年在英国科学促进会会议上所发表的著名论断，即细胞的生命是“一个多相系统内某种独特的动态平衡现象”。胶质理论虽不够完善，但是我们还没有找到一种新的理论来取代它。彼得斯提出了“细胞骨架”学说，解释了细胞内代谢发生的时空有序性，这个学说在今天看来是非常有预见性的，不过至今尚未找到很直接的证据支持该假说，相反，倒是有很多证据看起来与这个学说相矛盾。

“生命的物质基础”的胶质概念被结构概念替代，是现代生物学最伟大的变革之一；但是这个变革却是在潜移默化中发生的，因为没有人对它提出反对意见，我猜测正是由于这个原因，没有人为原生质体学说致悼词。

Cellular Differentiation in Embryonic Development

Embryology is in some ways a model science. It has always been distinguished by the exactitude, even punctilio, of its anatomical descriptions. An experiment by one of the grand masters of embryology could be made the text of a discourse on scientific method. But something is wrong; or has been wrong. There is no *theory* of development, in the sense in which Mendelism is a theory that accounts for the results of breeding experiments. There has therefore been little sense of progression or timeliness about embryological research. Of many papers delivered at embryological meetings, however good they may be in themselves—in themselves they are sometimes marvels of analysis, and complete and satisfying within their own limits—one too often feels that they might have been delivered five years beforehand without making anyone much the wiser, or deferred for five years without making anyone conscious of great loss.

It was not always so. In the 1930's experimental embryology had much the same appeal as molecular biology has today: students felt it to be the most rapidly advancing front of biological research. This was partly due to the work of Vogt, who had shown that the mobilization and deployment of cellular envelopes, tubes and sheets was the fundamental stratagem of early vertebrate development (thus relaying the foundations of comparative vertebrate embryology); but it was mainly due to the "organizer theory" of Hans Spemann, the theory that differentiation in development is the outcome of an orderly sequence of specific inductive stimuli. The underlying assumption of the theory (though not then so expressed) was that we should look to the chemical properties of the inductive agent to find out why the amino-acid sequence of one enzyme or organ-specific protein should differ from the amino-acid sequence of another. The reactive capabilities of the responding tissue were emphasized repeatedly, but only at a theoretical level, for "competence" did not lend itself to experimental analysis, and the centre of gravity of actual research lay in the chemical definition of inductive agents.

Wise after the event, we can now see that embryology simply did not have, and could not have created, the background of genetical reasoning which would have made it possible to formulate a theory of development. It is not now generally believed that a stimulus external to the system on which it acts can specify the primary structure of a protein, that is, convey instructions that amino-acids shall be assembled in a given order. The "instructive" stimulus has gone the way of the philosopher's stone, an agent dimly akin to it in certain ways. Embryonic development at the level of molecular differentiation must therefore be an unfolding of pre-existing capabilities, an acting-out of genetically encoded instructions; the inductive stimulus is the agent that selects or activates one set of instructions rather than another. It is just possible to see how something of the kind happens in the induction of adaptive enzymes in bacteria—a phenomenon of which the older description, the "training" of bacteria, reminds us that it too, at one time, was thought to be "instructive" in nature. All this applies only to biological order at the level of the amino-acid sequences of proteins or the nucleotide sequences of nucleic acids. Nothing is yet known about the genetic specification of order at levels above the molecular level.

胚胎发育中的细胞分化

从某种程度上讲，胚胎学是一门模式学科，其特征是对解剖结构的描述极为精确，甚至有些过分拘泥细节。一位胚胎学大师所做的实验可能只是将一系列科学方法的叙述做成文本。但是胚胎学在某处错了，或者一直存在错误。没有发育的**理论**，在这个意义上说，孟德尔遗传学说是一个理论，它解释了杂交实验的结果。因此关于胚胎学研究的进展或时效性没有意义。然而，在胚胎学会议上提交的许多文章无论它们本身多么好——许多文章是分析史上的杰作，在本领域内可称完美——总令人觉得这些文章如果提前五年发表，不会让人更明智；如果延迟五年发表，不会让人感到巨大的损失。

当然，事实也不尽如此。20 世纪 30 年代的实验胚胎学就像今天的分子生物学一样别具吸引力：那时，研究者们认为胚胎学是发展最快速的生物学研究的前沿。这部分要归功于沃格特的工作，他指出细胞膜、管状结构以及片层结构的流动性和展开是脊椎动物胚胎早期发育的主要策略（这为脊椎动物比较胚胎学的建立提供了基础），不过他的观点主要是基于汉斯·施佩曼的“组织者理论”，该理论认为发育分化是胚胎受到有序特定诱导刺激的结果。这一理论的言外之意（尽管当时没有这么说）是我们应该去研究诱导物的化学成分，以探知为什么不同酶或器官特异性的蛋白质的氨基酸序列会各不相同。虽然反复强调反应组织的反应能力，但只是在理论层面上，因为“全能性”尚未得到实验的验证，实际研究工作的重心应是确定诱导物的化学组分。

事后诸葛亮，现在我们知道仅仅胚胎学没有，也不可能形成遗传学理论的基础，而后者本来会使前者可能发展出一套发育理论。现在，人们一般不相信作用于系统的外来的诱导物能够指定蛋白质的一级结构，即传递氨基酸以特定顺序聚集起来的指令。具有“指导”作用的诱导物已经重蹈点金石的覆辙，在某些方面依稀与点金石类似。因此在分子水平的胚胎发育的分化是先前存在能力的展现和遗传编码指令的行为，诱导物是一种起选择或激活作用的物质，而不是具有其他作用的物质。这只有在诱导细菌适应酶（以前称为细菌“驯化”的现象，同时，也提醒我们它在自然界中被认为有“指导”作用）时，才能看到类似事件如何发生。这一切只适用于在蛋白质氨基酸序列水平或核酸的核苷酸序列水平上的生物顺序，而对于上述分子水平之上的顺序的遗传特性我们尚且知之甚少。

The function performed by the hierarchy of inductive stimuli as it occurs in vertebrate development is to determine the specificities of time and place: it is an inductive stimulus which determines that a lens shall form just here and just now—not elsewhere, and at no other time. As I see it, it is the inductive process that allows vertebrate eggs and embryos before gastrulation to indulge in the prodigious range of adaptive radiation to be seen in germs as disparate as a dogfish's egg and a human being's—a case I have argued elsewhere and need not go over here again[8].

Biology of the Organism: Animal Behaviour

If experimental embryology was the subject that seemed most exciting to students of the 'thirties, that most nearly on the threshold of a grand revelation, the study of animal behaviour (in the sense in which we now tend to use the word "ethology"), seemed just as clearly the most frustrating and unrewarding. Twenty years later it was the other way about: embryology had lost much of its fascination and many of the ablest students were recruited into research on behaviour instead. What had happened in the meantime?

In the early 1930's we had one new behavioural concept to ponder on: the idea that an animal might in some way apprehend a sensory pattern or a behavioural situation as a whole and not by a piecing together of its sensory or motor parts. That was the lesson of *Gestalt* theory. We had also learnt finally, and I hope for ever, the methodological lesson of behaviourism: that statements about what an animal feels or is conscious of, and what its motives are, belong to an altogether different class from statements about what it does and how it acts. I say the "methodological" lesson of behaviourism, because that word also stands for a certain psychological theory, namely, that the phenomenology of behaviour is the whole of behaviour—a theory of which I shall only say that, in my opinion, it is not nearly as silly as it sounds. Even the methodology of behaviourism seemed cruelly austere to a generation not yet weaned from the doctrine of privileged insight through introspection. But what comparable revolution of thought ushered in the study of animal behaviour in the style of Lorenz and Tinbergen and led to the foundation of flourishing schools of behaviour in Oxford, here in Cambridge, and throughout the world?

I believe the following extremely simple answer to be the right one. In the 'thirties it did not seem to us that there *was* any way of studying behaviour "scientifically" except through some kind of experimental intervention—except by confronting the subject of our observations with a "situation" or with a nicely contrived stimulus and then recording what the animal did. The situation would then be varied in some way that seemed appropriate, whereupon the animal's behaviour would also vary. Even poking an animal would surely be better than just looking at it: that would lead to anecdotalism: that was what bird-watchers did.

Yet it was also what the pioneers of ethology did. They studied natural behaviour instead of contrived behaviour, and were thus able for the first time to discern natural behaviour structures or episodes—a style of analysis helped very greatly by the comparative

在脊椎动物发育过程中，通过诱导刺激层次发挥的作用决定分化的时空特异性：诱导刺激决定晶状体现在就在这里形成——而不是别的地点和时间。在我看来，正是诱导过程允许脊椎动物的卵细胞和胚胎在原肠胚形成前进入适应辐射的惊人范围中，就如同在细菌与狗鲨和人类卵细胞发育过程中看到的区别一样——这点我曾在其他地方讨论过[8]，不再在此重复。

个体生物学：动物行为

如果实验胚胎学看起来是最令 30 年代研究者兴奋的学科和最接近重大启示起点的学科，那么显然对动物行为的研究（在这个意义上，现在我们倾向于使用“动物行为学”这个词），似乎是最令人沮丧和不值得做的。20 年后，相反地，胚胎学失去了大部分魅力，许多最有能力的学者转而研究动物行为。当时发生了些什么事情呢？

在 20 世纪 30 年代初期，我们有一个新的行为学概念要仔细考虑：动物可能以某种方式从总体上领会感官模式或行为状况，而不是靠动物感官或运动部分的拼凑。这是**格式塔**理论的内容。我们后来也了解了行为主义方法论，并且我希望能一直如此：它陈述的是动物的感受是什么或能意识到什么以及它的动机是什么，它与动物做了什么和怎样做的陈述属于完全不同的一类。我称它为行为主义“方法论”是因为，这个词代表着特定的心理学理论，即行为的现象学是行为的全部——以我看来，这个理论远不像它的名字一样听起来无聊。尽管行为主义方法学看起来过于严谨以至于产生了尚未丢弃，通过内省获得的特殊洞察力的教条，但是洛伦兹和丁伯根研究动物行为的方式近乎引领了一场思维上的革命，并使牛津、剑桥和遍布世界各地的多家学校纷纷建立起动物行为学学院，又有哪个学科能与之相提并论呢？

我认为下面这个非常简单回复就是正确答案。在 30 年代，除了通过某种实验干预（即通过一定的方法刺激动物或者将动物置于一定的“情境”之下，然后观察并记录动物的行为外），对我们来说没有“科学地”研究行为的方法。当情境以某种看起来恰当的方式变化时，动物的行为也会发生变化。当然戳一下动物的反应效果肯定会强于单纯的观察，后者称得上是件趣闻轶事，但是只有观鸟者才会这么做。

不过，动物行为学的先行者们也做了这样的事情。他们研究自然状态下的行为而非人为的行为，因此他们能够首次识别自然行为结构或部分——一种通过比较法

approach, for the occurrence of the same or similar behavioural sequences in members of related species reinforced the idea that there was a certain natural connectedness between its various terms, as if they represented the playing out of a certain instinctual programme. Then, and only then, was it possible to start to obtain significant information from the study of contrived behaviour—from the application or withholding of stimuli—for it is not informative to study variations of behaviour unless we know beforehand the norm from which the variants depart.

The form of address I chose—to trace the recent growth and transformation of ideas in four "subjects" belonging to four levels of biological analysis—gave me no opportunity to mention some of the greatest innovations of modern scientific thought: the dynamical state of bodily constituents, for example, the perpetual flux of the material ingredients of the body. Nor have I said anything except by implication of the greatest discoveries in modern science, those which revealed the genetical functions of the nucleic acids. Yet I feel I have said enough of the growth of biology in the recent past to draw some morals, however trite. The history of animal behaviour—in particular the sterility of the older experimental approach—illustrates the danger of doing experiments in the Baconian style; that is to say, the danger of contriving "experiences" intended merely to enlarge our general store of empirical knowledge rather than to sustain or confute a specific hypothesis or pre-supposition. The history of embryology shows the dangers of an imagined self-sufficiency, for embryology is an inviable fragment of knowledge without genetics. (I often wonder what academics mean when they say of a certain subject that it is a "discipline in its own right"; for what science is entire of itself?) You may think our recent history entitles us to feel pretty pleased with ourselves. Perhaps: but then we felt pretty pleased with ourselves twenty-five years ago, and in twenty-five years time people will look back on us and wonder at our obtuseness. However, if complacency is to be deplored, so also is humility. Humility is not a state of mind conducive to the advancement of learning. No one formula will satisfy that purpose, for there is no one kind of scientist; but a certain mixture of confidence and restless dissatisfaction will be an ingredient of most formulae. Confident we may surely be, for the next twenty-five years will throw up several new ideas as profound and astonishing as any I have yet described, namely ... but I have no space left to tell you what they are.

(**207**, 1327-1330; 1965)

Peter. Medawar: F.R.S., Director, National Institute for Medical Research.

References:

1. See *The Mneme* by R. Semon, London, 1921, particularly pp. 24, 113, 180, 211; and Hering's paper "On Memory, a Universal Attribute of organized Matter" in *Alm. Akad. Wiss. Wien.*, **20**, 253 (1870).
2. *The Philosophy of a Biologist*, 162 (London, 1931).
3. "A Cybernetical Aspect of Genetics", *J. Hered.*, **41**, 19 (1950).
4. Schrödinger, E., *What is Life?*, especially pp. 19-20, 61-62, 68 (Cambridge, 1944). For Weismann's far-sighted views on the matter, see *The Architecture of Matter* by Toulmin, S., and Goodfield, J. (London, 1962).

非常便于分析的类型，因为相关物种中相同或相似行为序列的发生强化了在其多种行为方式间存在某种特定的自然联系的观点，可能它们代表着特定本能程序的发挥。接下来，也只有在那时，才可能开始从人为行为的研究中获得重要信息——使用或不使用刺激物，因为除非我们事先知道变体偏离的标准，否则研究的行为变异是无益的。

为了追溯历属生物分析四个水平的四个“主题”目前增加的观念和转变的观念，我选择的称谓形式没有机会提及一些现代科学思想中的最伟大的革新，即生物体组分的动态，如生物体组成成分是不停流动的，除了暗示，我也没谈及现代科学中最伟大的发现，即关于核酸的遗传功能的揭示。但我觉得我已经讲了许多近年来生物学的发展，这些足以使我们吸取一些教训，虽然是平庸的。动物行为的历史——尤其是成效甚微的传统实验方法——例证了以培根的方式做实验的危险性，也就是说，人为“实验”的危险性仅意味着扩大了经验知识的一般储存而不是支持或驳斥某个特定的假说或预想。胚胎学的历史表明了想象的自我满足思想的危险性，因为离开了遗传学，胚胎学是不独存的知识片段。（我经常在想，当有些人提起某个学科时常说这个学科独树一帜，可事实上哪门科学又能自成一体呢？）你可能对近来的历史感到非常满意。可是我们在 25 年前自我感觉极好，但是，25 年后人们也会回过头来看我们并惊讶于我们的愚钝。然而，如果自满是悲叹的，谦逊也会这样。谦逊不是传导学术进步的心理状态，没有一个准则符合那个目的，因为没有这类的科学家，但是信心和永不自满的心态的组合将是绝大多数准则中的一个因素。当然，我们是有信心的，在将来的 25 年里将提出几个如同我曾描述过的那样深刻和令人吃惊的新观念，那就是……不过这次我没时间告诉你们具体究竟是什么了。

（高如丽 翻译；金侠 审稿）

5. In my Tizard Memorial Lecture, *Encounter* (August 1965).

6. A term coined by J. Oudin to describe γ-globulin variants: it might well be generalized to include all molecular polymorphism.

7. Pirie, N. W., "Patterns of Assumption about Large Molecules", *Arch. Biochem. Biophys.*, Supp. **1**, 21 (1962).

8. *J. Embryol. Exp. Morph.*, **2**, 172 (1954).

Recent Developments in Cosmology*

F. Hoyle

Editor's Note

Fred Hoyle was one of the most versatile and productive of astronomers in the first decades after the Second World War. When this paper was published, he was the director of the Institute of Theoretical Astronomy at Cambridge (then being constructed). This article is the text of a talk largely concerned with the implications of the newly discovered class of celestrial objects called quasi-stellar objects or quasars. That Hoyle did not win a Nobel Prize for his seminal work on the formation of elements in stars is now widely considered a grave injustice.

I shall start from the observed shift of the spectrum lines of galaxies interpreted in terms of the expansion of the universe. The red shift implies that distances between galaxies, measured with an imaginary ruler for example, increase with time. An immediate question is whether the universe was denser in the past than it is today. If so, how much denser was the universe?

A definitive answer to this critical problem could be obtained in principle by observing the state of the universe in the past. This is possible because of the finite speed of light. We do not observe a galaxy as it is now but as it was at the moment the light started on its journey. In the case of very distant galaxies the light started several billion years ago, so we have direct evidence of the state of affairs several billion years ago. All that need be done, again in principle, is to observe the density of galaxies as it was a few billion years ago and to compare it with the density in our immediate neighbourhood. This would be a direct way of settling the density problem. This indeed was the way in which Hubble tried to settle it more than thirty years ago. He failed to do so because of the extreme difficulty of making a fair count of distant galaxies. The tendency is to count the brighter galaxies but to miss the fainter ones. Since Hubble's attempt nobody has had the hardihood to make a direct assault on the problem by attempting to count galaxies.

Ryle and his associates have counted radio sources instead of galaxies, and here the result has turned out to be much more clear-cut, at any rate so far as the counting process itself is concerned. The difficulty with radio sources is that we are still far from sure exactly what it is that is being counted. Developments in the past two years, the discovery of the quasi-stellar sources in particular, have shown the situation to be more complex than it was at first thought to be. The indication of the radio counts is that the universe was more dense in the past than it is today. However, further knowledge is needed concerning the

* Substance of an Evening Discourse delivered on September 6 at the Annual Meeting in Cambridge of the British Association for the Advancement of Science.

宇宙学的新进展*

霍伊尔

编者按

弗雷德·霍伊尔是在二战后最初十年里天文学界最博学、最多产的科学家之一。本文发表时，他是剑桥大学理论天文研究所（当时还正在建设中）的所长。本文是一篇演讲的文字稿，主要是探讨关于新发现的一类被称作类星体的天体的宇宙学含义。霍伊尔没有凭借在恒星内元素形成方面的开创性工作而获得诺贝尔奖，现在人们普遍认为这是很不公正的。

我将从观测到的星系谱线红移被解释为宇宙膨胀开始。假设我们用一把想象的尺子去测量，红移暗示着星系间距离会随着时间而增加。紧接着会产生的问题就是，过去的宇宙是不是比现在的密度要大。如果是的话，密度要大多少？

原则上，通过观测宇宙过去的状态就可以给出这个关键问题的确切答案。因为光速的有限性使得这种观测成为可能。我们看到的不是这个星系当前的状态，而是其在光发出时刻的状态。在观测远距离星系的情况下，我们有可能看到的是其数十亿年前发出的光，所以我们可以直接观测到宇宙数十亿年前的状态。同样从原则上说，我们需要做的仅仅是观测几十亿年前的星系的密度并和我们近邻星系的密度比较。这将是解决密度问题的最直接的方法。三十多年前哈勃就曾试图这样做。但由于对远距离星系做准确的计数极其困难而未能成功。观测愈远愈倾向记录更亮的星系而丢失较暗的星系。从哈勃尝试至今，再没有人试图直接计数星系以破解这个难题。

赖尔和其合作者们选择对射电源而不是星系进行计数，如果仅就计数过程本身而言，这时结果显得更为清楚。用射电源计数的困难在于我们至今还远未准确地知道我们计数的是什么。过去两年中的发展，尤其是类星射电源的发现使人们认识到真实情况远非我们一开始设想的那么简单。射电源的计数结果暗示了宇宙过去比现在要更致密。但是，在我们对射电源本质做出更为准确的了解前，我们还不能给出

* 于9月6日在剑桥大学召开的英国科学促进会年度会议上发表的晚间演讲的内容。

nature of the radio sources before this conclusion can be regarded as definitive.

If the quasi-stellar objects are truly cosmological a great deal becomes pretty well settled. Imagine an object of fixed intrinsic brightness to be moved to increasingly great distances. Two things will happen. The apparent luminosity of the object will decrease and the red-shift of the spectrum lines will increase. A theoretical relation between these quantities can be determined for any specified cosmological theory. The relation is different in different theories, so that in principle it would be possible to distinguish between one cosmological theory and another if we could experiment in this way with a standard object of fixed brightness. Unfortunately it is impossible to move a single object to increasing distances; so the astronomer must rely on similar objects just happening to lie at different distances. The question then arises of how sure we can be that the objects are really similar to each other. Massive galaxies do seem to be quite remarkably similar, but the theoretical differences we are looking for are rather slight in the case of galaxies. This is because galaxies, even the brightest galaxies, cannot be observed far enough away for the theoretical differences to be more than slight. At greater distances the theoretical differences become much more appreciable, however. The technical problem is that of photographing spectrum lines when the light intensity is very small. What is needed is more light. It is here that the quasi-stellar sources are of critical importance. Accepting for the moment that the red-shift of the spectrum lines in these sources is cosmological in character, the quasi-stellar sources are brighter than the most massive galaxies by about four magnitudes, a factor of about forty.

At present, red-shift measurements are available for about fifteen quasi-stellar objects. The shifts are dimensionless numbers given by dividing the wave-length shift of any spectrum line by the laboratory wave-length of the same line. The result is the same for all lines. The measured values range from quite small values, for example 0.16 for 3*C* 273, up to the enormous value of 2 for the source 3*C* 9. The theoretical differences become quite large for red-shifts as great as this, so that a distinction between different cosmological theories should be straightforward once a sample of the order of a hundred quasi-stellar objects has been obtained. The present indication based on the small sample of fifteen is that the universe has expanded from a state of higher density, although the statistical scatter in the sample is large enough to be comparable to the effects that are being looked for.

For spectral shifts as large as two, the Lyman-α line is displaced from the unobservable ultra-violet into the blue, at about 3,700 Å. It is possible to look for a continuum on the blueward side of Lyman-α. This continuum is subject to absorption by neutral hydrogen atoms in intergalactic space. A very small density of neutral atoms would be sufficient to absorb out the light completely. Schmidt's observation of 3*C* 9 shows the continuum to be present but to be weakened, that is, to be lower than the continuum on the redward side of Lyman-α. The implication is that intergalactic gas, if it exists, must be hot, perhaps above 10^6°K. The weakening of the continuum is rather strange, for in a sensitive situation like this one would expect either the continuum to be essentially unweakened or to be

一个确切的定论。

如果类星体确实是宇宙学的，那么许多问题就能够较好地确定下来。想象一下一个本身亮度固定的天体逐渐离我们远去的情况。这时将出现两个现象：该天体的视亮度会降低，同时观测到谱线红移会增加。这些量之间的理论关系对于任一特定的宇宙学理论可由计算确定。不同的宇宙学理论所对应的关系不同，所以，原则上，如果我们有一个本身亮度固定的天体并用上述实验方法将可以甄别不同的宇宙学理论。不幸的是，不可能将一个天体移到愈来愈远的距离，所以天文学家们只能依靠处于不同距离上的相似的天体。于是问题又变成了我们能在多大程度上肯定这些天体彼此间是类似的。从观测上来看，大质量星系看起来确实是很类似的，但就星系而言，我们所要寻求的理论上的差异相当小。这是由于即便是最亮的星系也无法在理论差异稍稍明显的距离上被观测到。在更遥远的距离尺度上，不同理论的差异将变得明显起来。然而，技术上的困难是当光强度非常小时，不能获得照相光谱谱线数据。需要的是更亮的天体。类星射电源正是在此刻成了具有关键重要性的观测对象。在接受这些类星体光谱谱线的红移具备宇宙学特性之后，可以发现类星射电源的光度比最大星系还要高约 4 个星等，即大约亮 40 倍。

迄今为止，人们已经得到了大约 15 个类星体的红移数据。在这里我们定义红移为任意谱线的波长移动除以实验室中该谱线的波长，是无量纲的量。其结果对所有谱线均是相同的。测量得到的谱线红移量范围从十分小的值如类星体 3*C* 273 的 0.16 到非常大的值如 3*C* 9 的 2。在红移如此巨大的情况下，理论的差异将会变得十分明显，一旦我们得到了上百量级类星体样本，不同宇宙学理论中差异的区分也就简单易行了。根据当前我们得到的 15 个类星体的小样本数据，有迹象表明，宇宙可能是由更高密度的状态膨胀而来，尽管在样本中统计弥散跟观测效应差不多明显。

红移大到 2 时，赖曼–α 线将从不可见的紫外区移动到可见光的蓝色区域，大约 3,700 埃。我们将有望观测到赖曼–α 线蓝端出现的连续谱。该连续谱是由星系际空间的中性氢原子对辐射的吸收造成的。密度非常低的中性氢原子就足以将这些光全部吸收。施密特对 3*C* 9 的观测发现了这样的连续谱的确存在，但却被减弱，即要比赖曼–α 线红端的连续谱强度低。这暗示了，如果存在星系际气体的话，这些气体必然非常热，可能超过 10^6K。连续谱的减弱是一个相当奇怪的结果，在这样的十分敏感的情况下，应当期望连续谱基本不被减弱或者完全消失。事先并不认为会发生介

absent. The intermediate case seems *a priori* unlikely, since it depends on a closely defined value of the hydrogen density. It is rather in the nature of a coincidence that the density has this critical value.

These remarks are all subject to a cosmological interpretation of the red-shift of the spectrum lines of the quasi-stellar objects. If much smaller, fainter objects were fired out of our own galaxy, or out of some neighbouring galaxy, with speeds close to light the same red-shifts would be observed. Can we be sure that such a "local" interpretation is wrong?

Even though on a "local" hypothesis the quasi-stellars are much less spectacular objects, the total mass involved in all such objects must be as high as $10^6 M_\odot$, or perhaps even more. For such a quantity of matter ejected at speeds close to light, the kinetic energy must be comparable with the rest mass energy, 10^{60} ergs. This is of a similar order of magnitude to the energy involved in the outburst of a major radio galaxy. The energy in the latter case is also in the form of particle motions. The difference is that the particles in the radio galaxies have been thought of in the past as occupying large volumes, not as being condensed into compact objects. However, we now have to ask whether a radio galaxy may not eject compact pieces as well as diffuse clouds of high-speed particles.

Radio galaxies do not eject their material with an initial isotropy. The typical pattern is of two centres of radio emission on opposite sides of a galaxy, with the two centres and the nucleus of the galaxy more or less collinear. To me personally, this has always suggested that an object in the nucleus of the galaxy separates violently into two pieces with a large relative motion. The collinear property then follows from conservation of momentum. Exactly the same phenomenon is observed in the quasi-stellar source *MH* 14-121, two regions of radio emission on opposite sides of, and collinear with, a centre of optical emission. The possibility must be considered that a cascade process is involved. An initial object in the centre of a galaxy breaks violently into two pieces. Later, each of these pieces breaks into two further pieces; and so on. As the cascade develops, and as the objects spread out from the parent galaxy, an approximation to an isotropic situation would then gradually develop.

From independent evidence it has been suggested that an explosion occurred in the nucleus of our own galaxy about ten million years ago. If the quasi-stellar objects emerged in this explosion, as Terrell has suggested, the brightest of the objects, 3*C* 273, would now be distant about 0.5 million parsecs, about one-thousandth of the cosmological distance. The optical emission, instead of the enormous cosmological value of 10^{46} ergs sec^{-1}, would be 10^{40} ergs sec^{-1}. The burning of some 300 solar masses of hydrogen gives sufficient energy to supply such an output for as long as ten million years. Since the mass of 3*C* 273 could be set as $10^4 M_\odot$ there would seem to be no difficulty in explaining the optical output. The kinetic energy of 3*C* 273 would then be $\sim 10^{56}$ ergs, about one order of magnitude less than the total energy of the galactic explosion, as estimated by Burbidge and Hoyle. The masses of other quasi-stellar objects can be set lower than 3*C* 273, because 3*C* 273 is intrinsically considerably brighter than the others, at any rate for

乎中间的情况，因为它取决于非常确定的氢密度值，密度恰巧处于这种临界值将仅仅会是自然界中的一种巧合。

我们以上的评论都是基于这些类星体谱线红移的宇宙学解释。但如果是从我们自己所处的银河系或者一些近邻星系中以接近光速的速度抛射出一个比较小、比较暗的天体，我们也能够观测到类似的红移。我们能完全肯定这种“局域”解释是错误的呢？

尽管在这种“局域”假说下类星体远不是如此令人惊奇的天体，但在所有这样的天体中，其总质量都高达 10^6 个太阳质量甚至更多。这样大质量的天体要被以接近光速的速度抛射出去，其动能必然与其静止质能，10^{60} 尔格相似。差不多是一个大射电星系爆发的总能量的量级。而后者大多数的能量也是以粒子运动形式出现的。其差异在于射电星系中的粒子被认为占有一个很大的体积，而不是凝聚成一个致密天体。我们现在要问的是，射电星系是不是不可以抛出致密碎片以及弥散的高速粒子云。

射电星系最初并不是各向同性地抛射物质。典型的图样是两个射电辐射中心在星系的两边，两个中心和星系核或多或少是共线的。就我个人而言，我认为这总是表示星系核中的某个天体剧烈地分裂成了具有很大相对速度的两部分。而共线性是动量守恒的结果。完全相同的现象也出现在类星射电源 *MH* 14-121 中：两个射电辐射区域分别在中心光学发射的两边并与其共线。因此必须考虑到发生级联过程的可能性。在星系中心的天体最初剧烈的分裂成两部分。接着这两部分又经历各自的分裂过程，如此继续。当其级联过程发生，并随着天体从母星系中散发出来，一个近似各向同性的状态将逐步形成。

有独立的证据显示在我们星系核中在大约一千万年前曾经有一次剧烈的爆炸。如特雷尔所猜想的那样，如果类星体是在这次爆炸中产生的，那么这些类星体中最亮的 3*C* 273 将大约距离我们 50 万秒差距，而这大约是宇宙学距离的千分之一。它的光学发射能流密度也将从以前宇宙学距离所估算的 10^{46} 尔格 / 秒变成 10^{40} 尔格 / 秒。燃烧大约 300 个太阳质量的氢就足以提供这样的能量来输出一千万年。由于 3*C* 273 的质量可设为 10^4 个太阳质量，所以在解释类星体光能输出方面并不存在困难。根据伯比奇和霍伊尔的估算，3*C* 273 的动能约为 10^{56} 尔格，比银河系爆炸的总能量低一个数量级。由于 3*C* 273 的内禀光度比其他类星体都高（仅对于目前观测到的射电源），所以其他类星体的质量应低于 3*C* 273 的质量。取每个天体的质量为 10^3 个太

the sources so far observed. Setting $10^3 M_\odot$ as the mass per object, and taking the mean speed as half the velocity of light, the kinetic energy per object is comparable with that of 3*C* 273. The total energy estimated by Burbidge and Hoyle, 10^{57} ergs, would provide only for ~10 objects. It would seem therefore that either Burbidge and Hoyle underestimated the violence of the galactic explosion, or an energy difficulty arises.

The same difficulty does not arise in the case of the galaxy *NGC* 5128. This is a nearby massive elliptical, distant about four million parsec. At least one major outburst is known to have occurred in the nucleus of this galaxy within the past ten million years. The probability must also be considered that both *NGC* 5128 and our galaxy are involved, with our galaxy contributing the comparatively low-speed objects and *NGC* 5128 contributing the high-speed objects.

These questions can undoubtedly be resolved by observation. Observations leading to size estimates for the quasi-stellar objects are coming along with rapidly mounting impetus. The light from 3*C* 273 has been known to be variable in a characteristic time of about ten years. This sets the maximum radius of the optical object at ten light years. In addition, rapid flashes in the light over only a few weeks have been suggested. Largely because the maximum radius would have to be reduced to a tenth of a light-year, or even less, there has been a disposition not to believe this evidence in the case of 3*C* 273. On the cosmological hypothesis, how can one have an optical emission a hundred times brighter than the most luminous galaxies pouring out of an object only a tenth of a light-year in diameter? The issue appears to have been resolved by a recent observation of a doubling of the light of a quasi-stellar source in less than a month.

On the radio side, fluctuations from 3*C* 273 have been found, first by Dent and more recently by Moffet and Maltby. The radio data set stronger constraints than the optical data, particularly for the cosmological theory. The present state of the argument is that the cosmological theory just survives the existing data. Whether it will continue to do so remains to be seen. My judgment of the situation is that survival for the cosmological theory depends on there being a sharp saturation in the accumulation of fluctuation data, that not much more in the way of fluctuations can be tolerated. If we are already near the end of the road, the theory will survive and will then probably turn out the correct theory. But if we are still near the beginning of the road, the prospects for the theory will be slight. I would say we have to do with a fifty-fifty situation.

I would like to turn now to quite different issues; but still bearing on the question I asked at the beginning: Has the universe emerged from a more dense state? The kinds of observation I have discussed so far all relate to great distances. Observations can be made in our own neighbourhood which also bear on the problem. I am now going to describe three such observations, together with the related arguments. The three are utterly different in character, illustrating how wide are the issues in cosmology, and how very many phenomena have to be made to fit into a consistent picture.

阳质量，并取其平均速度为光速的一半，依照这样的估计这些天体将会有与3*C* 273大致相同的动能。但是按照伯比奇和霍伊尔估计的总能量值，10^{57}尔格，那场大爆炸的能量就只能供给大约10个这样的天体。所以要么是伯比奇和霍伊尔低估了银河系爆炸的强度，要么就要出现能量困难。

但在星系*NGC* 5128中不会出现类似的困难。这是一个距离银河系大约四百万秒差距的近邻大质量椭圆星系。在过去的一千万年中，至少有一次大的爆发在这个星系的星系核中发生。当然，我们也必须考虑这种可能性，即观察到的类星体是银河系与这个星系*NGC* 5128共同产生的：银河系产生相对低速的天体，而*NGC* 5128产生速度较大的天体。

上面谈到的这些问题毫无疑问可以通过观测解决。随着快速积累的观测资料，观测正导致我们对类星体尺度的估算。观测发现，来自3*C* 273的光大约以10年为特征时标在变化。这说明该光学天体的最大半径为10光年。不仅如此，3*C* 273的辐射中也发现了存在持续时间仅为数周的光闪。主要是因为最大半径会缩小为1/10光年或是更少，现在有一种倾向不相信3*C* 273提供的证据。因为按宇宙学假设，怎么可能存在直径只有1/10光年的天体，却能够释放出比最亮的星系都还要亮100倍的光能？最近有观测发现有个类星射电源在一个月之内增亮了一倍，这看起来解决了上面的问题了。

在射电观测方面，登特率先发现了类星体3*C* 273辐射的起伏，这个结果随后也被莫菲特和莫尔特比证实。射电数据提供了比光学数据更强的限制，特别是对宇宙学理论而言。现在论据的状态是宇宙学理论仅仅勉强能够满足现有的数据。该结果是不是仍然能够满足以后的数据仍有待观察。我个人的观点是，宇宙学理论是否能够仍然成立取决于积累的光起伏的数据存在很快的饱和，理论已经难以再承受更快的光变了。如果我们已经接近路的终点，理论将经受住考验而被证明是正确的。但如果我们才踏上路的起点，那么这个理论的未来将会非常渺茫。我想说这两种可能性大概对半分。

现在我想谈谈另一个十分不同的话题，但并不会偏离我在本文开头提出的问题：宇宙是否是从一个更为致密的状态演化而来？直到现在，我谈的观测都是与远距离有关的。我们也可以对我们的附近进行观测而这些观测也与这个问题有关。现在我就要谈谈三个这类的观测和与之相关的讨论。这三项观测的特征是完全不同的，显示了宇宙学问题涵盖领域的广阔性，也说明了一个自恰的宇宙学理论必须要能够解释多少现象。

Recently, Penzias and Wilson have observed a radio background at a wave-length of about 7 cm, which they do not believe to be due to their equipment or to the nearby terrestrial environment. The intensity is between 10 and 100 times greater than can be attributed to radio sources. The suggestion is that the universe has a thermodynamic radiation background corresponding to about 3.5°K. Observations at two other wave-lengths at least are needed to confirm this suggestion. One such observation is now being planned by Dicke at Princeton.

There seems no way in which such a background can be explained in terms of current astrophysical processes. Hence, if we accept the suggestion of Penzias and Wilson, the immediate implication is that the universe must have been different in the past from what it is today. Particularly, a higher density is needed to generate the background.

A similar result follows from the entirely different consideration of the helium-to-hydrogen ratio in stars and gaseous nebulae within our galaxy. Determinations of this ratio range from 0.08 to 0.18; and the ratio seems to be just as high in old stars as in most young stars. The ratio to be expected from current stellar activity is only 0.01. So either activity in the galaxy was much greater in the past, or the helium cannot be explained in terms of production from hydrogen through thermonuclear processes within the galaxy. Failure to observe any stars or any object with a low helium content points to the second of these possibilities.

It is possible to show by detailed calculation that, if matter in the universe has emerged from a state in which the temperature was above 10^{10} °K, the helium-to-hydrogen ratio must be about 0.14, a value which falls in the centre of the observed range. However, no values less than a truly universal value should be found. Two independent determinations for the Sun, one from structure calculations, one from observations of solar cosmic rays, give concordant results close to 0.09. This seems significantly below the expected universal value; but further work is needed to establish whether the discrepancy is real or not.

All the lines of investigation which I have mentioned so far point to an affirmative answer to the initial question: they point to the universal density in the past being higher than it is at present. Yet in every case the argument has been fraught with uncertainty. The probability seems against a negative answer, yet the possibility cannot be excluded. Speaking personally, I believe the case for a negative answer would still be arguable if it were not for the third of my three lines of attack. This again is entirely different in character from the helium/hydrogen ratio and from the microwave observation of Penzias and Wilson. I refer to the problem of the origin of elliptical galaxies. In my view, a consideration of this problem points decisively toward the universe having been very much denser in the past than it is at present.

Galaxies have been broadly classified into two types—ellipticals and spirals. There is an incontrovertible argument to show that spirals must have condensed from a more diffuse form. The spirals are rotating. Their angular momenta prevent them from being

最近，彭齐亚斯和威尔逊发现了一种波长在 7 厘米附近的射电背景辐射，他们坚信这个背景与设备和周围环境无关。因为该背景辐射的强度是由射电源辐射产生强度的 10 到 100 倍。所以这说明我们的宇宙有一个大约 3.5 K 的热力学辐射背景。要证实这个结论，还至少需要其他两个波长的观测数据，普林斯顿的迪克正在准备其中一个观测。

现有天体物理过程似乎无法解释这样的宇宙背景辐射。所以如果我们接受彭齐亚斯和威尔逊的结论，那么直接的推论就是宇宙过去处在与现在不同的状态中。特别要指出的是，要产生这样一个背景辐射就需要密度更高的宇宙。

下面一个相似的结论来自一个完全不同的研究方向：对银河系中恒星和气体星云里氦和氢比例的测量。这个比例测定结果大约是 0.08 到 0.18，并且该值似乎在年老的恒星和大多数年轻的恒星中都是类似的。而根据现有恒星活动强度对这个数值的期望值仅为 0.01。这要么说明过去星系中的活动性远比现在更强，要么说明星系中的氦不能被解释为氢在星系里的热核过程的产物。我们在任何恒星或天体中都没有观测到低的氦含量，所以有可能第二种可能性是正确的。

仔细的计算可以证明，如果宇宙中的物质都是经过 10^{10}K 以上的高温状态产生的，那么氦和氢比例将必然是约为 0.14，该值恰好在观测到的数据范围中心。但是不应该发现比实际的普遍值还要低的结果。对太阳的氦和氢比例现有两种独立的推算方法，一是从太阳的恒星结构进行计算，另一是根据太阳宇宙线的观测，而这两种方法都给出了一致的结果近似 0.09。这个结果看起来似乎明显小于所期望的普遍值，但是，我们还需要做进一步的工作来确认这个差异是否是真实的。

至此我介绍的各种不同方向的研究结果对最初的问题都给出了肯定的答复：过去的宇宙的密度比现在的要更高。但是，每项研究工作的论据均具有不确定性。这些结果看上去似乎不支持否定的答案，但是也不能排除这种可能。就我个人而言，如果没有我下面将要介绍的 3 条线中的第 3 条线索，我也会同意否定答案也许还是可以争辩的。这第 3 条线在性质上与氦 / 氢比例、彭齐亚斯和威尔逊的微波背景辐射完全不同。我称这个问题为椭圆星系起源问题。我认为对这个问题的考虑有力地表明了宇宙的过去比现在要更为致密。

星系可以被大致分为两类：椭圆星系和旋涡星系。毋庸置疑，那些旋涡星系肯定是从某种较为疏散的形态凝聚而来。旋涡星系是在旋转的，它们的角动量阻止其被压缩为更致密的形式。尽管从来没有从观测上认真检验过，扁平的椭圆星系也总

compressed into more compact forms. The flattened ellipticals have always been supposed to be similarly in rotation, but this has never been properly checked by observation. Because the ellipticals were thought to be in rotation it was similarly supposed that they were formed by a condensation process. This, I am now convinced, is wrong. I believe ellipticals to have formed through expansion from a higher density state.

Elliptical galaxies are remarkably amorphous. The star distribution is everywhere smooth. If one measures the surface brightness it is found to behave very nearly as an inverse square law, rising with great steepness toward the centre. The centres possess extremely bright central pips. How sharp these centres really are, how star-like, is impossible to say at the moment, for atmospheric seeing effects smear the central pip into an apparent disk.

Suppose the universe expanded from a much denser state, say 10^{-12} g cm^{-3}, and suppose the gas at the beginning of the expansion was not entirely smooth, suppose there were condensation knots already within it. It appears that such condensation knots can restrain the expanding gas to a degree which can be subject to precise calculation. A knot of 10^9 $M_\odot$ can restrain a total mass of 10^{12} $M_\odot$ within a region of galactic dimensions. A knot of 10^7 $M_\odot$ can restrain a mass of about $5 \cdot 10^{10}$ $M_\odot$. The critical point now emerges, that the surface brightness of the resulting aggregation can be calculated (assuming the material forms into stars) and the calculations yield quite unambiguously a law close to the inverse square, in fact just what is observed.

The point I wish to make is that whereas the steep rise towards the centre is expected, and is predicted, by the expansion picture, this characteristic feature of elliptical galaxies cannot, I believe, be understood at all within the condensation picture.

The clinching factor, it seems to me, is that a condensation knot—a memory of the initial dense state—is to be expected at the centre of every major elliptical galaxy. It is these condensation knots that give rise to the phenomenon of the radio galaxy. These are the massive objects which Fowler and I postulated some three years ago. Questions were asked of us at the time as to how our objects ever managed to form. Difficulties of angular momentum were raised. The answer which can now be given is that the objects never formed, in the sense in which the questions were asked. They are relics of a much higher density phase of the universe. They have been there since the galaxies themselves were formed, and in the sense of the radio astronomer they have been smouldering throughout the lifetimes of the galaxies. They are systems which remain at the very edge of stability. Whenever instabilities occur, violent outbursts serve to restabilize them.

Why is my initial question so important? Why make such a fuss about whether the universe has been in a more dense state? Because the present physical theory suggests that there is no limit to how great the density must have been in the past. I use the word "suggests" because the physical divergence of the density was first demonstrated for a homogeneous and isotropic universe. Divergence also occurs when the isotropic restriction is removed. Does it also occur when homogeneity is removed? I have always believed the

是被假定在做类似的旋转。因为认为椭圆星系是在旋转的，所以可以假设它们也经过了一个类似的凝聚过程而形成。但是现在我认为这是错误的。我相信椭圆星系是从一个更高密度态膨胀形成的。

椭圆星系是显著的无定形的，恒星在其中的分布是处处平滑的。如果测量椭圆星系的表面亮度，会发现某一点的面亮度和其距中心的距离非常接近平方反比定律。在接近中心点处面亮度上升十分陡。中心有一个极亮的中心核，但由于大气视宁度效应，将中心点涂抹成看起来成盘状，这让我们现在无法定出其中心有多锐，多像恒星。

假设宇宙是从一个密度高得多，比如，10^{-12} 克 / 厘米^3 的状态膨胀演化而来，并假定刚开始膨胀的气体并非完全平滑的，其中已经存在一些气体凝聚形成的团块，而这些凝聚团块能够在一定程度上使保持住的气体质量将能够被准确地计算。例如，一个大约有十亿个太阳质量的团块将能够使得大约一万亿个太阳质量的气体被束缚在星系大小的范围内。一个大约有一千万个太阳质量的团块将能够使得大约五百亿个太阳质量的气体被束缚。这样就有一个临界点出现了，那么总的聚合体的表面亮度是可以通过计算（假设这些物质形成恒星）得到的，而且计算产生的结果也会很好地符合平方反比定律，即正如我们观测到的。

而我想指明的一点是，鉴于在趋近中心时面亮度很陡的增加是被膨胀图像所期望和预言的，我相信，椭圆星系的这一特征是上面提到的凝聚模型所不能解释的。

就我看来决定因素是质量凝聚的团块，它们含有原初致密态的记忆，应存在于所有大椭圆星系中心。而也正是这些质量凝聚团块产生了射电星系。这就是大约三年前福勒和我提出的大质量天体。我们当时被问到，我们的这些天体是怎么形成的。角动量困难因而产生。而现在对此问题的答案是它们从来没有在问题所问的意义上形成过。那就是这样的大质量天体不是由某种现象或是天文学过程产生的，而是宇宙早期高密度状态至今留下的遗迹。星系形成时它们已经存在在那里了，而从射电天文学家的角度来看它们是贯穿星系寿命期一直保持在焖烧状态的处于稳定性边沿的系统。一旦不稳定性产生，强烈的爆发会使它们恢复稳定。

为什么我最初的问题这么重要？为什么我们要如此关心宇宙早期是不是比现在更致密？因为现有的物理学理论暗示了过去宇宙密度并不存在任何上限。我之所以用“暗示”，是因为物理密度的发散第一次在均匀各向同性宇宙中显示出来。即使我们去掉宇宙各向同性，发散仍然会发生。那么如果我们也不要求宇宙是均匀的，发散也会出现吗？我个人认为答案仍然是肯定的，但我必须指出，我对这个答案的信

answer to this question was also affirmative, but my belief was based more on the failure of those who maintained the opposite to demonstrate their case than on any positive demonstration on the affirmative side. However, progress on the affirmative side has been made very recently, and opinion has generally moved toward the view that the equations of physics contain a universal singularity.

I have always had a rooted objection to this conclusion. It seems as objectionable to me as if phenomena should be discovered in the laboratory which not only defied present physical laws but which also defied all possible physical laws. On the other hand, I see no objection to supposing that present laws are incomplete, for they are almost surely incomplete. The issue therefore presents itself as to how the physical laws must be modified in order to prevent a universal singularity, in other words how to prevent a collapse of physics.

It was with this background to the problem that several of us suggested, some twenty years ago, that matter might be created continuously. The idea was to keep the universe in a steady-state with creation of matter compensating the effects of expansion. In such a theory the density in the universe would not be higher in the past than it is at present. From the data I have presented here it seems likely that the idea will now have to be discarded, at any rate in the form it has become widely known—the steady-state universe. But let me proceed with the theoretical ideas which have grown out of the notions of twenty years ago, for they may turn out to have a value going beyond the first suggestions.

During the past ten years the struggle has been to invent a form of mathematics operating in the manner customary in physics, namely, starting from an action principle. It was found possible to represent the creation of matter through the introduction of a new field. The manner in which the field was treated was quite normal. What was different from ordinary physics was the motive underlying the investigation, the avoidance of a universal singularity, rather than an experiment in the laboratory. Physicists will introduce a new field at the drop of a hat, if experiments in the laboratory should direct them so; but the physicist is unhappy to do so for any other reason.

Having obtained the mathematical structure of the new field it was found that singularities never occur, quite regardless of whether matter is being created or not. So long as the new field exists there will be no singularity either of the universe or of a local imploding body. In other words, the models available for investigation, the models without singularities, were very much wider than the old steady-state theory. During the past few years it is these other models which have been under investigation. What has turned out?

The simplest case is that in which the new field exists but in which there is no creation of matter. It is then possible to obtain a finite, oscillating universe of the kind that has been sought for so long in the usual theory. The universe alternately expands and contracts. Gravitation causes the reversal from expansion to contraction, while the new field causes the rebound from contraction to expansion.

心更多的是建立在试图给出否定答案的人们的失败经历上的，而不是建立在支持方的正确论述上。尽管如此，最近支持方所取得的新进展和看法使得更多人相信我们现有的物理学方程包含着一个一般性的奇点。

事实上，我对这一结论有着根深蒂固的排斥。在我看来，如果一个在实验室中发现的现象不仅抵触现有的物理学定律，还抵触所有可能的物理学定律，那这将是不可接受的。另一方面，我相信现有的物理学定律是不完备的，事实上它们也必然是不完备的。那么我们现在面对的问题就是如何寻找一个方案来修改物理学定律以便消除一般性奇点的出现，换句话说就是要防止整个物理学的坍塌。

正是在这样的背景下，我们中的几个人在大约二十年前提出宇宙中的物质也许是持续不断产生的。提出这个理论的想法是让不断产生的物质来补偿宇宙的膨胀效应，使宇宙保持稳恒态。在这样的理论中过去的宇宙密度并不比现在高。就今天我在此给出的观测数据来看，这样的理论现在应该被抛弃，无论如何，其广为人知的形式，即稳恒态宇宙应该被抛弃。但是，让我进一步阐述其理论概念，它正是从上面那个二十年以前的理论衍生出来的，因为该理论的价值已经超过了其最初所设想的了。

在过去的十年间，人们一直努力于创造一种物理学所熟悉的数学运算形式，即，从作用量原理出发。人们发现，通过引入某种新场以代表物质的产生是可能的。而对场的处理也是很正常的。但这次与通常的物理学不同的是我们的研究的隐含动机不在于在实验室中进行的实验，而是为了消除一般性奇点。物理学家会立刻引入一个全新的场，如果实验室的实验需要他们这样做，但物理学家却不愿意为了任何其他理由而这么做。

在得到了新场的数学结构后，人们发现奇点确实不会出现，而与物质是否产生也没有什么关系。只要这种新的场存在，无论是宇宙还是在我们周围的爆炸天体都不可能有奇异性存在。换句话说，这是一个可用于探讨无奇异性的模型，而它比从前的稳恒态宇宙模型要广泛得多。它是最近的几年中人们一直在研究的另一个模型。那么研究的结果怎样呢？

最简单的一种情况是，存在这种新的场，但没有物质产生。那么我们可以得到有限而振荡的宇宙。这正是迄今为止很多通常理论所寻求的。宇宙交替地膨胀和收缩。引力使得宇宙从膨胀转为收缩，而新的场使宇宙从收缩转为膨胀。

So far as I am aware, such an oscillating model is in satisfactory agreement with all available data. The model is less dull than it seems at first sight, for it contains the possibility of some carry-through from one cycle to the next. Suppose the universe as we observe it eventually stops expanding. Suppose it falls back to a state of comparatively high density, a state in which stars are evaporated, a state in which even the nuclei of heavy elements are disrupted, a state from which matter emerges with the helium-to-hydrogen ratio I described before, about 0.14. In the state of high density things will not be quite uniform. Because of the existence of galaxies, and of clusters of galaxies, there will inevitably be some departures from uniformity. These departures will form the condensation knots round which a new generation of galaxies will form. Thus the condensation knots of which I spoke at an earlier stage are not merely random perturbations. One generation of galaxies acts as the seeds for the next generation. Magnetic fields will also persist from cycle to cycle.

There are two objections to this model. The new field is without sources. It is introduced *ad hoc*, along with the matter. There is never any coupling between the matter and the field. Then there is the subtle, but I believe the correct, objection that a series of oscillations must eventually damp out. Unless dissipative processes are precisely zero, which seems unlikely, the amplitude of the oscillation will gradually die away and the universe will come to rest in an intermediate static state.

For these reasons it is of interest to examine the models with creation of matter, noticing there is no specification from theory as to what the density must be in the steady-state situation. In the past the density was set empirically, by requiring it to be equal to the present-day density. Perhaps this step was wrong. Perhaps the true steady-state density should be very much higher.

During the past year, Dr. Narlikar and I managed to investigate a possibility which had previously proved too difficult to handle, the case in which there are departures from homogeneity, the case in which there are fluctuations from one region of space to another. To our surprise we found that under certain conditions the creation of matter could fall away in a localized region, and that if it did so the region would break into a series of oscillations of a kind that were closely analogous to the oscillations I have just been describing. In the former case we had oscillations of the whole universe, but of a universe of finite volume and finite mass. In this new case we have oscillations of a finite region of an infinite universe. From the point of view of an observer living in such a region it would be difficult to tell the difference. The oscillations would eventually damp away, but in this second case there would simply be a return to the steady-state condition. In this second case there will be many localized oscillating regions, not merely one. The regions will not in general be in juxtaposition with each other; they will usually be separated like islands in an ocean: and, like islands, they will be of different sizes and the amplitudes of their oscillations will be different.

I have already mentioned the philosophy of the physicist, that the whole of physics is

据我所知，这个振荡模型和现在所有数据都能很好地吻合。这个模型并不像乍看起来那样死板，因为其中包含着从一个循环转入下一个循环的可能性。如果我们现在的这个宇宙最终停止膨胀了，并且返回相对高的密度状态，在这种状态中，恒星将会蒸发，甚至重元素原子核也将瓦解，物质将形成，而氦和氢的比例也如我在上面提到的约为 0.14。在高密度状态，物质分布并非是十分均匀的。因为存在着星系或星系团，所以将不可避免地偏离均匀分布。而这样的不均匀将形成凝聚的团块，新一代的星系将会围绕它们形成。这样，我前面提到的凝聚的团块将不仅仅是来源于随机的扰动。上一代的星系将会成为下一代星系的种子。磁场也将在一次次循环中保存下来。

对于该模型，现在有两方面的反对意见。首先是这个模型中新引入的场是无源的。该场是我们为了此问题特别引入的。这个场与物质也绝不会有任何耦合。另一个微妙的但我相信是正确的问题是，经过一系列的振荡后，这种振荡将会逐渐衰减掉。除非宇宙的耗散过程精确地为零，而这几乎是不可能的。所以随着漫长的振荡，振幅逐渐减小，宇宙将会逐渐停止于一个中间静态。

正因为如此，又由于现在没有特定的由理论给出的明确的稳恒态宇宙的密度值，所以考察一下有物质产生的模型是有意义的。过去我们是经验地设定宇宙过去的密度，设定其大约与现在密度相同的数值。也许这一步是错误的。或许真正的稳恒态宇宙密度应当远高于此。

过去的几年间，纳利卡博士和我一直致力于研究宇宙显著偏离均匀性和各向同性状态的可能性，在此状态下空间从一个区域到另一个区域之间存在起伏，这种状态因为过于复杂而没有被人研究过。我们惊讶地发现，在某些条件下，在一个局部区域的物质产生有可能消失，如果这真的发生了，那么这个特定的区域也会进入一系列振荡的状态中，该状态非常类似于前面提到的宇宙振荡。前者是在宇宙中整体发生振荡，但是一个有限体积和有限质量的宇宙。而新的情况是在无限宇宙中的有限区域内发生的振荡。如果从正好生活在这样的一个区域中的观测者的观点，将无法区别两者的不同。同样，这种局部区域发生的振荡也可能衰减掉，但在第二种情况下振荡一旦衰减了，这片区域将就是回到稳恒态条件。在这第二种情况下，有可能存在非常多的局部振荡区域，而不仅仅只有一处。它们通常并不是并列相连的，而一般是像大海中分离的孤岛一样。它们有着不同的大小，其振荡的幅度也不相同。

我曾经提到过，物理学家的哲学是所有物理均能够在实验室中发现。而我们现

discoverable in the laboratory. What has been discovered is a remarkable mixture of elegance—invariance properties for example—and of ugliness, the fine structure constant being 137 ... for example. The properties of matter depend critically on the dimensionless numbers of physics, as well as on the structure of the laws. One can take three views on the dimensionless numbers:

(1) They just happen to have the values we find for them and no explanation of these values will ever be found.

(2) The observed values are necessary to the logical consistency of physics.

(3) The observed values are of non-local origin.

I imagine few will be satisfied with the first of these possibilities. I also imagine most physicists prefer (2). But what if (3) should be correct? Could the curious values we observe for the dimensionless numbers be connected with the particular oscillating and finite region in which we happen to live? If this were so, the universe would be far richer in its possibilities and content than we normally imagine. In other regions the numbers would be different and the gross properties of matter, the science of chemistry for example, would be entirely changed.

(**208**, 111-114; 1965)

F. Hoyle: F. R.S., Professor of Astronomy and Experimental Philosophy, University of Cambridge.

在所发现的是如守恒性质般优雅和如精细结构常数 137 般丑陋的异常混合体。物质的性质不仅取决于物理定律，也十分敏感的依赖于一些无量纲的数。人们对这些无量纲的数可以有三种看法：

（1）我们获得这些常数值纯粹巧合，并没有什么特别的解释。

（2）这些观测值是与物理学具有逻辑一致性所必需的。

（3）这些观测值并非局部起源。

我相信大多数人对第一个观点都不会满意，并且我也相信大多数物理学家会倾向于第二个观点。但是有没有人考虑过如果第三个观点是正确的呢？可不可能这些奇怪的无量纲数值恰好与特定的振荡现象及我们现在所处的宇宙区域有关？如果是这样的话，那么宇宙的可能及内容就可能远比我们想象的要丰富得多。在宇宙的其他区域中，这些数值会不同，物质的总体性质将完全不同，例如化学科学。

（樊彬 翻译；邓祖淦 审稿）

Pleistocene Glacial-Marine Zones in North Atlantic Deep-Sea Sediments

J. R. Conolly and M. Ewing

Editor's Note

Reconstruction of ancient climate from geological records began in the nineteenth century with studies of features carved by glaciers. By the 1960s there were new windows on the past, such as the analysis of cores drilled into marine sediments as described in this paper from John Conolly and Maurice Ewing of Columbia University. Ewing founded the Lamont Geological Observatory there in 1949. They report detritus from melted icebergs in cores from the North Atlantic, and point out that its geographical extent could enable reconstruction of fluctuations in ice-age climate—a technique now central to understanding the mechanisms and speed by which climate has switched in the past between glacial and warm conditions.

SINCE Bramlette and Bradley[1] first described glacial marine sediment zones in deep-sea cores across the North Atlantic, there has been no further attempt to use these zones as criteria for interpretation of Pleistocene climates. The occurrence of glacial erratics in the North Atlantic has been described by several authors[2-6]. One of the most recent accounts was given by Pratt[6], who described erratic boulders of granite, schist, diorite and quartzite from cores and dredges on the Great Meteor Seamount. These accounts indicate that icebergs floated much farther south in the North Atlantic during the cold periods of the Pleistocene, dropping considerable continental material as far south as 30° N.

An investigation was made of the occurrence of ice-rafted material in the Lamont cores from the North Atlantic to find cores in pelagic sediment which contained large variations in the vertical distribution of ice-rafted debris. In general, all cores taken in pelagic sediment north of 50° N. contained abundant glacial debris. In many areas near Labrador, Greenland and Iceland there was so much glacial debris that obvious variations in the amount of intensity of ice-rafting could not be measured. Farther south, cores described by Ericson *et al.*[7] consist of zones of sediment containing abundant ice-rafted grains. Cores taken south of 35° N. contain little or no ice-rafted grains. Hence it was decided to examine the variation in ice-rafted material in the cores between 40° and 50° N., particularly since Ericson *et al.* had already shown that they contained zones consisting of different Foraminifera assemblages deposited during cold and warm periods of the Pleistocene. The zones delineated by Ericson *et al.* can also be defined using the relative abundance of ice-rafted detritus present in the cores.

The amount of ice-rafted detritus present in the sand fraction of 13 cores taken from the

北大西洋深海沉积物中的更新世冰海区

康诺利，尤因

编者按

从19世纪起，以研究冰蚀地貌特征为开端，人们开始通过地质记录重建古气候。20世纪60年代，人们又发现了一些新的研究方法。正如哥伦比亚大学的约翰·康诺利和莫里斯·尤因在本文所介绍的，我们可以从海洋沉积物中钻取岩芯并对其进行分析。1949年，尤因在哥伦比亚大学建立了拉蒙特地质观测站。康诺利和尤因发现北大西洋的岩芯中含有来自融化冰川的碎屑，并提出根据这些碎屑的地理分布能够再现冰河期气候的波动。现在这一方法对于了解地质历史时期气候在冰期与间冰期之间的转换机制和转换速度非常重要。

自布拉姆利特和布拉德利[1]首次报道了北大西洋深海岩芯中存在冰海沉积物区段以来，目前还没有将这些区段作为解释更新世气候依据的进一步研究。一些学者[2-6]曾报道过北大西洋存在冰川漂砾。一份最新的报告来自普拉特[6]，他描述了来自大米蒂厄海山的岩芯与泥沙中的花岗岩、片岩、闪长岩和石英岩漂砾。这些研究表明，北大西洋的冰山在更新世寒冷期往南漂浮了相当远的距离，甚至在北纬30°处留下了大量的陆源物质。

为了在远洋沉积物中找到冰筏碎屑在垂向上具有明显变化的岩芯，我们对拉蒙特观测站的北大西洋岩芯的冰筏的材料进行了研究。来自北纬50°以北的远洋沉积物中的岩芯中一般都含有大量的冰川碎屑。在拉布拉多、格陵兰岛和冰岛附近的许多地区都存在冰川碎屑，其含量非常大以至于无法测定冰筏强度的明显变化。再往南，埃里克森等人[7]报道的岩芯皆含冰筏颗粒丰富的沉积区段。北纬35°以南的岩芯则仅含少量或根本不含冰筏颗粒。因此，以北纬40°和50°为界，我们决定检测该区域内的岩芯冰筏碎屑含量的变化，尤其是埃里克森等人指出，这一区域的岩芯在更新世的寒冷期与温暖期含有不同类型的有孔虫组合沉积。埃里克森等人划定的区域也可以用岩芯中冰筏碎屑的相对含量来限定。

我们对埃里克森等人[7]曾经描述过的13个北大西洋（图1）岩芯开展了研究，

North Atlantic (Fig. 1) previously described by Ericson *et al.*[7] was estimated at intervals down the cores (Fig. 2) by examination of the sand fraction under a binocular microscope. The cores lie between latitudes 40° and 50° N. and consist almost entirely of pelagic sediment containing varying percentages of pelagic organisms. Cores *A*157-5 and *A*180-14 were taken near the edge of the Sohm Abyssal Plain and contain one or two very thin quartz silt beds, presumably deposited by turbidity currents; but the rest of the sediment in these two cores is mainly pelagic. The remainder of the cores is located in positions in the deep-sea floor favourable for pelagic deposition.

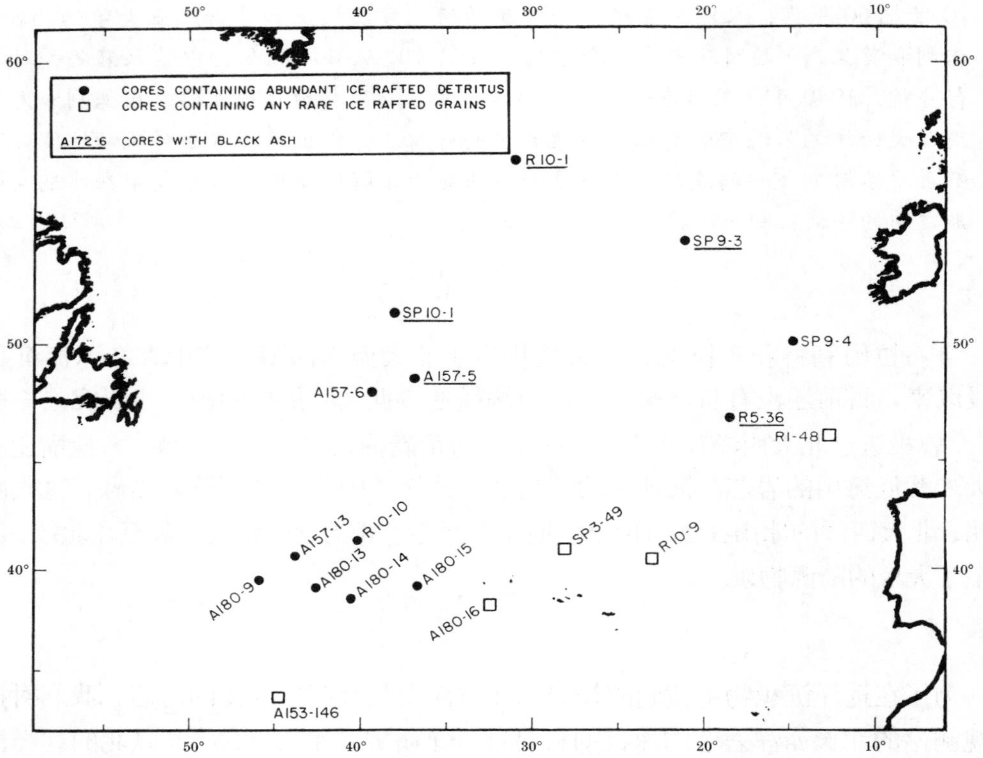

Fig. 1. North Atlantic Ocean showing the location of cores described in this investigation with abundant ice-rafted sand and pebbles and the location of cores containing only rare ice-rafted grains. Cores in the north and north-western North Atlantic contain black pumice and brown and black glass probably derived by ice-rafting from near Iceland

通过双目显微镜分析岩芯中的砂粒组分，估测了由上到下每隔一段芯中的冰筏碎屑量（图 2）。这些岩芯位于北纬 40° 和 50° 之间，成分几乎全是远洋沉积物，只不过其中远洋生物的含量不同。岩芯 *A*157-5 和 *A*180-14 取自索姆深海平原的边缘附近，它们含有一层或两层可能由浊流沉积的石英粉砂薄层，在这两个岩芯中的其他沉积物则主要是远洋沉积。其余岩芯均位于有利于远洋沉积的深海底部。

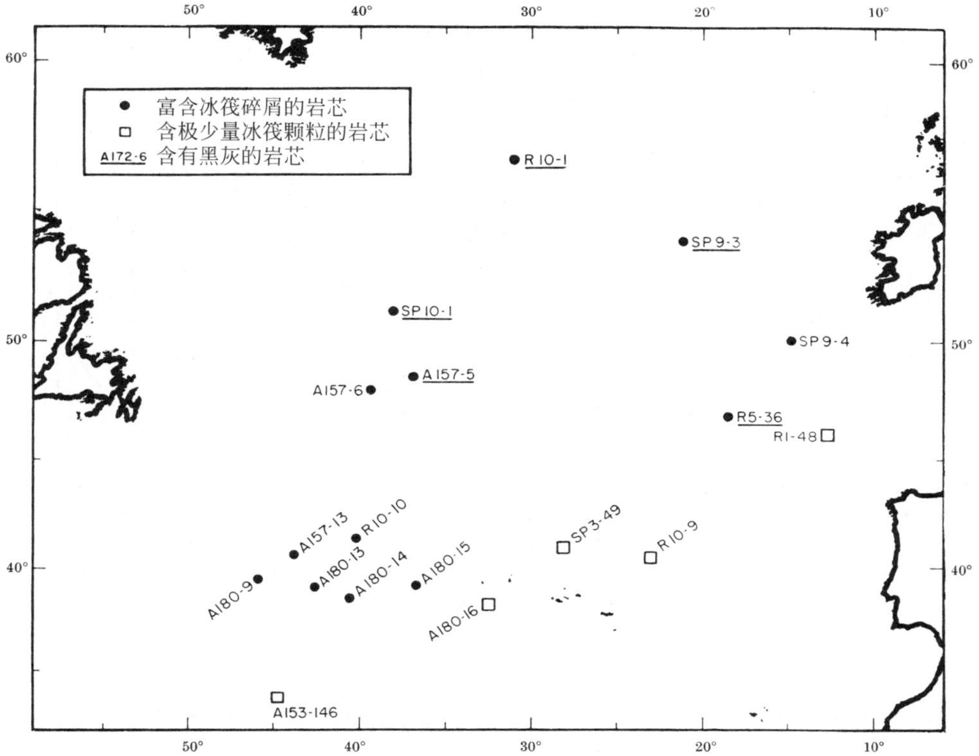

图 1. 本研究中描述的北大西洋地区富含冰筏砂及冰筏砾的岩芯位置和仅含极少量冰筏颗粒的岩芯位置简图。位于北大西洋北部和西北部的岩芯含有黑色浮石以及褐色和黑色玻璃，它们可能与冰岛附近的冰筏有关。

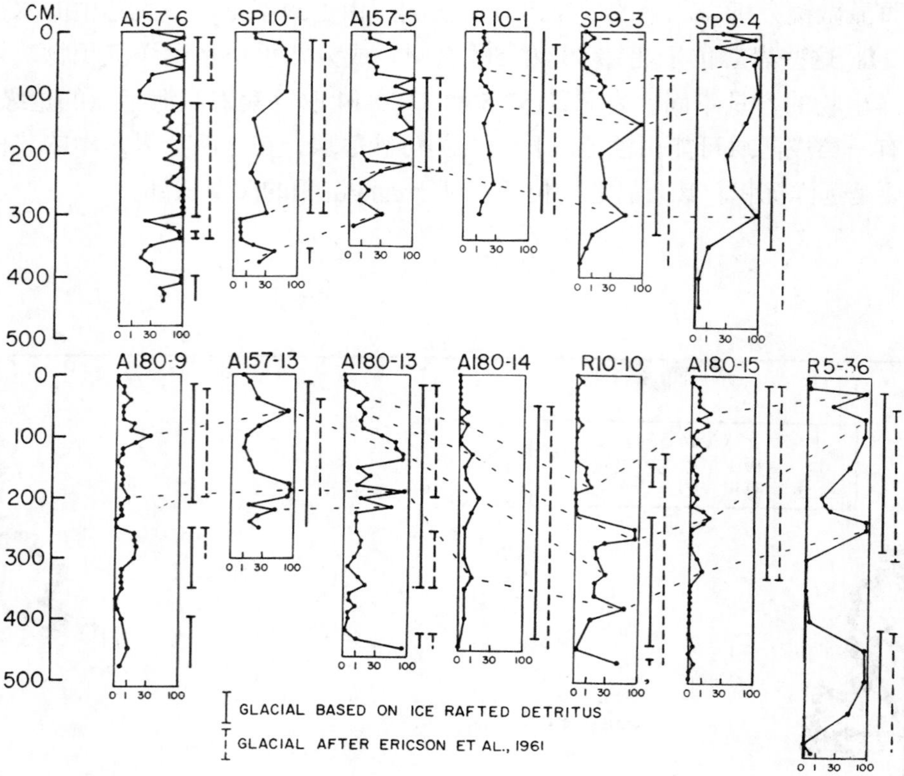

Fig. 2. The amount of ice-rafted detritus in the sand fraction is expressed as a percentage of the total sand fraction at intervals down 13 cores from the North Atlantic. Zones defined as glacials by Ericson *et al.* (ref. 7) in these cores can also be defined on the relative abundance of ice-rafted detritus. Tentative correlations are made between areas of cores containing high amounts of ice-rafted detritus. These areas may represent deposition during the major cold periods of the late Pleistocene

Table 1. Location of Cores used for Ice-rafting Distribution Analyses (Fig. 2)

Core	Latitude	Longitude	Water depth (metres)
*A*157-5	48°35′N	36°51′W	4,500
*A*157-6	48°03′N	39°20′W	4,500
*A*157-13	40°34′N	43°51′W	4,680
*A*180-9	39°27′N	45°57′W	4,060
*A*180-13	39°08′N	42°39′W	4,880
*A*180-14	38°41′N	40°40′W	5,020
*A*180-15	39°16′N	36°42′W	4,610
*R*5-36	46°55′N	18°35′W	4,500
*R*10-1	56°47′N	31°00′W	2,375
*R*10-10	41°24′N	40°06′W	4,755
*SP*9-3	53°53′N	21°06′W	2,745
*SP*9-4	50°02′N	14°46′W	4,205
SP10-1	51°23′N	38°04′W	3,695

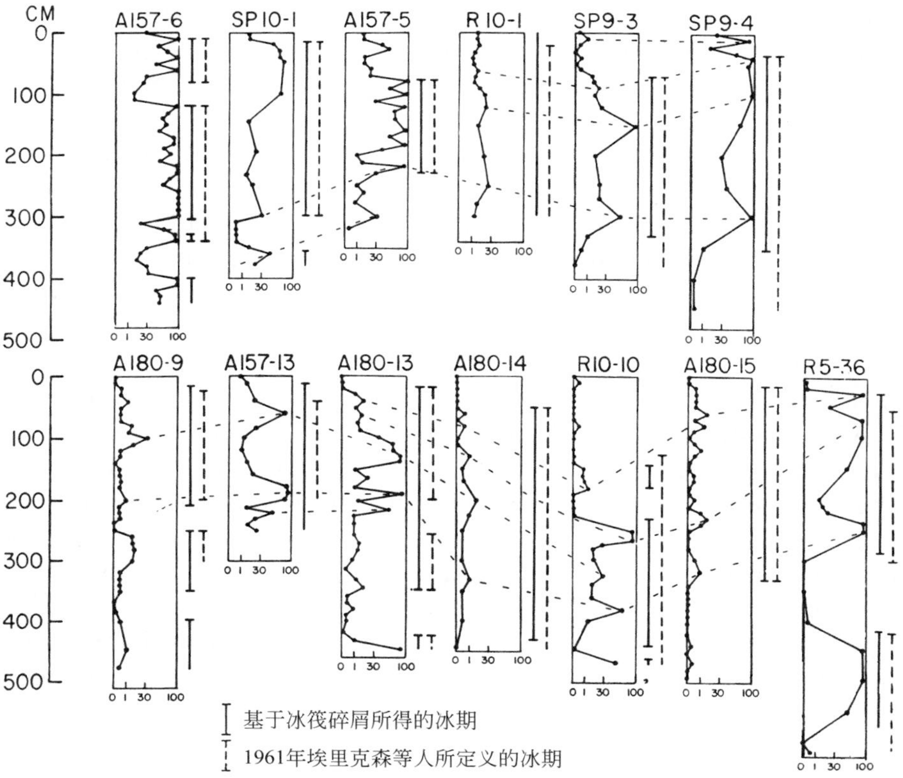

图 2. 对13个北大西洋岩芯自上而下每隔一段砂粒组分中冰筏碎屑进行了分析，含量表示为其占整个砂粒组分的百分比。岩芯中由埃里克森等人（参考文献7）所定义的冰期区域也可根据冰筏碎屑物的相对含量来确定。我们对富含冰筏碎屑的岩芯区段进行了对比。这些区域可能代表了晚更新世主要寒冷期沉积。

表 1. 图 2 中用于冰筏分布分析的岩芯的位置

岩芯	纬度	经度	水深（米）
*A*157-5	48°35′N	36°51′W	4,500
*A*157-6	48°03′N	39°20′W	4,500
*A*157-13	40°34′N	43°51′W	4,680
*A*180-9	39°27′N	45°57′W	4,060
*A*180-13	39°08′N	42°39′W	4,880
*A*180-14	38°41′N	40°40′W	5,020
*A*180-15	39°16′N	36°42′W	4,610
*R*5-36	46°55′N	18°35′W	4,500
*R*10-1	56°47′N	31°00′W	2,375
*R*10-10	41°24′N	40°06′W	4,755
*SP*9-3	53°53′N	21°06′W	2,745
*SP*9-4	50°02′N	14°46′W	4,205
SP10-1	51°23′N	38°04′W	3,695

In general, the sand fraction consists mainly of tests of pelagic Foraminifera mixed with ice-rafted sand and minor amounts of volcanic ash. The ice-rafted detritus is easily identifiable, as it characteristically consists of very poorly sorted, and mainly angular, sand and pebbles of a variety of mineral and rock types. The size, poor sorting, general angularity and wide lithological range of this detritus that occurs in pelagic sediment, far from land, indicate that it has dropped from melting ice. Many of the large pebbles are striated or faceted and large quartz grains are commonly frosted and pitted. Quartz is most abundant and commonly makes up 50-70 percent of the sand fraction. Pebbles of granitic, gneissic, regional metamorphic and sedimentary rocks of all kinds make up the bulk of the fraction coarser than 1 mm.

Black pumice and brown and black glass occur associated with ice-rafted sand in cores from the eastern North Atlantic. Since the amount of black volcanic detritus present bears a constant relation to the amount of poorly sorted ice-rafted sand, it must also be ice-rafted. The black pumice and glass are most abundant in cores taken close to Iceland (Fig. 1), as has been previously noted by Ericson *et al*[8], and the amount of black pumice decreases southwards, indicating dilution of this volcanic detritus from Iceland with detritus from eastern Greenland and the British Isles. In the western North Atlantic, quartz is less common and makes up only 30-50 percent of the ice-rafted sand. Large quantities of hornblende and garnet are particularly characteristic of the sand in cores *A*157-5 and *A*157-6.

The amount of ice-rafted sand present increases from a few grains in the southernmost cores to 20-30 percent of the total volume of sediment in the glacial marine zones in cores *SP*10-1 and *SP*9-3. The variation in the percentage of ice-rafted detritus in the sand fraction at intervals down the cores (Fig. 2) can be interpreted as a measure of the effects of climate on deposition. Zones containing a relatively high percentage of ice-rafted detritus correlate very closely with zones containing colder-water foraminiferal assemblages described by Ericson *et al.*[7].

There is considerable fluctuation in the amount of ice-rafted detritus deposited during these cold periods, suggesting that it might be possible to determine the major cold and warm zones within each glacial by correlating areas representing maximum and minimum amounts of ice-rafted detritus in different cores across the North Atlantic.

If it is assumed that the zones which Ericson *et al.*[7] considered to have been deposited during the last glacial (the period from about 11,000 to 60,000 years ago), and shown in Fig. 2, are correct, then it is possible to sub-divide further this cold period on the basis of the relative abundance of ice-rafted detritus. For example, core *R*10-10 contains a distinct zone containing abundant ice-rafted detritus between 150 and 180 cm from the top of the core. This zone occurs between areas dated as 11,800±480 and 15,820±200 years old[7] and probably contains ice-rafted detritus deposited during the last major glaciation of the last glacial period. Beneath this zone there are three more zones in which the sand fraction is made up almost entirely of ice-rafted detritus, suggesting that there were probably three

一般来讲，砂粒组分主要由远洋有孔虫组成，同时还混有冰筏砂和少量火山灰。冰筏碎屑很容易识别，它们主要由分选较差、大多呈棱角状、含多种矿物和岩石组分的砂和砾石组成。碎屑具有较大的颗粒、较差的分选、棱角状的形态，以及多种岩石类型的特征，这些表明出现在远洋沉积物中的碎屑是冰融沉积的产物。许多大砾石具有擦痕或磨蚀面，较大石英颗粒常呈毛玻璃或麻坑状。石英组分非常丰富，通常占到砂粒组分的 50%~70%。粒度大于 1 毫米的部分主要由花岗岩、片麻岩、区域变质岩和各类沉积岩组成。

在北大西洋东部的岩芯中，冰筏砂与黑色浮石以及褐色和黑色的玻璃共生。由于黑色火山碎屑的含量与分选较差的冰筏砂的含量具有稳定的关系，所以这类碎屑也应属于冰筏成因的漂砾。正如此前埃里克森等人[8]曾注意到的一样，冰岛附近岩芯中的黑色浮石和玻璃最为丰富（图 1），而黑色浮石的含量向南逐渐降低。这些现象表明来自东格陵兰岛和不列颠群岛的碎屑物稀释了来自冰岛的火山碎屑物。在北大西洋西部，石英含量较小，仅占冰筏砂的 30%~50%。岩芯 *A*157-5 和 *A*157-6 中冰筏砂的典型特征是含有大量的角闪石和石榴石。

冰筏砂的含量从南至北逐渐增加，在最南端钻取的岩芯中只含极少量颗粒，而位于冰海区的 *SP*10-1 和 *SP*9-3 岩芯中，冰筏砂占到沉积物总体积的 20%~30%。自上而下每隔一段对岩芯砂粒组分中冰筏碎屑的百分含量变化进行测量（图 2），可以用来衡量气候对沉积作用的影响程度。冰筏碎屑物百分含量相对较高的区段与埃里克森等人[7]描述的含冷水有孔虫组合的区段密切相关。

寒冷期沉积的冰筏碎屑的含量具有相当大的波动性。这表明，如果对北大西洋岩芯中冰筏碎屑含量最大和最小的区段进行对比，则有可能确定每次冰期的主要寒冷区和温暖区的位置。

图 2 给出了埃里克森等人[7]认为的末次冰期（约 11,000 年 ~60,000 年以前）的沉积区段，如果这些区段位置正确的话，那么就有可能根据冰筏碎屑的相对丰度进一步划分该寒冷期。例如，在岩芯 *R*10-10 中，距岩芯顶部 150 厘米 ~180 厘米之间是一个明显含有大量冰筏碎屑的区段。这个区段的年龄在 11,800±480 年和 15,820±200 年之间[7]，可能包含末次冰期最后一次主要冰川沉积的冰筏碎屑。在这个区段之下还有另外三个区段，其砂粒组分几乎全由冰筏碎屑组成，表明末次冰期内还可能包含另外三个重要的寒冷期。其他许多岩芯中也存在类似的富含冰筏碎屑

more major cold periods during the last glacial period. Similar zones containing high amounts of ice-rafted detritus occur in many of the other cores and possible correlations between them are shown in Fig. 2.

These results indicate that the abundance and distribution of ice-rafted detritus in deep-sea cores in the North Atlantic could provide a powerful tool for delineating even minor fluctuations in the Pleistocene climate. Cores taken in pelagic sediment in the vicinity of cores *R*5-36, *R*10-10 and *A*180-13 in particular should contain easily determinable ice-rafted zones that might eventually lead to a better understanding of the fluctuations in climate and rates of sedimentation during the Pleistocene in the North Atlantic. Furthermore, it may be possible to delineate the Pliocene-Pleistocene boundary, using the first appearance of ice-rafted detritus in deep-sea pelagic cores as a criterion. The disappearance of ice-rafted detritus with depth occurs in sediment cores raised from the deep ocean floor surrounding Antarctica[9,10] and occurs just beneath the Pliocene-Pleistocene boundary based on radiolarian assemblages[11].

So far, none of the cores taken in the North Atlantic ice-rafting area passes by continuous section through the Pleistocene and none has been identified as containing the Pliocene-Pleistocene boundary; but further attempts to take such cores are now in progress.

We thank D. B. Ericson, who kindly lent us samples of sand from Lamont cores. Important support for this work was provided by a Ford Foundation fellowship and a Fulbright travel grant for Dr. J. R. Conolly. This work was also supported by the Office of Naval Research and by the U.S. National Science Foundation.

(**208**, 135-138; 1965)

John.R. Conolly and Maurice. Ewing: Lamont Geological Observatory of Columbia University, Palisades, New York.

References:

1. Bramlette, M. N., and Bradley, W. H., *U.S. Geol. Surv., Prof. Paper*, **196**, A, Part 1 (1940).
2. Murray, J., and Renard, A. F., *Challenger Rep.*, 322 (1891).
3. Andree, K., *Geologie des Meereskoden*, **2** (Gebouder Borntraeger, Leipzig, 1891).
4. Ewing, M., *Nat. Geog. Mag.*, **96**, 611 (1949).
5. Heezen, B. C., *Geol. Soc. Amer. Spec. Paper*, **65**, 99 (1959).
6. Pratt, R. M., *Deep-Sea Res.*, **8**, 152 (1961).
7. Ericson, D. B., Ewing, M., Wollin, G., and Heezen, B. C., *Geol. Soc. Amer.*, **72**, 193 (1961).
8. Ericson, D. B., Ewing, M., and Wollin, G., *Science*, **144**, 1183 (1964).
9. Krinsley, D. H., and Newman, W. S., *Science*, **149**, 442 (1965).
10. Conolly, J. R., and Ewing, M., *Science* (in the press).
11. Hays, J. D., *Amer. Geophys. Union Antarctic Research Series*, **6**, 125 (1965).

物的区段，图 2 显示了它们之间可能的关系。

上述结果表明，北大西洋深海岩芯中冰筏碎屑物的含量和分布为描绘更新世更小幅度的气候波动提供了一个强有力的工具。尤其是在岩芯 *R*5-36、*R*10-10 和 *A*180-13 附近的远洋沉积物中所获取的岩芯，它们应该含有易于鉴定的冰筏带，从而有助于更好地了解更新世北大西洋地区的气候波动以及沉积速率。此外，利用深海远洋岩芯中冰筏碎屑的首次出现作为判别条件，我们有可能划定上新世–更新世的界限。在南极 [9,10] 周围，深海沉积物岩芯中的冰筏碎屑随深度增加而消失，这一现象恰好发生在根据放射虫组合 [11] 所确定的上新世–更新世的界面之下。

迄今为止，取自北大西洋冰筏地区的岩芯没有一个能代表更新世完整的连续剖面，也没有一个岩芯能跨越上新世–更新世的界限。但获取此类岩芯的工作正在进行中。

感谢埃里克森为我们慷慨地提供了拉蒙特岩芯库的砂样。福特基金会为本项工作提供了重要资助，康诺利博士得到了富布莱特基金的赞助。此外，美国海军研究办公室和美国国家科学基金会也为本研究提供了支持。

（李任伟 翻译；孟庆任 审稿）

Structural Basis of Neutron and Proton Magic Numbers in Atomic Nuclei

L. Pauling

Editor's Note

Physicists by the mid 1960s had noted the surprising stability of atomic nuclei having certain "magic numbers" of either protons or neutrons, including 2, 8, 20, 50, 82 and 126. Here American chemist Linus Pauling offers an explanation. These numbers do not correspond to atomic shells being completely filled with fermions (particles with spin 1/2, like protons and neutrons). However, they do appear to correspond to closed shells of nucleons which achieve efficient packing in space, possibly with an extra halo of alpha particles. For example, the magic number 50 arises as 8 neutrons or protons in a closed-shell core, and another 42 in an outer halo. These magic-number nuclei have a higher average binding energy than other nuclei.

IN 1933 Elsasser[1] pointed out that some of the properties of atomic nuclei correspond to greater stability for certain numbers of neutrons and protons (given the name magic numbers) than for other numbers; the magic numbers for both N (neutron number) and Z (proton number) are 2, 8, 20, 50, 82 and 126. (Less-pronounced effects are observed also for N or Z equal to 6, 14, 28, 40, and some larger numbers. The set of magic numbers is often assumed to include 28.)

The magic numbers do not have the values ($2n^2$) for completed shells of fermions (with all states with total quantum number n, azimuthal quantum number $l \leqslant n-1$, occupied by pairs), which are 2, 8, 18, 32, 50, ..., nor the values for certain shells and sub-shells that lead to maximum stability for electrons in atoms, which are 2, 10, 18, 36, 54 and 86.

It was discovered by Mayer[2] and by Haxel, Jensen and Suess[3] that the magic numbers can be accounted for by use of the sub-sub-shells corresponding to spin-orbit coupling of individual nucleons; that is, to the values of $j = l + 1/2$ and $l - 1/2$ for the two sub-sub-shells of each sub-shell. For example, they[4] assign to N or $Z = 50$ the configuration $(1s1/2)^2(1p3/2)^4(1p1/2)^2(1d5/2)^6(2s1/2)^2(1d3/2)^4(1f7/2)^8(2p3/2)^4(1f5/2)^6(2p1/2)^2(1g9/2)^{10}$, which may be written more briefly as $1s^2 1p^6 1d^{10} 2s^2 2p^6 1f^{14}(1g9/2)^{10}$.

The evidence for spin-orbit coupling and for the Mayer-Jensen shell model is convincing. It is, however, difficult to understand, on the basis of their arguments, why the six magic numbers should be outstanding among the many numbers corresponding to the completion of spin-orbit sub-sub-shells, which (for the Mayer-Jensen sequence[4] of energy-levels) are 2, 6, 8, 14, 16, 20, 28, 32, 38, 40, 50, 56, 64, 68, 70, 82, 92, 100, 106, 110, 112, 126, 136, 142, ...

中子和质子在原子核中的幻数的结构基础

鲍林

编者按

在 20 世纪 60 年代中期，物理学家注意到，那些出奇稳定的原子核都含有一些特定“幻数”的质子或中子，这些“幻数”包括 2、8、20、50、82 和 126。本文中，美国化学家莱纳斯·鲍林提出了一种解释：他认为这些幻数并不对应于那些完全被费米子（自旋为 1/2 的粒子，例如质子和中子）填满的原子壳层。而是看起来对应于在空间中被有效堆积的核子的闭壳层，可能还带有一圈外加的 α 粒子晕。例如，幻数 50 就意味着在闭壳层核心内有 8 个中子或质子，另外 42 个在外层晕中。与其他原子核相比，这些幻数核具有更高的平均结合能。

艾尔萨瑟[1]于 1933 年指出，较之于其他数，具有某些特定中子数和质子数（将其命名为幻数）的原子核的一些性质更为稳定。对于 N（中子数）和 Z（质子数），这些幻数是 2、8、20、50、82 和 126。（对于 N 或 Z 等于 6、14、28、40 以及某些更大的数，也能注意到不太明显的效应。通常认为幻数序列包括 28。）

幻数既不是与费米子满壳层（或者说费米子成对填满主量子数为 n、角量子数为 $l \leqslant n-1$ 的所有状态）有关的数值 ($2n^2$)，即 2、8、18、32、50……也不是与某些可导致电子在原子中有最大稳定性的壳层和子壳层有关的数值：2、10、18、36、54 和 86。

梅耶夫人[2]以及哈克塞尔、延森和苏斯[3]都发现，幻数可以利用对应于独立核子的自旋–轨道耦合的支壳层来进行解释；也就是说，对应于某一子壳层的总角动量分别为 $j = l + 1/2$ 和 $l - 1/2$ 的两个支壳层。例如，他们[4]将 N 或 Z 为 50 的组态标记为 $(1s1/2)^2$ $(1p3/2)^4$ $(1p1/2)^2$ $(1d5/2)^6$ $(2s1/2)^2$ $(1d3/2)^4$ $(1f7/2)^8$ $(2p3/2)^4$ $(1f5/2)^6$ $(2p1/2)^2$ $(1g9/2)^{10}$，或更简略地写成 $1s^2$ $1p^6$ $1d^{10}$ $2s^2$ $2p^6$ $1f^{14}$ $(1g9/2)^{10}$。

有关自旋–轨道耦合和梅耶夫人–延森壳层模型的证据是令人信服的。然而，对于他们的论据，让人难以理解的是，为什么这 6 个幻数在可以填满自旋–轨道耦合的支壳层的数字集合中是如此与众不同，这个集合（对于能级的梅耶夫人–延森序列[4]）是 2、6、8、14、16、20、28、32、38、40、50、56、64、68、70、82、92、100、106、110、112、126、136、142……

In the course of developing a theory of nuclear structure based on the assumption of closest packing of clusters of nucleons[5], I have found that the magic numbers have a very simple structural significance: 2 and 8 correspond to the closed shells $1s^2$ and $1s^21p^6$, and the others to a closed-shell core with an outer layer (the mantle of the nucleus) containing the number of spherons (helions[6], He^4, tritons, H^3, or dineutrons) required to surround the core in closest packing.

Triangular (icosahedral) closest packing, as found, for example, in the intermetallic compound[7] $Mg_{32}(Al,Zn)_{49}$, involves the sequence 1, 12, 32, 72 of spheres in successive layers. These numbers are approximated by the equation $n_0 = (n_i^{1/3} + 1.30)^3 - n_i$, in which n_0 is the number of spheres in an outer layer and n_i is the number in the core. (The form of this equation corresponds to assigning equal effective volumes to the spheres, and the value of the constant reflects the nubbling of the surface and the packing of outer spheres into pockets of the core.) This equation can be applied to obtain the number of spherons in the successive layers in a nucleus, and thus to obtain the sequence of nucleonic energy-levels. Sub-shells (with given value of l) occurring once (as $1s$, $1p$, etc.) are assigned to the mantle of spherons, those occurring twice ($1s$ and $2s$, for example) to the mantle and next inner layer, and so on. Thus I interpret the configuration for N or Z = 50, given above, as representing 8 neutrons or protons in the core ($1s^21p^6$) and 42 in the outer layer ($2s^22p^61d^{10}1f^{14}(1g9/2)^{10}$).

The application of the packing equation leads to a sequence of levels essentially as given by Mayer and Jensen, but often with sub-sub-shells for different layers being filled over overlapping ranges of values of N or Z. For example, the $3s1/2$, $2d3/2$, and $1h11/2$ sub-sub-shells all begin to be occupied at about N or Z = 60 and are all completed at about N or Z = 82.

The configurations found in this way for the magic numbers are given in Table 1 and Fig. 1. Each of the first two represents a completed shell. The third (20) has a completed shell as core and another as mantle. Each of the others has a core of a completed shell or two completed shells, with a mantle that is required by the packing to include a sub-sub-shell $(1g9/2)^{10}$ for 50, $(1h11/2)^{12}$ for 82, and $(1i13/2)^{14}$ for 126. Until 184 is reached, there are no other values of N or Z for which the packing equation leads to a core consisting of layers that are completed shells.

Table 1. Nucleon configurations for magic numbers

N or Z	Mantle	Core or outer core	Inner core
2	$1s^2$		
8	$1s^21p^6$		
20	$2s^21p^61d^{10}$	$1s^2$	
50	$2s^22p^61d^{10}1f^{14}(1g9/2)^{10}$	$1s^21p^6$	
82	$3s^22p^62d^{10}1f^{14}1g^{18}(1h11/2)^{12}$	$2s^21p^61d^{10}$	$1s^2$
126	$3s^23p^62d^{10}2f^{14}1g^{18}1h^{22}(1i13/2)^{14}$	$2s^22p^61d^{10}1f^{14}$	$1s^21p^6$

在构建基于核子集团最密堆积假设的核结构理论[5]的过程中，我已发现，幻数具有非常简单的结构意义：2 和 8 对应于闭壳层组态 $1s^2$ 和 $1s^21p^6$，而其他的则对应于带有一个外层（称为核的幔壳层）的闭壳层核，其中外层内含有一定数量的球子（氦核[6]、He[4]、氚核、H[3] 或双中子），这些球子以堆积的方式围绕在核心周围。

例如，在金属间化合物[7] $Mg_{32}(Al,Zn)_{49}$ 中发现的（二十面体的）三角形最密堆积各外层中包含的球子数按顺序依次为 1、12、32、72。这些数可用方程 $n_0=(n_i^{1/3}+1.30)^3-n_i$ 近似表示，其中 n_0 是在一个外（壳）层中球子的数目，n_i 是核中球子的数目。（这个方程的形式相当于为球子赋予等量的有效体积，常数值反映了表面的小块和外部球子的堆积进入到了核心的内部。）这个方程可用来计算核内相继外层中球子的数目，进而获得核子能级的序列数。子壳层（具有特定的角量子数 l）一旦出现（如组态 $1s1p$ 等）就分配给球子的幔壳层，那些出现二次的（如 $1s$ 和 $2s$）就分配给幔壳层和下一个内层，等等。因此，对于上述给定的 N 或 Z = 50 的组态，我的解释是：在核心 $(1s^21p^6)$ 中有 8 个中子或质子，另外 42 个中子或质子在外层 $(2s^22p^61d^{10}1f^{14}(1g9/2)^{10})$ 里。

堆积方程的应用基本上导出了梅耶夫人和延森给出的能级序列，但通常是在 N 或 Z 值有重叠的范围内填满不同外层的支壳层。例如，支壳层 $3s1/2$，$2d3/2$ 和 $1h11/2$ 都在 N 或 Z 约为 60 时开始填充，直到 N 或 Z 约为 82 时才都被填满。

在表 1 和图 1 中分别给出了将这种方法应用于幻数后得到的组态。前两个幻数都表示满壳层，第三个幻数（20）则有一个满壳层作为核心和另一个作为幔壳层。其他每一个幻数都包含一个或两个满壳层作为核心，至于它们的幔壳层，在幻数是 50 的情况下，堆积要求其包含组态为 $(1g9/2)^{10}$ 的支壳层，在幻数为 82 的状态下，包含 $(1h11/2)^{12}$ 的支壳层，而幻数 126 则包含 $(1i13/2)^{14}$ 的支壳层，一直至幻数 184，不存在 N 或 Z 的其他数值，由堆积方程导出的仅包含满壳层的核。

表 1. 对于各种幻数的核子组态

N 或 Z	幔壳层	核心或外层核心	内层核心
2	$1s^2$		
8	$1s^21p^6$		
20	$2s^21p^61d^{10}$	$1s^2$	
50	$2s^22p^61d^{10}1f^{14}(1g9/2)^{10}$	$1s^21p^6$	
82	$3s^22p^62d^{10}1f^{14}1g^{18}(1h11/2)^{12}$	$2s^21p^61d^{10}$	$1s^2$
126	$3s^23p^62d^{10}2f^{14}1g^{18}1h^{22}(1i13/2)^{14}$	$2s^22p^61d^{10}1f^{14}$	$1s^21p^6$

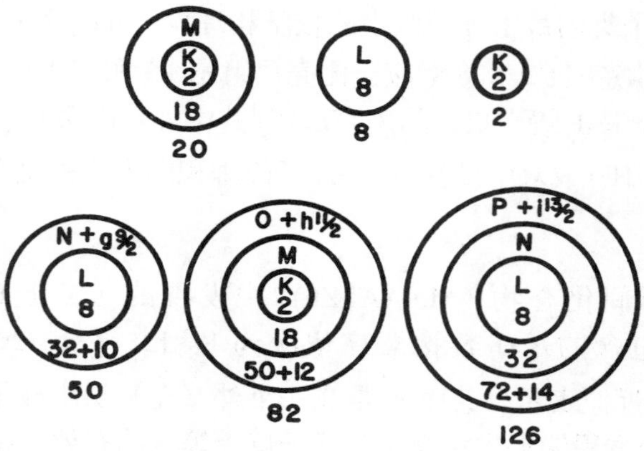

Fig. 1. The magic-number structures of atomic nuclei

I conclude that the stability that characterizes the magic numbers results from the completion of shells for a single layer (2, 8) or two layers (20) of spherons, or, for the larger magic numbers (50, 82, 126), for the core layers, the mantle having a completed shell plus a completed sub-sub-shell.

(**208**, 174; 1965)

L. Pauling: Big Sur, California.

References:

1. Elsasser, W. M., *J. Phys. et Radium*, **4**, 549 (1933); **5**, 389, 635 (1934).

2. Mayer, M. Goeppert, *Phys. Rev.*, 75, 1969 (1949).

3. Haxel, O., Jensen, J. H. D., and Suess, H. E., *Phys. Rev.*, 75, 1766 (1949); *Z. Physik*, **128**, 295 (1950).

4. Mayer, M. Goeppert, and Jensen, J. H. D., *Elementary Theory of Nuclear Shell Structure*, 58 (John Wiley and Sons, Inc., New York and London, 1955).

5. This theory is described in papers to be published in *Phys. Rev. Letters, Proc. U. S. Nat. Acad. Sci.*, and *Science*.

6. Pauling, L., *Nature*, **201**, 61 (1964): Proposal of the name helion for the α-particle.

7. Bergman, G., Waugh, J. L. T., and Pauling, L., *Nature*, **169**, 1057 (1952); *Acta Cryst.*, **10**, 254 (1957). Pauling, L., *The Nature of the Chemical Bond*, third ed., 427 (Cornell University Press, Ithaca, New York, 1960).

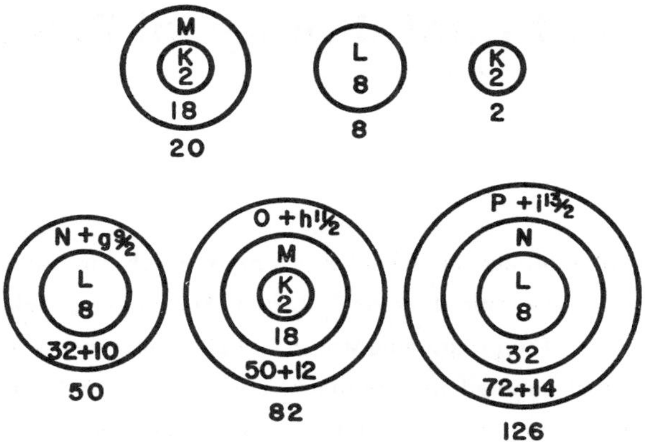

图 1. 原子核的幻数结构

我的结论是，幻数所体现的稳定性来自于由球子组成的单层（2、8）或者双层（20）满壳层，或者对于更大的幻数（50、82、126）和具有核心的层，则幔壳层是由一个满壳层加上一个填满的支壳层构成。

（沈乃澂 翻译；厉光烈 审稿）

The International Biological Programme*

E. B. Worthington

Editor's Note

The context of the International Biological Programme which ran during the 1960s and 1970s, as explained here by its scientific director E. Barton Worthington, looks astonishingly prescient from today's perspective. The programme was essentially concerned with environmental biology and conservation, but it adopted the approach, now very much in vogue again, of regarding nature as a resource on which human welfare depends. It developed the notion of the biosphere, or as Worthington puts it, "the living layer around the Earth". And in considering such issues as human impact on fish stocks, human adaptability to environmental change and the robustness of ecosystems, the IBP anticipated some of the major themes in environmental research today.

THE International Biological Programme is now well into its first year—the first of seven or eight. It is concerned with "the biological basis of productivity and human welfare". It is divided into two phases: Phase I, which consists mainly of design and feasibility studies, to occupy most of 1965 and 1966; Phase II, the operational programme, to commence in 1967 and carry on for about five years. Beyond these simple facts I doubt if there are many people who know much about the Programme, for we have been so busy planning it that little thought has been given to advertising it.

The International Biological Programme is a programme which, because of the effects of various factors, particularly the climate, must extend over a number of years, since it is obvious that an investigation of growth in a summer such as we have had this year would be quite different from a similar study undertaken last year. It has, however, drawn some of its inspiration from the International Geophysical Year. Indeed, if one looks at the development of the sciences during the past few decades one is struck by the high peaks of achievement reached in international collaboration and also through international competition in the physical sciences. Research on the ionosphere, the atmosphere, and the geosphere has been greatly stimulated by organized activities—the International Polar Years, the International Geophysical Year and the International Years of the Quiet Sun which have developed one from the other. Programmes are going forward strongly, too, in connexion with the hydrosphere, as arranged by the Intergovernmental Oceanographic Commission and the International Hydrological Decade. But in such investigations the biosphere has been almost completely neglected. Yet on the natural resources of this Earth—especially the renewable ones which come from biological productivity—the future

* Substance of an Evening Discourse delivered on September 3 at the meeting in Cambridge of the British Association for the Advancement of Science.

国际生物学计划*

沃辛顿

编者按

站在今天的角度看，国际生物学计划是一个非常具有前瞻性的计划，本文中该计划的科学主任巴顿·沃辛顿指出它是在20世纪六七十年代期间实施的。虽然该计划的重点是关于环境生物学和环境保护，但它采用了将自然看作人类福利所依赖的资源的方法，现在这种方法又流行了起来。该计划还提出了生物圈或沃辛顿所说的“围绕地球表面的生命层”的概念。国际生物学计划预见到了现在环境研究中的一些重大议题，如人类对鱼类资源的影响，人类对环境变化的适应性以及生态系统的稳定性。

现在是国际生物学计划实施的第一年——该项目计划实施七至八年，是关于“生产力和人类福利的生物学基础”方面的研究。它被分成两个阶段：阶段 I 主要是在1965 年和 1966 年的大部分时间里设计计划并对其可行性进行分析；阶段 II 是方案执行阶段，开始于 1967 年并将持续大约 5 年。除了这些简单的事实外，我估计没有多少人对这个计划有更多的了解，因为我们一直忙于制订计划以至于几乎没有考虑去宣传它。

由于受到各种因素的影响，特别是气候影响，国际生物学计划必须持续若干年，因为很显然我们今年夏天对生长情况的调查结果可能显著不同于去年进行的类似的调查。然而，从国际地球物理年中我们能得到一些鼓励。实际上，如果人类回顾过去数十年间的科学发展，那么一定会对物理科学中通过国际合作和国际竞争所获得的辉煌成就而感到吃惊。通过有组织的活动大大促进了对电离层、大气层和地圈的研究，这些活动包括相继举办的国际极地年、国际地球物理年和国际宁静太阳年。由政府间海洋学委员会和国际水文十年计划举办的与水圈相关的计划也将得到迅速的发展。但是在诸如此类的研究中，生物圈已经几乎完全被忽略了。然而人类的将来必须依赖地球上的自然资源，特别是来源于生物生产力区域的可再生资源。相比于登陆月球或抓拍火星的特写镜头而言，这些对人类要重要得多。有人甚至认为，对人类来说保证北海鱼类的稳定产量要比探测与开采可能存在于北海下的石油更重要。

---

* 在 9 月 3 日剑桥的英国科学促进会会议上发表的晚间演说的内容。

of mankind depends. They are much more important to most human beings than getting to the Moon or taking close-up photographs of Mars. One could even argue that it is more important to humankind to ensure a sustained yield of fish from the North Sea than to discover and extract the oil that may lie beneath it.

What do we mean by biology within the context of the International Biological Programme? To some, biology means the life sciences as opposed to the earth sciences; to some it stimulates thoughts of the inner workings of the cell; and to some perhaps, merely the facts of human reproduction. For the purposes of an International Biological Programme, I think the best definition is the biosphere, that is the living layer around the Earth, on land, in the waters and in the air.

This word biosphere, by the way, seems to present a problem in semantics. I have heard it explained by a television astronomer as a concentric region of the solar system, comprising the orbits of Venus, the Earth and Mars, where there is some reason to believe that life as we know it exists. I use it, however, as the layer which supports life in, on and around the Earth, for the International Biological Programme is likely to have little time or opportunity to extend its activities to other planets.

Some biologists are inclined to think that the International Biological Programme is rather a waste of effort and money. They argue that opportunities for the exchange of knowledge and ideas are not lacking, but are almost overburdening, for international unions and associations exist in every branch of biology. From spring to autumn scarcely a week passes without some international biological congress, often several running contemporaneously, even in the same country. Is this not enough?

The counter argument is that we scientists concerned with environmental biology have to take but one look at our colleagues concerned with the physical environment to appreciate what a degree of organization can do. Few would deny that studies of this kind of biology, concerned with the organism in relation to its environment, which had such a splendid start in the past century, have been sadly overtaken in this century by studies in the physical sciences. In the long run, I believe that the International Biological Programme will be looked on as a major effort—and a successful one—to redress this balance. In doing so it will provide a part of the fundamental knowledge which today is so much needed so that biological science can be applied more effectively to the provision of human needs.

History

Before examining the content of the International Biological Programme we should consider how the idea came into being. British scientists have taken a prominent part in this. Sir Rudolph Peters some years ago, when president of the International Council of Scientific Unions (ICSU), took a major part in the conception of the International Biological Programme. Prof. H. W. Thompson of Oxford, the current president of ICSU, did a good job as midwife during the first International Biological Programme Assembly

在实施国际生物学计划的大背景下，我们所说的生物学具体指的是什么呢？对某些人来说，生物学指的是生命科学而不是地球科学；对有些人来说，它促使其思考细胞内部的运行方式；或许还有些人认为，它仅指人类繁殖这一事实。在国际生物学计划里，我认为最好的定义是生物圈，也就是围绕地球表面的，存在于陆地上、水中还有空中的生命层。

顺便说一下，生物圈这个词似乎在语义上存在一个问题。我曾听过一个电视天文学家将其解释为太阳系的同心区域，包括金星、地球和火星的轨道，也就是那些我们有理由相信存在生命的地方。然而，我指的是用以维持生命的地球的下层、表层和周围，就国际生物学计划而言，它可能没有时间或机会将其活动扩展到其他的行星上。

一些生物学家倾向于认为国际生物学计划是相当浪费精力和金钱的。他们认为交流知识和想法的机会并不缺乏而是几乎过盛，因为国际联盟和协会包含生物学的各个分支。从春季到秋季几乎每个星期都会有一些国际生物学大会，常常几个会议同时举行甚至是在一个国家举行。难道这还不够吗？

与之背道而驰的观点是我们环境生物学科学家只需稍微关注研究自然环境的同事们，就可以领悟组织能够做到何种程度。很少有人会不认可对这类涉及生物与环境之间联系的生物学的研究，它在上个世纪有着相当好的开端，但在本世纪却不幸地被自然科学研究超越了。从长远来看，我相信国际生物学计划在成功恢复这种平衡的过程中，将发挥主要作用。通过这样做，它将提供一些我们现在迫切需要的基本知识，以便更有效地应用生物科学来满足人类的需要。

历　史

在详阅国际生物学计划的内容之前，我们应该知道这个想法是如何产生的。英国的科学家在这里扮演了非常重要的角色。多年前，时任国际科学联合会理事会（ICSU）主席的鲁道夫·彼得斯爵士在国际生物学计划的构思中发挥了重要作用。去年，来自牛津大学的现任国际科学联合会理事会主席汤普森教授在巴黎举行的第一届国际生物学计划大会中扮演了一个非常好的助产士的角色。而作为国际生物科

held in Paris last year. Prof. C. H. Waddington, as president of IUBS, has been a good doctor in the pre- and post-natal clinics; while the president, officers and secretariat of the Royal Society, by priming and holding the feeding-bottle, have enormously helped the infant's early growth.

How the ideas leading up to the International Biological Programme have fluctuated and developed has been related by Prof. Montalenti, the Italian geneticist who led much of the preparatory work. Initially, it was thought that the programme should concentrate on the human organism, and especially population dynamics and genetics. Later there was a body of opinion which thought it could involve itself best on the preservation and conservation of biological systems in different parts of the world, especially those which are most endangered by economic progress. Finally, these and other approaches have been brought together in such a way as to be of interest to a rather broad spectrum of biological scientists. The objective, as defined in 1964, is to ensure a world-wide study of: (*a*) organic production on the land, in fresh waters, and in the seas, and the potentialities and uses of new as well as of existing natural resources; (*b*) human adaptability to changing conditions. The programme should not range through the entire field of biology but should be limited to basic biological studies, related to productivity and human welfare, which will benefit from international collaboration, and are urgent because of the rapid rate of the changes taking place in all environments throughout the world.

Thus, of two major problems now facing the human species on Earth—of controlling his rate of reproduction and of increasing the biological product on which he subsists—the International Biological Programme is concerned with the second. The advances in techniques to control reproduction which have been produced in the past decade have reached a point at which there is more need for sociologists to apply them than for biologists to invent new ones. Yet the attributes and potentialities of man are by no means left out of the programme, as I will explain.

Principles

The programme is based on a number of principles. First, it is a directional and a selected programme. It is not a free-for-all, nor is all research bearing on productivity and human adaptability automatically incorporated into it. The initials IBP can be regarded, if you like, as a kind of status symbol, and to ensure that this is not misused we have a sifting arrangement for projects at the national level and later at international level before admission into the programme. The tag of IBP does not, of course, mean that the project is necessarily good science, nor that other work on biological productivity conducted outside IBP is not good science. It merely implies that those immediately concerned with IBP agree that the project fits in and is likely to advance materially the objects of the programme.

Secondly, the programme is concerned throughout with the fundamental approach to research. It starts from the premise that the applied sciences of biological production, such as agriculture, forestry, fisheries, have in recent decades gone striding ahead more quickly

学联合会主席的沃丁顿教授，就像是产前产后诊所里一个称职的医生；同时英国皇家学会的主席、工作人员还有秘书兢兢业业的工作为国际生物学计划这个婴儿的早期成长做出了较大的贡献。

蒙塔伦蒂教授讲述了这些想法是如何促成国际生物学计划在曲折中发展的，这个意大利遗传学家为这项计划做了大量的筹备工作。首先，有人认为这个计划应该关注人体组织，特别是种群动力学和遗传学。之后，大量的主张认为该计划应致力于保存和保护世界不同地区的生物系统，特别是那些因为经济发展而濒临灭绝的生物系统。最后，这些观点和其他想法以这样一种方式整合起来以引起众多生物学家的注意。1964 年确定出其目标旨在保证世界范围内的以下研究：(*a*) 陆地上、淡水中以及海水中的有机质生产，新能源以及现有自然资源的潜力和使用；(*b*) 人类对环境变化的适应性。这项计划并没有囊括生物学的所有领域，而是仅限于与人类生产和人类福利相关的基础生物学研究，这些项目将在国际合作中受益，同时也是迫在眉睫的，因为全世界的环境都在发生着快速的变化。

因此，地球上的人类现在面临两个主要的问题——控制人类的繁殖速率和增加其赖以生存的生物产品——国际生物学计划关注的是第二点。过去十年内，人类已经拥有了控制繁殖率的技术，现在最需要的是社会学家去应用它而不是生物学家发明新的技术。然而这项计划并不忽视人类的作用和潜力，我将对此作出解释。

原　则

这个计划建立在许多原则的基础上。首先，它是一个有着明确目标的精心筛选出的计划。它不是对任何人开放的，也不是所有涉及人类生产力和人类适应性的研究就能自动加入到这个计划中。如果你愿意的话，可以将国际生物学计划看作一种社会地位的象征，在获准进入这个计划之前，为了确保其不被滥用，我们会对项目进行国家级水平的筛选，然后是国际级水平的筛选。当然，附有国际生物学计划这个标签的项目并不一定是好的科学，也不意味着在国际生物学计划管理范围之外的和生物生产力相关的项目就不是好的科学。它仅仅意味着那些与国际生物学计划直接相关的项目很快就会被认同并且可能在本质上促进项目的实施。

第二，这个计划普遍关注的是研究的基础方法。这个计划以生物生产的应用科学这一前提为出发点，例如农业、林业和渔业在近几十年里的发展速度远超过我们

than the fundamental understanding of the causes of productivity. Similarly the sciences of man, medicine and some of the applied social sciences, have in some ways outpaced fundamental understanding of mankind and the differences between one man and another. The International Biological Programme is an opportunity to restore the balance and to provide new organized knowledge as a springboard for the technologies to take further plunges into progress.

Thirdly, the International Biological Programme is urgent. This is not only because of the steady growth of the pressure of human populations on renewable resources, but also because many of the situations in the world, both biological and human, are changing so rapidly that they will soon cease to exist. The International Biological Programme is not a preservationist body, for our approach is dynamic not static, conservation rather than preservation; but the perpetuation of sample biological systems for future biologists to study is definitely among its objectives.

Fourthly, and this could perhaps almost go without saying, the International Biological Programme is limited to research which could benefit from international co-operation. There are some scientists, and great ones at that, who do not readily co-operate with others and whose special attributes lead them to penetrate deeply on a narrow front the unknown, behind locked doors so to speak, rather than, by a sharing of knowledge, to advance with others along a broad one. The International Biological Programme is clearly not designed for the isolationist researcher, although his findings might well be picked up and developed as a Programme project.

Divisions of the Programme

In order to get to grips with what inevitably is a very large content, the International Biological Programme is divided into seven sections. One of the first and most obvious divisions was into the biological communities of the land, of fresh waters, and of the sea, because terrestrial ecology, limnology, and oceanography have each developed their own discipline of research, although biological energy often flows from one to another. These three sections are known by their initials; PT for Productivity of Terrestrial Communities; PF for Productivity of Freshwater Communities; PM for Productivity of Marine Communities.

All three have their problems of conservation, including the definition, description and management of prescribed areas or samples of living communities. The problems of conservation on the land are more extensive and generally more complex than those of the waters. They include such concepts as national parks, nature reserves, and sites of special scientific interest. Therefore, there is a special section of IBP labelled CT for Conservation of Terrestrial Communities. Each of the three, moreover, presents different facets of the processes of production—photosynthesis (utilization of solar energy) and the nitrogen cycle—this section is called Production Processes (PP). Each of the three may reveal new resources of value to mankind or new methods applicable to the use and conservation of resources, which require fundamental study; this will be carried out

对生产力提高原因的基本理解。同样，人类科学、医学和一些应用社会科学在某些方面已经超过了对人类以及人与人之间差异的基本理解。国际生物学计划为重新建立这种平衡，以及提供可作为技术进步的跳板的系统化知识提供了契机。

第三，国际生物学计划是势在必行的。这不仅仅是因为人口对可再生资源需求的压力不断增长，也是因为许多世界形势（包括生物的和人类的）正在发生着如此快速的变化以至于他们在不久将会灭绝。由于我们的方法是动态的而不是静态的，是保护而不是保存，因此国际生物学计划不是一个保存机构；但是延续样本生物系统以便将来生物学家进行研究的目标是非常明确的。

第四，国际生物学计划仅限于通过国际合作能够获益的研究，这一点可能几乎是众所周知的。有一些科学家特别是一些优秀的科学家不愿意与其他人合作，可谓闭门造车，由于其特殊的性格导致他们深陷狭窄的未知前沿而不是通过知识的共享与其他人在宽广的前沿上共同进步。很明显国际生物学计划不是为孤立主义研究者制定的，尽管他的发现可能被重视并采纳为国际生物学计划中的一个项目。

计划的分工

这项计划将会很庞大，为能掌握要领，国际生物学计划分为七个部分。第一个也是最明显的部分是陆地、淡水和海洋生物群落，因为尽管生物能源常从一处流向另一处，但是陆地生态学、湖沼学和海洋学都已各自发展成为研究学科。这三个部分由于它们的缩写而为人们所熟知：PT 代表陆地生物群落生产力；PF 代表淡水生物群落生产力；PM 代表海洋生物群落生产力。

这三个部分都面临着保护方面的问题，包括对生物群落指定区域或现存标本的定义、描述和管理。与水域生物群落相比，陆地生物群落的保护问题更为广泛且通常更为复杂。这些问题包括国家公园、自然保护区及具有特别科学价值的地方等概念。因此，国际生物学计划中有一个特殊的陆地生物群落保护（CT）的部分。此外，这三个部分中的每一个都代表着生产过程的不同方面——光合作用（太阳能的利用）和氮循环——这个部分被称为生产过程（PP）。三个部分中的每一个都可能向人类展示出有价值的新能源或适用于使用和保护能源的新方法，这就需要进行基础研究；这将在被称为生物能源使用和管理（UM）的部分内进行。最后，人类问题产生了

within the section named UM for Use and Management of biological resources. Finally, the human problems, which bring in another series of disciplines, notably physiology and anthropology, will be studied within the Section of HA, Human Adaptability. This makes seven: PT, PP, CT, PF, PM, HA and UM.

Each of these sections is headed by an international convener and sectional committee, and is busy in producing a five-year programme of its own. Two of the conveners are British—Mr. Max Nicholson of CT and Prof. J. S. Weiner of HA. The seven sections are, of course, closely related to each other, but also to other programmes going on during the same period, for example PF to the International Hydrological Decade.

IBP consists of the sum of its parts, not only in the sense of containing seven different programmes, but also in the sense that the bulk of the research will be undertaken and financed nationally, not internationally. Many countries are at present busy preparing their national programmes, and of these one of the most advanced is that for the United Kingdom, now published by the Royal Society.

Examples of Research

Let us take a few examples of the kind of work which IBP will contain, and think especially of the British contribution. Although a great deal has yet to be learned about our own biological communities and our own people, some of the thinking has been on the lines that we should use the knowledge and abilities of a good many scientists overseas, where ignorance about biological productivity is still very great. Thus the U.K. programme in its PT section aims to establish two bases for IBP work in the warmer regions overseas, in co-operation, of course, with the countries concerned. One of these is likely to be in savannah country, at the Cambridge Nuffield Unit of Tropical Animal Ecology, situated in the Queen Elizabeth Park in Uganda; another at a site yet to be determined in an area of tropical rain forest. At these bases, in co-operation with local scientists, it is hoped to undertake investigations of productivity in depth—primary production of the trees, shrubs, grasses and herbs, secondary by herbivorous mammals and insects, tertiary by predators and parasites.

It is hoped to quantify as well as qualify each link in the food chain so as to obtain data to compare production in the wild with production from the tame, for example, where domestic animals and plants have been established on land used for agriculture.

Passing to another section, namely CT, it is pleasing to report that something has been actually achieved. In the spring of 1964 and again in 1965, expeditions went from Great Britain to the desert lands of Jordan, and made a survey especially of the Azraq Oasis and its environs, to the east of Amman. This has resulted in several things: a useful IBP booklet entitled *An Approach to the Rapid Description and Mapping of Biological Habitats*, and more important, in detailed recommendations about the creation of national parks in Jordan. Further preparatory work has been based on the Azraq Oasis where the park

另外一系列的学科特别是生理学和人类学，将在人类适应性（HA）的部分内得到研究。这个计划共分为七个部分：PT、PP、CT、PF、PM、HA 和 UM。

每个部分由一名国际会议召集人和分科委员会负责，他们正忙着制定各自的 5 年计划。会议召集人中有两个英国人——负责陆地生物群落保护部分的马克斯·尼克尔森先生和负责人类适应性部分的韦纳教授。当然，这七个部分不仅彼此之间紧密联系，并且与同一时期进行的其他计划也是紧密联系的，例如淡水生物群落生产力部分和国际水文十年计划之间存在联系。

国际生物学计划由它的各个部分共同组成，其意义不仅仅在于包含七个不同的部分，而且在于大部分研究的开展和资助都是在国家层面而非国际层面上进行的。目前许多国家正忙着准备他们自己的国家级项目，其中一个最先进的项目是英国的，目前由皇家学会公布。

研究例子

让我们来举些例子来说明国际生物学计划所要从事的这种工作，尤其是要看看英国所做的贡献。虽然我们对国内生物群落和人群了解的还不多，但一些流行的想法是我们应当利用海外优秀科学家的知识和能力，那里对生物生产力仍然知之甚少。因而英国陆地生物群落生产力部分的目标是在海外较温暖地区建立两个基地，当然，这要与相关国家进行合作。其中一个基地可能在草原地区，坐落于乌干达的伊丽莎白女王公园的剑桥纳菲尔德热带动物生态学研究组；另一个设在热带雨林地区，场地仍未确定。我们希望与当地科学家们一起在基地中能够承担较深入的生产力方面的研究——树木、灌木、禾本科植物和草本植物的初级生产力，食草性哺乳动物和昆虫的二级生产力，食肉动物和寄生虫的三级生产力。

我们希望能定量并定性地分析食物链中的每个环节，以获取能够对野生生物与驯养生物（例如，陆地上已用于农业生产的家养动物和植物）的生产力进行比较的数据。

下面谈谈另一个被称为陆地生物群落保护的部分，令人高兴是这部分已经有了实质性的进展。在 1964 年和 1965 年春天，分别从英国直至约旦的沙漠地区组织探险，并且沿途作了调查，特别是对安曼东部的阿兹拉克绿洲及其附近地区进行了调查。这个调查导致几件事情的发生：它促成了一本名为“生物栖息地快速描述和绘制方法”的实用的国际生物学计划小册子的产生，更重要的是，它详细地介绍了约旦国家公园的建造。以阿兹拉克绿洲为基础，进一步的筹备工作正在进行着，在美国人

headquarters and warden are now established with American aid. Within a week or two, two experienced members of the Nature Conservancy's staff are going there to prepare a management plan, applying the experience in management of wild areas gained in this country. Meanwhile, in August H.M. The King of Jordan publicly announced that he will set up the Azraq National Park, and also that Jordan will participate in the IBP by establishing at the Park's centre an institute for biological and human investigations of desert and oasis conditions. This indeed will make a useful counterpart to the proposed IBP bases in savannah and rain forest to which I have already referred.

From the PF section I will draw two examples of British initiative: one is an intensive study of the biological productivity of a reach of the Thames, organized from the University of Reading. This is dealing with primary and secondary production and will include studies on the feeding and population dynamics of a considerable number of fish species. It will fill a major gap in our knowledge of British fresh waters, for most intensive work has been devoted to lakes and very little to rivers. The other example relates to research in tropical lakes. In terms of food supplies through fisheries, and water supplies for irrigated agriculture, they are of much greater importance to the world than the little lakes in our own country. So the programme includes the establishment, based on Britain, of a team of limnologists for work in the tropics, especially Africa. This takes advantage of the fact that we happen to have in Britain a rather particular expertise in tropical lakes.

During the present planning phase each of the seven sections has already held, or has arranged, a number of symposia consisting of selected specialists from all over the world to discuss methods of research in particular spheres and to prepare handbooks. The object here is not to "straight-jacket" the methods in use in IBP, for field biology is at present advancing very rapidly through the development of old methods and the devising of new ones; but it is to agree on those proved methods which can be advised for general use throughout the world and can be relied on to produce comparable results. A good example was a symposium held in Aberdeen and Cambridge in September concerning research on large herbivorous mammals. In Australia, studies of kangaroos and introduced sheep suggest that the former may be more effective converters of grass into meat than the latter; if only kangaroos produced wool instead of hair, they might be the basis of Australian prosperity. In Africa there are indications that the broad spectrum of indigenous African mammals, such as giraffe, antelopes, buffalo and wart hog, may be better agents of secondary production of meat than the exotic cattle, sheep and goats which have replaced them in many areas and are apt to depress the yield of the habitat. In Scotland we have the Island of Rhum, where management of red deer by the Nature Conservancy has resulted in more venison coming off the island than mutton under the former agricultural management and at the same time it seems as though the level of primary production of the vegetation has been raised. This symposium brought experiences of this sort together and advised on methods for future work under IBP from the three points of view—the ecological, the physiological and the pathological.

Another example I want to give is one with which I am personally involved just at present,

的帮助下公园的总部和管理区现在都已经完工。在一两个星期内，大自然保护协会两个经验丰富的工作人员将到那里制定管理计划，在这个国家获取有关野生保护区管理的经验。与此同时，八月约旦国王陛下公开宣布他将建立阿兹拉克国家公园；通过在公园中心建立研究所以便在沙漠和绿洲环境下进行生物和人类调查，约旦也将参与到国际生物学计划中。这确实与我之前所提到的在草原和雨林地区建立国际生物学计划基地不谋而合。

在淡水生物群落生产力部分，我将举两例英国人发起的项目：一个是由雷丁大学组织的对泰晤士河某河段生物生产力进行的一次深入研究。这涉及初级生产力和次级生产力，也将包括对相当数量的鱼类种群摄食及种群动态进行研究。由于大部分集中性的研究一直针对湖泊，而几乎没有河流，因此这一研究将填补我们在英国淡水知识中的一大空白。另一个例子与热带湖泊研究有关。从渔业供应食物、水灌溉农田方面来讲，它们对世界的重要性要比小湖对我们国家的重要性大得多。因此，这个计划包括成立一个在英国的湖泊生物学家团队，其工作致力于热带地区，特别是非洲。这利用了英国碰巧拥有关于热带湖泊的独特经验这一事实。

在目前的规划阶段里，七个部分中的每一个或已经开展起来或正在筹备中，由来自全世界的经过挑选的专家组成专题讨论会，商讨特殊领域的研究方法并制定手册。这里的目的不是“限制”用于国际生物学计划的方法，因为通过旧方法的发展和新方法的发明，目前生物学领域发展非常迅速；而是它将认同那些被证明了的、被建议在全世界范围内普遍使用的方法，并通过这些方法获得对比结果。一个很好的例子是九月在阿伯丁和剑桥举行的关于大型食草哺乳动物的研讨会。在澳大利亚对袋鼠和引进羊种进行的研究表明，前者比后者能更有效地将草转化为肉；如果只有袋鼠生产羊毛而不是毛发，那么它们将是澳大利亚繁荣的基石。在非洲有迹象表明大量的非洲本土哺乳动物诸如长颈鹿、羚羊、水牛和疣猪，相比于多年前就已经在许多地区取代它们的、使其栖息地产量趋于减少的外来牛、绵羊和山羊来说，是更好的肉类的次级生产者。在苏格兰拉姆岛，我们通过大自然保护协会对马鹿进行管理，从岛上获取的鹿肉比先前在农业管理下产出的要更多，与此同时，植物的初级生产水平似乎比以前提高了。本次研讨会将这些经验整理在一起并从三个方面对国际生物学计划未来的工作方法提出了建议，这三个方向分别是：生态学、生理学和病理学。

我要举的另一个例子是目前我亲自参与的研究，即大型人工湖的研究工作。建

namely research on large man-made lakes. The basic reason for creating these is generally for hydroelectric power: for example, at Kariba, Volta and Kainji in Africa, Brokopondo in Surinam, and a number of large impoundments in North America. Sometimes water conservation for irrigation is equally or more important, as in the Aswan High Dam in Egypt. But the influence of these great sheets of water will extend not only to producing power and water but also to many other human needs, and has a profound bearing on the biology of large regions. Anyone familiar with Africa, for example, will realize the fundamental influence of the great natural lakes on climate, vegetation, fisheries, water supply for man and stock, transport, sites for urban development, and the rest. Since the period of IBP happens to coincide with the period of constructing several new great impoundments and of the biological changes consequent on several of those already completed, their study will take quite a significant place in the programme. Here again, it is good to note that Britain has taken an initiative, and as I speak a group of eight scientists drawn from Liverpool and other universities in Britain and Nigeria, and supported financially by the Ministry of Overseas Development, are undertaking a preliminary investigation of the part of the River Niger where Mungo Park met his end in 1806, the reaches which, in a year or more, will form a five-hundred square mile lake impounded by the dam at Kainji. The group has now been joined by several American and African sociologists who are extending the aquatic study to the 50,000 or so people now living below the future water-level. Under the leadership of local people, assisted by scientists from outside, and with funds which we hope will be provided by the special fund of the United Nations, it is hoped to establish a co-ordinated programme of study on these great impoundments.

I have been speaking mainly about the purely biological aspects of IBP, but the section on human adaptability has so far been quite one of the most active. It brings in a lot of scientists in the spheres of medicine and of physical anthropology, and its programme is designed rather differently from some of the other sections. It is wide and comprehensive, divided into a large number of headings and subheadings. Research topics include environmental physiology, including tolerance of different human groups to cold, heat, and high altitude; fitness, growth and physique, which, incidentally, will include a survey of highly fit athletes; the genetics of populations, with international data centres to be developed on existing national ones such as the blood-group centre of the Medical Research Council in London; and lastly health, nutritional and epidemiological topics. Clearly a lot of this work will need to be done by groups of research workers traveling with their equipment to study communities in their natural environments. This involves mounting a good many quite complex expeditions to remote places. British workers under IBP/HA expect, for example, to work this autumn on the Hazda tribe around Lake Eyassi in Tanzania and the people of Bhutan in the very high Himalayas.

Organization

There is a school of scientific thought that resents all forms of direction or organization. Science is free: give us the funds and let us go unfettered in any direction where research leads, and we will show results. Good scientists should not become administrators; any

造这些大型人工湖最根本的原因通常是为了水力发电：例如，非洲的卡巴里、沃尔塔和卡因吉、苏里南的布罗科蓬多以及北美许多大型水库。有时对灌溉用水的保护同等重要或更加重要，就像埃及的阿斯旺高坝一样。而这些贮存的大量的水不仅用于发电和灌溉，而且能满足人类的许多其他需求，并且也对较大区域里的生物产生了深远的影响。例如，熟悉非洲的任何人都能认识到大型自然湖泊对天气、植被、渔业和人类用水以及水资源的贮存、运输、城市发展的地理位置和其他方面造成的重要影响。国际生物学计划执行的时期碰巧与在建的几座新的大型水库及已完工的几座水库引起的生物变化所处的时期相同，对它们的研究将在这项计划中占据重要地位。在这里，我们再次表扬英国采取的主动行动，在我演讲的这一刻，由 8 名分别来自利物浦以及英国和尼日利亚的其他一些大学的科学家组成的团队正承担着对尼日尔河部分河段的初步研究工作，该项目由海外发展部给予资金支持。1806 年芒戈·帕克曾来过这些河段，这些河段将在一年内或更长的时间里被卡因吉大坝拦截从而形成一个 500 平方英里的蓄水湖。几位来自美国和非洲的社会学家现在也加入了这个团队，将研究从水生生物扩展到约 5 万人，这些人现在居住的位置在将来的水平面以下。在当地人的领导下，通过外来科学家的帮助以及我们所期待的联合国提供的专项资金，有望制定关于这些大型水库的统筹方案。

上面我主要从纯生物方面谈了国际生物学计划，但是到目前为止，有关人类适应性的部分是相当热门的。它引进了许多来自医学和体质人类学领域的科学家，并且制定的计划显著不同于其他部分。它广泛而全面，分为非常多的课题和副课题。研究课题包括环境生理学（包括不同人群对冷、热和高海拔的耐受性）、适应性、生长发育和体质（顺便说一下，这包括调查非常健康的运动员）、人口遗传学（由现有的国家数据中心发展起来的国际数据中心，如伦敦医学研究理事会的血型中心）、最后是与健康、营养和流行病有关的课题。很显然，这些工作需要大量的研究人员带着他们的设备外出研究自然环境中的群落。这包括组织相当综合的探险队去偏远的地方。例如，隶属于国际生物学计划中人类适应性部分的英国工作者们期望在这个秋天研究坦桑尼亚埃亚西湖周围的哈次达族和海拔非常高的喜马拉雅山上的不丹人。

组　织

有一支科学思想学派反对所有形式的指导或组织机构。科学是自由的：给我们经费并允许我们在感兴趣的任何方向上进行不受限制的研究，我们将给出成果。好

who do so are so much loss to science. This is an attitude which some of us associate with the older universities, but it is quite widespread, within Government scientific service as well as outside it. I met it strongly expressed when discussing IBP recently in Uganda. Now this libertine approach to science does not face the realities of how the funds and facilities for research are to be produced, how the results are to be discussed and published, or how those results which have an element of application in them might be turned to practical use. Nevertheless, it is an attitude with which I personally, and many others who are concerned with IBP, have a good deal of sympathy. We have been influenced by it in thinking up the organization necessary for IBP, at least to the extent that we have devised this as lightly as possible. We are trying to build a simple structure from the foundations and to make the roof no heavier than is necessary to protect those inside from the weather.

Starting from the top there is ICSU which has set up the Special Committee for the International Biological Programme (SCIBP), comparable with its scientific committees for Oceanic Research (SCOR) and Antarctic Research (SCAR). SCIBP is a democratic organization which holds a general assembly about every two years. It has a Swiss president, Prof. Jean Baer, vice-presidents from Italy, Poland, the United States and Great Britain, and a number of other members, some representing the main international unions in the biological sciences and some drawn from the different bio-geographical regions of the world. It includes also the seven international conveners of the sections of IBP. Unesco, FAO, WHO, SCOR, and SCAR have representatives on it. Each of the conveners has also his sectional committee of specialist members drawn from all over the world.

The central office for IBP is at 7 Marylebone Road, Regent's Park, London, in accommodation generously provided and furnished by the Government and the Royal Society. Each of the seven international conveners has his own office, although only four of them as yet have whole-time staff.

Publications of IBP are so far very few: a journal called *IBP News* was started in October 1964, and so far three numbers have been published. We are also starting a series of handbooks, and the first of these, being a general guide to the activities of HA section, has just gone to press.

The central funds, for running the offices and holding meetings and for publications, come from national dues paid in by each participating country. These are on a rather modest scale and in fact are at present insufficient. I am glad to say they are augmented by grants and loans from ICSU and Unesco, and a particularly generous grant recently made by the U.S. National Academy of Sciences. It is hoped that other countries will follow this excellent example.

The finance I have spoken of is concerned only with the organizational framework and, by international standards, is quite small. The cost of the actual research undertaken under

的科学家不应该成为管理者；无论谁这样做对科学来说都是严重损失。我们中的一些人常将这种态度与历史悠久的大学相关联，其实这在政府科学服务部门的内部和外部也都相当普遍。最近在乌干达国际生物学计划的讨论中，我对这个观点深有感受。而这种自由主义的科学态度没有面对现实，即研究经费和设备从何而来，研究结果将怎样被讨论和发表，或者研究结果的应用价值怎样被实际应用。即便如此，我和许多其他关注国际生物学计划的人对这种态度都深有同感。我们在筹建国际生物学计划的必要组织时受其影响，至少在一定程度上我们尽可能精简组织结构。我们一直尝试着在地基上建立一个简单的组织结构，使屋顶轻到只够保护其内部免受外界环境的影响。

最高级的部门是国际科学联合会理事会，它设立了国际生物学计划特别委员会（SCIBP）、海洋研究科学委员会（SCOR）和南极研究科学委员会（SCAR）。国际生物学计划特别委员会是一个民主的组织，通常每两年组织一次会员大会。该组织的主席是来自瑞士的琼·贝尔教授，副主席分别来自意大利、波兰、美国和英国，还有许多会员，其中一些是生物科学领域内主要国际联盟的代表，还有一些来自世界不同的生物地理区域。这也包括国际生物学计划中七个部门的国际会议召集人。联合国教科文组织、联合国粮农组织、世界卫生组织、海洋研究科学委员会和南极研究科学委员会都有代表出席这个会议。每个会议召集人也属于他们各自部分的专家成员委员会，这些专家成员来自世界各地。

国际生物学计划的中央办公室位于伦敦的马里波恩路 7 号丽晶公园，由政府和皇家学会慷慨提供并装修。七个国际会议召集人都有属于他们自己的办公室，尽管至今他们中只有四人有全职的工作人员。

到目前为止，由国际生物学计划发行的出版物还很少：一本名为《国际生物学计划消息》的杂志创办于 1964 年 10 月，到目前为止已经出版了三期。我们也开始制定一系列手册，其中作为人类适应性部分通用指南的第一本小手册刚刚出版。

办公室日常运作、会议举行和出版物发行所需的经费主要由每个参会国提供。但他们提供的经费数量是有限的，事实上目前并不足以维持工作的正常开展。令人高兴的是国际科学联合会理事会和联合国教科文组织为我们提供了贷款和捐助，以及最近美国国家科学院提供了特殊慷慨的捐助，希望其他国家能效仿这样好的例子。

我所谈及的经费仅与组织框架有关，与国际标准相比是非常少的。如果国际生物学计划的各部分都体现价值，那么由其主持的对世界各处进行实际研究所需的费

the auspices of IBP in all parts of the world will naturally be quite large if the programme is to be at all worth while. As yet it is impossible to say how much it may cost, because very few national programmes have yet been prepared in detail although a number are in active preparation. If we take the British programme as a model, and if some twenty major nations have comparable programmes and twenty or thirty others prepare smaller programmes, the total is bound to run to several million pounds. The finance for national programmes will of course be provided nationally: in this first year of design and feasibility studies, the British Treasury has provided some £80,000 specially for IBP; added to the normal votes for the Royal Society and the Nature Conservancy. This will enable some appointments to be made and some research of a trial nature to be started. A number of other countries have acted somewhat similarly. Czechoslovakia, for example, in addition to financing its own planning phase, has provided from its own funds the office and staff for one of the international conveners, Prof. Malek, who is based in Prague.

In order to plan and carry out national programmes, many countries are setting up their own national committees, often with sub-committees equivalent to the international sectional committees of SCIBP. Thus the United Kingdom, through its committee structure which operates under the patronage of the Royal Society, brings about 150 British scientists into the active planning stage. The United States now has a national committee under Dr. Roger Revelle. Poland one under Prof. Petrusewicz; Japan not only has a national committee but has already submitted a programme. I believe that before long a major problem of SCIBP and of its Central Office will be, not so much to get IBP in motion which has been a preoccupation up until now, but to prevent it running away from itself by becoming too large and unmanageable.

Conclusion

The gestation period of the Programme has been long, but recent progress is at a much greater rate than we had dared to hope a couple of years ago, for the world needs an IBP. What, then, is the philosophy behind it? What is the driving force that causes many busy people about the world to devote their time and energy to helping it on? I suggest it is a spirit of service to our fellow men and to all the other animals and plants that make up the very varied living communities of the Earth. Even in these days of rather selfish approach to living, apparent in the political, commercial and even scientific spheres, I suppose there is some feeling of service in all of us, even if it is only an instinct towards conserving the race, after conserving the individual. Here in IBP is the opportunity for very many biologists, whose efforts may have been not perhaps of very high value to others, to bring their researches together, to focus them and to make them more useful. Here in IBP is the opportunity of showing the world the value of field biology as well as laboratory biology. New resources will undoubtedly be discovered, and so also will be the aesthetic as well as the scientific and economic value of plants and animals in their natural and also in their man-made environments.

An important part of the service IBP hopes to render will be to ensure that at least

用自然是相当大的。迄今为止，还不能估算出到底要花费多少钱，因为很少的国家项目已经有了详细的计划，尽管有一些正在积极地准备着。如果我们以英国的计划为例，若二十个左右的主要国家能有类似的计划并且还有二三十个其他准备好的小计划，那么执行这些计划所需的总费用一定会达到几百万英镑。当然，国家计划的经费将由该国提供：在制订计划和可行性研究的第一年，英国财政部专门为国际生物学计划拨款了 80,000 英镑；为英国皇家学会和大自然保护协会增加合法投票权。这有益于进行委任并开始开展一些野外实验研究。很多其他国家也有些许类似的做法。例如，捷克斯洛伐克除了支付规划阶段的资金外，还为其中一个国际召集人（在布拉格基地的马利克教授）提供办公室日常运转和员工费用。

为了制定和执行国家计划，许多国家正在成立他们自己的全国委员会，通常该委员会设置小组委员会，这类似于国际生物学计划特别委员会的国际分科委员会。因而英国在皇家学会的赞助下来运作委员会机构，并引入了约 150 名英国科学家积极筹备计划。现在美国有一个由罗杰·雷维尔博士负责的国家委员会，波兰的国家委员会由彼得鲁塞维奇教授负责；日本不仅有一个国家委员会而且已经提交了计划。我认为不久以后国际生物学计划特别委员会及其中央办公室的一个主要的问题不是获得较多的现在已经引起关注的国际生物学计划议题，而是防止它由于发展太大造成难以管理而最后脱离了自己的轨道。

结　论

这个计划经历了一个较长的酝酿期，但其目前的发展速率比我们两年前所希望的还要快，因为世界需要国际生物学计划。那么这一计划背后蕴含了什么样的哲学思想？能吸引世界上许多忙碌的人们把他们的时间和精力花费在该计划上的驱动力是什么？我认为，对于我们的同胞和其他组成地球上多样生物群落的动植物来说，它是一种服务的精神。即使是在生活方式（尤其在政治、商业甚至是科学领域中）相当自私的现在，我认为我们所有人都是有一些服务理念的，尽管保护好个体之后再保护种族仅是一种本能。对于那些曾经努力但没有给他人带来很大价值的生物学家们来说，国际生物学计划是一个机遇，因为它可以将这些研究者聚集起来，关注他们并使他们发挥自己的价值。国际生物学计划也为野外生物学和实验室生物学向全世界展示其价值提供了机会。毫无疑问新型能源将被发现，同样地，生活在自然和人工环境中的动植物的审美价值、科学价值及经济价值也将被发现。

国际生物学计划希望提供的服务中，一个重要的部分是确保至少这些令人惊奇

samples of these wonderful creations of evolution, so different and yet so similar in the several bio-geographical zones, will continue and flourish for subsequent generations of humans to appreciate and use. Nor should we forget the many and diverse races of man himself, with their separate and particular attributes. Unless we understand these matters and use our understanding to plan the future, they will go down before the axe and fire, the bulldozer or the hypodermic needle. This marvellous biological differentiation on the Earth would then tend towards dull uniformity and even obliteration.

(**208**, 223-226; 1965)

Dr. E. B. Worthington: Scientific Director (Designate).

的进化演变样本（它们在多个生物地理区域如此不同却又如此相似）将继续存在并生长良好，使得人类的后代将有机会欣赏和使用到。我们也不应该忘记人类自身种族的多样性，及其所具有的分散性和独特性。除非我们已经理解了这些问题并能根据我们的理解去规划未来，否则他们将在斧头、火、推土机或注射器针头面前衰退。地球上非凡的生物分化将趋于单一甚至消失。

（尹金 翻译；金侠 审稿）

New Limits to the Angular Sizes of Some Quasars

R. L. Adgie *et al.*

Editor's Note

Quasars were first recognized as powerful sources of radio emission a very great distance from our own galaxy. By the mid-1960s, radioastronomers energetically set about gathering information about these mysterious objects. This paper describes the use of two radiotelescopes separated by 134 km (one at Jodrell Bank at the University of Manchester in the north of England and one at the Radar Research Laboratory at Malvern, further south), which enabled the size of some quasars to be deduced using the Technique of interferometry

IN previous experiments at Jodrell Bank the angular sizes of discrete radio sources have been investigated by means of long baseline interferometers[1,2]. The highest resolving power used previously was obtained during observations at a wave-length $\lambda=0.73$ m with telescopes 180,000 wave-lengths apart (134 km). Four quasi-stellar and one unidentified source were found to be unresolved in those observations. Their angular sizes were thus shown to be smaller than 0.4 sec of arc. In a further attempt to resolve these sources another experiment has been carried out using the Mark I 250-ft. radio telescope at Jodrell Bank, and one of the 82-ft. radio telescopes operated by the Royal Radar Establishment, Malvern. The separation of these telescopes is 127 km, in a direction which is close to north-south. This interferometer worked on a wave-length $\lambda=0.21$ m, so that the maximum resolving power was more than three times greater than had been obtained in the previous observations. The effective resolving power changes as sources are observed in different directions, but its maximum value is greater than 600,000 wave-lengths for most sources. With this baseline the output fringe frequency produced as the radio source moves through the lobes of the interferometer pattern varies with hour angle from 0 to as much as 40 c/s. An almost identical frequency was produced continuously by a digital "fringe speed machine" and this was subtracted from the interferometer output, so that the fringe patterns displayed on the chart recorder were normally slower than 0.5 cycles/min. A microwave link system was established between the two observatories, via two repeater stations. A new very-high-frequency phase-locking system was also developed, with equipment at each site.

During these observations, the five sources which had not been resolved previously (3*C* 119, 286, 287, *CTA* 21 and 102) all gave clear fringe patterns over a wide range of hour angles, though for only one source did the amplitude remain approximately constant. These sources are listed in column 1 of Table 1. Column 2 shows their catalogued[8] flux density, *S*, at $\lambda=0.21$ m. The observed fringe amplitudes were normalized by daily observations of the source 3*C* 147, which was found to give clear fringe patterns at all hour angles. Corrections arising from various instrumental effects have been applied to these

类星体角大小的新极限

阿吉等

编者按

类星体最早是作为离我们星系非常遥远的强大射电源而为人所知的。在 20 世纪 60 年代中期，射电天文学家们开始积极着手对这些神秘天体的信息进行收集汇总。本文叙述了两架相隔了 134 千米射电望远镜的观测应用（一架在英国北部曼彻斯特大学的焦德雷尔班克，另一架在莫尔文以南的雷达研究实验室），这使人们能够通过干涉测量技术推断类星体的大小。

在焦德雷尔班克之前的实验中，人们曾用长基线干涉仪对分立射电源的角大小做了研究[1,2]。从前进行的最高分辨率的观测是在波长 $\lambda = 0.73$ 米处，用相隔 180,000 倍波长（即 134 千米）距离的望远镜观测到的。在这些观测中，发现有 4 个类星体和 1 个未证认源未能被分辨。它们显示的角大小小于 0.4 角秒。为了进一步分辨这些射电源，采用位于焦德雷尔班克的马克 I 250 英尺射电望远镜以及莫尔文的皇家雷达研究所的 82 英尺射电望远镜进行另一项实验。这两个望远镜大致以南北方向排列，间距为 127 千米。其干涉仪的工作波段是 $\lambda=0.21$ 米，因此测得的极限分辨率提高为之前实验结果的 3 倍多。尽管有效分辨率会随着观测角度的改变而改变，但对大多数源来说其基线最大值超过 600,000 个波长。在这一基线下，当射电源随观测时角穿越干涉图样的波瓣时，会使输出的条纹频率发生 0 周 / 秒 ~40 周 / 秒的变化。而利用一台数字式的“条纹变速机”可以连续得到非常接近的频率值，然后可将此值从干涉仪的输出结果中剔出，这样在记录仪中显示的载波条纹通常就要低于 0.5 周 / 分。在两个天文台之间已借助两个中继站建立了微波连接系统。现已在每个台站新安装了甚高频锁相系统装置。

在这些观测中，之前尚未分辨的 5 个源（3*C* 119，286，287，*CTA* 21 和 102）在较宽的时角变化范围内均给出了清晰的条纹图样，但这其中也只有一个源的振幅大致保持恒定。这些源列于表 1 中的第 1 列。第 2 列给出了 $\lambda=0.21$ 米波段处各编目对应的[8] 流量密度 S。由于 3*C* 147 的源在任何时角情况下都给出了清晰的条纹图样，所以对观测到的条纹振幅都用 3*C* 147 的日观测数据进行了归一化。对这些条纹振幅

normalized values of fringe amplitude. It was found that when the sources were observed at elevations less than 15° these corrections were frequently greater than 20 percent, and such observations have not been used. The corrected values of fringe amplitude have been calibrated by considering the maximum value observed for each source, which is shown in column 3 of Table 1. It was found that these maximum values are in an almost constant ratio to the total flux from each source, as shown in column 4, the mean value of these ratios being 14.1±0.9.

Table 1. Radio Sources Smaller than 0.1 Sec of Arc in at Least One Dimension

Source	Flux S at λ=0.21m (flux units)*	Max, fringe amplitude, A, observed with tracking interferometer of aerial spacing 605,000λ (arbitrary units)	A/S
3*C* 119	8.5±0.8	125±10	14.7±1.8
3*C* 286	16.1±0.4	245±20	15.2±1.5
3*C* 287	7.6±1.5	95±5	12.5±2.5
CTA 21	8.0±0.8	115±10	14.4±2.0
CTA 102	6.6±1.6	95±10	14.4±2.0
			Mean value 14.1±0.9

*One flux unit = 10^{-28} $Wm^{-2}(c/s)^{-1}$

A constant ratio in column 4 would be obtained if the minimum linear dimensions of all these sources were similar, and they were at comparable distances, and were partially resolved to the same extent by effective baselines between 500,000λ and 600,000λ. This is an improbable situation, and it seems more likely, as we assume, that each source was unresolved by the effective baseline at which the maximum value of fringe amplitude was observed. This means that each of these sources is smaller than 0.1 sec of arc in at least one direction. The source *CTA* 102 did not appear to be resolved at any hour angle when its elevation was greater than 15°, so that its angular size is shown to be less than 0.1 sec of arc in all position angles. Each of the other sources was partially resolved at some hour angle, and the corresponding maximum angular dimensions (assuming gaussian source models) were in the range 0.12-0.16 sec of arc, as shown in column 5 of Table 1.

The quasar 3*C* 273 was also observed and was found to give clear fringe patterns of unexpectedly large amplitude with one well-marked minimum near meridian transit. Observations of lunar occultations of this source show that it consists of two components, *A* and *B*, the centres of which are 19.5 sec apart in position angle 044°. If both these components had contributed to the fringe patterns observed at this baseline, a pronounced minimum would have been observed every 10-15 min at most hour angles. As these frequent minima were not observed, it follows that only one component of the source is small enough to give fringe patterns at this baseline, and that it, in turn, probably consists of two parts, which are each smaller that 0.1 sec of arc.

As only one minimum was observed, the angular separation of these parts and the position angle cannot, by inspection, be determined uniquely, though they may be obtained in due course by more detailed analyses. If it is assumed that this position angle is also 044°, the

归一化值的修正考虑到了多种仪器效应。具体观测发现，当射电源的仰角低于 15°时，往往修正幅度会大于 20%，这种观测结果没有被采用。修正后的条纹振幅值在参考了每个源的观测极大值后进行了标定，这些极大值列于表 1 中的第 3 列。由表可知，如第 4 列所示这些极大值与每个源的总流量呈恒定的比例关系，这些比例的平均大小为 14.1 ± 0.9。

表 1. 角尺度至少在一个方向上小于 0.1 角秒的射电源

源	在 λ=0.21 米处的流量 S（流量单位）*	用天线间距 605,000λ 的追踪干涉仪观测的最大条纹振幅 A（任意单位）	振幅 / 流量
3*C* 119	8.5 ± 0.8	125 ± 10	14.7 ± 1.8
3*C* 286	16.1 ± 0.4	245 ± 20	15.2 ± 1.5
3*C* 287	7.6 ± 1.5	95 ± 5	12.5 ± 2.5
CTA 21	8.0 ± 0.8	115 ± 10	14.4 ± 2.0
CTA 102	6.6 ± 1.6	95 ± 10	14.4 ± 2.0
			平均值 14.1 ± 0.9

*1 流量单位 = 10^{-28} 瓦 · 米$^{-2}$（周 / 秒）$^{-1}$

如果所有这些源都具有相近的最小线尺度，离我们的距离也差不多，并且能利用 500,000λ~600,000λ 范围内的基线进行有效的分辨，在满足所有这些条件时表中第 4 列才会看到一个常值。当然这不大现实，正如我们所猜测的，更有可能的情况是每一个源都未能被有效基线所分辨，观测到的都是条纹幅度的最大值而已。这意味着每个源至少在一个方向上小于 0.1 角秒。当源 *CTA* 102 仰角大于 15° 时，在任何时角处都不能分辨它，因此其角大小在所有方位角上均小于 0.1 角秒。如表 1 的第 5 行所示，其他源在某些时角处仍能部分分辨，相应的角大小极大值（假定是高斯源模型）出现在 0.12 角秒 ~ 0.16 角秒范围内。

类星体 3*C* 273 也曾被观测到，并被发现它能给出清晰的条纹图样，其出人意料的大振幅在其经过子午线附近时存在一个明显的极小值。该源的月掩星观测表明，它由两个子源 *A* 和 *B* 组成，其中心偏离 044° 的方位角 19.5 角秒。如果这两个子源对基线上观测到的条纹图样都有贡献，那么在大多数时角处，每 10~15 分钟将都可以观测到明显的极小值。由于这些频繁的极小值并未被观测到，可知两者之中可能只有一个子源足够小以产生在此基线上观测到的条纹图样；反之，也可能存在两个部分，但每个都小于 0.1 角秒。

尽管经过更进一步的分析也许能得出确定的结果，但由于仅观测到一个最小值，因此根据这些观测值要唯一地确定出这些部分之间的角距离和方位角还是有困难的。

separation is of the order 0.4 sec of arc.

This interpretation of our observations, when calibrated with the factor derived from the sources discussed earlier, shows that the two parts of one component of 3*C* 273 are now giving a flux density not less than 30±2 flux units. As may be seen in Table 2, this is significantly greater than the value of 23.3 flux units derived for the brighter component, *B*, from the ratio given by the occultation observations of 1962.9. The total flux from this source was therefore re-measured recently, with the Mark I telescope at Jodrell Bank, and compared with the radio galaxies 3*C* 348 and 353. These measurements show that, on the assumption that the radio galaxies have remained constant, the value of total flux from 3*C* 273 in 1965.6 was 46±1.5 flux units. This is compatible with the other results if it is assumed that the interferometer observations refer to the component *B*, and that the flux of this component has now increased to 30 flux units, that is, by approximately 30 percent in three years. It is not known which part of component *B* has increased. This conclusion may be compared with the measurements reported by Dent[3] which show that at 8,000 Mc/s, where almost all the radiation comes from component *B*, the flux has increased by 40 percent in 2.5 years.

Table 2. Data on 3*C* 273 at 0.21 M

Total flux density (1962-3)	39.8±2 flux units
Flux ratio component *B* : *A* (1962.9)	1.40
Therefore component *A* was then 16.5 and *B*,	23.3 flux units
Long baseline interferometer (1965.5) Two parts of one component gave	30±2 flux units
Total power measurements (1965.6) *A*+*B* Provisional interpretation (1965.7)	46±1.5 flux units

Component *A* is still 16.6 flux units, and component *B* is now 30 flux units. Flux ratio *B* : *A* now 1.84.

We have summarized in Table 3 our current interpretations, based on these and earlier measurements, of the angular dimensions of the ten quasi-stellar sources the redshifts of which have been published[4,5]. Possible values of the linear dimensions of the radio-emitting regions of these sources are shown in columns 4 and 5. Those in column 4 have been calculated on the hypothesis that the redshifts of these sources arise from the general expansion of the Universe, and so correspond to distances greater than 600 Mpc. The values given in column 5 are calculated on the hypothesis suggested by Hoyle and Burbidge[6], that the emitting regions are at distances of order 10 Mpc, and their redshifts arise from very high intrinsic velocities of recession of the individual objects.

如果假设这个方位角也是 044°，那么各部分之间的角距离则在 0.4 角秒的量级。

在先前讨论源因子的标定时，我们对这类观测的讨论表明，3*C* 273 的一个子源中的两个部分在现阶段辐射出的流量密度不小于 30±2 个流量单位。如将在表 2 中所见的，该值要远大于较亮的子源 *B*，*B* 在 1962.9 掩星观测比值中所得到的结果是 23.3 个流量单位。因此，最近用焦德雷尔班克的马克 I 望远镜重新测量了这个源的总流量，并与射电星系 3*C* 348 和 353 作了比较。这些观测表明，如果假定射电星系保持稳定，那么在 1965.6 射电星系 3*C* 273 的总辐射流量约为 46±1.5 个流量单位。如果假设干涉仪的观测结果是参照子源 *B* 的，而且这个子源的流量在 3 年里大致增加了 30%，即现在增至 30 个流量单位，那么这是与其他结果相一致的。但并不清楚子源 *B* 中哪个区的辐射流量在增加。这个结论可与登特 [3] 给出的测量结果相比较，登特指出在 8,000 兆周 / 秒时，几乎所有的辐射均来自子源 *B*，而其对应的流量在 2.5 年里增大了 40%。

表 2. 3*C* 273 在 0.21 米处的数据

总流量密度（1962-3）	39.8±2 个流量单位
流量比例子源 *B* : *A*（1962.9）	1.40
当时子源 *A* 是 16.5 而 *B* 为	23.3 个流量单位
长基线干涉仪（1965.5） 一个子源的两部分测出	30±2 个流量单位
总功率测量（1965.6）*A*+*B* 临时的解释（1965.7）	46±1.5 个流量单位

A 部分仍为 16.6 个流量单位，*B* 部分现在是 30 个流量单位。流量比 *B*:*A* 现在是 1.84。

我们在表 3 中汇总了当前的结果，这是基于对 10 个已发表红移测量结果 [4,5] 的类星体射电源的本次及以前的角大小的测量而得到的，其中第 4 列和第 5 列中给出了这些源的射电发射区域可能的线尺度大小。假设这些射电源的红移是由宇宙学膨胀造成的，那即可计算得出第 4 列中的数值，相应的离我们的距离大于 600 兆秒差距。第 5 列中给出的数值是根据霍伊尔和伯比奇 [6] 提出的假设计算的，即认为其中发射区距离我们 10 兆秒差距量级，并且其红移是由各个天体非常高的内禀退行速度产生的。

Table 3. Current Interpretations of the Radio Measurements of the Angular and Linear Dimensions of some Quasars

Source	Redshift z	Remarks on individual sources	Approximate linear dimensions (parsecs)	
			If redshifts cosmological*	If sources "local" at about 10 Mpc
		Source has two components 19.5 sec apart in position angle 044°	Separation of *A* and *B* 32,000	950
3*C* 273	0.158	*Component B*, coincident with optical quasi-stellar object, has two parts, each smaller than 0.1 sec, separation probably 0.4 sec. At λ=0.21m flux of component B has increased by approx. 30 percent in 2.7 yr	Each part smaller than 170 separation probably 700	5 20
		Component A has dimensions 5×1.5 sec flux probably unchanged	8,500×2,500	240×70
3*C* 48	0.367	At λ=0.73 m, elliptical, 0.4 by <0.3 sec †‡§	1,100× $\leqslant$ 900	20× $\leqslant$ 15
3*C* 47	0.425	At λ=0.21 m, this source has two components (ref. 9) Separation 62 sec	$\geqslant$ 180,000	$\geqslant$ 3,000
		Each component $\leqslant$ 10 sec, but little structure $\leqslant$ 2 sec ¶	<30,000 but > 6,000	<500 but >100
3*C* 147	0.545	At λ=0.73 m, elliptical 0.6 by <0.4 sec †‡§	2,000× $\leqslant$ 1,300	30× $\leqslant$ 20
3*C* 254	0.734	At λ=1.89 m, ≈6 sec. No structure measurements at any wave-length	≈21,000	≈300
3*C* 286	0.86	At λ=0.21 m, 0.12 by <0.1 sec ‡	420×<350	6×<5
3*C* 245	1.029	At λ=1.89 m, >12 sec. No structure measurements at any wave-length ¶	>41,000	>600
CTA 102	1.037	At λ=0.21 m, <0.1 sec in all position angles	<360	<5
3*C* 287	1.055	At λ=0.21 m, 0.14× <0.1 sec ‡	500×<360	7.0×<5
3*C* 9	2.012	At λ=1.89 m, >10 sec. No structure measurements at any wave-length ¶	>32,000	>450

* These linear dimensions have been calculated for model universes (ref. 4) in which the acceleration parameter q_0=+1. If q_0=0, these values must be multiplied by a factor $(1+0.5z)$ which for these sources lies in the range 1-2.01.

† Results (ref. 7) of detailed analysis of observations at λ=0.73 m.

‡ None of the available evidence suggests that the source contains fine structure within this elliptical component, but further analyses or observations at even higher resolution could conceivably reveal a more complex structure, within these overall dimensions, as in the case of 3*C* 273 *B*.

§ Fringe patterns corresponding to partial resolution of this source were recorded during the observations at λ=0.21 m described above. They have not yet been analysed in sufficient detail to improve significantly the earlier interpretation of the angular structure of this source.

¶ A weak source at λ=0.73 and λ=0.21 m. Ever if it were unresolved, the signal-to-noise ratio would be poor under optimum conditions, and the fringe pattern might not have been recognized during those observations which were attempted.

(**208**, 275-276; 1965)

R. L. Adgie, H. Gent and O. B. Slee: Royal Radar Establishment, Great Malvern.
A. D. Frost, H. P. Palmer and B. Rowson: University of Manchester, Nuffield Radio Astronomy Laboratories, Jodrell Bank.

References:

1. Allen, L. R., Anderson, B., Conway, R. G., Palmer, H. P., Reddish, V. C., and Rowson, B., *Mon. Not. Roy. Astro. Soc.*, **124**, 477 (1962).

表 3. 目前对部分类星体角大小和线尺度的射电观测说明

源	红移 z	对各源注解	近似线尺度（秒差距）	
			假设红移是宇宙学红移*	假设源是“本地的”，距离约 10 兆秒差距
3*C* 273	0.158	源有两个成分，在方向角 044° 处分开 19.5 角秒	*A* 和 *B* 的距离为 32,000	950
		B 部分，与光学类星体一致，由两部分组成，每个都小于 0.1 角秒，且大约间距 0.4 角秒。在 λ=0.21 米波段上 B 部分在 2.7 年里流量增加了大约 30%	每部分小于 170 大致距离 700	5 20
		A 部分尺度为 5 × 1.5 角秒，其流量大致不变	8,500 × 2,500	240 × 70
3*C* 48	0.367	在 λ=0.73 米，尺度小于 0.3 角秒时椭率为 0.4 †‡§	1,100 × ⩽ 900	20 × ⩽ 15
3*C* 47	0.425	在 λ=0.21 米，源由两部分组成（参考文献 9），相距 62 角秒	⩾180,000	⩾ 3,000
		每部分均⩽ 10 角秒，但细致结构⩽ 2 角秒 ¶	＜ 30,000 但＞ 6,000	＜ 500 但＞ 100
3*C* 147	0.545	在 λ=0.73 米，小于 0.4 角秒时椭率为 0.6 †‡§	2,000 × ⩽ 1,300	30 × ⩽ 20
3*C* 254	0.734	在 λ=1.89 米，约 6 角秒。任何波长均未测出结构	≈ 21,000	≈ 300
3*C* 286	0.86	在 λ=0.21 米，小于 0.1 角秒时椭率为 0.12 ‡	420 × ＜ 350	6 × ＜ 5
3*C* 245	1.029	在 λ=1.89 米，大于 12 角秒。任何波长均未测出结构 ¶	＞ 41,000	＞ 600
CTA 102	1.037	在 λ=0.21 米，在任何方位角观测都小于 0.1 角秒	＜ 360	＜ 5
3*C* 287	1.055	在 λ=0.21 米，0.14 × ＜ 0.1 角秒 ‡	500 × ＜ 360	7.0 × ＜ 5
3*C* 9	2.012	在 λ=1.89 米，大于 10 角秒。任何波长均未测出结构 ¶	＞ 32,000	＞ 450

* 这些线性尺寸是在加速因子为 q_0 =+1 的宇宙模型（参考文献 4）下进行计算得到的。如果 q_0 = 0，对那些红移在 1~2.01 范围内的源，结果必须乘上因子（1+0.5z）。

† 在 λ=0.73 米处观测值的详细分析结果 (参考文献 7)。

‡ 还没有证据表明，在源的这个椭圆部分内包含精细结构，但将来更高分辨率的分析或观测将肯定能在此轮廓内揭示一个更复杂的结构，就如 3*C* 273 *B* 那样。

§ 相对应的该源部分分辨条纹图样是在上文中提到的 λ=0.21 米波段观测得到的。它们还尚未得到足够详细的分析以对该源角结构的早期解释做出重要改进。

¶ 在 λ=0.73 米和 λ=0.21 米处存在一个弱源。它一直都未能被解析，在最佳条件下其信噪比也很小，并且在其他尝试观测中对条纹图样甚至无法认证。

（沈乃澂 翻译；肖伟科 审稿）

2. Anderson, B., Donaldson, W., Palmer, H. P., and Rowson, B., *Nature*, **205**, 375 (1965).
3. Dent, W. A., *Science*, **148**, 1458 (1965).
4. Schmidt, M., *Astrophys. J.*, **141**, 1295 (1965).
5. Shklovsky, I. S., *Astro, Circ., U.S.S.R.*, No. 250 (1963).
6. Hoyle, F., and Burbidge, G. R. (personal communication).
7. Anderson, B., Ph.D. thesis, Univ. Manch. (1965).
8. Conway, R. G., Kellerman, K. I., and Long, R. J., *Mon. Not. Roy. Astro. Soc.*, **125**, 261 (1963).
9. Ryle, M., Elsmore, B., and Neville, Ann C., *Nature*, **207**, 1024 (1965).

Double Chromosome Reduction in a Tetraploid *Solanum*

G. E. Marks *et al.*

Editor's Note

Meiosis, the process that produces sex cells with a single set of chromosomes, occurs via a process of reductional division that halves chromosome number. Unusual plant hybrids, thought to be produced by double chromosome reduction, had been reported before but definitive proof of their origin was lacking. Here British botanist Jeffrey B. Harborne and colleagues present biochemical and morphological data confirming the production of an unusual *Solanum* hybrid by this method. The potato plant was more like its female parent, suggesting that the double reduction occurred in the male plant, which contained four sets of chromosomes.

REPEATED attempts to cross *Solanum demissum* ($2n = 6x = 72$) with *S. stoloniferum* ($2n = 4x = 48$) gave one seeded berry containing one seed. This yielded a plant (*M.* 271) which had $2n = 4x = 48$, instead of the expected $2n = 5x = 60$. The cytological, morphological and biochemical studies of *M.* 271 reported here provide good evidence that it is a true hybrid and therefore the product of double chromosome reduction.

The plants used in this investigation were as follows: *Parents. Solanum demissum* (C.P.C. 2249) (*dms* 2249). This clone, collected by Dr. J. G. Hawkes in 1949 in Hidalgo State, Real del Monte, Mexico, is morphologically typical of the species. It is both male and female fertile, producing 94.6 (±1.64) percent stainable pollen of a regular diameter and a mean of 96 seeds per berry on self-pollination. *Solanum stoloniferum* (C.P.C. 2282.2) (*sto* 2282.2). This clone was grown from seed collected by Dr. J. G. Hawkes in 1949 in Puebla State, Mexico. It is a form of the species characterized by dark green leaves, many interjected leaflets, a high leaflet index and blue flowers. It sets abundantly seeded berries by self-pollination.

*Hybrid M.*271. This one seed obtained in the cross *dms* 2249 (♀) × *sto* 2282.2 (♂) germinated and grew very slowly into a small plant with extremely short internodes and a tufted, almost cushiony habit; it produced only a single flower. By contrast, when grafted on tomato, its growth was upright and vigorous, it produced long internodes and flowering was profuse and continuous. Comparison of the leaf and flower characters of *M.* 271 with those of its parents (Table 1) shows that in most ways it resembles the *demissum* parent more closely than it does *sto* 2282.2. A predominance of *demissum* would also be expected in a pentaploid hybrid ($2n = 60$—3 *dms* +2 *sto* genomes). Morphologically, *M.* 271 resembles polyhaploid *S. demissum* ($2n = 3x = 36$)[1-3] and could be taken for one were it not for its chromosome number. An analysis of meiosis gave the results shown in Table 2.

四倍体茄属植物中染色体的双减数

马克斯等

编者按

减数分裂是产生只含有一套染色体的生殖细胞的过程，在这个过程中，染色体数目减半。曾有报道认为一些异常杂种植株可能是由染色体双减数引起的，但是缺乏关于其起源的确切证据。本文中，英国植物学家杰弗里·哈本及其同事们提供的生物化学和形态学方面的数据证实了茄属中的异常杂种植株是通过这种方式产生的。该马铃薯植株的性状更接近其母本，表明杂种产生是由于含有四套染色体的父本发生了染色体双减数。

反复尝试将 *Solanum demissum*（$2n = 6x = 72$）和 *S. stoloniferum*（$2n = 4x = 48$）杂交，使其最终获得含有一粒种子的结实浆果。这粒种子萌发长成的植株（*M.* 271）体细胞染色体数目为 $2n = 4x = 48$，而不是预期的 $2n = 5x = 60$。本文对 *M.* 271 进行了细胞学、形态学和生物化学方面的研究，均提供了确凿的证据证明 *M.* 271 确实是一个由于发生染色体双减数而产生的真杂种。

本研究所用的实验材料如下：**亲本**。*Solanum demissum* (C.P.C.2249) (*dms* 2249) 是由霍克斯博士于 1949 年在墨西哥雷亚尔–德尔蒙特的伊达尔戈州收集到的克隆株，其具有该物种典型的形态特征：雄性雌性均可育，花粉直径正常，可染花粉粒占 94.6(±1.64)%，自花授粉时每个浆果平均可结 96 粒种子。*Solanum stoloniferum* (C.P.C. 2282.2) (*sto* 2282.2) 是霍克斯博士于 1949 年在墨西哥普埃布拉州所采集种子的后代，它是该物种的一种变型，其特点是长有深绿色叶子和许多嵌入小叶，小叶指数较高，花朵呈现为蓝色。它可以通过自花授粉产生大量的结实浆果。

杂种 *M.* 271 这是由 *dms* 2249 (♀) × *sto* 2282.2 (♂) 杂交得到的种子，该种子萌发后逐渐长为节间极短的簇生盘状的小植株，仅生长出一朵花。相比之下，若将其嫁接在番茄上，则生长直立且旺盛，节间长，花多且持续产生。对 *M.* 271 与其亲本的叶片和花器官性状进行比较（表 1）表明，它在许多方面更接近亲本 *demissum* 而不是 *sto* 2282.2。五倍体杂种（$2n = 60$）应该也更偏向于 *demissum*，因为其基因组组成为 3 *dms*+2 *sto*。如果不考虑染色体数量，*M.* 271 应该在形态上更像多元单倍体 *S. demissum*（$2n = 3x = 36$）[1-3]。表 2 是减数分裂的分析结果。

Table 1. Leaf Characters of Parents and Hybrid

	dms 2249 Mean* (range)	*M.* 271 Mean* (range)	*sto* 2282.2 Mean* (range)
Pairs of lateral leaflets	2.90 (2-3)	2.00 (0)	3.40 (3-4)
Number of interjected leaflets	2.55 (1-4)	0.90 (0-1)	6.40 (3-10)
Terminal leaflet index $\left(\frac{\text{Breadth}}{\text{Length}}\%\right)$	58 (52-68)	61 (50-72)	66 (60-73)

* Based on ten measurements.

Table 2. Meiotic and Fertility Data

Plant	Meiosis in pollen mother cells							Percent ± *S.E.* stainable pollen
	No. of cells	Mean ± *S.E.* per cell					Term. coeff.	
		IV	III	II	I	Xta		
sto 2282.2	25	0	0	24.00	0	32.64 ± 0.51	0.56	60.4 ± 4.02
M. 271	25	0.08	1.48 ± 0.25	12.64 ± 0.36	17.96 ± 0.40	22.4 ± 0.73	0.72	0

M. 271 has no stainable pollen and attempts to backcross it by both parents as males gave one berry when *sto* 2282.2 was used. This contained two seeds, but neither germinated.

Possible Origins

There is no definite morphological evidence to suggest, let alone prove, that *M.* 271 is a true hybrid of *S. demissum* × *S. stoloniferum*. Before giving the biochemical evidence on this point, we may consider three other possible origins, as follows:

(1) *contamination*. It is possible that *M.* 271 is a hybrid between *dms* 2249 and a diploid *Solanum*, since three such species, *S. chomatophyllum*, *S. santolallae* and *S. verrucosum*, were growing in the same glasshouse as *S. demissum* and were being used in the same crossing programme. However, all attempts to cross *demissum* with these diploids failed, and, in addition, *M.* 271 shows no evidence of the characteristic morphology or phenolic pattern (see later) of any of these species. Hybrids between *demissum* and *verrucosum* have been recorded[4,5]: they differ both morphologically and cytologically from *M.* 271.

(2) *Female parthenogenesis*. Polyhaploid plants of *S. demissum* are occasionally produced as a result of female parthenogenesis in selfed progenies of *S. demissum*[3] or in progenies obtained from crosses between *demissum* and diploid species[2,6,7]. All had $2n = 3x = 36$ except for two plants: one which Dodds[2] found to have $2n = 3x + 3 = 39$ and another which Beamish[7] found to have $2n = 2x + 2 = 26$.

A tetraploid plant could arise parthenogenetically from a hexaploid only by an extremely abnormal maternal meiosis. Meiosis and embryo-sac development were therefore studied in ovules of *dms* 2249, using sections stained with Heidenhain's haematoxylin. Meiosis was regular and embryo-sac development was of the type normal for *S. demissum*[8] . Thus the

表 1. 亲本与杂种的叶片性状

	dms 2249 均值 *（范围）	*M.* 271 均值 *（范围）	*sto* 2282.2 均值 *（范围）
侧生小叶的对数	2.90(2~3)	2.00(0)	3.40(3~4)
嵌入小叶的数量	2.55(1~4)	0.90(0~1)	6.40(3~10)
顶生小叶指数 $\left(\frac{宽度}{长度}\%\right)$	58(52~68)	61(50~72)	66(60~73)

* 基于 10 次测量得到。

表 2. 减数分裂和育性分析

植株	花粉母细胞减数分裂							可染花粉百分比 ± 标准误差
	细胞数量	每个细胞的均值 ± 标准误差					顶端系数	
		IV	III	II	I	Xta		
sto 2282.2	25	0	0	24.00	0	32.64 ± 0.51	0.56	60.4 ± 4.02
M. 271	25	0.08	1.48 ± 0.25	12.64 ± 0.36	17.96 ± 0.40	22.4 ± 0.73	0.72	0

M. 271 不能产生可染花粉，因此尝试将其两亲本作为父本与其回交，当以 *sto* 2282.2 为父本时结出了一个浆果，它含有两粒种子，但均不能发芽。

可能的起源

迄今尚无确切的形态学证据表明 *M.* 271 是 *S. demissum* × *S. stoloniferum* 的真杂种，更不用说证明了。在获得生物化学证据之前，我们考虑了以下三种其他可能的起源：

（1）**污染**　*M.* 271 有可能是一个由 *dms* 2249 与一种二倍体茄属植株产生的杂种，因为 *S. chomatophyllum*、*S. santolallae* 和 *S. verrucosum* 这三个物种的植株与 *S. demissum* 生长在同一个温室中，而且被用于同样的杂交项目。然而，所有试图将 *demissum* 与这些二倍体杂交的努力都以失败告终，另外 *M.* 271 也没有表现出任何上述物种的特征性的形态学或酚型特征（见后）。以前报道的 *demissum* 和 *verrucosum* 的杂种 [4,5] 的形态学和细胞学特征均与 *M.* 271 不同。

（2）**孤雌生殖**　*S. demissum*[3] 自交后代或其与二倍体物种 [2,6,7] 杂交后代的孤雌生殖有时会产生多元单倍体植株。这些多元单倍体植株染色体组成均为 $2n = 3x = 36$，只有以下两个植株例外：一个是多兹 [2] 发现的植株 ($2n = 3x + 3 = 39$)，另一个是比米什 [7] 发现的植株 ($2n = 2x + 2 = 26$)。

仅通过六倍体母本植株的极度异常减数分裂而导致的孤雌生殖就可能产生四倍体植株。本研究利用海登海因苏木素切片染色法，观察了 *dms* 2249 胚珠中的减数分裂和胚囊发育的情况，结果发现其减数分裂正常，其胚囊发育是正常的 *S. demissum*

occurrence of a parthenogenetic tetraploid seedling of *demissum* is extremely unlikely.

(3) *Male parthenogenesis*. *M.* 271 could have conceivably arisen by male parthenogenesis, in which case it would be genetically equivalent to a segregate in a progeny raised by selfing *sto* 2282.2. Such a progeny was grown and all the individuals were found to resemble closely the parent plant; furthermore, all were fertile and set berries by selfpollination. Thus, this parental clone is highly homozygous, and it is therefore inconceivable that a male parthenogenetic seedling should resemble *demissum* rather than its *stoloniferum* parent.

Biochemical Evidence

Except for the anthocyanin pigments of flowers which exhibit dominant-recessive relationships in their inheritance, the genetic control of most chemical constituents is more or less quantitative and hybrids contain most or all of the substances present in the parents[9]. Thus chemical constituents characteristic of presumed parents can give good evidence of the origin of a putative hybrid. On this assumption, the flavonol glycosides of the flowers and the leaf alkaloids of *dms*, *sto* and *M.* 271 were examined, since these substances were known to show significant variation among the wild tuber-bearing *Solanum* species.

Phenolic patterns in flowers. Ten flavonol glycosides are known to occur (and vary) in potato flowers[10]. Their distributions in *M.* 271, in its putative parents and in three related diploid species were therefore examined (Table 3). The results eliminate the possibility that *M.*271 could have arisen by a chance hybridization between *demissum* and a related diploid species. The following points about the phenolic patterns of the flowers may be noted.

Table 3. Phenolic Constituents of Flowers

	dms 2249	*M.* 271	*sto* 2282.2	*chm** 2708	*san* 2519	*ver* 2644
Flavonol glycosides						
Kaempferol 3-glucoside	−	−	−	−	+	−
Kaempferol 3-rutinoside	−	−	−	−	−	+
Kaempferol 3-sophoroside	−	−	−	+	+	−
Kaempferol 3-(2^G-glucosylrutinoside)	−	−	−	+	−	+
Quercatin 3-glucoside	−	−	−	−	+	−
Quercetin 3-rutinoside	+	+	+	−	−	+
Querectin 3-sophoroside	−	−	−	−	+	−
Quercetin 3-(2^G-glucosylrutinoside)	−	−	−	+	−	+
Myricetin 3-rutinoside	+	+	−	+	−	−
Luteolin 7-glucoside	−	−	+	−	−	−
Other phenolics						
Caffcic-glucose-quinic complex	+	+	−	−	−	+
Unknown colourless→mauve	−	−	−	+	−	−

* Also contains two other unidentified flavonol glycosides.

Key: *dms*—*demissum*; *sto*—*stoloniferum*; *chm*—*chomatophyllum*; *san*—*santollalae*; *ver*—*verrucosum*.

植株的类型[8]。由此可见，通过 *demissum* 孤雌生殖产生四倍体是完全不可能的。

（3）**孤雄生殖** *M.* 271 可能是通过孤雄生殖产生的，在这种情况下，它与 *sto* 2282.2 自交后代的某个分离个体在遗传组成上将完全相同。种植这样的后代后，其所有个体均表现出与亲本植株相似的性状；而且所有个体均可育，并可通过自花授粉产生浆果。因此这个亲本克隆株是高度纯合的，另外，我们也很难相信一个孤雄生殖产生的幼苗会与 *demissum* 相似，而不是与其亲本 *stoloniferum* 相似。

生物化学证据

除了花朵的花青素在遗传上表现为显隐性关系外，绝大多数化学成分的遗传控制或多或少都是数量性的，而且杂种含有存在于亲本植株内的大多数或所有化学物质[9]。因此，研究可能亲本的化学成分特征可以为某些假定的杂种的起源提供有力的证据。根据这一假设，本研究检测了材料 *dms*、*sto* 和 *M.* 271 花中的黄酮醇糖苷含量以及叶片中的生物碱含量，因为人们知道这些物质的含量在野生茄属块茎物种中存在显著差异。

花朵中酚的类型的分布特征 已知在马铃薯的花中含有 10 种黄酮醇糖苷，而且其含量存在差异[10]。因此本研究检测了这些物质在 *M.* 271、其可能的亲本以及相关的 3 个二倍体物种中的分布特征（表 3）。研究结果表明，*M.* 271 不可能来自于 *demissum* 和任何一个相关的二倍体物种间的偶然杂交。关于花中酚的类型的分布特征，以下几点值得关注。

表 3. 花中酚类成分分析

	dms 2249	*M.* 271	*sto* 2282.2	*chm** 2708	*san* 2519	*ver* 2644
黄酮醇糖苷						
山奈酚 3–葡糖苷	−	−	−	−	+	−
山奈酚 3–芸香糖苷	−	−	−	−	−	+
山奈酚 3–槐糖苷	−	−	−	+	+	−
山奈酚 3–(2^G– 葡糖基芸香糖苷)	−	−	−	+	−	+
槲皮素 3–葡糖苷	−	−	−	−	+	−
槲皮素 3–芸香糖苷	+	+	+	−	−	+
槲皮素 3–槐糖苷	−	−	−	−	+	−
槲皮素 3–(2^G– 葡糖基芸香糖苷)	−	−	−	+	−	+
杨梅酮 3–芸香糖苷	+	+	−	+	−	−
木樨草素 7–葡糖苷	−	−	+	−	−	−
其他酚						
咖啡 – 葡萄糖 – 奎宁复合物	+	+	−	−	−	+
未知无色→紫红色	−	−	−	+	−	−

* 还包含其他两种未鉴定的黄酮醇糖苷。

缩写：*dms*—*demissum*; *sto*—*stoloniferum*; *chm*—*chomatophyllum*; *san*—*santollalae*; *ver*—*verrucosum*.

(1) The pattern of *M.* 271 is identical with that of *demissum*, agreeing with the morphological evidence (see earlier) showing that *demissum* is the predominant parent.

(2) The pattern of *M.* 271 does not disagree with the idea that *stoloniferum* is the other parent. One constituent of *stoloniferum*, it is true, is not present in the hybrid. This substance, luteolin 7-glucoside, though characteristic of the species, is not always present: it was lacking in four out of 38 clones examined[10]. Its absence from *M.* 271 is therefore not critical.

(3) The pattern of *M.* 271 is quite different from those of the three diploid species (Table 2), which makes it very unlikely that any of these species is involved in its parentage. Thus, all three not only contain kaempferol as well as quercetin glycosides but, in addition, the glycosidic patterns (sophoroside, glucoside and (2^G-glucosylrutinoside)) are quite different from *M.* 271 or its parents (which have only the 3-rutinoside). Production of (2^G-glucosylrutinoside) in flowers of *S. stoloniferum* and *S. chacoense* is known[10] to be controlled by a dominant gene *Gl* (3-rutinoside being the recessive character), and it is unlikely that this glycosidic form would not appear in hybrids involving *chomatophyllum* or *verrucosum*.

Alkaloids of the leaves. Steroidal alkaloids occur, combined with sugars (branched tri- or tetra-saccharides), quite characteristically in the genus *Solanum*, and their distribution has been studied intensively in recent years[11]. While glycosides of solanidine are widely distributed in the tuberous solanums, those based on demissidine are found only in *S. demissum.* Thus it should be possible to characterize hybrids of *demissum* with other species on the basis of their alkaloid content and this has, in fact, been done with *M.* 271.

The alkaloids of both parents were examined, with the results shown in Table 4. The clone of *S. demissum* contained the expected demissine[12] and *S. stoloniferum* contained solanine and α-chaconine, the two commonest potato alkaloids. *M.* 271 contained three glycosides of which two corresponded in R_F value with glycosides from the different parents, that is with demissine and α-chaconine; the third appeared to be a new demissidine glycoside. On acid hydrolysis, these glycosides together yielded demissidine, with traces of solanidine, and four sugars: glucose, galactose, xylose and rhamnose. Thus, *M.* 271 has the aglycones of both parents and also the constituent sugars of both, since the bound xylose is derived from *S. demissum* and the bound rhamnose can only have come from *S. stoloniferum.*

Since major intraspecific variation in alkaloid content is unknown in the potatoes, this result is effective proof that *M.* 271 is a true hybrid between *S. demissum* and *S. stoloniferum.*

(1)杂种 *M.* 271 的酚型与 *demissum* 的相同,这与形态学证据是吻合的(见上文),表明 *demissum* 是其主要亲本。

(2)杂种 *M.* 271 的酚型并不能否定 *stoloniferum* 是其另外一个亲本。的确，在杂种中没有检测到 *stoloniferum* 的一种成分，但也有研究表明虽然木樨草素 7– 葡糖苷是该物种的特征性物质，但并非总能被检测到：在所有检测过的 38 个克隆体中，4 个克隆体中未检测到木樨草素 7– 葡糖苷 [10]，因此该物质在 *M.* 271 中不存在就不能证明 *stoloniferum* 不是该杂种的亲本之一。

(3)杂种 *M.* 271 的酚型与本研究所分析的 3 个二倍体物种中的酚型存在显著差异（表 2），由此推测这些二倍体物种不可能参与该杂种的形成。因为这 3 种二倍体不仅含有山奈酚和槲皮素苷，还含有槐糖苷、葡糖苷和 2^G– 葡糖基芸香糖苷等糖苷，这与 *M.* 271 或其亲本（仅含 3– 芸香糖苷）显著不同。已知 *S. stoloniferum* 和 *S. chacoense* 的花朵产生的 2^G– 葡糖芸香糖苷 [10] 受一个显性基因 *Gl* 控制（3– 芸香糖苷是隐性性状），这种类型的糖苷应该在与 *chomatophyllum* 或 *verrucosum* 有关的杂种中出现。

叶片中的生物碱　茄属植物的重要特征是存在甾体生物碱与糖类（带分支的三糖或四糖），近年来已对它们的分布情况进行了深入研究 [11]。糖苷茄啶在有块茎的茄属中广泛分布，而糖苷垂茄碱仅在 *S. demissum* 中存在。因此，可以根据生物碱的含量区分来自 *demissum* 和其他物种的杂种。本研究正是对 *M.* 271 进行了这样的分析。

检测了两个亲本的生物碱组成情况，结果见表 4。*S. demissum* 的克隆体含有预期的垂茄碱 [12]，而 *S. stoloniferum* 则含有两种最常见的马铃薯生物碱：茄碱和 α– 卡茄碱。杂种 *M.* 271 含有 3 种糖苷，其中两种的 R_F 值分别与来自不同亲本的糖苷相对应，即对应于垂茄碱和 α– 卡茄碱，第三种则是一种新的糖苷垂茄碱。这些糖苷碱在酸水解时共同产生垂茄碱、痕量的茄啶和 4 种糖：葡萄糖、半乳糖、木糖和鼠李糖。因此，*M.* 271 含有两个亲本的糖苷配基和糖类，其木糖来自 *S. demissum*，而鼠李糖则只能来自 *S. stoloniferum*。

因为在马铃薯中尚未发现其生物碱含量在种内有较大的差异，所以本研究结果有效地证明了 *M.* 271 是 *S. demissum* 和 *S. stoloniferum* 间的真杂种。

Table 4. Alkaloids in the Leaves

Plant	Alkaloid	R^*a-s	R_F†	Products of acid hydrolysis	
				Aglycone(s)	Sugars
dms 2249	Demissine	0.94	0.29	Demissidine	Xylose, glucose and galactose
sto 2282.2	Solanine α-chaconine	1.0 1.35	0.28 0.46	Solanidine	Rhamnose, glucose and galactose
M. 271	Demissine (?)	0.88	0.30	Demissidine + traces of solanidine§	Rhamnose, xylose, glucose and galactose
	New demissidine glycoside α-chaconine (?)	‡1.37	0.48		

* R_F relative to α-solanine: chromatograms run on citrate-buffered whatman No.1 paper in butanol-citric acid-water.

† Chromatograms run on silica-gel plates in acetic acid-ethanol (1 : 3).

‡ Identified as a mixture of two components, since this spot gave a strong Dragendorf reaction for alkalold but only a weak reaction with Clarke's reagent (used for detecting solanidine glycosides in the presence of demissidine glycosides, which do not react).

§ Solanidine was detected, in the presence of demissidine, by the use of Sarett's reagent (compare ref. 13). The crude mixture of alkaloid aglycones failed to respond to the nitroso test, indicating that tomadine was absent.

Origin of *M.* 271

The morphology and biochemistry of *M.* 271 indicate that it is far nearer its female parent, *demissum*, than it is to *stoloniferum*, suggesting that double chromosome reduction occurred in the latter, the male parent.

Meiosis was normal in the sample of pollen mother cells examined from *sto* 2282.2 (Table 1). However, pollen grain measurements from ten different anthers showed a range of size within each anther. Using within-anther variance as a measure of this variation, Bartlett's test showed a highly significant heterogeneity between anthers (χ^2[9]487.4). Furthermore, the mean variance within anthers of *sto* 2282.2 was above that for other *stoloniferum* clones. Pollen stainability was also extremely variable in *sto* 2282.2, ranging from 12 to 75 percent per anther. Of a sample of 1,000 "good" pollen grains 5.6 percent had diameters equal to or below the modal diameter of pollen grains measured in a diploid species. Since, within species, the size of a pollen grain is often correlated with its chromosome number, it is quite likely that some of the small pollen grains found in *sto* 2282.2 were double-reduced, with 12 chromosomes.

Matsubayashi[14] found that certain clones of *stoloniferum* produced occasional tripolar spindles at *M*I of meiosis which resulted in hexads containing six nuclei of almost equal size. Such a mechanism could well be the source of double-reduced pollen grains. Unfortunately a re-investigation of meiosis in *sto* 2282.2 is impossible since the clone was lost through virus infection. There is therefore no information about the cytological mechanism of the presumed double reduction.

Discussion

Double reduction has been invoked on a number of occasions to account for the appearance of unusual hybrids. Thus Steere[15] obtained diploid progeny which resembled

表 4. 叶片中的生物碱

植物	生物碱	R^*a-s	R_F†	酸水解产物	
				糖苷配基	糖类
dms 2249	垂茄碱	0.94	0.29	垂茄碱	木糖、葡萄糖和半乳糖
sto 2282.2	茄碱	1.0	0.28	茄啶	鼠李糖、葡萄糖和半乳糖
	α – 卡茄碱	1.35	0.46		
M. 271	垂茄碱 (?)	0.88	0.30	垂茄碱 + 痕量茄啶 §	鼠李糖、木糖、葡萄糖和半乳糖
	新的糖苷垂茄碱 α – 卡茄碱 (?)	‡1.37	0.48		

* R_F 与 α– 茄碱的相对量：在丁醇 – 柠檬酸 – 水中，在浸有柠檬酸盐缓冲液的沃特曼 1 号纸张上跑色谱。
† 在乙酸和乙醇（1:3）的混合液中，在硅酸凝胶平板上跑色谱。
‡ 被鉴定为两种组分的混合物，因为在该点有强烈的生物碱德拉根多夫反应，但与克拉克试剂只有微弱反应（该试剂用于在不发生反应的垂茄碱糖苷存在时检测茄啶糖苷）。
§ 使用萨雷特试剂（见参考文献 13）在垂茄碱存在时检测到了茄啶。生物碱糖苷配基的粗混合物未对亚硝基检测发生反应，表明番茄碱缺失。

M. 271 的来源

M. 271 的形态学和生物化学特征表明，它更接近于其母本 *demissum*，而不是父本 *stoloniferum*，说明其父本染色体发生了双减数。

检查发现来自 *sto* 2282.2 的花粉母细胞样品的减数分裂正常（表 1）。不过，对 10 个不同花药的花粉粒大小的测定表明，每个花药中花粉粒大小存在差异。把同一花药内的数据方差作为这种变化的量度，巴特利特的测验结果表明在花药之间存在着明显的异质性（χ^2[9]487.4）。此外，*sto* 2282.2 花药内的均方差高于其他的 *stoloniferum* 克隆株。*sto* 2282.2 每个花药中花粉的可染能力也存在很大差异，从 12% 至 75% 不等。选取 1000 个“好”的花粉粒样品进行测量，其中 5.6% 的直径等于或低于在二倍体物种中测量获得的花粉粒的标准直径。由于在同一物种内，花粉粒的大小通常与其染色体的数量相关，很可能在 *sto* 2282.2 中发现的某些较小的花粉粒发生了染色体双减数，只有 12 条染色体。

松林 [14] 发现 *stoloniferum* 的某些克隆株有时会在减数第一次分裂中期产生三极纺锤体，导致形成包含 6 个几乎同等大小核子的六核体。这种机制非常有可能是产生发生染色体双减数的花粉粒的原因。遗憾的是，由于病毒感染使克隆体丢失，未能对 *sto* 2282.2 的减数分裂进行再次研究。因此，尚缺乏双减数假说的细胞学证据。

讨　论

双减数常被用来解释许多异常杂种的产生。例如，斯蒂尔 [15] 通过将腋花矮牵牛 ($2n = 2x = 14$) 和碧冬茄 ($2n = 4x = 28$) 杂交，获得了与其两亲本均相似的二倍体后代。

both parents, from the cross *Petunia axillaris* ($2n = 2x = 14$) × *P. hybrida* ($2n = 4x = 28$). Nishiyama[16] made similar observations on *Avena* hybrids, Karprechenko[17] on *Brassica* × *Raphanus* crosses and Ewart and Walker[18] on *Poinsettia*. In the cherry, three diploid cultivars are reputed to have arisen from crosses between diploid *Prunus avium* and a tetraploid cultivar, "May Duke"[19]; Darlington[20] thought that the chromosome number of the parents disproved the supposed origin of these cultivars but, in retrospect, it now seems that the original interpretation is worth reconsideration.

In none of these examples is there definite proof of double chromosome reduction: for the potato hybrid, although direct cytological evidence is lacking, the biochemical data appear to be decisive. The fact that Matsubayashi[14] independently obtained a tetraploid plant from the same cross that produced *M.* 271 suggests that double chromosome reduction may be less uncommon than we think. But it seems unlikely that it is an important general mechanism in Nature for decreasing chromosome numbers.

From a biochemical point of view, *M.* 271 is particularly interesting since it contains a new hybrid substance, a glycoside of demissidine not present in either parent. The identification of the sugar linkages in this glycoside will clearly be of interest, as it should throw some light on the control of alkaloid glycoside synthesis, about which very little is at present known.

(**208**, 359-361; 1965)

G. E. Marks, R. K. Mckee and J. B. Harborne: John Innes Institute, Bayfordbury, Hertford.

References:

1. Howard, H. W., and Swaminathan, M. S., *Genetica*, **26**, 381 (1953).
2. Dodds, K. S., *Nature*, **166**, 795 (1950).
3. Marks, G. E., *J. Genet.*, **53**, 262 (1955).
4. Propach, H., *Z. Indukt. Abstamn. Vererb.*, **74**, 376 (1937).
5. Kawakami, K., and Matsubayashi, M., *Sci. Rep. Myogo Univ. Agric.*, 3, 17 (1957).
6. Bains, G. S., and Howard, H. W., *Nature*, **166**, 795 (1950).
7. Beamish, K., *Amer. J. Bot.*, **43**, 297 (1955).
8. Walker, R. I., *Bull. Torrey Bot. Club*, **82**, 87 (1955).
9. Alston, R. E., and Turner, B. L., *Biochemical Systematics*, 295 (Prentice-Hall, 1963).
10. Harborne, J. B., *Biochem. J.*, **84**, 100 (1962).
11. Schreiber, K., *Die Kulturpflanze*, **11**, 422 (1963).
12. Schreiber, K., and Aurich, O., *Z. Naturforschg.*, 18*b*, 471 (1963).
13. Schreiber, K., Aurich, O., and Osske, G., *J. Chromatog.*, **12**, 63 (1963).
14. Matsubayashi, M., *Chromosome Information Service*, No. 3, 7 (1962) and personal communication.
15. Steere, W. C., *Amer. J. Bot.*, **19**, 340 (1932).
16. Nishiyama, I., *Cytologia*, **5**, 146 (1933).
17. Karprechenko, G. D., in *Recent Advances in Cytology*, edit. by Darlington, C. D., 193 (Churchill, 1937).
18. Ewart, L. C., and Walker, D. E., *J. Heredity*, **50**, 203 (1960).
19. Knight, T. A., quoted by Darlington, C. D., *J. Genet.*, **22**, 19 (1928).
20. Darlingron, C. D., *J. Genet.*, **28**, 327 (1934).

西山[16]在燕麦属杂种研究中，卡尔佩琴科[17]在芸薹属植物和萝卜属植物杂交实验中，尤尔特和沃克[18]在对一品红的研究中都观察到了类似的现象。在对樱桃的研究中，研究者认为 3 个二倍体樱桃栽培品种是由二倍体物种欧洲甜樱桃和四倍体栽培品种“五月爵士樱桃”杂交产生的[19]。达林顿[20]认为亲本中染色体的数量证明了这些栽培品种的假定起源是不正确的，但是现在看来最初的解释值得重新考虑。

以上这些研究例子中均没有给出染色体双减数的确切证据：在关于马铃薯杂种的研究中，尽管缺乏直接的细胞学证据，但提供了确切的生物化学数据。松林[14]从得到 *M*. 271 的同一杂交过程中还获得了一个四倍体植株，这一事实表明染色体双减数也许不像我们想象的那样少见。但是在自然界中这种机制可能并不是染色体数量减少的一个重要的常规机制。

在生化水平上，尤其令人感兴趣的是，*M*. 271 包含了一种新的糖苷垂茄碱，这种新的杂交物质在任何一个亲本中都不存在。有必要鉴别该糖苷中的糖链连接，以便帮助人们更好地了解糖苷生物碱的合成，因为目前我们对此还所知甚少。

（周志华 翻译；王秀娥 审稿）

Structure of the Quasi-Stellar Radio Source 3C 273 B

M. J. Rees and D. W. Sciama

Editor's Note

The radio source known as *3C* 273 *B*—the designation "*3C*" refers to the third catalogue of radio sources in the sky compiled by the radioastronomy station at Cambridge—is one of the first to be studied in detail. This paper was based both on radioastronomy measurements and optical observations of the source of the radio waves. Of the two authors, Martin Rees is now Lord Rees of Ludlow and became president of the Royal Society of London in 2005. Dennis Sciama was a theoretical astronomer at Cambridge.

IN this article we show that: (1) the radio variations[1] of *3C* 273 *B* are consistent with its red shift being cosmological; (2) the variable component of the optical continuum[2] of *3C* 273 *B* may be partly due to inverse Compton collisions between relativistic electrons and their own synchrotron radiation. In this case the optical variations would be correlated with the radio variations, though with a phase delay.

The problem involved in (1) is to reconcile (*a*) the upper limit on the size of the source derived from the period of the variations[3]; (*b*) the lower limit on the angular diameter of the source derived from the absence of self-absorption down to some particular frequency[4,5] (assuming the synchrotron mechanism and that the electrons are radiating incoherently); (*c*) the distance derived from the red shift of the optical counterpart of the radio source. This problem first arose with the quasi-stellar source *CTA* 102, which Sholomitsky[6] reported to vary with a period of about 100 days at 940 Mc/s. In this case the distance derived from the red shift of 1.037 (ref. 7) is ~1,500 times greater than the upper limit permitted by (*a*) and (*b*). We recently proposed[8] a model of *CTA* 102 which would resolve this discrepancy, but recognized that it required a rather improbable geometry and so was very implausible. Since then Maltby and Moffet[9] have reported that *CTA* 102 did not vary appreciably at 970 Mc/s over a 3-year period ending about 2 years before Sholomitsky's observations began. While it is possible that *CTA* 102 varies sporadically, the more likely inference is that Sholomitsky's observations are in error.

The same problem arises with the quasi-stellar source *3C* 273 *B*, the flux density of which at 8,000 Mc/s was found by Dent[1] to have increased by about 40 percent in 3 years. This source shows no self-absorption in its spectrum down to at least 200 Mc/s (ref. 10) (in fact the spectrum is flat down to this frequency). For a magnetic field strength of 10^{-3} gauss this implies a lower limit on the angular diameter of 0.03 sec (while the observed[11] angular diameter is 0.5 sec). If the period of the radio variations is comparable with that of the

类星体射电源3*C* 273 *B*的结构

瑞斯，夏玛

编者按

众所周知，3*C* 273 *B* 是最早被详细研究的射电源之一。此处“3*C*”是指在剑桥射电天文学观测站收集整理的射电源星表中的第三表。本文的研究是在对该射电源的射电天文学测量和光学观测的基础上进行的。本文的两位作者之一瑞斯（即现在的瑞斯勋爵）于2005年当选英国皇家学会主席，另一位丹尼斯·夏玛则是剑桥大学理论天文学家。

我们在本文中阐明以下两点：（1）3*C* 273 *B* 的射电变化与它的宇宙学红移相一致[1]；（2）3*C* 273 *B* 的连续光谱中的可变部分（即光变）可能部分是由于相对论电子与其同步辐射之间发生逆康普顿碰撞[2]。这种情况下，光学波段变化与射电变化相关联，只是存在一定的相位延迟。

上面（1）中的内容需要满足：(*a*) 根据变化周期推出的射电源尺寸的上限[3]；(*b*) 根据不发生自吸收的特定频率推出的射电源角直径的下限[4,5]（假设存在同步辐射机制，并且电子是非相干辐射的）；(*c*) 通过射电源光学对应体红移推出的距离。这一问题最初出现于类星体射电源 *CTA* 102，据肖洛米斯基报道，该射电源在 940 兆周 / 秒处的变化周期大约为 100 天[6]，在此由它的红移 1.037（参考文献 7）计算出来的距离是（*a*）和（*b*）所允许的上限的近 1,500 倍。事实上，在最近的研究中，我们已经提出了 *CTA* 102 的一个模型[8]以解决上面的分歧，但是该模型构建的不大可能的几何形态却令人难以接受。自那以后，莫尔特比和莫菲特就曾报道[9]，在肖洛米斯基的观测开始之前两年，*CTA* 102 在 970 兆周 / 秒附近大约三年的时间都没有发生明显变化。因此，*CTA* 102 可能只是偶尔变化，而肖洛米斯基的观测很可能存在错误。

类星体射电源 3*C* 273 *B* 也存在相同的问题。登特发现在频率为 8,000 兆周 / 秒处，该射电源的流量密度在 3 年时间里增加了大约 40%[1]。该射电源在至少大于 200 兆周 / 秒的频谱区域内是不存在自吸收的（参考文献 10）（事实上，其频谱在高于 200 兆周 / 秒的频率范围内都是很平坦的）。对于大小为 10^{-3} 高斯的磁场强度，其角直径下限为 0.03 角秒（角直径观测值为 0.5 角秒[11]）。如果射电变化的周期与光学波段变化的周期（约 12 年）相当，那么该射电源的尺寸不可能超过 3 秒差距，其距

optical variations, that is ~12 years. The size of the radio source cannot exceed 3 pc and its distance cannot exceed 20 Mpc. On the other hand, the red shift of 0.158 (ref. 12) implies a distance of 470 Mpc.

The discrepancy would be resolved if the varying part of the source had an angular diameter $\sim 10^{-3}$ sec. We therefore propose[13]:

Model I. This model consists of a source of angular diameter 0.5 sec and (roughly constant) flux density ~25 flux units down to at least 200 Mc/s, in the centre of which is a varying source of angular diameter 1.3×10^{-3} sec (corresponding to a linear diameter of 3 pc), and at minimum a flux density ~2.5 flux units down to the frequency ν_a at which self-absorption sets in. Such self-absorption would not show up in the observed spectrum of this composite source. For a magnetic field H gauss in the central source, $\nu_a \sim 4{,}000\, H^{1/5}$ Mc/s. For simplicity we assume that the central source varies because of an increase in its relativistic electron flux, while its angular diameter and magnetic field are unchanged. If the total flux density of the source is doubled at high frequencies at maximum, the flux from the central source must increase by a factor ~10. Thus the frequency ν_b at which self-absorption sets in at maximum is given by $(\nu_b/\nu_a)^{2.5} \sim 10$, so $\nu_b \sim 10{,}000\, H^{1/5}$ Mc/s.

We can now predict the time variations that would be observed at various frequencies. For simplicity we take the central source to vary sinusoidally at high frequencies. For $\nu > \nu_b$ no self-absorption occurs, so the observed variation would be sinusoidal. In the intermediate range $\nu_b > \nu > \nu_a$ the flux density would at first increase sinusoidally, but when it reaches the level at which it would be self-absorbed at that frequency the increase would be cut off, and the flux density would remain constant until it decreases again in the second half of the cycle. For $\nu < \nu_a$ the variations would be negligible.

A lower limit on H (the value of which has not yet been specified) can be obtained if we require that the energy density of relativistic particles shall not exceed the magnetic energy density. If only ~1 percent of the total energy is in the electrons, we find that the field strength cannot be much less than 1 gauss. If $H = 1$ gauss, ν_a and ν_b have the values ~4,000 and ~10,000 Mc/s respectively, and the expected variations at 8,000 Mc/s are large enough to account for the observations. Our estimates for ν_a and ν_b are only rough, but they indicate what might be expected, and the measurement of their values and of the variations at intermediate frequencies would be a useful test of the model and would provide considerable information about the structure of the source.

It is not known how electrons attain relativistic energies in radio sources. The generation process may occur throughout the volume of the source, or the electrons may be ejected from a massive object at its centre. It is easily seen that the electrons must be produced by a mechanism of the former kind if the source in fact resembles Model I. The reason is that the lifetime of an electron which radiates at, say, 10^4 Mc/s in a field of 1 gauss is only $\sim 5\times10^6$ sec, which is much less than the time taken to cross the source, even for an electron moving at the speed of light. If such an electron were ejected from the centre it

离不会超过 20 兆秒差距。另一方面，大小为 0.158（参考文献 12）的红移量意味着其距离为 470 兆秒差距。

如果射电源可变部分的角直径约为 10^{-3} 角秒，那么上文中的不一致就会得到解决。因此，我们提出了以下模型 [13]：

模型 I　在该模型中，射电源角直径为 0.5 角秒，在大于 200 兆周 / 秒的频谱范围内流量密度（基本恒定）约为 25 个流量单位；在该射电源的中心区域，存在一个角直径为 1.3×10^{-3} 角秒的变源（对应线直径为 3 秒差距），在自吸收频率 ν_a 内，其最小流量密度约为 2.5 个流量单位。但是，自吸收在该复合源的观测谱中并不会出现。若该中心源磁场强度为 H 高斯，那么频率 ν_a 约为 4,000 $H^{1/5}$ 兆周 / 秒。为了简化模型，我们假设中心源由于其相对论电子流量的增加而发生变化，但是其角直径和磁场保持不变。如果该射电源极大时在高频的总流量密度增加一倍，那么中心源的流量则必须增加到近 10 倍。因此，自吸收区最高频率 ν_b 可以由 $(\nu_b/\nu_a)^{2.5}$ 约为 10 得出，即 ν_b 约为 10,000 $H^{1/5}$ 兆周 / 秒。

下面，我们预估各种频率下可能观测到的时变。为了简化，我们假定中心源在高频区域按正弦变化。由于在 $\nu > \nu_b$ 的区域不存在自吸收，因此实际观测到的时变应是正弦变化。在频率区间 $\nu_b > \nu > \nu_a$ 范围内，某频率处的流量密度首先按正弦变化增加，当达到自吸收阈值时就会停止增加，并保持恒定直至在后半周期继续降低。$\nu < \nu_a$ 范围内的变化可以忽略。

如果要求相对论性粒子的能量密度不能超过磁场能量密度的话，我们就可以得到 H 的下限（这个值尚未指定）。如果电子的能量只占总能量的 1%，我们发现磁场强度不可能远小于 1 高斯。如果 H=1 高斯，那么 ν_a、ν_b 的大小分别约为 4,000 兆周 / 秒和 10,000 兆周 / 秒，频率 8,000 兆周 / 秒处的预期变化足够大，以解释观测结果。尽管我们对 ν_a、ν_b 的估计有些粗略，但是在一定程度上仍然可以说明问题。实际测量 ν_a、ν_b 的频率值，以及测量的该频率区间内的流量变化，对于检验这一模型是非常有用的，同时可以提供关于该射电源结构的重要信息。

电子在射电源中是如何获取相对论能量的，这一问题尚不清楚。这一能量产生过程可能遍布于整个射电源，也可能是电子被射电源中心处的致密天体喷射出。然而，很显然的一点是，如果射电源符合模型 I，电子的能量产生机制必须符合前一种情况。原因在于，在强度为 1 高斯的磁场中，辐射频率为 10^4 兆周 / 秒的电子的寿命仅为 5×10^6 秒左右，远小于它穿过该射电源所需的时间（即使以光速射出）。如果电子由中心喷射出，它将难以到达射电源的边缘，除非射电源对于电子的辐射频率

would not reach the edge, unless it were emitting radiation at a frequency at which the source was opaque. Thus for frequencies exceeding v_a our discussion of the variations will be incorrect. To allow for this we now introduce:

Model II. In this model we assume that the electrons are all generated in a very small region (with diameter < 0.1 pc), which presumably contains a massive object. As in Model I, nearly all the flux at frequencies < ~4,000 Mc/s is assumed to come from a halo, and we only concern ourselves with an intense spherically symmetric core with radius ~1 pc, in which the variable higher frequency radio flux is supposed to originate. We assume that H ~1 gauss throughout this region, and that its radio emission has a flux density $S(\nu)$ which may be variable. For each ν we can determine the minimum radius $R(\nu)$ of a sphere from which $S(\nu)$ could come, if it in fact comes from a region which is opaque at all frequencies up to ν. We find that $R(\nu) \sim 0.3\ (S(\nu))^{1/2}(\nu/10^4)^{1.25}$ parsecs, when S is measured in flux units and ν in Mc/s. This radius can be compared with the distance $r(\nu)$ which an electron radiating at frequencies $\sim\nu$ would travel in its lifetime, assuming that it moves with speed $\sim c$. This is $\sim 5\times10^{-2}(\nu/10^4)^{-1/2}$ pc. If $R(\nu) > r(\nu)$, electrons moving outward from the centre cannot radiate freely without producing a radiation field the brightness temperature of which at frequency ν is higher than their kinetic temperature. Therefore they will conserve most of their energy until they reach a distance ~ $R\ (\nu)$ from the centre, where they can radiate freely.

The available data do not enable us to specify the flux density of the core precisely, but it is consistent with the observations to take $S(\nu)$ to be 10-30 flux units in the frequency range from 5,000 up to $\sim 10^5$ Mc/s. $R(\nu)$ is then several times greater than $r(\nu)$ throughout this range, and so we conclude that the radiation at frequency ν comes from the surface of a sphere of radius $R(\nu)$.

If electrons are ejected from the centre at a steady rate, $S(\nu)$ and $R(\nu)$ will adjust themselves to values which depend on the energy spectrum of the input electrons, and the flux of the source will be constant. If, however. The rate of input of electrons alters, $R(\nu)$ (and consequently $S(\nu)$) will change after the lapse of an interval of the order of the time for light signals to travel a distance $R(\nu)$. Thus changes in the behaviour of the massive object will cause changes in the radio flux. The maximum late of increase of flux will be attained if $R(\nu)$ expands with speed $\sim c$. An increase of $S(8\times10^3)$ from 2.5 to 25 flux units. Which corresponds to an increase in $R(8\times10^3)$ from ~0.6 to ~1.9 pc, could therefore certainly occur rapidly enough to explain Dent's observations. We can also predict, on the basis of this model, that more rapid variations could occur at higher frequencies. Furthermore, if a sudden change in the rate of injection of particles produces changes in $S(\nu)$ at different frequencies, we would expect to observe the variations at higher frequencies before those at lower (even in the absence of intergalactic dispersion[14]).

We have seen that, if the core emits a significant amount of radiation at, say, 10^5 Mc/s, this radiation must come mainly from a sphere which is opaque up to that frequency. The total energy density of all the radio frequency radiation up to 10^5 Mc/s within it will be

是不透明的。因此，对于大于 ν_a 的频率范围，我们关于流量变化的讨论存在不妥之处，所以我们现在需要引入下面的模型：

模型 II 在该模型中，我们假设所有的电子均产生于一个非常小的区域（直径小于 0.1 秒差距），该区域可能包含了一个大质量天体。正如模型 I 中，假定小于约 4,000 兆周 / 秒的频率范围内的所有流量几乎全部来自一个晕。这样，我们只需关心半径近为 1 秒差距的致密球形对称核，并假定高频可变射电流量就来自该区域。不妨设整个区域内的磁场强度 H 约为 1 高斯，射电辐射的流量密度为可变的 $S(\nu)$。如果辐射流量确实来自某一区域，而该区域对小于 ν 的频率都不透明，那么对于每个频率 ν，我们就可以确定一个最小半径 $R(\nu)$ 的球体，而 $S(\nu)$ 就来自该球体。我们发现，半径 $R(\nu)$ 约为 $0.3(S(\nu))^{1/2}(\nu/10^4)^{1.25}$ 秒差距，其中 S 的单位为流量单位，ν 的单位为兆周 / 秒。即使假设电子的速度近似为光速，半径 $R(\nu)$ 与辐射频率近似 ν 的电子在其寿命内所走的距离 $r(\nu)$ 也是可比较的，该距离约为 $5\times10^{-2}(\nu/10^4)^{-1/2}$ 秒差距。如果 $R(\nu) > r(\nu)$，那么从中心向外运动的电子就不能够自由辐射，除非产生一个在频率 ν 时的亮温度大于动力学温度的辐射场。这样，电子就会一直保存大部分能量，直至接近到达某一距离 $R(\nu)$ 后才能够自由辐射。

目前，我们尚不能通过已有的数据准确确定核心区域的流量密度。但如果将从 5,000 兆周 / 秒到 10^5 兆周 / 秒的频率区间内的流量密度取为 10~30 个流量单位，这些数据就会符合观测结果。那么，在这一区间内，$R(\nu)$ 就会比 $r(\nu)$ 大若干倍。这样，我们可以得出结论，频率为 ν 的辐射主要来自半径为 $R(\nu)$ 的球的表面。

如果电子以稳定速率从中心喷射出，$S(\nu)$ 与 $R(\nu)$ 就会根据输入电子的能谱适当调整到某一取值，该射电源的流量将保持恒定。然而，如果电子的输入速率改变，$R(\nu)$（与对应的 $S(\nu)$）将在某一时间间隔（量级与光穿过距离 $R(\nu)$ 所需时间相当）之后随之改变。因此，大质量天体的行为改变将会导致射电辐射流量的变化。如果 $R(\nu)$ 以近似光速 c 膨胀，则可以求得流量增加的最大速率。$R(8\times10^3)$ 从 0.6 秒差距左右增加到 1.9 秒差距左右，$S(8\times10^3)$ 将随之从 2.5 个流量单位增加到 25 个流量单位，这个增加速率足以解释登特的观测结果。基于这一模型，我们也可以预测，在更高的频率可以出现更快的变化。而且，如果注入粒子速率的突然改变将导致 $S(\nu)$ 在不同频率时的变化，我们可以预期在高频观测到的变化会比低频出现的早（即使不存在星系间散射 [14]）。

在上文中，我们已经分析，如果核心区域在某频率（比如 10^5 兆周 / 秒）发射大量的辐射，这些辐射一定主要来自对小于该值的频率范围不透明的某一球体。那么，该球体内频率小于 10^5 兆周 / 秒的所有射电辐射的总能量密度约为 6×10^{-3} 尔格 / 厘米^3

$\sim 6\times 10^{-3}$ ergs/c.c.(compared with $\sim 10^{-6}$ ergs/c.c. within Model I), and this very high value suggests that inverse Compton scattering might be important. The Compton lifetime of an electron of energy $\gamma m_0 c^2$ in this radiation field is $8\times 10^9/\gamma$ sec. If $S(10^5)\sim 25$ flux units, $R(10^5)\sim 0.1$ pc and the time which an electron takes to drift out of this sphere is $\sim 2\times 10^7$ sec if its outward velocity $\sim c/2$. But the electrons radiating at 10^5 Mc/s have $\gamma \sim 300$, and so their Compton lifetime is of the same order. The most energetic photons would result from the scattering of 10^5 Mc/s photons by electrons with $\gamma \sim 300$, and their frequency would be[15] $\sim 10^{10}$ Mc/s, which is in the ultra-violet range. Photons of lower energy (including the whole visible range) would be produced, and the spectrum of the scattered radiation would have a low-energy cut-off at a frequency depending on the smallest value of γ represented in the electron energy spectrum. The energy radiated by this process in the visible range may well be greater than that of the synchrotron radio emission. The exact relative importance of the Compton and synchrotron losses is very sensitive to the high-frequency cut-off in the radio spectrum (which we have taken as 10^5 Mc/s) to the value of H. to the precise position where the electrons are accelerated. And to their mean rate of outward drift. It would therefore clearly not be worth while to base an exact calculation on this crude model.

The foregoing rough arguments do, however, suggest that at least a part of the visible light emitted by 3*C* 273 *B* may have been produced by Compton scattering. Moreover, such a hypothesis would provide a natural explanation for the observed optical fluctuations of the source, since, if electrons are accelerated in the massive object in irregular bursts, there will be variations in the intensity of the scattered light. Nearly all the scattering occurs in a region of radius ~ 0.1 parsecs (since not only the radiation energy density, but also the particle density, is much higher near the centre). Therefore, fluctuations with time-scales of the order of months, or even less may occur, and these are in fact observed[16]. The long period variations[2] (~ 12 years) in the optical luminosity may also arise from periodic variations in the rate of injection electrons, which, as we have already seen, can produce the observed variation at radio frequencies. This model therefore suggests that the radio and the long-period optical variations may be connected.

The increase in the radio flux observed by Dent coincided with a decrease in the optical luminosity, which had the most recent of its 12-yearly maxima in 1962. But according to this model one would expect periodic radio variations to lag (perhaps by several years) behind the variations at centre which cause them, so this fact also accords with our model, and suggests that the radio variations, when they have been observed for longer, will also turn out to have a period ~ 12 years.

The visible light from 3*C* 273 *B* is unpolarized[17] whereas the radio flux (at $\sim 3{,}000$ Mc/s) is ~ 3 percent polarized[18]. It will not be possible to find out whether the central part of the source is polarized at radio frequencies until the extent to which the degree of polarization changes when the flux varies has been examined. However, even if the radio flux from the core were polarized (implying large-scale uniformity in the direction of H), it would not follow that the scattered visible light must appear polarized, since it is mainly produced

（在模型 I 中，该值约为 10^{-6} 尔格 / 厘米^3），这么高的密度值表明，逆康普顿散射可能起到了很重要的作用。在该辐射场中，能量为 γm_0c^2 的电子的康普顿寿命为 $8\times10^9/\gamma$ 秒。如果流量密度 $S(10^5)$ 取值约为 25 个流量单位，那么 $R(10^5)$ 约为 0.1 秒差距；假定电子向外的运动速率约为 $c/2$，那么电子穿出球体的时间约为 2×10^7 秒。对于辐射频率为 10^5 兆周 / 秒的电子，γ 取值约为 300，则电子的康普顿寿命和电子穿出球体的时间为同一量级。电子（γ 约为 300）对频率为 10^5 兆周 / 秒的光子的散射，将使这些光子获得最大能量，使其频率达到 [15] 约 10^{10} 兆周 / 秒，位于紫外光谱区。同时，散射也会产生较低能量（包括可见光范围）的光子，因此散射辐射谱存在一个较低的截止能量，对应的截止频率取决于电子能量谱中 γ 的最小值。这一过程产生的可见光辐射能量可能远大于同步射电辐射的能量。至于康普顿能量损失和同步辐射能量损失二者的相对重要性，则取决于以下若干因素：射电谱中的高频截止频率（我们取值为 10^5 兆周 / 秒）、磁场强度 H、电子加速的准确位置以及电子向外漂移的平均速率。由于这一模型较为粗糙，我们也无需进行过多的精确计算。

尽管上文论述略显粗糙，但是说明了 3*C* 273 *B* 发射的可见光至少有一部分是由康普顿散射产生的。而且，这一假说为观测到的射电源光变提供了自然合理的解释，即如果电子在不规则爆发的大质量天体中加速，散射光的强度就会发生变化。几乎所有的散射都发生在一个半径约为 0.1 秒差距的区域（因为在靠近中心的区域，辐射能量密度和粒子密度都高得多），所以会发生周期为数月（或更短）的起伏，这也正是实验所观测到的结果 [16]。光学波段的长周期变化 [2]（约 12 年）也可能是由于电子注入速率的周期变化造成，而这也可以引起（正如我们所观测到的）射电频率的变化。所以，这一模型认为射电频段变化和长周期光学变化可能是彼此联系的。

登特观测到的射电流量的增加正好与光学光度的减小相符合，该光学光度值曾在 1962 年达到 12 年以来的最大值。另外，这个模型认为射电的周期性变化落后（可能是几年）于中心区域的变化，而后者恰恰是前者形成的原因，因此该模型与前面的观测事实也一致，这意味着，如果对射电变化进行长期观测，就会发现其周期也近似为 12 年。

3*C* 273 *B* 发射的可见光是非偏振的 [17]，但射电流量（在频率约为 3,000 兆周 / 秒处）存在大约 3% 的偏振 [18]。在我们检测确定流量变化时偏振度的变化达到何种程度之前，我们仍无法弄清射电源中心区域在射电频段是否偏振。然而，即使来自中心区域的射电流量是偏振的（这意味着在磁场强度 H 方向存在大尺度的均匀性），散射的可见光也不一定是偏振的。因为这些可见光主要产生于一个极不透明的区域，

in an extremely opaque region, where the radio-frequency radiation will not be polarized even if the field is uniform.

It has been assumed in the foregoing that H does not change significantly when the density of the relativistic particles alters. This will be a good approximation if the magnetic energy is greater than the particle energy (a strength of 1 gauss is sufficient). The field is presumably "anchored" to the massive object.

It should be emphasized that the Compton losses are significant in this model mainly because of the occurrence of synchrotron self-absorption, which prevents the electrons from radiating away their energy as fast as they otherwise would. Any electrons which are accelerated to high energies ($\gamma > 300$, say), and which therefore emit synchrotron radiation at frequencies which can escape freely from the source, will lose their energy in a time much shorter than the Compton lifetime, so they will contribute to the radiation at high radio frequencies ($> 10^5$ Mc/s), rather than in the far ultra-violet. ($> 10^{10}$ Mc/s).

Model III. The first two models have taken no account of the fact that lines are present in the optical spectrum of 3*C* 273 *B*. According to Greenstein and Schmidt[19], these lines could be produced by gas of density $\sim 10^7$ particles/c.c., temperature $\sim 2 \times 10^4$ °K, and mass $\sim 10^5\ M_\odot$. Though this gas need not radiate all the optical continuum, it must be incorporated in a complete model of the source. The model which we shall now describe indicates one way in which this can be done.

If the gas were in the form of a uniform spherical cloud, its diameter would be ~ 0.5 pc, and it would be opaque to light of all frequencies because of scattering by free electrons. It would therefore be difficult to account for the observed fluctuations in optical luminosity with a time-scale of a few months, since if the variable flux were emitted by a small region within the cloud its variations would be smeared out and would not be observed. This difficulty would be eased if the density within the cloud were non-uniform, or if it had a filamentary structure[20], but there would remain the problem of feeding energy into the gas to balance its losses.

In an alternative configuration, suggested by Shklovsky[21], the gas is distributed in a thin spherical shell. We shall adopt this suggestion, and show that a model can be constructed on the basis of which the radio variations, and both the long and short period optical variations, can be explained.

If the radius of the shell is taken[21] as 4×10^{18} cm, and its density as $\sim 10^7$ particles/c.c., its thickness will be $\sim 10^{17}$ cm if its total mass is $\sim 10^5\ M_\odot$. The observed broadening of the spectral lines places an upper limit of $\sim 1{,}500$ km/sec on the velocity of the shell if it is expanding. If there is a mass of $\sim 10^9\ M_\odot$ at its centre, a field of ~ 1 gauss would be strong enough to prevent the shell collapsing. Scattering by free electrons would be unimportant at all frequencies. The shell will be transparent to most photons of optical frequency, but will be opaque to radio waves at all frequencies below $\sim 10^5$ Mc/s because of free-free

即使该区域的场是均匀的，射频辐射在该区域也不会发生偏振。

在上述分析中，我们已经假定，当相对论性粒子密度发生变动时，磁场强度 H 并不会明显变化。如果磁能大于粒子的能量（1 高斯的磁场强度足够），上面的假定将是一个很好的近似。因此可以推测，磁场主要“固定于”大质量天体。

需要强调的一点是，在该模型中，只有在出现同步加速自吸收时康普顿耗损才会变得明显，因为自吸收会阻止电子能量快速的辐射。当加速电子达到很高的能量（比如说 $\gamma > 300$）时，就会在那些能够自由穿透射电源的频率上产生同步辐射，之后这些电子会在很短的时间内（比康普顿寿命小得多）损失掉能量。因此，这些高能电子产生高频（$> 10^5$ 兆周 / 秒）辐射，而不是远紫外（$> 10^{10}$ 兆周 / 秒）辐射。

模型 III 上面的两个模型并没有考虑出现在 3*C* 273 *B* 光谱中的光学波段谱线。根据格林斯坦和施密特的研究 [19]，这些谱线可能由密度约为每立方厘米 10^7 个粒子、温度约为 2×10^4 K、质量约为 10^5 个太阳质量的气体产生。尽管这些气体并不辐射所有的光学波段连续谱，但必须将其整合到射电源完整模型中。下面我们将阐述一种整合的思路。

如果这些气体是以均匀球状云的形式存在的话，其直径将为 0.5 秒差距左右。由于自由电子的散射，这些气体对于所有频率的光都将是不透明的。如果变化的流量来自这团气体云中的一小块区域，则这种变化就会变得模糊不清并且难以观察，因此实际观测到的周期为数月的光度起伏会难以解释。如果气体云的密度分布是不均匀的，或具有丝状结构 [20]，则以上困难就会消失。然而，这样就会遇到另一问题，即如何将能量输入气体以平衡其损失。

什克洛夫斯基曾经提出另一种结构 [21]，认为气体分布在一个薄球壳中。下面我们将采纳这一建议，并以射电变化为基础建立一个模型，从而可以同时解释长周期和短周期的光学波段的变化。

不妨令该球壳的半径 [21] 为 4×10^{18} 厘米，密度约为每立方厘米 10^7 个粒子，总质量约为 10^5 个太阳质量，那么球壳的厚度约为 10^{17} 厘米。如果该球壳在膨胀的话，可以通过观测到的谱线展宽计算出膨胀速度的上限近似为 1,500 千米 / 秒。如果其中心质量约为 10^9 个太阳质量，那么约 1 高斯的磁场强度足以支撑球壳。这样，在所有频率上，自由电子的散射变得不再重要。该球壳对于光学波段的大多数光子都是透明的，但是由于自由–自由吸收，对于低于约 10^5 兆周 / 秒的所有射电频段都是不

absorption. The observed radio flux must therefore originate outside the shell.

The gas in the shell would produce the observed line emission, and would radiate at a rate $\sim 10^{46}$ ergs/sec, mainly at visible wave-lengths. Its thermal energy content is insufficient to maintain this rate of energy loss for more than a few weeks, and so it must be absorbing energy at an equal rate from the interior. Since the shell absorbs radio waves, intense but unobserved radio radiation may exist in the spherical region within it, and this suggests the possibility that the shell may be absorbing enough energy in the form of radio waves to compensate for its losses in the visible range. This would require the production of $\sim 10^{46}$ ergs/sec at frequencies below $\sim 10^5$ Mc/s, which is ~ 30 times as great as the observed power radiated in this frequency range. However, such a high rate of energy production is not unreasonable since a sphere within which synchrotron self-absorption were taking place at all frequencies up to 10^5 Mc/s would need to have a radius of only ~ 0.8 pc (little more than half the radius of the shell) to emit $\sim 10^{46}$ ergs/sec. Alternatively the required amount could be produced if the whole interior were opaque up to $\sim 7 \times 10^4$ Mc/s. The exact situation within the shell will depend on the energy spectrum of the electrons injected into it, but a sufficiently high rate of energy generation will be achieved if relativistic electrons with $\gamma < 300$ are produced at a rate $\sim 10^{46}$ ergs/sec. We must assume that there is a cut-off in the electron energy spectrum for $\gamma > 300$, since otherwise there would be intense radiation at frequencies above 10^5 Mc/s which would escape through the shell and produce observable radiation with a higher flux-density than is observed.

The observed radiation at frequencies below 10^5 Mc/s (apart from the component which comes from the halo) is, according to this model, emitted outside the shell by electrons which have escaped from the interior. An electron ejected from the massive object at the centre will be absorbing and emitting radiation at the same rate until it approaches the shell. Since the synchrotron lifetime of the electrons (in the absence of self-absorption) is of the order of the time which they take to pass through the shell, most electrons will lose their energy before reaching the exterior. Thus there radiation will not be observed directly, but will simply heat the gas. However, since the power of the observed radio radiation is much less than the power required to heat the gas, the observed radio flux would be produced even if only a few percent of the electrons succeeded in escaping. Despite the high density of the gas in the shell, an electron passing through it has a 90 percent chance of reaching the exterior without losing a significant amount of energy in ionization and collisional losses. If the field ~ 1 gauss extends outside the shell, these electrons will radiate away their energy before they have travelled a further distance ~ 0.1 pc unless self-absorption occurs outside the shell as well. Such self-absorption will occur at sufficiently low frequencies, though the situation is somewhat complicated by the fact that the electrons can radiate energy inwards into the shell.

The production of the visible light is more complicated. Much of it, both in spectral lines and in the continuum, comes from the gas in the shell. However, Compton scattering may also, as in Model II, produce radiation at optical frequencies. The radio radiation

透明的。因此，观测到的射电流量一定来自球壳之外。

球壳中的气体将以约 10^{46} 尔格 / 秒的速率辐射观测到的谱线，且辐射主要集中在可见光波段。由于其热能难以在数周之内一直维持其能量损失速率，因此必须还要以相同速率从内部吸收能量。既然该壳层吸收射电波段，那么其内部的球形区域也可能存在着难以观测的强射电辐射。这表明，球壳很可能依靠吸收射电波段能量来补偿其可见光波段的能量损失。为了维持这种平衡，在低于约 10^5 兆周 / 秒的频段能量生成速率需要达到约 10^{46} 尔格 / 秒，而这一理论值约是该频段实际观测功率值的 30 倍。但是如此高的功率并不是不合理，由于在低于 10^5 兆周 / 秒频率下发生同步辐射自吸收的球体半径仅需要 0.8 秒差距（和球壳的半径一半差不多）来进行约为 10^{46} 尔格 / 秒的放射。另外，如果整个球壳内部对小于约 7×10^4 兆周 / 秒的频率都是不透明的，则可以得到另一数值。球壳内的具体情况依赖于注入该壳层的电子的能量谱，如果 $\gamma < 300$ 的相对论电子以约 10^{46} 尔格 / 秒的速率产生，就能达到足够高的能量产生率。我们必须假设对于 $\gamma > 300$ 的电子能量谱存在着截止，否则在高于 10^5 兆周 / 秒的频段也会出现强辐射，这些辐射将穿出球壳，产生的流量密度就会高于实际观测值。

根据该模型，实际观测到的低于 10^5 兆周 / 秒频段的辐射（除了其中一部分来自晕）是由内部逃逸出的电子发射的。由中心大质量天体喷射出的电子将以相同的速率吸收和发射辐射，直至这些电子到达球壳。既然电子同步辐射的寿命（不存在自吸收的情况下）与它们穿出球壳的时间同量级，那么大多数电子在到达外部之前将损失掉能量。所以，相应的辐射只是将气体加热，但不能直接观测到。然而，由于可被观测的射电辐射的功率比用于加热气体的功率小得多，那么即使只有一小部分电子成功逃逸，也可以产生出观测到的射电流量。事实上，尽管球壳中的气体密度很高，电子经电离和碰撞穿过球壳到达外部而不明显损失能量的概率仍高达 90%。如果磁场强度（约 1 高斯）延伸至球壳外面，这些电子在运动约 0.1 秒差距的距离之前就已经辐射掉了能量，除非球壳外面也存在自吸收。但这些自吸收一般只发生于足够低的频率。事实上，逃逸出球壳的电子也会向球壳内辐射能量，此时的情况会变得有些复杂。

可见光的产生会更复杂一些。无论是谱线还是连续谱，大部分可见光来自球壳中的气体。然而，正如模型 II 那样，康普顿散射可能也会产生光学波段的辐射。如果同步加速自吸收存在于低于约 7×10^4 兆周 / 秒的频段，那么球壳所包围的射电辐

energy density in the volume enclosed by the shell is $\sim 2\times 10^{-3}$ erg/c.c. if synchrotron self-absorption occurs at frequencies up to $\sim 7\times 10^{4}$ Mc/s, and the corresponding Compton lifetime of an electron is $2\times 10^{10}\ /\gamma$ sec. The highest energy electrons the synchrotron losses of which are balanced by self-absorption have $\gamma \sim 250$, and their Compton lifetimes are of the same order as the time they would take to travel outwards from the centre to the shell. The Compton losses, therefore, are significant, though their exact magnitude is highly sensitive to the precise model adopted. The frequencies of the scattered photons will, as in Model II, be mainly in the visible and near-ultra-violet, and most photons will escape through the shell, though those the frequencies of which correspond to intense spectral lines may the absorbed. Compton scattering of radio frequency radiation outside the shell will be insignificant.

We now consider how the observed variations in flux can occur in this model. We discuss first the long period variations. If there were fluctuations with a time-scale ~12 years in the rate of production of relativistic particles at the centre, there would be changes in the radiation density in the sphere enclosed by the shell, and a consequent change in the temperature of the gas. The rate of radiation of visible light by the shell would therefore alter. There would also be changes in the rate at which electrons escape through the shell, and consequently in the observed radio flux. Variations with periods less than, say, 5 years would be partly smeared out and so could not have a large amplitude.

The observed short period fluctuations in the optical luminosity have a time-scale of a few months, and obviously cannot be produced in the shell, which has a radius of ~4 light years. In Model II they were attributed to the inverse Compton effect. Since we have shown that light will be produced by Compton scattering in this model, a similar explanation might also be possible here. This would require the scattering to occur in a region smaller than a few light months in radius. However, the scattering will not be concentrated in such a small region as in Model II, where the radiation energy density was high enough for scattering to be significant only within a sphere of radius ~0.1 pc. Nevertheless, if all the electrons are ejected from a massive object, their number density will be higher near the centre, and the amount of scattering will be greater there even if the radiation density is no higher. Consequently, the variations in the component of the optical continuum produced by the Compton effect may be sufficiently rapid to account for the observed variations with time-scales of a few months.

We note that whereas the line strengths will alter with the slow period ~12 years, it would be inconsistent with this model for them to be involved in the rapid fluctuations in optical luminosity. We understand that attempts are now being made to see whether the lines do in fact vary in intensity. This feature of our model will thus soon be tested.

If we could construct a complete model of this kind, we would be able to calculate the expected phase lag between the variations in luminosity at optical frequencies and the related radio variations. However, we lack sufficient information to enable us to do this. To illustrate the complexity of the problem we enumerate some of the factors which would

射能量密度约为 2×10^{-3} 尔格 / 厘米^3，而电子相应的康普顿寿命则为 $2\times10^{10}/\gamma$ 秒。其中，具有最高能量的电子的 γ 值大约为 250，其同步辐射损失由自吸收进行补偿，并且这些电子的康普顿寿命与电子从中心到穿出球壳的时间具有相同的量级。因此，尽管康普顿耗损的具体值与采用的精确模型密切相关，但其损失无疑是很明显的。如模型 II，散射光子的频率主要位于可见光和近紫外区，而且尽管一些较强的谱线对应的频率可能会被吸收，但大多数的光子可以从球壳逃逸出。在球壳外，射频辐射的康普顿散射将变得很少。

下面，我们用模型分析所观测到的流量变化是怎样产生的。我们首先分析长周期变化。如果球心相对论性粒子的产率存在约 12 年时标的起伏，那么壳层包含的球体内的辐射密度就会发生变化，气体的温度也会随之变化。这样，由壳层产生的可见光辐射的速率会因此改变，而同时电子逃逸出球壳的速率以及观测到的射电流量也会发生变化。周期小于 5 年的变动则会部分消减，因此相应的起伏幅度会变小。

观测到的光学波段的短周期光度起伏，时间周期为数月，而球壳的半径大约为 4 光年，因此这种短周期起伏显然不可能是由球壳内部产生的。在模型 II 中，认为这种短周期起伏是由于逆康普顿效应产生的。上文中已经提到，该模型中康普顿散射可以产生光，那么类似的原理也可以在这儿用于解释短周期起伏。这就要求散射必须发生于一个较小的区域（半径小于数光月）。然而，这种散射并不会集中于类似模型 II 那么小的区域（在模型 II 中，辐射能量密度足够高，因此使得散射主要集中在一个半径约为 0.1 秒差距的球形区域）。不过，如果所有的电子都是由一个大质量天体喷射出来的，靠近中心的粒子数密度自然会很高，那么即使辐射密度不是很高，散射光强度也会很大。因此，由康普顿效应产生的光学波段连续谱的变化可能足够快，进而可以解释观测到的周期为数月的变化。

然而，我们注意到，在该模型中谱线的强度将以约 12 年的周期缓慢变化，这与上面光度快速起伏的模型不符。我们知道人们正在进行尝试，以确定观测谱线的强度是否真的存在变化。这样就可以很快验证我们模型的这一特征了。

如果我们能够建立一个类似的完整模型，那么我们就可以通过计算来预测光学波段光度变化与相关的射电变化的相位差。遗憾的是，目前我们仍然缺少足够的信息来这样做。为了说明这一问题的复杂性，我们在下面列举了一些用于决定相位差

determine the magnitude of the lag.

(1) The variations in particle density and radiation energy density propagate outwards with different velocities.

(2) The phase delay of the radio variations will depend on whether self-absorption is taking place outside the shell at the frequency of observation. If it is taking place the observed flux would come from the surface of a sphere with radius greater than 1.5 pc, rather than from just outside the shell, thus increasing the lag of the radio variations. At 8,000 Mc/s, the frequency of Dent's observations, self-absorption would occur if more than ~14 flux units of the observed flux density were coming from the compact source (rather than from the halo). Since the observed variations amount to 10 flux units (and this flux cannot come from the halo), it is likely, though not certain, that self-absorption is in fact occurring.

(3) The sense in which the emission rate of the gas in the shell varies as the additional radio energy falls on is must be known.

(4) The relative intensity of the light produced by the inverse Compton effect and the light emitted by the shell must be known. These two components will have the same period, but may be out of phase with one another. The times at which maxima in the resultant optical luminosity occur will thus depend on the phase lag between the two components, and on the ratio of the amplitude of their variations.

This discussion shows that existing observations do not suffice to determine a well-defined working model of 3*C* 273 *B*. However, we can draw the important conclusion that neither the optical nor the radio variations require the source to be closer to us than the 470 Mpc implied by a cosmological red shift of 0.158. This conclusion considerably weakens the case for the local model[3,22] of quasi-stellar radio sources which places them a few megaparsecs away and in which the observed red shift implies a large velocity relative to their surroundings. More detailed observations of optical variations, and of radio variations as a function of frequency, should enable us to decide whether models of the type described here are appropriate for 3*C* 273 *B*, and for other quasi-stellar sources as well.

Note added in proof. H. Gent and H. P. Palmer reported at the Dublin meeting of the Royal Astronomical Society (September 7, 1965) that they have succeeded in resolving 3*C* 273 *B* at 21 cm with a long base-line interferometer. Their proposed interpretation of their observations is that the source consists of two components separated by ~0.4 sec of arc, the angular diameter of each component being less than ~0.1 sec. This limit on the angular size of the components is still much greater than the angular diameter of the variable core in our model ($\sim 10^{-3}$ sec), and of the lower limit of 3×10^{-2} sec for the halo.

(**208**, 371-374; 1965)

M. J. Rees and D. W. Sciama: Department of Applied Mathematics and Theoretical Physics, University of Cambridge.

大小的因素。

（1）以不同速度向外传播的粒子密度的变化和辐射能量密度的变化。

（2）射电变化的相位滞后取决于在观测频段自吸收是否发生于球壳之外。如果确实发生于球壳外，则观测到的流量来自半径大于 1.5 秒差距的球壳表面，而不是刚好在球壳外，因此也增加了射电变化的相位延迟。在频率 8,000 兆周 / 秒时，即登特观测所使用的频率，如果观测到的流量密度中超过近 14 个流量单位来自致密射电源（而不是来自晕）的话,就会发生自吸收。由于观测到的变化为 10 个流量单位（而这些流量不可能来自于晕），因此虽不能肯定，但很可能实际上发生了自吸收。

（3）必须清楚球壳气体的发射速率随额外射电能量进入球壳的变化。

（4）必须清楚逆康普顿效应产生的光以及球壳发射的光的相对强度。二者具有相同的周期，但是可能存在相位差。合成后的光度最大值的发生时刻，取决于二者的相位差以及二者变化幅度的比值。

以上的讨论表明，已有的观测尚不足以确定 3*C* 273 *B* 完备的有效模型。然而，我们可以得出以下重要结论：无论是光学波段变化还是射电波段变化，都不需要射电源与我们的距离小于 470 兆秒差距（由宇宙学红移量 0.158 得出）。这一结论相当程度上削弱了类星体射电源的局域模型 [3,22]，该模型认为，观测到的红移意味着百万秒差距外的射电源与周围存在很大的相对速度。继续全面深入地观测光学波段和射电波段随频率的变化，可以使我们最终确定本文所描述的模型是否适用于 3*C* 273 *B* 以及其他类星体射电源。

附加说明：根据亨特和帕尔默最近在皇家天文学会都柏林会议上的报道（1965 年 9 月 7 日），他们已经使用长基线干涉仪在 21 厘米波段成功分辨 3*C* 273 *B*。他们认为，该射电源结构包含两部分，二者间隔约 0.4 角秒，其中每部分的角直径小于约 0.1 角秒。但是，在我们的模型中，可变内核的角直径约为 10^{-3} 角秒，晕的角直径下限为 3×10^{-2} 角秒，显然比观测值小很多。

（金世超 翻译；蒋世仰 审稿）

References:

1. Dent, W. A., *Science*, **148**, 1458 (1965).
2. Smith, H. J., *Quasi-stellar Sources and Gravitational Collapse*, 221 (Univ. Chicago Press, 1965).
3. Terrell, J., *Science*, **145**, 918 (1964).
4. Slish, V. I., *Nature*, **199**, 682 (1963).
5. Williams, P. J. S., *Nature*, **200**, 56 (1963).
6. Sholomitsky, G. B., *I. A. U. Inf. Sull. Variable Stars*, No. 83 (Feb. 27, 1965).
7. Schmidt, M., *Astrophys. J.*, **141**, 1295 (1965).
8. Rees, M. J., and Sciama, D. W., *Nature*, **207**, 738 (1965).
9. Maltby, P., and Moffet, A. T., *Astrophys. J.*, **142**, 409 (1965).
10. Dent, W. A., and Haddock, F. T., *Quasi-stellar Sources and Gravitational Collapse*, 381 (Univ. Chicago Press, 1965).
11. Hazard, C., Mackey, M. B., and Shimmins, A. J., *Nature*, **197**, 1037 (1963).
12. Schmidt, M., *Nature*, **197**, 1040 (1963).
13. Sciama, D. W., *Proc. Intern. School of Physics "Enrico Fermi", Course* 35, July 12-24, 1965 (to be published).
14. Haddock, F. T., and Sciama, D. W., *Phys. Rev. Letters*, **14**, 1007 (1965).
15. Feenberg, E., and Primakoff, H., *Phys. Rev.*, **73**, 449 (1948).
16. Sandage, A., *Astrophys. J.*, **139**, 416 (1964).
17. Moroz, V. I., and Yesipov, V. R., *I. A. U. Inf. Bull. Variable Stars*, No. 31 (1963).
18. Morris, D., and Berge, G. L., *Astro. J.*, **69**, 641 (1964).
19. Greenstein, J. L., and Schmidt, M., *Astrophys, J.*, **140**, 1 (1964).
20. Schmidt, M., *Proc. Second Texas Conf. Relativistic Astrophysics* (to be published).
21. Shklovsky, I. S., *Soviet Astronomy*, **8**, 638 (1965).
22. Hoyle, F., and Burbidge, G. R. (to be published).

Character Recognition by Holography

D. Gabor

Editor's Note

Dennis Gabor, the inventor of the theory of holography, here suggests an application of the technique, recently improved by the development of the laser, to a long-standing problem in engineering: the automatic recognition of characters, such as printed letters. Holography produces an image of an object based on information contained in a scattered coherent light wave. If one builds up a hologram progressively by scattering light from many possible variants of a single character, then illumination of a character similar to any such variant can be made to produce a visual code easily readable by a machine. Gabor's basic idea, with many modifications, is now commonly used in pattern recognition techniques based on holography.

WAVE-FRONT reconstruction or holography, on which the first report[1] was published in Nature seventeen years ago, had a powerful renaissance in the past years. E. N. Leith and J. Upatnieks[2], G. W. Stroke[3] and others have greatly improved the original method, and showed that it was possible to reconstruct complicated two- and three-dimensional objects, with half-tones, in previously unattainable perfection. The revival of holography owed much of its impulse to the invention of the laser, which made it possible to produce holograms with interferences of the order of 10,000, and thus to make full use of the information capacity of fine-grain photographic plates.

I wish to show that it has now become possible to harness holography for the solution of one of the most urgent problems of computers and other date-processing devices; the recognition of characters with many variants.

Wave-front reconstruction contains a principle which has not yet been fully exploited. Expressed in a general form: two coherent waves are made to fall simultaneously on a photographic plate, one coming from an object A, the other from an object B. The photograph links these together in such a way that if the hologram is illuminated by A alone, B will appear too, and vice versa. So far this principle has been applied in the form that A was the object of interest and B a light source, usually a simple one, and in the reconstruction the hologram was illuminated by B. I now propose to turn this around. Let A be a character, such as a printed or hand-written letter or numeral, which can be read by human beings but not by a machine, and let B be a combination of point-sources, forming a code-word which can be read by a machine. Produce the hologram by combining A and B. When A, or a character sufficiently close to it is presented to the hologram, with the original illumination, the code-word B will flash out. This means that the hologram can act as a translator, or coding device.

利用全息术的字符识别

盖伯

编者按

全息术理论的发明者丹尼斯·盖伯在本文中提出了该技术（最近因激光器的发展而有所改进）的一项应用，即应用于工程技术中长期存在的一个问题：字符（例如印刷字体）自动识别。全息术产生物体的像建立在包含有相干光波散射信息的基础之上。如果将同一个字符各种可能的变形所散射的光递增地制作出一张全息图，那么与任何一个变形相似的字符的照明就能够产生一个便于机器读出的视觉编码。盖伯的基本创意经过多次改进后，现在已经普遍用在基于全息术的图形识别技术中。

17 年前《自然》首次报道[1]了波前重建，即全息术，近年来这项技术又再次兴起，势头强劲。利思和乌帕特尼克斯[2]、斯托克[3]以及其他一些人已经对原来的方法做了重大的改进，并表明有可能利用半色调重建复杂的二维物体和三维物体，并达到过去不能实现的完美程度。激光器的发明在很大程度上推动了全息术的复苏，因为它使利用量级为 10,000 的干涉产生全息图成为可能，这样也可以充分利用细粒照相干板上的信息容量。

我要说明的是，现在利用全息术有望解决计算机和其他数据处理装置中最为紧迫的问题之一——对具有多种变形字符的识别。

波前重建包含了一个尚未被充分应用的原理。通常表现为：两束相干波同时照射在一张照相干板上，其中一束来自物体 A，另一束来自物体 B。如果全息图单独用 A 照明，B 也会出现，反之亦然，全息图就是通过这样的方式将它们联系在一起的。至今，这个原理已经通过下述方式加以利用：若 A 是被关注的物体，B 是光源（通常是简单的一个单个的光源），在重建中，全息图用 B 照明。现在我要对此进行一些改动。设 A 是一个字符，例如一个印刷的或手写的字母或数字，它可以被人读出，但不能被机器识别，再设 B 是点光源的一个组合，它形成了一个可被机器识别的编码。将 A 和 B 混合便可产生全息图。当 A 或一个与它十分相似的字符呈现在全息图前，并使用原来的照明光照亮时，编码 B 将立刻浮现出来。这表明全息图起到了转换器或编码装置的作用。

The interest of this principle is in the enormous recognition capacity which can be stored in a single hologram, and which one might not perhaps suspect at first sight. I wish to show that with N characters to be discriminated, each with M variants, the product $M{\cdot}N$ can be made of the order of a thousand or even more.

Fig. 1 shows the optics for producing the master hologram, and for using it in the read-out. The recording medium is assumed to be a transparency, such as a microfilm; but reflecting media can also be used. The hologram is built up by repeated exposures in what may be called "layers". These are not, of course, physically separated in the emulsion. Each layer corresponds to one of the N characters to be discriminated, with all its M variants, and is marked with one code-word. The layer contains the part-holograms, to be called "engrams" of the variants side by side, with little overlap. Each engram is produced with one direction of illumination, and as the photographic plate is arranged in the rear focal plane of a lens viewing the character, it is a "Fourier-hologram". This has the advantage that the hologram is translation-invariant, that is to say, independent of the position of the character so long as this appears alone in the window. An engram need not occupy much more area in a photographic plate than would be needed for a good record of the corresponding character, but as a cautious example we will assume 120 engrams, each with a diameter of about 5 mm, on a photographic plate of 50 mm × 50mm. This is sufficient to record without overlap 30 variants, each in four or six "identical" engrams. Fig. 1 shows how this is achieved.

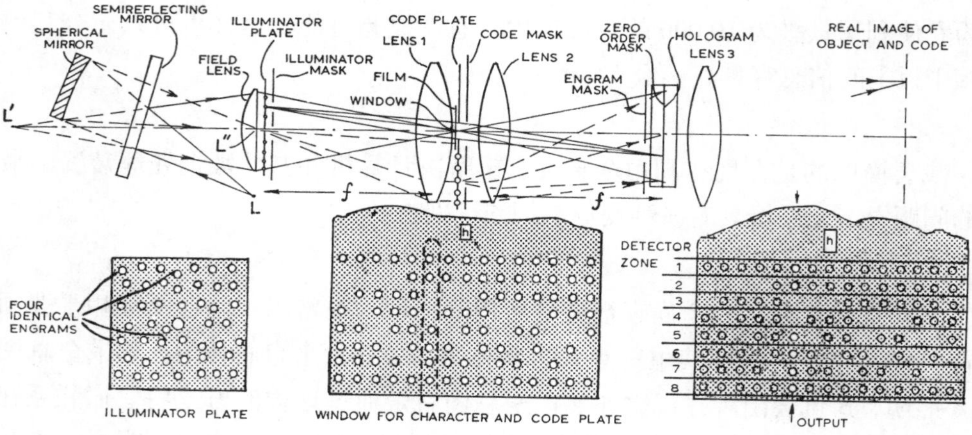

Fig. 1. Apparatus for producing a coding hologram and using it for the read-out.

The light of a laser issues from a point L, and a beam splitter consisting of a spherical mirror and a semi-reflecting mirror produces of this two images L' and L''. The first of those serves the illuminator; the second, in the centre hole of the illuminator plate, serves the code plate. The illuminator plate, backed by a field lens, consists of a plastic plate embossed with, say, 120 lenticules, and is black outside the lenticules. These produce 120 point sources which illuminate the window containing the character through a lens 1, which removes the illuminator points into star space. The point sources correspond one-

这个原理的价值在于它所具有的巨大的识别容量，并且能存储在单个全息图中，对此人们最初也许不会察觉得到。我要说明的是，要对 N 个字符进行辨别，每个有 M 种变形，其乘积 $M \cdot N$ 能够达到上千甚至更高的量级。

制作主全息图并利用它进行读取的光学装置如图 1 所示。假定记录介质是透射型的，例如显微胶片，不过也能够使用反射型介质。通过在“层”（姑且这样命名）上重复曝光而产生全息图。当然，这并不是说乳胶中存在物理上的分离。每一层都对应 N 个字符中的一个字符，每个都具有 M 种变形的待辨别字符，并用一个编码字标记。这个层包含了部分全息图，称为各个变形的“忆迹”，它们并排相连并略微重叠。每个忆迹是用一个方向上的光束照射产生的，又因为照相干板位于观测字符的透镜的后焦平面上，因此是一个“傅里叶全息图”。其优点在于全息图具有平移不变性，换言之，字符只需在窗口中单独出现，而其所处的位置是无关紧要的。与良好地记录一个字符所需要的面积相比，相应的一个忆迹并不需要占用照相干板更大的面积。而作为一个严谨的例子，我们将假设在 50 毫米 × 50 毫米的照相干板上有 120 个直径约为 5 毫米的忆迹，这就足够在无需重叠的方式下记录 30 个变形，其中每个有 4 个或 6 个“同样的”忆迹。图 1 显示了这是如何实现的。

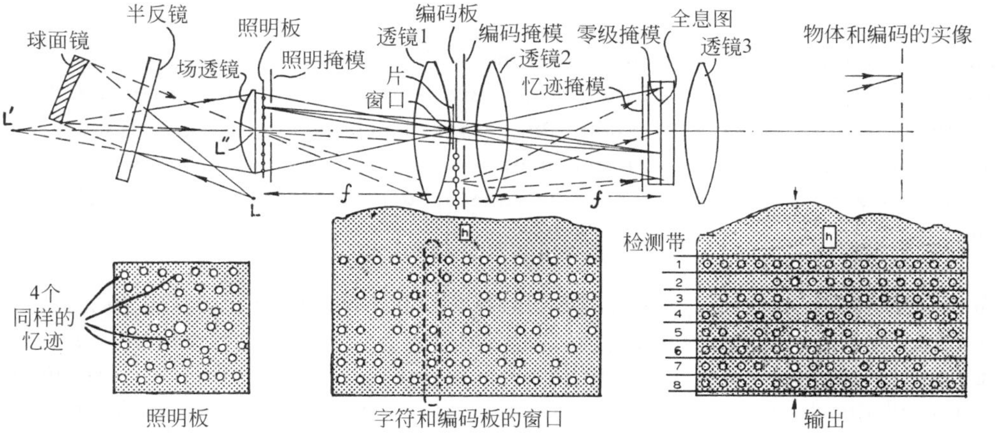

图 1. 制作编码全息图并将它读出的装置

激光器的光束从点 L 射出，通过一个包含有一个球面镜和一个半反镜的分束器后产生两个像 L' 和 L''。其中第一个像被用作照明光；位于照明板中心孔处的第二个像被用作编码板。照明板在场透镜的背后，其由一片有 120 个微透镜的模压塑料板构成，在微透镜外为黑色。这些微透镜形成了 120 个点光源，它们穿过透镜 1 照射在包含字符的窗口上，使照明点移入了星空。点光源与忆迹一一对应。它们的排列稍有随机性是有利的。当任何一个变形发生时，一次均可获得 4 个同样的忆迹。

by-one to the engrams. There is a certain advantage in randomizing them slightly. Four identical engrams are taken at a time of any one variant. These are spaced out, as far as possible, to increase the resolving power of the hologram. They are selected with a mask, and a different mask with four holes is used for every variant.

The point source L'' in the centre of the illuminator plate illuminates the code-plate, through the same lens 1, which serves in this area as a field lens. The code-plate, like the illuminator, is an embossed plastic plate, which contains the code-word in the form of groups of luminous points, arranged in one or several arrays. It is advantageous to use self-checking codes, in which every word has the same number of code-points. In the example there are six positions, of which two remain dark and four light up. This code has $6{\cdot}5/1{\cdot}2 = 15$ words. Two more positions have been added. There do not contribute to the discrimination of characters, but improve the signal-to-noise ratio, as eight points have to light up for every valid character.

In the making of the master hologram all engrams in one layer are marked, that is to say, exposed simultaneously, with one distinctive code-word, which is selected by a mask. But as each code-word illuminates the whole area of the hologram, a further mask must be used near the plane of the photographic plate, which cuts out the light except in the area of the engrams which are made at any one time. This makes it possible to observe the rule of optimum illumination, which postulates about equal light sums on any engram from the character and from its code-word.

Black-on-white letters are less suitable for discrimination than their negatives, because they have too much in common; all their white area. But this disadvantage can be eliminated by a further mask, in the plane of the hologram, which cuts out all undiffracted light. By Babinet's principle this turns a character into its negative. Such a mask can be easily made by exposing a photographic plate through a clear window simultaneously to all illuminator points.

After $M{\cdot}N$ successive exposures of the photographic plate, which add up to a convenient medium density, the master hologram is made by processing and printing it, preferably with an overall gamma of 2, and the print is put back in the original position. In the reading all the point-sources of the illuminator are used, while the whole code-plate is covered up. A lens 3 is used for observation, which produces a real image of the code-plate. If now the recording medium is dragged across the window, whenever a character or a variant appears in it, its code-word will flash up. It is advantageous to arrange in the image plane a mask, which is a replica of the code-plate, with very fine holes, so as to exclude all but the signalling light. This mask, too, can be made photographically.

A method of reading the code-words is to sum up all the light which appears in one zone, corresponding to one position in the code, and guide it to a separate photoelectric detector. Each detector is fitted with a level discriminator, so as to reject spurious signals below a certain level. This method is simple; but it has only moderate discriminating

为了提高全息图的分辨率，这些忆迹要尽可能地相互远离。用掩模对它们进行挑选，每个变形使用一个不同的带有 4 个孔的掩模。

位于照明板中心的点光源 L'' 同样通过透镜 1 照明编码板，透镜 1 在这一区域作为场透镜使用。与照明器类似，编码板是一块模压塑料板。它包含的编码字以一群照明点的形式存在，它们排成一个或几个阵列。使用自检编码具有一定的优点，因为其中每个字都具有相同数目的编码点。在这个例子中有 6 个位置，其中 2 个始终为暗，另外 4 个被照亮。这个编码具有的字数为 $(6\times5)/(1\times2)=15$。已经又增加了 2 个位置。这对字符的分辨率并没有贡献，但提高了信噪比，因为每个有效的字符必须有 8 个点被照亮。

在主全息图的制作过程中，用一个独特的编码字来标记一个层中所有的忆迹，换言之，它们是同时曝光的，而每个编码字的选择取决于掩模。但由于每个编码字都照明了全息图的整个区域，因此必须在靠近照相干板的平面附近再使用一个掩模，它遮去了在任何时刻获得的忆迹区域以外的光。这样就有可能观测到最佳照明的规律，最佳照明要求对于任一忆迹，来自于字符和其编码字的光的总和都大致相等。

相比于其负片，白底黑字的字母不太适合于鉴别，因为它们之间共同的部分即它们所有的白色区域太多。但这一不利条件可以通过在全息图平面中再加一个掩模来消除，这个掩模遮去了所有的非衍射光。根据巴比涅原理，这样可使一个字符转换为它的负片。令所有的照明点通过一个清晰的窗口同时对照相干板曝光就可以很容易地制作出这类掩模。

照相干板经 $M\cdot N$ 次连续曝光后，增至一个适合介质的光密度，再通过处理和洗印就制成了主全息图，总伽马值最好为 2，并将照片放回原始位置。在读取过程中使用了照明光的所有点源，而整个编码板是被遮盖住的。透镜 3 用于观测，它产生了一个编码板的实像。这时如果记录介质被拖过窗口，只要有字符或其变形在其中出现，其编码字便会立刻显现出来。在像平面放置一个掩模是有好处的，这个掩模是编码板的复制品，具有很细的孔，因此可以排除信号光外的所有光。这类掩模也能通过照相而制得。

读取编码字的方法是：将与编码中某一位置相对应的一个带中出现的所有的光相加，并将它导入一个单独的光电探测器。每个探测器与一水平鉴别器相配，以排除低于一定水平的乱真信号。这种方法简单，但只具有一般的鉴别能力，因为如果

power, because if the characters are not clearly distinct, some light might show up in the same zone in the code-words of other characters. One can reduce this by making the code-words of characters which are not clearly distinct as different as possible. But the maximum of discrimination is achieved by a somewhat more complicated apparatus. In this the image of the code-plate is projected on the screen of an image camera. The code-words flash up at intervals corresponding to the time allotted to each letter, during 10-30 percent of this period. In the time between flashes all code positions are scanned word by word, and points above a certain level of intensity are transferred to a memory organ, such as a core store. But unless the full number of points appear in a word, the record is erased. If the full number is counted, the code-word is transferred to the computer.

The great discriminating power of the holographic method stems from its high angular resolution. Assume, for example, $N = 35$, $M = 30$, $M{\cdot}N = 1050$. The group of four engrams corresponding to the character presented to the reader receives 1/30 of the light, and can diffract about 1/35 of it, altogether about 10^{-3} of the total. (Not counting, of course, in black-on-white records, the undiffracted light which goes into the zero order.) Of the diffracted light, under the proper conditions, that is to say, when the engrams were taken with about equal light sums from the letter and from the code-word, one-quarter will go into the reconstruction of the code-word. One half appears in the object, another quarter goes into the "twin" image of the code-word, which, however, is washed out by intermodulation with the character, and is useless for recognition. But the useful quarter is concentrated in extremely small solid angles. For example, if four or six identical engrams are spaced out by about 25 mm, the solid angle in which the major part of the light corresponding to a code-point is concentrated will be of the order 10^{-8}. Let the light of, say, 10^{-4} of the total be distributed among ten code-points, this means that 10^{-5} of the light appears in one code-point, in a solid angle which is perhaps 10^{-6} of the solid angle covered by the whole code; a concentration of the order ten. Moreover, this estimate is somewhat pessimistic, because it takes no account of the confirmation of the character by the engrams of slightly different variants in the same layer.

In conclusion, there is good reason to believe that a single hologram may discriminate between all the numerals and the letters of the alphabet, each with 30 variants.

(**208**, 422-423; 1965)

D. Gabor: Department of Electrical Engineering, Imperial College of Science and Technology, London.

References:

1. Gabor, D., *Nature*, **161**, 777 (1948); *Proc. Roy. Soc.*, A, **197**, 475 (1949); *Proc. Phys. Soc.*, B, **64**, 244 (1951).
2. Leith, E. N., and Upatnieks, J., *J. Opt. Soc. Amer.*, **53**, 1377 (1963); **54**, 1295 (1964); **55**, 569 (1965).
3. Stroke, G. W., *Optics of Coherent and Non-coherent Electromagnetic Radiations, Univ. Michigan* (1965), with Falconer, D. G., *Physics Letters*, **13**, 306 (1964); **15**, 283 (1965).

有些字符没有明显的区别，那么其他字符的编码字的光可能会出现在同一带内。对于那些没有明显区别的字符，可以通过制作尽可能不同的编码字来减少这种情况。但通过更加复杂的装置可以达到最大的鉴别力。在这个装置中，编码板的像投影在相机的屏上。编码字每隔一段时间闪现，占这个周期的 10%~30%，而闪现的时间间隔与分配给每个字母的时间相对应。在闪现间隔的时间内，所有的编码位置被逐一扫描，那些高于一定强度水平的点被传送到一个存储元件上，例如磁心存储器。但是直到一个字中全部的点都出现，这个记录才会被清除。如果点的总数被记录下来，那么这个编码字就会被传送到计算机中。

全息照相方法的高辨别能力来自于其角度的高分辨率。例如假定 N=35，M=30，则 $M{\cdot}N$=1050。提交给读出器的字符所对应的 4 个忆迹的组接收到光的 1/30，其中约 1/35 会发生衍射，因此全部的光约占总数的 $1/10^3$。（当然，没有将白底黑字的记录计算在内，因为其非衍射光的量级接近于零。）也就是说，在适当的条件下，当忆迹从字符中和从编码字中接收到的光近乎相等时，衍射光的 1/4 将进入编码字的重建中去。此外，一半出现在物体中，另外的 1/4 进入编码字的“孪生”像中，然而，由于这部分与字符交互调制，并且对于识别没有帮助，所以被消除了。但是有用的 1/4 集中在极小的立体角中。例如，如果 4 个或 6 个同样的忆迹彼此之间的距离间隔约为 25 毫米，那么与一个编码点相对应的光将大部分集中在量级为 10^{-8} 的立体角内。也就是说，占总量 $1/10^4$ 的光分布在 10 个编码点上，这意味着一个编码点上出现的光为 $1/10^5$，并且集中在一个可能为布满全部编码的 10^{-6} 的立体角中，汇集度为 10。此外，这种估计有些悲观，因为它忽略了在同一层中略有差异的变形忆迹对字符的证实。

总之，我们完全有理由相信，单个全息图可以在所有的数字和字母表中的字母之间进行辨别，其中每个有 30 个变形。

（沈乃澂 翻译；熊秉衡 审稿）

"Pink Spot" in the Urine of Schizophrenics

R. E. Bourdillon *et al.*

Editor's Note

Here Raymond Bourdillon and colleagues add fuel to the "pink spot" controversy. Three years earlier, psychiatrist Arnold Friedhoff and biochemist Elnora Van Winkle used paper chromatography to identify a "pink spot" in the urine of patients with schizophrenia. Subsequent studies, often done non-blind and with small subject numbers, yielded conflicting results. So Bourdillon and colleagues set up a blind, controlled study of 808 samples, concluding that there is a strong link between the pink spot and schizophrenia. Diet and drugs were, they thought, unlikely to bias the results. But the theory was later abandoned when it was found that the pink spot was a probable metabolite of both tea and the anti-psychotic chlorpromazine.

SINCE Friedhoff and van Winkle[1] reported that they had isolated the compound 3,4-dimethoxyphenyl-ethylamine (DMPE)—the "pink spot"—from the urine of 15 out of 19 schizophrenics whereas they found it was absent in 14 mentally normal people, other workers have carried out similar investigations. Of these, Sen and McGeer[2], Kuehl *et al.*[3] and Horwitt[4] were confirmatory, Perry *et al.*[5] and Faurbye and Pind[6] were not, and Takesada *et al.*[7] found that the compound was also present in nearly half their controls. In all these series the number of individuals tested was small, and moreover it appears that in none of them were the tests done in ignorance of the diagnosis. In the past many metabolic abnormalities have been described in schizophrenia, but none has since been shown to have any fundamental bearing on the disease. It therefore seemed important to us to investigate the pink spot further, for if it could be shown to be causally related to schizophrenia this would provide important evidence favouring the abnormal methylation hypothesis as put forward by Osmond and Smythies[8] and Harley-Mason[9].

We have tested for the pink spot in the urine of 808 individuals to try to find out how often it is found: (*a*) in the different forms of schizophrenia; (*b*) in different types of mental disease; (*c*) in close relatives of schizophrenics; (*d*) in mentally normal people. To try to answer these problems, four experiments were planned:

Exps. I and II: Here two independent and "blind" surveys were carried out in which separate workers ascertained the incidence of the pink spot using different methods for its detection and also different criteria for the assessment of schizophrenia.

Exp. III: A small series of family studies in which the close relatives of pink spot positive schizophrenic propositi were investigated.

精神分裂症患者尿中的“粉红色斑点”

鲍迪伦等

编者按

本文中，雷蒙德·鲍迪伦及其同事们的研究使得关于“粉红色斑点”的争议更加激烈。3 年前，精神病专家阿诺尔德·弗里德霍夫和生物化学家埃尔诺拉·范温克尔采用纸层析法在精神分裂症患者的尿液中发现了“粉红色斑点”。随后进行的研究（经常是针对小部分患者进行的非盲法研究）产生了相互矛盾的结果。因此鲍迪伦及其同事们对 808 份样品作了一个盲点对照研究，结果显示粉红色斑点与精神分裂症密切相关。他们认为日常饮食和药物不会影响这种结果。但是后来，当发现粉红色斑点可能是茶和抗精神病药氯丙嗪的代谢物时，这种观点被抛弃了。

自从弗里德霍夫和范温克尔[1]报道他们从 19 名精神分裂症患者中的 15 个人的尿液中分离出化合物 3,4–二甲氧基苯基乙胺（DMPE）——“粉红色斑点”——而在 14 名精神正常的人中没有发现这一物质之后，其他工作者也开始进行类似的研究。其中，森和麦克吉尔[2]、屈尔等人[3]以及霍威特[4]的研究证实了这一结果，而佩里等人[5]以及福尔拜和平德[6]的研究没有得到这种结果，武贞等人[7]发现在他们近一半的对照样品中也存在该化合物。在这一系列实验中，被测个体的数目少，而且他们中没有一个是在忽视诊断的前提下进行检测的。过去，在精神分裂症患者中发现过很多代谢异常现象，但之后没有一种被证明与该病有根本上的关系。因此，进一步研究粉红色斑点很重要，因为如果这种斑点与精神分裂症密切相关，就可以作为支持异常甲基化假说的重要证据，这一假说由奥斯蒙德和斯迈西斯[8]以及哈利–梅森[9]提出。

我们已经测试了 808 个人尿液中的粉红色斑点，试图找出该斑点在以下几种情况中存在的概率：(*a*) 在不同类型的精神分裂症中；(*b*) 在不同类型的精神病中；(*c*) 在精神分裂症患者的近亲属中；(*d*) 在精神正常的人中。为了回答这些问题，我们设计了 4 组实验：

实验 I 和实验 II：这是两个独立的“盲法”实验，研究中每个工作人员都单独使用不同的检测方法和不同的评价标准来鉴定精神分裂症患者中粉红色斑点的发生率。

实验 III：这是一个小系列的家庭研究，对家族中粉红色斑点阳性的精神分裂症患者的近亲属进行调查研究。

Exp. IV: A survey of mentally normal individuals some of whom were apparently healthy in every way and some of whom were in-patients in the wards of two general hospitals.

Exp. I. The urines of 101 mental hospital in-patients, all "possible schizophrenics", were tested with the primary object of finding the incidence of pink spot in the disease. The patients, who were drawn from three mental hospitals, consisted of acute and chronic cases and some had been off drug therapy for up to two months. All had at one time been given a provisional diagnosis of schizophrenia, and this and the drug therapy were known to the investigator (R. E. B.) who was testing for the pink spot. After he had assessed the presence or absence of this, each patient was interviewed and re-assessed by a psychiatrist (S. A. L.) who was ignorant of the pink spot finding. It was she who made the final assessment, and in about 17 percent of the patients she thought the original diagnosis of schizophrenia was substantially in doubt; when this was so they were classed as non-schizophrenic. Where the diagnosis of schizophrenia was definitely upheld the patients were grouped into those who at any time had exhibited one or more of Schneider's first-rank symptoms[10] and those who had not (these are referred to as Schneider positive and Schneider negative respectively). Afterwards the patients were also sub-divided into classical schizophrenics and those who showed only paranoid features without formal thought disorder or flattening of affect. The former for convenience are referred to as "non-paranoid" and the latter as "paranoid". In five patients the information necessary for diagnosis was unobtainable either because the patients were unco-operative or because of language difficulties, and these five are classed as "impossible to assess".

The urine sample was, whenever possible, collected over 20h, though in some cases shorter periods of collection proved more practicable. The extraction and the paper chromatography were carried out as described by Friedhoff and van Winkle[1] and this is referred to here as Method 1. Where there was marked interference by drugs the presence or absence of the pink spot sometimes had to be classed as "impossible to assess".

Because a much more detailed investigation would be necessary to ascertain that 3,4-DMPE was in fact being demonstrated we have, throughout this article, preferred to use the term "pink stop" rather than "presence of DMPE" in reporting the results.

These are given in Table 1 and the statistical analysis in Table 2. This consists of various comparisons using the χ^2 test or Fisher's two-tailed test for exact probability, whichever seemed the more appropriate. The control group were 149 mentally normal individuals (tested by Method 1) none of whom had the pink spot. Given also (Table 3) are the percentages of individuals with the pink spot within sub-classes.

实验 IV：对精神正常的个体进行调查研究，其中一部分人从各方面看都明显健康，而另一部分是在两个综合医院住院的患者。

实验 I 为了调查粉红色斑点的可能发生率，对 101 例在精神病院住院的患者的尿样进行了检测。这些患者来自 3 个精神病院并且“可能都是精神分裂症患者”。他们中有急性和慢性患者，其中一些人已经停止药物治疗达 2 个月之久了。在同一时间对所有患者进行精神分裂症的临时诊断，负责检测粉红色斑点的研究者雷蒙德·鲍迪伦熟悉这种诊断和药物治疗。当他检测完斑点是否存在后，每个患者还要与不了解粉红色斑点的精神病学家雪莉·莱斯利会面并进行再次检测。据其做出的最后评估，她对约 17% 精神分裂症患者的最初诊断结果持怀疑态度；鉴于此，他们被归为非精神分裂症患者。已经确诊的精神分裂症患者被分成两组，一组是在任何时候都会表现出一种或多种施奈德一级症状的患者[10]，另一组是从来不表现症状的患者（这分别被称为施奈德阳性和施奈德阴性精神分裂症）。然后患者也被细分为典型的精神分裂症患者和只显示有妄想症特性而没有思维形式障碍或是情感偏激的患者。为了方便起见，前者被称为“非妄想症者”，后者称为“妄想症者”。由于患者不合作或语言障碍的原因，我们在 5 名患者中没有获得诊断所需的必要信息，因此将他们划分为“无法评估”类。

要尽可能收集超过 20 小时的尿样，尽管已经证实对某些患者而言短时间收集更有效。尿样的萃取和纸层析按弗里德霍夫和范温克尔[1]所描述的方法进行，本文中将其定义为方法 1。当被药物显著干扰时，粉红色斑点时有时无，我们有时不得不将其划分为“无法评估”类。

因为还有必要作更详细的研究以明确事实上正被我们所论证的 3,4–二甲氧基苯基乙胺,所以整篇文章中我们更倾向于使用术语“粉红色斑点”而不是“存在 3,4–二甲氧基苯基乙胺”来报道实验结果。

表 1 和表 2 分别表示研究的结果和统计分析。其中包括了对确切的发生概率用卡方检验或费希尔双边检验而得到的多项比较结果，任何一种方法似乎都更加合适。对照组是 149 个精神正常的个体，没有检测到粉红色斑点（通过方法 1 测定）。表 3 同样给出在亚群中粉红色斑点个体的出现比例。

Table 1. Experiment I

(*a*) Pink spot in relation to Schneider's first-rank symptoms

Schneider rating	Pink spot rating			
	Positive	Negative	Impossible to assess	Totals
Positive	35	11	6	52
Negative	7	16	4	27
Impossible to assess	4	0	1	5
Non-schizophrenic	0	16	1	17
Totals	46	43	12	101

(*b*) Pink spot in relation to non-paranoid and paranoid classification

Psychiatric assessment		Pink spot rating		
		Positive	Negative	Totals
Schneider positive	Non-paranoid	35	7	42
	Paranoid	0	4	4
Schneider negative	Non-paranoid	5	5	10
	Paranoid	2	11	13
Totals		42	27	69

Table 2. Experiment I. Comparison of Incidence of Pink Spot between Classes

Comparison	χ^2	d.f.	Probability
Schneider positive with Schneider negative	11.57	1	< 0.001
Schneider positive with non-schizophrenic	24.95	1	< 0.001
Schneider positive with control			$= 2.5\times10^{-39}$
Schneider negative with non-schizophrenic			= 0.029
Schneider negative with control			$= 3.1\times10^{-7}$
Non-paranoid with paranoid	20.18	1	< 0.001
Non-paranoid with non-schizophrenic	26.80	1	< 0.001
Non-paranoid with control			$= 8.06\times10^{-32}$
Paranoid with non-schizophrenic			N.S.
Paranoid with control			0.0099
Schneider positive with Schneider negative Within non-paranoid			0.0388
Schneider positive with Schneider negative within paranoid			N.S.
Paranoid with non-paranoid within Schneider positive			= 0.0020
Paranoid with non-paranoid within Schneider negative			N.S.

Table 3. Experiment I. Percentage of Individuals with Pink Spot within Sub-classes

Sub-class	Percentage with pink spot
Schneider positive, non-paranoid	83.3 ± 5.75
Schneider positive, paranoid	0.0
Schneider negative, non-paranoid	50 ±15.8
Schneider negative, paranoid	15.4 ± 10.0

表 1. 实验 I

(*a*) 与施奈德一级症状相关的粉红色斑点

施奈德评价	粉红色斑点评价			
	阳性	阴性	无法评估	合计
阳性	35	11	6	52
阴性	7	16	4	27
无法评估	4	0	1	5
非精神分裂症	0	16	1	17
合计	46	43	12	101

(*b*) 与非妄想症和妄想症相关的粉红色斑点

精神病评估		粉红色斑点评价		
		阳性	阴性	合计
施奈德阳性	非妄想症	35	7	42
	妄想症	0	4	4
施奈德阴性	非妄想症	5	5	10
	妄想症	2	11	13
合计		42	27	69

表 2. 实验 I. 不同类群间粉红色斑点发生率的比较

比较	χ^2	自由度	概率
施奈德阴性和施奈德阳性	11.57	1	< 0.001
施奈德阳性和非精神分裂症	24.95	1	< 0.001
施奈德阳性和对照			$= 2.5 \times 10^{-39}$
施奈德阴性和非精神分裂症			$= 0.029$
施奈德阴性和对照			$= 3.1 \times 10^{-7}$
非妄想症和妄想症	20.18	1	< 0.001
非妄想症和非精神分裂症	26.80	1	< 0.001
非妄想症和对照			$= 8.06 \times 10^{-32}$
妄想症和非精神分裂症			无显著性差异
妄想症和对照			0.0099
施奈德阳性和非妄想性施奈德阴性			0.0388
施奈德阳性和妄想性施奈德阴性			无显著性差异
妄想症和施奈德阳性非妄想症			$= 0.0020$
妄想症和施奈德阴性非妄想症			无显著性差异

表 3. 实验 I. 亚群中粉红色斑点个体的出现比例

亚群	粉红色斑点比例
施奈德阳性，非妄想症	83.3 ± 5.75
施奈德阳性，妄想症	0.0
施奈德阴性，非妄想症	50 ± 15.8
施奈德阴性，妄想症	15.4 ± 10.0

Exp. II. In the second experiment a different psychiatrist (P. H.) and biochemist (A. P. R.) worked together. The urines of 296 psychiatric in-patients drawn from two hospitals were investigated for the pink spot. The patients had often been in hospital for many years and included a larger proportion of chronic cases than in the first experiment. The samples of urine were analysed in ignorance both of the diagnosis and of the nature and quantity of drugs being received, so that a different part of the work was "blind" from that in Exp. I. The psychiatrist selected the patients so as to include a variety of mental diseases, and he accepted the diagnosis given in the case-sheets and did not interview the patients personally as did the psychiatrist in Exp. I. He divided the cases into four groups: (*a*) "non-paranoid" schizophrenics; (*b*) "paranoid" schizophrenics; (*c*) schizophreniform syndromes (where although some features of schizophrenia were present it was uncertain whether or not the primary diagnosis was schizophrenia); (*d*) non-schizophrenics, which included such conditions as manic depressive psychosis, organic dementia and mental defect.

Since a different psychiatrist was scoring the cases and the diagnosis was assessed from the case sheets, the classes are probably not strictly comparable with those of Exp. I.

The chromatographic procedures were the same as those described by Friedhoff and van Winkle[1] (our "Method 1"), but a different extraction procedure was used and the technique is referred to by us as "Method 2". A volume of 300-500 ml. of a 16-h overnight sample of urine was adjusted to *p*H 9.0 with 2 N sodium hydroxide. This was extracted three times with 100-ml. portions of 1,2-dichloroethane and the extracts dried over anhydrous sodium sulphate. The first extract was examined by ultra-violet absorption at 279 mμ. A peak at this value is a useful indicator of DMPE in the absence of interfering substances such as drug metabolites. The ultra-violet absorption spectrum helps particularly to distinguish DMPE from any closely related compounds which could not satisfactorily be resolved from it by the chromatographic procedures used. The three extracts were then combined and evaporated to dryness on a rotary evaporator. The residue was redissolved in dichloroethane for application to the chromatography paper. Authentic 3,4-dimethoxyphenyl-ethylamino (K and K Laboratories) and mixed spots of urine extracts and authentic DMPE were applied alongside the urine extracts on the chromatography papers and the separation carried out.

The results of Exp. II are given in Table 4 and the statistical analysis in Table 5. The controls are 310 mentally normal individuals (tested by Method 2) one of whom had the pink spot. The results for the schizophrenform syndrome class have not been analysed because the group was probably very heterogeneous.

实验 II 第二个实验由另一位精神病学家哈珀和生物化学家保利娜·布里奇斯共同完成。他们检测了来自两个医院的 296 例住院精神病患者尿样中的粉红色斑点。这些患者经常长期住院，而且其中慢性病例的比例比第一次实验中的大。为了与实验 I 相区别，部分工作采用的是“盲法”实验，即尿样的分析是在不了解诊断情况和所使用药品的性能和数量的情况下进行的。精神病学家挑选了多种类型的精神病患者，同时他接受病历中的诊断结果，并没有像实验 I 中的精神病学家那样亲自会见患者。他把患者分为 4 组：(*a*)“非妄想症”精神分裂症；(*b*)“妄想症”精神分裂症；(*c*) 精神分裂症样综合征（尽管有一些精神分裂症的特征，但最初诊断不能确定是否是精神分裂症）；(*d*) 非精神分裂征，包括躁狂抑郁症、器官性痴呆和心理缺陷。

因为病例是由不同的精神病专家根据病历中的诊断结果进行评判的，所以这些分类可能没有实验 I 那样严格。

纸层析过程也是按照弗里德霍夫和范温克尔[1]所述的方法（我们称为“方法 1”）进行的，但使用的萃取过程是不同的，是按照我们定义的方法 2 进行的。使用 2 摩尔 / 升的氢氧化钠溶液将过夜 16 小时的体积为 300 毫升 ~500 毫升尿样的 pH 值调至 9.0。然后用 100 毫升 1,2– 二氯乙烷萃取 3 次后再用无水硫酸钠干燥萃取物。通过紫外分光光度计在波长为 279 纳米下检测第一次萃取物。在没有干扰物质（比如药物代谢物）的情况下，所检测到的峰值是鉴定 3,4– 二甲氧基苯基乙胺的有用指标。紫外分光光度法特别有助于将 3,4– 二甲氧基苯基乙胺从其他相近的混合物中区分出来，而层析法则不能达到这个水平。然后将 3 种萃取物混合在一起并在旋转蒸发器中脱水蒸干。残余物用二氯乙烷再次溶解后进行纸层析。高纯度的 3,4– 二甲基苯乙胺（K&K 实验室）及其与尿液萃取物斑点的混合物和尿液提取物一起进行纸层析和分离实验。

表 4 和表 5 分别是实验 II 的研究结果和统计分析。以 310 例精神正常个体为对照，通过方法 2 对其进行检测发现只有一例呈现粉红色斑点。因为精神分裂症样综合征患者的种类非常多，所以没有分析这类患者的结果。

Table 4. Experiment II. Pink Spot Assessment in 296 Psychiatric Patients

Psychiatric assessment	Pink spot rating			
	Present	Absent	Impossible to assess	Totals
Non-paranoid schizophrenics	20	30	19	69
Paranoid schizophrenics	2	54	6	62
"Schizophreniform syndromes"	5	58	25	88
Non-schizophrenics	1	68	8	77
Totals	28	210	58	296

Table 5. Experiment II. Comparison of Incidence of Pink Spot between Classes

Comparison	χ^2	d.f.	Probability
Non-paranoid with paranoid	19.16	1	< 0.001
Non-paranoid with non-schizophrenic	27.05	1	< 0.001
Non-paranoid with control			$= 2.81\times10^{-18}$
Paranoid with non-schizophrenic			N.S.
Paranoid with control			N.S.

Exp. III. The pink spot was investigated in 20 close relatives of three schizophrenic propositi, all three of whom were found (by one or both of the two methods) to excrete the pink spot. None of the relatives was schizophrenic though some were reported as having other mental abnormalities.

The pink spot was not found in the urine of any of the close relatives, and these therefore are not significantly different from the control group of mentally normal individuals.

Exp. IV: *Investigation of mentally normal individuals.* These consisted of two groups. The first was made up of 265 healthy individuals, mostly undergraduates or university staff. The second was composed of 126 mentally normal in-patients, comprising 54 pre-operative and 20 post-operative cases, 10 patients with liver disease, 20 with chronic neurological states and 22 with general medical conditions. The pink spot was assessed by one or both of the two methods previously described and the series has acted as the control for the various comparisons.

All the controls were negative for the pink spot with the exception of one healthy individual, a woman aged 54. She suffered from migraine but was mentally normal and so was her family.

Comparison between Method 1 (Friedhoff and van Winkle) and Method 2 (ultra-violet + chromatography) in the investigation of the pink spot. In 133 people both methods for assessing the pink spot were used (Table 6).

表 4. 实验 II. 在 296 例精神分裂症患者中检测粉红色斑点

精神病评估	粉红色斑点评价			
	存在	不存在	无法评估	合计
非妄想性精神分裂症	20	30	19	69
妄想性精神分裂症	2	54	6	62
“精神分裂样综合征”	5	58	25	88
非精神分裂症	1	68	8	77
合计	28	210	58	296

表 5. 实验 II. 各种类型之间粉红色斑点发生率的比较

比较	χ^2	自由度	可能性
非妄想症和妄想症	19.16	1	< 0.001
非妄想症和非精神分裂症	27.05	1	< 0.001
非妄想症和对照			$= 2.81 \times 10^{-18}$
妄想症和非精神分裂症			无显著性差异
妄想症和对照			无显著性差异

实验 III　在 3 例精神分裂症患者的 20 个近亲属中检测粉红色斑点。使用一种或同时使用这两种方法均能在这 3 个患者中检测出粉红色斑点，而他们的近亲属中没有一人患有精神分裂症，尽管有些人被报道有其他精神异常症状。

在所有近亲属的尿液中没有检测到粉红色斑点，因此他们与作为对照的精神正常的个体相比无显著性差异。

实验 IV：对精神正常的个体进行的研究　他们被分为两组：第 1 组由 265 例健康个体组成，他们大部分是大学生或大学职工。第 2 组是由 126 例精神正常的住院患者组成，包括 54 例手术前患者和 20 例手术后患者、10 例有肝病的患者、20 例有慢性神经功能缺损的患者和 22 例有常见疾病的患者。使用前面提到的一种方法或同时使用两种方法检测粉红色斑点，同时该系列已作为各种比较的对照。

除了一个 54 岁的健康女性外，所有对照的红色斑点检测均为阴性。她患有偏头痛但精神正常，她的家人也是这样。

使用方法 1（弗里德霍夫和范温克尔）和方法 2（紫外分光光度法和层析法）研究粉红色斑点进行的比较　同时使用这两种方法对 133 例个体进行粉红色斑点检测（表 6）。

Table 6. Comparison of Method 1 and Method 2 in Investigation of the Pink Spot

	Ultra-violet + chrom. (Method II)		
Friedhoff and van Winkle (Method 1)	Pink spot positive	Pink spot negative	Totals
Pink spot positive	12	7	19
Pink spot negative	2	112	114
Totals	14	119	133

Though there is a significant correlation, $P = 1.06 \times 10^{-10}$, between the results given by the two methods, there are discrepancies.

There are several reasons which might account for this non-concordance: (1) Method 2 may be less sensitive in detecting the pink spot (as opposed to DMPE); (2) slightly different substances may be being estimated; (3) one method may be more likely to produce undetectable false readings because of the presence of drugs; (4) there may be observer discrepancies. There possibilities are being investigated and will be the subject of a further article.

The association previously found between the pink spot and schizophrenia has been confirmed using large numbers. The results of Exp. I give compelling evidence that its presence is particularly associated with Schneider-positive individuals. It is much rarer in those who are Schneider negative and rarer still (if present at all) in non-schizophrenics.

In Exp. I the same patients have also been classified as to whether or not they only have paranoid features. The presence of the pink spot is particularly associated with the non-paranoid group but is significantly higher among the paranoid group than among the mentally normal controls.

When the individuals are classified as being Schneider positive and non-paranoid this sub-class has a significantly higher incidence of the pink spot than does any other group (83.3 ± 5.75 percent). Thus to predict the presence of the pink spot the double classification is the most efficient.

Five individuals were so seriously disturbed that they could not be interviewed or assessed on the Schneider rating. The fact that four of them showed the pink spot suggests that these were true Schneider-positive non-paranoid cases as judged by our other results.

The second experiment using a different method for detecting the pink spot again shows the very strong association between the presence of the pink spot and "non-paranoid" schizophrenia. The lower frequency of the pink spot may be due to any of the four reasons mentioned above and/or to the cases being loss florid than in Exp. I. However, not enough have been scored by the Schneider rating to show whether the association is particularly with the Schneider-positive "non-paranoid" group although the data show a strong tendency in this direction.

表 6. 使用方法 1 和方法 2 研究粉红色斑点的比较

	紫外分光光度计法和层析法（方法 2）		
弗里德霍夫和范温克尔（方法 1）	阳性粉红色斑点	阴性粉红色斑点	合计
阳性粉红色斑点	12	7	19
阴性粉红色斑点	2	112	114
合计	14	119	133

虽然这两种方法的研究结果显著相关（P 值为 1.06×10^{-10}），但仍存在差异。

结果出现差异的原因可能有如下几点：(1) 在检测粉红色斑点时，方法 2 的敏感性可能更低（3,4– 二甲氧基苯基乙胺与之相反）；(2) 可能检测到了一些差异较小的物质；(3) 由于药物的存在，其中的一种方法更有可能产生觉察不到的错误读数；(4) 可能存在测者差异。这些可能的原因正在被研究并作为将来更深层研究文章的主题。

通过检测大量样品，证实了先前提出的粉红色斑点和精神分裂症之间存在联系的观点。实验 I 的研究结果为粉红色斑点与施奈德阳性个体间存在密切联系提供了有力的证据。在施奈德阴性个体中这是很少见的，在非精神分裂症（如果存在的话）个体中出现的概率更小。

实验 I 中相同的患者也按照是否只有妄想症特征来分类。粉红色斑点与非妄想症组存在特别密切的关系，但在妄想症组中出现的概率明显高于精神正常的对照组。

当个体被划分为施奈德阳性和非妄想症类型时，其粉红色斑点发生率明显高于其他组（83.3% ± 5.75%）。因此对于预测粉红色斑点的出现，这种双重分类法最有效。

由于 5 个人受到严重干扰，以至于不能与他们进行面谈或按照施奈德的方法对其进行分类。实际上，在其中的 4 个人中检测到了粉红色斑点，就像我们得到的其他结果一样，他们都是施奈德阳性非妄想症患者。

第二次实验使用不同的方法检测粉红色斑点，结果再次表明斑点的出现和“非妄想症”精神分裂症有紧密的联系。粉红色斑点出现的频率较低可能是由于上述提到的 4 个原因中的任何一个，或由于患者不如实验 I 中的健康。然而按照施奈德的方法，没有足够的证据显示施奈德阳性“非妄想症”组与粉红色斑点之间有明确关系，尽管数据强烈地倾向于这一方向。

The evidence from the two experiments suggests that the pink spot is highly associated with schizophrenia and is not often present in other forms of mental disorder or in close relatives or in controls. Moreover, from our survey it seems highly improbable that diet and institution life play any part in producing the pink spot. An important problem is whether the abnormal metabolite precedes or is a result of the disease. The family data point to the latter conclusion, but it is possible that the pink spot only appears shortly before the disorder manifests itself, and that more refined techniques might demonstrate it in sibs. It would be interesting to follow pink-spot-positive patients with florid schizophrenia during remissions since these data might indicate whether the acuteness of the disease was associated with the quantity of pink spot material. If it did, this might explain its absence in sibs. The possibility has to be considered that drugs might be the cause of the pink spot. This is refuted by our data. Thus the relationship between schizophrenia and pink spot is at least as marked in those who had been off drugs for two weeks or more as in those who had not. Moreover, the non-schizophrenics on drugs showed no elevation of the frequency of the pink spot over those not on drugs. However, a complicating factor in using the pink spot for diagnosis is that drugs interfere both with the chromatography and with the ultra-violet absorption and it is difficult to obtain patients (particularly acute cases) who are not on drug therapy.

We thank Dr. B. Finkleman, Prof. F. J. Fish, Dr. A. V. de P. Kelly, Dr. I. Leveson, and Dr. B. Ward for allowing us to examine and test their patients, and the staffs of the hospitals concerned for help in the collection of samples. We also thank the Hon. Miriam Rothschild for obtaining the co-operation of certain of the individuals investigated.

(**208**, 453-455; 1965)

R. E. Bourdillon, C. A. Clarke, A. Pauline Ridges and P. M. Sheppard: Nuffield Unit of Medical Genetics, Department of Medicine, University of Liverpool.

P. Harper: Department of Psychological Medicine, University of Liverpool.

Shirley A. Leslie: Psychiatric Registrar, Royal Liverpool Children's Hospital, Liverpool.

References:

1. Friedhoff, A. J., and van Winkle, E., *Nature*, **194**, 897 (1962).
2. Sen, N. P., and McGeer, P. H., *Biochem. Biophys. Res. Comm.*, **14**, 227 (1964).
3. Kuehl, F. A., Hichens, M., Ormond, R. E., Meisinger, M. A. P., Gale, P. H., Cirillo, V. J., and Brink, N. G., *Nature*, **203**, 154 (1964).
4. Horwitt, M. K., contribution to discussion at *Symp. Amine Metabolism in Schizophrenia*, Atlantic City, April 1965 (in the press).
5. Perry, T. L., Hansen, S., and Macintyre, L., *Nature*, **202**, 519 (1964).
6. Faurbye, A., and Pind, K., *Acta Psychiat. Scand.*, **40**, 540 (1964).
7. Takesada, M., Kakimoto, Y., Sano, I., and Kaneko, Z., *Nature*, **199**, 203 (1963).
8. Osmond, H., and Smythies, J., *J. Ment. Sci.*, **98**, 309 (1952).
9. Harley-Mason, J., *J. Ment. Sci.*, **98**, 313 (1952).
10. Schneider, K., *Fortschr. Neurol. Psych.*, **25**, 487 (1957).

两个实验给出的证据表明粉红色斑点与精神分裂症高度相关，而在其他的精神障碍类型、近亲属或对照组中并不经常出现。此外，根据我们的调查，日常饮食和日常生活不大可能对粉红色斑点的产生起到非常重要的作用。异常代谢物是先于疾病产生还是由疾病引起，这是一个重要的问题。家族数据指向后者，但粉红色斑点可能只在精神障碍发生前短暂地显现，而且许多精细技术可以验证出近亲属中的斑点。密切注意处于康复期的粉红色斑点呈阳性的妄想症型精神分裂症患者将很有趣，因为这些数据可能暗示疾病的严重程度是否与粉红色斑点的数量有关。如果真是这样的话，将有助于解释在近亲属中不出现粉红色斑点的原因。必须考虑药物可能导致出现粉红色斑点这种可能性。我们的研究数据否定了这一点。因此精神分裂症与粉红色斑点之间的关系至少应标记在那些已经停药两周以上或者没有服药的人身上。此外，服药的非精神分裂症患者与那些没有服药的患者相比，粉红色斑点出现的概率并没有提高。然而，在使用粉红色斑点作诊断时，一个复杂的因素是药物会干扰层析法和紫外吸收光谱法的检测，并且很难找到那些没有进行药物治疗的患者（尤其是急性患者）。

我们感谢芬克莱曼医生、菲什教授、凯利医生、莱韦森医生和沃德医生允许我们检测他们的患者，也感谢关心和帮助我们收集样品的医院的全体员工。我们还要感谢米丽娅姆 · 罗思柴尔德阁下在个体研究时所给予的合作。

（郭娟 翻译；刘京国 审稿）

The Juvenile Hormone*

V. Wigglesworth

Editor's Note

Here British entomologist Vincent Wigglesworth extols the virtues of "one of the most outstanding morphogenetic hormones known"—the juvenile hormone, which he himself had recently discovered. The hormone, which is released from a pair of endocrine glands behind the brain, controls metamorphosis by maintaining larval features in many different kinds of insects. Decapitating kissing bug larvae, Wigglesworth had shown, triggers premature metamorphosis. In this paper, his opening address to the third conference of European Comparative Endocrinologists, Wigglesworth sums up what is known about the juvenile hormone, including its role in metamorphosis and reproduction, and its chemical nature. He also believes that the hormone brings about "gene switching" and so may affect more complex behaviours, such as sociability.

IN choosing this topic for the opening address to the third conference of European Comparative Endocrinologists, I had in mind the consideration of the juvenile hormone in general terms—as an agent with properties that must be of interest to all endocrinologists. I shall not therefore attempt a complete or specialized survey of this very complex subject, but will select only a limited number of points for discussion.

A Morphogenetic Hormone

The juvenile hormone is a morphogenetic hormone—one of the most outstanding morphogenetic hormones known. The existence of a hormone responsible for maintaining larval characters was first revealed by the fact that decapitation in young *Rhodnius* larvae causes premature metamorphosis[1]. Parabiosis showed that this hormone was freely circulating in the blood; and by removing progressively more and more of the anterior parts of the head from the insects used in the parabiosis experiments, it was shown that the hormone came not from the brain but from the corpus allatum—an endocrine organ that buds off from the ectoderm at the base of the mouthparts and comes to lie just behind the brain[1]. This conclusion was confirmed by the implantation of corpora allata from young (3rd- or 4th-stage) larvae into 5th-stage larvae. These 5th-stage larvae then moulted not into adults but into giant 6th-stage larvae[2].

The juvenile hormone acts directly on the epidermal cells responsible for laying down the cuticle at moulting; restricted local application of the hormone results in a restricted

* Substance of an opening address to the third conference of European Comparative Endocrinologists held in Copenhagen during August 1965.

保幼激素*

威格尔斯沃思

编者按

本文中，英国昆虫学家文森特·威格尔斯沃思盛赞了由他自己在不久前发现的一种重要的形态发生激素——保幼激素的优点。保幼激素是由位于脑后的一对内分泌腺分泌的，在许多不同种类的昆虫体内，该激素通过保持幼虫特征来控制变态。威格尔斯沃思的实验表明，切除接吻虫幼虫的头部会使其提前变态。这篇文章是威格尔斯沃思在第三届欧洲比较内分泌学家大会上致的开幕词。在这里，他总结了已知的保幼激素的知识，包括它在变态和繁殖中的作用以及它的化学性质。他也相信该激素可以引起"基因转换"，并可能因此而影响到更为复杂的行为，例如社会行为。

选择保幼激素作为第三届欧洲比较内分泌学家大会开幕演讲的题目，是因为我认为一般来说保幼激素这种物质的属性一定会引起所有内分泌学家的兴趣。但是我并没有因此而试图对这个复杂的题目进行一个完整或专业的纵览，而只是选取了有限的几个点以供讨论。

形态发生激素

保幼激素是一种形态发生激素——是已知最重要的形态发生激素之一。这种负责保持幼虫特性的激素的发现源于切除红猎蝽幼小的幼虫头部引起了过早的变态发育[1]。异种共生实验显示这种激素在血液中自由循环；通过逐渐延长异种共生实验中昆虫头部前段的切除范围，发现这种激素不是来源于大脑，而是来源于咽侧体——外胚层的一种内分泌器官，位于口器的底部，正好在脑后[1]。将幼小的幼虫（第三龄或第四龄）的咽侧体移植到第五龄的幼虫后，发现这些第五龄的幼虫并没有蜕变为成虫，而是成为巨型第六龄幼虫[2]，此发现进一步证实了这个结论。

保幼激素直接作用于负责在蜕皮阶段产生外皮的表皮细胞；限制激素的局部应用会使受限部分的幼虫表皮变为成虫表皮[2]。例如，有可能产生一只带有幼虫翅膀

* 这篇文章是 1965 年 8 月于哥本哈根举行的第三届欧洲比较内分泌学家大会的开幕词。

local patch of larval cuticle in an otherwise adult insect[2]. It is possible, for example, to produce adult insects with one larval wing[3]. The self-same cell has the capacity for laying down larval cuticle or adult cuticle. That is most clearly shown in the sensory bristles or hairs: the trichogen cells which form the bristles persist from one stage to the next; in the presence of a large amount of juvenile hormone these cells lay down larval-type bristles; in the absence of the hormone they lay down adult-type bristles, and with intermediate amounts of juvenile hormone, brestles of intermediate type are developed[1]. Under natural conditions intermediate forms do not commonly occur. There is a strong tendency for the insect to develop either larval or adult characters.

Experiments by many authors have shown that the juvenile hormone controls metamorphosis in insects of all kinds. In holometabolous insects, which have a pupal stage between the larva and the adult, the juvenile hormone again controls the morphogenetic change; a large amount of the hormone ensures retention or re-development of larval characters; absence of the hormone results in metamorphosis to the adult; the presence of a very small amount of juvenile hormone leads to the appearance of the pupal form[4]. This result not only confirms the importance of the juvenile hormone in controlling morphogenesis, but it illustrates in a most striking way a point often made by C. M. Child: that the same inductor substance can evoke totally different results depending on its concentration or the timing of its action.

Here again intermediate forms rarely occur in Nature. But they can be induced experimentally: if the corpus allatum is removed from the last-stage larva of the honeybee[5] or of the giant silkmoth *Hyalophora*[6] the supply of juvenile hormone falls below the level necessary to produce the pupa, and monstrous forms intermediate between pupa and adult develop. Some caterpillars pass through a regular succession of morphological stages in successive instars. These forms also seem to be regulated by levels of juvenile hormone secretion—but the detailed evidence for this has not yet been fully worked out[7].

The Nature of Hormone-controlled Metamorphosis

It has long been recognized that the effect of the juvenile hormone is to control the realization or suppression of inborn potencies. In other words, it brings about "gene switching". In this regard it resembles the inductor substances which control morphogenesis in different parts of the body during differentiation; and the factors which lead to the differences in form if different individuals in environmentally induced polymorphism[8]. Indeed, there are a number of polymorphic changes in which there is evidence that the level of juvenile hormone activity may itself be involved, notably (i) the change over from the "solitary" to the "gregarious" form in locusts[9]; (ii) the switch from apterous to alate forms among parthenogenesis aphids[10]; (iii) the production of the soldier caste in termites[11,12].

Just how and where the juvenile hormone is acting is not known. Twelve years ago I wrote "it is a matter for discussion whether the simultaneous inheritance of the dual potentialities for larval and adult differentiation within these societies of cells is by way of the nucleus

的成虫[3]。同一种细胞既能产生幼虫表皮，也能产生成虫表皮。这种现象在感觉器官的刚毛或绒毛上体现得最为明显：产生刚毛的毛原细胞持续存在于昆虫发育的过程中；当存在大量的保幼激素时，这些细胞产生幼虫型刚毛；当缺乏这种激素时，它们产生成虫型刚毛，当保幼激素处于中等水平时，就会产生处于中间状态的刚毛[1]。在自然情况下中间状态并不普遍存在。昆虫的发育有很强的倾向，不是发育为幼虫就是发育为成虫。

很多科学家的实验结果显示保幼激素调控着各种昆虫的变态。对于完全变态的昆虫来说，在幼虫阶段和成虫阶段之间存在蛹的阶段，保幼激素在这里也调控着昆虫的形态变化；大量激素的存在会确保幼虫特性的维持或再发育；激素缺乏的结果是变态为成虫，只存在极小量保幼激素时幼虫会化成蛹[4]。这个结果不仅肯定了保幼激素在调控变态发育中的重要性，而且用最惊人的方式阐明了蔡尔德经常提及的观点：相同的感应物质可能产生截然不同的作用，这取决于它的浓度和作用时间。

这里再次指出昆虫发育的中间状态在自然界中很少出现。但是它们可以在实验中被诱导产生：如果摘除蜜蜂[5]或巨蚕蛾[6]的最后阶段的幼虫的咽侧体，使供给的保幼激素降低到化蛹所必需的含量以下，这时就会产生介于蛹和成虫之间的巨型虫。一些幼虫会以连续中间状态的形式经过常规的连续形态学阶段。这些形态变化似乎也由保幼激素的分泌水平进行调节——但是有关这一点的详细证据仍不充分[7]。

受激素调节的变态的本质

我们很久以前就已经认识到，保幼激素的作用是对某些先天潜能的实现或抑制进行调节。换句话说，它导致“基因转换”。从这方面考虑，它类似于可以在分化过程中调节身体不同部位形态发育的感应物质，也与由环境导致的昆虫多态性中导致个体间形态差异的因子[8]类似。实际上，有证据显示昆虫的多态性变化都涉及保幼激素的分泌水平，比较显著的是（i）蝗虫由“独居型”转变为“群居型”[9]；（ii）孤雌生殖的蚜虫由无翅转变为有翅[10]；（iii）白蚁中兵蚁等级的产生[11,12]。

保幼激素如何发挥作用以及在哪里发挥作用仍不得而知。12年前我曾经写过“这些细胞群既能分化为幼虫又能分化为成虫的双重潜能，是取决于细胞核遗传还是细

or cytoplasm or both"[13]. Eight years ago I submitted that the juvenile hormone "controls the manifestation of alternative genetically controlled forms" and I suggested that "it is possible to conceive it as being concerned in the regulation of permeability relations within the cells—in such a way that the gene-controlled enzyme system responsible for larval characters is brought increasingly into action when the juvenile hormone is present"[14].

The position is unchanged today—except that tissue-specific puffing patterns in the chromosomes of *Drosophila*[15], on one hand, and the theories of enzyme induction in bacteria as developed by Jacob and Monod[16] *et al.*, on the other, render us much more prepared to accept the idea of a primary action of the hormone at the level of the gene. Experimental evidence has yet to come.

Reversal of Metamorphosis

The question was early raised whether the genetic system responsible for the production of larval characters was still capable of re-activation by the juvenile hormone in the adult insect. In other words, whether metamorphosis can be reversed. Of course, this can only be tested by making the adult moult again by exposing it artificially to the moulting hormone.

In general it can be said that in most adult tissues it is not possible to induce any reversal of metamorphosis. But there are certain undoubted examples of such reversal: in the abdominal cuticle of *Rhodnius*[17] and of *Oncopeltus*[18], in the thoracic cuticle of the earwig *Auisolabis*, where the "ecdysial line" characteristic of the larva can be re-induced in a moulting adult[19], and in the integument of Lepidoptera where larval cuticle can be re-induced in fragments of pupal and imaginal integument[20,21].

Reversal of metamorphosis is an abnormal phenomenon. There has been no selection for its occurrence and it is not surprising that it occurs with difficulty. Likewise the production of stages intermediate between the normal stages in metamorphosis is an abnormal phenomenon and selection will have acted against it.

Time of Action of the Juvenile Hormone

The most effective moment for exposing the tissues to the juvenile hormone seems to be just before they begin the synthetic activities characteristic of the larval stage. Hormone administered too early is less effective—presumably because it is broken down in metabolism before the time for its action has arrived[22,23].

But there are certain effects which are induced in the cells long before they become manifest. A very small dose of juvenile hormone administered soon after feeding in the 5th-stage larva of *Rhodnius* has no effect on the type of cuticle laid down: normal adult cuticle is produced over the abdomen. But it does have the effect of ensuring the survival of the trichogen cells (almost all of which normally break down and disappear from the

胞质遗传还是两者兼有，这是一个值得讨论的问题”[13]。8 年前我提出保幼激素“调节可供选择的遗传调控方式的表现”，并且我认为“它在细胞内很可能与渗透性关系的调节有关——通过这种方式，当存在保幼激素时，负责幼虫特性的由基因控制的酶系统能够更多地发挥作用”[14]。

此立场至今没有改变——只不过果蝇染色体中的组织特异性膨胀方式[15]以及雅各布和莫诺等人提出的细菌中酶诱导的理论[16]让我们更加容易接受激素在基因水平发挥初级作用这一观点。目前还没有获得具体的实验证据。

变态发育的逆转

人们很早就提出一个问题：负责产生幼虫特征的遗传系统在成虫中是否仍然有可能被保幼激素重新激活。换句话说，变态发育是否可以逆转。当然，这只能通过让成虫暴露于人工合成的蜕皮激素而使它再次蜕皮来进行检验。

一般来说，在大多数成虫组织中不可能引发任何变态发育逆转，但是也存在一些确定无疑发生了这种逆转的例子：对于红猎蝽[17]和突角长蝽[18]的腹部表皮以及矮蠼螋的胸部表皮来说，在正在蜕皮的成虫体内能诱导出幼虫的特征“蜕皮线”[19]，对于鳞翅目昆虫的表皮来说，能再次诱导蛹的片段和成虫的表皮成为幼虫表皮[20,21]。

变态发育的逆转是一种异常现象。它的发生不被选择，这种情况很难发生也就不足为奇了。同样地，在变态反应中介于正常阶段之间的中间状态的产生也是异常现象，自然选择会抵制这种情况的发生。

保幼激素作用的时间

组织暴露于保幼激素下的最有效时刻似乎恰好是在它们开始显示幼虫阶段的合成活性特征之前。激素施用得太早，效率会降低——大概是因为在它起作用之前就在代谢过程中分解了[22,23]。

但是，早在激素效应出现之前，在细胞中就已诱导出一些效应。对刚喂完食的第五龄的红猎蝽幼虫施用很小剂量的保幼激素，不会对表皮类型产生影响：腹部产生了正常的成虫表皮。但是它确保毛原细胞(在变态过程中毛原细胞几乎会全部脱落，并从腹部的背面消失) 全部继续存在，因此在成虫的腹部出现了多余的绒毛[23]。

dorsum of the abdomen during metamorphosis), so that an excessive number of hairs appears on the abdomen of the adult[23].

The juvenile hormone has a comparable effect on the survival of the thoracic gland. The thoracic gland (the source of the moulting hormone) normally undergoes autolysis in *Rhodnius* within 24 h after moulting to the adult. This is a response to some hormonal factor in the newly moulted adult. But if the gland has been exposed to juvenile hormone during the pre-moulting period, it does not respond in this way and fails to undergo autolysis[24]. (The breakdown of certain muscles after metamorphosis in the silkmoth *Hyalophora cecropia* has recently been shown to be regulated in much the same way[25].)

Influence of the Juvenile Hormone on Behaviour

In certain caterpillars, behaviour is different in the final stage before pupation than it is before moulting in the earlier larval stages. The wax moth *Galleria* spins a tough cocoon before pupation, a flimsy web before a larval moult[26]. The sphingid *Mimas tiliae* crawls down the tree-trunk to the soil before pupation, but rests on the foliage before each larval moult[27]. These differences result from the presence or absence of juvenile hormone and are attributed to a direct effect on the nervous system. But the possibility remains that they could result from a nervous feed-back effect from other organs, for example from the distended silk glands.

Gonadotrophic Effects of the Juvenile Hormone

Secretion of the juvenile hormone ceases in *Rhodnius* in the 5th-stage larva before metamorphosis, but begins again in the adult. The hormone is then necessary for yolk formation in the female and for the full activity of the accessory glands in the male, which serve to produce the spermatophores to enclose the sperm[2]. In *Hyalophora cecropia*, in which the eggs are developed during the pupal stage, very little juvenile hormone is secreted in the adult female, but large amounts are produced in the adult male[28], which secretes a succession of spermatophores.

The precise nature of the gonadotrophic effect of the juvenile hormone is uncertain. The position is complicated by the fact that in some insects the secretion from the neuro-secretory cells in the brain seems to be more important than the juvenile hormone in ensuring yolk production. In the case of *Rhodnius*, G. C. Coles[29] concluded that the juvenile hormone acts on the fat body cells and serves to activate those components of the gene system which lead to the synthesis of the specific proteins that are discharged into the blood and are taken up by the acolytes and added to the yolk. In the male locust, *Schistocerca*, T. R. Odhiambo[30] considers that the juvenile hormone activates the many systems concerned in protein synthesis in the nuclei of the accessory glands.

Metabolic Action of the Juvenile Hormone

The juvenile hormone is often said to be a "metabolic hormone"—by which is meant that it sets going metabolic processes, either of synthesis or of combustion, whether or not

保幼激素对于胸腺的继续存在也具有类似的作用。正常情况下，在红猎蝽蜕变为成虫后的 24 小时内胸腺（蜕皮激素的来源）自溶。这个过程是新蜕变的成虫中的某些激素因子作用的结果。但是如果在蜕变前这一时期，胸腺暴露在保幼激素中，就不会发生这样的反应，腺体也不会自溶 [24]。（最近发现惜古比天蚕蛾变态后特定肌肉的分解也通过与之非常相似的方式被调节 [25]。）

保幼激素对行为的影响

在某些毛虫中，即将化蛹前的最后阶段的行为与早先幼虫阶段蜕皮前的行为不同。蜡螟在化蛹前会织一个坚韧的茧，但幼虫每次蜕皮前只是结一个轻薄的网 [26]。椴天蛾化蛹前会爬下树干到土壤中，但幼虫每次蜕皮前都栖息在树叶上 [27]。这些差异是由保幼激素的存在或缺乏造成的，并且是对神经系统直接作用的结果。但也有可能是由来自其他器官（比如，来自膨大的吐丝腺）的神经反馈调节导致的。

保幼激素的促性腺作用

变态前，在第五龄的红猎蝽幼虫中保幼激素的分泌停止，但在成虫时期又重新开始分泌保幼激素。这种激素对于雌性的卵黄形成和雄性副腺（负责产生包裹精子的精子包囊）的完全活力是必不可少的 [2]。对于惜古比天蚕蛾，卵在化蛹阶段发育，雌性成虫几乎不分泌保幼激素，但连续不断地分泌精子包囊的雄性成虫却产生大量保幼激素 [28]。

保幼激素促性腺作用的精确机制仍不确定。在卵黄形成的过程中，一些昆虫脑部神经分泌细胞的分泌物似乎比保幼激素更重要，这个事实使情况更加复杂。以红猎蝽为例，科勒斯 [29] 得出如下结论：保幼激素作用于脂肪体细胞并激活了那些基因系统组分，引发特定蛋白质的合成。蛋白质被释放到血液中，之后被卵母细胞吸收，加入卵黄。对于雄性沙漠蝗来说，奥德西亚姆波 [30] 认为保幼激素激活了许多与副腺细胞核中蛋白质合成相关的系统。

保幼激素的代谢活动

保幼激素经常被称为“代谢激素”——这意味着它调节合成代谢过程或者氧化代谢过程，无论怎样，这两个过程都是正常运转的身体所必需的。从这个意义上讲，

these are required for the working body. I am sceptical about the existence of metabolic hormones in this sense; I think they are unphysiological. I fancy that in most cases of this kind the hormone is setting in motion some physiological process, and the observed changes in metabolism are feed-back effects. (But, of course, abnormally large doses of hormones may have an abnormal pharmacological effect on metabolism which has little relation to their normal influence in the body.)

A well-known example of a metabolic effect of the juvenile hormone is the accumulation of reserves of fat and glycogen in the fat body of the grasshopper *Melanoplus* when the corpora allata are removed[31]. But Odhiambo[32] has shown that in the locust *Schistocerca* the juvenile hormone acts on the central nervous system and causes continuous activity. After allatectomy the insect continues to feed normally but it becomes inactive; consequently reserves pile up. The accumulation of reserves is not a feed-back effect from the gonads; the same effects are seen in males with or without their accessory glands.

In the blowfly *Calliphora*[33] and in the cockroach *Leucophaea*[34] the corpora allata are necessary to maintain the normal high level of oxygen consumption. But here again the juvenile hormone may be initiating some physiological activity (perhaps the synthesis of ovarial proteins) which demands increased oxygen consumption. In these cases it is not known whether nervous or muscular activity is changed. In the bug *Pyrrhocoris* the effect of the corpus sllarum on metabolism is seen only if the gonads are present: it appears to be a feed-back effect from the activated ovaries which are demanding nutrients[35]. Likewise in *Rhodnius*, the accelerated rate of digestion in the presence of the corpus allatum is a feed-back effect from the developing ovaries[36].

In *Leptinotarsa* the adult female goes into diapause when the juvenile hormone is absent or the corpora allata are removed. The rate of metabolism falls to a very low level and egg development ceases. In this state the thoracic muscles and their mitochondria degenerate almost completely. When juvenile hormone is supplied everything is restored: the beetles become active, the ovaries develop, muscles and sarcosomes are fully regenerated[37]. The metabolic effects are profound—but just where the juvenile hormone is acting is not known.

It is, of course, self-evident that hormones can influence the body only by bringing about chemical changes in the cells. In this sense they are always "metabolic hormones". Within a few hours the moulting hormone restores nucleoprotein synthesis in dormant epidermal cells of *Rhodnius*[14]; the juvenile hormone seems specifically to induce the synthesis of yolk proteins in the fat body of *Rhodnius*[29]; as Gilbert[38] has recently shown, the juvenile hormone will induce the fat body of the cockroach *Leucophaea* to synthesize ovarian lipids. But these, and many similar effects, are elements in a pattern of development evoked by the hormone. They are not simply quantitative changes in metabolism unrelated to growth requirements—as is commonly implied by the expression "metabolic hormone".

我怀疑代谢激素的存在；我认为它们不符合生理规律。我想在大多数情况下这种激素在动态中调节一些生理活动，并且在代谢中观察到的变化是具有反馈效应的。(但毫无疑问的是，异常大剂量的激素可能会对代谢产生一种异常的药理效应影响，这在体内与它们的正常影响几乎没有关系。)

一个著名的关于保幼激素代谢效应的例子是，当切除黑蝗的咽侧体后，其脂肪体内的脂肪和糖原储备发生积聚[31]。但是奥德西亚姆波[32]指出沙漠蝗的保幼激素作用于中枢神经系统并产生持续活性。咽侧体切除后，昆虫能继续正常进食，但是它变得不活跃；因此储备发生积聚。这种储备的积聚并不是来自性腺的反馈效应；同样的效应也发生在带有或切除了副腺的雄性昆虫中。

对于丽蝇[33]和蜚蠊[34]，咽侧体是保持正常高水平的氧气消耗所必需的。但是这里再次指出保幼激素也可能启动某些要求增加氧气消耗的生理活性（也许是卵蛋白的合成）。在这些例子中还不清楚神经或肌肉活性是否改变。只有当性腺存在时红蝽咽侧体在代谢中的作用才能看得出来：这看上去是由于正需要营养的被激活的卵巢所产生的反馈效应[35]。类似地，对于红猎蝽，当咽侧体存在时消化速率的提高是发育中的卵巢的反馈效应[36]。

对于瘦跗叶甲属昆虫，当保幼激素缺乏或咽侧体被切除时雌性成虫出现滞育。代谢率降到一个非常低的水平，卵的发育也停止了。在这种情况下胸部肌肉及其线粒体几乎全部退化了。一旦提供保幼激素，一切又恢复了：甲虫又变得活跃，卵巢开始发育，肌肉和肌细胞线粒体充分再生[37]。保幼激素对代谢的影响是深远的——但是激素作用位点仍不清楚。

当然，很明显激素只是通过引起细胞内的化学变化来影响整体。在这个意义上，它们永远是“代谢激素”。蜕皮激素在几个小时内就恢复了红猎蝽休眠表皮细胞的核蛋白的合成[14]；保幼激素似乎能特异性地诱导红猎蝽脂肪体中卵黄蛋白的合成[29]；如吉尔伯特[38]最近发表的结果所示，保幼激素能诱导蜚蠊的脂肪体合成卵巢的脂质。但是这些以及很多相似的效应只是激素引发的一种发育模式中的部分。它们不是与生长需求无关的代谢过程中的简单量变——如同通常“代谢激素”所表达的那样。

Chemical Nature of the Juvenile Hormone

The large accumulation of juvenile hormone in the adult moth of *Hyalophora cecropia* provided a source of active extract. Ether extracts from the abdomen of the male moth gave an orange-coloured oil rich in juvenile hormone activity[28]. This material was utilized to develop methods of assay[3,22] and methods for concentrating the active principle by countercurrent separation[22]. These procedures were applied to extracts from many sources and have shown that material with roughly the same partition properties, and with juvenile hormone activity, is widely spread throughout the animal and plant kingdoms: in the tissues of invertebrates and vertebrates, in higher plants, some bacteria and yeasts.

The material extracted from two of these sources, namely from the excrement of the mealworm, *Tenebrio*, and from yeast, was examined chemically by Schmialek[39]; the active principle was isolated and shown to be a mixture of *trans-trans*-farnesol and its aldehyde farnesal. The question arises whether the natural juvenile hormone in the insect has any relation to farnesol or is of a totally different nature.

At the present time the answer to this question is not known. Farnesol will certainly reproduce all the morphogenetic and gonadotrophic effects of the juvenile hormone in *Rhodnius*[40]. It is particularly effective if its stability is increased by blocking the alcohol end of the molecule in the form of an ether (for example, farnesyl methyl ether) or as the farnesyl acetone[41].

In the form of the methyl ether, a 0.06 percent solution of the active *trans-trans* isomer is far more effective than the natural extract from *cecropia*. 1.2 μg will cause a partial retention of larval characters in *Rhodnius*—a dose of 5.2 μg/g of body-weight[23]. In *Antheraea*, 20,000 μg of the natural extract from *cecropia* will cause a partial retention of pupal characters—a does of 4,000 μg/g of body-weight[42].

By repeated partition with methyl alcohol, chromatographic separation on silicic acid columns, followed by the crystallization of impurities, a "non-crystalline fraction" has been isolated which will produce this same effect in *Antheraea* at dose of 5 μg, that is, 1 μg/g of body-weight[42]. Accepting these results at their face value this product is about five times as effective as farnesyl methyl ether in *Rhodnius*.

Further attempted purification by gas-liquid chromatography leads to heat destruction of the natural substance, but one fraction isolated in this way had an activity twelve times that of the "non-crystalline fraction"[42]. Meyer, Schneiderman and Gilbert[43] report similar results, showing pyrolytic breakdown of the material in the gas-liquid chromatography column, but with some highly active fractions. Röller, Bjerke and McShan[44] have isolated a well-defined active substance which is certainly not farnesol.

The significance of these results is uncertain. Assay methods for material that is exerting its action over a period of many days of development, and which is continuously being

保幼激素的化学属性

保幼激素在惜古比天蚕蛾成虫中的大量积聚为含激素活性的提取物提供了来源。雄性飞蛾腹部的乙醚提取物是橙色油状物，富有保幼激素活性[28]。这种物质可以用于发展化验方法[3,22]，也可以用于发展通过逆流分离浓缩活性物质的方法[22]。很多原始材料的提取物适用这些过程，并且显示出在动植物中广泛存在具有大致相同分离特性和保幼激素活性的材料：如在无脊椎动物和脊椎动物的组织中，在高等植物、部分细菌和部分酵母中。

施麦阿来克对从其中两种原始材料（即拟步行虫幼虫的排泄物和酵母）提取出的物质进行了化学检验[39]；分离出活性物质，结果显示是反–反–法呢醇及其乙醛法呢醛混合物。这就提出了一个问题，即昆虫中的天然保幼激素是否与法呢醇有关或是具有完全不同的天然性质。

目前这个问题的答案仍然未知。法呢醇确实可以在红猎蝽身上重现保幼激素的所有形态发生效应和促性腺效应[40]。如果通过阻断醇基从而提高它的稳定性将会特别有效，包括醚（比如法呢甲醚）形式分子或法呢丙酮形式分子[41]。

在甲醚形式中，0.06% 的活性反–反异构体溶液远比惜古比天蚕蛾的天然提取物有效。1.2 微克就会使长红锥蝽一定程度地保留幼虫特性——剂量为 5.2 微克 / 克体重[23]。对于柞蚕，20,000 微克来自惜古比天蚕蛾的天然提取物能使蛹的特性得到一定程度的保留——剂量为 4,000 微克 / 克体重[42]。

通过甲醇多次分离、硅酸柱色谱分离以及随后的杂质结晶，分离出来一种“非晶体馏分”，它可以在柞蚕中产生同样的作用，剂量为 5 微克，即 1 微克 / 克体重[42]。如果在它们的表面数值上接受这些结果，那么这个产物在红猎蝽中的效率大约是法呢甲醚的 5 倍。

利用气液相色谱纯化会导致这种天然物质热分解，但是用这种方法分离出的一种馏分的活性是“非晶体馏分”的 12 倍[42]。迈耶、施奈德曼和吉尔伯特[43]报道了相似的结果，显示出材料在气液相色谱柱中发生热分解，但是伴有更高活性的馏分。罗勒、毕尔克和麦克沙恩[44]已经分离出了一种明确的活性物质，确定其不是法呢醇。

这些结果的重要性还不能确定。材料能在很多天内不断发挥作用，并且在代谢过程中持续分解，其化验方法还没有非常精确的定义。（通过稍微地修改施用材料的

broken down in metabolism, have no very precise meaning. (By modifying slightly the means of administering the material I have recently repeated the results on *Rhodnius* as described here with half the earlier dose, that is, with about 2.5 μg of the active isomer of farnesyl methyl ether per gram of body-weight.) At the present time farnesol derivatives are the only compounds of known chemical composition with juvenile hormone activity. They were identified as the substance with juvenile hormone activity in the extracts of non-insect material. They have been found in the extracts of *cecropia* and other silkmoths, Until other known compounds have been isolated, I am inclined to hold to the provisional hypothesis that the active group in the juvenile hormone is indeed the triple isoprene unit of farnesol, and that this exists in the natural hormone in some form that has not yet been defined.

(**208**, 522-524; 1965)

V. Wigglesworth: C. B. E., F. R. S., Department of Zoology, University of Cambridge.

References:

1. Wigglesworth, V. B., *Quart. J. Micro. Sci.*, 77, 191 (1934).
2. Wigglesworth, V. B., *Quart. J. Micro. Sci.*, **79**, 91 (1936).
3. Wigglesworth, V. B., *J. Insect Physiol.*, **2**, 73 (1958).
4. Piepho, H., *Verh. Dtsch. Zoo. Ges.* (Wilhelmshaven), **62** (1951).
5. Schaller, F., *Bull. Soc. Zoo Fr.*, 77, 195 (1952).
6. Williams, C. M., *Biol. Bull., Woods Hole*, **121**, 572 (1961).
7. Staal, G. B., *Entom. Bericht.*, **25**, 34 (1965).
8. Wigglesworth, V. B., *The Physiology of Insect Metamorphosis* (Cambridge University Press, 1954).
9. Joly, P., *Insectes Sociaux*, **3**, 17 (1956).
10. Lees, A. D., *Symp. Roy. Entomol. Soc. Lond.*, **1** (Insect Polymorphism), 68 (1961).
11. Kaiser, P., *Naturwiss.*, **42**, 303 (1955).
12. Lüscher, M., *Naturwiss.*, **45**, 69 (1958).
13. Wigglesworth, V. B., *J. Embryol. Exp. Morph.*, **1**, 269 (1958).
14. Wigglesworth, V. B., *Symp. Soc. Exp. Biol.*, **11**, 204 (1957).
15. Beermann, W., *Chromosoma*, **5**, 138 (1952).
16. Jacob, J., and Monod, J., *Cold Spring Harbor Symp. Quant. Biol.*, **26**, 193 (1961).
17. Wigglesworth, V. B., *Naturwiss.*, **27**, 301 (1939).
18. Lawrence, P., thesis, Univ. Camb. (1965).
19. Ozeki, K., *Sci. Papers Coll. Gen. Educ. Univ. Tokyo*, **11**, 102 (1961).
20. Piepho, H., *Naturwiss.*, **27**, 301 (1939).
21. Piepho, H., and Meyer, H., *Biol. Zbl.*, **70**, 252 (1951).
22. Gilbert, L. I., and Schneiderman, H. A., *Trans. Amer. Micro. Soc.*, **79**, 38 (1960).
23. Wigglesworth, V. B., *J. Insect Physiol.*, **9**, 105 (1963).
24. Wigglesworth, V. B., *J. Exp. Biol.*, **32**, 485 (1955).
25. Lockshin, R. A., and Williams, C. M., *J. Insect Physiol.*, **10**, 642 (1965).
26. Piepho, H., *Z. Tierpsychol.*, 7, 424 (1950).
27. Piepho, H., Böden, E., and Holz, I., *Z. Tierpsychol.*, **17**, 261 (1960).
28. Williams, C. M., *Nature*, **178**, 212 (1956).
29. Coles, G. C., *Nature*, **203**, 323 (1964).
30. Odhiambo, T. R., thesis, Univ. Cambridge (1965).

方法，我最近重复了上面描述的红猎蝽的实验结果，所用剂量是早期的一半，也就是大约每克体重用 2.5 微克法呢甲醚的活性异构体。）目前法呢醇衍生物是具有保幼激素活性的化合物中唯一已知的化学组分。它们在非昆虫原料的提取物中作为具有保幼激素活性的物质被鉴别出来。在惜古比天蚕蛾和其他蚕蛾的提取物中也发现了它们。在分离出其他已知化合物之前，我倾向于坚持这个临时性的假说，即保幼激素中的活性基团实际上是法呢醇的三异戊二烯单元，并且以某种还没有被定义的形式存在于天然激素中。

（李响 翻译；崔巍 审稿）

31. Pfeiffer, L. W., *J. Exp. Zool.*, **99**, 183 (1945).
32. Odhiambo, T. R., *Nature.*, **207**, 1314 (1965).
33. Thomsen, E., *J. Exp. Biol.*, **26**, 137 (1949).
34. Sägesser, H., *J. Insect Physiol.*, **5**, 204 (1960).
35. Novák, V. J. A., Slama, K., and Wenig, K., *The Ontogeny of Insects*, Symposium in Prague 1959, 147 (1961).
36. Wigglesworth, V. B., *J. Exp. Biol.*, **25**, 1 (1948).
37. Stegwee, D., *J. Insect Physiol.*, **10**, 97 (1964).
38. Gilbert, L. I. (unpublished results).
39. Schmialek, P., *Z. Naturf.*, **16*b***, 461 (1961).
40. Wigglesworth, V. B., *J. Insect Physiol.*, 7, 73 (1961).
41. Schmialek, P., *Z. Naturf.*, **18**b, 516 (1963).
42. Williams, C. M., and Law, J. H., *J. Insect Physiol.*, **11**, 569 (1965).
43. Meyer, A. S., Schneiderman, H. A., and Gilbert, L. I., *Nature.*, **206**, 272 (1965).
44. Röller, H., Bjerke, J. S., and McShan, W. H., *J. Insect Physiol.*, **11**, 1185 (1965).

Propagation and Properties of Hepatitis Virus

Z. F. Ch. Kachani

Editor's Note

Here German researcher Zarah. F. Kachani argues that the hepatitis virus is made of DNA, rather than RNA. She manages to isolate the virus from patients with acute and chronic forms of the illness, normal donors, and from sewage and faeces. It is now known that several different hepatitis viruses can trigger the illness, and that they store their genetic information in different forms. Hepatitis C, for example, uses RNA, whereas hepatitis B uses DNA. It is also recognised that transmission routes vary: hepatitis B can be transferred via blood, while hepatitis A can be transferred via contaminated sewage and faeces.

TESTING a newly developed chemical reaction, we found the virus of hepatitis to consist of pure deoxyribonucleic acid without proteins, contrary to other known forms. This was investigated and confirmed as follows: by treatment with alcohol the virus can be precipitated like the nucleic acids and can be dissolved afterwards without loss of activity. With other virus such treatment led to total inactivation[1,2]. This property of the hepatitis virus enables one to prepare highly concentrated and pure samples, which do not contain proteins from tissues or other virus.

The hepatitis virus itself cannot permeate into the cell, the protein hull of virus being, as is well known, responsible for the affinity to the host cells. However, if the virus is brought into the cell by special treatment, then propagation and formation of plaques occur as with other viruses. The fact that, in such cases, the virus can be propagated in many tissue cultures confirms its character as a pure nucleic acid[3].

Enzymes that cleave nucleic acids degrade the virus, but trypsin, papain, Na-deoxycholate and ether are without any effect.

In vitro, the virus can be fixed by actinomycin like other deoxyribonucleic acids.

The following factors also indicate that the nucleic acid of the hepatitis virus is deoxyribonucleic acid (DNA): (1) Total inactivation by DNase, but not RNase; (2) 5-iodo-2′-deoxyuridine yielding an inhibition of propagation *in vivo*, while substances influencing the metabolism of RNA, such as 8-azaguanine, 2-thiouracil and 5-fluorouracil, have no influence; (3) actinomycin inactivates the virus *in vivo* as well as *in vitro*; it is known that actinomycin blocks DNA, but not RNA, *in vitro*; (4) estimation by the method of Schmidt and Thannhauser[5] confirms the DNA character of the virus.

肝炎病毒的繁殖及其特性

卡切尼

编者按

在这篇文章中，德国研究人员扎拉·卡切尼认为肝炎病毒是由DNA而不是由RNA组成的。她分别从患有急性疾病和慢性疾病的患者体内、正常人体内以及污水和粪便中分离出该病毒。人们现在已经知道几种不同的肝炎病毒都能够引发疾病，并且它们以不同的形式存储自身的遗传信息。例如，C型肝炎病毒使用RNA而B型肝炎病毒使用DNA。现在人们也已经认识到它们的传播途径不同：B型肝炎通过血液传播，而A型肝炎通过受污染的污水及粪便传播。

在验证一个新发现的化学反应时，我们发现肝炎病毒仅由脱氧核糖核酸组成而不包含蛋白质，这和其他已知肝炎病毒的组成形式不同。通过如下实验对这种肝炎病毒进行了检验和证实：经过乙醇处理后的肝炎病毒可以像核酸一样发生沉淀，将沉淀重新溶解后病毒的活性依然存在。而其他病毒在经过这样的处理后会完全丧失活性[1,2]。利用肝炎病毒的这种特性，可以制备出高浓度的不含任何组织蛋白质或其他病毒蛋白质的纯肝炎病毒。

众所周知，病毒一般通过衣壳蛋白黏附到宿主细胞上，因此，肝炎病毒本身不能侵入细胞。然而，如果经过特殊的处理将肝炎病毒引入到细胞中，它会像其他病毒一样繁殖并形成噬菌斑。在这种情况下，肝炎病毒能够在多种组织培养物中繁殖这一事实证实了其仅由核酸构成[3]。

核酸剪切酶能够降解肝炎病毒，但是胰蛋白酶、木瓜蛋白酶、脱氧胆酸钠和乙醚对它则没有任何影响。

在体外实验中，肝炎病毒同其他脱氧核糖核酸一样能被放线菌素固定。

以下几个方面也表明肝炎病毒中的核酸是脱氧核糖核酸（DNA）：(1) 肝炎病毒能被DNA酶完全灭活，却不被RNA酶灭活；(2) 在体内实验中，5–碘–2′–脱氧尿苷能抑制肝炎病毒的繁殖，然而影响RNA代谢的物质，如8–氮鸟嘌呤、2–硫尿嘧啶和5–氟尿嘧啶对其繁殖则没有影响；(3) 在体内实验和体外实验中，放线菌素都能使肝炎病毒失活，而一般认为放线菌素在体外实验中抑制了DNA而不是RNA；(4) 采用施密特和汤恩豪瑟[5]的方法进行的推测证实了肝炎病毒是DNA型病毒。

The hepatitis virus can be propagated on the chicken embryo by the following technique: (1) Treating the chorio-allantoic membrane with hyaluronidase just before inoculation; this loosens the tissue and thereafter the virus can passively permeate into the tissue; (2) the cytotoxic effect, especially from sera, can be removed by dilution, otherwise it prohibits multiplication of the virus; (3) the effect of DNA in cleaving enzymes such as DNase I and DNase of tissue origin will be greatly reduced by adding 0.01 moles Na-citrate and shifting the *p*H up to 8.5.

In tissue cultures the cells were washed before inoculation with 1 M NaCl, *p*H 8.2. The inoculation fluid contained hyaluronidase. Further propagation for many passages in tissue cultures is possible only if the *p*H of the medium does not go below 7, since *p*H 6.5 strongly decreases the active virus particles. The optimum *p*H for preservation of the hepatitis virus is between 8.5 and 9.5.

Plaque formation on the chorio-allantoic membrane appeared on the third day, and in liver and spleen on the fourth day after inoculation, the foci being similar to those of other virus, both morphologically and histologically[6]. In tissue cultures the beginning of the cytopathogenic effect was seen on days 3-4 after inoculation.

Electron microscopy shows the virus to have a polyhedral shape (Fig. 1). Negative staining with 1 percent uranyl acetate makes it possible to measure the diameter, which is between 40 and 150 mμ. To determine whether the smaller particles are parts of larger ones, or are the virus itself, we separated the particles by ultracentrifugation. These were then tested for infectivity and diameters measured. The results showed that the smallest particles represent the virus itself.

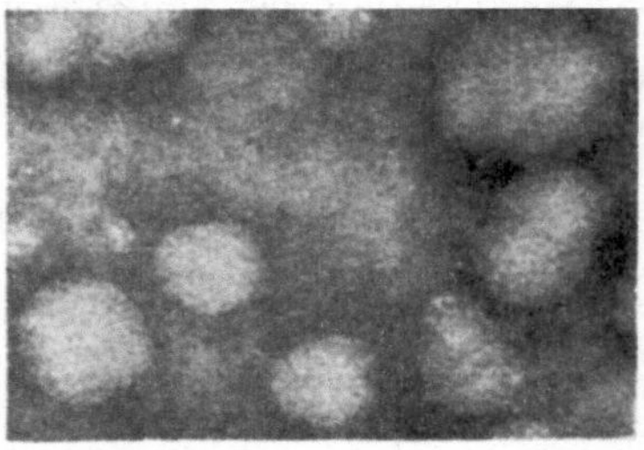

Fig. 1. Human hepatitis virus stained with uranyl acctate (× 100,000)

The virus was propagated from 144 cases of acute and chronic hepatitis epidemica, from serum hepatitis and from a series of normal blood donors. The virus was found in sewage as well as in blood and in faeces. All 144 virus stems tested were identical in electron micrographs and by immunological tests.

For preparation of immune serum from rabbits, the injection of the pure virus suspension with Freund's adjuvant is recommended together with simultaneous application of anabolic steroids. With immune sera prepared in this way 144 stems were tested by

通过如下方法可以在鸡胚中成功繁殖肝炎病毒：(1) 接种前用透明质酸酶处理绒毛尿囊膜，这样可以使组织松弛，之后病毒被动进入组织中；(2) 通过稀释能够消除细胞毒素特别是来自血清的毒素的影响，否则病毒的繁殖会受到抑制；(3) 通过加入 0.01 摩尔的柠檬酸钠并将 pH 值调至 8.5，可以明显减少组织中的 DNA 酶 I 和 DNA 酶等剪切酶对 DNA 的降解作用。

接种前，用 pH 值为 8.2 的 1 摩尔 / 升 NaCl 溶液洗涤组织培养物中的细胞，接种液中要加入透明质酸酶。由于当 pH 值为 6.5 时病毒颗粒的活性会显著降低，因此只有当培养基的 pH 值不低于 7 时，在组织培养物中病毒才可能发生更多代繁殖。保存肝炎病毒的最适 pH 值介于 8.5~9.5 间。

接种后第 3 天，绒毛尿囊膜上形成噬菌斑，接种后第 4 天，在肝脏和脾脏上形成噬菌斑。从形态学和组织学来看[6]，这些斑点与其他病毒的噬菌斑十分相似。接种 3~4 天后，组织培养物中就开始出现细胞病变了。

电子显微镜下观察发现肝炎病毒呈多面体形（图 1）。采用 1% 的醋酸铀负染法可以测算肝炎病毒的直径，其直径大小约在 40 纳米至 150 纳米之间。为了鉴别较小颗粒是较大的肝炎病毒的碎片还是肝炎病毒本身，我们用超速离心法分离不同尺寸的颗粒，然后检测了颗粒的感染性并测算了其直径，结果表明最小的颗粒就是病毒本身。

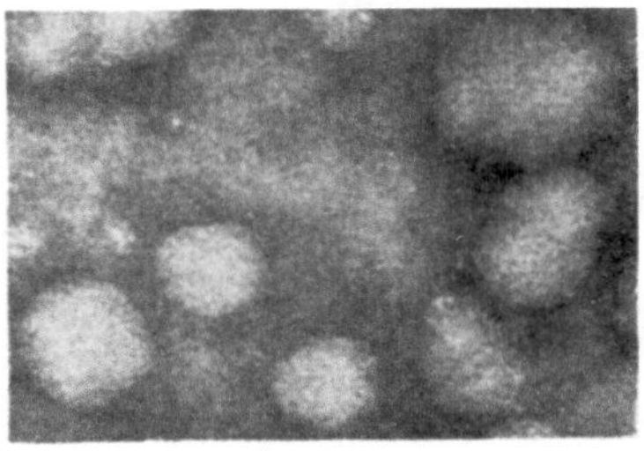

图 1. 醋酸铀染色的人肝炎病毒（放大 100,000 倍）

实验所用的病毒是由 144 个急性和慢性流行性肝炎病毒繁殖而来的，它们来自含肝炎病毒的血清以及一些正常的供血者。在污水、血液和粪便中也发现了肝炎病毒。电子显微镜观察和免疫学检测表明这 144 个肝炎病毒株属于同一家系。

在制备兔源免疫血清时，建议在注射含弗氏佐剂的纯病毒悬液的同时注射合成类固醇。用这种方法制备的免疫血清被用来进行豚鼠红细胞血凝反应和病毒中和反

neutralization and haemagglutination with erythrocytes of guinea-pig, and a complement fixation test. As has been stated, they all gave the same reaction.

Neutralizing and haemagglutination-inhibiting antibodies were found in patients after complete healing, while complement-fixing antibody was present as well as the virus only in chronically active cases. An efficient disinfectant is "Havisol" (Schulke and Mayr G.m.b.H., Hamburg), based on phenol. The 6 percent solution inactivates massive, protein-poor virus suspensions in 2 min. With more proteins present the virus was inactivated by "Havisol" and "Parmetol" in 2 percent solution after 15 min.

As expected, the virus was much more resistant to heat than other viruses, and heating to 75°C for 1 h had no effect at all. Heating above 170°C was necessary to inactivate pure virus suspension with 10 P. F. U., within 1 h. The same suspension was inactivated in the autoclave after 30 min at 2 atmospheres at 134°C. With protein and cations, present heating for 1 h at 195°C, or at two atmospheres, was required to kill the virus. The addition of 2 percent sodium carbonate led to the total loss of activity within 20 min at 100°C.

The hepatitis virus was more resistant to ultra-violet radiation. Irradiation of 0.5 ml. solutions in Petri dishes at a distance of 10 cm, using a mercury vapour lamp giving 2,540 Å emission, produced an area of inactivation of 8.5 cm diameter after 6 min.

Since it was not possible to inoculate man with the virus, we performed the classical experiment of Neefe *et al.*[7] on human volunteers, as with the propagated virus in chicken embryo. The results were exactly as described by these authors.

(**208**, 605-606; 1965)

Z. F. Ch. Kachani: Department of Colloid Chemistry, University of Kiel.

References:

1. Chargaff, E., and Davidson, J. N., in *The Nucleic Acids*, **1**, 382 (Academic Press, New York, 1955).
2. Maassah, H. F., *J. Immunol.*, **90**, 265 (1963).
3. Herriot, R. M., *Science*, **134**, 256 (1961).
4. Tatum, E. L., *Proc. U.S. Nat. Acad. Sci.*, **48**, 1238 (1962).
5. Schmidt, G., and Thannhauser, S. J., *J. Biol. Chem.*, **161**, 83 (1945).
6. Kachani, Z. F. Ch., *Arch. Hyg. Bakt.*, 147, 546 (1963).
7. Neefe, J. R., Stokes, J., Baty, J. B., and Reinhold, J. G., *J. Amer. Med. Assoc.*, **128**, 1076 (1945).

应，及补体结合实验以检测这 144 个病毒株。结果如前所述，它们的反应一致。

在完全康复的患者中发现了中和抗体和血凝抑制抗体，而补体结合抗体只和病毒共存于慢性肝炎患者体内。以苯酚为主要成分的“Havisol”（许尔克和马尔有限公司，汉堡）能有效地灭活病毒。用 6% 的“Havisol”溶液处理病毒悬液，2 分钟内大部分不含蛋白质的病毒都会失活。如果病毒中蛋白质含量较高，可以用 2% 的“Havisol”和“Parmetol”溶液作用 15 分钟使病毒失活。

同预期的一样，肝炎病毒比其他病毒更耐热，75℃加热 1 小时对它根本没有影响。要灭活 10 个蚀斑形成单位的纯病毒悬液，需要在高于 170℃的条件下加热 1 小时。该病毒悬液在 2 个大气压下 134℃加热 30 分钟后也能被灭活。如果病毒中含有蛋白质和阳离子，则要在 195℃加热 1 小时或者在 2 个大气压下加热才能灭活病毒。如果在病毒悬液中加入 2% 的碳酸钠，那么在 100℃的条件下，加热不到 20 分钟就可以使病毒完全失活了。

肝炎病毒抗紫外线辐射的能力也很强。用汞蒸气灯发射 2,540 埃的紫外线，照射距其 10 厘米的含有 0.5 毫升病毒溶液的培养皿，6 分钟后产生了一个直径为 8.5 厘米的失活区。

由于不能在人身上接种肝炎病毒，我们对志愿者采用了尼夫等 [7] 提出的经典实验方法，如同对鸡胚接种繁殖的肝炎病毒一样。我们得到的实验结果同这些作者在他们的论文中给出的结果完全一致。

（彭丽霞 翻译；金侠 审稿）

Three Haemoglobins K: Woolwich, an Abnormal, Cameroon and Ibadan, Two Unusual Variants of Human Haemoglobin A

N. Allan *et al.*

Editor's Note

Here, biologist Hermann Lehmann from Cambridge University and colleagues, continue their catalogue of haemoglobin variants, describing and characterising three types of haemoglobin K. Two, denoted Cameroon and Ibadan, are unusual variants of the more common haemoglobin A. The third, an abnormal haemoglobin denoted Woolwich, is of particular interest because it contains an amino-acid substitution at a position that had been thought immutable to change. The lysine group normally present in this position was thought to stabilize the molecule, and the team conclude that its replacement in haemoglobin K Woolwich may interfere with the molecule's "status quo".

HAEMOGLOBIN K was first described by Cabannes and Buhr[1] and is a "fast" variant of normal adult haemoglobin (haemoglobin A). It moves further towards the anode on electrophoresis at alkaline *p*H than haemoglobin A, but only just separates from it.

A haemoglobin K with its abnormality in the β-chain has been reported to occur in combination with haemoglobin S (ref. 2). The proportion of S : K was 3 : 2, and there was a mild haemoglobinopathy. The family in which this haemoglobin K was observed came from the West Indies and was of African ancestry. This haemoglobin K was first noted at Woolwich, England, and it will be denoted as K β Woolwich.

We have now found a second instance of the combination of a haemoglobin K with haemoglobin S. By hybridization with canine haemoglobin[3] this haemoglobin K could be shown to be a β-chain variant. Unlike haemoglobin K Woolwich, the proportion of this haemoglobin K to haemoglobin S was 3 : 1, similar to that of haemoglobin A in the sickle-cell trait (A + S). There was no haemoglobinopathy. Indeed, the carrier of this K + S combination was found in the course of routine screening of healthy blood donors at University College Hospital, Ibadan, Nigeria. The blood donor, a woman, came from Cameroon, and neither she herself nor her relatives could be examined further. This new haemoglobin K will be denoted as haemoglobin K β Cameroon (Figs. 1 and 2).

三种血红蛋白K：一种异常的伍力奇血红蛋白、两种人血红蛋白A的稀有变体——喀麦隆和伊巴丹血红蛋白

艾伦等

编者按

在本文中，来自剑桥大学的生物学家赫尔曼·莱曼及其同事们继续他们关于血红蛋白变体目录的研究，他们描述并定义了三种血红蛋白 K。其中两种蛋白是常见的血红蛋白 A 的稀有变体，分别被命名为喀麦隆和伊巴丹。第三种是异常血红蛋白，被命名为伍力奇，它的分子中有一个原本被认为不可变更的氨基酸被取代，因此非常有趣。通常在这一位置上的赖氨酸残基被认为能够使蛋白分子稳定。研究组认为，血红蛋白 K 伍力奇中这一氨基酸的取代可能会影响蛋白分子的“现状”。

卡巴纳和布尔[1]首先对血红蛋白 K 进行了描述，它是正常成人血红蛋白（血红蛋白 A）的一种“快速”变体。在碱性 pH 条件下，血红蛋白 K 在电泳中向正极移动的距离稍远于血红蛋白 A，两者恰好能够区分开。

早先已经报道过 β 链异常的血红蛋白 K 与血红蛋白 S 组合存在的情况（参考文献 2）。S 与 K 的比例是 3∶2，伴有轻度血红蛋白病。携带此血红蛋白 K 的家庭来自西印度群岛，其祖先来自非洲。这种血红蛋白 K 首先在英国的伍力奇被发现，因此以 Kβ 伍力奇来表示。

现在我们发现了血红蛋白 K 与血红蛋白 S 组合存在的另一个实例。与犬血红蛋白的杂交表明，该血红蛋白 K 的 β 链发生了变异[3]。与血红蛋白 K 伍力奇不同，这种血红蛋白 K 与血红蛋白 S 的比例是 3∶1，这类似于镰刀形红细胞性状（A+S）中的血红蛋白 A 与 S 的比例，但不伴有血红蛋白病。实际上，尼日利亚伊巴丹大学学院附属医院在常规筛选健康供血者的过程中发现了这种血红蛋白 K+S 组合的携带者。供血者是一位来自喀麦隆的妇女，但是未能对她及其亲戚作进一步的检查。这种新的血红蛋白 K 以血红蛋白 K β 喀麦隆来表示（图 1 和图 2）。

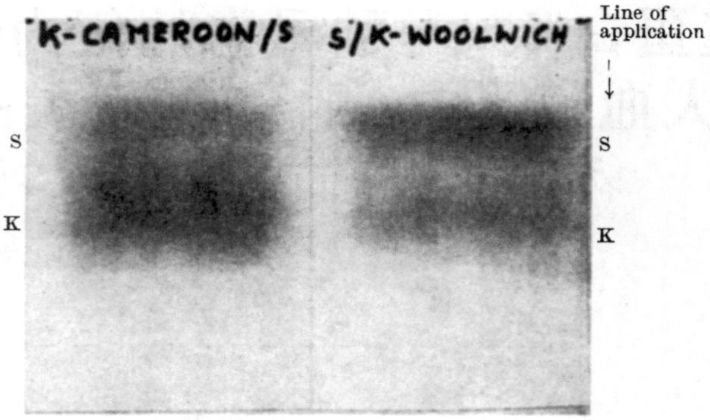

Fig. 1. Paper electrophoresis at *p*H 8.6 of haemoglobins K Cameroon + S (left) and S + K Woolwich (right). The proportion of K Cameroon to S is that found for A in sickle-cell trait (see Fig. 2)

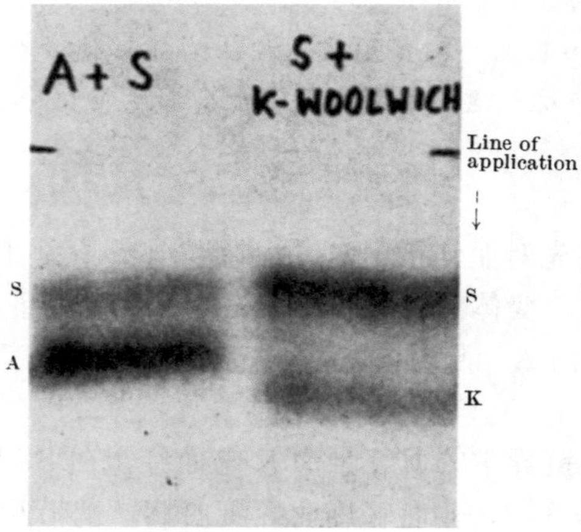

Fig. 2. Paper electrophoresis at *p*H 8.9 of haemoglobins from sickle-cell trait (A + S) and of haemoglobins S + K Woolwich. The combination of haemoglobin S and K Woolwich shows a greater proportion of S and results in a mild haemoglobinopathy

A third sample of haemoglobin K, this time in combination with haemoglobin A, was found in a Yoruba adolescent in Ibadan, in the course of an anthropological survey. Hybridization with canine haemoglobin showed the variant to have its amino-acid substitution in the β-chain. The proportion of A : K was 1 : 1, and there was no anaemia. The body was repeatedly examined; but in the members of the family available for examination no further instances of haemoglobin K were found. This haemoglobin K will be denoted as haemoglobin K β Ibadan.

It has previously been discussed that some haemoglobin variants may be recognized as "abnormal"when in combination with haemoglobin A they are found to form less than half the total haemoglobin[4]. Others may be considered as merely unusual, and they can

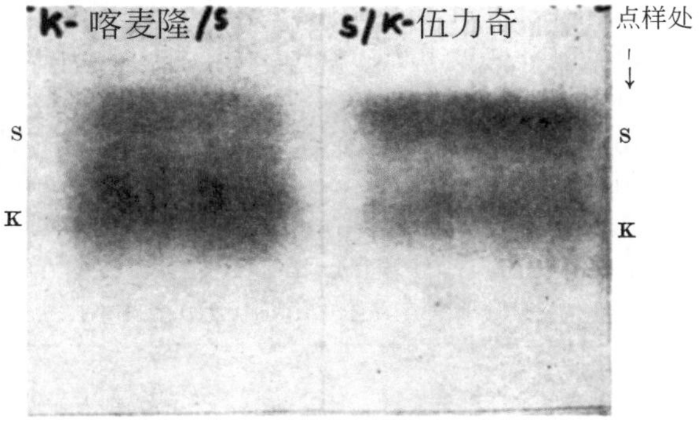

图 1. pH 8.6 条件下的血红蛋白 K 喀麦隆 + S(左) 和 S+K 伍力奇 (右) 的纸电泳。K 喀麦隆与 S 的比例与镰刀形红细胞性状血红蛋白 A 与 S 的比例一致（均为 3 : 1)。(见图 2)

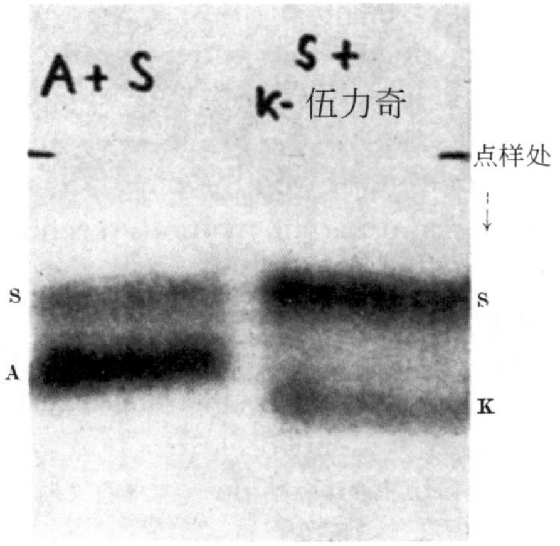

图 2. 来自镰刀形红细胞性状（A+S）的血红蛋白和来自血红蛋白 S+K 伍力奇的血红蛋白在 pH 8.9 条件下的纸电泳。血红蛋白 S 和血红蛋白 K 伍力奇的组合显示 S 所占比例较大，结果伴有轻度血红蛋白病。

第 3 例血红蛋白 K 是在伊巴丹进行人类学普查过程中在一个约鲁巴青年的血液中发现的，其血红蛋白 K 与血红蛋白 A 相结合。与犬血红蛋白的杂交表明，该变体的 β 链中发生了氨基酸替换。A 与 K 的比例是 1 : 1，不伴有贫血症。反复检查了该患者，但在经检查的家庭成员中再没有发现血红蛋白 K 的例子。这种血红蛋白 K 被定名为血红蛋白 K β 伊巴丹。

以前曾经讨论过，当一些血红蛋白变体与血红蛋白 A 组合时，若血红蛋白变体占血红蛋白总量的一半以下时，即可被当作“异常”变体 [4]；但若它们与血红蛋白

be recognized by being found in equal proportion to haemoglobin A. The combination A + S (A > S) is an example of the first, abnormal type, and that for A + G Accra (A = G) represents the second unusual type. On two occasions a combination of unusual haemoglobins with haemoglobin S was observed. Haemoglobin S was present as the lesser fraction, as it is found in sickle-cell trait carriers with haemoglobin A (A > S). Haemoglobin J Baltimore[5] and haemoglobin D Ibadan[6] were the two unusual haemoglobins which in combination with S formed the greater part of the total pigment. In both instances the carriers of the haemoglobin mixtures had no sickle-cell disease but were sickle-cell trait carriers.

Of our three haemoglobins K, the Woolwich variant can be described as abnormal, and the combination haemoglobin K Woolwich and haemoglobin S (K < S) causes a mild haemoglobinopathy. Haemoglobin K Cameroon together with haemoglobin S results in the sickle-cell trait (K > S), and haemoglobins K Ibadan and A are found in equal proportions (K = A). The two latter haemoglobins K are therefore unusual rather than abnormal. It was of interest to investigate these three haemoglobins which are similar in their electrophoretic properties, and if possible to see which amino-acid substitution in the β-chain changed the physiological value of the resulting variant, and which did not. The haemoglobins were isolated, peptide maps were prepared, and when possible the variant peptides were separated and analysed using the methods recently listed in detail[6].

Haemoglobin K Woolwich. The peptide map of haemoglobin K Woolwich is shown in Fig. 3. It will be noted that the tyrosine peptide representing β^ATpXIII and the histidine peptide β^ATpXIV are missing, as well as a small spot near to β^ATpVI that is usually present in peptide maps of haemoglobin A. An extended electrophoretogram (Fig. 5) showed these differences more clearly. βTpXIII represents residues 121-132 of the β-chain and βTpXIV residues 133-144.

Peptide β^ATpXIII

121 122 123 124 125 126 127 128 129 130 131 132
Glu-Phe-Thr-Pro-Pro-Val-Gln-Ala-Ala-Tyr-Gln-Lys
↑
chymotryptic splitting

Peptide β^ATpXIV

133 134 135 136 137 138 139 140 141 142 143 144
Val-Val-Ala-Gly-Val-Ala-Asn-Ala-Leu-Ala-His-Lys

A 含量相等，则只被认为是稀有变体。A+S（A>S）组合是第一种异常类型的例子。而 A+G 阿克拉（A=G）代表第二种稀有类型。还观察到以下两种情况是稀有血红蛋白与血红蛋白 S 的组合。血红蛋白 S 所占比例较少，就像在镰刀形红细胞性状携带者的血红蛋白 A（A>S）组合中所发现的情况那样。血红蛋白 J 巴尔的摩 [5] 和血红蛋白 D 伊巴丹 [6] 是两种稀有血红蛋白，它们与血红蛋白 S 结合时构成总色素的大部分。在这两个例子中，含有组合血红蛋白的携带者没有镰刀形红细胞疾病，但他们是镰刀形红细胞性状的携带者。

在我们的 3 种血红蛋白 K 中，伍力奇变体可被描述为异常蛋白，血红蛋白 K 伍力奇和血红蛋白 S（K<S）的组合引起轻度血红蛋白病。血红蛋白 K 喀麦隆与血红蛋白 S 在一起就产生镰刀形红细胞性状（K>S），并发现血红蛋白 K 伊巴丹和血红蛋白 A 等量存在（K=A）。因此后两种血红蛋白 K 是稀有血红蛋白，而不是异常的血红蛋白。研究这 3 种血红蛋白是有趣的，因为它们的电泳性质相似。如果有可能，还应观察在 β 链中，哪个氨基酸的取代改变了所得变体的生理学功能，哪个取代不引起改变。于是我们分离了血红蛋白，进行了肽谱分析，并在可能的情况下对变异的肽链进行了分离和分析，采用的是最近详细阐述过的方法 [6]。

血红蛋白 K 伍力奇　图 3 显示了血红蛋白 K 伍力奇的肽谱，可以看到，代表 β^ATpXIII 的酪氨酸肽和组氨酸肽 β^ATpXIV 缺失，在血红蛋白 A 肽谱中通常存在的靠近 β^ATpVI 的小点也消失。延长的电泳图（图 5）更加清楚地显示了这些差别。βTpXIII 代表了 β 链第 121~132 位残基，βTpXIV 代表了第 133~144 位残基。

β^ATpXIII 肽

121 122 123 124 125 126 127 128 129 130 131 132

Glu-Phe-Thr-Pro-Pro-Val-Gln-Ala-Ala-Tyr-Gln-Lys

↑

胰凝乳蛋白酶裂解处

β^ATpXIV 肽

133 134 135 136 137 138 139 140 141 142 143 144

Val-Val-Ala-Gly-Val-Ala-Asn-Ala-Leu-Ala-His-Lys

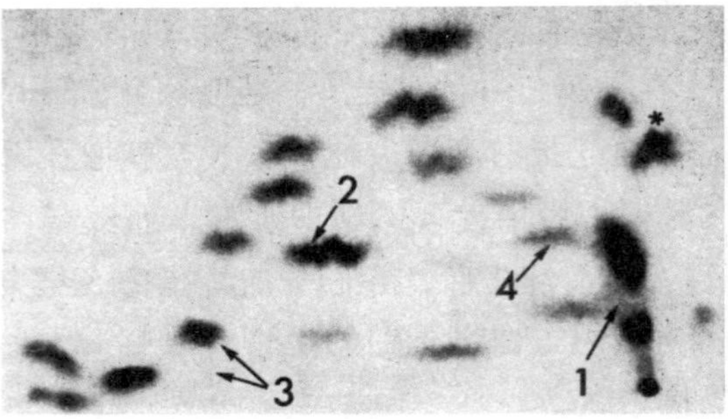

Fig. 3. Peptide map of haemoglobin K Woolwich. Note that at 1 β^ATpXIII (positive for tyrosine), and at 2 β^ATpXIV (positive for histidine) are missing. The incidental chymotryptic peptide β131-132 derived from β^ATpXIII is also missing at 3 (lower arrow) just below β^ATpVI 3 (top arrow). A new peptide which was found to represent β^ATpXIII-XIV can be seen at 4. The starred peptide is β^ATpV in its usual position—compare with Fig. 6

A mutation affecting the mobility of both these tryptic peptides is likely to involve the lysine residue at position 132 because a change in the nature of this residue, apart from Lys→Arg, would result in a peptide bond at β132 which could not be broken by tryptic hydrolysis. In this case βTpXIII and βTpXIV would form one new peptide containing both tyrosine and histidine. Such a new peptide can be seen in Fig. 3, and it will be noted that it has moved somewhat towards the cathode, thus indicating a slight positive charge. This would eliminate the possibility of a Lys→Glu mutation which would have given rise to a negatively charged peptide. This mutation was already unlikely on the basis of the electrophoretie mobility of haemoglobin K Woolwich. The mutation Lys→Glu results in the acquisition of two negative charges per half molecule of haemoglobin and this would produce a variant with an electrophoretic mobility resembling that of haemoglobin I or haemoglobin N rather than that of haemoglobin K. The mutation Lys→Arg has already been excluded. It would not give rise to a charge change and would not resist the tryptic separation of the βXIII and βXIV peptides. The remaining single mutations permitted by the genetic code[7] are Lys→Gln, Lys→Asn, Lys→Thr and Lys→Met. The amino-acid analysis of the new peptide is given in Table 1. It will be seen that all the residues of βTpXIII and βTpXIV are present except for one lysine residue, and that one additional residue of glutamic acid was found. Glutamine is hydrolysed to glutamic acid when peptides are hydrolysed into their amino-acid constituents and the additional glutamic acid had to come from a glutamine, as the observed electrophoretic mobility of the new peptide demands. The lysine residue in position β132 of the β-chain had thus been substituted by one of glutamine. Haemoglobin K Woolwich may be described as $\alpha_2\beta_2^{132Lys\rightarrow Gln}$. This represents the first observation of a Lys→Gln mutation in human haemoglobin. The mutation also explains the absence of the small spot usually found near βTpVI. This spot represents a dipeptide β131-132 (Gln-Lys) resulting from an incidental chymotryptic splitting of the β130 tyrosyl peptide bond during tryptic hydrolysis. No such dipeptide could, of course, arise when β132 is Gln instead of Lys because the residues β131-132 would remain attached to βTpXIV.

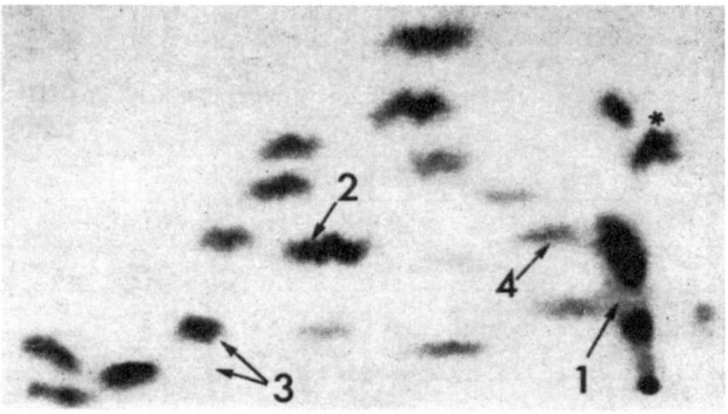

图 3. 血红蛋白K伍力奇的肽谱。注意1处的β^{A}TpXIII（存在酪氨酸）和2处的β^{A}TpXIV（存在组氨酸）缺失；来自β^{A}TpXIII的附带的胰凝乳蛋白酶裂解肽β131-132在3处（下箭头）也消失，其位置恰好在β^{A}TpVI 3(上箭头)的下面。在4处可看到代表β^{A}TpXIII-XIV的一个新肽。带星号的肽是β^{A}TpV，处于其正常位置，可与图6相比较。

影响这两个胰蛋白酶裂解肽迁移率的突变可能与第132位的赖氨酸残基有关，因为除去Lys（赖氨酸）转变为Arg（精氨酸）的情况外，该残基性质的变化都可能导致β132位形成的肽键不能被胰蛋白酶水解断裂。在这种情况下，βTpXIII和 βTpXIV可能形成含有酪氨酸和组氨酸的一个新肽。在图3中可以看到这个新肽，还可以注意到它有些向负极偏移，因而显示有轻微的正电荷变化。这就排除了产生Lys → Glu（谷氨酸）突变的可能性，因为这种突变会产生一个带负电荷的肽。基于血红蛋白K伍力奇的电泳迁移率，这种突变本来就不可能发生。Lys → Glu突变的结果使每半个血红蛋白分子得到2个负电荷，这会产生一个变体，其电泳迁移率类似于血红蛋白I或血红蛋白N，而非血红蛋白K。已经排除了Lys → Arg的突变，因为它不会产生电荷的变化，也不会抑制胰蛋白酶对βXIII和βXIV的裂解作用。遗传密码[7]容许的其他点突变还有Lys → Gln（谷氨酰胺）、Lys → Asn（天冬酰胺）、Lys → Thr（苏氨酸）和Lys → Met（甲硫氨酸）。表1列出了新肽的氨基酸分析的结果，可以看出βTpXIII和βTpXIV中所有氨基酸残基都存在，只有一个赖氨酸除外，而且还发现了一个额外的谷氨酸残基。当肽被水解成其氨基酸组分时，谷氨酰胺被水解成谷氨酸。根据所观察到的新肽的电泳迁移率，额外的谷氨酸一定来自谷氨酰胺。因此，在β链β132位的赖氨酸残基必然被一个谷氨酰胺所取代。血红蛋白K伍力奇可以表示成$\alpha_2\beta_2^{132\mathrm{Lys}\rightarrow\mathrm{Gln}}$。这是在人血红蛋白中首次观察到Lys → Gln突变。这种突变也可以解释通常在βTpVI附近存在的小点的缺失。这个点代表了一个二肽β131-132（Gln-Lys），它是在胰蛋白酶水解作用期间β130酪氨酰肽键被胰凝乳蛋白酶附带裂解产生的。当β132是Gln而不是Lys时，由于β131-132残基可能仍然保持连接于βTpXIV，那么就不会产生这种二肽。

Table 1. Haemoglobin K Woolwich

Amino-acid analysis (molar ratio) of the variant peptide β^KTp (XIII-XIV)

	Known values for haemoglobin A			haemoglobin K βTp(XIII-XIV)
	βTpXIII	βTpXIV	βTpXIII +βTpXIV	
Asp		1	1	0.9
Thr	1		1	1.2
Ser				0.3
Glu	3		3	3.8
Pro	2		2	2.1
Gly		1	1	1.1
Ala	2	4	6	5.8
Val	1	3	4	3.5
Leu		1	1	1.0
Tyr	1		1	0.7
Phe	1		1	0.8
Lys	1	1	2	1.0
His		1		0.9

Low recovery of valine is probably due to slight resistance of Val-Val bond to acid hydrolysis.

Haemoglobin K Cameroon. Unfortunately there was insufficient material available to make a complete structural investigation, and in spite of all efforts the donor could not be contacted again. The peptide map of this haemoglobin is shown in Fig. 4. It will be seen that the small spot usually found near βTpVI is missing and it is known that this spot represents the dipeptide β131-132 (Gln-Lys) arising from an incidental chymotryptic splitting of βTpXIII during tryptic digestion. A very small shift of βTpXIII towards the anode is also noticeable. This alteration in the electrophoretic mobility of βTpXIII was confirmed by an extended electrophoretogram (Fig. 5). The increase in negative charge of βTpXIII is compatible with a haemoglobin K which differs from haemoglobin A by an additional negative charge per half-molecule. This, in βTpXIII, could only be the substitution of a neutral amino-acid residue by Glu or Asp. The absence of the incidental chymotryptic peptide from βTpXIII suggests that there was an inhibition of the chymotryptic splitting of the β130 tyrosyl bond. Such an inhibition could be caused by a substitution of the neutral β129 Ala residue by an acidic residue. Thus it seems likely that in haemoglobin K Cameroon a Glu or an Asp has replaced the Ala at β130. Clearly these observations need substantiating when the opportunity arises.

表 1. 血红蛋白 K 伍力奇

变体肽 β^{K}Tp(XIII-XIV) 的氨基酸分析 (摩尔比)

	已知值的血红蛋白 A			血红蛋白 K βTp(XIII-XIV)
	βTpXIII	βTpXIV	βTpXIII +βTpXIV	
Asp		1	1	0.9
Thr	1		1	1.2
Ser				0.3
Glu	3		3	3.8
Pro	2		2	2.1
Gly		1	1	1.1
Ala	2	4	6	5.8
Val	1	3	4	3.5
Leu		1	1	1.0
Tyr	1		1	0.7
Phe	1		1	0.8
Lys	1	1	2	1.0
His		1		0.9

缬氨酸的回收率低可能是由于 Val（缬氨酸）–Val 肽键对酸水解有一定抗性。

血红蛋白 K 喀麦隆　遗憾的是没有足够的样品来进行完整的结构研究，尽管进行了不懈努力，但是仍然不能再联系到供血人。这种血红蛋白的肽谱见图 4。可以看到通常靠近 βTpVI 的小点缺失了。已知这个小点代表二肽 β131-132（Gln-Lys），它是胰蛋白酶消化时，胰凝乳蛋白酶附带裂解 βTpXIII 产生的。还可以注意到 βTpXIII 向正极有很小的偏移。延长的电泳图确认了 βTpXIII 电泳迁移率的这一变化（图 5）。βTpXIII 负电荷的增加与血红蛋白 K 一致，因为血红蛋白 K 与血红蛋白 A 的不同之处在于血红蛋白 K 每半个分子增加了一个负电荷。在 βTpXIII 中，这只可能是一个中性氨基酸残基被 Glu 或 Asp（天冬氨酸）所取代。来自 βTpXIII 的附带的胰凝乳蛋白酶裂解肽缺失，提示 β130 酪氨酰肽键被附带胰凝乳蛋白酶裂解的作用受到抑制。这种抑制作用的产生，可能是因为 β129 的中性残基 Ala（丙氨酸）被一个酸性氨基酸残基所取代。因此，很有可能是血红蛋白 K 喀麦隆的 β130 位上的 Ala 被 Glu 或 Asp 所取代。显然，如果有机会的话，这些观察结果还需要进一步确证。

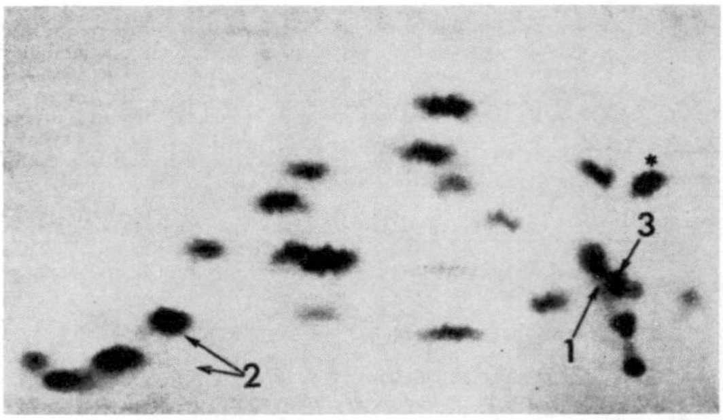

Fig. 4. Peptide map of haemoglobin K Cameroon. Note that at 1 β^{A}TpXIII (positive for tyrosine) is missing. The chymotryptic dipeptide β131-132 derived from β^{A}TpXIII is also missing at 2 (lower arrow), just below β^{A}TpVI 2 (top arrow). 3 indicates the new peptide β^{K}TpXIII. The starred peptide is β^{A}TpV in its usual position—compare with Fig. 6

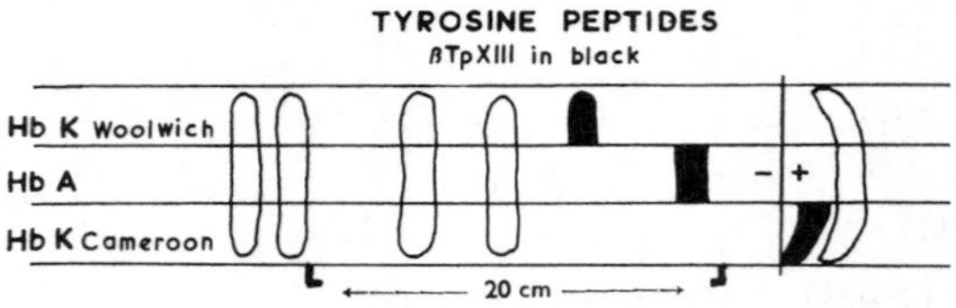

Fig. 5. Paper electrophoresis (90 min at *p*H 6.4) of tyrosine containing peptides from haemoglobin A compared with those from haemoglobins K Woolwich and K Cameroon. βTpXIII from haemoglobin K Woolwich is combined with βTpXIV and remains positively charged. βTpXIII from haemoglobin K Cameroon is negatively charged.

Haemoglobin K Ibadan. The peptide map of haemoglobin K Ibadan is shown in Fig. 6. It will be seen that the methionine peptide β^{A}TpV is missing, and a new methionine peptide has appeared moving further towards the anode with an electrophoretic mobility similar to that of βTpIII. This alteration in electrophoretic mobility of βTpV could be confirmed in an extended electrophoretogram (Fig. 7). βTpV represents residues 41-59 of the β-chain.

β^{A}TpV

41 42 43 44 45 46 47 48 49 50 51 52 53 54 55 56 57 58 59
Phe-Phe-Glu-Ser-Phe-Gly-Asp-Leu-Ser-Thr-Pro-Asp-Ala-Val-Met-Gly-Asn-Pro-Lys
↑
Splitting with cyanogen bromide

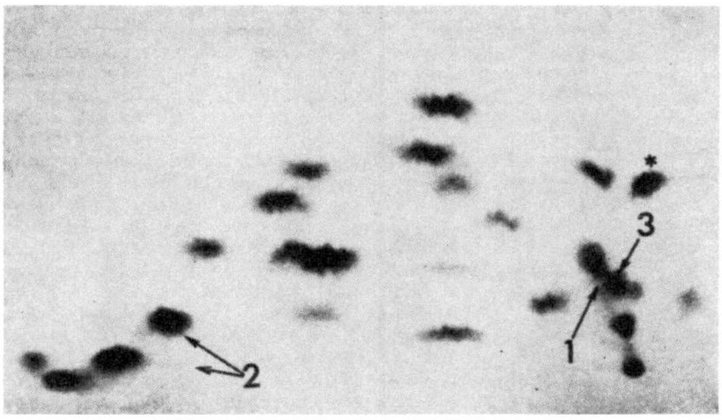

图 4. 血红蛋白 K 喀麦隆的肽谱。注意在 1 处的 β^{A}TpXIII(存在酪氨酸)缺失。在 2 处（下箭头）来自 β^{A}TpXIII 的胰凝乳蛋白酶二肽 β131-132 也缺失。它正好位于 β^{A}TpVI 2 处（上箭头）的下方。3 表示新肽 β^{K}TpXIII。加星号的肽是 β^{A}TpV，处于它的正常位置，可与图 6 相比较。

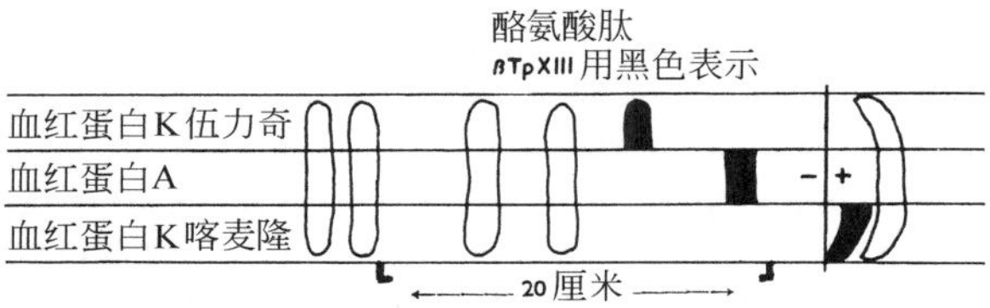

图 5. 来自血红蛋白 A 的含酪氨酸肽的纸电泳（pH 6.4，90 分钟），与来自血红蛋白 K 伍力奇和血红蛋白 K 喀麦隆的含酪氨酸纸电泳相比较。来自血红蛋白 K 伍力奇的 βTpXIII 与 βTpXIV 相组合，并保持带正电荷。来自血红蛋白 K 喀麦隆的 βTpXIII 带负电荷。

血红蛋白 K 伊巴丹 血红蛋白 K 伊巴丹的肽谱如图 6 所示，可以看到甲硫氨酸肽 β^{A}TpV 缺失，而一个新的甲硫氨酸肽出现，并进一步向正极移动，其电泳迁移率类似于 βTpIII。βTpV 电泳迁移率的这种变化可以在延长的电泳图中得到证实(图 7)。βTpV 代表着 β 链的 41~59 残基。

β^{A}TpV

41 42 43 44 45 46 47 48 49 50 51 52 53 54 55 56 57 58 59

Phe-Phe-Glu-Ser-Phe-Gly-Asp-Leu-Ser-Thr-Pro-Asp-Ala-Val-Met-Gly-Asn-Pro-Lys

↑

用溴化氰裂解

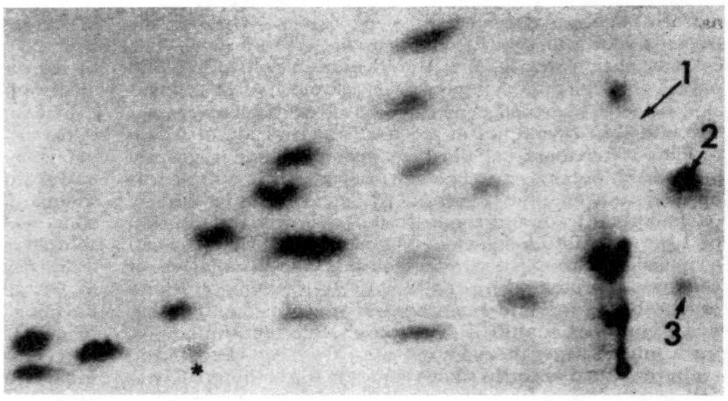

Fig. 6. Peptide map of haemoglobin K Ibadan. β^{A}TpV is missing at 1, and a new peptide can be seen at 2, with the electrophoretic mobility of β^{A}TpIII(3). The starred peptide is the incidental chymotryptic β131-132 from β^{A}TpXIII which is missing in Figs.3 and 4

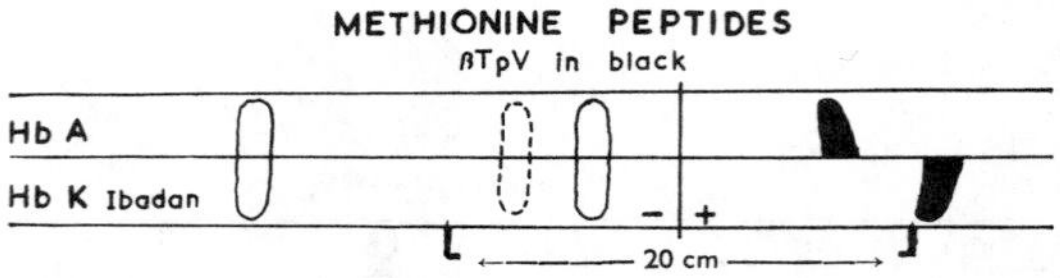

Fig. 7. Paper electrophoresis (90 min at *p*H 6.4) of methionine containing peptides from haemoglobin A and haemoglobin K Ibadan. Note the increase in mobility of the negatively charged βTpV from haemoglobin K Ibadan

The amino-acid analysis of the new peptide, from haemoglobin A, is shown in Table 2. It will be seen that the new peptide contains one glycine residue less and one glutamic acid residue more than the haemoglobin A peptide. A mutation Gly→Glu would explain the increase in the negative charge of β^{K}TpV and would be compatible with the new variant being a haemoglobin K which has one negative charge per half-molecule more than haemoglobin A. Consistently low recoveries were obtained for phenylalanine. This can be seen also in a previous analysis of βTpV[8]. The Phe-Phe bond may be difficult to hydrolyse because of steric effects. Increasing the time of hydrolysis from 20 h to 40 h at 108° did not improve recovery.

Table 2. Haemoglobin A and Haemoglobin K Ibadan

Amino-acid analysis (molar ratio) of peptide βTpV

	β^{A}TpV	β^{K}TpV
Asp	3.0	2.9
Thr	1.0	1.0
Ser	2.0	1.8
Glu	1.0	2.0
Pro	2.0	1.9
Gly	1.8	1.0
Ala	1.2	1.0
Val	1.1	0.8
Met	0.8	Present*
Leu	1.1	1.1
Phe	2.4	2.5
Lys	1.2	1.1

* Methionine and sulphone together amounted to about 1 residue.

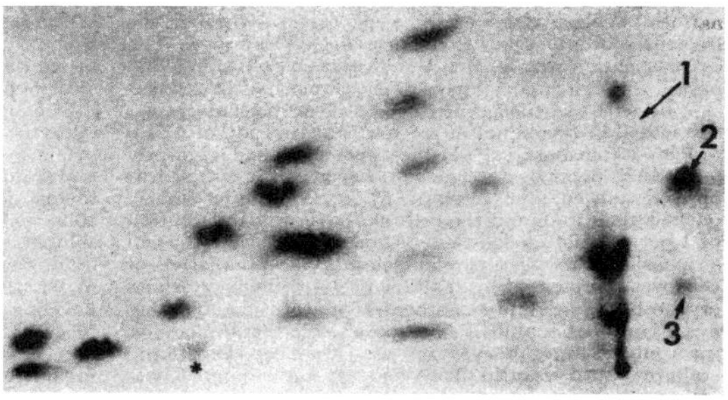

图 6. 血红蛋白 K 伊巴丹的肽谱。 在 1 处的 β^{A}TpV 缺失，在 2 处可以看到一个新肽，它具有 β^{A}TpIII（3）的电泳迁移率。带星号的肽是来自 β^{A}TpIII 附带的胰凝乳蛋白酶解的二肽 β131-132，β^{A}TpXIII 在图 3 和图 4 中消失。

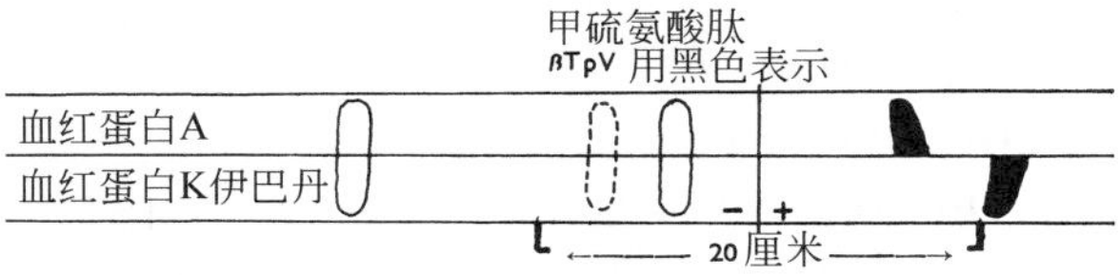

图 7. 来自血红蛋白 A 和血红蛋白 K 伊巴丹的含甲硫氨酸肽的纸电泳 (pH 6.4，90 分钟)。注意来自血红蛋白 K 伊巴丹的带负电荷的 βTpV 的迁移率增加。

表2显示了来自血红蛋白A的新肽的氨基酸分析，可以看到，与血红蛋白A肽相比，这个新肽减少了一个甘氨酸残基，增加了一个谷氨酸残基。Gly（甘氨酸）→ Glu 的突变可以解释 β^{K}TpV 所带负电荷的增加，也可以与这种新变体是血红蛋白 K 的新变体相一致，因为与血红蛋白 A 相比，血红蛋白 K 每半个分子多含有一个负电荷。苯丙氨酸的回收率一直很低。这在以前对 βTpV 的分析 [8] 中也可以看到。Phe（苯丙氨酸）-Phe 肽键可能由于立体效应而难于水解。在 108° 将水解时间从 20 小时增加到 40 小时也没能改善回收率。

表 2. 血红蛋白 A 和血红蛋白 K 伊巴丹

βTpV 肽的氨基酸分析（摩尔比）

	β^{A}TpV	β^{K}TpV
Asp	3.0	2.9
Thr	1.0	1.0
Ser	2.0	1.8
Glu	1.0	2.0
Pro	2.0	1.9
Gly	1.8	1.0
Ala	1.2	1.0
Val	1.1	0.8
Met	0.8	存在 *
Leu	1.1	1.1
Phe	2.4	2.5
Lys	1.2	1.1

* 甲硫氨酸和砜共约等同于 1 个残基。

β^{A}TpV contains two glycine residues: β46 and β56. In order to determine which of the two possible glycine residues had been replaced by glutamyl, the methionyl bond at β55 was split with cyanogens bromide[9]. The resulting peptides were separated by paper electrophoresis at *p*H 6.4. β^{A}TpV isolated from haemoglobin A was treated similarly. From both β^{K}TpV and β^{A}TpV two fragments each were obtained, one charged positively, and one charged negatively. The positively charged peptides obtained from β^{K}TpV and β^{A}TpV had the same electrophoretic mobility, whereas of the two negatively charged peptides, that from haemoglobin K had a greater mobility. If the amino-acid substitution Gly→Glu in haemoglobin K Ibadan had been at β56 no positively charged peptide would have resulted from the cleavage of the methionyl bond at β55. Both the positively charged peptides from A and K, presumably representing residues β56-59, stained transiently yellow with ninhydrin, indicating the N-terminal glycyl. The increased mobility of the negatively charged peptide from haemoglobin K Ibadan indicated that the mutation had occurred at position β46. The results of the amino-acid analysis of the four fragments are shown in Table 3. The basic amino-acids were not determined as this was not relevant to the position of the Gly→Glu mutation. It will be seen that the positively charged peptides (56-59) from β^{K}TpV and β^{A}TpV have an identical amino-acid composition. However, the negatively charged peptide representing residues 41-55 from β^{K}TpV has one glutamic acid residue more and one glycine residue loss than the corresponding negatively charged peptide from β^{A}TpV. This indicates that of the two glycine residues 46 and 56 the first has been substituted by glutamyl and that the formula of haemoglobin K Ibadan is $\alpha_2\beta_2^{46Gly\rightarrow Glu}$. This is the first observation of a Gly→Glu mutation in human haemoglobin although a mutation Glu→Gly has been observed[10].

Table 3. Haemoglobin A and Haemoglobin K Ibadan

Amino-acid analysis (molar ratio) of peptides arising from splitting βTpV (β41-59) at β55 methionyl with cyanogen bromide

	Negatively charged peptides(β41-55)		Positively charged peptides (β56-59)	
	Hb A	Hb K	Hb A	Hb K
Electrophoretic mobility at *p*H 6.4 (Glu, −1.0, Lys, + 1.0)	−0.42	−0.59	+0.57	+0.57
Asp	2.0	2.2	1.0	1.0
Thr	1.0	1.0		
Ser	2.0	1.8		
Homoserine	Present	Present		
Glu	1.2	1.9		
Pro	1.0	1.1	1.0	0.9
Gly	1.0	0.3	0.9	1.0
Ala	1.1	1.0		
Val	1.1	1.0		
Leu	1.0	1.0		
Phe	2.4	2.3		

It has been suggested here that haemoglobin K Cameroon (mutation of β130 Ala to

β^{A}TpV 有 2 个甘氨酸残基：β46 和 β56。为了测定这两个可能的甘氨酸残基中哪一个被谷胺酰残基取代，将 β55 的甲硫氨酰键用溴化氰裂解 [9]。在 pH 值为 6.4 的条件下将所得的肽用纸电泳分离。从血红蛋白 A 分离得到的 β^{A}TpV 也用类似的方法处理。从 β^{K}TpV 和 β^{A}TpV 中各获得两个分别带正电荷和负电荷的片段。从 β^{K}TpV 和 β^{A}TpV 得到的正电荷肽段有相同的电泳迁移率，而在两条带负电荷的肽段中，来自血红蛋白 K 的肽段有较大的迁移率。如果血红蛋白 K 伊巴丹中的 Gly → Glu 取代发生在 β56 位，那么 β55 位的甲硫氨酰键的裂解就不会产生带正电荷的肽。血红蛋白 A 和 K 产生的 2 个带正电荷的肽，假定是 β56~59 的残基，茚三酮染色瞬间变黄，表明 N 端是甘氨酰。来自血红蛋白 K 伊巴丹的带负电荷的肽的迁移率有提高，这表明在 β46 位发生了突变作用。表 3 列出了这四个肽的氨基酸分析结果。由于与 Gly → Glu 的突变位置不相关，没有测定其碱性氨基酸。可以看到来自 β^{K}TpV 和 β^{A}TpV 的带正电荷的肽（56~59）有相同的氨基酸组分。但是代表 β^{K}TpV 的 41~55 位残基的带负电荷的肽比从 β^{A}TpV 中得到的相应的带负电荷的肽多一个谷氨酸残基，少一个甘氨酸残基。这就表明在 46 位和 56 位的两个甘氨酸残基中，前一个已被谷氨酰取代，因而血红蛋白 K 伊巴丹可表示为 $\alpha_2\beta_2^{46Gly\rightarrow Glu}$。这是第一次在人血红蛋白中观察到 Gly → Glu 的突变，虽然以前已经见到过 Glu → Gly 突变的发生 [10]。

表 3. 血红蛋白 A 和血红蛋白 K 伊巴丹

用溴化氰裂解 βTpV（β41~59）β55 甲硫酰胺处得到的肽的氨基酸分析（摩尔比）

	带负电荷的肽（β41~55）		带正电荷的肽（β56~59）	
	血红蛋白 A	血红蛋白 K	血红蛋白 A	血红蛋白 K
pH 6.4 电泳迁移率 (Glu，−1.0，Lys，+1.0)	−0.42	−0.59	+0.57	+0.57
Asp	2.0	2.2	1.0	1.0
Thr	1.0	1.0		
Ser	2.0	1.8		
Homoserine（高丝氨酸）	存在	存在		
Glu	1.2	1.9		
Pro	1.0	1.1	1.0	0.9
Gly	1.0	0.3	0.9	1.0
Ala	1.1	1.0		
Val	1.1	1.0		
Leu	1.0	1.0		
Phe	2.4	2.3		

这表明血红蛋白 K 喀麦隆（β130 Ala → Asp 或 Glu?）和血红蛋白 K 伊巴丹

Asp or Glu?) and haemoglobin K Ibadan ($\alpha_2\beta_2{}^{46Glu}$) are unusual haemoglobins whereas haemoglobin K Woolwich ($\alpha_2\beta_2{}^{132Gln}$) is abnormal. It is remarkable that the β132 lysine residue, which is substituted by one of glutamine in haemoglobin K Woolwich, is one of the most immutable residues in the evolution of haemoglobin. It is also found in myoglobin, and indeed no haemoglobin has as yet been described in which this β132 lysyl is not present. The lysyl in this position must obviously serve some purpose in stabilizing the molecule and its replacement by an amino-acid with a neutral side-chain may thus be expected to interfere with the *status quo* within the molecule.

(**208**, 658-661; 1965)

N. Allan: Subdepartment of Haematology, University College Hospital, Ibadan, Nigeria.

D. Beale, D. Irvine and H. Lehmann: Medical Research Council Abnormal Haemoglobin Research Unit, University Department of Biochemistry, Cambridge.

References:

1. Cabannes, R., and Buhr, L., *Pédiatrie*, **10**, 888 (1955).
2. O'Gorman, P., Allsopp, K. M., Lehmann, H., and Sukumaran, P. K., *Brit. Med. J.*, ii, 1381 (1963).
3. Huehns, E. R., Shooter, E. M., and Beaven, G. H., *J. Mol. Biol.*, **4**, 323 (1962).
4. Lehmann, H., Beale, D., and Boi Doku, F. S., *Nature*, **203**, 363 (1964).
5. Charache, S., and Conley, C. L., *Blood*, **24**, 25 (1964).
6. Watson-Williams, E. J., Beale, D., Irvine, D., and Lehmann, H., *Nature*, **205**, 1273 (1965).
7. Nirenberg, M., Leder, P., Bernfield, M., Brimacombe, R., Trupin, J., Rottman, F., and O'Neal, C., *Proc. U.S. Nat. Acad. Sci.*, **53**, 1161 (1965).
8. Bowman, B. H., Oliver, C. P., Barnett, D. R., Cunningham, J. E., and Schneider, R., *Blood*, **23**, 193 (1964).
9. Gross, E., and Witkop, B., *J. Biol. Chem.*, **237**, 1856 (1962).
10. Hill, R. L., Swenson, R. T., and Schwartz, H. O., *J. Biol. Chem.*, **235**, 3182 (1960).

($\alpha_2\beta_2{}^{46Glu}$) 是稀有血红蛋白，而血红蛋白 K 伍力奇 ($\alpha_2\beta_2{}^{132Gln}$) 是异常血红蛋白。值得注意的是在血红蛋白 K 伍力奇中，被谷氨酰胺取代的 β132 赖氨酸残基是在血红蛋白演化过程中最稳定的残基之一。在肌红蛋白中也发现了这种情况，但在此之前却没有关于血红蛋白中不存在这个 β132 赖氨酰的记载。显然，这个位置上的赖氨酰必然对稳定分子起到某种作用。因此，当它被含有中性侧链的氨基酸取代后，可以预期蛋白质分子内部的“现状”会受到影响。

（荆玉祥 翻译；顾孝诚 审稿）

A Dense Packing of Hard Spheres with Five-Fold Symmetry

B. G. Bagley

Editor's Note

Crystals are forbidden from having five-fold symmetry on geometric grounds: it is impossible to pack pentagons without gaps. The discovery in 1984 of a metal alloy with apparent ten-fold symmetry seemed to challenge that idea, but this so-called quasicrystal proved to lack true crystallinity. This paper from B. G. Bagley describes, two decades earlier, another way to create five-fold symmetry from a dense, infinitely extended packing of spheres. The packing is not periodic in three dimensions, however, but has a definite centre. The following year, an example of Bagley's scheme was reported for virus particles. Bagley also cites five-fold-symmetric clusters proposed by Desmond Bernal to exist in simple liquids, which were later invoked as possible nuclei of incipient quasicrystals.

SUPPOSE a plane of hard spheres is constructed such that the spheres form concentric pentagons with an odd number of balls per pentagon side. A second plane of hard spheres is now constructed such that the spheres form concentric pentagons with an even number of spheres per pentagon side. If this second plane is placed in intimate contact with the first, with their five-fold axes coincident, there results a layer which, within the plane of the layer, can be continuously packed to infinity (Fig. 1). Identical layers can then be stacked one on another, with their five-fold axes coincident, to give an infinite packing along the five-fold axis. An infinite structure can thus be constructed the nucleus of which is a pentagonal dipyramid of seven spheres.

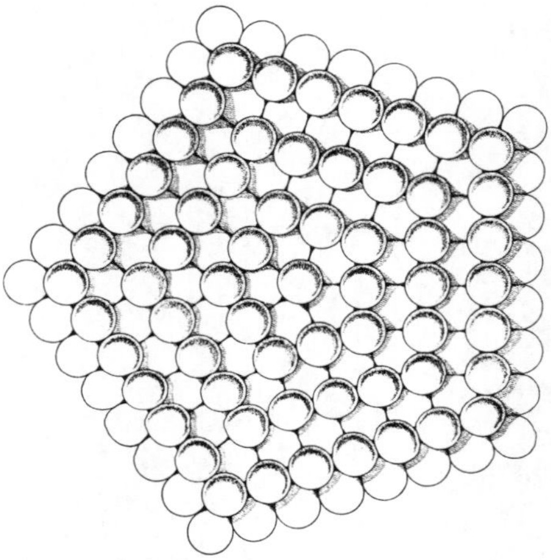

Fig. 1. A layer of hard spheres based on a packing sequence of concentric pentagons.

具有五重对称性的硬球的密堆积

巴格利

编者按

根据几何学原理，晶体不能具有五重对称性：做五边形堆积而不产生空隙是不可能的。1984 年人们发现一种金属合金具有明显的十重对称性，这一发现似乎是对上述观点的挑战，但是后来发现这个所谓的准晶体缺乏真正的晶体性质。巴格利的这篇文章发表于此前 20 年，文中他介绍了另外一种利用无限外延密堆积小球而构建出五重对称结构的方法。然而，这种堆积在三维空间中不具有周期性，但是却具有一个明确的中心。第二年，人们在病毒粒子中发现了一个巴格利方案的实例。巴格利还引用了德斯蒙德·贝尔纳提出的、存在于简单液体中的五重对称性团簇结构，而后来这被认为是初期准晶体的晶核。

假定如此构建一个硬球的平面，使若干硬球形成许多同心五边形，且每个五边形边上的硬球数为奇数。而第二个硬球的平面虽也由硬球构成同心五边形，但每个五边形边上的硬球数为偶数。如果将第二个硬球平面与第一个硬球平面紧密接触，且使它们的五重轴一致，这样就形成了一个在层的平面内可以无限连续堆积的硬球层（如图 1 所示），那么相同的这些层在五重轴一致的方向上可以连续地堆积，这样就可以沿着五重轴的方向形成一个无限堆积。一个无限堆积的结构也因此被构建出来，这个结构的核是由 7 个球构成的五边形双棱锥体。

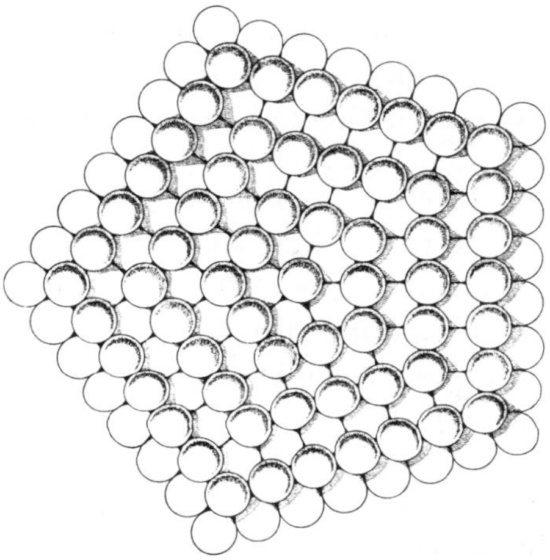

图 1. 一个基于同心五边形堆积序列的硬球层

Following the foregoing packing sequence with polygons other than the pentagon results in other, well-known structures. The same sequence with squares yields cubic close packing[1] and, with hexagons, primitive hexagonal. A difficulty arises when attempts are made to apply the exact sequence to triangles, because concentric triangles with an even (or odd) number of spheres per side cannot be made coplanar. It is important that, of these polygons, only the pentagon cannot form a regular tessellation and therefore, although it can be packed to infinity, it has a unique axis, the single five-fold rotation axis.

An alternative way of generating the same pentagonal structure is as follows: Construct n ($n = 1, 2, 3, \cdots \infty$) pentagonal pyramidal shells of hard spheres such that each face is an equilateral triangle of side length n (spheres). If shell 1 is placed in the cavity of shell 2 there results a pentagonal dipyramid of seven atoms. Likewise when shell 3 is placed on the structure there results a pentagonal dipyramid of twenty-three spheres. In fact, as each subsequent shell is placed on the growing structure there always results a pentagonal dipyramid bounded by close-packed planes, each face of which is an equilateral triangle with n (shell number) spheres to a side. This pentagonal dipyramid consists of five distorted tetrahedral the edges parallel to the five-fold axis being expanded by 5.15 percent. Within each tetrahedron the structure is body-centred orthorhombic with cell dimensions chosen such that the pentagonal dipyramid faces will be close packed and two adjacent tetrahedra will be joined by a coincidence boundary. These conditions yield a body-centred orthorhombic cell with dimensions (diameter of sphere=1.000), a=1.000, $b=\cot 36° = 1.3764$, $c=(2^2-\csc^2 36°)^{1/2}=1.0515$. Thus this pentagonal structure has a density independent of position of 0.72357. This density is slightly lower than that for close packing (0.74048), but higher than body-centred cubic (0.68017) or icosahedral shell packing (0.68818) (ref. 2). The co-ordination is 10 at a distance of 1.000 and 2 at a distance of 1.052. This structure is an example of G_3^1 type symmetry, that is, a one-dimensionally periodic group in three dimensions, and its symmetry group is $5mP2ml$ (Niggli's[3] nomenclature).

Structures which have the symmetry described here have been observed experimentally. Gedwill, Altstetter and Wayman[4], using optical microscopy, observed five-fold symmetry in cobalt crystals produced by the hydrogen reduction of cobaltous bromide. Wentorf[5], also using optical microscopy (external morphology), observed five-fold symmetry in synthetic diamonds. Ogburn, Paretzkin and Peiser[6], using X-rays, found pentagonal symmetry in copper [110] dendrites grown by electrodeposition. The most striking examples, however, are the sub-micron whiskers of nickel, iron and platinum grown from the vapour by Melmed and Hayward[7]. These whiskers, 50-200 Å in diameter, had a five-fold rotational symmetry observed by field emission microscopy. The five-fold symmetry was found not to be limited to the surface, as no change in symmetry was observed in the continuous reduction in length of several iron whiskers.

In all these cases the structure was explained as a quintuple twin ((111) twinning plane) with five face-centred cubic individual crystals about a common [110] axis, the 7°20′ difference between 5×70°32′ and 360° being made up with lattice strain or imperfections. It is

接着如果将上述五边形的堆积序列换成其他多边形堆积序列，那么我们就可以得到另外一些大家所熟知的结构。例如，正方形按相同序列堆积便可得到立方密堆积[1]，六边形按相同序列堆积则可得到简单的六方密堆积。但是，人们在试图做一个精确的三角形序列时出现了困难，因为在共面上不能形成每边具有偶数（或奇数）个球的同心的三角形。重要的是，在这些多边形中，只有五边形不能形成规则的镶嵌，因此，尽管它能无限堆积，却只具有一个特殊的轴，即唯一的五重旋转轴。

产生相同的五边形结构的另一种方法如下：构建 n（$n = 1, 2, 3, \cdots \infty$）的五边形棱锥的硬球壳层，使它的每个面都是一个边长为 n（球）的等边三角形。如果将壳层 1 置于壳层 2 的腔体内，结果就形成了一个具有 7 个原子的五边形双棱锥体。同样，将壳层 3 置于上述结构上时，它就形成了一个 23 个球的五边形双棱锥体。实际上，当每个次级壳层置于这种生长的结构上，总可形成一个以密堆积平面为界面的五边形双棱锥体，其中每个面都是边长为 n 个（壳层数）球的等边三角形。这种五边形双棱锥体是由五个畸变的四面体组成的，它的边平行于向外扩展 5.15% 的五重轴。每个四面体内都是体心正交晶结构，具有的单胞尺度能使五边形双棱锥体的面可以呈密堆积，且两个相邻的四面体通过重合边界连接在一起。这些条件所产生的体心正交单胞的尺度是（球的直径 =1.000）：a=1.000、b=cot36°=1.3764、$c=(2^2-\csc^2 36^\circ)^{1/2}$=1.0515。因此，这个五边形结构具有的密度值为 0.72357，它与位置无关。这个密度比密堆积密度（0.74048）稍低，但高于体心立方堆积（0.68017），或二十面体的壳层堆积（0.68818）（参考文献 2）。在距离为 1.000 时，配位数为 10，在距离为 1.052 时，配位数就为 2。这种结构是 G_3^1 型对称性的一个例子，也就是说，在三维中的一维的周期群，其对称群为 *5mP2ml*（尼格利[3]的命名法）。

本文描述的对称性结构已在实验中观测到。格德威尔、阿尔特施泰特和韦曼[4]用光学显微镜观测到了由氢还原溴化钴所产生的钴晶体的五重对称性。温托夫[5]也用光学显微镜（外形貌学）观测到了合成金刚石的五重对称性。奥格本、帕雷茨金和派泽[6]用 X 射线发现了通过电沉积生长的铜 [110] 枝晶的五角对称性。然而，最显著的例子是梅尔梅德和海沃德[7]利用蒸汽生长出镍、铁和铂的亚微米晶须。这些晶须的直径为 50 埃 ~200 埃，通过场发射显微镜观测到其具有五重旋转对称性。这种五重对称性不只限于表面，因为在一些铁晶须的连续剥离的过程中，并没有观测到对称性的变化。

在所有这些情况下，该结构都解释为五重孪晶（(111）孪晶平面），即在共同的 [110] 轴的周围有 5 个面心立方的晶体，$5 \times 70^\circ 32'$与 360° 之间的 $7^\circ 20'$ 之差是点阵应变或欠完美性引起的。然而，不同的是孪晶机制未必能产生梅尔梅德和海沃德[7]

unlikely, however, that a twinning mechanism could generate a structure having the small size (50-200 Å) and atomic perfection (at the five-fold axis) of Melmed and Hayward's[7] whiskers. On the other hand, it appears that the formation of a pentagonal dipyramid nucleus and its subsequent growth is a more probable and simpler mechanism for the formation of this structure. Furthermore, if a twinning mechanism were responsible for the five-fold symmetry one would expect [110] to be an observed whisker orientation in normal, non-pentagonal, whiskers. This is indeed the case for nickel and platinum, but the observed orientation for face-centred cubic iron is [100] (ref. 8).

It is also to be noted that the pentagonal nucleus for the structure described here has the same form as one of the configurations which has been proposed as an important element of liquid structure by Bernal[9,10]. It is evident from the foregoing discussion that crystallization can occur by the growth of such a configuration.

I thank Profs. F. C. Frank, C. S. Smith, and D. Turnbull for their advice, and the Xerox Corporation for a fellowship. This work was supported in part by the Office of Naval Research under contract *Nonr* 1866 (50), and by the Division of Engineering and Applied Physics, Harvard University.

(**208**, 674-675; 1965)

B. G. Bagley: Division of Engineering and Applied Physics, Harvard University, Cambridge, Massachusetts.

References:

1. Coxeter, H. S. M., *Illinois J. Math.*, **2**, 746 (1958).
2. Mackay, A. L., *Acta Cryst.*, **15**, 916 (1962).
3. Niggli, A., *Zeit. Krist.*, **111**, 288 (1959).
4. Gedwill, M. A., Altstetter, C. J., and Wayman, C. M., *J. App. Phys.*, **35**, 2266 (1964).
5. Wentorf, R. H., jun., in *The Art and Science of Growing Crystals*, edit. by Gilman, J. J., 192 (Wiley, New York, 1963).
6. Ogburn, F., Paretzkin, B., and Peiser, H. S., *Acta Cryst.*, **17**, 774 (1964).
7. Melmed, A. J., and Hayward, D. O., *J. Chem. Phys.*, **31**, 545 (1959).
8. Melmed, A. J., and Gomer, R., *J. Chem. Phys.*, **34**, 1802 (1961).
9. Bernal, J. D., *Nature*, **183**, 141 (1959).
10. Bernal, J. D., *Nature*, **185**, 68 (1960).

晶须的小尺寸（50 埃～200 埃）结构以及在五重轴上的原子完美性。另一方面，五边形双棱锥体晶核的形成以及其随后的生长，也许是这种结构形成的更可能且更简单的机制。而且，如果孪晶机制是造成五重对称性的原因，可以预期在通常的、非五边形的晶须中法向取向应为 [110]。这确实符合镍和铂的情况，但在面心立方的铁中观测到的方向却是 [100]（参考文献 8）。

还应注意到，本文所述结构的五边形核与由贝尔纳 [9,10] 提出的液体结构的重要组态之一具有相同的形式。从上述讨论中我们可以明显得出，这类组态在生长的过程中能够产生结晶。

我要感谢弗兰克教授、史密斯教授和特恩布尔教授提供的意见，同时也感谢施乐公司提供的科研经费。这项研究的部分工作得到了海军研究办公室（合同为 *Nonr* 1866（50））以及哈佛大学工程与应用物理学院的支持。

（沈乃澂 翻译；赵见高 审稿）

Antimatter and Tree Rings

V. S. Venkatavaradan

Editor's Note

Physicists attempting to explain the vast energy released in the Tunguska meteor strike of 1908 in Siberia had been driven to a radical hypothesis: that part of the meteor may have been made of antimatter. Researchers had indeed found evidence in the area for an altered ratio of the abundance of the isotopes carbon-14 and carbon-12, consistent with significant annihilation of matter and antimatter. Here, however, Indian physicist V. S. Venkatavaradan of the Tata Institute of Fundamental Research in Bombay notes that the isotope ratios observed vary also with sunspot activity, and that this evidence therefore does not support the antimatter hypothesis. Scientists today believe the Tunguska event was caused by the impact of a large rock meteor.

RECENTLY, Cowan *et al.*[1] discussed the interesting case of the Tunguska meteor—the event and its origin mainly in the context of release of a rather high energy of $\sim 10^{24}$ ergs on its impact. Various theories concerning its origin and the nature of the energy source were discussed (for example, asteroidal origin and energy from impact or nuclear reactions). They have shown that none of the theories can satisfactorily explain the amount of energy released during the impact. The authors have invoked the antimatter hypothesis and, as an experimental verification to this, have calculated the expected increase in the carbon-14/carbon-12 ratios in the atmosphere subsequent to the fall of the meteorite. Considering the total energy release, they obtained a value of 7 percent for the expected increase in activity. Their measurements of the atmospheric carbon-14/carbon-12 ratios, based on annual rings of a 300-yr.-old tree, show a possible increase of 1 percent in the year 1909, leading them to the conclusion that probably 1/7th of the energy release in the Tunguska meteorite impact came from antimatter annihilation.

It is the purpose of this communication to point out that the probability of such an interesting conclusion is unfortunately very much reduced if one considers the nature of secular variations of carbon-14/carbon-12 ratios in the atmosphere. It was Stuiver[2] who first pointed out that there existed a good inverse correlation, for the past 1,300 yr. of record, between the solar activity and carbon-14/carbon-12 ratios in the atmosphere. (In what manner sunspot activity brings about this correlation is, however, not well understood as yet.) If we compare the solar activity and the observed carbon-14/carbon-12 ratio during 1870-1933, within the errors of measurements, we do find a fair anticorrelation between the sunspot activity and the carbon-14 deviations (see Fig. 1), there being some phase differences which are not unexpected because of time delays in interactions of relevance to the carbon-14/carbon-12 ratios, for example, air-biosphere and air-sea exchange.

反物质与树木年轮

文卡塔瓦拉丹

编者按

多年来，物理学家们都在试图解释 1908 年发生在西伯利亚的通古斯陨石撞击所释放出的巨大能量，甚至得出了一个极端的猜测：即一部分通古斯陨石可能是由反物质构成的。研究者们确实在这一地区发现了证据，即同位素碳-14 与碳-12 丰度的比例变化，这符合物质和反物质重要的相互湮灭原理。然而在本文中，孟买塔塔基础研究所的印度物理学家文卡塔瓦拉丹指出，这种同位素比例的变化同样与太阳黑子的活动有关，因此上述证据不足以支持这个反物质的猜测。今天，科学家都认为通古斯事件是由于一块巨大的陨石撞击地球引起的。

最近，考恩等人[1] 讨论了有趣的通古斯陨石撞击事件——他们主要根据撞击时释放出的极高能量（约 10^{24} 尔格）对该事件及其起因进行了讨论。讨论内容涉及关于事件起因的各种理论以及能量来源的性质（例如，小行星起源，能量来自于撞击还是核反应）。最后他们认为，没有一种理论能够圆满地解释撞击时所释放出的巨大能量。他们提出了反物质的假设，而且作为其假设的实验证据，他们还计算了陨石降落后大气中碳-14 与碳-12 比值增加的预期值。考虑到总的能量释放，他们计算出放射性强度的增加值为 7%。根据一棵树龄为 300 年的老树的年轮所测得的大气中碳-14 与碳-12 的比值，他们指出，在 1909 年该值可能增加了 1%，并因此得出结论：在通古斯陨石撞击中大约 1/7 的能量释放来自反物质的湮灭。

这篇通讯的目的在于指出：假如人们考虑到大气中碳-14 与碳-12 比值长期变化的特征，那么上述这个有趣结论成立的可能性就会大大降低。斯蒂尤艾弗[2] 最先指出，在过去 1,300 年的记录中太阳活动与大气中碳-14 和碳-12 比值存在良好的反相关性。（但是，太阳黑子活动何以能产生此种相关性现在还不甚清楚。）假如我们比较一下 1870 年 ~1933 年期间的太阳活动和观测到的碳-14 与碳-12 的比值，在测量误差范围内我们确实可以发现在太阳黑子活动与碳-14 偏离值之间有相当好的反相关（参见图 1），由于一些与碳-14 和碳-12 比值相关的相互作用，例如大气–生物圈和大气–海洋间的物质交换存在时间滞后，所以图中太阳黑子与碳-14 偏离值存在一些相位差也在意料之中。

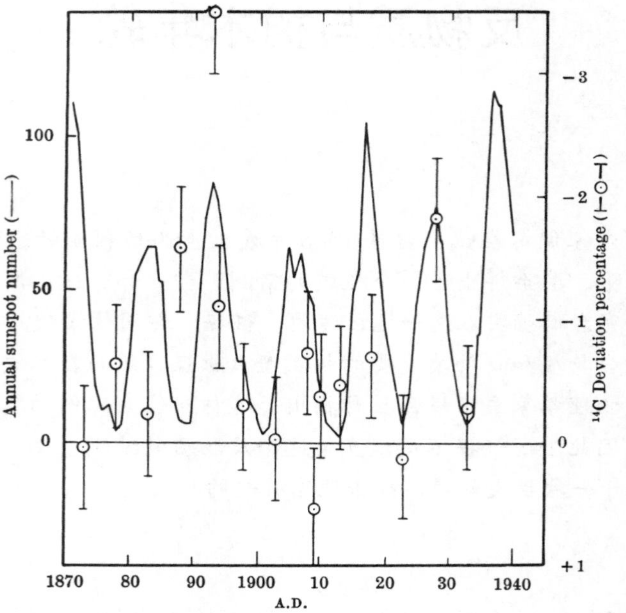

Fig. 1. Measured carbon-14 activity in tree rings (ref. 1) and sunspot activity during the same period

Thus, it is clear that if one takes into account the nature of secular variations of carbon-14/carbon-12 ratios in the atmosphere, it becomes difficult to reach any conclusions which may be of significance to a possible antimatter content of the Tunguska meteorite.

(**208**, 772; 1965)

V. S. Venkatavaradan: Tata Institute of Fundamental Research, Colaba, Bombay-5.

References:

1. Cowan, C., Atlurl, C. R., and Libby, W. F., *Nature*, **206**, 861 (1965).
2. Stuiver, M., *J. Geophys. Res.*, **66**, 273 (1961).

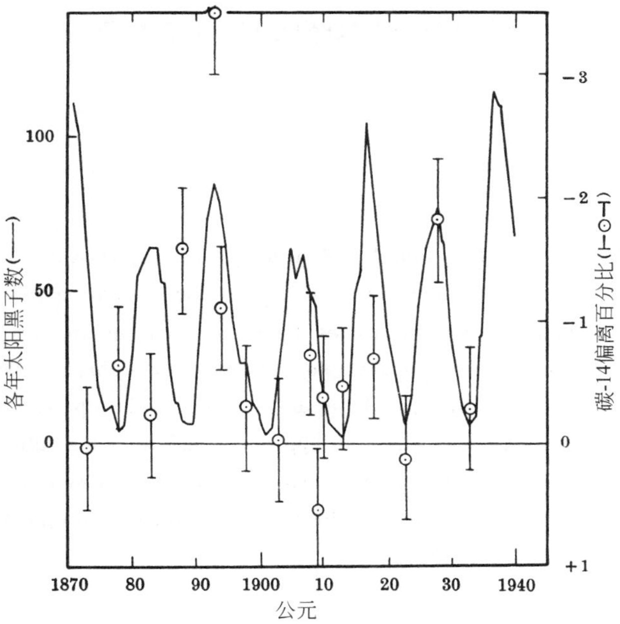

图 1. 树木年轮中所测得的碳-14 放射性强度（参考文献 1）和同时期太阳黑子活动

因此，很明显的是，若考虑到大气中碳-14 与碳-12 比值长期变化的特征，我们就难以得到任何有利于通古斯陨石中可能存在反物质的结论。

（李任伟 翻译；肖伟科 审稿）

Drug-Dependence

W. R. Brain*

Editor's Note

In this Inaugural Address to the School of Pharmacy, neurologist Walter Russell Brain discusses the issues surrounding drug-dependence and abuse. The increasing prescription of sedatives, stimulants and tranquilizers may, he argues, be cause for concern, but the beneficial effects cannot be ignored. Tranquilizers, for example, can help schizophrenics reintegrate with society and lessen the need for shock therapy. He argues for research into prescription and consumption patterns, with the hope that an integrated approach will influence future drug design. In the meantime, he adds, "there is still much to be said for the ideal of fighting our own battles if we can without the aid of pharmacy, but with the support of some philosophy which gives a meaning to life."

WHEN I chose the present subject, I hoped that before I presented it the new report of the Interdepartmental Committee on Drug Addiction would have been published. However, it is still in the printer's hands, so I can say nothing about that now. When the report appears, however, as I hope it will soon, I believe it will be self-explanatory and call for no comments from me. The report of the earlier Committee, of which also I was chairman, raised a general question which seems to me important enough to call for further discussion. I can best explain this by quoting from the report. We said: "Most of our witnesses affirmed that, today, drugs acting on the central nervous system are being used excessively, but they were unable to furnish records in support of this contention". We obtained some information about the quantity of barbiturates prescribed annually in England and Wales over the previous two years and said: "It is obvious that usage has expanded both progressively and substantially so that, in 1959, it was almost twice what it was in 1951". We also stated that analysis of National Health prescriptions showed that "barbiturates, other sedatives and hypnotics, together with analgesics and antipyretics (excluding dangerous drugs), account for no less than about 19 percent of all the prescriptions issued". There was also reason to believe that the prescription of tranquillizers had also increased, and we noted that the amount spent on one particular tranquillizer by nine selected mental hospitals had increased ten-fold over a course of five years. After mentioning the dangers of addiction to amphetamine and phenmetrazine, we noted that an analysis of some 214 million National Health Service prescriptions in 1959 indicated that some 5,600,000 or approximately 2.5 percent were for preparations of the amphetamines and phenmetrazines.

* Substance of the Address at the Inaugural Ceremony of the School of Pharmacy, University of London, delivered on October 13.

药物依赖

布雷恩*

编者按

本文是神经学家沃尔特·罗素·布雷恩在药学院的就职演说，他围绕药物依赖和滥用问题进行了讨论。他认为越来越多的含有镇静剂、兴奋剂和安定药的处方应当引起关注，但是其益处不能被忽视。拿安定药来讲，它确实可以让精神分裂症患者重新回归社会，减少对休克疗法的需求。他主张对药物处方和消耗模式进行一些研究，希望拿出一个可以影响未来药物设计的综合方案。同时，他补充道："还有许多要说的是，我们的理想状态是在没有药物帮助的情况下，只是借助某种赋予生命一定意义的人生观，依靠身体自身与疾病做斗争。"

在我选择这个题目时，我希望在我演讲之前药物成瘾跨部门委员会的新报告就已经公布了。但是现在仍然在印刷中，因此关于那份报告我现在不能说任何事情。在这份报告公布后（正如我所希望的很快就会），我相信它会是不言自明的，不需要我进行评论。先前委员会(我也担任这个委员会的主席)的报告提出了一个普遍问题，这个问题对我来说很重要，需要进一步的讨论。引用报告的原文能更好地说明这个问题，即："我们大多数的见证人都承认，如今作用于中枢神经系统的药物正在被过量地使用，但是他们不能提供支持这一论点的证据。"我们获得了一些关于前两年英格兰和威尔士每年使用的巴比妥类药物数量的信息，并写道："很明显，药物用量已经逐步大幅增加，以至于 1959 年的用量几乎是 1951 年的两倍。"我们还陈述了对全民健康处方的分析，表明"巴比妥类药物、其他镇静剂和催眠剂以及止痛药和退烧药（不包括危险药物）在所有开出的处方药中不少于 19%"。还有理由相信开安定药的处方也增加了，我们注意到在调查的 9 所精神疾病医院消耗的某种安定剂的量在 5 年的时间里增加到了 10 倍。提到安非他明和苯甲吗啉易上瘾的危险，我们注意到对 1959 年全民健康服务的约有 2.14 亿份处方药的分析显示，大约有 560 万份或近似 2.5% 准备用安非他明和苯甲吗啉制剂。

* 本文是在伦敦大学药学院的就职仪式上的演讲内容，演讲致词是在 10 月 13 日。

Reviewing these facts, we made the following observations "To explain this trend in medication directed at the central nervous system, we have found no single answer. In part it must be due to the vigorous advertising of these drugs and their preparations by the pharmaceutical industry, both to the medical profession and to the public. To some extent the accelerated tempo and heightened anxieties of modern life have been held to blame; but this is an assertion based on assumption more than fact. Thirdly, and possibly of considerable consequence, there is the materialistic attitude adopted nowadays to therapeutics in general. This is one feature of an age which owes so much to science. For every deviation from health, great or small, a specific, chemical corrective is sought and, if possible, applied, and it is also widely believed that health may be positively enhanced by the use of drugs. When dealing with mental disease, psychotherapy may still be invoked. Often, however, a prescription is given for a drug when the patient's real need is a discussion of his psychological difficulties with the doctor. An obvious danger arises when the drugs so employed, far from being placebos, are undeniably potent, frequently toxic, and sometimes habit-forming as well. On the other hand, the newer drugs are proving of great value in psychiatry where they are to some extent replacing other methods of treatment. This increasing use of sedatives, stimulants and tranquillizers raises issues on which we do not as a Committee feel confident to pronounce. In particular, it is not for us to decide whether their occasional or even regular use is justified if it enables that person to lead a happier and more useful life. In any case, if resort to potentially habit-forming drugs is sometimes to be regarded as a symptom of psychological maladjustment, it should be treated as a symptom, and its cause sought, perhaps as much in social conditions as in the mind of the individual. These are questions which should be considered not only by doctors, but by all concerned with social welfare."

These are certainly difficult questions, and I do not propose to try to answer them all now. What I shall try to do instead is to clarify them, to look at their implications, and to suggest ways in which we may hope to contribute towards answering them. Basic to the whole problem are the meaning and implications of drug-dependence.

This term was introduced by the World Health Organization Expert Committee on Addiction-producing Drugs in their thirteenth report, published in 1964. In the fourth section, with the significant title "Terminology in Regard to Drug Abuse", it directs attention to some confusion which had arisen in the use of the term "drug addiction" and "drug habituation". Because, it said, "the list of drugs abused increased in number and diversity" it sought a term which could be applied to drug abuse generally, and since "the component in common appears to be dependence, whether psychic or physical or both", it adopted the term "drug dependence", which it defined as "a state arising from repeated administration of a drug, often on a periodic or continuous basis. ... Its characteristics will vary with the agent involved and this must be made clear by designating the particular type of drug-dependence in each specific case—for example, drug-dependence of morphine-type, of cocaine-type, of cannabis-type, of barbiturate-type, of amphetamine-type, etc.". In using the term "drug dependence", and relating it to the abuse of drugs, it may seem that the World Health Organization Committee was only emphasizing

鉴于以上这些事实，我们得到的结论如下：“要解释针对中枢神经系统进行药物治疗这一趋势，我们发现答案并不是唯一的。部分原因一定是制药企业向从医人员和公众有力地宣传推广了这些药物及其制剂。在某种程度上也归咎于现代生活的快节奏和高度焦虑，但这个论断更多的是根据假设提出的，而不是根据事实。第三（这一点可能带来相当严重的后果），就是目前在治疗上人们总体上都持唯物主义的态度，这是科学时代的一个特征。对于每一次出现的健康问题，不管大小，如果可能的话，人们都会去寻找并服用某种特定的化学药物，人们也普遍相信药物能够让人变得更健康。对于精神疾病，也许仍然会采用心理治疗方法。但是当一名患者的真正需求是和医生讨论其心理问题时医生经常会给他开药。这样用药远比安慰剂有更明显的危险，毫无疑问用药是有效的，但通常具有一定毒性并且有时会成瘾。另一方面，较新的药物被证明在治疗精神疾病方面具有重要的价值，在某种程度上会取代其他的治疗方法。我们委员会不能够自信地宣布因镇静剂、兴奋剂和安定药的用量增加会产生问题，尤其当这些药物能够使得某些人过上更幸福并且更有益的生活时，不是我们来决定他们偶尔或者甚至定期地使用这些药物是否合理。不管怎样，如果依赖于有潜在成瘾性的药物有时被视为心理失调的症状，那么就应该视它为一种症状来治疗，而这种失调的原因可能与社会环境有关，也可能与个人心态有关。这些问题不仅仅需要由医生来考虑，还应当由所有关心社会福利的人来考虑。”

这些当然都是很难的问题，我现在不打算尝试回答所有的问题。反而我应该尽力去做的是讲清楚它们、认清它们的影响以及提出有助于我们回答这些问题的方法。所有问题的基础是药物依赖的含义及其影响。

这个术语是在 1964 年世界卫生组织药物依赖专家委员会公布的第 13 份报告中提出的。这份报告第四部分的标题很显眼，就是“与药物滥用相关的术语”，它将注意力转移到了在使用术语“药物成瘾”与“服药习惯化”所产生的混淆上。因为文中提到：“滥用药物的数量和种类都有所增加”，我们需要寻找一个适用于通常的药物滥用的术语，而且由于“相同点似乎都是依赖性，无论是心理或生理上的或二者兼而有之”，因此它采用“药物依赖”这个术语，其定义是“重复使用一种药物，通常是周期性或者持续性地使用而产生的一种状态……其特征根据涉及药剂的不同而不同，而且必须指明每种情况下特定的药物依赖类型，比如吗啡类的药物依赖、可卡因类的药物依赖、大麻类的药物依赖、巴比妥类的药物依赖和安非他明类的药物依赖等等”。在“药物依赖”术语的使用和它与药物滥用的关系上，似乎世界卫生组织委员会只是强调了一些显而易见的问题。但我想说的是“药物滥用”这个术语本

the obvious; but my object is to suggest that the term "drug abuse" itself raises some important questions which are not only unanswered but which we have not at present the knowledge to answer.

At least one valuable thing has emerged from the philosophy of the present century—its emphasis on the importance of words. So let us begin by asking what the word "drug" means, and why it means what it does. *Webster's Dictionary* defines "drug" as "any substance used as a medicine, or in the composition of medicine, for internal or external use", and then it goes on, "whether or not a given substance should be included under the term drug depends upon the purpose for which it is sold (as regards the seller) or used (as regards the purchaser) ". So it would seem that the same substance may sometimes be a drug and sometimes not. When we get to the verb "to drug" a new meaning creeps in, for Webster gives three definitions: "(1) to affect or season with drugs or ingredients; especially to stupefy by a narcotic drug; (2) to tincture with something offensive or injurious; (3) to dose to excess with or as with drugs". So a sinister note has already appeared: though we begin with drugs as any ingredients of a medicine, the average person hearing that someone has been "drugged" would not imagine that he had been given penicillin. This is sometimes reflected in what patients will say to a doctor, for example: "I don't mind taking medicine, but I hope you won't put me on any drugs, doctor!" Or: "I hope that this is not a habit-forming drug". So far as the public Press is concerned, if you see the word "drugs" in a headline you may be fairly sure that what follows refers to some sinister aspect of pharmacy, either "drug-addiction" or the supposed danger of taking some particular drug or group of drugs. In the annual report of the Chief Medical Officer of the Ministry of Health, though there is a chapter called "Therapeutic Agents: Control and Toxicology", when reference is made to the possible dangers of therapeutic agents the word "drugs" appears, and the relevant committee is called not a Committee on the Safety of Therapeutic Agents, but a Committee on the Safety of Drugs.

This pejorative meaning of the word "drug" is relevant to this article, for the subject of drug-dependence is a highly emotional one. "Drug addiction" hits the headlines frequently in the Press, and is the subject of plays and broadcasts. As a social problem, it excites an interest out of all proportion to its magnitude. In Great Britain, the total number of addicts to heroin, cocaine and morphine is well short of a thousand, and we are fortunate compared with Canada, where there are at least four thousand, and the United State where there are a great many more. But the number of men and women who will die of lung cancer this year in Britain is 25,000. Most of these are men in middle life. Their sufferings, the distress of their families and the loss to the community are collectively enormously greater than the effects of what is normally called "drug addiction", yet these deaths excite no similar emotional interest, although they, too, are the indirect result of a form of drug addiction, addiction to cigarettes.

I am not a psychologist, and perhaps the psychologists can tell us why drug addicts to morphine, heroin and cocaine arouse such a disproportionate amount of interest; even without going very deeply into the matter, however, one may surmise that it is partly

身带来了一些不仅没有被解答的重要问题，并且以我们目前所知也没有办法解答。

本世纪的哲学至少带来了一件有价值的事情——就是强调词的重要性。因此让我们先看看“药物”这个词的含义，以及为什么它会有这种含义。《韦氏字典》对“药物”的定义是“作为药品或者药品成分的任何物质，内服或者外用”，接着它继续写道“一种特定的物质能否被包含在药物术语的范畴内取决于它售卖（与销售者有关）或者使用（与购买者有关）的目的”。因此有可能同一种物质有时候是药物而有时候不是。当我们开始使用其动词形式“给药”时，一个新的含义产生了，《韦氏字典》给出了三个定义：“（1）用药物或者其成分影响或者调节，尤其是用麻醉药麻醉；（2）用刺激性或者损伤性的东西使略受影响；（3）服用过量的或等量的药物”。因此一个不好的注解已经出现了：尽管我们说药物是药品的任何成分，但是普通人在听到某人被“给药”后不会认为他是服用了青霉素。这有时候反映在病人对医生所说的话中，比如：“医生，我不介意服药，但是请不要让我使用任何的药物！”或者：“我希望这不是容易成瘾的药物”。就公共媒体而言，如果你在标题中见到了药物这个词，你可能会很确定之后的内容将是药物的一些不光彩的方面，或者是“药物成瘾”，或者是服用某个或某类药物可能具有的危险性。在卫生部首席医疗官的年度报告中尽管有一章称为“治疗药剂：管理和毒理学”，但每当提到治疗药剂可能带来危害时“药物”这个词就会出现，而且相关的委员会的名称也不是治疗药剂安全委员会，而是药物安全委员会。

“药物”这个词的贬义在本文中被提及，因为药物依赖这个话题总能调动起人们的情绪。“药物成瘾”经常见诸媒体的头条，并且是戏剧和广播节目的常见题材。作为一个社会问题，它能引起最广泛的关注。在英国，对海洛因、可卡因和吗啡成瘾的人的总数可能不到1,000，加拿大至少有4,000人成瘾，而美国则拥有更多数量的瘾君子，相对来讲我们很幸运。但英国今年死于肺癌的总人数是25,000，且大部分都是中年男性。他们遭受的痛苦、家人的悲伤和给社会带来的损失总体上要远远大于“药物成瘾”所带来的影响，但是这些死亡并没有引起类似的情绪上的关注。尽管肺癌也可以看作一种药物成瘾方式（香烟成瘾）的间接结果。

我不是心理学家，可能心理学家能够告诉我们为什么吗啡、海洛因和可卡因成瘾能够激发如此不成比例的关注。甚至在没有对这个问题进行非常深入的调查，我

because these drugs are potent, mysterious and potentially dangerous: and one of their most mysterious characteristics is their power of temporarily or permanently changing the personality. Add to that the association of "drug addiction" with crime and violence and we reach the conception of "potions ... drunk of Siren tears, distill'd from limbecks foul as hell within".

This is no exaggeration. The drug addict in this narrower sense is indeed a pathetic figure and a potentially dangerous one, too, if he or she becomes a source of infection to others. But, as the World Health Organization Committee recognizes, these drug addicts, though creating special problems, are only part of the broader spectrum of drug dependence.

It is obvious that there is nothing wrong with drug dependence as such. If a diabetic requires regular dosage of a drug to maintain his blood sugar at a normal level, or if a patient suffering from a collagen disease requires regular amounts of steroids, such patients are drug-dependent as already defined, their dependence being a physical one. But no one would describe this kind of drug-dependence as drug abuse: exactly the contrary. So it would seem that something more than mere drug-dependence is necessary to create drug-abuse, and if we look at the list of such drugs of both abuse and dependence which appears in the report of the World Health Organization Committee, I think the basis of the distinction becomes clear, for they are all drugs which are taken for their psychological effects. This brings us to the next stage of our enquiry, which is the crucial one. Is dependence on a drug which is taken for its psychological effects necessarily an abuse of that drug? Few people would, I suppose, quarrel with the view that this is true of morphine, heroin and cocaine, though someone recently wrote to the Press and complained that, since he found it necessary to take heroin, he did not see why his freedom to do so should be interfered with. But there is rather less unanimity about cannabis, and where do alcohol and tobacco stand? (I use the term tobacco here comprehensively to include whatever its pharmacologically potent constituents may be.)

Tobacco and alcohol may both be drugs of dependence. Their action is pharmacological, and in extreme cases the addict attempting to give them up suffers deprivation symptoms, which may be so severe that he is unable to do without them. The fact that they are both drugs which you prescribe and obtain for yourself, instead of through a doctor, and that there are social aspects of their use, is irrelevant to their pharmacological action. As in the case of other drugs of dependence, people vary very greatly in their liability to become addicted, and serious dependence is much more common in the case of tobacco than alcohol. I know of no evidence that tobacco-dependence has any bad psychological effects; but it undoubtedly may have bad physical effects, and it is here that the dependence becomes important, because it may make it extremely difficult for the addict to give up smoking. Alcohol-dependence, in its extreme forms, is recognized to be a manifestation of a psychological illness, and calls for treatment accordingly, but as in Britain that cannot be carried out without the willing co-operation of the patient, which is usually difficult to obtain, the serious alcohol addict is a difficult medical and social problem.

们就可以推测部分是因为这些药物都是药效强的、神秘的并且有潜在危害的。它们最神秘的特点之一是其能够暂时或者永久地改变人格的能力。再加上“药物成瘾”和暴力与犯罪的结合，我们就能理解这些描述：“魔药——如喝了鲛人的泪珠，从心中地狱般的锅里蒸出来”。

这并非夸大其词。如果狭义上的药物成瘾者成为影响其他人的根源，他或她确实是一个悲情的角色，也是一个潜在的危险人物。但是世界卫生组织委员会承认这些药物成瘾者尽管带来了特殊的问题，但也仅仅是药物依赖这个大群体的一部分。

显然，药物依赖本身同样没有什么错。如果一个糖尿病患者需要常规剂量的药物来维持其血糖在正常的水平上，或者一位胶原病患者需要定期服用类固醇，这些患者属于已被定义过的药物依赖，他们的依赖是身体上的。但是没有人会将这种药物依赖描绘成药物滥用，事实上恰恰相反。因此似乎要成为药物滥用，那么仅仅有药物依赖是不够的。如果我们查看世界卫生组织委员会的报告中既是滥用药物又是依赖性药物的清单，我想它们的基本区别就显而易见了，即它们都是因为会产生心理作用才被服用的药物。这样就进入到我们调查的下一个很关键的阶段。因为心理作用而服用的药物的依赖一定是药物滥用吗？我想几乎没有人会否认在吗啡、海洛因和可卡因中的确是这样。尽管最近有人写信给出版社并抱怨他不明白为什么自己服用海洛因的自由应该受到干涉，因为他发现服用海洛因是必要的。但是关于大麻却很少有一致性意见，更别说酒精和烟草了。（我这里使用烟草这个词，无论其药理上的有效成分是什么。）

烟草和酒精可能都是依赖性的药物。它们具有药理学作用，并且在极个别情况下，想要戒掉的成瘾者都会受戒断症状的折磨，这些症状是如此严重以至于患者不得不继续服药。事实上一方面它们都是无须经过医生，自己就可以给自己开的药物；另一方面它们又具有社交方面的用途，而这与它们的药理学作用无关。和其他依赖性的药物一样，成瘾倾向的个体差别非常大，对烟草具有严重依赖的情况比酒精更常见。我知道没有证据表明对烟草的依赖有负面的心理影响，但是毫无疑问它可能对身体有不好的影响。这里的依赖性就很重要，因为这使得成瘾者极难戒烟。酒精依赖在极端情况下被认为是心理疾病的表现，并且需要相应的治疗，但是在英国这种治疗在没有病人的主动配合下是无法完成的，而这种配合常常很难获得，因此严重的酒精成瘾者对于医疗和社会都是一个很头疼的问题。

I have mentioned both tobacco and alcohol addiction not only because of their intrinsic importance, though that is considerable, but in order to bring out a point of more general relevance. The World Health Organization Committee points out that the characteristic feature of drug-dependence is the strong desire or need to continue taking the drug. Leaving on one side the chronic alcoholic, using that term to describe people whose consumption of alcohol leads to such psychological or physical ill-effects that they are in need of medical treatment, there are many others who habitually take alcohol in more moderate amounts and claim that they feel and are the better for it, and miss it, if for some reason they are unable to get it. They would agree with a patient of mine who once said: "Alcohol has been a very good friend to me". This is a point to which I shall return.

What are we to think of this steadily rising consumption of barbiturates and tranquillizers? Before we can answer this question, which is a very complex one, we need a great deal of information which is not at present available. As the first Drug Addiction Committee said in its report: "It is clear that there is scope and a need for operation research into the prescribing pattern in this country with particular reference to habit-forming drugs". We need to know first how many patients are receiving prescriptions for barbiturates, and what is the average amount prescribed for these patients per annum. Then we must know what proportion of them are receiving barbiturates for treatment of epilepsy. An epileptic patient on barbiturates is drug-dependent because he cannot give up the drugs without serious ill-effects, but this type of drug-dependence is a use and not an abuse of the drug. Having eliminated those prescriptions, the next thing we need to know is what proportion of the tablets prescribed the patient actually consumes. Doctors, I am sure, would over-estimate their patients' faith in their prescriptions if they supposed that the tablets they prescribe are regularly and faithfully consumed by every patient. So we need to know from an appropriate sample of patients what proportion of the barbiturates prescribed for them they actually take; and if they do not take them all, what do they do with the rest? This is a question with several practical implications. Are the superfluous tablets locked up, or thrown away, or left about, where perhaps a child can find them? Moreover, if the patient puts them safely away, does he himself know what they are when he turns them out again in a year's time? It has sometimes been suggested that the prescription of excessive amounts of barbiturates by some doctors may be a source of such drugs for the black market. In any event, I think it is clear that prescription figures are likely to be a very misleading guide to actual consumption.

Nevertheless, let us assume—and experience shows that this is a reasonable assumption—that there are patients who are drug-dependent on barbiturates, not in the sense that they are in a state of chronic barbiturate intoxication, but that they are more or less regular consumers of barbiturates, either as hypnotics or as general sedatives to blunt the sense of being stretched on "the rack of this tough life". If this is drug-dependence, is it a use or an abuse of the drug? In the passage I quoted from the first report of the Drug Addiction Committee, it will be remembered, occur the words "often, however, a prescription is given for a drug when the patient's real need is a discussion of his psychological difficulties with the doctor". No doubt, this is sometimes true, but we have to remember that the average

我提到的烟草和酒精成瘾不仅因为它们固有的重要性（虽然是值得考虑的），也是为了提出更具有普遍意义的一点。世界卫生组织委员会指出，药物依赖的典型特征是继续服药的强烈欲望或需求。暂且不说慢性嗜酒者，即那些由于消耗大量的酒精而导致心理或身体上的副作用以至于需要医学治疗的人，还有许多习惯于饮用大于适量酒精的人声称因为饮酒他们感觉良好，如果因为某种原因他们无法获得酒精的话也会非常想念。他们会同意我的一位患者曾经说过的："酒精已经是我的一个非常好的朋友。"这是我要说的一点。

我们对巴比妥类药物和安定药消耗量的稳定增长怎么看呢？在回答这个非常复杂的问题之前，我们需要很多现在尚未获得的信息。正如第一届药物成瘾委员会在报告里说的："很清楚的是，现在有对国内的开药模式尤其是针对成瘾性药物进行研究的机会和需求"。我们首先需要知道有多少患者正在使用巴比妥类药物，以及每年为这些患者开药的平均量是多少。然后我们必须知道有多大比例的人使用巴比妥类药物是为了治疗癫痫。癫痫患者对巴比妥类药物是具有依赖性的，因为他们一停药就会有严重的后果，但是这种形式的药物依赖是正常的使用而不是滥用。在排除了这些处方之后，下一步我们需要知道的就是在开出的药物中有多大的比例真正被患者用掉了。如果医生们认为每一位患者都会定期如实地服用开出的药物，我可以肯定地说他们高估了患者对他们所开处方的信心。因此我们需要在合适的患者样本中调查开出的巴比妥类药物中到底有多大比例真正被患者使用，以及如果他们没有全部按照处方用掉，剩下的如何处置？这是一个具有许多实际意义的问题。这些剩余的药物是被储存起来、丢弃还是放在儿童可及的地方？此外，如果患者将其安全地储存起来，那一年之后再翻出来时他自己是否还能记得这是什么药？有时候人们就认为一些医生开出的过量巴比妥类药物可能是黑市中这类药物的来源。不管怎样，我想显然开药的数目误导了实际消耗的药量。

不过，让我们假设一下——经验告诉我们这是一个合理的假设——那些对巴比妥类药物有依赖的患者（并非处于慢性巴比妥类药物中毒的状态中，仅仅是巴比妥类药物的或多或少的定期服用者），用来作为催眠剂或者通用镇静剂以麻木他们"在艰苦生活拷问台上"被拉长的感觉。如果这也是药物依赖，那么到底是正常使用还是药物滥用？在我引用的药物成瘾委员会第一份报告的一段中，大家会记起的一句话就是"然而，当一名患者的真正需求是和医生讨论其心理问题时，医生经常会给他开药"。毫无疑问有些时候确实是这样的，但是我们要记住，当今普通的医生太忙

doctor today is much too busy to be able to spare the time for that kind of psychotherapy except on rare occasions, and though it would undoubtedly sometimes be helpful, many people would doubt whether psychotherapy, even if it were available, is the most suitable form of treatment for many such patients. Underlying a critical attitude to the regular prescription of barbiturates or other sedatives for the purpose I have mentioned, I think I can detect a hidden assumption. Let us look for a moment at another instance, namely, the administration of tranquillizers, which amounts to drug-dependence, but is nevertheless universally regarded as a use and not an abuse: I refer to the modern pharmacological treatment of schizophrenia. The regular administration of chlorpromazine and similar drugs to schizophrenics has enabled many of them to leave a mental hospital and live in the community so long as they take the drug regularly. Comparable beneficial results have been achieved by the treatment of patients suffering from depression by the antidepressant drugs. The authors of a recent monograph on the subject summarized the results of these forms of treatment as follows: "In general, these psychopharmacological agents have facilitated the control of mood and behavioural disturbances. In the mental hospital setting, they have induced a more quiet and more orderly atmosphere. They have enabled the discharge of an increasing number of patients and the return of many, previously resistant to treatment, to their appropriate places in society. In addition, they have facilitated ambulatory and outpatient treatment and have lessened the need for shock therapy"[1]. Here, then, is a beneficent form of drug-dependence in the case of patients suffering from major psychological disorders. Why, then, or in what circumstances, should we question the use of similar drugs in the doctor's consulting room for the treatment of patients suffering from minor psychological disorders? Is it perhaps because we are inclined to draw a line between gross psychiatric illnesses, for which we feel the patient cannot in any way be held responsible, and which are due to the operation of unknown physical factors, which may turn out to be biochemical, and the minor psychological disorders for which we do not postulate any physical cause but tend to attribute to psychological causes, and to regard as reactions to stresses and strains to which, perhaps we think, the fortunate majority of us are too tough to succumb. We recognize that it is of no use to admonish the schizophrenic as a general rule, but would not many of our neurotic patients, we wonder, be better as a result of some effort on their own part? This, of course, raises a difficult philosophical question involving the relationship between the mind and the brain. I shall not discuss this further now, but I doubt whether it is philosophically sound to make any such distinction between the major and the minor psychological disorders. We cannot interpret schizophrenia or depression purely in psychological terms, nor, for that matter, can we at present give a physiological explanation for them. It often appears easier to give a psychological explanation of the minor neurotic disorders from which many people suffer; but that does not exclude the probability that they, too have physiological explanations which we shall one day discover. The mind and body constitute a complex unity, and when we are dealing with psychological disorders, we always need to take account of both psychological and physiological interpretations so far as we can achieve them. It may well be that for the kind of reasons I have already mentioned some patients receive prescriptions for sedatives indiscriminately; but that is a long way from saying their continuing use involves a form of drug-dependence which is an abuse. I quote once more

以至于不能抽出时间进行这种心理治疗，除了极少数的情况。尽管毫无疑问心理治疗有时候是有帮助的，但是很多人会怀疑这些心理治疗（即使可以提供的话）是不是治疗多数的这种患者的最合适的方式。在我上文提到的目的而定期开巴比妥类药物或者其他镇静剂的批判态度之下，我想我又发现了一种隐藏的假设。让我们来看另一个例子，即镇静剂的使用达到了依赖性的程度但是仍然被普遍认为是正常使用而不是滥用，我指的是精神分裂症的现代药物治疗。定期地服用氯丙嗪和类似的药物治疗精神分裂症已经使得患者离开了精神病医院并重新回到社会，只要他们能够定期地服用这些药物。用抗抑郁药来治疗受抑郁症折磨的患者也取得了类似的好结果。最近在有关这个主题的专著中作者们总结了这些方式的治疗效果：“总体来说，这些治疗心理疾病的药物有助于控制情绪和行为紊乱。在精神病医院，它们创造了更加安静、更加有序的环境。它们使得出院患者的数量越来越多，并使许多先前对治疗很抵抗的患者回归到了社会中合适的位置。此外，它们也促进了不卧床和门诊患者的治疗并减少了对休克治疗的需求。”[1] 这就是药物依赖对患有重度心理紊乱的患者的有益方面。那么为什么或者我们在何种情况下才应该质疑医生在诊察室里开出类似的药物来治疗有轻度的心理疾病的患者呢？可能是因为我们倾向于对所有的心理疾病进行分类（我们无论如何也不应该让患者为此负责），哪些是由于未知的身体因素产生的（证明可能是生化方面的），对于轻度的心理紊乱我们不会假定任何身体因素而将其归因于心理原因，可以看作对压力和紧张的反应，可能我们认为很幸运我们大部分人足够坚强从而未被压垮。我们认识到一般来说劝诫精神分裂症患者是没有用处的，但是我们想知道神经官能症患者在自己的一些努力下能否好转？当然这提出了一个涉及思维和脑之间关系的困难的哲学问题。我现在不再深入谈这个问题，但是我怀疑在重度和轻度的心理紊乱之间所做的任何区分在哲学上是否合理。我们不能单纯用心理学术语去解释精神分裂症或者抑郁症，而且我们目前也不能够给出生理学方面的解释。对很多人患有的轻度神经官能症给出心理学解释常常比较简单，但是这不能排除某一天我们可能会发现它们也有生理学解释的可能性。思维和躯体形成一个复杂的整体，当我们处理心理紊乱时，我们常常需要尽可能地把目前已知的心理和生理两方面的解释考虑进来。恰恰是由于我已经提到的这类原因，患者会不加选择地接受镇静剂的处方。但是还不能说他们持续服用这些药物是药物滥用。我再一次引用第一届药物成瘾委员会的报告：“当药物能够让他们过上更幸福更有益的生活时，不是我们来决定他们偶尔或者定期地服用这些药物是否合理”。如果你是把酒精当成朋友的人，你当然认同在适宜的病例中定期服用镇静剂。

from the report of the first Drug Addiction Committee: "it is not for us to decide whether their occasional or even regular use is justified if it enables a person to lead a happier and more useful life". If you are among those who regard alcohol as a friend, you may also think the same of the regular use of sedatives in suitable cases.

But, in my view, the real limitation to the best possible use of such drugs springs from our ignorance. Let me end by looking into the future. I foresee a day when we shall understand much more than we do now about the relationship between the brain and the mind. On one hand we shall have methods of making accurate psychological assessments of the personality, very possibly in terms of factors which find no place in our present psychological vocabulary. We shall then be able to interpret psychological disorders in terms of these functions, their mutual interplay, and their reactions to our experiences. Parallel with these developments, psychopharmacology will have been placed on a rational instead of an empirical basis. We shall think in terms of the normal biochemistry of nerve cells and synapses, their groupings and interactions, their disorders and the effect of drugs on them. As a result, correlating in this way psychology, physiology, biochemistry and pharmacology, we shall have not only a more comprehensive armamentarium of drugs, but much more precision and individualization in their use. All we shall need then will be enough doctors with time to use them. But it would be wrong to leave the matter there. If mind and body are a unity we must not concentrate on the physical treatment of stress to the exclusion of its psychological aspects. Here, however, we need to look beyond individual psychotherapy and take a broader view. As the first Drug Addiction Committee said in its report, the cause of psychological maladjustment should be sought perhaps as much in social conditions as in the mind of the individual. So far as we know, life has always been stressful, and looking back over history and prehistory, it becomes clear that, although we have our own peculiar stresses, we have eliminated a great many which our ancestors had to put up with. Indeed, stress seems inherent in the evolutionary principle. There will always be some who find life too much for them, and they will continue to need help from pharmacology and supportive psychotherapy. We are all aware of the challenge to international and social organization which some of our major current stresses present. Beyond that, there is still much to be said for the ideal of fighting our own battles if we can without the aid of pharmacy, but with the support of some philosophy which gives a meaning to life, and from which we can draw strength and support.

(**208**, 825-827; 1965)

Reference:

1. Benson, W. M., and Schicle, B. C., *Tranquillising and Antidepressive Drugs* (C. C. Thomas, Springfield, Illinois, 1962).

但是，在我看来，对这些药物可能的最佳用途的真正限制源自我们的无知。我想通过展望未来来结束这次演讲。我预知有一天我们能够比现在更加了解大脑和思维之间的关系。一方面我们会有能够对人格做出准确的心理学评估的方法，很有可能用一些在我们现在的心理学词汇中还没有的因素。然后我们能够根据这些功能、它们之间的相互作用和它们对于我们体验的反应来解释心理紊乱。与这些进展同步的是，精神药理学将建立在理性基础上而不是经验主义基础上。我们应该从神经细胞和突触的正常生物化学、它们的分类和联系、它们的紊乱和药物对它们的作用方面进行考虑。结果，以这种方式将心理学、生理学、生物化学和药理学结合起来，我们不仅能够有更加充足的药物，而且在使用这些药物时可以更加精确和个性化。那时我们所需要的就是足够的医生有时间来使用它们。但是仅仅做到这些是不对的。如果思维和躯体是一个整体，我们一定不能仅仅将压力的治疗局限于身体层面上，而忽略了心理方面。然而，此时我们需要一个更广阔的视角来看问题，而不只局限于个体的心理治疗。正如第一届药物成瘾委员会在其报告中所说，精神失调的原因可能与社会环境有关，也可能与个人心态有关。就我们目前所知，生活总是充满压力的。回望历史以及史前时期，显而易见，虽然我们有我们自己特有的压力，但我们已经免去了太多先辈们不得不承受的压力。的确在进化原则中压力可能是与生俱来的。有些人经常觉得生活让他们难以承受，他们需要持续的药物和支持性心理治疗的帮助。我们都意识到自身巨大的压力给国际和社会组织所带来的挑战。此外，还有很多要说的是，我们的理想状态是在没有药物帮助的情况下，只是借助某种赋予生命一定意义的人生观，依靠身体自身与疾病做斗争，我们能从这种人生观中获得力量和支撑。

（毛晨晖 翻译；张旭 审稿）

A New Model for Virus Ribonucleic Acid Replication

F. Brown and S. J. Martin

Editor's Note

How do viruses replicate? Many have genes encoded not in DNA but in RNA, and in 1963 Luc Montagnier and F. K. Sanders proposed that single-stranded viral RNA could become a replicating double-stranded form inside host cells. Here researchers at the UK's Animal Virus Research Institute propose a more complicated replication strategy that involves circular forms of single- and double-stranded RNA, inspired by the way some bacterial viruses (phage) replicate their DNA. It is now known that RNA viruses employ several different strategies for replication—some make their own replication enzymes, others use the RNA to imprint their genes in the DNA of the host.

SUBSTANTIAL evidence now exists to support the initial observations of Montagnier and Sanders[1] that the multiplication of virus RNA proceeds via a replicating form. This form is readily differentiated from the RNA which is present in the complete virus particles by its considerably slower rate of sedimentation in sucrose, lower buoyant density in caesium sulphate and resistance to degradation by ribonuclease. It has been postulated that this replicating form permits the preferential synthesis of new virus RNA (corresponding to the plus strand) on a primer (minus strand) which is initially coded for by the ingoing virus RNA. This replicating form is envisaged as containing a double-stranded region as well as a number of single-stranded tails, corresponding to partially formed plus strands (Fig. 1*a*)[2-4]. Such a molecule would possess a lower buoyant density than single-stranded RNA and it has been assumed that ribonuclease will remove the single-stranded tails, leaving only a double-stranded molecule (Fig. 1*b*).

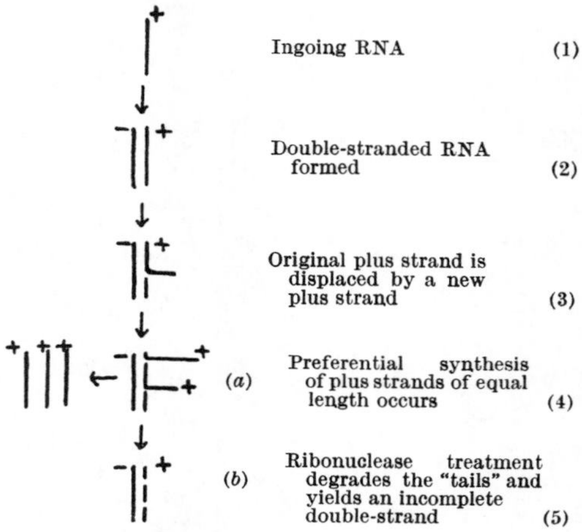

Fig. 1. Diagrammatic representation of the replicating mechanism of virus RNA which is at present accepted

病毒RNA复制的新模式

布朗，马丁

编者按

病毒如何复制？很多病毒的基因并不是编码在DNA上而是编码在RNA上，1963年吕克·蒙塔尼耶和桑德斯提出，在宿主细胞中的单链病毒RNA能够变为正在复制中的双链形式。本文中，来自英国动物病毒研究所的研究人员在一些细菌病毒（噬菌体）的DNA复制方式的启发下，提出了一种更为复杂的、涉及单链及双链RNA环状结构的复制策略。现在我们已经知道，RNA病毒使用多种不同的复制策略——有些病毒利用自己的复制酶来进行复制，其他病毒则是利用RNA把它们的基因编码在宿主的DNA上。

现在存在实证支持蒙塔尼耶和桑德斯[1]最初观察到的病毒RNA繁殖经历的一种复制模式。通过其在蔗糖中相对较慢的沉降速度、在硫酸铯中较低的浮力密度以及对核糖核酸酶降解作用的耐受，可以很容易将这种形式的RNA和存在于完整病毒颗粒中的RNA区分开来。据推测，在这种复制模式中，侵入宿主的病毒首先以其RNA为模板编码产生引物链（负链），然后再根据引物链选择合成新的病毒RNA（与正链一致）。估计这一复制模式中会出现一段双链区域，以及很多相当于正链片段的单链尾巴（图1*a*）[2-4]。这种RNA复合体分子的浮力密度比单链RNA分子的浮力密度更低，目前认为核糖核酸酶会降解掉单链尾巴，仅留下一个双链分子（图1*b*）。

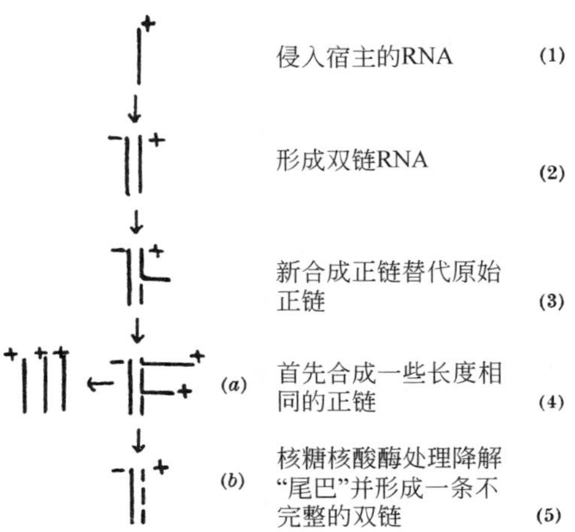

图1. 目前公认的病毒RNA复制机制的示意图

Certain features of this model, however, do not account for all the experimental evidence available. In the first place, it has been shown that the ribonuclease-resistant RNAs present in cells infected with EMC[1], foot-and-mouth disease[5] and poliomyelitis[6] viruses possess low but significant infectivity. Unless the minus strand is infective, which is extremely unlikely, the infectivity must be contained in the plus strand. In the model which is at present favoured, the plus strand of the ribonuclease-resistant RNA would not be an intact virus RNA strand but a collection of RNA molecules, each shorter in length than the virus RNA. All the evidence so far accumulated in a number of laboratories has shown that the intact virus RNA molecule is required for infectivity[7,8]. Secondly, the ribonuclease-resistant RNA in the model shown in Fig. 1*b* is a double-stranded molecule which has gaps between adjoining segments of the residual plus strands. It is questionable whether such a molecule would be stable to relatively high concentrations of ribonuclease, for example, 50 μg/ml.[9].

A model for the replicating form which accounts for these experimental findings should contain a complete double strand as the ribonuclease-resistant part of the structure. Additional experimental evidence which we have derived from an examination of the RNA molecules synthesized in baby hamster kidney cells infected with foot-and-mouth disease virus supports this supposition and has led us to propose a new hypothesis for virus RNA replication. Our hypothesis is based on a cyclic mechanism similar to that which is thought to be involved in the replication of DNA phages.

In a previous report from this laboratory, Brown and Cartwright[5] demonstrated that three peaks of ^{32}P-labelled RNA were formed in the presence of actinomycin *D* during foot-and-mouth disease virus replication in baby hamster kidney cells. These fractions were separated by sucrose-gradient sedimentation and have approximate sedimentation coefficients of 37*S*, 20*S* and 16*S* (peaks *A*, *B* and *C*, Fig. 2*A*).

This work has now been extended to a more detailed investigation of the individual fractions obtained from sucrose gradients. For the determination of the base composition, aliquots of each fraction were precipitated with 2 volumes of ethanol at –20° following addition of purified yeast RNA. The precipitates were then hydrolysed in 0.3 N potassium hydroxide and the distribution of radioactivity in the 2′-3′ -nucleotides was determined. Aliquots of individual fractions were precipitated with ethanol in the presence of unlabelled baby hamster kidney cell RNA, which was added to serve as an internal marker, and then recentrifuged in a second sucrose gradient. The results in Table 1 show that the RNA sedimenting in fractions 1-15 of virus-induced RNA has the same base composition as RNA extracted from purified virus[10,11]. Recycling of the individual fractions showed, however, that peak *A* was not homogeneous but consisted of a spectrum of fractions which differed in their sedimentation coefficients (Fig. 2*B*, *C*, *D*). In contrast, different fractions of the RNA from purified radioactive virus obtained in a similar way by sedimentation in a sucrose gradient had the same sedimentation coefficient (Fig. 3). The spectrum of sedimentation values present in virus-induced RNA has therefore been interpreted as being due to molecules of different chain-lengths. It is considered unlikely that these differences in sedimentation values, which are not found in RNA from

但是这种复制模式的某些特征不能解释所有已获得的实验证据。首先，研究发现在感染脑心肌炎病毒[1]、口蹄疫病毒[5]和脊髓灰质炎病毒[6]的细胞中，耐核糖核酸酶的RNA具有低的但是显著的感染性。负链具有感染性的可能性极小，因此这一感染性应该来源于正链。在目前较为认可的复制模式中，耐核糖核酸酶的RNA中的正链并不是完整的病毒RNA链，而是一组RNA分子，其每个分子的长度都比病毒RNA的长度短。到目前为止，许多实验室积累的证据表明，完整的病毒RNA分子对于感染是必需的[7,8]。其次，如图1*b*所示的模型中的耐核糖核酸酶RNA是一个双链的分子，其邻接的正链片段之间都有缺口。这样的分子在较高浓度的核糖核酸酶下（比如50微克/毫升[9]）能否保持稳定是值得怀疑的。

要想解释这些实验结果，病毒RNA复制形式的模型应该包含一个类似于耐核糖核酸酶的RNA部分结构的完整双链。在检测感染了口蹄疫病毒的幼仓鼠肾细胞中RNA分子合成情况时，我们得到的实验证据支持这一假设，并提出病毒RNA复制的一种新假说。这一假说基于一个环状机制，它类似于噬菌体DNA复制过程中所涉及的环状机制。

在本实验室先前的报道中，布朗和卡特赖特[5]证明，在存在放线菌素*D*的情况下，幼仓鼠肾细胞中的口蹄疫病毒复制时会形成3个^{32}P标记的RNA高峰。这3个组分可以用蔗糖梯度沉降法进行分离，它们的沉降系数大约分别为37*S*、20*S*和16*S*（图2*A*中的峰*A*、峰*B*和峰*C*）。

现在这项工作已经延伸到对通过蔗糖梯度得到的各种组分进行更加详细的研究。为了测定碱基组成，我们向等份的各组分中加入纯化的酵母RNA，再加入2倍体积的乙醇后在–20℃下沉淀。接着沉淀物在0.3摩尔/升的氢氧化钾溶液中进行水解，然后测定2′, 3′–核苷酸的放射性分布情况。向等份的各组分中加入未标记的幼仓鼠肾细胞RNA，作为内参，也用乙醇进行沉淀，然后在另一蔗糖梯度中再次离心。结果如表1所示，病毒感染组沉降分离后的第1~15组分沉淀得到的RNA，在碱基组成上和提取的纯病毒的RNA是相同的[10,11]。然而对各组分进行二次沉降分析的结果表明，峰*A*并不是由单一成分组成的，而是包含一系列沉降系数互不相同的组分（如图2中的*B*、*C*、*D*）。相比之下，对于来自纯化的具有放射性的病毒RNA，用同样的蔗糖梯度沉降法分离得到的不同组分则具有相同的沉降系数（图3）。因此，病毒感染得到的RNA具有多个不同的沉降系数值，这一现象应该解释为其中含有链长度不同的多种RNA分子。由于用相同步骤分离纯化的病毒中的RNA时并没有出现沉降系数的多样化，因此沉降系数多样化不太可能是由于存在多种稳定的构型造成的。

purified virus isolated by the same procedure, are due to the presence of different stable configurations. The results in Figs. 2 and 3 also reveal that peak *A* from virus-infected cells sediments more quickly than the RNA isolated from purified virus. This suggests that the RNA isolated from virus-infected cells contains some molecules which are larger than those which are incorporated into the virus particles. These molecules, as shown in Table 1, have the same base composition as virus RNA. Molecules of a length greater than that of virus RNA could not be formed on the basis of the displacement mechanism shown in Fig. 1. The maximum length that could be obtained by this mechanism would be the same as that of the primer RNA.

Table 1. Base Composition of Foot-and-Mouth Disease Virus RNA

Fraction No.	Base composition (counts/100 counts)			
	A	*U*	*G*	*C*
1	26.6	21.8	23.3	28.3
2	26.7	21.7	23.4	28.2
3	25.9	22.0	24.2	27.9
4	26.9	21.3	23.0	28.8
5	26.7	21.7	23.7	27.9
6	26.2	21.9	23.9	28.0
7	26.2	22.2	24.3	27.3
8	26.9	21.7	23.2	28.2
9	26.2	21.9	23.7	28.2
10	25.8	21.4	23.6	29.2
11	26.0	21.9	23.3	28.8
12	25.5	21.7	23.6	29.2
13	24.8	22.1	24.5	28.6
14	24.5	23.1	24.3	28.1
15	25.4	22.8	23.7	28.1
Purified virus RNA	26.0	21.8	24.1	27.8
RNase-resistant RNA	23.8	24.2	25.6	26.4
Calculated duplex	24.0	24.0	26.0	26.0

Individual fractions from gradients were precipitated with 1 mg yeast RNA any hydrolysed in 0.3 N potassium hydroxide for 18 h at 37°. The 2′-3′-nucleotides were separated by paper electrophoresis at pH 3.5 in sodium citrate buffer. The distribution of phosphorus-32 in the ultra-violet absorbing regions was determined after elution

We have also examined the structure of the ribonuclease-resistant RNA obtained by two successive centrifugations in sucrose gradients of virus-induced RNA which had been treated with 0.01 μg RNase/ml. This has a base composition which is in agreement with its being a duplex structure consisting of a plus and a minus strand (Table 1). Heating this molecule at various temperatures up to 110°C for 5 min, followed by rapid cooling, has failed to produce any molecules sedimenting at the same position as virus RNA (peak *A*, Fig. 3). A typical result is shown in Fig. 4, which indicates that both heated and unheated RNA sediment in approximately the same position. Nevertheless, after heating at 110°C the ribonuclease-resistant RNA is degraded by the enzyme. Single-stranded RNA isolated from purified virus also sedimented to the same position as the ribonuclease-resistant RNA after heating under these conditions (Fig. 4*C*). Apparently, heating single-stranded virus RNA in this manner produces structural or configurational changes in the molecule which

图 2 和图 3 的结果也表明，被病毒感染细胞的峰 *A* 比从纯病毒中分离得到的 RNA 沉降得更快。这说明从病毒感染细胞中分离得到的 RNA 中包含一些分子，它们比组成病毒颗粒的 RNA 分子更大。正如表 1 所示，这些分子和病毒 RNA 具有相同的碱基组成。而通过图 1 所示的置换机制是无法形成比病毒 RNA 更长的分子的，因为通过置换机制得到的最长的分子也只能同 RNA 引物链一样长。

表1. 口蹄疫病毒RNA的碱基组成

管号	碱基组成（计数/100计数）			
	A	*U*	*G*	*C*
1	26.6	21.8	23.3	28.3
2	26.7	21.7	23.4	28.2
3	25.9	22.0	24.2	27.9
4	26.9	21.3	23.0	28.8
5	26.7	21.7	23.7	27.9
6	26.2	21.9	23.9	28.0
7	26.2	22.2	24.3	27.3
8	26.9	21.7	23.2	28.2
9	26.2	21.9	23.7	28.2
10	25.8	21.4	23.6	29.2
11	26.0	21.9	23.3	28.8
12	25.5	21.7	23.6	29.2
13	24.8	22.1	24.5	28.6
14	24.5	23.1	24.3	28.1
15	25.4	22.8	23.7	28.1
纯化病毒的RNA	26.0	21.8	24.1	27.8
耐核糖核酸酶的RNA	23.8	24.2	25.6	26.4
理论上的双链	24.0	24.0	26.0	26.0

分别向密度梯度分离得到的各组分中加入 1 毫克酵母 RNA 并沉淀，然后在 37℃、0.3 摩尔 / 升的氢氧化钾溶液中水解 18 小时。在 pH 为 3.5 的柠檬酸钠缓冲液中通过纸电泳对 2′,3′– 核苷酸进行分离。洗脱后测定 ^{32}P 在紫外吸收区的分布

我们也分析了病毒感染产生的 RNA 经 0.01 微克 / 毫升核糖核酸酶处理并进行连续两次蔗糖梯度沉降后得到的耐核糖核酸酶的 RNA 的结构。其碱基组成表明它是由一条正链和一条负链组成的双链结构（表 1）。在包括高达 110℃的各种温度下将该分子加热 5 分钟，迅速冷却后，并不能得到任何与病毒 RNA（图 3 中的峰 *A*）具有相同沉降位置的分子。图 4 显示了一个典型的结果，可以看出，不管是经过加热处理还是没有经过加热处理，这种 RNA 总是在几乎相同的位置发生沉降。不过，经过 110℃加热处理后，这种耐核糖核酸酶的 RNA 能够被酶降解。在此条件加热处理后，从纯化的病毒中分离得到的单链 RNA 的沉降位置也与耐核糖核酸酶的 RNA 的沉降位置相同（图 4*C*）。很明显，用这种方法加热单链病毒 RNA 可以改变其原来的分子

are sufficient to greatly reduce its sedimentation coefficient. The fact that heating the ribonuclease-resistant RNA at 110°C did not produce any molecules with sedimentation coefficients smaller than that of heated virus RNA has been taken as evidence for the absence of a double-stranded structure in which the plus strand is composed of segments (cf. Fig. 1*b*).

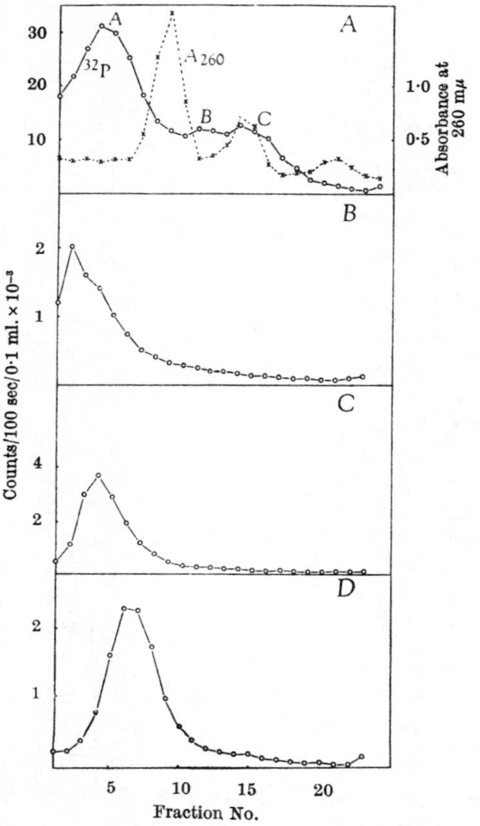

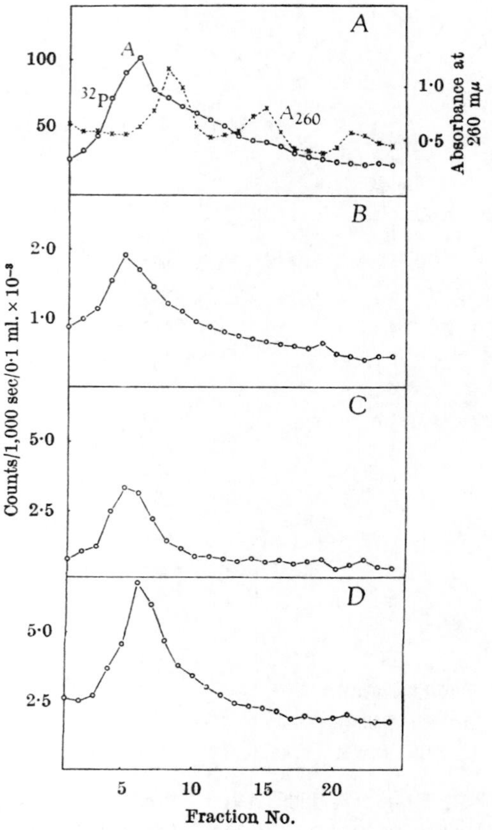

Fig. 2. Sedimentation in sucrose gradients (5-25 percent sucrose in 0.1 M acetate, *p*H 5.0) of "Sephadex *G*-200" filtered RNA from actinomycin *D* treated *BHK* cells, 4 h after infection with *FMD* virus. (*A*), Total RNA; (*B*), fraction 2 from first sedimentation recycled in a second gradient; (*C*), recycled fraction 4; (*D*), recycled fraction 6. The RNA was centrifuged for 16 h at 20,000 r. p. m. in an *SW* 25 rotor in a Spinco ultracentrifuge at 4°. Unlabelled *BHK* cell RNA was added to each sample before centrifuging to serve as an internal marker

Fig. 3. Sedimentation in sucrose gradients of RNA from purified ^{32}P-labelled *FMD* virus. (*A*), Total RNA; (*B*), fraction 3 from first sedimentation recycled in second gradient; (*C*), recycled fraction 5; (*D*), recycled fraction 6. Unlabelled *BHK* cell RNA was added to each sample before centrifuging to serve as an internal marker

结构或者构型，并足以降低其沉降系数。耐核糖核酸酶的 RNA 在 110℃ 下加热处理后并不能得到沉降系数比经同样加热处理的病毒 RNA 的沉降系数更小的任何分子，这一事实已经作为并不存在那种正链是由一些小片段组成的双链结构的证据（参见图 1*b*）。

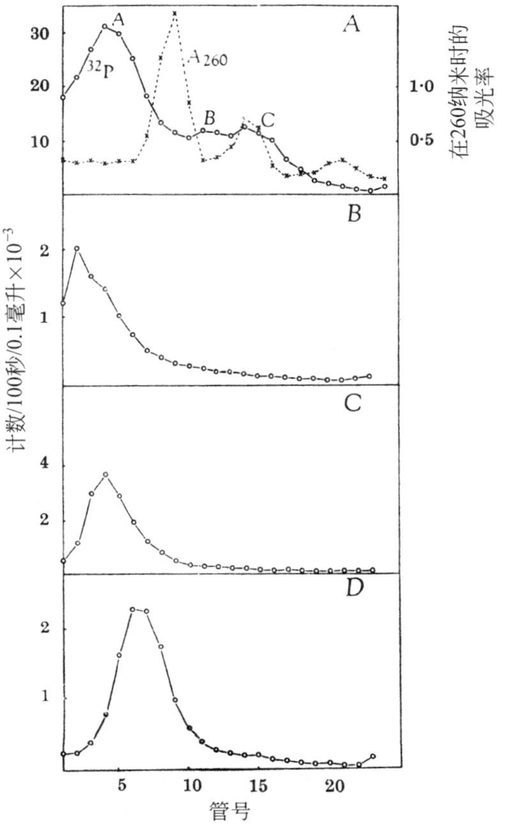

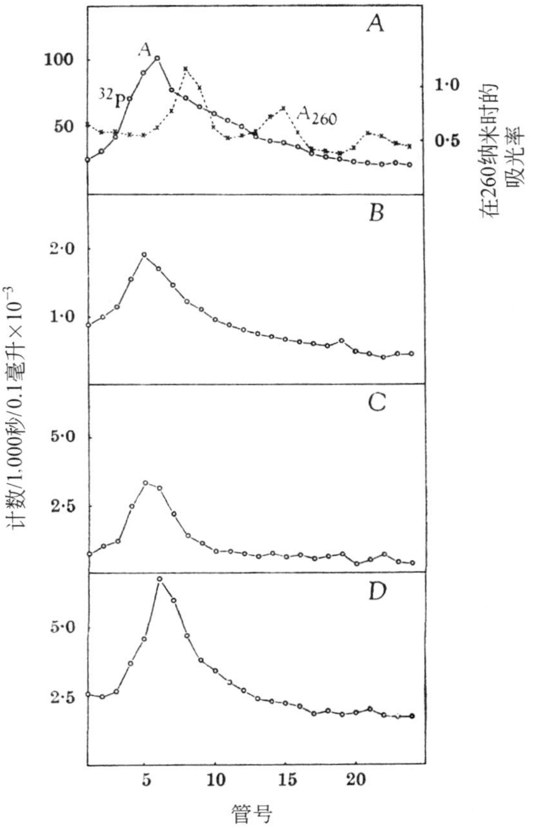

图 2. 幼仓鼠肾细胞用口蹄疫病毒感染 4 小时，再经放线菌素 *D* 处理后通过“葡聚糖 *G*–200”进行凝胶过滤，得到的 RNA 进行蔗糖梯度（0.1 摩尔 / 升乙酸盐中含 5% ~ 25% 的蔗糖，pH 5.0）沉降的情况。（*A*）总 RNA；（*B*）第一次沉降后的第 2 组分进行二次沉降的结果；（*C*）第 4 组分二次沉降的结果；（*D*）第 6 组分二次沉降的结果。在 4℃ 下，将 RNA 在斯宾诺超速离心机的 *SW*25 转子上以每分钟 20,000 转离心 16 小时。以离心前加入未标记的幼仓鼠肾细胞 RNA 的样品作为内参。

图 3. 纯化的 ^{32}P 标记的口蹄疫病毒中的 RNA 进行蔗糖梯度沉降的情况。（*A*）总 RNA；（*B*）第一次沉降后的第 3 组分进行二次沉降的结果；（*C*）第 5 组分进行二次沉降的结果；（*D*）第 6 组分进行二次沉降的结果。以离心前加入未标记的幼仓鼠肾细胞 RNA 的样品作为内参。

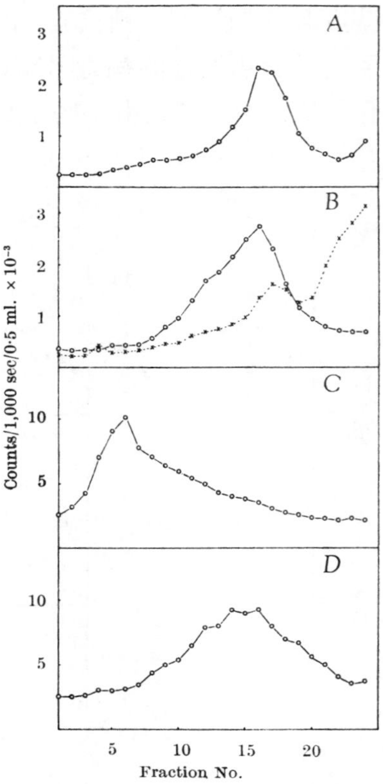

Fig. 4. Effect of heating at 110° in 10^{-2} M EDTA on the sedimentation in sucrose gradients of RNase-resistant RNA and virus RNA. (*A*), Unheated RNase-resistant RNA; (*B*), heated RNase-resistant RNA; ○ , without RNase; ×, with 0.01 μg RNase/ml.; (*C*), unheated virus RNA; (*D*), heated virus RNA

All the evidence at present available leads us to propose a replicating form which will release an intact double strand on ribonuclease treatment and also permit the synthesis of molecules with different chain-lengths. Neither of these requirements can be met with the displacement mechanism at present held. It is postulated that the ingoing virus RNA (plus strand) codes for a complementary minus strand (Fig. 5). This minus strand takes up the configuration of a circle, or is synthesized as a cyclic structure. The RNA polymerase which produces the new plus strands can rotate around this cyclic primer producing a long chain of plus strand, which is repetitive in sequence. This long chain is then broken down by an enzyme into segments of approximately the correct length for viral RNA. Molecules of shorter length may function as specific messenger RNAs for the synthesis of virus coat protein. This may be the function of the molecules present in peak *B* of the virus-induced RNA. Only those molecules of the correct length are finally incorporated into virus.

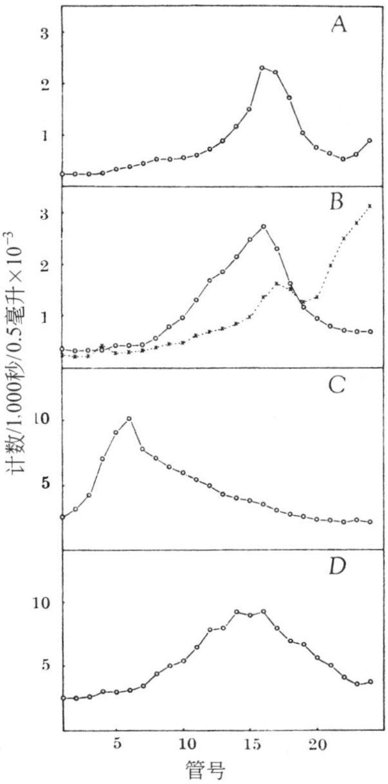

图 4. 耐核糖核酸酶的 RNA 和病毒 RNA 在 10^{-2} 摩尔 / 升的 EDTA 中进行 110℃ 加热处理对其蔗糖密度梯度沉降情况的影响。(*A*) 未加热的耐核糖核酸酶的 RNA；(*B*) 加热的耐核糖核酸酶的 RNA；○代表没有加核糖核酸酶的实验组，× 代表每毫升溶液中加入 0.01 微克核糖核酸酶的实验组；(*C*) 未加热的病毒 RNA；(*D*) 加热的病毒 RNA。

基于目前获得的所有证据，我们提出了一种复制模式，在这种复制模式中经核糖核酸酶处理后，会释放完整的双链，也允许合成链长度不同的多种分子。这两点完全不符合目前支持的置换机制。我们猜测，侵入宿主的病毒 RNA（正链）能够编码一条互补的负链（图 5），这条负链形成环状构型，或者其本来就被合成为环形结构。合成新正链的 RNA 聚合酶能够绕着这种环状的引物链合成一条在序列上重复的很长的正链。之后，在酶的剪切作用下，这条长链被切割成与病毒 RNA 长度相当的片段。那些长度较短的 RNA 片段可能充当合成病毒外壳蛋白的特异信使 RNA。病毒感染产生的 RNA 的峰 *B* 中的分子可能就具有这种功能。只有那些长度相当的 RNA 分子最后才会组装到病毒中。

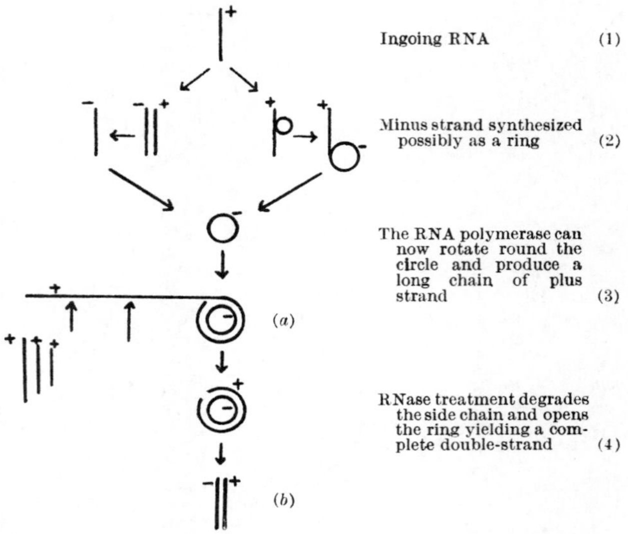
Ingoing RNA (1)
Minus strand synthesized possibly as a ring (2)
The RNA polymerase can now rotate round the circle and produce a long chain of plus strand (3)
(a)
RNase treatment degrades the side chain and opens the ring yielding a complete double-strand (4)
(b)

Fig. 5. Diagrammatic representation of the proposed model for virus RNA replication

This cyclic replicating form is consistent with the evidence available at present. On ribonuclease treatment the side chain will be removed and the ring probably opened at the growing point to yield a complete double strand. The hypothesis also explains the presence of virus-like RNA in virus-infected cells that has longer chain-lengths than the RNA extracted from purified virus.

(**208**, 861-863; 1965)

F. Brown and S. J. Martin: Animal Virus Research Institute, Pirbright, Woking, Surrey.

References:

1. Montagnier, L., and Sanders, F. K., *Nature*, **199**, 664 (1963).
2. Weissmann, C., Borst, P., Burdon, R. H., Billeter, M. A., and Ochoa, S., *Proc. U.S. Nat. Acad. Sci.*, **51**, 682 (1964).
3. Fenwick, M. L., Erikson, R. L., and Franklin, R. M., *Science*, **146**, 527 (1964).
4. Hausen, P., *Virology*, **25**, 523 (1965).
5. Brown, F., and Cartwright, B., *Nature*, **204**, 855 (1964).
6. Pons, M., *Virology*, **24**, 467 (1964).
7. Gierer, A., *Nature*, **179**, 1297 (1957).
8. Ginoya, W., *Nature*, **181**, 958 (1958).
9. Weissmann, C., Billeter, M. A., Schneider, M. C., Knight, C. A., and Ochoa, S., *Proc. U.S. Nat. Acad. Sci.*, **53**, 653 (1965).
10. Brown, F., and Cartwright, B., *Nature*, **199**, 1168 (1963).
11. Bachrach, H. L., Trautman, R., and Breese, S. S., *Amer. J. Vet. Res.*, **25**, 333 (1964).

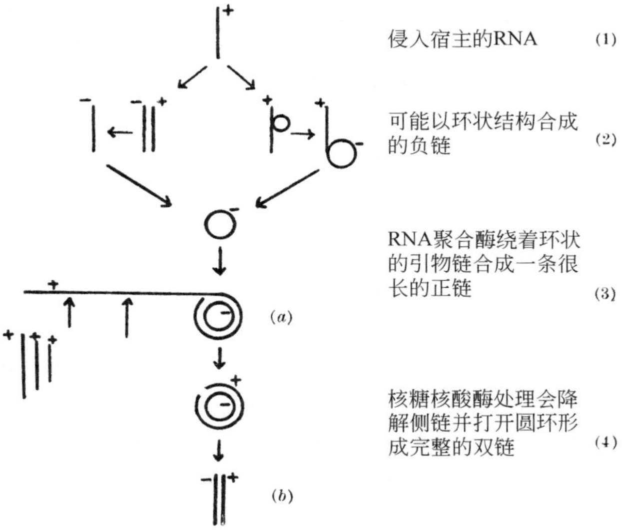

图 5. 我们提出的病毒 RNA 复制模型的示意图

这种环状复制模式和目前获得的证据是相吻合的。经核糖核酸酶处理后，侧链会被移除，环可能会在生长点处被打开从而形成一条完整的双链。这种假设也能够解释在病毒感染细胞中存在着比从纯化病毒中提取的 RNA 更长的病毒状 RNA。

（彭丽霞 翻译；王晓晨 审稿）

Virus Aetiology for Down's Syndrome (Mongolism)

A. Stoller and R. D. Collmann

Editor's Note

Today it is known that people with Down's syndrome have an extra copy of chromosome 21, and that the condition is more common in children born to older mothers. In this paper, Australian mental health researchers Alan Stoller and R. D. Collmann suggest instead a viral cause. They plot 12 years worth of Australian data on graph, demonstrating a correlation between maternal hepatitis infection and the occurrence of "mongol" births nine months later. The theory did not survive, and today the ultimate cause of Down's syndrome still remains uncertain.

FOR many years now, we have been working on the epidemiology of Down's syndrome (mongolism) in the State of Victoria, Australia, and have charted its occurrences during 1942-64. Peaks of incidence, of 2-year duration have been recorded at 5-7 year intervals from 1942 until 1957 and, as a result of this, a further peak of occurrence for this congenital anomaly was forecast for 1962-63. This was the first time ever that such a forecast had been able to be made and, in fact, this eventuated[1,2]. On the basis of our original findings[1,2], we had postulated a hypothesis of an infective virus, of long incubation, affecting mostly, but not exclusively, the ovum of the ageing mother, either directly or through some immunity pattern. Our reasons for this were not only the perception by one of us (A. S.) of a possible clinical relationship between the exposure of the mother to infective hepatitis prior to conception, but also the epidemiological findings that cases of mongol births clustered significantly in time and place, that urban peaks of annual incidence were in every case greater than rural peaks (higher contact rates), and rural peaks followed on one year after urban peaks (suggesting a slow spread of infection out of the high-contact urban areas into the rural areas). Our latest investigations have consisted of an attempt to match the annual occurrence of mongolism in the Melbourne area with the annual occurrence of notifiable infectious diseases during 1952-64, 1952 being the year that infective hepatitis first became notifiable in the State of Victoria. Of all infections diseases, the incidence of infective hepatitis, charted nine months prior to that of mongolism, has alone shown concordance (Fig. 1): another link in the chain of evidence we had forged relating mongolism to the virus of infective hepatitis, or some process associated with the infection, affecting the ovum prior to, or about the time of, conception. The correlation coefficient between the incidences of mongols, per 100,000 live births, and those of infective hepatitis, per million of population, was 0.81, significant at the level of $P<0.01$.

唐氏综合征（先天愚型）的病毒病因学

斯托勒，科尔曼

编者按

现在人们已经知道唐氏综合征患者多一条21号染色体，而高龄孕妇所生的孩子中患病的情况更为常见。在本文中，澳大利亚心理健康研究者艾伦·斯托勒和科尔曼认为该病是由病毒引起的。他们将12年间澳大利亚的数据进行绘图分析，指出孕妇肝炎感染和9个月后产出“先天愚型”患儿这两者之间存在相关性。这个理论没能站住脚跟。迄今为止，唐氏综合征的根本原因仍然不确定。

多年来我们致力于研究澳大利亚维多利亚州唐氏综合征（先天愚型）的流行病学，并对1942年~1964年间的发病情况进行了作图分析。从1942年到1957年，每隔5~7年就会出现一个持续2年的发病高峰，根据这一结果我们预测在1962年~1963年间将会出现这种先天性异常疾病发病的下一个高峰。这是首次对该病的流行性进行预测，事实上也的确发生了[1,2]。根据我们最初的发现[1,2]，我们提出一个假说，即可能有一种潜伏期很长的传染性病毒，主要但非专一地感染高龄孕妇的卵子，这种病毒或直接感染或经由某种免疫机制间接感染。我们之所以提出这一假说，不仅由于我们研究团队中的一员斯托勒发现先天愚型患儿的出生和产妇在受孕前感染肝炎可能在临床上有联系；而且流行病学的研究发现先天愚型的发病在时间和地点上具有明显的群发性，即每年城市发病高峰的病例都比农村发病高峰的病例多（接触率更高），在城市发病高峰一年后，农村才出现发病高峰（表明传染病从高接触率的城市地区慢慢传播到农村地区）。在最近的一项调查中，我们试图将1952年~1964年间墨尔本地区每年先天愚型的发病情况和每年呈报的传染性疾病的发病情况联系起来。1952年维多利亚州开始呈现传染性肝炎。在所有的传染性疾病中，只有传染性肝炎与先天愚型的发病情况具有一致性（图1），如图中所示，传染性肝炎的发病时间比先天愚型早9个月。这种一致性是我们把先天愚型和肝炎病毒感染，或者说与受孕前或受孕期间影响卵子的病毒感染过程联系起来的又一例证。每100,000个新生儿中先天愚型的患儿数与每1,000,000人中感染肝炎的人数之间的相关系数为0.81，在$P<0.01$的水平上两者具有显著的相关性。

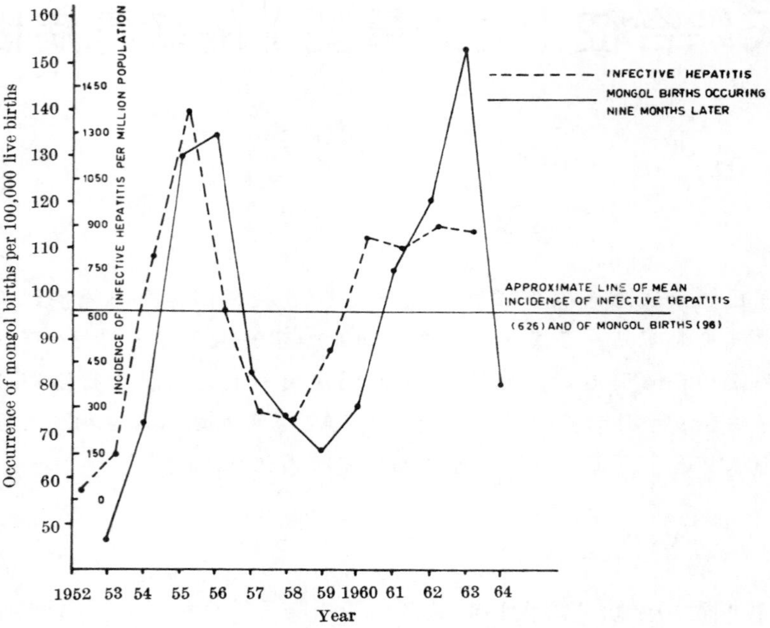

Fig. 1. Annual incidence of Infective hepatitis in Melbourne, and of mongol births 9 months later for the period 1952 to 1964

We would, in fact, postulate that such a process of virus human interaction could well be the basis of other genetic anomalies. We have already noted some degree of concordance between peaks of hydrocephaly and mongolism[3], even though, in the former, no visible chromosomal abnormality is apparent. A prospective clinical investigation is being put into operation to test the association between infective hepatitis and the occurrence of mongolism; and immunity patterns for this virus, as soon as feasible, will need to be tested on a large group of mothers "at risk". Meanwhile, also, examination of the effects of viruses on human cells in culture, and of ovarian tissue in particular, might well open up an undreamed of prospect of obtaining insight into the production, and thence prevention, of many gene disturbances.

(**208**, 903-904; 1965)

Alan. Stoller and R. D. Collmann: Mental Health Research Institute, Royal Park, N.2., Victoria, Australia.

References:

1. Collmann, R. D., and Stoller, A., *Amer. J. Publ. Hlth.*, 52, 813 (1962).

2. Stoller, A., and Collmann, R. D., *Med. J. Austral.*, 1, 1 (1965).

3. Collmann, R. D., and Stoller, A., *J. Ment. Defic. Res.*, 76, 22 (1962).

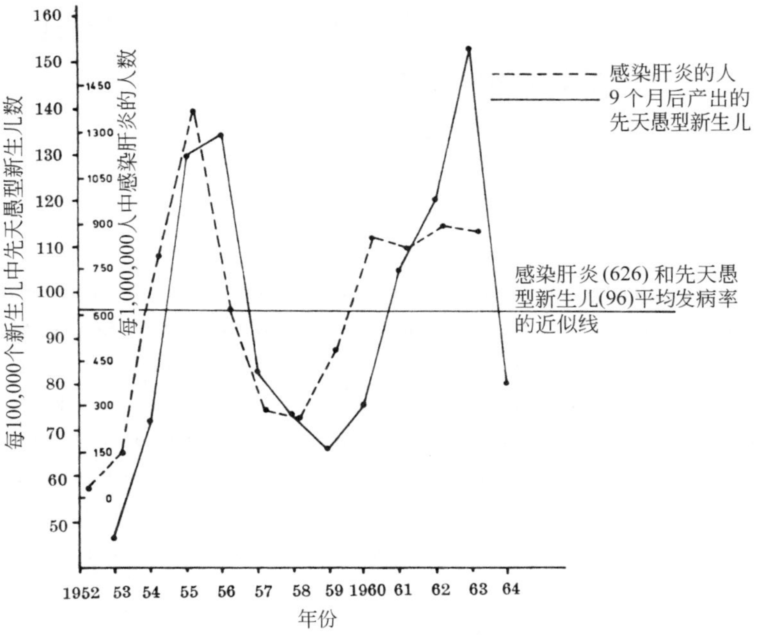

图 1. 1952 年 ~1964 年间墨尔本每年感染肝炎的人数以及 9 个月后产出的先天愚型新生儿数

事实上，我们推测病毒与人体相互作用的这一过程很可能是其他遗传异常发生的基础。我们已经发现脑积水发病高峰和先天愚型具有一定的相关性[3]，尽管在脑积水病例中没有观察到明显的染色体异常现象。正在进行一项具有前瞻性的临床调查以检测肝炎感染和先天愚型发病之间的联系；一旦可行，将要在大量“高危”的母亲中检测该病毒的免疫机制。同时，检测病毒对体外培养的人类细胞尤其是卵巢组织的影响也许会揭示出许多令人意想不到的基因异常发生的原因，进而预防许多基因异常的发生。

（彭丽霞 翻译；金侠 审稿）

Biological and Mental Evolution: an Exercise in Analogy*

A. Koestler

Editor's Note

Here the Hungarian writer and philosopher Arthur Koestler contributes a paper to *Nature* based on an address commemorating the mineralogist James Smithson, who bequeathed the funds for the Smithsonian Institution in Washington DC. Koestler draws an analogy between biological and mental evolution. He suggests that the former can be considered a "history of escapes from over-specialization", and that "breakthroughs" in art and science can be thought of this way too, for example in reference to Thomas Kuhn's model of scientific "revolutions" occurring via paradigm shifts. Koestler's argument looks somewhat dated now, but his suggestion that evolution has "structural constraints" that limit what random mutation may create remains relevant.

ALLOW me to take you on a ride on the treacherous wings of analogy, starting with an excursion into genetics. Creativity is a concept notoriously difficult to define; and it is sometimes useful to approach a difficult subject by way of contrast. The opposite of the creative individual is the pedant, the slave of habit, whose thinking and behaviour move in rigid grooves. His biological equivalent is the over-specialized animal. Take, for example, that charming and pathetic creature, the koala bear, which specializes in feeding on the leaves of a particular variety of eucalyptus tree and on nothing else; and which, in lieu of fingers, has hook-like claws, ideally suited for clinging to the bark of the tree—and for nothing else. Some of our departments of higher learning seem expressly designed for breeding koala bears.

Sir Julian Huxley has described over-specialization as the principal cause why evolution in all branches of the animal kingdom—except man's—seems to have ended either in stagnation or in extinction. But, having made his point, he drew a conclusion which you may find less convincing. "Evolution," be concluded, "is thus seen as an enormous number of blind alleys with a very occasional path to progress. It is like a maze in which almost all turnings are wrong turnings[1]." With due respect, I think this metaphor is suspiciously close to the old-fashioned behaviourist's views of the rat in the maze as a paradigm of human learning. In both cases the explicit or tacit assumption is that progress results from a kind of blind man's buff—random mutations preserved by natural selection, or random tries preserved by reinforcement—and that that is all there is to it. However, it is possible to dissent from this view without invoking a *deus ex machina*, or a Socratic *daimon*, by making

* Substance of an address delivered on September 18 at the Bicentennial Celebration commemorating the birth of James Smithson, held in Washington during September 16-18 (see *Nature*, **208**, 320; 1965).

生物进化与心理演进：类推法运用*

凯斯特勒

编者按

本文是匈牙利作家、哲学家阿瑟·凯斯特勒基于纪念矿物学家詹姆斯·史密森（其遗赠资金建立了位于华盛顿的史密森学会）的致词而发表在《自然》上的一篇论文。凯斯特勒运用类推法来研究生物进化和心理演进。他认为前者可以被看作一段“逃离高度特化的历史”，这也同样可以用来理解艺术和科学中的“突破”，比如托马斯·库恩建立的通过典范式转移而引发“革命”的科学模型。现在看来凯斯特勒的论点有些过时了，但是他提出的进化中存在着能够限制随机突变发生的“结构限制”这一论断仍然适用。

让我们从遗传学的角度出发去领略一下类推法的奥妙。创造是一个很难界定的概念，而有时候通过对照或许可以有效地解决这个难题。创造的对立面是教条、惯性思维，即思考和行动严格地按照常理来办。从生物学的角度来看，这等价于高度特化的动物。例如，树袋熊是一种迷人而又让人怜爱的动物，它专门以一种特定桉树叶为食，绝不以其他食物为食；其指被钩状的爪代替，非常适合紧紧握住树皮——除此以外，便也没有其他用处了。高校的一些院系就好像是为了“培养树袋熊”而设置的一样。

朱利安·赫胥黎爵士认为高度特化是动物界所有进化分支（除了人类之外）最终停滞或消失的主要原因。不过，为了表达他的观点，他做出这样一个也许你会认为并不那么可信的结论：将“进化”总结为“就好比是众多死胡同中偶然向前伸展出来的一条小道，这就像迷宫一样，无论向哪个方向转弯都是错误的[1]。”恕我直言，我认为这一比喻可能类似于传统行为学家利用老鼠迷宫研究人类学习模式的观点。两者都直接或默认地做出了这样的假设，即发展是源于一种类似捉迷藏的过程而获得的——源于经过自然选择或强化后所保存下来的随机突变——并且就是这样简单。然而，这种观点可能不被人接受，因为仅仅通过简单的假设，我们并不能排除这是

* 于9月18日发表在纪念詹姆斯·史密森诞辰200周年庆典上的演讲，该庆典于9月16日～18日在华盛顿举行（见《自然》第208卷，第320页；1965年）。

the simple assumption that, while random events no doubt play an important part in the picture, that is not all there is to it.

One line of escape from the maze is indicated by a phenomenon known to students of evolution by the ugly name of paedomorphism, a term coined by Garstang[2] some forty years ago. The existence of the phenomenon is well established; but there is little mention of it in the text-books, perhaps because it runs against the *Zeitgeist*. It indicates that in certain circumstances evolution can re-trace its steps, as it were, along the path which led to the dead-end and make a fresh start in a more promising direction. To put it simply, paedomorphism means the appearance of some evolutionary novelty in the larval or embryonic stage of the ancestral animal, a novelty which may disappear before the adult stage is reached, but which reappears in the adult descendant. This bit of evolutionary magic is made possible by the well-known mechanism of neoteny, that is to say, the gradual retardation of bodily development beyond the age of sexual maturity, with the result that breeding takes place while the animal still displays larval or juvenile features. Hardy[3], de Beer[4] and others have pointed out that if this tendency toward "prolonged childhood" were accompanied by a corresponding squeezing out of the later adult stages of ontogeny, the result would be a rejuvenation and despecialization of the race which would thus regain some of its lost adaptive plasticity. But of even greater importance than this re-winding of the biological clock is the fact that in the paedomorphic type of evolution selective pressure operates on the early, malleable stages of ontogeny. In contrast to this, gerontomorphism—the appearance of novel characters in the late-adult stages—can only modify structures which are already highly specialized. One is accordingly led to expect that the major evolutionary advances were due to paedomorphism and not to gerontomorphism—to changes in the larval or embryonic, and not in the adult, stage.

Let me give an example, which will make clearer what I am driving at. There is now strong evidence in favour of the theory, proposed by Garstang[2] in 1922, that the chordates, and thus we, the vertebrates, descended from the larval state of some primitive echinoderm, perhaps rather like the sea-urchin or sea-cucumber. Now an adult sea-cucumber would not be a very inspiring ancestor—it is a sluggish creature which looks like an ill-stuffed sausage, lying on the sea-bottom. But its free-floating larva is a much more promising proposition: unlike the adult, it has bilateral symmetry, a ciliary band presumed to be the forerunner of the neural fold, and other sophisticated features not found in the adult animal. We must assume that the sedentary adult residing on the sea-bottom had to rely on mobile larvae to spread the species far and wide in the ocean, as plants scatter their seeds in the wind; and that the larvae, which had to fend for themselves, exposed to much stronger selective pressures than the adults, gradually became more fish-like; and lastly because sexually mature while still in the free-swimming; larval state—thus giving rise to a new type of animal which never settled on the bottom at all and altogether eliminated the senile, sessile cucumber stage from its life-history.

It seems that the same re-tracing of steps to escape the dead-ends of the maze was repeated at each decisive evolutionary turning-point—the last time, so far as we know,

一种任意的巧合或者是苏格拉底式的迷局，毫无疑问随机事件在全局中发挥着重要作用，但这并不是全部。

逃离迷宫的一条路线可以用进化学习者所熟知的一种现象来说明，这一现象有一个难听的名字叫做幼稚形态，是加斯唐[2]在大约四十年前提出的一个概念。已经明确证实该现象是存在的；但是在教科书中却很少被提及，这也许是因为它违背了**时代精神**。该概念指出，在特定环境下进化可以重演，犹如沿着一条通往死胡同的道路，转入一个更有希望的方向重新开始一样。简单说来，幼稚形态就是指动物祖先的幼体或胚胎期出现的一些进化的新表型可能在成熟期到来前就消失了，但却又会重新出现在成体的后代当中。这种令人不可思议的进化可能是由人们熟知的幼态持续机制导致的，也就是说，越过了正常的性成熟年龄之后，身体发育逐步延迟，以至于在它开始出现繁殖行为时仍表现出幼体的形态特征。哈迪[3]、德比尔[4]及其他学者均指出：如果这种“幼稚期延长”的趋势伴随着之后的成体发育阶段相应地减少，结果便产生了返老还童的特征和种族的去高度特化性，这种性质能够使其重新获得一些曾经失去的适应可塑性。但是，较之生物钟重绕，更为重要的是以下事实，即幼体形态类型的进化选择压力发生在个体发育可延展性的早期。相反地，老龄形态——在成熟阶段晚期出现的新表型——则只能调控已经高度特化的结构。可以认为进化过程主要是由幼稚形态而非老龄形态所致，即在幼体期或胚胎期而非在成熟期发生改变。

举个可以令我的讲述更为清楚的例子。1922 年，加斯唐[2]提出的一个现在已经得到强有力的证据支持的理论，即脊索动物及脊椎动物（包括人类）来源于一些原始棘皮动物的幼期形态，这种形态可能与海胆或者海参非常相似，但这却不是一种令人鼓舞的祖先形态，它行动迟缓，深躺海底，犹如一根未塞满的腊肠。然而，它的自由漂浮生活的幼虫是一个更有研究前景的命题：幼虫与成虫不同，它具有双面对称结构，一个被推测认为可能是神经褶前体的纤毛环，和其他一些成虫不具有的复杂特征。我们推测：驻留在海底生活的成虫依赖于可运动的幼虫在海里向更远处及更大范围散播其物种，就像植物通过风来散播种子一样；而且必须努力谋生的幼虫较成虫暴露在更大的选择压力下，便逐渐地变得与鱼类更为相似，最后在浮游期就发生了性成熟，从而产生出一种新的动物类型，这种类型的动物从来不驻留在海底生活，其衰老时的驻留生活状态在其生活史中完全消失。

仿佛避开迷宫的死胡同一样，在每一个决定进化方向的转折时刻都重复发生着重演的步骤——目前我们所知的最后一次转折是人类从一些原始的灵长类动物中分

when the line which bore our own species branched off from some ancestral primate. It is now generally recognized that the human adult resembles more the embryo of an ape than an adult ape. In both, the ratio of brain-weight to body-weight is disproportionately high; in both, the closing of the sutures of the skull is retarded to allow for further brain growth. The back to front axis through man's head—the direction of his line of sight—forms an angle of ninety degrees with his spinal column; a condition which, in apes and other mammals, is only found in the embryonic stage. The same applies to the angle between the uro-genital canal and the backbone, which accounts for the singularity of the human way of mating. Other embryonic—or, to use Bolk's[5] term, foetalized—features are the absence of brow-ridges, scantness of body-hair, retarded development of the teeth, and so on. As Haldane[6] has said: "If human evolution is to continue along the same lines as in the past, it will probably involve a still greater prolongation of childhood and retardation of maturity. Some of the characters distinguishing adult man will be lost." But there is a reverse to the medal, which Aldous Huxley gleefully showed us in *After Many A Summer*: artificial prolongation of the absolute life-span of man might provide an opportunity for features of the adult ape to re-appear in Methuselah. But this only by the way.

The essence of the process which I have described is a retreat from highly specialized adult forms of bodily structure and behaviour to an earlier, more plastic and less committed stage—followed by a sudden advance in a new direction. It is as if the stream of life had momentarily reversed its course, flowing uphill for a while, then opened up a new stream-bed—leaving the koala bear stranded on its tree like a discarded hypothesis. We have now reached the crucial point in our excursion, because it seems to me that this process of *reculer pour mieux sauter*—of drawing back to leap, of undoing and re-doing—is a basic feature of all significant progress, both in biological and mental evolution.

It can be shown, I think, that these two types of progress—the emergence of biological novelties and the creation of mental novelties—are analogous processes on different levels of the developmental hierarchy. But to demonstrate the connexion we must proceed stepwise from lower to higher organisms. One of the fundamental properties of living organisms is their power of self-repair, and the most dramatic manifestations of this power are the phenomena of regeneration (which Needham[7] called "one of the more spectacular pieces of magic in the repertoire of living organisms"). Primitive creatures, like flatworms, when cut into slices, can regenerate a whole animal from a tiny fragment; Amphibia can regenerate limbs and organs; and once more the "magic" is performed by *reculer pour mieux sauter*—the regression of specialized tissues to a genetically less committed, quasi-embryonic stage, a de-differentiation or de-specialization followed by a re-differentiation.

Now the replacement of a lost limb or lost eye is a phenomenon of a quite different order from the adaptive processes in a normal environment. Regeneration could be called a meta-adaptation to traumatizing challenges. The power to perform such meta-adaptations manifests itself only when the challenge exceeds a critical limit and can only be met by having recourse to the genetic plasticity of the embryonic stage. We have just seen that

支出来的时候。现在一般认为，相比成熟猿类的形态，成人与猿类的胚胎期更为相似。两者的脑重与体重比都高得不成比例；两者的大脑都因头骨缝闭合时间推迟而得以进一步发育。人体头部的后前轴（参照头部视线方向）与脊柱成九十度角；而这种情形对于猿类和其他哺乳动物来说只出现在胚胎时期。在泌尿生殖器道与脊柱间也呈现同样的九十度角，这是与人类所特有的交配方式相适应的。其他的胚胎的特征或似胚胎状（运用博尔克[5]的术语）的特征有：没有眉梁、缺少体毛、牙齿发育迟缓等等。正如霍尔丹[6]所说："如果人类进化是在原有基础上的继续发展，其幼体期也将很可能会进一步延长，而成熟期将被延后。一些区别于成人的特征也将消失。"但是，相反地，如奥尔德斯·赫胥黎在《多少个夏天之后》中欣慰地向我们展示一样：人为延长人类的绝对寿命可能会使成年猿类所具有的特征在高龄的个体中再次出现。但这只是顺便提一下而已。

我所描绘的这个过程的本质是从身体结构形式和行为方式高度特化的成年期回到一个更早、更具有可塑性而定向性较低的时期，该时期过后紧随着会出现一个朝着新方向的突发性的提高。这就像一条生命的溪流突然改变其进程，向上流动一会儿，之后就打开了一个新的河床，就像一个被抛弃的假说所描述的那样将树袋熊留在树上使其进退两难。现在，我们已经到达了进化中的关键时刻，因为似乎对我来讲，在生物进化和心理演进中，以退为进、撤销与重建是所有重要过程的一种基本特征。

我认为可以将生物学新事物的出现与新思维的产生这两种过程看作在不同的发展等级水平上的两个相互类似的过程。然而，为了论证两者的关系，我们应该遵循逐步由低等生物体到高等生物体的步骤。生命有机体的一个基本特征是具有自我修复功能，而再生现象则是这种功能的最生动的体现（尼达姆[7]曾称这种再生现象是"生命有机体中令人惊叹的魔法中的一个片断"）。当将原始生物体（如扁形虫）切成几个片断时，每个小片断都可以再生出一个完整的个体；两栖动物可以再生出肢体和器官；这种"魔法"再一次由以退为进来完成，即特化组织经过去分化或紧随着再分化的去特化退行到定向性较低的准胚胎期。

此时，丢失肢体或丢失眼的替换过程完全不同于在正常环境中的适应过程的顺序。再生可以被称为是挑战中受创伤后的一种超适应性，这种超适应性只有当其受到的挑战超过一定的临界点才会表现出来，且只有具备胚胎期遗传可塑性的生命有机体才会表现出来。我们刚才已经了解到系统发生的主要变化是在成体退回到胚胎

the major phylogenetic changes were brought about by a similar retreat from adult to embryonic forms. Indeed, the main line of development which led up to our species could be described as a series of operations of phylogenetic self-repair: of escapes from blind alleys by the undoing and re-moulding of maladapted structures.

Evidently, self-repair by the individual produces no evolutionary novelty, it merely restores the *status quo ante*. But that is all the individual needs in order to regain its normal adaptive balance in a static environment (assuming that the traumatizing disturbance was only a momentary one). Phylogenetic "self-repair", on the other hand, implies changes in the genotype to restore the adaptive balance in a changing environment.

As we move toward the higher animals, the power of regenerating physical structures is superseded by the equally remarkable power of the nervous system to reorganize its mode of function. (Ultimately, of course, these reorganizations must also involve structural changes of a fine-grained nature in terms of circuitry, molecular chemistry or both, and so we are still moving along a continuous line.) Lashley[8] taught his rats certain visual discrimination skills; when he removed their optical cortex, the learning was gone, as one would expect; but, contrary to what one would expect, the mutilated rats were able to learn the same tasks again. Some other brain area, not normally specializing in visual learning, must have taken over this function, deputizing for the lost area.

Similar feats of meta-adaptation have been reported in insects, birds, chimpanzees and so on. But let us get on to man, and to those lofty forms of self-repair which we call self-realization, and which include creativity in its broadest sense. Psycho-therapy, ancient and modern, from shamanism down to contemporary forms of abreaction therapy, has always relied on what Ernst Kris[9] has called "regression in the service of the ego". The neurotic with his compulsions, phobias and elaborate defence-mechanisms is a victim of maladaptive specialization—a koala bear hanging on for dear life to a barren telegraph pole. The therapist's aim is to regress the patient to an infantile or primitive condition; to make him retrace his steps to the point where they went wrong, and to come up again, metamorphosed, re-born. Goethe's *Stirb und Werde*, the inexhaustible variations of the archetype of death and resurrection, dark night and spiritual rebirth, all revolve around this basic paradigm—Joseph in the well, Jesus in the tomb, Buddha in the desert, Jonah in the belly of the whale.

There is no sharp dividing line between self-repair and self-realization. All creative activity is a kind of do-it-yourself therapy, an attempt to come to terms with traumatizing experiences. In the scientist's case the trauma is some apparent paradox of Nature, some anomaly in the motion of the planets, the sting of data which contradict each other, disrupt an established theory, and make nonsense of his cherished beliefs. In the artist's case, challenge and response are manifested in his tantalizing struggle to express the inexpressible, to conquer the resistance of his medium, to escape from the distortions and restraints imposed by the conventional styles and techniques of his time.

形式时产生的。事实上，发展到我们人类物种的主要线路可以被形容为是一系列系统发生的自我修复的结果，通过对适应不良的机体结构进行淘汰和重塑来避开进化过程中的死胡同。

显然，个体的自我修复并没有产生进化上的新事物，它只是恢复了原状。然而，这却是所有个体在静态环境中重获正常适应性平衡所必须经历的过程（假定损伤干扰只是暂时的）。另外，系统发生的“自我修复”也暗示着在变化的环境中基因型的改变能够修复适应性平衡。

当我们向着高等动物发展时，身体结构的再生功能则被功能同样显著的神经系统所替代，以便重组其功能模式。（当然，最后这些重组也必然涉及天然精细结构的改变，如循环结构、化学分子物质或两者兼有，所以我们仍朝着原有的线路进行演进。）拉什利[8]教授训练他的大鼠某些视觉辨别技巧，而正如我们可以预计的一样，当他将大鼠的视觉皮层切除后，这种辨别能力便消失了。然而，与我们预计的结果不同的是：这些被切除视觉皮层的大鼠可以通过再学习获得这种技巧，这说明大脑内其他非视觉学习区域必定接替了这种任务，从而取代了被切除的区域。

相似的超适应能力在昆虫、鸟类、黑猩猩等中也有过报道。但让我们回到人类，回到那些我们称之为自我实现的在广义上具有创造性的自我修复的高级形式。无论是古代还是现代的精神疗法，从萨满教到当代的情感发泄疗法，都依赖于恩斯特·克里斯[9]所提出的“自我机能的退行”。具有强迫症、恐惧症和精细防御机制的神经病患者是不适应特化的牺牲品，如同把树袋熊挂在单调乏味的电线杆上虚度宝贵生命。治疗师的目的在于引导病人恢复到婴幼儿或原来的状态，折回到错位点上，并再次向前发展、改变，进而获得重生。在歌德的“死去重生”中，死亡与复活、黑暗之夜和精神复活原型的无穷无尽的变化都围绕着这一基本模式——井里的约瑟，坟墓里的耶稣，沙漠里的佛陀，鲸鱼肚里的约拿。

自我修复与自我实现之间没有一个确切的分界线。所有创造性的活动都是一种自我完成的疗法，都是一种恢复精神创伤体验的尝试。对于科学家来讲，损伤是自然界的一种明显的自我矛盾形式，是行星运行的异常形式，是相互矛盾的棘手的数据，它使原有理论陷于混乱，使人们珍视的信念变得一文不值。对于艺术家来说，挑战与响应可以在以下情形中得到证明，当他们急切努力去表达那些难以表达的事物时，当他们去征服其媒介的阻力时，当他们努力挣脱其所处时代的传统的方法与形式强加给他们的扭曲与抑制时。

In other words, the so-called revolutions in the history of both science and art are successful escapes from blind alleys. The evolution of science is neither continuous nor strictly cumulative except for those periods of consolidation and elaboration which follow immediately after a major breakthrough. Sooner or later, however, the process of consolidation leads to increasing rigidity and orthodoxy, and so into the dead-end of over-specialization. The proliferation of esoteric jargons which seems to characterize this phase reminds one sometimes of the monstrous antlers of the Irish elk, and sometimes of the neurotic's elaborate defence-mechanisms against the threats of reality. Eventually, the process leads to a crisis, and thus to a new revolutionary break-through—followed by another period of consolidation, a new orthodoxy, and so the cycle starts again.

In the history of art, this cyclic process is even more obvious: periods of cumulative progress within a given school and technique end inevitably in stagnation, mannerism or decadence, until the crisis is resolved by a revolutionary shift in sensibility, emphasis, style.

Every revolution has a destructive and a constructive aspect. In science the destruction is wrought by jettisoning previously unassailable doctrines, including some seemingly self-evident axioms of thought. In art, it involves an equally agonizing re-appraisal of accepted values, criteria of relevance, frames of perception. When we discuss the evolution of art and science from the historian's detached point of view, this un-doing and re-doing process appears as a normal and inevitable part of the whole story. But when we focus our attention on any concrete individual who initiated a revolutionary change, we are immediately made to realize the immense intellectual and emotional obstacles he had to overcome. I mean not only the inertial forces of society; the primary locus of resistance against heretical novelty is inside the skull of the individual who conceives of it. It reverberates in Kepler's agonized cry when he discovered that the planets move in elliptical pathways: "who am I, Johannes Kepler, to destroy the divine symmetry of the circular orbits!". On a more down-to-earth level the same agony is reflected in Jerome Bruner's[10] experimental subjects who, when shown for a split second a playing card with a black queen of hearts, saw it as red, as it should be; and when the card was shown again, reacted with nausea at such a perversion of the laws of Nature. To unlearn is more difficult than to learn; and it seems that the task of breaking up rigid cognitive structures and reassembling them into a new synthesis cannot, as a rule, be performed in the full daylight of the conscious, rational mind. It can only be done by reverting to those more fluid, less committed and specialized forms of ideation which normally operate in the twilight below the level of focal awareness. Such intervention of unconscious processes in the creative act is now generally, if sometimes reluctantly, accepted even by behaviourists with a strong positivist bias. Allow me, therefore, to take it for granted that in the period of incubation—to use Graham Wallas's[11] term—the creative individual experiences a temporary regression to patterns of thinking which are normally inhibited in the rational adult.

But it would be a gross over-simplification to identify—as is sometimes done—these patterns with Freud's so-called "Primary Process". The primary process is supposedly

换句话讲，科学和艺术的历史上所谓的革命就是成功逃离死胡同后的结果。科学进展除了那些在产生重大突破后进一步巩固强化和精心加工的阶段之外都不是持续的，也并非严格地累积起来的。然而，巩固过程迟早将进入到越发刻板与保守的阶段，从而进入到高度特化的尽头。增殖是一个能表征这个阶段的深奥的专业术语，它时而让人想起爱尔兰麋鹿的巨大鹿角，时而让人想起神经病患者面对现实威胁的精细防御机制。最后，这一过程导致了危机的产生，并因此爆发一场新的革命，之后又到达了一个新的巩固时期，产生了新的正统观念，进而循环又开始了。

在艺术的历史上，这种循环过程甚至更为明显，即原有学派和技巧经过不断发展的累积期之后，不可避免地进入到发展停滞、特殊习惯成形的颓废期，直到在感性、重点、风格上出现的又一次革新，危机才得以解决。

每一次革命都具有破坏性和建设性两个方面。在科学上，破坏就等于抛弃以前的教条思想，包括一些看起来好像不证自明的公理性思想。在艺术上，破坏涉及对已经被人们接受的价值、中肯标准和理念框架进行公平而痛苦的再评估。当我们从历史学家各种超然的观点来探讨艺术和科学的发展时，毁灭和重建过程在整个历史中是正常的不可缺少的部分。但是，当我们将注意力聚焦于任何一个具体的具有革命导火线性质的事物时，便立刻认识到了那些不得不克服的巨大的心理障碍和情感障碍。这里，我指的不仅是社会的惯常势力，还有存在于头脑中的反对异端新事物的原有思想。当开普勒发现行星的运行轨道是椭圆形时，他极度痛苦地喊出："我是谁，约翰内斯·开普勒，怎么就毁灭了神圣的对称性的圆形轨道论了呢？"更为实际的是，杰罗姆·布鲁纳[10]实验中的被试者们也曾表达过同样的痛苦，当在一瞬间亮出一张黑心皇后牌时，他们看到的却是红色，就像它本来就应该是红色一样，而当牌再次亮出时，被试者们便对这种颠倒自然规律的现象感到反胃。忘却比学习更加困难；在白天意识清醒时和处于理性思维状态时，要打破严格的认知结构并将其重新组合成一个新的系统似乎是行不通的，这已经成为一种规律。只有当大脑回复到更为流畅的、较少教条化和特化的构思状态时，这种任务才得以完成，而这种构思状态通常在黎明时分运作，因为此时集中意识水平较低。现在，无意识过程对创造性行为的干涉作用甚至被带有较强实证主义偏见的行为主义者所普遍接受，虽然他们有时并不十分情愿。因此，请允许我理所当然地认为，在潜伏期（用格雷厄姆·沃拉斯[11]的术语来说），创造性个体经历了思维模式暂时性的退行，这种思维模式通常在理性的成年期被抑制。

但是，有时用弗洛伊德的所谓的“初级过程”来鉴别这些模式总显得高度单纯化。一般说来初级过程是缺乏逻辑性的，是被快乐原则所支配的，是易于混淆感知与幻

devoid of logic, governed by the pleasure principle, apt to confuse perception and hallucination, expressed in spontaneous action, and accompanied by massive affective discharge. I believe that between this very primary process, and the so-called secondary process governed by the reality principle, we must interpolate a whole hierarchy of cognitive structures which are not simply mixtures of primary and secondary processes, but are autonomous systems in their own right, each governed by a distinct set of rules. The paranoid delusion, the dream, the daydream, free association, the mentality of children at various ages and of primitives at various stages, should not be lumped together, for each has its own logic or rules of the game. But while clearly different in many respects, all these forms of ideation have certain features in common, since they are ontogenetically, and perhaps phylogenetically, older than those of the civilized adult. I have elsewhere[12] called them "games of the underground", because if not kept under restraint they would play havoc with the routines of disciplined thinking. But under exceptional conditions, when disciplined thinking is at the end of its tether, a temporary indulgence in these underground games may suddenly produce a solution which was beyond the reach of the conscious, rational mind—that new synthesis which Poincare[13] called the happy combination of ideas, and which I like to call "bisociation" (as distinct from associative routine). I have discussed this process in some detail in a recent book[12] and shall not dwell on its intricate details. The point I want to make here is that the creation of novelty in mental evolution follows the same pattern of *reculer pour mieux sauter*, of a temporary regression to a naive or juvenile level, followed by a forward leap, which we have found in biological evolution. We can carry the analogy further and interpret the Aha reaction, or "Eureka!" cry, as the signal of a happy escape from a blind alley—an act of mental self-repair, achieved by the de-differentiation of cognitive structures to a more plastic state, and the resulting liberation of creative potentials—the equivalent of the release of genetic growth-potentials in regenerating tissues.

It is a truism to say that in mental evolution social inheritance replaces genetic inheritance. But there is a less trivial parallel between phylogenesis and the evolution of ideas: neither of them proceeds along a continuous curve in a strictly cumulative manner. Newton said that if he saw farther than others it was because he stood on the shoulders of giants. But did he really stand on their shoulders or some other part of their anatomy? He adopted Galileo's laws of free fall, but rejected Galileo's astronomy. He adopted Kepler's planetary laws, but demolished the rest of the Keplerian edifice. He did not take as his point of departure their completed "adult" theories, but retraced their development to the point where it had gone wrong. Nor was the Keplerian edifice built on top of the Copernican structure. That ramshackle structure of epicycles he tore down and kept only its foundations. Nor did Copernicus continue to build where Ptolemy had left off. He went back two thousand years to Aristarchus. The great revolutionary turns in the evolution of ideas have a decidedly paedomorphic character. The new paradigm, to use Thomas Kuhn's[14] term, which emerges from the revolution is not derived from a previous adult paradigm; not from the aged sea-urchin but from its mobile larva, floating in the currents of the ocean. Only in the relatively peaceful periods of consolidation and elaboration do we find gerontomorphism—small improvements to a fully mature body of knowledge. In

觉的，是由自发行为所表达出来的，并且伴随着大量的情感释放。我认为，在这种初级过程与所谓的由现实原则所支配的次级过程之间应当插入一个完整的认知结构等级，这一等级并不是初级过程与次级过程的简单融合，而是在其自身范围的一个自治系统，且受一套不同的规律所支配。妄想症患者的错觉、梦、白日梦、自由联想，儿童不同年龄的心理状态以及不同阶段的原始心理都有着各自的逻辑和规则，因而不能归并在一起考虑。但是，尽管所有这些构思过程在许多方面都存在明显差异，它们依然具有一定的共性特征，因为它们在个体发生上，或者可能在系统发生上都早于那些正常的成人。我在以前的著作[12]中称它们为“地下游戏”，这是因为如果不对其进行克制，他们将严重破坏那些因训练而形成的常规思维。但是，在异常条件下，当常规思维的使用已经达到极限时，短暂地放任这些地下游戏可能会突然产生出一个解决方案，这一解决方案是意识和理性头脑所不能到达的，它是一个新的合成，普安卡雷[13]称其为思想的愉悦合并，而我则喜欢称其为“异缘联想”以区别于联合程序。我已经在最近的一本书[12]里详细地讨论了这一过程，这里就不再赘述。在本文中我想说明的一点是：在心理演进中新事物的产生遵循着与以退为进相似的模式，即经过短暂退行至幼稚水平后，又跳跃式地向前演进，这在生物进化中同样被发现过。我们仍然可以通过运用类推法来解释“啊哈”的反应或“找到了！”的惊呼，它们可以被看作避开死胡同后的一种幸福信号，即一种心理自我修复行为，它经过认知结构去分化后变得更具可塑性，并且同时释放创造性潜能，而这种创造性潜能相当于再生组织中释放的遗传性生长潜能。

众所周知，在心理演进中社会遗传取代了基因遗传。但是，在系统发生与思想进化之间存在一些微小的相似，即两者都不符合连续曲线那样严格的累积方式。牛顿曾说过，如果说他比别人看得更远，那是因为他站在了巨人的肩膀上。但是，他真的就站在巨人的肩膀上或是他们身体的其他部位上吗？他吸收了伽利略的自由落体定律，但却反对其在天文学上的观点。他接受了开普勒的行星定律，但却推翻其所有其他建树。他没有直接以他们完整而“成熟”的理论作为基础继续前进，而是折回到他们理论发展中的错误点。而开普勒的理论大厦也不是在哥白尼的理论上建成的，他将摇摇欲坠的本轮理论推翻，而只保留其基础部分。同样，哥白尼也不是在托勒密的理论上继续前进，而是回溯到两千年前的阿利斯塔克的理论。思想演进中那些伟大的革命性的转折点具有明显的“幼稚形态”特点。用托马斯·库恩[14]的话来讲，从革命中产生的新的范式并不是来源于先前的成熟的范式；不是来源于成年的海胆，而是来源于那些可游动的、在海浪中漂浮的幼虫。只有在相对平静的巩固强化和精心加工的时期，我们才会发现老龄形态，即对完全成熟的知识体系微

the history of art the process is again all too obvious; there is no need to elaborate on it.

I began with a wistful remark about the treacherous wings of analogy, aware of the fact that those who trust these waxen wings usually share the fate of Icarus. But it is one thing to argue from analogy, and quite another to point to an apparent similarity which has perhaps not been paid sufficient attention, and then to ask whether that similarity has some significance or whether it is trivial and deceptive. I believe that the parallel between certain processes underlying biological and mental evolution has some significance. Biological evolution could be described as a history of escapes from over-specialization, the evolution of ideas as a series of escapes from the bondage of mental habit; and the escape-mechanism in both cases is based on the same principles. We get an inkling of them through the phenomena of regeneration—the remoulding of structures and reorganization of functions—which only enter into action when the challenge exceeds a critical limit. They point to the existence of unsuspected "meta-adaptive" potentials which are inhibited or dormant in the normal routines of existence, and, when revealed, make us sometimes feel that we move like sleepwalkers in a world of untapped resources and unexplored possibilities.

It could be objected that I have presented a reductionist view; that it is sacrilegious to call the creation of a Brahms symphony or of Maxwell's field equations an act of self-repair, and to compare it with the mutation of a sea-squirt larva, the regeneration of a newt-tail, the relearning process in the rat or the rehabilitation of patients by psycho-therapy. But I think that such a view is the opposite of sacrilegious. It points, however tentatively, at a common denominator, a factor of purposiveness, without invoking a *deus ex machina*. It does not deny that trial and error are inherent in all progressive development. But there is a world of difference between the random tries of the monkey at the typewriter, and the process which I called, for lack of a better name, *reculer pour mieux sauter*. The first means reeling off all possible responses in the organism's repertory until the correct one is hit on by chance and stamped in by reinforcement. The second may still be called trial and error, but of a purposive kind, using more complex, sophisticated methods: a groping and searching, retreating and advancing towards a goal. "Purpose," to quote Herbert J. Muller[15], "is not imported into Nature and need not be puzzled over as a strange or divine something. ... It is simply implicit in the fact or organisation." This directiveness of vital processes is present all along the line, from conscious behaviour down to what Needham[7] called "the striving of the blastula to grow into a chicken". How tenacious and resourceful that striving is has been demonstrated by experimental embryology, from Speeman to Paul Weiss—though its lessons have not yet been fully digested.

Thus to talk of goal-directedness or purpose in ontogeny has become respectable again. In phylogeny the monkey still seems to be hammering away at the typewriter, perhaps because the crude alternatives that had been offered—amorphous entelechies, or the Lysenko brand of Lamarckism—were even more repellent to the scientific mind. On the other hand, some evolutionary geneticists are beginning to discover that the typewriter is structured and organized in such a way as to defeat the monkey, because it will print

小的提高。在艺术历史上，这个过程依然是十分明显的，这里也不必再赘述。

关于类推法的奥妙，我想以一个引人深思的评论作为开始，我意识到这样一个事实，那就是那些信任蜡质双翼的人往往要面对伊卡洛斯般的命运。但是，这只是类推法争论中的一个方面，另一个方面指的是或许还没有被我们足够重视的外观上的相似性，接着则要思考这种相似性是否具有一定的意义，抑或是微不足道的、具有欺骗性的。我相信，某些潜藏于生物进化过程与心理演进过程之间的相似性具有一定的意义。生物进化可以被描述为是一个逃离高度特化的历史，而心理演进则是逃离心理习惯束缚的一系列事件；两者的逃离机制都是建立在同样的原理上。通过再生现象（即结构重组和功能重塑）我们对它们产生了一个粗浅的认识，再生现象只有当面临的挑战超过临界限度时才发挥作用。它们都指出“超适应”潜能毫无疑问是存在的，它通常以压抑或潜伏的形式存在，而当我们揭开它时，则会使我们感到自己就像梦游者一样，在一个充满着待开发资源和待探索的可能事物中遨游。

人们可能会反对我提出的缩影式观点；将一曲勃拉姆斯交响乐或麦克斯韦电磁方程组的创作称为自我修复行为，并将其与真海鞘幼虫的突变、蝾螈尾部的再生、大鼠的再学习过程或心理治疗后患者的复原一起相提并论，这是亵渎神明的。但是，我的看法却刚好相反，因为它试探性地指出了目的形成因素的共同特性，而没有当成任意的巧合。不能否定尝试与错误在所有发展进程中是固有存在的。但是，猴子在打字机上的随机尝试与我所称之为以退为进的过程完全不是一回事。前者指的是在有机体所有可能的反应库中随意抽取，直到偶然地做出了一次正确的输入为止，之后通过强化而铭刻于心；而后者可能仍然被称为尝试和错误，但是却是有目的性地通过利用更为复杂的方法，如探索和搜寻，向着目标迂回前进。引用赫伯特·马勒[15]的话来讲，“目的不是被引入到自然界的，是不应该像陌生的或神圣的事情一样让人迷惑的。……它只是隐含在事实或组织之中”。重要过程的发展趋向性是确定的，沿着从有意识的行为到尼达姆[7]所称的“囊胚发育成为一个幼仔的努力”的线路进行。这种努力是不屈不挠的，是足智多谋的，这已经被实验胚胎学研究（从施佩曼到保罗·韦斯）所证实——尽管这些研究成果尚未被人们完全接受。

因此，关于个体发生的目的性或目标的讨论又重新变得很有价值。在系统发生的研究中，猴子似乎依然在打字机上敲打，或许这是因为那些已经被提出的粗略的备选方案——模糊的生命原理或拉马克学说下的李森科主义——被科学思想更多地排斥。另一方面，一些进化遗传学家开始发现打字机的这种结构和组织形式对猴子

only meaningful words and sentences. In recent years the rigid, atomistic concepts of Mendelian genetics have undergone a softening process and have been supplemented by a whole series of new terms with an almost holistic ring. Thus we learn that the genetic system represents a "micro-hierarchy" which exercises its selective and regulative control on the molecular, chromosomal and cellular level; that development is "canalized", stabilized by "developmental homeostasis" or "evolutionary homeostasis"[16] so that mutations affect not a single unit character but a "whole organ in a harmonious way"[17], and, finally, that these various forms of "internal selection" create a restricted "mutation spectrum"[18] or may even have a "direct, moulding influence guiding evolutionary change along certain avenues"[19]—and all this happens long before external, Darwinian selection gets to work. But if this is the case, then the part played by a lucky chance mutation is reduced to that of the trigger which releases the co-ordinated action of the system; and to maintain that evolution is the product of blind chance means to confuse the simple action of the trigger, governed by the laws of statistics, with the complex, purposive processes which it sets off. Their purposiveness is manifested in different ways on different levels of the hierarchy, from the self-regulating properties of the genetic system through internal and external selection, culminating perhaps in the phenomena of phylogenetic self-repair: escapes from blind alleys and departures in new directions. On each level there is trial and error, but on each level it takes a more sophisticated form. Some twenty years ago, Tolman and Krechevsky[20] created a stir by proclaiming that the rat learns to run a maze by forming hypotheses; soon it may be permissible to extend the metaphor and to say that evolution progresses by making and discarding hypotheses.

Any directive process, whether you call it selective, adaptive or expectative, implies a reference to the future. The equifinality of developmental processes, the striving of the blastula to grow into an embryo, regardless of the obstacles and hazards to which it is exposed, might lead the unprejudiced observer to the conclusion that the pull of the future is as real and sometimes more important than the pressure of the past. The pressure may be compared to the action of a compressed spring, the pull to that of an extended spring, threaded on the axis of time. Neither of them is more or less mechanistic than the other. If the future is completely determined in the Laplacian sense, then there is nothing to choose between the actions of the two springs. If it is indeterminate in the Heisenbergian sense, then indeterminacy works in both directions, and the distant past is as blurred and unknowable as the future; and if there is something like a free choice operating within the air-bubbles in the stream of causality, then it must be directed towards the future and oriented by feed-back from the past.

(**208**, 1033-1036; 1965)

References:

1. Huxley, J., *Man in the Modern World*, 13 (New York, 1948).

2. Garstang, W., *J. Linnean Soc. Lond.* (*Zoology*), **35**, 81 (1922).

3. Hardy, A. C., in *Evolution as a Process* (New York, 1954).

也是不利的，因为它打印出来的只是一些有意义的词和句子。近些年来，孟德尔遗传学严格的原子论概念已经经历了一个软化过程，并且一整套的新术语已经被补充进去，这些术语几乎可以自成一个完整的体系。因此，我们了解到遗传系统表现出了一种可以在分子、染色体和细胞水平发生选择性调控的“微层次”；我们了解到发育是被“发育动态平衡”或者“进化动态平衡”[16]所“定向的”，从而突变不仅仅是改变一个特征，而是“以和谐的方式影响到所有的器官”[17]，最后，这些不同形式的“内在选择”创建了一个有限的“突变谱”[18]，或者甚至是“直接引导着进化向着某一个方向演进”[19]，并且这些不同形式的内在选择都发生在达尔文自然选择（外在选择）发挥作用之前。但是，如果情况确实如此的话，那么由碰巧产生的随机突变引起的变化部分则是引发系统协同变化的触发器，而要维持进化是偶然变化的产物这一主张，就意味着用已经启动的复杂的有目的的过程去扰乱那个遵循统计学规律的简单的触发行为。从遗传系统在内外部选择下的自我调控，到系统发生的自我修复这一可能的终点，即避开死胡同之后再开启新的方向，它们的目的性在不同的等级水平上表现方式显然不尽相同。在任一水平上都存在尝试和错误，但在任一水平上都以一种更为复杂的方式进行。大约二十多年前，托尔曼和克雷契夫斯基[20]宣布的关于大鼠学会走迷宫的形成假说在科学界引起了轰动；不久，假说在隐喻意义上得到延伸，并又有了关于进化发展的制造和抛弃假说。

任何定向过程，不管你将其称之为选择、适应或是预期，都暗示着未来的可能情形。不考虑所面临的那些障碍和危险时，发育过程（囊胚长成胚胎的努力过程）最终得到同样的结果，这可能会使公正的观测者得出这样的结论：未来的引力是真实存在的，并且有时它比过去的压力更加重要。压力好比是被压缩的弹簧在时间轴上所表现出来的行为，引力则好比是被拉伸的弹簧在时间轴上的行为，两者的力量大小相当。如果未来完全由拉普拉斯的理论所决定，那么不用在这两种弹簧的行为之间做出选择。如果在海森堡的理论中它是不确定的，那么在两个方向上都有不确定的功，则遥远的过去就如未来一样模糊而不可知；而且如果有什么事物（比如自由选择）像一个在众多因果关系的洪流之中的气泡一样，则它必定会在过去的反馈信息的引导下向着未来发展。

（曾菊平 翻译；刘京国 审稿）

4. de Beer, G. R., *Embryos and Ancestors* (Oxford, 1940).
5. Bolk, L., *Das Problem der Menschwerdung* (Jena, 1926).
6. Haldane, J. B. S., *The Causes of Evolution*, 150 (London, 1932).
7. Needham, A. E., *New Scientist*, London, November 2, 1961.
8. Lashley, K. S., *Brain Mechanisms and Intelligence* (Chicago, 1929).
9. Kris, E., *Psychoanalytic Explorations in Art* (New York, 1952).
10. Bruner, J. S., and Postman, L., *J. of Personality*, XVIII (1949).
11. Wallas, G., *The Art of Thought* (London, 1954).
12. Koestler, A., *The Act of Creation* (New York, 1964).
13. Poincare, H., in *The Creative Process* (Berkeley, Calif., 1952).
14. Kuhn, T. H., *The Structure of Scientific Revolutions* (Chicago, 1962).
15. Muller, H. J., *Science and Criticism* (New Haven, Conn., 1943).
16. Cannon, H. G., *The Evolution of Living Things* (Manchester, 1958).
17. Waddington, C. H., *The Listener*, London (Nov. 13, 1952).
18. Spurway, H., in *Supplemento. La Ricerca Scientifica* (Pallanza Symp.), 18 (Cons. Naz. delle Richerche, Rome, 1949).
19. For a survey of literature in this field see Whyte, L. L., *Internal Factors in Evolution* (London, 1965).
20. Krechevsky, I., *Psychol. Rev.*, 39 (1932).

Biological Systems at the Molecular Level

B. Askonas *et al.*

Editor's Note

This report of a meeting of the International Union of Pure and Applied Biophysics in Naples offers a snapshot of what biophysics meant in the 1960s. By this time the key characteristics of the molecular structures of proteins were known, although a seemingly inordinately large part of the discussion here was taken up with issue of how the various amino acids along a protein chain are rotationally ordered. There is little sense yet that it is the more global three-dimensional arrangement that determines a protein enzyme's function. The possibility of cloning antibody-forming immune cells to make specific types of antibody, mentioned here, does however presage the immensely valuable production of "monoclonal antibodies" in the mid-1970s.

A SYMPOSIUM was organized by the Commission of Molecular Biophysics of the International Union of Pure and Applied Biophysics during September 8-11, under the auspices of the International Laboratory of Genetics and Biophysics, Naples—the local arrangements being made by Prof. A. Buzatti-Traverso.

The first day's discussions, under the chairmanship of Prof. H. A. Scheraga (Cornell), were concerned fundamentally with the problem of predicting the conformations of proteins from their primary structure.

In the first paper Dr. S. Lifson (Rehovoth) gave an account of his recent statistical-mechanical investigations of conformational changes in polypeptides. His method consisted in defining sequences, sequence partition functions and sequence-generating functions and in using them to derive an equation for the contribution of each chain element to the partition function of the whole molecule. The results make possible, for example, an assessment of the relative importance of hydrogen bonding and hydrophobic interactions in determining the conformation of poly-L-alanine at different temperatures.

The remaining papers were more closely concerned with the investigation of specific conformations and the limitations imposed on them by interactions between non-bonded atoms. Given that the conformation of the peptide group is generally *trans* and planar, the most important variables determining the conformation of a polypeptide chain are the angles ψ and φ for rotation about the N–C_α and C_α–C^1 bonds respectively. Prof. G. N. Ramachandran (Madras) reviewed the earlier work in which he and his colleagues had studied the values of ψ and φ that are allowed when fixed minimum distances of approach are set for the atoms of a dipeptide unit comprising the two peptide groups and the β-carbon joined to an α-carbon atom. This had shown that only certain regions in a

分子水平的生物系统

阿斯康纳斯等

编者按

这篇是在那不勒斯召开的国际纯粹与应用生物物理学联合会的某次会议的报告。它为20世纪60年代生物物理学的含义提供了一个简要的全景概括。尽管看起来这里所讨论的绝大部分内容都是关于各种氨基酸是如何在多肽链中有序旋转的，但那时候人们已经知道蛋白质分子结构中的关键特点。那时尚未了解到是更为全局的三维排布决定了蛋白酶的功能。这里提到了通过克隆抗体的免疫细胞来产生特异性抗体的可能性，不管怎样，这确实预言了20世纪70年代中期具有重大意义的"单克隆抗体"的生产。

9 月 8 日至 11 日，由国际纯粹与应用生物物理学联合会的分子生物物理学委员会组织的一次研讨会，在位于那不勒斯的国际遗传和生物物理实验室的支持下召开，本次会议的当地筹办工作由布扎蒂–特拉韦尔索教授负责。

第一天的讨论由施拉格教授（康奈尔）担任主席并主持会议，从根本上涉及了由蛋白质一级结构来预测其构象的问题。

在第一个报告中，里夫森博士（雷霍沃特）给出了他最近对多肽构象变化的统计力学研究结果。他的方法包括了定义出序列，序列分区函数以及序列生成函数，以及运用它们得出等式，此等式关乎构成整个分子的分区函数的每一个肽链元素的贡献。例如，这些结果使得我们有可能去评估氢键和疏水相互作用在决定多聚–L–丙氨酸在不同温度下的构象中的相对重要性。

其余报告与特定构象及其被非键合原子间相互作用所强加的局限性的研究密切相关。既然肽基团的构象大体上都是反式和平面化的，那么决定多肽链构象的最重要变量分别是 N–C_α 旋转时的键角 ψ 和 C_α–C^1 旋转时的键角 φ。拉马钱德兰（马德拉斯）教授回顾了早先的工作，在这项工作中，他和他的同事们对组成两个肽基团的二肽单元的原子以及连接 α–碳原子的 β–碳原子间的最小距离确定时的 ψ 和 φ 的允许值进行了研究。他们的研究结果表明，在 ψ、φ 图中，只有特定区域是空间允许的，多肽中已经提出的大多数构象，或在相关结构分析中观测到的大多数构象都分布或

ψ, φ-diagram are sterically allowed and that these regions enclose, or nearly enclose, most of the conformations that have been proposed for polypeptides or observed in analyses of relevant structures. He then described an investigation of the effect of allowing the angle $NC_{\alpha}C^{1}$ to vary by $\pm 5^{\circ}$ from the tetrahedral value (while the deviations from 110° of the other angles at C_{α} were minimized), which showed that the allowed regions in the ψ, φ-diagram are increased, by the introduction of this flexibility, to embrace most of the observed conformations that were previously just forbidden.

Prof. Ramachandran went on to consider the properties of helical polypeptide chains, in which the angles ψ and φ are kept constant at each α-carbon, with particular reference to the main chain—NH · · · O hydrogen bonding. He showed that families of helices of the right- and left-handed 3.6_{13} or α-type and of the 3.0_{10} type (with hydrogen bonds from peptides 1 to 4, and 1 to 3, respectively) are sterically allowed, with hydrogen bonds of acceptable length that depart from colinearity by less than 30°, provided that the bond angle at C_{α} is close to 110°. On the other hand, right- and left-handed π-helices (1-5 hydrogen bonded) are allowed only when the angle at C_{α} is 115°, and the 2.2_7 ribbon structure (1-2 bonded) is permitted only with hydrogen-bond-angles greater than 20°. The triple helix structure for collagen with two inter-chain hydrogen bonds (angles of 27° and 30°) for every three residues, as proposed in Madras, falls within a fully allowed region in the ψ, φ-diagram, and a new suggestion was put forward that this structure also includes additional CH · · · O hydrogen bonds between neighbouring chains. When collagen has the sequence gly-pro-hyp in all three chains, however, it appears that only one hydrogen bond can occur for every three residues and the preferred structural parameters closely follow those given by Rich and Crick.

Finally, Prof. Ramachandran discussed the conformations of amino-acid side-chains that have been observed in crystal structures, showing (in keeping with earlier reviews) that they usually adopt fully staggered conformations, but that any one of the possible variants may be adopted in response to a particular environment.

Developments of the limiting-contact approach to the analysis of polypeptide conformations were also described by Dr. G. Némethy. In these studies the influence of various amino-acid side-chains on the conformation of the dipeptide unit was investigated, the results being presented again in terms of the allowed regions in the ψ, φ-diagram. It was shown that the addition of a γ-carbon atom reduces the percentage of allowed conformations form 16 percent for C_{β} alone to 14 percent, even though there are three rotational positions giving staggered conformations of the side-chain from which to choose. The addition of atoms beyond C_{γ} in an unbranched side-chain does not limit the range of allowed conformations any more, but the presence of more than one δ-atom, as in leu, reduces the allowed conformations to 11 percent of the possible, and branching at C_{β}, as in val, ile or thr, reduces this total to only 4.5 percent.

From all these analyses by the limiting-contact method it is clear, therefore, that local steric restrictions, quite apart from the interaction of groups widely separated in the primary

者基本分布在这些特定区域内。他接下来描述了一份当允许角 $NC_\alpha C^1$ 发生偏离四面体值 ±5°（当 C_α 的其他角偏离 110° 的值最小时）以内时所产生的影响的研究报告。这表明通过引入这种灵活性，ψ、φ 图中的允许区域增加了，以接受先前禁止的多数观察到的构象。

拉马钱德兰教授接下来考虑螺旋多肽链的特征，其每个 α 碳原子的键角 ψ 和 φ 都保持一致（特别参考了主链中的 NH···O 氢键）。他指出右手螺旋家族和左手螺旋家族的 3.6_{13} 或 α 型，以及 3.0_{10} 型（其肽 1 与肽 4，以及肽 1 与肽 3 分别形成氢键）在空间上都是允许的，倘若 C_α 的键角接近 110°，其氢键长度位于可接受的范围并且距离共线性最大不超过 30°。另一方面，只有在 C_α 的键角为 115° 时才允许存在右手和左手 π 螺旋（1–5 氢键连接）；只有在氢键–氢键夹角大于 20° 时允许存在 2.2_7 带状结构（靠 1–2 氢键连接）。正如马德拉斯所提出的那样，在胶原蛋白的三重螺旋结构中，每三个残基内就有两个链间氢键（键角分别为 27° 和 30°），落在 ψ，φ 图中的完全允许范围内，并且提出了一个新建议，即这一结构也包括相邻链间额外的 CH···O 氢键。胶原蛋白在全部三条链中均含有 gly（甘氨酸）-pro（脯氨酸）-hyp（羟脯氨酸）序列，但看起来每三个残基中只能产生一个氢键，并且这种优势结构的参数接近里奇和克里克给出的数据。

最后，拉马钱德兰教授讨论了在晶体结构中已经观测到的氨基酸侧链的构象，显示（与此前综述一致）它们经常采用完全交错的构象，但是，在特殊的环境中，任一可能变体都有可能被采用。

内梅蒂博士也描述了用于分析多肽构象的限制接触法的发展。在这些研究中，调查了各种氨基酸侧链对二肽单元构象的影响，这些结果同样用 ψ，φ 图的允许区域来表示。尽管存在三种旋转位置能够形成侧链的交错构象以供选择，但结果显示，每增加一个 γ 碳原子，所允许构象的百分比会从 C_β 单独存在时的 16% 减少为 14%。在无分支侧链中，C_γ 之外原子的加入一点也不限制所允许构象的范围，但是一个以上 δ 原子的存在，例如在 leu（亮氨酸）中，会使可能的允许构象减少至 11%，并且 C_β 处所产生的分支，例如 val（缬氨酸），ile（异亮氨酸）或 thr（苏氨酸），会使这一总值减少至只有 4.5%。

因此，从所有这些利用限制接触法分析得出的结论很明确：除了一级结构中距离很远的基团间的相互作用之外，局部空间位阻大大限制了多肽链能够形成的构象

structure, severely restrict the number of conformations accessible to a polypeptide chain and go some way (though not yet far enough) towards making practicable the calculation of conformation from amino-acid sequence. A general method for handling such calculations has been pioneered by Prof. A. M. Liquori (Naples), and his colleagues, who described his preliminary attempts to calculate the helical conformations of minimum potential energy, taking into account the forces between non-covalently-bonded atoms. These calculations have led to diagrams of the potential energy as functions of ψ and φ which indicate, for example, that the right-handed α-helix with the original Pauling and Corey parameters is a very stable conformation even without consideration of the hydrogen-bonding that stabilizes it still further. There are four other potential-energy minima, including one corresponding to the left-handed α-helix which is shown, encouragingly, to be less stable than its right-handed counterpart.

Analysis of the structure of myoglobin has shown that these stable helical values of ψ and φ also occur frequently in non-helical regions of the molecule. Prof. Liquori suggested, therefore, that it might be interesting to investigate an idealized structure for myoglobin in which all the dihedral angles were constrained to take the values at the closest of these favoured pairs. Here again, of course, the aim was to reduce the number of conformations that has to be considered to manageable proportions.

Unfortunately there are very few reliable data from which the conformational potential energy of a polypeptide can be calculated. Prof. Liquori presented some evidence to suggest that the general features of the ψ, φ potential energy diagram for helices do not depend very sensitively on the exact shape of the interaction potential curves used in the calculations. He emphasized his belief that while precise energy values are not yet available, proper use of the relatively reliable van der Waals's radii may enable progress to be made towards the prediction of conformations.

In a final short paper in this session, Dr. D. C. Phillips (London) described the structure of lysozyme, recently determined at the Royal Institution, remarking particularly on the occurrence in it of some residues forming an anti-parallel pleated sheet and of some others in the conformation of the 3.0_{10} helix with corresponding hydrogen bonding. Nearly all the helices in the molecule appear to be distorted to some extent from the standard α-structure and there is evidence that the hydrogen bonds in them sometimes depart from linearity by 20° or more. He described how comparison of the main features of the structure with the varying hydrophobicity of the amino-acid residues in the primary structure had suggested that the polypeptide chain folds itself from the terminal amino-end, forming first a compact unit with a hydrophobic core, then an extended arm of hydrophilic residues, partly in the β-conformation, and finally a coil that nearly closes the gap between the two parts, leaving a cleft that appears to be the active region, before winding itself around the terminal amino-end. Following ideas developed in collaboration with Dr. P. Dunnill, he noted that analysis of the distribution of hydrophobicity along a polypeptide chain might be useful in predicting conformations if enough guiding principles could be established.

的数量，并且在某种程度上（尽管还不够成熟）使根据氨基酸序列来计算构象变得可行。利阔里教授（那不勒斯）和他的同事们首先提出一种处理这种计算的普遍方法，利阔里描述了在计算具有最小势能的螺旋构象的同时将由非共价键连接的原子间的作用力考虑进去的初步尝试。这些计算推导出作为 ψ、φ 的函数的势能图，例如，它表明带有最初的鲍林和科里参数的右手 α 螺旋即使在不考虑使它更加稳定的氢键时也是一种非常稳定的构象。还有另外四个势能最小值，包括已经展示过的一种相当于左手 α 螺旋的结构，令人鼓舞的是，这种左手 α 螺旋结构不如与之对应的右手 α 螺旋结构稳定。

对肌红蛋白结构的分析表明，这些稳定螺旋的 ψ、φ 值也常常出现在分子的非螺旋区域。因此利阔里教授认为对肌红蛋白的一种理想结构进行研究可能是有趣的，这种结构中所有二面角都受到限制，取最接近这些有利于形成配对的数值。当然，这里进行这样研究的目的是为了将不得不考虑的构象个数减少至容易管理的程度。

不幸的是，几乎没有可靠的数据能够用于计算多肽构象的势能。利阔里教授给出的一些证据显示，螺旋所具备的 ψ、φ 势能图的总体特征并不十分敏感地依赖于计算中所使用的相互作用潜在曲线的准确形状。他强调他所相信的，即在仍未获得准确能量值的情况下，合理运用相对可靠的范德华半径也许可以完成预测构象的过程。

在这部分的最后一个小报告中，菲利普斯博士（伦敦）描述了最近由皇家研究院确定的溶菌酶的结构，特别引人注意的是在蛋白内部的一些氨基酸残基形成了一种反平行的折叠片，其他一些残基形成了具有相应氢键的 3.0_{10} 螺旋构象。分子中几乎所有螺旋看上去都发生了相对于标准 α 螺旋结构的不同程度的扭曲，有证据表明，它们中的氢键偏离线性达 20° 或更多。他描述了此结构的主要特征与一级结构中氨基酸残基的不同疏水性间的比较，结果认为多肽链从氨基末端开始自我折叠，首先形成一个具有疏水核心的紧密单元，然后形成由亲水残基组成的部分为 β 构象的延伸臂，最终，一个卷曲结构几乎封闭了这两部分间的间隔，在尚未围绕氨基末端完成自我缠绕时，留下了一个看似是活性区域的裂缝。随后的想法是在与丹尼尔博士的合作中发展而来的，他注意到如果建立起足够的指导原则，那么对多肽链的疏水性分布的分析将可能有助于预测构象。

A preliminary calculation of the dihedral angles ψ, φ in lysozyme had shown them to be nearly all in allowed regions of a potential energy diagram calculated for a peptide unit by the use of Lennard-Jones type interaction potentials. This diagram, which was similar to that calculated by Brant and Flory, differed from the original limiting-contact diagram mainly in allowing a greater range of conformations near those appropriate to the 3.0_{10} and the left-handed α-helices. This was presumably because in these regions the occurrence of marginally short contacts, which are forbidden in the limiting-contact analysis, are outweighed, in the calculation of potential energies, by the presence of a large number of favourable contacts. The effect on the ψ, φ-diagram is very similar to that reported by Prof. Ramachandran to result from allowing the $NC_{\alpha}C^{1}$ angle to depart from 110°.

These papers provoked a lively discussion in the course of which Dr. F. H. C. Crick (Cambridge) remarked that the study of allowed helical conformations has really progressed very little beyond the results obtained by Donohue from the careful measurement of models. He urged strongly that rigorous attempts should be made to distinguish the important conformational variables, by comparison of the relative energies involved, from among covalent bond-lengths and bond angles, hydrogen bond lengths and angles, van der Waals's contact distances and rotations about bonds, suggesting that calculations based on simple crystal structures might provide necessary criteria for the establishment of valid energy parameters. Dr. J. C. Kendrew (Cambridge) described the helices found in myoglobin, noting that they are less regular than was first supposed and that some residues, particularly at the carboxyl ends of α-helices, are in the 3.0_{10} conformation. There was general agreement that models based only on α-helices and "random coils" must be considered inadequate. In view of the present very large number of investigations in which peptide conformations are described in terms of ψ, φ-diagrams, a plea was made for the general adoption of the standard conventions for labelling rotations that have been drawn up by Dr. G. Némethy. These are shortly to be published in the leading journals.

The second day, under the chairmanship of Dr. G. M. Edelman (New York), was devoted to the structural basis of the immune response. Dr. A. Nisonoff (Urbana) gave an extensive review of work done on structure of immunoglobulins over many years, leading up to the present-day concept of a divalent multi-chain structure consisting of two heavy chains, and two light chains with two antigen-binding sites per molecule. Even specific antibody directed to a single antigen is highly heterogeneous. Four classes of immunoglobulins are known, which share light chains but differ in heavy chains. Although the main antigen-binding site is on the heavy chain, a consensus of opinion is that both light and heavy chains contribute to the configuration of the antigen-binding site. Recent studies suggested that the two heavy chains are held together by only one S—S bond. In closing, Dr. Nisonoff discussed recent work by Drs. Hilschmann and Craig and Dr. Putnam and his colleagues, who have determined a partial amino-acid sequence of three Bence Jones proteins of type I (equivalent or similar to light chains of type I immunoglobulins). The C-terminal half of the molecule is constant in the three Bence Jones proteins, while the

初步计算溶菌酶中的二面角 ψ、φ，结果表明它们几乎都落在了运用伦纳德–琼斯型相互作用势计算得到的多肽单元势能图中的允许区域。此图与布兰特和弗洛里的计算结果相似，而与最初利用限制接触法获得的图不同，主要区别在于它允许更大范围的接近于 3.0_{10} 和左手 α 螺旋的构象。这可能是因为在这些区域中发生了少量短接触，这在限制接触法分析中是不允许的，在大量有利接触存在的情况下，它们在势能的计算中被高估了。这对 ψ、φ 图的影响与拉马钱德兰教授所报道的在允许 $NC_{\alpha}C^{1}$ 角偏离 110° 时所得到的结论非常相似。

这些报告引发了活跃的讨论，在此期间，克里克博士（剑桥）评论道，除了多诺霍从对模型的仔细测量中所获得的结果外，对于被允许的螺旋构象的研究几乎没有取得进展。克里克博士极力主张通过对所涉及的能量进行比较，来进行缜密的尝试以区分出由共价键长和键角、氢键长和键角、范德华接触距离及围绕键的旋转所引起的重要的构象变量，由此指出，基于简单晶体结构的计算也许能为有效能量参数的建立提供必要的标准。肯德鲁博士（剑桥）描述了肌红蛋白中发现的螺旋，它们并不像最初想象的那样规则，一些残基特别是在 α 螺旋的羧基末端的残基形成了 3.0_{10} 的构象。仅基于 α 螺旋和“无规卷曲”的模型肯定会被认为是不完善的，这一观点大家基本达成一致。鉴于目前有非常大量的调查以 ψ、φ 图的形式描述肽段构象，由此恳请大家普遍采用由内梅蒂博士所绘图中所示旋转的标准协议。这些将很快发表于前沿期刊中。

第二天，在埃德尔曼博士（纽约）主持下，主要致力于讨论免疫应答的结构基础。尼索诺夫博士（乌尔瓦纳）全面综述了多年来对免疫球蛋白结构所做的工作，引入当前的这一概念，即二价多链结构由两条重链和两条轻链组成，每个分子带有两个抗原结合位点。甚至指向单个抗原的特异性抗体也是高度异质性的，已知存在四类免疫球蛋白，它们轻链相同，但重链不同。虽然主要抗原结合位点位于重链，但是一致认为轻链和重链都对抗原结合位点的构型有贡献。近期的研究表明两条重链只通过一个 S–S 键结合在一起。最后，尼索诺夫博士讨论了希尔施曼博士、克雷格博士和帕特南博士及其同事们近期的工作，他们测定了三种 I 型本周蛋白的部分氨基酸序列（等于或类似于 I 型免疫球蛋白的轻链）。三种本周蛋白分子中靠近 C 末端的一半保持一致，但靠近 N 末端的另一半则表现出很大的差异性。米尔斯坦博士（剑桥）给出了几种抗原蛋白结构的进一步的数据，表明结果与变异源于单点

N-terminal half shows wide variation. Dr. Milstein (Cambridge) gave further data on the structures of several antigen proteins and suggested that the results were incompatible with the concept that the variations are due to single point mutations. We all await further sequence studies to throw light on the constant and variable regions of the antibody molecules.

Next, Prof. Jerne (Pittsburg) discussed the cellular kinetics of the antibody response when antigen is injected into the whole animal. Studying haemolytic antibody formation by individual spleen cells, using his plaque assay technique, he observed the events following the injection of sheep red blood cells. There is a rapid rise and fall in the number of antibody-forming cells. Subsequent to the injection of sheep red blood cells one is dealing with a cell population multiplying for a few days, after which time the cells reach an end-stage and to not divide into further antibody-forming cells. Dosage of sheep red blood cells affects the slope of the increase in antibody-forming cells as well as the time (in days) taken to reach a peak number of antibody-forming cells. At low doses of sheep red blood cells only two-thirds of the animals tend to respond and the slope of the increase of antibody-forming cells is much flatter. This is not easily explained by a population of reactive cells multiplying at a certain rate. Prof. Jerne discussed various possibilities. He suggested that perhaps the most likely explanation would be that lymph gland has several compartments, and that contact of antigen with reactive cells can only occur in certain parts of the lymph gland, perhaps the germinal follicles.

In the third paper in this section, Dr. M. Cohn (La Jolla) gave a lucid discussion of the potentiality of single cells. Since it has not been possible to clone antibody-forming cells in tissue culture, three approaches have been used. Different investigators have studied: (1) antibodies formed by single cells; (2) immunoglobulins formed by clones of transplantable murine plasma cell tumours; (3) the use of fluorescent staining techniques to detect different types of immunoglobulins in individual cells. The various studies agreed in finding that at least 90-95 percent of the cells make only one antibody, one class of immunoglobulin and one type of light or heavy chain. In an investigation testing for genetic markers on heavy chains less than 5 percent of the cells had a potential to express both alleles. Therefore, only one structural gene appears to be expressed by the majority of cells. The significance of the low percentage of apparently multi-potential cells is not clear at present. No two myeloma proteins have been found to be alike. Therefore, the number of possible light and heavy chains must be very large.

In closing, Dr. Cohn discussed theories of antibody formation, germ-line versus soma. Soma would rely on mutation during the life of the cell and be less useful than the germ-line, which would follow Mendelian genetics.

Dr. B. Askonas (London) discussed the processing of antigens and the role of information at macromolecules in the immune response. She stated that the problem of control of antibody synthesis by antigen runs far behind the other problems. The fate of antigen was discussed at the cellular and biochemical level. Radioactive antigen is taken up by

突变这一概念不符。我们都期待进一步的序列研究能弄清楚抗体分子中的恒定区和变化区。

接下来，杰尼教授（匹兹堡）讨论了将抗原注入动物时的抗体应答的细胞动力学。通过采用他的斑块测定技术，研究了由单个脾细胞形成溶血抗体的过程，他观测了在注射了绵羊的红细胞后发生的现象。抗体生成细胞的数量出现快速增长和减少。在注入绵羊的红细胞后，随后几天内，被处理的细胞数量倍增，之后细胞达到末期，不再进一步分裂产生抗体生成细胞。绵羊的红细胞的注入剂量影响着抗体生成细胞的增长斜率，同时也影响着抗体生成细胞的数量达到峰值所需的时间（天数）。当注入低剂量的绵羊红细胞时，只有三分之二的动物倾向于产生反应，而且抗体生成细胞增长曲线的斜率非常平缓。用反应细胞的数量以某一特定速率倍增来解释这些现象并不容易。杰尼教授讨论了多种可能性。他认为也许最有可能的解释是淋巴腺具有很多隔间，而抗原与反应细胞的接触只能发生在淋巴腺的某些部分，有可能是新发生的滤泡。

在这一部分的第三个报告中，科恩博士（拉荷亚）就单个细胞的潜能作了浅显易懂的讨论。由于还不可能在组织培养中克隆抗体生成细胞，那么只好采用以下三种方法。不同的研究者已经对此进行了研究：(1) 由单一细胞系生成抗体；(2) 由可移植的鼠类血浆细胞瘤的克隆生成免疫球蛋白；(3) 用荧光染色技术来检测单个细胞系中的不同类型的免疫球蛋白。这些不同的研究都发现，至少 90% ~ 95% 的细胞只能产生一种抗体、一类免疫球蛋白，以及一种类型的轻链或重链。在一项检测重链遗传标记的研究中，不到 5%的细胞具有同时表达两个等位基因的潜力。因此，看上去大多数细胞只表达一个结构基因。目前只有少量明显具有多潜能的细胞的意义尚不清楚。目前没有发现任何两种骨髓瘤蛋白是相似的，因此，可能存在的轻链和重链的数量必然非常庞大。

最后，科恩博士讨论了抗体形成的理论，比较了种系细胞形成的方式和体细胞形成的方式。体细胞形成的方式依赖细胞周期中发生的突变并且不如种系细胞中发生的突变有效，后者遵循孟德尔遗传学规律。

阿斯康纳斯博士（伦敦）讨论了抗原的处理以及在免疫应答过程中在大分子层面上信息所扮演的角色。她指出通过抗原对抗体合成进行控制这一问题的开展远远落后于其他问题。她在细胞和生化水平上讨论了抗原的命运。放射性抗原被遍布于

phagocytic cells throughout the lymph gland; in the secondary response it is particularly concentrated in the dendritic cells in the germinal centre. Although a major part of the antigen taken up is degraded very rapidly, the remaining antigen persists for weeks and is lost only gradually from the cells. The failure to detect radioactively labelled antigen in antibody-forming cells by G. J. V. Nossall and J. H. Humphrey and their collaborators has shown that there can be only very few antigenic determinants present in the antibody-forming cell.

The question of how antigen stimulates the potential antibody-forming cell is still a vital problem. Whether it does so by direct interaction with the reactive cell or has to go through an intermediary cell needs further clarification. Since the phagocytic cells, the macrophages, take up the antigen they have been implicated as possible intermediary cells. RNA preparations containing antigen can be extracted from macrophages and they are highly active in inducing antibody, but whether this is an essential step in the induction of antibody is not clear. Suggestions that antigen-free informational molecules are transferred from macrophages to the reactive cells have also been made, but this has not been shown convincingly. Further experimentation is required to throw light on this problem.

On the third day a discussion on allosteric enzymes was held with Dr. F. Jacob (Paris) as chairman. The fact that a combination of one molecule of ligand with a macromolecule can influence the combination of another, the same or different, has been known for a long time. The term "allosteric" proteins was introduced by Monod and Jacob to describe proteins in which such interactions occur. Although it is to be expected that many proteins are in some degree allostoric, the introduction of this term has been especially useful in directing attention to a particularly important class of phenomena involving enzymes which, potentially at least, provide an explanation of the regulation of metabolic processes in the organism.

The original observations of such interactions were on haemoglobin which may be considered as a type case of an allosteric protein. This was the subject of Dr. Wyman's talk. Dr. Wyman discussed mainly the haem-haem interaction, considered as a model of interaction between sites for the same ligand.

The second speaker, Dr. J. Monod (Paris), described a model which aims at explaining both the interactions between similar and between different ligands, in terms of quaternary structures of proteins. In this model an allosteric protein is considered to be a polymer with an axis of symmetry, which can exist under at least two different states which are assumed to differ between them by the degree of association between the sub-units. The two states are supposed to differ in their affinity for the ligands which the protein can bind so that the presence of a given ligand can push the equilibrium towards a given state.

The third speaker was Dr. H. K. Schachman (Berkeley, California), who gave a physico-chemical description of the enzyme aspartyl transcarbamylase of *E. coli*. Dr. Schachman showed that the enzyme is made of different sub-units, some of which possess a site

淋巴腺内的吞噬细胞吸收；在二级应答中，放射性抗原特别集中在树突状细胞的生发中心。尽管被吸收抗原的主要部分很快就被降解了，但是抗原的剩余部分仍能维持几周，并且只能从细胞中逐渐消失。诺萨尔、汉弗莱和他们的同事们未能在抗体生成细胞中检测到放射性标记的抗原，这表明在抗体生成细胞中只会有极少量抗原决定簇出现。

抗原如何刺激潜在的抗体生成细胞仍是一个关键问题。它是直接与反应细胞作用还是必须通过中间细胞，这一点尚需进一步明确。因为吞噬细胞，如巨噬细胞吸收抗原，所以它们已经被认为可能是中间细胞。从巨噬细胞中可以提取出包含抗原的 RNA 制剂，它们在诱导抗体的过程中有很高的活性，但是这是否是抗体诱导中的必需步骤仍不清楚。有人也已经建议将无抗原信息的分子从巨噬细胞内转移到应答细胞中，但这尚未给出令人信服的结果，仍需进一步实验来阐明这个问题。

第三天，雅各布博士（巴黎）作为主席主持了一场关于变构酶的讨论。一个大分子与一个配体分子的结合可以影响它与另外一个相同或不同的配体分子的结合，人们很早之前就已经了解到这一事实。莫诺和雅各布引入“变构”蛋白这一术语，用来描述蛋白质中发生的这种相互作用。尽管希望许多蛋白都存在一定程度的变构，但此术语的引入在引起人们对包括酶在内的特别重要的一类现象的关注方面仍然是非常有用的，这些酶至少能为生物体内代谢过程的调节提供一种解释。

对这种相互作用的最初观察是在血红蛋白中进行的，血红蛋白可能被认为是某一类型的变构蛋白，这是怀曼博士的演讲主题。怀曼博士主要讨论了血红素间的相互作用，这被认为是相同配体的位点间相互作用的模型。

第二个报告人莫诺博士（巴黎）描述了一个模型，旨在根据蛋白质四级结构来解释相似配体间和不同配体间的相互作用。在这个模型中，变构蛋白被认为是拥有一个对称轴的多聚体，它至少以两种不同形态存在，假定用亚基间的结合程度来区别这几种不同形态。这两种形态的蛋白和能够与之结合的配体间的亲和力应当不同，因此已知配体的存在可以推动化学平衡向已知状态发展。

第三个报告人是沙赫曼博士（伯克利，加利福尼亚），他从物理化学的角度描述了大肠杆菌的天冬氨酸转氨甲酰酶。沙赫曼博士指出该酶由不同亚基组成，其中一些

specific for one of the substrates, aspartate, and others a site specific for CTP which inhibits the reaction catalysed by the enzyme. Isolated sub-units still exhibit affinity for their respective ligand but without co-operative effects, those being restricted to the complex polymer.

In the discussion, many other enzymes were discussed which exhibit similar behaviour. This is the case, for example, of the enzyme *d*CMP amino hydrolase which has been extensively investigated by Dr. Scarano. In contrast, other complex enzymes appear to operate on a different scheme. This is the case, for example, of the enzyme glutamine synthetase of *E. coli*, investigated by Dr. E. Stadtman, an enzyme the activity of which is susceptible to partial inhibition by eight different compounds of widely different structures.

In the final session on "Molecular Aspects of Differentiation", with Prof. J. Brachet (Brussels) as chairman, the main topic discussed was the synthesis of nucleic acids and proteins during early development. Prof. Monroy (Palermo) described in detail the significance of the events following the process of fertilization in sea-urchin eggs. Ribosomes from unfertilized eggs are not capable of incorporating amino-acids, while those obtained from fertilized eggs are capable of doing so. Prof. Monroy presented the following simple experiment. When RNA from unfertilized eggs was added to liver ribosomes the latter incorporated amino-acides. But no incorporation was detected when RNA from unfertilized eggs was added to ribosomes from unfertilized eggs. He has therefore suggested that some inhibitor is present on the ribosomes which prevents them from synthesizing protein. Though the unfertilized egg has a store of messenger RNA, the ribosomes become active only after fertilization. Prof. Monroy further indicated that inhibition on the inactive ribosomes could be lifted considerably by treating them with trypsin and removing the trypsin by washing through a sucrose layer.

Dr. D. Brown (Baltimore) examined the synthesis of ribosomal, soluble and DNA-like RNA during development of *Xenopus*. The kind of RNA synthesized varies conspicuously as development proceeds. Dr. Brown has been able to show that DNA-like RNA and soluble RNA are synthesized during late cleavage phase and the synthesis continues after gastrulation. The synthesis of ribosomal RNA starts only at the onset of gastrulation and increases as development proceeds.

The final paper was one on cell interactions and carcinogenesis by Dr. L. Sachs (Rehovoth), who discussed *in vitro* studies on the mechanism of carcinogenesis by polyoma virus and by carcinogenic hydrocarbons. In the experiments with polyoma it was shown that virus infection can induce the synthesis of cellular DNA after normal cell DNA synthesis has been repressed by contact inhibition or by X-irradiation, that each cell is induced to synthesize about double its DNA content, and that this induction is not dependent on the replication of viral DNA, but is a function of the viral genome. It was suggested that all the known experimental findings on cell-virus interactions with the small DNA tumour viruses can be explained by the synthesis of a messenger RNA early after virus infection that mediates the induction of cellular enzymes required for DNA synthesis by way of

亚基拥有一个底物（天冬氨酸）的特异结合位点，其他亚基则具有结合三磷酸胞苷的特异位点，与三磷酸胞苷的结合可以抑制该酶的催化反应。分离的亚基仍然对它们各自的配体具有亲和力，但是没有表现出那些限于发生在复杂多聚体中的协同效应。

在讨论中，也探讨了其他许多表现出相似行为的酶。例如已经被斯卡拉诺博士广泛研究的脱氧胞苷一磷酸氨基水解酶。相反，其他复杂的酶表现为不同的方式，例如，斯塔特曼博士研究的大肠杆菌谷氨酰胺合成酶，这种酶的部分活性容易被 8 种结构差异极大的化合物所抑制。

布拉谢教授（布鲁塞尔）作为主席主持了最后一部分关于“分化的分子方面”的会议，讨论的主题是早期发育中核酸与蛋白质的合成。蒙罗伊教授（巴勒莫）详细地描述了海胆卵受精后所发生的一系列事件的重要性。从未受精的卵中获得的核糖体不能结合氨基酸，而那些从受精卵中获得的核糖体则可以结合氨基酸。蒙罗伊教授介绍了下面的简单实验。将从未受精的卵中提取出的 RNA 加入肝脏的核糖体中，该核糖体能够结合氨基酸。但是，将从未受精的卵中提取的 RNA 加入到从未受精的卵中提取的核糖体中，却没有检测到这种结合。因此他认为在核糖体上存在可以阻止其合成蛋白质的一些抑制因子。虽然未受精的卵中存有很多信使 RNA，但是核糖体只在受精后才变得有活性。蒙罗伊教授进一步指出，先用胰蛋白酶处理非活性的核糖体，然后用蔗糖梯级溶液洗去胰蛋白酶，可以显著降低非活性核糖体的抑制作用。

布朗博士（巴尔的摩）检查了非洲爪蟾发育过程中核糖体的、可溶性的和 DNA 状的 RNA 的合成。在发育过程中，各种 RNA 的合成差异显著。布朗博士已能够表明 DNA 状 RNA 和可溶性 RNA 在卵裂后期合成并一直持续到原肠胚形成后。核糖体 RNA 的合成只起步于原肠胚形成的开始期，并且随着发育进行而增加。

最后是萨克斯博士（雷霍沃特）的关于细胞相互作用和癌症发生的一个报告，他讨论了对多瘤病毒和致癌烃类致癌机理的体外研究。多瘤病毒的实验显示出在正常细胞的 DNA 合成已经被接触抑制或被 X 射线抑制后，病毒感染能够引发细胞 DNA 的合成，被引发的每一个细胞的合成大约能使 DNA 的含量加倍，而且这种引发并不依赖于病毒 DNA 的复制，而是病毒基因组的功能。有人提出，所有已知关于细胞病毒与小 DNA 肿瘤病毒间的相互作用的实验发现都可以这样解释，即在病毒感染后的早期，信使 RNA 的合成通过改变细胞表面来调节 DNA 合成所需细胞酶的诱导。致癌烃的实验表明，在体外，这些化学物质能够直接且迅速地引发正常细

alteration of the cell surface. In the experiments with carcinogenic hydrocarbons it was shown that these chemicals can directly and rapidly induce *in vitro* a high frequency of transformation of normal cells to tumour cells. Such *in vitro* investigations provide evidence on the similarities between the two types of carcinogenesis.

(**208**, 1048-1050; 1965)

胞向肿瘤细胞的高频转变。这种体外研究为这两类致癌作用间的相似性提供了证据。

（孙玉诚 翻译；崔巍 审稿）

Globin Synthesis in Thalassaemia: an *in vitro* Study

D. J. Weatherall *et al.*

Editor's Note

Thalassaemia is an inherited disease of the blood which takes several forma, each corresponding to an abnormal configuration of the haemoglobin molecule. David Weatherall, a British physician and academic scientist, was the first to recognize the medical importance of these diseases, which are particularly common in the Middle East. This study describes the proofs that he and his colleagues obtained, that haemoglobin in thalassaemia is indeed wrongly synthesized, because the genes concerned have been mistakenly reproduced.

THE inherited haemoglobinopathies are of two main types. There are those, like sickle-cell disease, in which a structural change in one of the peptide chains of the globin fraction can be demonstrated, and there are others in which, despite evidence of an inherited defect in globin synthesis, no structural change in the globin moiety can be found. Disorders of haemoglobin synthesis of the second type are often found in patients with the clinical and haematological findings of thalassaemia and are, therefore, designated the "thalassaemia syndromes"[1].

Human adult haemoglobin has a major and a minor component called haemoglobins A and A_2 respectively[2]. Haemoglobin A has two α- and two β-peptide chains ($\alpha_2\beta_2$) and haemoglobin A_2 has two α- and two δ-chains ($\alpha_2\delta_2$) (ref. 3). Foetal haemoglobin, which has usually disappeared by the age of one year, has two α- and two γ-chains ($\alpha_2\gamma_2$) (ref. 4). There is good evidence that the structures of the α-, β-, γ-, and δ-chains are determined by separate pairs of genes[3].

In some patients with the clinical picture of thalassaemia, foetal haemoglobin synthesis persists beyond the first year of life and haemoglobin A_2-levels exceed the normal range of 1.5-3.5 percent of the total haemoglobin[2]. Furthermore, the genetic determinant for this type of thalassaemia behaves as though it were allelic or closely linked to the β-chain locus and also interacts with the sickle-cell (β^s-chain) gene[5]. These observations suggest that this form of thalassaemia results from an inherited defect in β-chain synthesis, the increased amounts of haemoglobins F and A_2 reflecting an attempt at compensation for the deficit in β-chains. The disorder is therefore designated β-thalassaemia.

Some patients with the clinical picture of thalassaemia do not have increased levels of haemoglobin A_2 and F, however, and the genetic determinant segregates separately from the β-chain gene[6]. Some, but not all, individuals in this group carry variable quantities

地中海贫血中珠蛋白的合成：一项体外研究

韦瑟罗尔等

编者按

地中海贫血是一种血液遗传性疾病，包括几种类型，每种类型对应于一种血红蛋白分子的异常构型。英国医生兼学术科学家戴维·韦瑟罗尔首先认识到了这些在中东地区尤为常见的疾病的医学重要性。这个研究描述了他和同事们所获得的实验证据，即在地中海贫血中血红蛋白的合成确实出现了错误，因为相关基因的复制出现了错误。

遗传性血红蛋白病有两种主要类型，一些能被证明的血红蛋白病（如镰状细胞贫血病）在其珠蛋白部分的一条肽链上发生了结构改变，而另一些血红蛋白病，尽管有证据表明，在珠蛋白合成时发生了遗传性缺陷，但珠蛋白部分未发现结构改变。在具有地中海贫血的临床和血液学表现的患者中，经常可以见到第二种类型的血红蛋白合成异常，因此被称为“地中海贫血综合征”[1]。

成年人血红蛋白有一种主要组分和一种次要组分，分别被称为血红蛋白 A 和血红蛋白 A_2[2]。血红蛋白 A 有两条 α 肽链和两条 β 肽链（$\alpha_2\beta_2$），血红蛋白 A_2 有两条 α 肽链和两条 δ 肽链（$\alpha_2\delta_2$）（参考文献 3）。通常到一岁时消失的胎儿血红蛋白，有两条 α 肽链和两条 γ 肽链（$\alpha_2\gamma_2$）（参考文献 4）。有确凿的证据表明，α 链、β 链、γ 链和 δ 链的结构是由单独成对的基因决定的[3]。

在某些有地中海贫血临床表现的患者中，胎儿血红蛋白的合成可持续到一周岁以后，且血红蛋白 A_2 的水平超出占总血红蛋白 1.5%~3.5% 的正常范围[2]。此外，该型地中海贫血的遗传定子似乎与 β 链基因座是等位基因或紧密连锁，并与镰状细胞（β^s 链）基因相互作用[5]。这些观测结果表明该型地中海贫血症是由 β 链合成期间遗传缺陷以及血红蛋白 F 和血红蛋白 A_2 的量增加（反映出试图补偿 β 链的缺陷）引起的。因此，这种疾病被称为 β– 地中海贫血。

然而，某些有地中海贫血临床表现的患者并不出现血红蛋白 A_2 和血红蛋白 F 水平的升高，且遗传定子与 β 链基因是单独分离的[6]。其中，本组中部分个体并不是全部携带有不同数量的血红蛋白 H 和巴特血红蛋白。血红蛋白 H 是正常 β 链的四聚

of haemoglobins H and Bart's. Haemoglobin H is a tetramer of normal β-chains (β_4), while haemoglobin Bart's is composed of four normal γ-chains (γ_4) (refs. 7, 8). It has been suggested, therefore, that this form of thalassaemia results from an inherited defect in α-chain synthesis, α-thalassaemia[9], the resulting excess of β-chains or γ-chains aggregating to form haemoglobins H or Bart's respectively. This concept of the genetic basis of the thalassaemias, while serving as a useful model for their further investigation, is incomplete since there is increasing evidence for the existence of several types of β-thalassaemia and, probably, of α-thalassemia[1].

Little is known about the mechanisms involved in the control of normal α- and β-chain synthesis in man, or about the factors which maintain δ-chain synthesis at about 1/40 of the level of β-chain synthesis. Furthermore, although there is evidence that the reticulocyte ribosomes of thalassaemic individuals have a reduced capacity for globin synthesis[10], there has been no direct evidence for defective α- and β-chain synthesis in these disorders. The chemical structure of these chains appears to be normal[11] and the nature of the apparent defect in synthesis remains quite obscure. The experiments to be described here were carried out in an attempt to clarify some of these problems by comparing the *in vitro* incorporation of radioactive amino-acids into α-, β-, and δ-chains in the reticulocytes of thalassemic and non-thalassaemic persons.

Reticulocyte-rich blood was obtained from 19 persons with the conditions listed in Tables 1, 2 and 3. 2-8 ml. of washed red cells was suspended in an amino-acid mixture[12] containing 25-100 μc. of uniformly labelled ^{14}C-leucine, and incubated in a Dubnoff metabolic shaker at 37°C, aliquots being removed at various times and immediately frozen. Haemoglobin fractions were purified by dialysis, column chromatography, and starch-block electrophoresis as previously deseribed[13].

Table 1. Relative Specific Activities of α- and β-Chains of Haemoglobin A prepared from Red Cells of Patients with a Variety of Haematological States. ^{14}C-Leucine was used in Each Case

Clinical disorder	Incubation time (min)	Specific activity of α-chain (c.p.m./mg)	Specific activity of β-chain (c.p.m./mg)
Hereditary spherocytosis	4	15	28
	15	88	77
	45	138	163
	240	422	439
Hereditary spherocytosis	2	39	93
	4	105	210
	200	1,617	1,652
Hereditary spherocytosis	2	189	616
	4	691	1,470
	300	8,960	9,296
Pyruvate kinase deficiency	4	418	595
	15	2,240	2,030
	60	3,780	4,116
	240	6,930	6,370

体（$β_4$），而巴特血红蛋白是由 4 条正常的 γ 链组成（$γ_4$）（参考文献 7,8）。因此，可以认为该型地中海贫血是由于 α 链合成期间的遗传缺陷引起的，即 α–地中海贫血[9]，由此产生的过量 β 链或 γ 链聚集，分别形成了血红蛋白 H 或巴特血红蛋白。关于地中海贫血遗传学基础的这种概念是不完整的，尽管在对其进一步研究中是个有用的模型，因为越来越多的证据表明存在多种类型的 β–地中海贫血，可能也存在多种类型的 α–地中海贫血[1]。

关于人体内正常 α 链与 β 链合成控制的机制，或者是什么因素让 δ 链的合成保持在 β 链合成水平的 1/40 左右，目前所知甚少。此外，尽管有证据表明，在地中海贫血个体中网织红细胞核糖体合成珠蛋白的能力下降[10]，但缺乏这些疾病 α 链、β 链合成缺陷的直接证据。这些链的化学结构看上去是正常的[11]，但在合成期间明显缺陷的本质仍然相当模糊。本文将要描述的实验是通过比较在体外将放射性氨基酸掺入地中海贫血患者和非地中海贫血患者的网织红细胞的 α 链、β 链和 δ 链中实现的，进而试图阐明其中的一些问题。

富含网织红细胞的血液来自 19 个受试者，其基本状况见表 1、表 2 和表 3。将 2 毫升 ~8 毫升洗过的红细胞悬浮于含有 25 微居里 ~100 微居里标记均匀的 ^{14}C–亮氨酸的氨基酸混合液中[12]，在 37℃下，在杜布诺夫代谢摇床中温育，在不同时间取出等份样品并立即冷冻。按以前所述的透析、柱层析和淀粉阻滞电泳纯化血红蛋白组分[13]。

表 1. 由各种血液病患者红细胞制备的血红蛋白 A 的 α 链和 β 链的相对比活。各例中均使用 ^{14}C–亮氨酸。

临床疾病	温育时间（分钟）	α 链的比活（每分钟计数 / 毫克）	β 链的比活（每分钟计数 / 毫克）
遗传性球形红细胞增多症	4	15	28
	15	88	77
	45	138	163
	240	422	439
遗传性球形红细胞增多症	2	39	93
	4	105	210
	200	1,617	1,652
遗传性球形红细胞增多症	2	189	616
	4	691	1,470
	300	8,960	9,296
丙酮酸激酶缺陷	4	418	595
	15	2,240	2,030
	60	3,780	4,116
	240	6,930	6,370

Table 2. Relative Specific Activities of α- and β-Chains of Haemoglobin A prepared from the Red Cells of Patients with β-Thalassaemia and Haemoglobin H Disease (α-Thalassaemia). ^{14}C-Leucine was used in Each Case

Clinical disorder	Incubation time (min)	Specific activity of α-chain (c.p.m./mg)	Specific activity of β-chain (c.p.m./mg)
Thalassaemia major	30	494	266
Thalassaemia major	30	840	470
Thalassaemia major	30	1,638	1,043
Thalassaemia major	30	242	61
Thalassaemia major	30	89	24
Thalassaemia major	60	126	180
Thalassaemia major	30	494	266
	180	3,064	1,904
	12 h	4,718	3,924
Thalassaemia major	3	627	373
	10	945	441
	30	1,638	1,043
	180	4,382	2,618
Haemoglobin H disease	30	1,660	277
Haemoglobin H disease	30	260	65
Haemoglobin H disease	30	80	10
Haemoglobin H disease	30	267	19
Haemoglobin H disease	240	67	13
	20 h	100	43
Haemoglobin H disease	10	35	2
	30	127	11
	180	189	32

Table 3. Distribution of Radioactivity in the Peptide Chains of Haemoglobins A and A_2 after 60-min Incubation of the Red Cells with ^{14}C-Leucine

Haemoglobin type	Specific activity of α-chain (c.p.m./mg)	Specific activity of β-chain (c.p.m./mg)	Specific activity of δ-chain (c.p.m./mg)
A	59.3	52.7	—
A_2	32.1	—	6.9

In some experiments ribosomes were prepared[14] before fractionation of the haemoglobins. Globin was prepared[15] from either purified haemoglobin fractions or, in some cases, directly from the washed whole-cell lysates without further purification. The α- and β-chains were separated by gradient elution chromatography on carboxymethylcellulose columns in urea/mercaptoethanol buffers as recently described[16]. In some experiments, chain separation was also achieved by hybridization with canine haemoglobin or by counter-current distribution[17]. The purity of each chain was checked by fingerprinting[16] and the radioactivity measured, after plating out about 0.5 mg of protein on aluminium planchets, using a low-background gas-flow counter[13]. In order to determine the distribution of radioactivity in finished or partly finished chains on the ribosomes, 5-10 mg of unlabelled carrier globin was added to the ribosomal pellets and the α- and β-chains of the mixture separated by carboxymethylcellulose chromatography[16].

Non-thalassaemic Reticulocytes

The specific activities of the separated α- and β-chains of purified haemoglobin A from

表 2. 由 β–地中海贫血患者和血红蛋白 H 病（α–地中海贫血）患者红细胞制备的血红蛋白 A 的 α 链和 β 链的相对比活。各例中均使用 ^{14}C–亮氨酸。

临床疾病	温育时间（分钟）	α 链的比活 （每分钟计数 / 毫克）	β 链的比活 （每分钟计数 / 毫克）
重型地中海贫血病	30	494	266
重型地中海贫血病	30	840	470
重型地中海贫血病	30	1,638	1,043
重型地中海贫血病	30	242	61
重型地中海贫血病	30	89	24
重型地中海贫血病	60	126	180
重型地中海贫血病	30	494	266
	180	3,064	1,904
	12 小时	4,718	3,924
重型地中海贫血病	3	627	373
	10	945	441
	30	1,638	1,043
	180	4,382	2,618
血红蛋白 H 病	30	1,660	277
血红蛋白 H 病	30	260	65
血红蛋白 H 病	30	80	10
血红蛋白 H 病	30	267	19
血红蛋白 H 病	240	67	13
	20 小时	100	43
血红蛋白 H 病	10	35	2
	30	127	11
	180	189	32

表 3. 红细胞在 ^{14}C–亮氨酸中温育 60 分钟后，血红蛋白 A 和 A_2 肽链中放射性分布情况。

血红蛋白类型	α 链的比活 （每分钟计数 / 毫克）	β 链的比活 （每分钟计数 / 毫克）	δ 链的比活 （每分钟计数 / 毫克）
A	59.3	52.7	–
A_2	32.1	–	6.9

在一些实验中，核糖体是在血红蛋白分离前制备的 [14]。珠蛋白或是由纯化的血红蛋白组分制备，或是在某些情况下由洗过的全细胞裂解物（未经进一步纯化）直接制备 [15]。α 链和 β 链的分离采用最近描述的方法 [16]，即在羧甲基纤维素柱上使用尿素 / 巯基乙醇缓冲液进行的梯度洗脱层析法。在一些实验中，通过与犬血红蛋白杂交或逆流分布法也能实现链的分离 [17]。采用指纹图谱法检测每种链的纯度 [16]，并将约 0.5 毫克蛋白铺在铝板上，用低背景气流计数仪测量放射性强度 [13]。为确定核糖体上已合成或部分合成的肽链的放射性分布情况，将 5 毫克 ~10 毫克未标记的载体珠蛋白加到核糖体沉淀物中，并用羧甲基纤维素层析法分离混合物中的 α 链和 β 链 [16]。

非地中海贫血的网织红细胞

表 1 总结了从各种非地中海贫血病症纯化的血红蛋白 A 的单独的 α 链和 β 链的

a variety of non-thalassaemic conditions are summarized in Table 1 and the distribution of radioactivity in a typical chain separation, after 30 min incubation, is shown in Fig. 1. Under all conditions investigated the specific activities of the α- and β-chains were very similar at incubation times of 5 min to 5 h. At shorter times, however, the specific activity of the β-chain was always significantly greater than that of the α-chain. The pattern of radioactivity in separated α- and β-chains obtained from addition of carrier globin to ribosomal pellets was always the same in this group. Thus, the radioactivity under the α-chain peak always exceeded that under the β-chain peak, the ratio α-chain/β-chain ranging from 1.5 to 2.1/1. Clear peaks of radioactivity were seen for both chains in each case, the radioactivity peak usually being slightly displaced from the protein peak. These results indicate that since the number of leucine residues in α- and β-chains is the same, α- and β-chain synthesis is normally synchronous. The fact that the specific activity of the β-chain is greater than that of the α-chain at short times of incubation, and the presence of an excess of radioactivity under the α-chain peak from the ribosomes after long periods of incubation, implies that a small pool of α-chain exists on the ribosomes. The existence of only a small peak of radioactivity associated with the β-chain from the ribosomes indicates that release of β-chains from the ribosomes is much more rapid than that of α-chains, but is not instantaneous. These observations suggest that finished β-chains are probably necessary for the removal of α-chains from the ribosomes. A similar situation has been described in the rabbit reticulocyte[18] where the discrepancy in chromatographic behaviour between radioactivity (newly made chain) and carrier chain was also noted. Whether this means that the newly made chain, while still on the ribosome, is chemically different from that found in finished haemoglobin is not clear, but this would seem very likely.

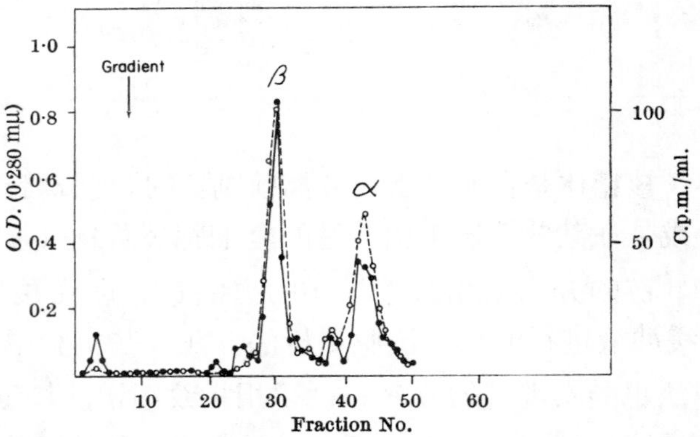

Fig. 1. Incorporation of radioactivity into the α- and β-chains of haemoglobin A prepared from the red cells of a patient with hereditary spherocytosis. Incubation period 45 min. ●—●, *O.D.* (0.280 mμ); ○ --- ○, radioactivity

In order to follow the incorporation of radioactive amino-acids into the α- and δ-chains of haemoglobin A_2, reticulocytes from an individual with hereditary spherocytosis were incubated with ^{14}C-leucine for 60 min and haemoglobins A and A_2 isolated[13]. The α- and β-chains of haemoglobin A and the α- and δ-chains of haemoglobin A_2 were then

比活，图 1 则给出了一种典型的分离链在温育 30 分钟后放射性的分布情况。在研究的所有病症中，当温育时间为 5 分钟 ~5 小时，α 链和 β 链的比活非常相似。但是，当温育时间较短时，β 链的比活总是显著大于 α 链的比活。在这一组，向核糖体沉淀物中加入载体珠蛋白，所得到的单独的 α 链和 β 链的放射性模式总是相同的。这样，α 链峰的放射性总是超过 β 链峰的放射性，α 链和 β 链的比值在 1.5∶1~2.1∶1 的范围内。在各例中都可见到两条链的清晰的放射性峰，放射性峰通常略偏离蛋白质峰。这些结果表明，由于 α 链和 β 链中亮氨酸残基的数目相同，所以 α 链和 β 链的合成通常是同步的。在较短的温育时间下，β 链的比活大于 α 链的比活，而长时间温育后，核糖体中 α 链峰出现过量的放射性这一事实表明核糖体上有一个小的 α 链库。只有一个小的与核糖体 β 链相关的放射性峰，这表明从核糖体中释放的 β 链要比 α 链快得多，但并不是瞬时的。这些观测结果表明，已合成的 β 链也许对核糖体中 α 链的释放是必要的。在兔网织红细胞中已描述了类似的情况[18]，人们也发现了带放射性的新合成链和载体链的色谱行为有区别。我们还不清楚这是否意味着仍位于核糖体上的新合成链与在已合成的血红蛋白中发现的化学结构不同，但很可能是这样的。

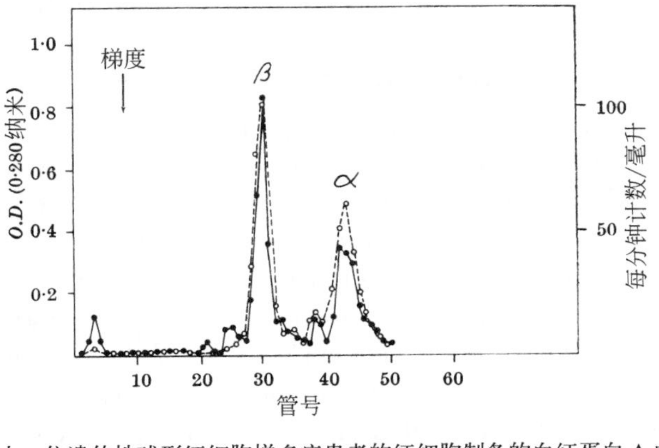

图 1. 掺入到由一位遗传性球形红细胞增多症患者的红细胞制备的血红蛋白 A 中 α 链和 β 链的放射性。温育时间为 45 分钟。●—●，*O.D.* (0.280 纳米)；○ --- ○，放射性。

为了跟踪放射性氨基酸掺入到血红蛋白 A_2 的 α 链和 δ 链的情况，将一位遗传性球形红细胞增多症个体的网织红细胞与 ^{14}C–亮氨酸温育 60 分钟，并将血红蛋白 A 和 A_2 分离[13]。然后将血红蛋白 A 的 α 链和 β 链及血红蛋白 A_2 的 α 链和 δ 链分开，

separated and the specific activities of the whole haemoglobin fractions and separated chains determined (Table 3). As in previous experiments[13] the specific activity of haemoglobin A was more than twice that of haemoglobin A_2. The specific activities of the α- and β-chains of haemoglobin A were very similar. The specific activity of the α-chain of haemoglobin A_2 was less than that of haemoglobin A—this finding being compatible with the finding[13] that, in the *in vitro* system, haemoglobin A_2 synthesis in reticulocytes is retarded before that of haemoglobin A. This observation cannot, however, explain the ratio of specific activity of α-chain to δ-chain of 5/1 in haemoglobin A_2. It has recently been suggested that one reason for the relatively slow rate of δ-chain synthesis might lie in the presence of one or more "slow points" during assembly of the δ-chain[20]. In such an event, δ-chain clearance from the ribosomes would be slow relative to α-chain clearance. Thus, in investigation of radioactive incorporation, the time taken to achieve uniform δ-chain labelling would be longer than that required for uniform α-chain labeling, resulting in the marked difference in specific activity between α-chain and δ-chain observed in these experiments. These findings are thus compatible with the recent observation that uniform labelling of the δ-chain does in fact take a long period of incubation[20]. Another explanation would be the exchange of α-chains between newly made haemoglobin A and haemoglobin A_2, the synthetic rate of which falls off so rapidly in peripheral blood, but this mechanism seems very unlikely.

These results suggest, therefore, that there are "slow points" in δ-chain synthesis giving rise to a relatively slow rate of clearance from the ribosomes. It is unlikely that the slow rate of δ-chain synthesis is associated with a quantitative reduction in messenger RNA since, although this would result in the production of fewer δ-chains, their specific activity would be similar to that of α-chains, if the rates of assembly of the two chains were comparable.

β-Thalassaemia Reticulocytes

The findings in the experiments utilizing cells from persons with β-thalassaemia, which were quite different from those in non-thalassaemic samples, are summarized in Table 2. The specific activity of the α-chain of purified haemoglobin A always exceeded that of the β-chain, the ratios α/β ranging from 1.5/1 to 7/1. These values were obtained at incubation times of 30 min-5 h, the differences being less marked after longer periods of incubation (Fig. 2). These ratios were similar to those recently reported[19]. In order to rule out the possibility of variation of leucine pool size for the two chains in this disorder, experiments were also performed with ^{14}C-lysine and ^{14}C-valine, similar differences in specific activity being noted. Such differences between the specific activities of the α- and β-chains in finished haemoglobin A could occur if a large intracellular pool of β-chain existed at any given time. After introduction of the radioisotope, newly made (and therefore labelled) β-chain would be diluted out by pre-existing unlabelled β-chains present in the pool. To examine this possibility, two experiments were carried out in which a chain separation was performed on a washed, whole-cell lysate without prior purification of haemoglobin fractions (Fig. 3). The recovery of protein and radioactivity exceeded 90 percent in each case. Fingerprinting of each peak showed only α- and β-chain peptides, no new spots being observed. In both experiments the amount of radioactivity under

测定全血红蛋白组分和单独链的比活（表 3）。与之前的实验[13]相同，血红蛋白 A 的比活是血红蛋白 A_2 比活的两倍多。血红蛋白 A 的 α 链和 β 链的比活非常接近，血红蛋白 A_2 的 α 链比活低于血红蛋白 A 的 α 链比活，这一结果与体外系统中网织红细胞血红蛋白 A_2 的合成滞后于血红蛋白 A 的合成的结果[13]是一致的。不过，这一观测结果不能解释为什么在血红蛋白 A_2 中 α 链和 δ 链的比活的比值是 5∶1。近来有人认为 δ 链的合成速度较慢的一个原因可能是 δ 链组装时存在一个或多个“限速位点”[20]。在这种情况下，δ 链从核糖体中的释放将相对慢于 α 链。这样，在放射性掺入的研究中，δ 链均一标记所需的时间将会长于 α 链均一标记所需的时间，导致在这些实验中观察到的 α 链和 δ 链的比活显著不同。这些结果也与最近观察到的 δ 链均一标记实际上确实需要很长的温育时间相一致[20]。另一解释是新生成的血红蛋白 A 和血红蛋白 A_2 间的 α 链相互交换，在外周血中，血红蛋白 A_2 的合成速率迅速下降，但这种机制似乎很不可能。

因而，这些结果表明，在 δ 链的合成中存在“限速位点”，导致其从核糖体中释放的速率相对慢。δ 链合成的速率降低不可能与信使 RNA 的量减少有关，因为尽管信使 RNA 量的减少会导致合成的 δ 链减少，但如果两条链组装的速度相似，那么它们的比活将与 α 链的比活相似。

β– 地中海贫血的网织红细胞

使用 β– 地中海贫血患者的细胞的实验结果与使用非地中海贫血患者的样品得到的结果完全不同，表 2 总结了这些结果。纯化的血红蛋白 A 中 α 链的比活总是高于 β 链的比活，当温育时间为 30 分钟~5 小时，两者比值在 1.5∶1~7∶1 范围内，较长时间温育后，两者的差异将不明显（图 2）。这些比值与最近报道的比值相似[19]。为了排除在这种疾病中两种链的亮氨酸库大小存在差异的可能性，我们还用 ^{14}C– 赖氨酸和 ^{14}C– 缬氨酸进行了实验，也发现了类似的比活差异。如果在任何给定时间，细胞内都存在一个大的 β 链库，则已合成的血红蛋白 A 的 α 链和 β 链之间的比活就会出现这种差异，在导入放射性同位素之后，新合成的（即被标记的）β 链会被库中已存在的、未标记的 β 链稀释。为了检查这种可能性，进行了两次实验，没有预先纯化血红蛋白组分，而是用洗涤过的全细胞裂解物进行链分离（图 3）。在各例中蛋白质与放射性的回收率都超过 90%。每个峰的指纹图谱只显示出 α 链和 β 链肽段，未观察到新斑点。在两个实验中，β 链峰的放射性量都与纯化的血红蛋白 A（用等量的初始红细胞裂解物制备）的 β 链的放射性量相似。在一次实验中，在 β 链峰之

the β-chain peak was similar to that found in the β-chain from purified haemoglobin A, which had been prepared from an equivalent amount of the original red-cell lysate. In one experiment a large peak of protein and radioactivity was eluted before the β-chain peak, this being the γ-chain of haemoglobin F, while in another too little haemoglobin F was present for clear separation of β- and γ-chains. These results thus excluded the presence of a large intracellular pool of β-chain, with subsequent dilution of newly labelled chains, as a basis for the observed differences in specific activity in α- and β-chains.

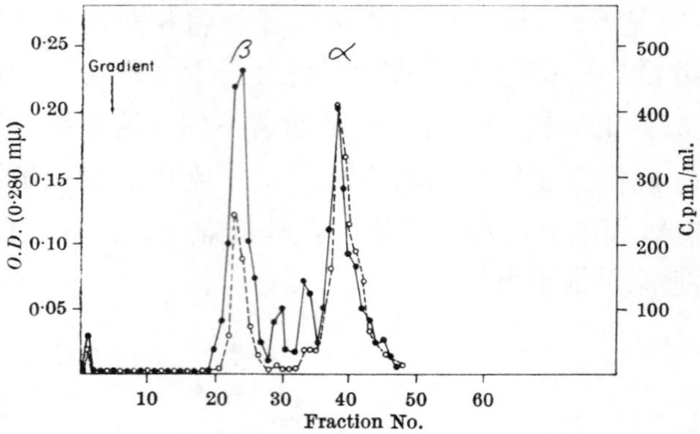

Fig. 2. Incorporation of radioactivity into the α- and β-chains of haemoglobin A prepared from the cells of a patient with β-thalassaemia major. Incubation time 60 min. ● — ●, *O.D.* (0.280 mμ); ○ --- ○, radioactivity

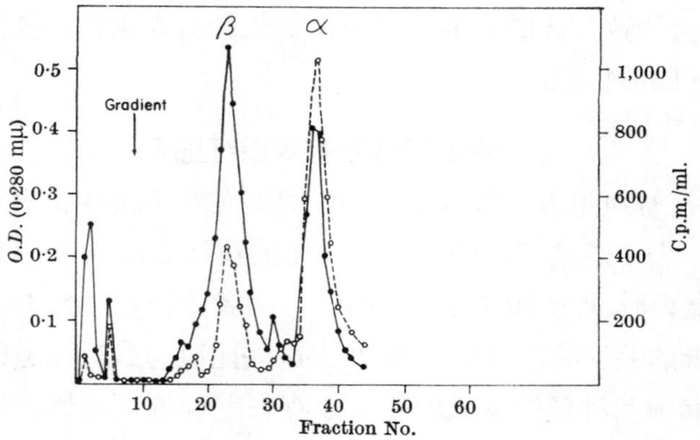

Fig. 3. Distribution of radioactivity compared with protein in a washed whole-cell lysate prepared from the red cells of a patient with β-thalassaemia major. Incubation time 60 min. ● — ●, *O. D.* (0.280 mμ); ○ --- ○, radioactivity

Such differences in specific activity could occur, however, if there were a large block (that is, rate-limiting step) at some point during the assembly of the β-chain or its release from the ribosome, associated with the presence on the ribosomes at any given time of many completed or partially completed chains. As in the case of normal δ-chains already discussed, relatively long periods of time would then be required to achieve uniform labelling of newly synthesized β-chain. At long times, each newly synthesized chain would

前洗脱出一个大的蛋白质和放射性峰，这是血红蛋白 F 的 γ 链，而在另一实验中，只有很少的血红蛋白 F，难以明确分开 β 链和 γ 链。因此，这些结果排除了在细胞内存在大的 β 链库的可能性，也不存在随后新标记的链被稀释，以及由此可能导致的 α 链和 β 链比活的差异。

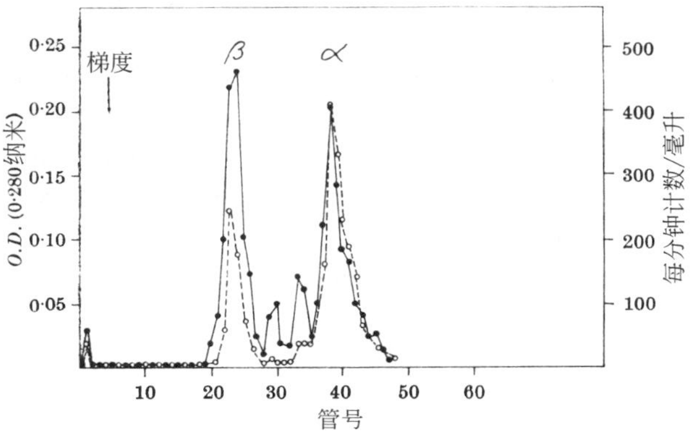

图 2. 掺入到由一位重型 β– 地中海贫血患者细胞制备的血红蛋白 A 中 α 链和 β 链的放射性。温育时间为 60 分钟。●—●，*O.D.* (0.280 纳米)；○ --- ○，放射性。

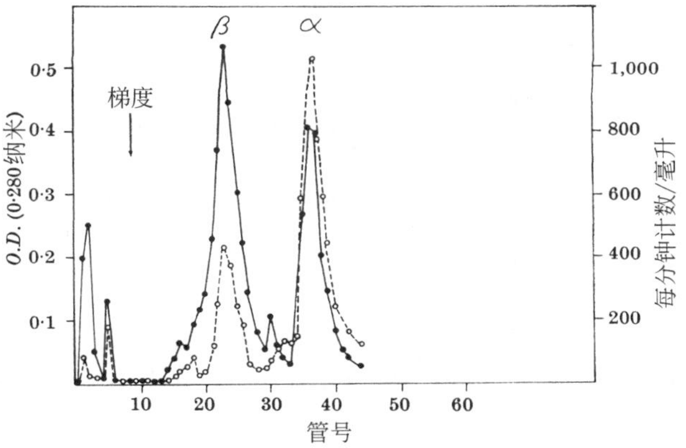

图 3. 在一位重型 β– 地中海贫血患者红细胞制备的洗涤过的全细胞裂解物中蛋白质与放射性分布的比较情况。温育时间为 60 分钟。●—●，*O.D.* (0.280 纳米)；○ --- ○，放射性。

然而，如果在 β 链组装或从核糖体上释放的过程中的某个点存在大的阻塞（即限速步骤），与在任何给定的时间核糖体上存在大量已合成或部分合成的肽链有关，也会发生这种比活的差异。正如已经讨论过的关于正常 δ 链的情况一样，要使新合成的 β 链达到均一标记则需要较长的时间。当时间较长时，每条新合成的肽链就会

then have the same specific activity as an α-chain synthesized from the same amino-acid pool. The time required to achieve uniform labelling would thus depend on the severity of the block, that is, of the ease with which unlabelled β-chains present at the time of introduction of the radioactive amino-acid were cleared from the ribosomes.

One consequence of a rate-limiting step in synthesis, of the sort already discussed, would be the absence of radioactivity associated with β-chain on the ribosomes, in contrast to normal ribosomes where both labelled α- and β-chains can be shown to be present after a few minutes incubation (see earlier). Prolonged periods of incubation would be required to clear pre-existing unlabelled β-chains from the ribosomes and replace them with labelled chains. Ribosomes were therefore prepared from the red cells of two patients, homozygous for β-thalassaemia, after incubation of the cells with ^{14}C-leucine for 45 min. After addition of carrier globin to the ribosome pellet, the chains were separated by column chromatography. No peak of radioactivity corresponding to the β-chain was observed, while a large peak was seen in the α-chain region in each case (Fig. 4).

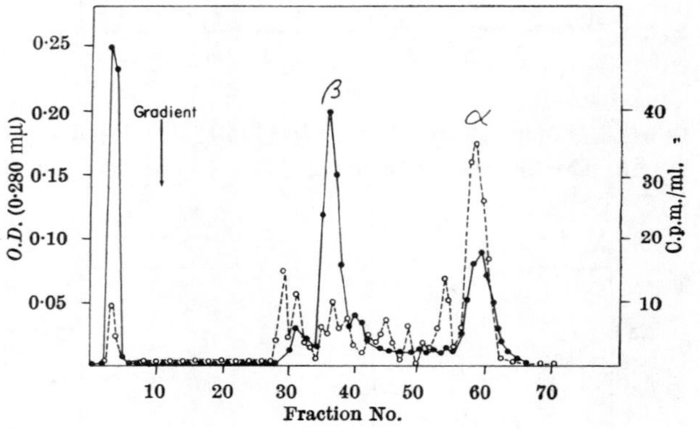

Fig. 4. Distribution of radioactivity after addition of 10 mg unlabelled carrier globin to the ribosomal pellet prepared from the cells of a patient with β-thalassaemin major, Incubation time 45min. ● — ● , *O. D.* (0.280 mμ); ○ --- ○ , radioactivity

These findings are thus compatible with the concept of a gross defect in β-chain synthesis at the ribosomal level in β-thalassaemia. Whether, since α-chains appear to require finished β-chains for their release from the ribosomes, this results in a secondary accumulation of finished α-chain on the ribosomes is uncertain, although this seems likely since the relative amount of radioactivity in the α-chain fraction was several times that observed in ribosomes obtained from non-thalassaemic reticulocytes. Further attempts to demonstrate the site of this proposed block in β-chain synthesis have been made by comparing the ratios of the specific activities of α- and β-chains of purified haemoglobin A prepared from four parallel incubations of aliquots of the same red cell sample using ^{14}C-labelled leucine, arginine, histidine, and tyrosine. Since these amino-acid are not distributed evenly along the peptide chain, the specific activities of non-uniformly labelled β-chains might be expected to differ with each amino-acid. The specific activities of individual peptides[14] of thalassaemic β-chain were also measured. No definite site of delay in synthesis has yet been demonstrated, although the results have not excluded a "slow point" either at, or

与从同样的氨基酸库中合成的 α 链有相同的比活。这样，使链达到均一标记所需的时间取决于阻塞的强度，即在轻度阻塞时，那些在导入放射性氨基酸时存在的未标记的 β 链将从核糖体中释放出来。

这类合成过程（已讨论过的那种）中限速步骤的后果之一，是造成核糖体上与 β 链相关的放射性的缺失，这与正常核糖体上标记的 α 链和 β 链均可在温育几分钟后出现的情况相反（见前文）。释放核糖体中已存在的未标记 β 链并用标记的 β 链将其替换，需要很长的温育时间。将两位纯合 β– 地中海贫血患者的红细胞与 ^{14}C– 亮氨酸温育 45 分钟，然后制备核糖体。向核糖体沉淀物中加入载体珠蛋白后，用柱层析分离两种肽链。在各例中均未观察到对应于 β 链的放射性峰，而在 α 链区域则见到一个大的峰（图 4）。

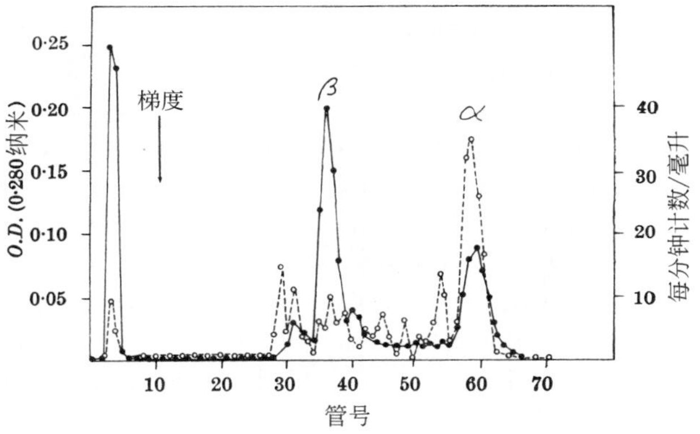

图 4. 将 10 毫克未标记的载体珠蛋白加到由一位重型 β– 地中海贫血患者细胞制备的核糖体沉淀物中后的放射性分布情况。温育时间为 45 分钟。●—●，*O.D.* (0.280 纳米)；○---○，放射性。

因此，这些结果与 β– 地中海贫血患者的 β 链在核糖体水平的合成存在严重缺陷这一观点是一致的。由于 α 链似乎需要已合成的 β 链才能从核糖体中释放，这是否会导致已合成的 α 链在核糖体上二次积累尚不清楚，尽管有可能如此，因为 α 链组分放射性的相对量是在非地中海贫血网织红细胞的核糖体中观察到的放射性相对量的数倍。为进一步确定在 β 链合成中这种提议的阻塞的位点，由同一红细胞样品的四种平行温育小样（分别用 ^{14}C– 亮氨酸、^{14}C– 精氨酸、^{14}C– 组氨酸和 ^{14}C– 酪氨酸温育）制备纯化血红蛋白 A，比较其 α 链和 β 链比活的比值。由于这些氨基酸在肽链中的分布不均匀，因此使用每种氨基酸非均一标记 β 链的比活预计会不同。同时还测量了地中海贫血每个 β 链的比活 [14]。尚未确定合成中确切的延迟位点，尽管这些结果尚未排除位于或者靠近 β 链的羧基末端存在一个“限速位点”。

near, the carboxyl-terminal end of the β-chain.

α-Thalassaemia (Haemoglobin H Disease) Reticulocytes

The results of six ^{14}C-leucine incubation experiments performed on the cells of persons with haemoglobin H thalassaemia are shown in Table 2. At incubation times of 30 min-5 h the specific activity of the α-chain of purified haemoglobin A was 1.5-15 times that of the β-chain (Fig. 5). This difference became less marked with more prolonged incubation of the red cells. Because of these findings, which were surprisingly like those in β-thalassaemia, the possibility of a large intracellular pool of β-chain diluting out newly made and, therefore, labelled β-chains again had to be examined. Washed whole-cell lysates from two persons with haemoglobin H disease were converted to globin without prior purification of the haemoglobins and the α- and β-chains separated (Fig. 6). The radioactivity in the β-chain fraction exceeded that in the α-chain fraction by a factor of 2.3/1 in one case and 3.0/1 in the second, while there was an associated increase in the optical density values for the β-chain peak. In a separate experiment using identical amounts of the same two samples of washed whole-cell lysates, the amounts of haemoglobin A and H were determined and the radioactivity in each fraction measured. The excess of both radioactivity and optical density associated with the β-chain (over that present in the α-chain) of the whole-cell lysate could all be accounted for by the amount of protein and radioactivity found in the purified haemoglobin H fraction in the second experiment. Similar results were observed with ^{14}C-lysine. These results suggest that in haemoglobin H disease β-chain synthesis occurs at a rate of about 2-3 times that of α-chain synthesis, and that β-chains are freely released into the red cell where they form a large pool from which they are capable of uniting with newly made α-chains as these become available. When the cell is haemolysed, most of these β-chains appear in the haemoglobin H fraction. The presence of this large pool of β-chains at any one time probably explains the striking difference between the specific activities of the α- and β-chains of haemoglobin A in haemoglobin H disease. Newly-made labelled α-chains will combine with unlabelled β-chains which were already present in this pool. Whether the excess β-chains exist as haemoglobin H (β_4) in the red cell is uncertain, but at least in an *in vitro* system haemoglobin H readily combines with α-chains to form haemoglobin A[21].

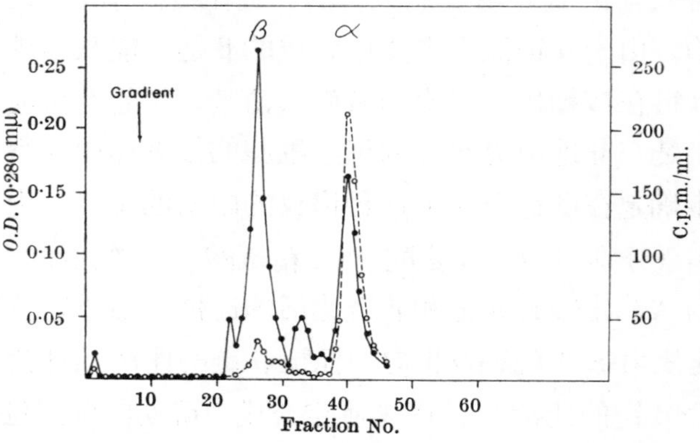

Fig. 5. Distribution of radioactivity in the α- and β-chains of haemoglobin A from the cells of a patient with haemoglobin H disease. Incubation time 45 min. ●—●, *O.D.* (0.280 mμ); ○ --- ○, radioactivity

α– 地中海贫血（血红蛋白 H 病）的网织红细胞

表 2 给出了对血红蛋白 H 地中海贫血患者的细胞进行 6 次 ^{14}C– 亮氨酸温育的实验结果。当温育时间在 30 分钟 ~5 小时之间时，纯化血红蛋白 A 中 α 链的比活是 β 链的 1.5~15 倍（图 5）。随着红细胞温育时间的延长，这一差异将变得不太明显。由于这些结果与 β– 地中海贫血的结果惊人地相似，所以必须再次检测大的胞内 β 链库稀释了新合成的和标记的 β 链可能性。将来自两位血红蛋白 H 病患者洗涤过的全细胞裂解物转化成珠蛋白（未事先纯化血红蛋白），并将 α 链和 β 链分开（图 6）。β 链组分的放射性超过了 α 链组分的放射性，在一个患者中超过了 2.3 倍，在另一个患者中超过了 3.0 倍，同时 β 链峰的光密度值出现了相应增长。在一次独立实验中，使用相同的洗涤过的全细胞裂解物的两个等量样品测定了血红蛋白 A 和 H 的量及各组分的放射性。在第二次实验中，纯化后血红蛋白 H 组分中蛋白质和放射性的量可以解释为什么全细胞裂解物中与 β 链相关的放射性和光密度值过量(超出 α 链的量)。采用 ^{14}C– 赖氨酸也观察到类似的结果。这些结果表明，在血红蛋白 H 病中，β 链合成的速率约为 α 链合成的 2~3 倍，β 链被自由释放到红细胞中，并在红细胞内形成一个大库，当有 α 链时，便可与新生成的 α 链结合。当细胞发生溶血时，这些 β 链中的绝大多数会出现在血红蛋白 H 的组分中。在任一时刻都存在这样一个大的 β 链库，这也许可以解释在血红蛋白 H 病中血红蛋白 A 的 α 链和 β 链比活的显著不同。新合成的标记的 α 链将与库中已经存在的未标记 β 链相结合。尚不能确定红细胞中过量的 β 链是否以血红蛋白 H（β_4）的形式存在，但至少在体外系统中，血红蛋白 H 可迅速与 α 链结合从而形成血红蛋白 A[21]。

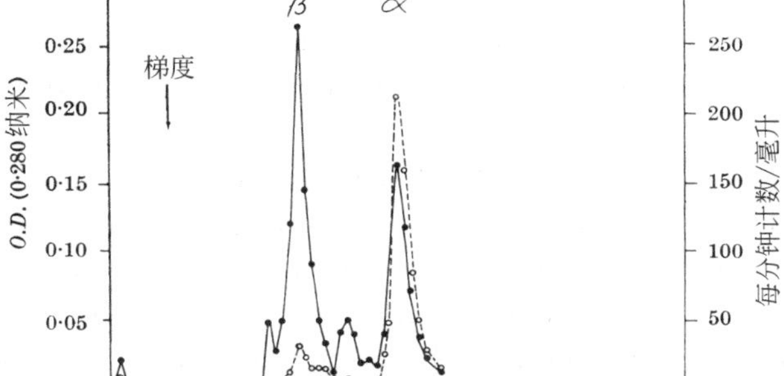

图 5. 由一位血红蛋白 H 病患者的红细胞制备的血红蛋白 A 中 α 链和 β 链的放射性分布情况。温育时间为 45 分钟。●—●，*O.D.* (0.280 纳米)；○ --- ○，放射性。

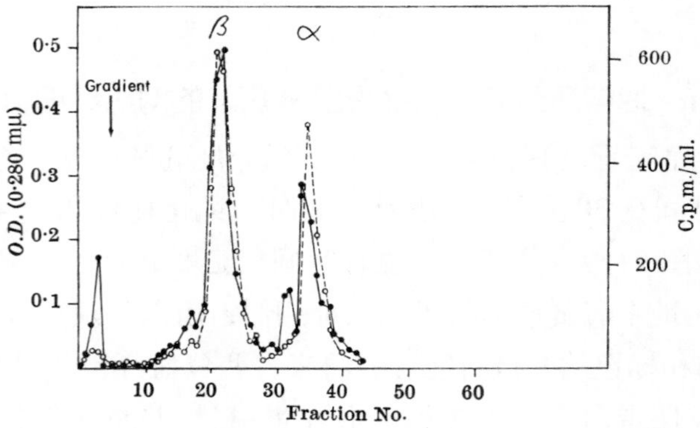

Fig. 6. Distribution of radioactivity compared with protein in a washed whole cell lysate prepared from the red cells of a patient with haemoglobin H disease. Incubation time 45 min. ●—●, *O.D.* (0.280 mμ); ○---○, radioactivity

These experimental results must, of course, be interpreted with caution since the behaviour of cells in an *in vitro* system may not fully reflect their *in vivo* properties. Furthermore, this type of experiment utilizing peripheral blood only measures the last vestiges of protein synthesis in reticulocytes. However, certain tentative conclusions can be drawn. It appears that in non-thalassaemic individuals, α- and β-chain synthesis is synchronous and that, as previously suggested[18], completed β-chains are required for the release of α-chains from the ribosomes. This probably results in a small number of finished α-chains being present on the ribosomes at any given time. Whether the peaks of radioactivity seen on ribosomal chain separations represent completed or partially completed chains is uncertain, although the high resolution of the chromatographic system used would have resulted in the separation of chains differing by as little as one charged residue[16].

From the results of experiments on the kinetics of α- and δ-chain synthesis of haemoglobin A_2, it seems likely that at least one mechanism whereby δ-chain synthesis occurs at a slower rate than α- and β-chain synthesis is the slow ribosomal release of δ-chains. This slow release may well be due to the presence of one or more "slow points" during assembly of the δ-chain.

In both forms of thalassaemia the specific activity of the α-chain of haemoglobin A exceeded that of the β-chain, even after long periods of cell incubation.

For α-thalassaemia, it has been clearly shown that α-chain synthesis occurs at about half the rate of β-chain synthesis, giving rise to a pool of free β-chain in the cell. Thus, although the rate of β-chain synthesis is greater than that of α-chain, the effect of the pre-existing pool of free β-chain is to dilute newly synthesized labelled β-chains. The specific activity of the β-chain is thus considerably lower than that of the α-chain even though synthesis of the latter is impaired.

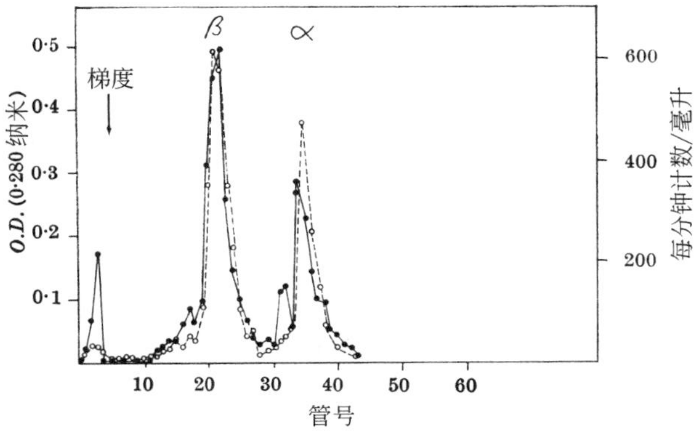

图 6. 由一位血红蛋白 H 病患者的红细胞制备的洗涤过的全细胞裂解物的蛋白质与放射性分布的比较。温育时间为 45 分钟。●—●，*O.D.* (0.280 纳米)；○ --- ○，放射性。

当然，必须慎重解释这些实验结果，因为体外系统中细胞的行为也许不能完全反映其在体内的特性。此外，这类使用外周血的实验仅测定了网织红细胞中蛋白质合成的最后痕迹。不过，我们仍然可以得出一些初步的结论。在非地中海贫血的个体内，α 链和 β 链的合成似乎是同步的，并且如前所述 [18]，从核糖体中释放 α 链需要已合成的 β 链，这也许会导致在任何给定的时间里，少量的已合成的 α 链会停留在核糖体上。还不能确定核糖体链分离的放射性峰是否代表已合成的或部分合成的肽链，尽管所用的色谱系统分辨率很高，能够分离只差一个带电残基的肽链 [16]。

根据血红蛋白 A_2 中 α 链和 δ 链合成动力学实验的结果，看起来 δ 链合成比 α 链和 β 链合成缓慢，至少有一种机制，那就是 δ 链从核糖体中释放较慢。这种缓慢释放很可能是由于在 δ 链组装的过程中存在一个或多个“限速位点”。

在两种地中海贫血中，即使细胞经过长时间的温育，血红蛋白 A 中 α 链的比活也都是超过 β 链的比活的。

对 α–地中海贫血来说，很显然 α 链的合成速率大约是 β 链合成速率的一半，导致在细胞中形成大的游离的 β 链的库。因此，尽管 β 链的合成速率大于 α 链合成速率，但已存在的游离 β 链的库的作用是稀释新合成的已标记的 β 链，因此，尽管 α 链的合成被削弱了，但 β 链的比活明显低于 α 链的比活。

In β-thalassaelmia, no such pool of β-chains could be demonstrated, nor was a large pool of free α-chain detected. However, excess α-chains do occur. Some are bound to γ-chain (as haemoglobin F), others appear to be attached to ribosomes, and some excess α-chain has been observed in chain separations of globin prepared from red cell stroma. These observations are in keeping with the suggestion[22] that excess α-chain may be insoluble and precipitates in the cell to form the inclusion bodies characteristic of β-thalassaemia.

From the date presented, the most probable explanation of the marked difference of specific activity between α- and β-chains in β-thalassaemia is a block or "slow point" during the assembly of the β-chain, resulting in an accumulation of completed or partially completed β-chains on the ribosomes. It seems likely that since α-chains require β-chains for their release, there is also a secondary accumulation of α-chains on the ribosomes. It is difficult to imagine a mechanism which could give rise to the differences in the specific activities of the α- and β-chains noted here, and yet at the same time leave the rate of assembly of the β-chain unaltered. If, for example, the defect were simply in the number of ribosomes active in β-chain synthesis, there would be a deficit in β-chains but those which were made would have the same specific activity as α-chains. Similarly, a net reduction of messenger RNA for β-chains would lead to a deficit in β-chains, but would not be expected to give rise to different specific activities of the α- and β-chains in completed haemoglobin A unless the rates of assembly of the two chains were also different. Experiments using multiple ^{14}C-labelled amino-acids have tentatively ruled out the N-terminal and central region of the chain as a site of a block in synthesis, but it could occur at or near the carboxyl-terminal end of the molecule. Whichever is true, it seems quite probable that in different instances of β-thalassaemia the site of the defect may not always be the same. The heterogeneity of β-thealassemias already recognized[1] may be, in some part, a reflexion of this. The similarity of the kinetics of peptide chain synthesis in thalassaemic β-chains and the δ-chains of normal haemoglobin A_2 suggests that a rewarding approach to the β-thalassaemia problem might be in the search for rate-limiting steps in synthesis. A reduction in the rate of α-chain synthesis in haemoglobin H disease has been shown and a similar search for the presence of "slow points" in α-chain synthesis in this disorder is indicated.

In the absence of evidence indicating structural changes in the α- and β-chains of haemoglobin A in thalassaemia, it seems likely that explanations for these disorders may be found in changes in one or more of the factors which affect the process of assembly of the protein on the ribosomes. Mutations leading to changes in messenger RNA codewords, for example, while producing no change in the sequence of amino-acids, might, nevertheless, alter the rates of translation by requiring recognition of the altered codons by other *s*RNA anti-codons. It is conceivable that if synthesis of the α- or β-chains is dependent on a polycistronic messenger RNA, then changes in messenger RNA at a site remote from the α- or β-chain cistron might in some way influence the rate of assembly or the α- or β-peptide chain[23]. However, this mechanism seems less probable than one directly involving the α-or β-chain messenger RNA. Alternatively, it is possible that mutations leading to changes in specific *s*RNAs or ribosomal RNA could also influence the rate of assembly of one peptide

在β–地中海贫血中，没能证实有这样的β链库，也未检测到大的游离α链库。但是的确出现了过量的α链。有些与γ链结合（如血红蛋白F），其他的似乎附着在核糖体上，在由红细胞基质制备的珠蛋白的链分离中可以观察到过量的α链。这些观测结果均与以下建议[22]相一致，即过量的α链在细胞中可能不溶，并沉淀形成β–地中海贫血的特征性包涵体。

根据已有的数据，在β–地中海贫血中α链和β链比活所出现的显著差异，最可能的解释是在β链组装的过程中出现了一个阻塞或“限速位点”，导致已合成或部分合成的β链在核糖体上积累。这很可能是由于α链的释放需要β链，所以在核糖体上也会存在α链的二次积累。很难设想一种引起在此观察到的α链和β链的比活存在差异的机制，而与此同时β链的组装速率不发生改变。举例来说，如果这种缺陷仅仅是由于β链合成时起作用的核糖体数量不足而引起的，那么β链的合成会不足，但所合成β链的比活应该与α链的相同。同样，β链信使RNA的净减少会导致β链不足，但是也不会导致所合成的血红蛋白A的α链和β链的比活不同，除非两条链的组装速率也不同。用多种^{14}C标记的氨基酸进行实验，初步排除了合成的阻塞位点位于链的N端或中间区域的可能性，但是可以位于或靠近分子的羧基末端。无论哪一种说法是对的，在不同的β–地中海贫血中缺陷的位点很可能并不总是相同的。已经认识到的β–地中海贫血的异质性[1]在某种程度上也许正好反映了这一点。地中海贫血β链和正常血红蛋白A_2中δ链合成动力学的相似性表明，解决β–地中海贫血这一问题的有效方法可能是寻找其合成过程中的限速步骤。已经证明血红蛋白H病中α链的合成速率降低，这意味着可以用同样的方法寻找该疾病中α链合成中“限速位点”的存在。

在没有证据表明地中海贫血中血红蛋白A的α链和β链结构改变的情况下，发现的影响核糖体上蛋白质组装过程的某一种或几种因子的改变似乎可以解释这些疾病。例如，导致信使RNA密码子改变（但氨基酸序列不变）的突变，由于需要*s*RNA反密码子识别改变的密码子，从而可能会改变翻译的速率。可以想象，如果α链或β链的合成依赖于一个多顺反子信使RNA，那么远离α链或β链信使RNA顺反子的一个位点发生改变会在某种程度上影响组装速率或α肽链或β肽链[23]。然而，这种机制的可能性似乎低于直接影响α链或β链信使RNA的可能性。另外，导致特异性*s*RNA或核糖体RNA改变的突变也可能会影响一条肽链相对于另外一条肽链的组装速率。例如，在兔血红蛋白分子中，一种亮氨酸特异性*s*RNA只编码约有三十

chain relative to another. An instance where a leucine-specific *s*RNA is involved in the coding of only one out of some 30 leucine residues in the rabbit haemoglobin molecule is already known[24]. The recent advances in the techniques for isolating and studying messenger RNA and *s*RNA from mammalian cells may eventually provide the necessary means of investigating the problem at this level.

We thank Dr. Marion Erlandson and Dr. Carl Smith for their help in obtaining blood samples for these investigations. We also thank Dr. S. H. Boyer, Dr. C. L. Conley, Dr. H. M. Dintzis and Dr. G. Von Ehrenstein for their advice.

This investigation was supported in part by grant *HE*-02799, U.S. Public Health Service, the National Heart Institute; grant *T*1-*AM*-5260, the National Institute of Arthritis and Metabolic Diseases; great *AM*-06006-03, National Institutes of Health; and grant *CB*-2630, National Science Foundation.

(**208**, 1061-1065; 1965)

D. J. Weatherall, J. B. Clegg and M. A. Naughton: Departments of Medicine and Biophysics, The John Hopkins University School of Medicine, Baltimore, Maryland.

References:

1. Weatherall, D. J., *The Thalassaemia Syndromes* (Blackwell Scientific Publications, Oxford, 1965).
2. Kunkel, H. G., Ceppellini, R., Muller-Eberhard, U., and Wolf, J., *J. Clin. Invest.*, **36**, 1615 (1957).
3. Baglioni, C., in *Molecular Biology*, edit. by Taylor, J. H., part I, 405 (Academic Press, New York, 1963).
4. Schroeder, W. A., and Matsuda, G., *J. Amer. Chem. Soc.*, **80**, 1521 (1958).
5. Ceppellini, R., in *Ciba Found. Symp. Biochem. Genet.*, edit. by Wolstenholme, G. E. W., and O'Connor, C. M., 133 (Churchill, London, 1959).
6. Cohen, F., Zuelzer, W. W., Neel, J. V., and Robinson, A. R., *Blood*, **14**, 816 (1959).
7. Jones, R. T., Schroeder, W. A., Balog, J. E., and Vinograd, J. R., *J. Amer. Chem. Soc.*, **81**, 3161 (1959).
8. Hunt, J. A., and Lehmann, H., *Nature*, **184**, 872 (1959).
9. Ingram, V. M., and Stretton, A. O. W., *Nature*, **184**, 1903 (1959).
10. Burka, E. R., and Marks, P. A., *Nature*, **199**, 706 (1963).
11. Guidotti, G., cited by Ingram, V. M., *Medicine*, **43**, 759 (1964).
12. Vinograd, J., and Hutchison, W. D., *Nature*, **187**, 216 (1960).
13. Rieder, R. F., and Weatherall, D. J., *J. Clin. Invest.*, **44**, 42 (1965).
14. Dintzis, H. M., *Proc. U.S. Nat. Acad. Sci.*, **47**, 247 (1961).
15. Anson, M. C., and Mirsky, A. E., *J. Gen. Physiol.*, **13**, 469 (1930).
16. Clegg, J. B., Naughton, M. A., and Weatherall, D. J., *Nature*, **207**, 945 (1965).
17. Ingram, V, M., and Stretton, A. O. W., *Biochim. Biophys. Acta*, **62**, 456 (1962).
18. Baglioni, C., and Colombo, B., *Cold Spring Harb. Symp. Quant. Biol.*, **29**, 347 (1964).
19. Heywood, J. D., Karon, M., and Weissman, S., *Science*, **146**, 530 (1964).
20. Ingram, V. M., *Medicine*, 43, 759 (1964).
21. Huchns, E. R., Beaven, G. H., and Stevens, B. C., *Biochem. J.*, **92**, 444 (1964).
22. Fessas, P., and Loukopoulos, D., *Science*, **143**, 590 (1964).
23. Stent, G. S., *Science*, **144**, 816 (1964).
24. Weisblum, B., Gonano, F., Von Ehrenstein, G., and Benzer, S., *Proc, U.S. Nat. Acad. Sci.*, **53**, 328 (1965).

个亮氨酸残基中的一个亮氨酸残基[24]。分离和研究哺乳动物的信使 RNA 和 *s*RNA 技术的最新进展为在这一水平上研究该问题提供了必要的方法。

我们感谢玛丽昂·厄兰森博士和卡尔·史密斯博士为本研究提供血液样品。也感谢博耶博士、康利博士、丹特齐斯博士和冯·埃伦施泰因博士给予本实验的建议。

本研究得到了：美国公共卫生署，国立心脏病研究所编号为 *HE*-02799 的研究经费的支持；美国国立关节炎和代谢病研究所编号为 *T*1-*AM*-5260 的研究经费的支持；美国国立卫生研究院编号为 *AM*-06006-03 的研究经费的支持；以及美国国家自然科学基金会编号为 *CB*-2630 的研究经费的支持。

（周志华 翻译；杨茂君 审稿）

Reconstruction of Phase Objects by Holography

D. Gabor *et al.*

Editor's Note

In 1948, Hungarian physicist Dennis Gabor reported in *Nature* a kind of three-dimensional imaging process which he called holography. He developed the idea initially in connection with the optics of electron beams, although he later generalized it to light. Holography relies on the interaction of the phases of reflected rays, but as Gabor and his coworkers say here, that phase information might appear to be lost in photographic images which merely record brightness of the beams. They show, however, a way to reconstruct both the phases and the amplitudes of the beams using optical holography, and thus to obtain all the available information about the object from which the rays are scattered.

THE principle of wave-front-reconstruction imaging, first described by one of us in 1948 (refs.1-3), has recently resulted in spectacular advances, notably in the form of three-dimensional "lensless" photography and imaging, with both macroscopic and microscopic objects[3-8]. Excellent images have been obtained in a number of variations of the basic method, notably when the objects used were "half-tone" intensity objects, or transparencies, rather than "phase" objects.

"Phase" objects may be of a primary interest in a number of holographic applications, notably in microscopy, and in several other applications, where phase rather than amplitude variations in the light field may be predominantly characteristic of the physical phenomena under investigation, for example, in work with wind tunnels and in acoustical applications.

As holograms are recorded on photographic emulsions which register only intensities, not phases, one might easily believe that a hologram is not a full substitute for a real object. Indeed, the total wave-front which issues from a hologram in the reconstruction cannot be the same as the original wave-front emitted by the object, because one half of the information is missing. In order to obtain the total information one requires two holograms, which are in sine-cosine relation to one another. Two such "complementary" or "quadrature" holograms have been used in the "total reconstruction microscope" by one of us[9]. Adding up the wave-fronts issuing from two such holograms, one obtains in the reconstruction the original wave-front, and nothing else, except a uniform background.

However, somewhat paradoxically, the original wave-front is also contained in the modified wave-front diffracted in the reconstruction by a single hologram. The incompleteness

用全息术实现的相位物体的重建

盖伯等

编者按

匈牙利物理学家丹尼斯·盖伯于1948年在《自然》上发表了一篇关于一种三维成像过程的报道，他把这种过程称作全息术。他提出的这个想法最初与电子束光学有关，但是后来他将其推广至光学。全息术依赖于反射光线相位的相互作用，但是正如盖伯及其同事们在本文中所说，在利用照相术得到的影像中相位信息似乎会丢失，这些影像记录到的只是光束的亮度。然而他们展示了一种能够通过光学全息术同时重建光束相位和振幅的方法，并通过这种方法获得了有关散射光线的物体的全部有效信息。

1948年，笔者之一首次描述了波前重建成像的原理（参考文献1~3），最近这个原理产生了惊人的进展，在宏观和微观物体的三维“无透镜”照相术和成像中尤其明显[3-8]。通过对基本方法做许多改进，人们已经获得了极好的图像，当所用的物体不是“相位”物体而是“半色调”强度物体或透明物体时，效果更为显著。

在许多全息的应用中，尤其是在显微术以及其他几种应用中，“相位”物体可能是首选，其中所研究物理现象的主要特征可能是光场的相位变化，而非振幅变化，例如在风道的研究和声学的应用中。

由于全息图是用照相感光乳胶记录的，且该乳胶记录的只是强度，而非相位，因此人们或许很容易相信全息图并不是一个实物的完全替代。实际上，由重建得到的全息图产生的总的波前并不等同于由物体发射的原始的波前，因为有一半的信息丢失了。为了获得全部信息，我们需要两个彼此之间是正弦–余弦关系的全息图。这样两个“互补的”或“正交的”全息图已被笔者之一[9]用于“完全重建显微术”中。把这样的两个全息图产生的波前相加，我们就得到了重建过程中的原波前，除此以外仅有均匀的背景。

然而，有些自相矛盾的是，原始的波前也包含在修正波前中（修正波前是单个全息图在重建中通过衍射得到的）。实际上这种不完整性本身表明，波前中混合了一

shows itself in the fact that this wave-front is mixed up with an additional wave, which appears to issue from a "conjugate object". But the two partial wave-fronts can be separated by various methods, the simplest of which is using a skew reference beam at an angle to the plate, in the taking of the hologram. The information-theoretical paradox that an incomplete record contains the full information in a retrievable form is explained by the fact that there is a loss of one half of the definition. This, however, is as good as unnoticeable in almost all present-day applications of holography.

Consequently, since one of the two (or more) waves diffracted by the hologram in the reconstruction process contains information on both the amplitude and the phase distribution in the object, both the phase and the amplitude information may be extracted from the reconstructed wave-front, for example, by suitable "filtering" of the aerial reconstructed images, or diffraction patterns, before the final image is recorded on a photographic film. In essence, the image-forming wave-fronts reconstructed from holograms are indistinguishable from the wave-front which would be obtained from an ideal lens or mirror looking directly at the object, when it is possible to form an image in the ordinary "one-step" imaging, for example, in microscopy. It has therefore been clear to us for some time that we may display the phase in the holographically reconstructed images of "phase" objects, when necessary, with the aid of any one of the several well-known methods[10,11] (for example, phase contrast, interferometry, Foucault or Schlieren methods) used to display the phase variations in the form of amplitude variations, as used in microscopy and other phase measuring applications in optics.

Because of the great present interest in holography, and because some of our recent advances seem to indicate a good likelihood that high resolutions may indeed be attainable in microscopy at very short wave-lengths (for example, X-rays), it may be of interest to demonstrate that phase-preserving imaging and "phase-contrast" image reconstruction may indeed be readily achieved in holography, using single holograms.

As one example of the "phase-preserving" reconstruction of the image of a phase object, we have used the arrangement shown in Fig. 1. The phase object used is shown (barely visible) in Fig. 2*a*, and an enlarged transmission two-beam interferogram of the object is shown in Fig. 2*b*. The phase object was formed by photographing the word "phase" and the letter "φ " on a Kodak 649*F* plate, and by bleaching the emulsion (using Kodak chromium intensifier as the bleacher). It is well known that photographic emulsions will shrink with the density of the exposure. (Typical emulsion shrinkage with exposure factors, 1, 2, 3, 4, is shown in Fig. 2*c*.) The phase object was recorded by projecting an image on to the plate deliberately slightly out of focus, in order to avoid steep gradients at the edges of the letters. (The amount of shrinkage shown in Fig. 2*b* was achieved in a 20-sec exposure, with a 75 W bulb, at *f*/11, in 1:1 imaging in the enlarger, and suitable bleaching.)

个似乎由“共轭物体”产生的附加波。但是这两个部分波前可用多种方法分离，其中最简单的方法是在记录全息图的过程中，使用与感光板呈一定角度的偏斜参考光束。一个不完整的记录包含并可以恢复得到完整的信息，这种信息 – 理论的矛盾可用精确度损失了一半的事实来解释。然而，在目前所有全息图的应用中这一点几乎没有引起人们的注意。

因此，既然在重建过程中通过全息图衍射得到的两个（或多个）波中，有一个包含了物体中振幅和相位分布的信息，那么相位和振幅的信息或许都可从重建的波前中提取出，例如，在感光胶片上记录下最终图像之前，对存在于空中的重建图像或衍射图样进行适当的“滤波”。本质上，从全息图重建形成的图像，其波前与从一个直接对准物体的理想透镜或镜子得到的波前几乎完全相同，在这种情况下像是通过通常的“一步”成像形成的，例如显微镜中的成像。因此，不久之前我们已经清楚，我们可以在“相位”物体的全息重建图像中显示相位，必要时，可从人们熟知的方法 [10,11]（例如相衬法、干涉测量法、傅科法或纹影法）中任意选取一种以振幅变化的形式来呈现相位变化，就像在显微术中和光学中其他相位测量应用中所使用的方法一样。

由于目前人们对全息术有很大的兴趣，并且我们最新取得的一些进展似乎表明在波长很短 (例如 X 射线) 的情况下可使显微镜得到非常高的分辨率，因此似乎有必要给出以下说明：利用全息术，使用单个全息图或许就可轻易实现保持相位的成像过程及“相衬”图像重建。

我们使用图 1 所示的装置，作为一个相位物体图像的“相位保持”重建的例子。所用的相位物体如图 2*a* 所示 (勉强可见)，图 2*b* 显示的是物体放大的透射型双光束干涉图。将单词“phase”和字母“φ”拍摄在一张柯达 649*F* 干板上，并漂白感光乳胶（使用柯达铬增强剂作为漂白剂）从而制得了相位物体。众所周知，感光乳胶将随着曝光强度的增加而收缩。（图 2*c* 为在曝光因子为 1、2、3、4 时，典型的感光乳胶的收缩。）为了避免字母边缘斜度过大，相位物体是通过将像投影在故意稍稍偏离焦点的胶片上来记录的。（图 2*b* 中所示的收缩量是用 75 瓦的灯泡在 *f*/11 和在 20 秒的曝光下以 1:1 在放大机内成像并作适当漂白而获得的。）

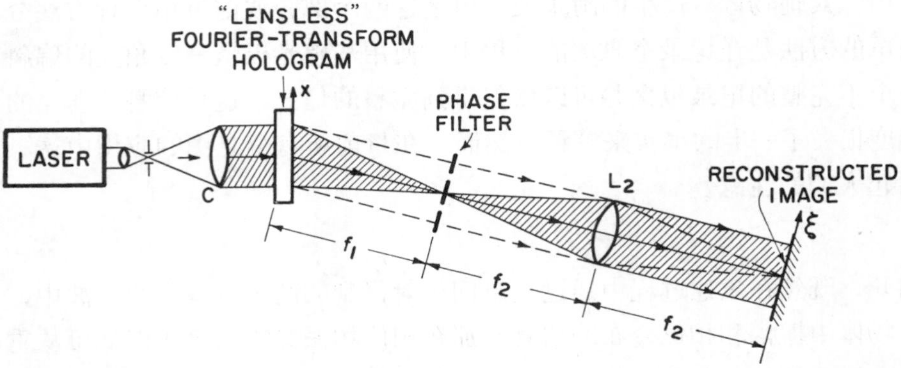

Fig. 1. Modified Fourier-transform holographic image-reconstruction arrangement, permitting "phase-contrast" detection and imaging of phase objects. The distance f_1 is equal to the distance of the object, respectively point-reference, from the hologram in the "lensless" recording of the Fourier-transform hologram[12,13]; "Conventional" Fourier-transform reconstruction of the images from the Fourier-transform holograms is obtained in the absence of the "phase filter". (The geometrical magnification obtained in Fourier-transform holographic imaging is equal to the ratio f_2/f_1. An additional magnification factor equal to λ_2/λ_1 is obtained, when the reconstructing wave-length λ_2 exceeds the recording wave-length λ_1. In this work, f_1=415 mm, f_2=600 mm, $\lambda_2=\lambda_1$=6,328 Å)

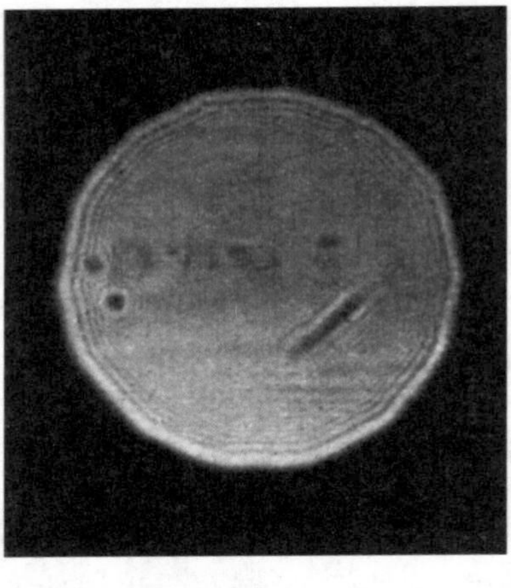

Fig. 2*a*. Direct (not holographic) image of phase object used in this work, showing degree to which a "pure" phase object was obtained by suitable bleaching of a Kodak 649*F* emulsion (see text, and Fig. 2*b*). The object is the word "phase" and the letter "φ" (the word phase being 20 mm long). The slight contrast detectable is due to some slight defocusing, and some residual absorption in the plate

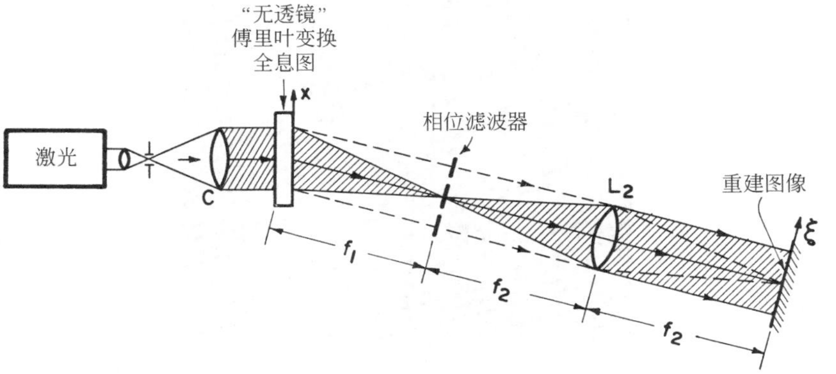

图 1. 改进型的傅里叶变换全息像重建装置，可以进行相位物体的“相衬”检测和相位物体的成像。在傅里叶变换全息图的“无透镜”记录中，距离 f_1 分别等于物体和点参考光源到全息图间的距离 [12,13]。从傅里叶变换全息图得到的像的“传统的”傅里叶变换重建是在无“相位滤波器”的情况下得到的。(在傅里叶变换全息成像过程中获得的几何放大倍率等于 f_2/f_1。当重建波长 λ_2 超过记录波长 λ_1 时，得到的附加放大倍数因子等于 λ_2/λ_1。在本文中，f_1 = 415 毫米，f_2= 600 毫米，$\lambda_2 = \lambda_1$ = 6,328 埃。)

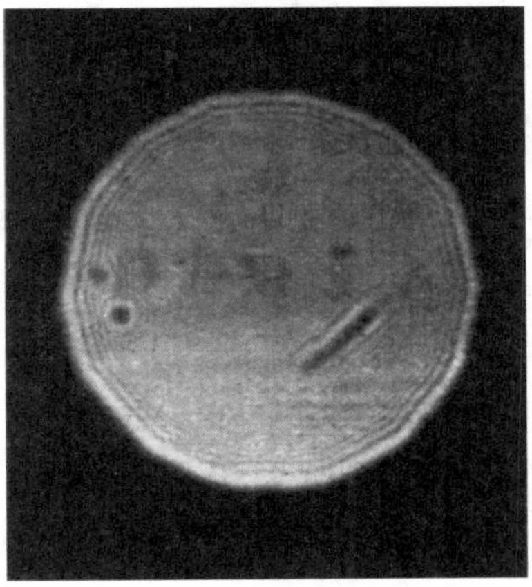

图 2*a*. 在本研究工作中使用的相位物体的直接（不是全息的）图像，这是用柯达 649*F* 感光乳胶（见正文和图 2*b*) 进行适当漂白得到的“纯”相位物体的程度。该物体是单词“phase”和字母“φ”（单词“phase”长 20 毫米）。可以检测到的微弱衬度是由于轻微的散焦以及干板上一些剩余吸收而产生的。

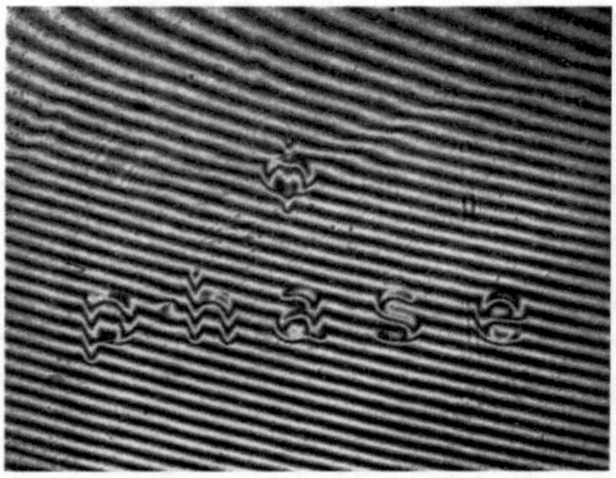

Fig. 2*b*. Two-beam single-pass interferogram (6,328 Å) of the phase object used in this work. The hologram of this phase object was recorded in the "lensless" Fourier-transform hologram recording arrangement according to ref. 12

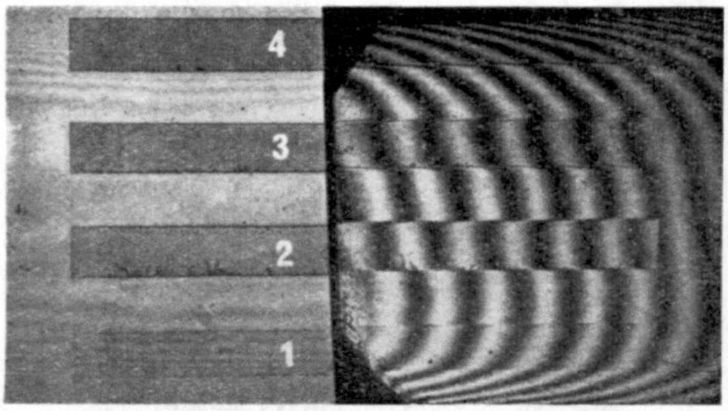

Fig. 2*c*. Two-beam single-pass interferogram (6,328 Å), illustrating the amount of emulsion shrinkage and corresponding phase variation achievable in a Kodak 649*F* emulsion with four different exposures (in ratios ×1, ×2, ×3, ×4), and suitable bleaching with Kodak chromium image intensifier, used to obtain almost pure "phase objects", with minimum residual absorption

The hologram of the phase object was recorded in the "lensless Fourier-transform" hologram recording arrangement, first described by one of us[12,13], in which the spherical waves originating from the various object points are made to interfere with a "single" spherical reference wave, originating from a source "point" in the mean plane next to the object. A reference wave of a radius f_1=415 mm was used in the recording. (We may note that the "lensless" recording of the hologram permits storage of the information about the phase distribution in the object without introducing any other optical elements between the object and the emulsion, thus avoiding any extraneous scattering, which might reduce the fidelity and sensitivity of the method.)

The images reconstructed from the "lensless Fourier-transform" hologram are shown in Figs. 3, 4 and 5. Fig. 3 shows a Fourier transform reconstruction, without filtering, obtained by simply projecting a plane monochromatic (6,328 Å) wave through the hologram, and by recording one of the side-band images in the focal pane of a f_2=600 mm lens. Unlike the reconstruction-imaging of intensity or amplitude objects, the reconstructed image

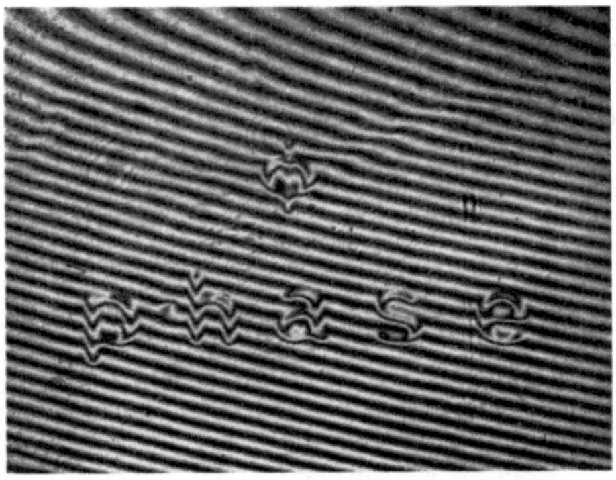

图 2*b*. 本研究工作中所使用的相位物体的双光束单通干涉图（6,328 埃）。这个相位物体的全息图是用参考文献 12 中记录的“无透镜”傅里叶变换全息图记录装置进行记录的。

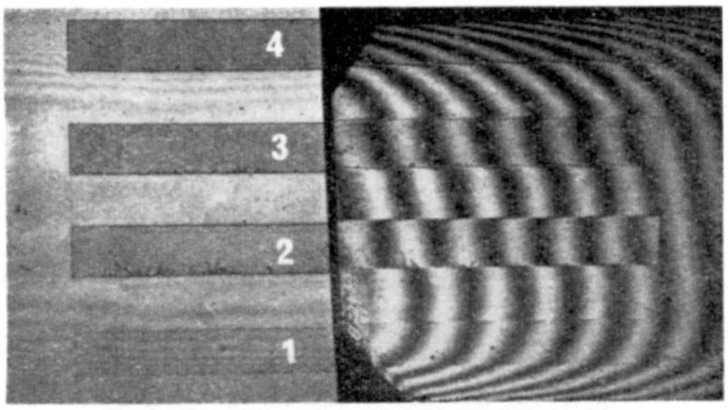

图 2*c*. 双光束单通干涉图（6,328 埃），它显示了感光乳胶的收缩程度以及在 4 种不同曝光量下（比例为 ×1、×2、×3、×4）用柯达 649*F* 感光乳胶得到的相应的相位变化，并用柯达铬像增强剂作了适当的漂白，以获得残余吸收量最小的近乎纯的“相位物体”。

相位物体的全息图是用“无透镜傅里叶变换”全息图记录装置记录的，笔者之一[12, 13]首次对这种装置进行了描述，其中，令各个物点发出的球面波与一个“单个”球面参考波相干，而这个参考波来自于与物体相邻的平均平面中的“点”源。记录中所用的参考波的半径 f_1 = 415 毫米。（我们可以注意到，在物体与感光乳胶之间不引入任何其他光学元件的情况下，全息图的“无透镜”记录可以对物体的相位分布信息进行存储，这避免了任何程度上的外来散射，而这种散射可能会降低所用方法的保真度和灵敏度。）

图 3、图 4 和图 5 是通过“无透镜傅里叶变换”全息图得到的重建图像。图 3 是一个傅里叶变换重建图像，其未经滤波，仅是用单色平面波 (6,328 埃) 透过全息图，并在一个 f_2=600 毫米的透镜的焦平面上记录一个边带像而得。与强度或振幅的重建图像不同，图 3 中相位物体的重建图像并没有表现出振幅衬度，这是由于物体具有

of the phase object in Fig. 3 shows no amplitude contrast, because of the "pure" phase nature of the object.

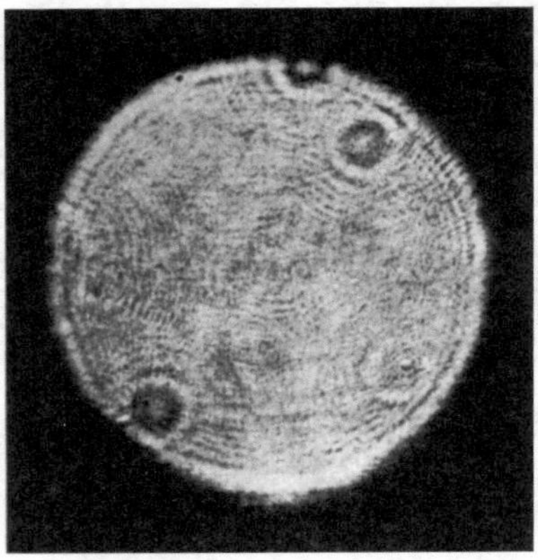

Fig. 3. Reconstructed image, obtained by Fourier-transform reconstruction in the arrangement of Fig. 1, without the use of any phase-contrast enhancement. (The "lensless" Fourier-transform recording of the hologram of the object was obtained according to ref. 12.) The image shown here is characterized by an almost complete absence of any amplitude contrast in the phase-portions of the image (the various interference effects are spurious, and are caused mainly by imperfectly clean reconstructing optics). It may be noted that excellent imaging is obtained under similar conditions when the original objects are amplitude or intensity objects[12,13], rather than pure phase objects

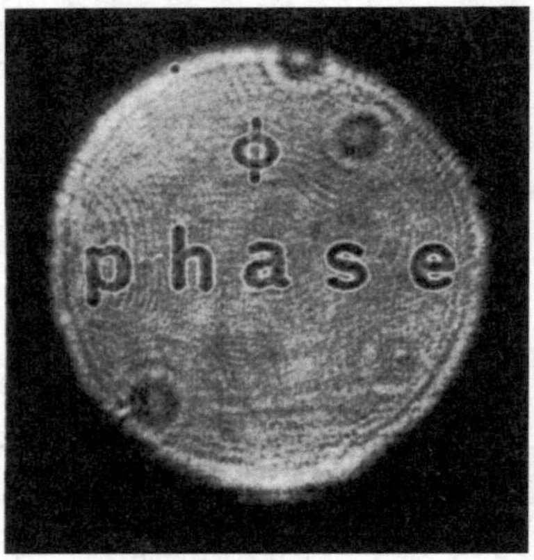

Fig. 4*a*. Reconstructed image of phase object, obtained with "phase-contrast" enhancement by defocusing (here towards the L_2 lens of Fig. 1 by $-f_2/4$, with f_2=600 mm). The length of the word in the object was 20 mm (in the image, it is 30 mm, because of the f_2/f_1 magnification (see Fig. 1))

"纯"相位性质。

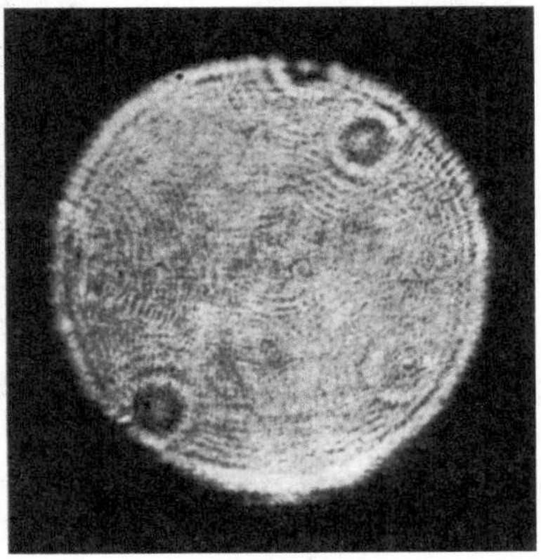

图 3. 用图 1 装置中的傅里叶变换重建得到的重建图像，没有做任何相衬增强处理。（根据参考文献 12 得到了物体的"无透镜"傅里叶变换全息图的记录。）这个像的特征是，在像的相位部分几乎没有任何振幅衬度。（各种各样的干涉效应都是干扰性的，这主要是由于重建光学元件不够干净而造成的。）可以注意到，当原物体是振幅或强度物体 [12,13] 而不是纯相位物体时，在相似条件下可以获得极好的像。

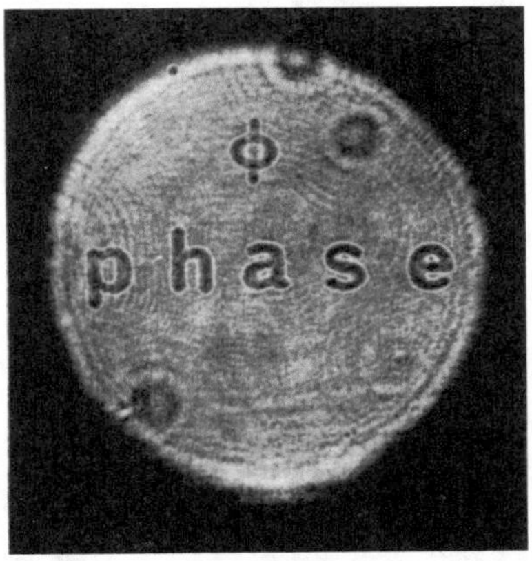

图 4*a*. 通过散焦增强"相衬"得到的相位物体的重建图像（与图 1 中透镜 L_2 的距离变化为 $-f_2/4$，其中 f_2= 600 毫米）。物体中单词的长度是 20 毫米（由于放大倍数为 f_2/f_1，因此像中长度是 30 毫米（见图 1））。

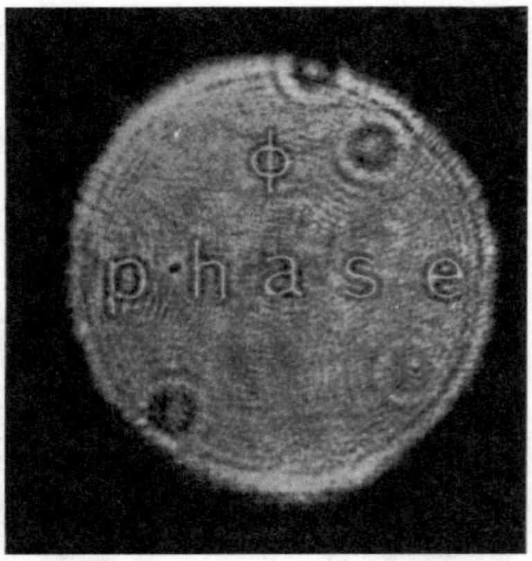

Fig. 4*b*. Reconstructed image of phase object, with "phase-contrast" enhancement, obtained by defocusing (here, out of focus, away from the lens L_2 by $+f_1/4$)

Fig. 4*c*. Reconstructed image of phase object, with phase-contrast enhancement obtained by using a phase-contrast filter (the corner of one of the rectangular phase strips, shown in Fig. 2*c*) in the arrangement of Fig. 1. (Here, the interference effects are spurious, and due to some imperfect cleanliness in the reconstruction optics)

Fig. 4*d*. Reconstructed image of phase object, with phase-contrast enhancement, obtained with a Foucault knife-edge used in the phase-filter plane of Fig. 1

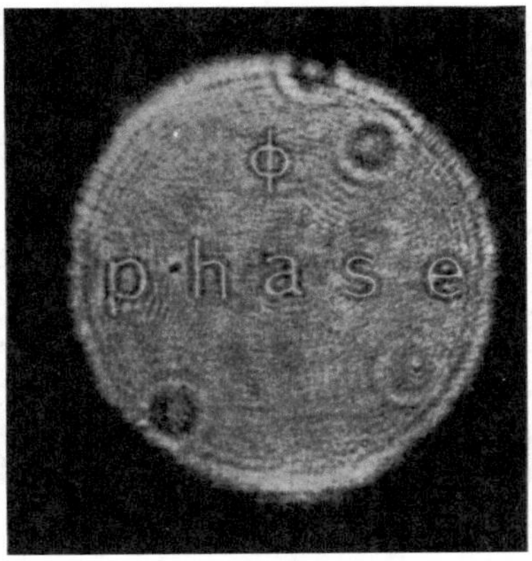

图 4*b*. 利用散焦增强“相衬”得到的相位物体的重建图像（此时散焦，与透镜 L_2 距离变化为 $+f_1/4$）。

图 4*c*. 在图 1 的装置中使用相衬滤波器（图 2*c* 中所示的其中一个矩形相位条的角）增强相衬而得到的相位物体的重建图像（这里的干涉效应是干扰性的，这是由重建光学器件不够干净造成的）。

图 4*d*. 在图 1 的相位滤波板中使用一个傅科刀口边沿增强相衬而得到的相位物体的重建图像。

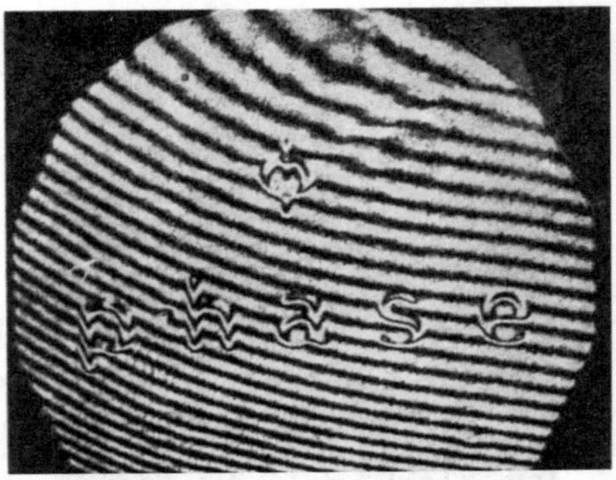

Fig. 5. "Hologram of the hologram." Two-beam single-pass interferogram (6,328 Å laser light) of the interference pattern between the reconstructed aerial image and a plane reference beam. Comparison of the image-interferogram shown here with the similarly obtained object-interferogram of Fig. 2*b* demonstrates that phase-distribution in the object is indeed preserved and completely reconstructed in Fourier-transform wavefront-reconstruction imaging, using a modified "phase-contrast" enhancing arrangement, such as that illustrated in Fig. 1. (We may note that phase preservation and phase-enhancing reconstruction apply to holograms recorded at one wave-length, and reconstructed in a second wave-length, for example, when λ_1 is in the X-ray domain and λ_2 in the visible-light laser domain)

Figs. 4 and 5 show well-contrasted images of the phase object, obtained by a number of the well-known phase filtering or phase-contrast methods, in which the phase variations are made visible in the form of amplitude (that is, intensity) variations in the image.

Figs. 4*a* and *b* show the reconstructed images, obtained by a "defocusing" phase-contrast enhancement, in a Fourier-transform reconstruction arrangement, as in the sharply focused Fig. 3, but now by recording the images together slightly ($\pm 1/4\, f_2$ at $f/24$) out of focus, with respect to the in-focus image of Fig. 3.

Fig. 4*c* shows an in-focus image, in which the phase-contrast enhancement was obtained in the filtering arrangement shown in Fig. 1, with the help of the corner of a phase-contrast filter (also recorded photographically, and bleached, similarly to the object recording already described here).

Fig. 4*d* shows an in-focus image, with "phase-contrast" enhancement obtained in the filtering arrangement of Fig. 1, with the help of a Foucault knife-edge filter (at right angles to the word "phase").

Fig. 5 shows a two-beam interferogram of the reconstructed aerial image, formed by interference of the aerial image with a plane wave (in a suitable beam-splitting arrangement): by comparing the interferogram of the phase object (Fig. 2*b*), the degree of phase preservation and of fidelity of "phase-preserving" reconstruction may be readily assessed.

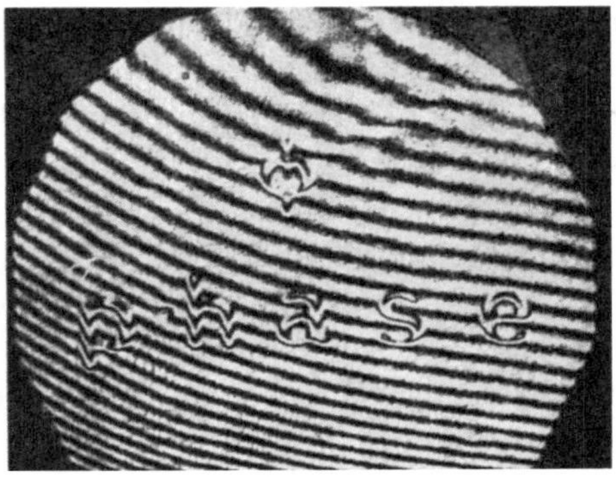

图 5.“全息图的全息图”。重建的空间像与平面参考光之间的干涉图样的双光束单通干涉图（激光波长为 6,328 埃）。将这里所示的像干涉图与通过相似方法得到的图 2*b* 中的物体干涉图进行比较，可以证明物体中的相位分布确实得到了保存，并在傅里叶变换波前重建中完全实现了重建。其中使用的是改进型的“相衬”增强装置，如图 1 所示。（我们可以注意到，相位保存和相位增强重建用作全息图记录时使用的是一个波长，而用于全息图重建时使用的是第二个波长。例如，当 λ_1 属于 X 射线波段时，λ_2 属于可见光激光波段。）

图 4 和图 5 是用人们熟知的相位滤波或相衬法得到的一些衬度很好的相位物体的像，其中相位变化是通过图像中的振幅（即强度）变化来体现的。

图 4*a* 和图 4*b* 是通过“散焦”相衬增强得到的重建图像，使用的傅里叶变换重建装置与经过严格对焦的图 3 所用的装置相同，但是相对于图 3 的准确对焦像，这里都是略微 ($f/24$ 处 $\pm 1/4f_2$) 偏离焦点对像进行记录的。

图 4*c* 是一个准确对焦的像，用图 1 所示的滤波装置中借助相衬滤波器的角来增强相衬（同样用照片做了记录，并进行了漂白，类似于前文描述的对物体所做的记录）。

图 4*d* 是在图 1 所示的滤波装置中借助傅科刀口滤波器（与单词“phase”垂直）增强“相衬”得到的一个准确对焦的像。

图 5 是一幅重建空间像的双光束干涉图，它由空间像与一个平面波（通过适当的光束分束装置）的干涉所形成：通过比较相位物体的干涉图（图 2*b*），可以很容易地对相位保持的程度和“相位保持”重建的保真度进行评估。

It is clear from a comparison of the images and interferogram of the image, of Fig. 4 and of Fig. 5, with the phase object and object-interferogram of Fig. 2, that the phase-distribution in the phase object was not only retrievably recorded in the hologram, but also that the phase in the image of the phase object can be readily displayed as an amplitude (respectively intensity) in the reconstructed image, with the aid of phase-contrast or other image-filtering methods, including interferometry of various types. We may note that there is some indication that holograms of phase objects, recorded with a 1/1 ratio of reference/diffracted field intensity (rather than the about 5/1 used here), appear to display some noticeable "phase-contrast" enhancement simply in the focus of the "conventional" Fourier-transform reconstruction arrangement.

We thank R. C. Restrick for his advice. This work was supported in part by the U.S. National Science Foundation and the U.S. Office of Naval Research.

(**208**, 1159-1162; 1965)

D. Gabor: F.R.S., Imperial College of Science and Technology, London.

G. W. Stroke, D. Brumm, A. Funkhouser and A. Labeyrid: University of Michigan, Ann Arbor, Michigan.

References:

1. Gabor, D., *Nature*, **161**, 777 (1948).
2. Gabor, D., *Proc. Roy. Soc.*, A, **197**, 475 (1949).
3. Gabor, D., *Proc. Phys. Soc.*, B, 244 (1951).
4. Leith, E. N., and Upatnieks, J., *J. Opt. Soc. Amer.*, **53**, 1377 (1963).
5. Leith, E. N., and Upatnieks, J., *J. Opt. Soc. Amer.*, **54**, 1295 (1964).
6. Leith, E. N., Upatnieks, J., and Haines, K. A., *J. Opt. Soc. Amer.*, **55**, 981 (1965).
7. Stroke, G. W., *Optics of Coherent and Non-Coherent Electromagnetic Radiations* (Univ. of Michigan, first ed., May 1964; second ed., March 1965).
8. Stroke, G. W., and Falconer, D. G., *Phys. Letters*, **13**, 306 (1964); **15**, 283 (1965); with Funkhouser, A., *Pyhys. Letters*, **16**, 272 (1965); with Restrick, R., Funkhouser, A., and Brumm, D., *Phys. Letters*, **18**, 274 (1965); *App. Phys. Letters*, 7,178 (1965).
9. Gabor, D., with Goss, W. P., British Patent No. 727, 893/1955, application date July 6, 1951.
10. Zernike, F., *Physica, Haag*, **1**, 43 (1934); *Physik. Z.*, **36**, 848 (1935); *Z. Techn. Physik.*, **16**, 454 (1935).
11. Francon, M., *Le Contraste de Phase en Optique et en Microscopie* (*Revue d'Oplique*, Paris, 1950).
12. Stroke, G. W., *App. Phys. Letters*, **6**, 201 (1965).
13. Stroke, G. W., Brumm, D., and Funkhouser, A., *J. Opt. Soc. Amer.*, **55**, 1327 (1965).

将图 4 和图 5 的像和像的干涉图与图 2 的相位物体和物体–干涉图对比，可以清晰地看出，记录在全息图内相位物体的相位分布不仅可以获取，而且相位物体中像的相位也能容易地借助于相衬法或其他图像–滤波方法，包括各种类型的干涉测量方法，以重建图像的振幅（各自强度）来表示。我们可能会注意到一些迹象，就是以 1/1 的参考 / 衍射场强比（而不是本文中所用的大约 5/1 的场强比）记录的相位物体的全息图，似乎可简单地在“传统的”傅里叶变换重建装置的焦点处表现出某些明显的“相衬”增强。

我们感谢雷斯特里克提出的建议。本项研究工作部分由美国国家科学基金会及美国海军研究办公室支持。

（沈乃澂 翻译；熊秉衡 审稿）

Radio Structure of the Galactic Centre Region

D. Downes *et al.*

Editor's Note

Optical astronomers were prevented in the 1960s from constructing a clear view of what the centre of our galaxy consists of because of the confusion between neighbouring bright sources of light and the large amounts of dust present there. Radioastronomy thus became the most effective means of exploring this crucial region of our own galaxy, and this is one of the first attempts to do so. The paper by Dennis Downes at Harvard, who went on to make several important contributions to the understanding of the Galactic Centre, and colleagues, describes a bright source adjacent to Sagittarius *A*, which was at that time suspected of being the galactic nucleus. This presages the discovery of Sagittarius *A in the 1970s, which is awarded that role today. It is widely thought that the Galactic Centre houses a very massive black hole, but this is still unconfirmed.**

RADIO observations have shown that the galactic centre region consists of a number of discrete sources. The brightest of these, Sagittarius *A*, is believed to represent the galactic nucleus. This communication describes a new series of observations of the region, made at frequencies of 8.25 and 15.50 Gc/s with a pencil-beam antenna. The angular resolutions were respectively 4.2 and 2.2 arc min, the latter being the highest pencil-beam resolution so far applied to the galactic centre region. The observations confirm that the microwave spectrum of Sagittarius *A* is non-thermal[1], show that the angular diameter of the source is approximately 3.5 arc min, and demonstrate that, adjacent to Sagittarius *A*, there is an irregular emission region, which is apparently thermal in nature. The relation between radio data concerning the galactic centre and optical information about the centres of nearby normal galaxies is also examined.

The observations were made with the 120-ft. paraboloid antenna at the Haystack field station of Massachusetts Institute of Technology, Lincoln Laboratory. The antenna has a Cassegrain feed system[2]. The receiver at 8.25 Gc/s had a band-width of 0.5 Gc/s, and with an output time constant of 1 sec the minimum detectable signal was of the order of 0.1°K. The receiver at 15.50 Gc/s used two channels centred at 15.25 and 15.75 Gc/s, each having a band-width of 0.5 Gc/s. With an output time constant of 1 sec the minimum detectable signal for this receiver was 0.2°K. The outputs from the receivers were recorded by both analogue and digital equipment. The observations were made by taking drift-scans, at spacings of 2 arc min in declination at 8.25 Gc/s, and at 1 arc min at 15.50 Gc/s. This procedure minimizes the effects of ground radiation scattered or diffracted into the antenna. The scans were taken when the galactic centre region was at meridian transit ±2 h, over which period its elevation ranged from 18 to 13 arc deg above the horizon.

银河系中心区域的射电结构

唐斯等

编者按

由于银河系近邻明亮光源的干扰以及空间中存在大量的尘埃，使得光学天文学家在20世纪60年代难以构建出银河系中心结构的清晰图像。因此射电天文学成为探索我们银河系关键区域最有效的方法，而本文正是最初的尝试之一。哈佛大学的丹尼斯·唐斯对理解银河系中心做出了重要的贡献，他及其同事们描述了邻近人马座 *A* 的明亮光源，在当时人们猜测人马座 *A* 是银河系的核心。这预示了现在确认为银河系核心的人马座 *A** 于20世纪70年代的发现。人们普遍认为银河系中心有一个质量很大的黑洞，但是尚未确认。

射电观测显示银河系中心区域由很多不连续的源组成。其中最亮的是人马座 *A*，人们认为它代表了银河系的核心。本文给出了在频率为8.25千兆周/秒和15.50千兆周/秒时用笔束天线对这个区域进行的一系列全新观测结果。其角分辨率分别是4.2角分和2.2角分，后者是目前用于银河系中心区域最高的笔束分辨率。这些观测证实了人马座 *A* 的微波频谱是非热辐射的[1]，并显示此源的角直径大约是3.5角分，还证实了在人马座 *A* 附近有一个不规则的、看似具有热辐射性质的辐射区域。本文也研究了银河系中心的射电数据和近邻普通星系中心光学信息之间的关系。

我们用麻省理工学院林肯实验室赫斯塔克野外观测站的120英尺抛物面天线进行观测。这个天线有一个卡赛格林馈源系统[2]。8.25千兆周/秒的接收机带宽是0.5千兆周/秒，输出时间常数1秒时可探测的最弱信号是0.1K量级。15.50千兆周/秒的接收机使用中心位于15.25千兆周/秒和15.75千兆周/秒的两个通道，每个通道带宽为0.5千兆周/秒。输出时间常数1秒时这个接收机可探测的最弱信号是0.2K。模拟以及数字设备记录接收机的输出。采用漂移扫描进行观测，在赤纬上8.25千兆周/秒处的间隔为2角分，15.50千兆周/秒处间隔为1角分。这个方法使散射或衍射进天线的地面辐射效应减到最小。当银河系中心区域位于中天附近±2小时的时候进行扫描，在这段时间中介于视界上的仰角范围为18弧度到13弧度。

Fig. 1*a* shows the radio brightness contours of the galactic centre region at 8.25 Gc/s and Fig. 1*b* shows the contours at 15.50 Gc/s. The bright source is Sagittarius *A*. To the north of Sagittarius *A*, and partially overlapping it, there is a complex emission region, which consists of an irregular curved ridge. This region may also be distinguished on contour maps at other frequencies[3,4]. Beneath these sources, there is a well-known emission region extending over several arc degrees, which is not indicated in the diagrams.

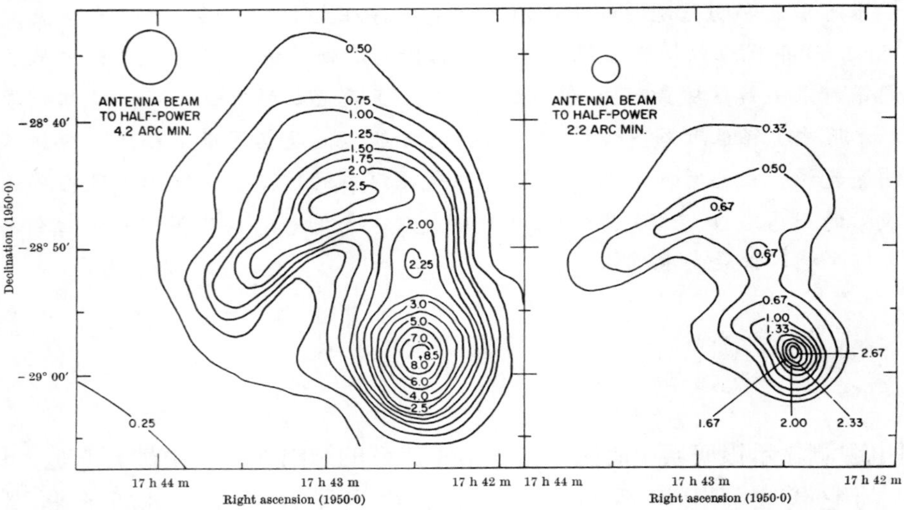

Fig. 1. *a* (Left), galactic centre region at 8.25 Gc/s. Contours represent antenna temperature in °K, corrected by 4 percent for extinction. *b* (Right), galactic centre region at 15.50 Gc/s. Contours represent antenna temperature in °K, corrected by 8 percent for extinction

Estimates of the flux densities of Sagittarius *A* at 8.25 and 15.50 Gc/s are given in Table 1. These values were derived on the assumption that the flux density of *M*87 was 47×10^{-26} M.K.S. units at 8.25 Gc/s and 28×10^{-26} units at 15.50 Gc/s. Beam-width corrections were made for both Sagittarius *A* and *M*87. The flux values for Sagittarius *A* fit closely on the intensity spectral curve of index $\alpha = -0.7$ given earlier by Maxwell and Downes[1], confirming the non-thermal character of the source. The position co-ordinates of Sagittarius *A* given in Table 1 are mean values taken from earlier position measurements of Maxwell and Downes, Hollinger[3] and Broten *et al.*[4].

Table 1. Flux Densities, Angular Diameters, and Positions of Radio Sources in Galactic Centre Region

	Sgr. *A*	Sgr. *B*1	Sgr. *B*2
Flux density ($\times 10^{-26}$ M.K.S.)			
at 8.25 Gc/s	150	35	125
at 15.50 Gc/s	100	60	190
Angular diameter(arc min)	4.0×2.5	7×5	17×5
Position (1950.0)			
right ascension	17h 42m 27s	17h 42m 34s	17h 42m 59s
declination	−28°58.5′	−28°51.0′	−28°47.0′

图 1*a* 显示了 8.25 千兆周 / 秒频率下银河系中心区域的射电强度等亮度线图，图 1*b* 显示了 15.50 千兆周 / 秒频率下银河系中心区域的射电强度等亮度线图。其中亮源是人马座 *A*。在人马座 *A* 的北边有一个和它部分重叠并且很复杂的辐射区域，由不规则的弯曲的隆起组成。也可以在其他频率的等亮度线图上辨别出这个区域[3,4]。在这些源之下有一个延展达几弧度的著名辐射区域，但它在图中没有表示出来。

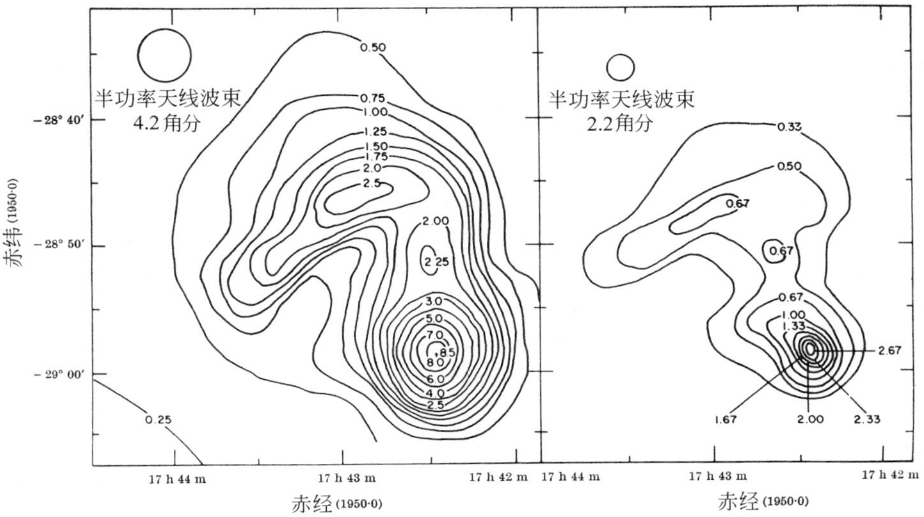

图 1. *a*（左边），8.25 千兆周 / 秒处观测到的银河系中心区域。等亮度线图表示了以 K 为单位的天线温度分布，对消光进行了 4% 的修正。*b*（右边），15.50 千兆周 / 秒处观测到的银河系中心区域。等亮度线图表示了以 K 为单位的天线温度分布，对消光进行了 8% 的修正。

表 1 给出了在 8.25 千兆周 / 秒和 15.50 千兆周 / 秒处对人马座 *A* 流量密度的估计。这些值是在这样的假设下导出的：在 8.25 千兆周 / 秒频率处 *M*87 的流量密度在 M.K.S.（米 · 千克 · 秒）制下为 47×10^{-26} 单位，在 15.50 千兆周 / 秒处是 28×10^{-26} 单位。对人马座 *A* 和 *M*87 都进行了波束宽度的修正。麦克斯韦和唐斯[1]早期指出，人马座 *A* 的流量值可以与指数为 α=−0.7 的谱线很好地拟合，这也证实了该源的非热辐射性质。表 1 中给出的人马座 *A* 的位置坐标取自早先麦克斯韦、唐斯、霍林格[3]和布拉滕等[4]所做位置测量的平均值。

表 1. 银河系中心区域射电源的流量密度、角直径和位置

	人马座 *A*	人马座 *B*1	人马座 *B*2
流量密度（$\times 10^{-26}$ 米 · 千克 · 秒单位制）			
8.25 千兆周 / 秒处	150	35	125
15.50 千兆周 / 秒处	100	60	190
角直径（角分）	4.0 × 2.5	7 × 5	17 × 5
位置 (1950.0)			
赤经	17 小时 42 分 27 秒	17 小时 42 分 34 秒	17 小时 42 分 59 秒
赤纬	−28°58.5′	−28°51.0′	−28°47.0′

To estimate flux densities from the irregular emission region north of Sagittarius *A*, we have divided it into two main areas, which we shall refer to as Sagittarius *B*1 and *B*2. The centres and angular diameters of these areas are listed in Table 1, the centres having been measured relative to the position of Sagittarius *A*. On Fig. 1*b* the centres are represented by the closed contours of antenna temperature 0.67°K. Integrated flux densities for Sagittarius *B*1 and *B*2 are given in Table 1. These values, however, should be regarded with caution, particularly at 15.50 Gc/s, since the present survey provides only a few brightness contours for the areas. Comparison of the integrated fluxed from these areas with data taken by Broten *et al.* at 5 Gc/s suggests that the sources are both thermal in nature and that they may therefore be H II regions. There is, however, no evidence to indicate that the sources are physically associated with Sagittarius *A*.

In considering the structure of the centre of our own galaxy, it is instructive to compare the existing radio data with optical data concerning the centres of two nearby normal galaxies, *M*31 and *M*51. (There is, of course, little optical evidence concerning the structure or nature of the centre of our own galaxy, since the centre is heavily obscured by intervening dust clouds.) Both *M*31 and *M*51 are observed optically to have a central nucleus of linear dimensions about 20 parsec[5,6]. In each case this nucleus is embedded in a larger nuclear bulge of dimensions about 1,000 parsec. In the case of our own galaxy, if we believe Sagittarius *A* to be at the galactic centre and at a distance of 10 kiloparsec[7], then its angular width of 3.5 arc min to half power would correspond to linear dimensions of the order of 10 parsec, which is comparable with the optical dimensions of the nuclei of the nearby normal galaxies. Similarly, if the extended source underlying Sagittarius *A* is regarded as radio evidence for a nuclear bulge at the centre of our own galaxy, the radio diameter of about 120 arc min[1] would correspond to linear dimensions of the order of 350 parsec.

Observations of the galactic centre by radio astronomers have now extended over some fifteen years, during which time angular discrimination has increased by a factor of about 30. With each improvement in resolution the central region has generally shown increasing structural complexity. Commencing in 1967, the region will be subject to a series of lunar occultations, and at that time we may look forward to a dramatic increase in the available angular resolution, perhaps by a factor of 100 or more. The detailed structure of this region should then be revealed much more fully.

We thank Mr. A. B. Hull and Dr. S. Weinreb of Lincoln Laboratory, and Mr. R. Rinehart and Mr. J. H. Taylor of Harvard University, for their assistance in making the observations. Lincoln Laboratory is a centre for research and development operated by the Massachusetts Institute of Technology with the support of the U.S. Air Force. The Harvard University part of the programme was supported by the U.S. National Science Foundation.

(**208**, 1189-1190; 1965)

D. Downes and A. Maxwell: Harvard Radio Astronomy Station, Fort Davis, Texas.

M. L. Meeks: Massachusetts Institute of Technology, Lincoln Laboratory, Lexington, Massachusetts.

为估计人马座 *A* 北边不规则辐射区域的流量密度，我们把它分为两个主要区域，我们将其称为人马座 *B*1 和 *B*2。这些区域的中心位置和角直径列于表 1，其中心位置是参照人马座 *A* 的位置测量的。在图 1*b* 中，0.67K 天线温度的闭合等亮度线图描绘出中心位置。表 1 给出了人马座 *B*1 和 *B*2 的流量密度积分。不过，对这些值的采用应该谨慎些，因为目前的巡天只提供了这些区域的几个等亮度线，特别是在 15.50 千兆周 / 秒处。通过比较来自这些区域的积分流量与布拉滕等人在 5 千兆周 / 秒得到的数据，人们发现这两个源实际上都是热辐射的，因此它们有可能是电离氢区。但是没有证据表明这些源和人马座 *A* 有物理上的联系。

在研究我们自己银河系中心的结构时，将已有的射电数据与两个近邻普通星系 *M*31 和 *M*51 中心的光学数据作比较是有意义的。（当然由于银河系中心大量尘埃云遮挡，所以得到的银河系中心结构或性质的光学证据很少。）在光学波段均观测到 *M*31 和 *M*51 具有线尺度大约 20 秒差距的中心核 [5,6]。对于每种情况，这个核都镶嵌于更大尺度的、约 1,000 秒差距的核球中。就我们自己银河系而言，如果我们认为人马座 *A* 是银河系中心并且距离是 10 千秒差距 [7]，那么它半功率处 3.5 角分的角宽度应该对应于 10 秒差距的线尺度，这与近邻普通星系核心的光学尺度差不多。类似地，如果人马座 *A* 背景上的展源被看作银河系存在中心核球的射电观测证据，那么大约 120 角分 [1] 的射电直径应该对应于 350 秒差距的线尺度。

射电天文学家对银河系中心的观测至今已经超过大约 15 年了，在这段时间里角分辨率已提高到原来的 30 倍左右。随着分辨率的每一次提高，中心区域逐渐显示出了不断增加的结构复杂性。从 1967 年开始，这个区域将出现一系列的月掩情况。那时，我们也许可以期待角分辨率大幅度地增加，如 100 倍或者更多，到那时人们可以更加充分地了解这个区域的细致结构。

感谢林肯实验室的赫耳先生和魏因雷布博士，以及哈佛大学的莱茵哈特先生和泰勒先生对观测给予的协助。林肯实验室是由麻省理工学院在美国空军的支持下运行的研发中心。该项目中哈佛大学部分由美国国家科学基金会支持。

（钱磊 翻译；王有刚 审稿）

References:

1. Maxwell, A., and Downes, D., *Nature*, **204**, 865 (1964).
2. Weiss, H. G., *IEEE Spectrum*, 2, No. 2, 50 (1965).
3. Hollinger, J. P., *Astrophys. J.*, **142**, 609 (1965).
4. Broten, N. W., Cooper, B. F. C., Gardner, F. F., Minnett, H. C., Price, R. M., Tonking, F. G., and Yabsley, D. E., *Austral. J. Phys.*, **18**, 85 (1965).
5. Lallemand, A., Duchesne, M., and Walker, M. F., *Pub. Astron. Soc. Pacific*, **72**, 76 (1960).
6. Burbidge, E. M., and Burbidge, G. R., *Astrophys. J.*, **140**, 1445 (1964).
7. *Intern. Astro. Union Inform. Bull.*, No. 11, 11 (1963).

Formation of Hydroxyl Molecules in Interstellar Space

J. L. Symonds

Editor's Note

In the mid-1960s radio astronomers were beginning the process of finding emission from molecules in space. J. L. Symonds here proposes a particular way in which the OH (hydroxyl) radical might be formed, which he crafted to avoid the problem that collisions of two particles seemed very unlikely in the low gas densities of interstellar space. What was missing at the time was the understanding that most of the gas was in the form of molecular hydrogen, and still unseen (only the more dilute atomic hydrogen was known). It would be another five years before molecular hydrogen was found in space, adding the missing part of the puzzle.

DURING the past year, radio astronomers[1,2] have been increasingly interested in microwave signals at frequencies of 1,612, 1,665, 1,667 and 1,720 Mc/s, produced by transitions between four energy levels of the OH molecule in the $^2\Pi_{8/2}$ state. Theoretical and laboratory intensity ratios[3] for the four microwave lines were found to be 1:5:9:1. It was reported[1] recently that anomalous intensity ratios had been measured in the strong OH absorption lines of the radio source Sagittarius *A*. McGee *et al.*[4] have extended their measurements to other radio sources and find emission and absorption at all four frequencies with instances of extremely anomalous intensity ratios.

Emission and absorption lines showing such anomalous intensity distributions indicate unusual populations of energy levels in the OH molecules. The observed distributions are more like those expected of a chemical reaction mechanism, followed by radiative deactivation, rather than those from thermal excitation. Since the gases are tenuous in the regions which produce these signals, the long time-scale between collisions will give the molecules, formed in an excited state, a greater probability of radiative rather than collisional deactivation.

The process of association of two atoms to form a molecule normally has a low probability. Since atomic recombination is known to proceed more rapidly in the presence of a third body, "dust" grains in space have been suggested as a suitable medium. The tenuous nature of the gas would seem to rule out a three-body process, however, and such reactions do not appear likely to produce the observed intensity anomalies. The processes for production and loss of OH molecules by two-body processes, therefore, deserve closer study.

In relation to the known concentrations of oxygen and hydrogen in our galaxy, the

羟基分子在星际空间中的形成

西蒙兹

编者按

20 世纪 60 年代中期，射电天文学家们开始了探寻星际空间分子辐射的历程，西蒙兹在本文中提出了一种可能形成羟基的特殊方法，避免了星际空间中低密度气体环境下两个粒子的碰撞概率过低的问题。那时，人们探测不到分子氢（只能探测到稀薄得多的原子氢），不知道大部分气体是以分子氢的形式存在的。直到 5 年后在星际空间中发现了分子氢，才补上了这一谜题中缺失的部分。

在过去的一年，射电天文学家们[1,2]对频率为 1,612 兆周 / 秒、1,665 兆周 / 秒、1,667 兆周 / 秒和 1,720 兆周 / 秒的微波信号产生了越来越浓厚的兴趣，这些信号都是由处于 $^2\Pi_{8/2}$ 状态的 OH 分子在 4 个能级间跃迁时产生的。4 条微波谱线的强度比的理论值和实验值[3]均为 1∶5∶9∶1。最近有研究称[1]，在观测来自人马座 *A* 射电源的强 OH 吸收谱线时发现了反常的强度比。随后麦吉等人[4]将观测对象扩展到其他射电源，发现不论是发射还是吸收，4 个频率的强度比都出现了极为反常的现象。

具有如此反常强度分布的发射谱线和吸收谱线，意味着 OH 分子的能级布居不同寻常。所观测到的布居似乎更有可能是发生了某种化学反应机制（以及随后的辐射退激发），而不是由热激发引起的。因为产生这些信号的区域中的气体非常稀薄，碰撞之间所具有的长时标将使在激发态形成的分子更有可能发生辐射退激发而不是碰撞退激发。

一般通过两个原子结合而形成一个分子的过程的可能性很低。因为原子复合需要一个第三体作为媒介才能加快进程，太空中的“尘埃”颗粒被认为是一种适当的媒介。但是太空内的气体非常稀薄，发生三体过程似乎是不可能的。而且，即使发生这样的反应也不大可能造成所观测到的反常强度。因此，经过两体过程产生和消耗 OH 分子值得进一步研究。

根据我们所在星系内氧和氢的已知浓度，OH 分子若是完全通过原子间的直接

concentration of OH molecules is such as to make it improbable that they are all formed by the direct collision process between atoms. In the study of gaseous processes in flames by spectroscopic means, OH spectra show evidence of pre-dissociation, made possible by radiationless transitions between states of nearly the same energy where the potential energy curves of the states cross or approach closely. The inverse pre-dissociation process[5] (pre-association) is also possible for forming molecules from a two-body collision. The pre-dissociation of the OH molecule to O and H atoms and its inverse are believed to occur, but with a small probability, because a normally forbidden transition is involved.

It is suggested that other two-body processes should be investigated for an alternative mechanism. Since the atom recombination is low, a mechanism worthy of consideration is the exothermic association of negative oxygen ions, O^-, and positive ions of hydrogen, H^+ (protons).

$$O^- + H^+ = OH + \text{approximately } 12\text{ eV}$$

The presence of O^- ions seems assured by the strong electron affinity of oxygen (1.45 eV) and the known presence of oxygen atoms in the regions under study. The anomalous emission and absorption has only been found in ionized regions[4,9] where large concentrations of electrons and protons must also exist. The pre-association of O^- and H^+ essentially may be a transition from the coulomb potential energy curve to the $^2\Sigma^+$ or, more probably, the $^2\Pi_{8/2}$ state curve, involving charge transfer. The interaction cross-section should have a maximum value when the relative velocity of the two ions produces kinetic energy close to the differences between the binding energy of the OH molecule and the electron affinity of the oxygen atom, that is , 4.45–1.45 = 3 eV.

In such circumstances, it is possible to form OH molecules in the $^2\Pi_{8/2}$ state with the population of each of the four levels depending greatly on the relative velocity of the O^- and H^+ ions. Whether the molecules emit or absorb energy will depend on the populations of the energy levels and, in bulk, one would not expect to see the theoretical intensity ratios. Situations could arise where the relationships between lines were completely unusual, for example, apparent absorption in some of the four lines and emission in the others. The actual result will depend strongly on the relative velocity distribution of the two ions. Investigation of the intensity ratios may, therefore, give a great deal of information on relative ion velocities.

Since the reaction has a "resonance" character, it will favour relative velocities producing about 3-eV kinetic energy between the ions. If the O^- ion were stationary, the proton velocity would need to be about 25 km/sec, which is certainly in the range found in the ionized regions of the galaxy. The lack of emission or absorption at the four frequencies in galactic regions of lower temperature may be explained in terms of a low cross-section at proton velocities well below 25 km/sec. An accurate calculation of the reaction cross-section and the state of the resulting molecule would be informative.

碰撞来产生，就不可能具有现有的浓度。借助分光镜方法研究火焰中的气体过程时，发现 OH 光谱显示出了预解离的迹象，这使具有几乎相同能量状态间的无辐射跃迁成为可能，这些状态的势能曲线相交或者紧密靠拢。对于以两体碰撞方式形成的分子来说，也有可能发生预解离的逆过程[5]（预结合过程）。OH 分子可以经过预解离过程形成 O 和 H 原子，也可以通过相反过程形成 OH 分子，但概率很低，因为涉及到通常条件下的禁戒跃迁。

为了探究是否存在其他机制，我们应当对其他两体化过程进行研究。鉴于原子直接复合的概率很低，值得研究的是带负电荷的氧离子 O^- 与带正电荷的氢阳离子 H^+（质子）结合并放热的机制。

$$O^- + H^+ = OH + \text{约 } 12 \text{ 电子伏}$$

已知在所研究区域中存在氧原子，并且氧原子具有强的电子亲和能（1.45 电子伏），这为 O^- 离子的存在提供了可能。目前仅在电离区[4,9]发现了反常的发射和吸收，而该区域也必定存在高浓度的电子和质子。O^- 和 H^+ 离子的预结合过程可能主要是从库仑势能曲线跃迁到 $^2\Sigma^+$ 状态曲线，或者更有可能是到 $^2\Pi_{8/2}$ 状态曲线，其间涉及电荷的转移。当两种离子的相对速度产生的动能接近于 OH 分子结合能与氧原子的电子亲和能之差（即 $4.45-1.45=3$ 电子伏）时，碰撞截面达到最大值。

在这种情况下，可能形成处于 $^2\Pi_{8/2}$ 状态下的 OH 分子，其中 4 个能级中每个能级的布居情况主要依赖于各自 O^- 和 H^+ 离子的相对速度。分子究竟是发射能量还是吸收能量取决于能级的布居情况，对于大量粒子而言，将与理论谱线强度比不符。当谱线间的关系完全不同时，就可能出现这种情形，例如 4 条谱线中的某些可能表现为吸收谱线而另外一些则为发射谱线。实际结果主要依赖于两种离子相对速度的分布情况。因此，对强度比值进行研究可以获取大量关于离子相对速度的信息。

由于反应具有“共振”特点，当离子间的相对速度产生大约 3 电子伏动能时是最有利的。如果固定 O^- 离子，则质子的速度大概需要达到 25 千米 / 秒，星系电离区中的粒子速度无疑可以达到这个要求。在星系低温区域 4 个频率处没有发生发射或吸收现象，这可能是由于质子速度明显低于 25 千米 / 秒导致碰撞截面过小而引起的。对反应碰撞截面和产物分子状态进行精确的计算将会获得更多的信息。

The process of association between O^- ions and protons, or for that matter any similar process between other ions, does not appear to have received great attention. The study of recombination rates in flames[6] shows evidence of a non-equilibrium condition in the excitation of molecules and atoms in the flame. Unexplained concentrations and intensity ratios exist which relate to OH molecule formations. These conditions may be the result of ionic recombination to form molecules and not atom-molecule reactions. Evidence of strong negative and positive ion concentrations has been found[7,8], but the result of their presence on the state of excitation of product molecules has not been elucidated.

If the reaction mechanism is as proposed, radiationless transitions will leave the OH molecule with a velocity similar to that of the O^- ion. However, it is not obvious what the "temperature" of the O^- ions will be since their velocity will depend on their mode of formation and their lifetime.

Two effects must be studied. First, the OH line will be shifted by Doppler effects resulting from mass motion relative to the observational point, and the mass motion may not necessarily be related to the motion of the O and H atoms. Secondly, the line broadening may differ from that produced by the "temperature" of the surrounding ionized gas region because the radiationless transitions occurring in pre-association results in some perturbation of the rotational levels in the states involved. Corresponding shifts in line positions and changes in the intensity distributions will occur, with widths also being reduced in the process.

Orientation of the magnetic moment of the O^- ion by a magnetic field should produce a modification of intensity ratios, possibly an alteration of frequency not associated with a mass movement, and certainly polarization effects. Viewing the OH radiation coming from an ionized region, the proposed mechanism suggests that the radiation will be linearly polarized[10] since the movement of hydrogen appears to be radially outward and the axis of rotation of the OH molecules will tend to be in a plane normal to the proton direction.

The known presence of OH molecules must also lead to the assumption that OH^- molecular ions are also present. The electron affinity of the OH molecule is greater than that of the oxygen atom, making possible two reactions of interest. The first is similar to that for the formation of OH and would lead to the formation of the H_2O molecule. The second is the charge transfer process which will result in the production of an atom of hydrogen and an excited OH molecule. Apart from ionizing and other processes which remove OH molecules, it is obvious that there are other modes of OH formation by collision processes between ions, atoms and molecules which must be taken into account.

Finally, the proposed mechanism offers some interesting prospects in relation to the formation of other molecules. Atoms with strong electron affinities are more likely to produce similar reactions with protons. Equally, the rotational states of such molecules will be excited. Atoms of hydrogen, carbon, oxygen, silicon and sulphur would be capable of forming negative ions. Whether the pre-association process is possible is not known for

O^- 离子和质子的结合过程或者其他离子发生的类似过程似乎还没有受到足够的重视。对火焰中复合速率进行研究[6]，表明在火焰中分子和原子的激发表现出非平衡态的迹象。在 OH 分子形成方面，浓度和强度比值问题仍未得到解释。这可能是离子复合形成分子的结果，而不是原子–分子反应的结果。已证实[7,8]存在正、负离子的高度聚集，但是它们的存在对产物分子激发态有何影响，尚未得到阐明。

如果反应机制确如前面所提出的那样，那么无辐射跃迁将使 OH 分子具有类似于 O^- 离子的速度。但是 O^- 离子所具有的“温度”是我们所不知道的，因为它们的初始速度依赖于其形成的方式和寿命。

有两种效应必须加以研究。首先，OH 谱线会因相对于观测点的该团块的整体运动所引起的多普勒效应而变化，而整体运动未必与 O 和 H 原子的运动相关。第二，谱线的致宽机制与由周围电离气体区域的“温度”所产生的 OH 的致宽情况可能是不同的，因为发生在预结合过程中的无辐射跃迁对相关状态中转动能级有些干扰。这些效应会造成相应的谱线位置和强度分布的变化，同时也伴随着谱线宽度的减小。

磁场对 O^- 离子的磁矩定向作用会改变强度比值和产生极化效应，强度比值的改变可能是通过一个与团块整体运动无关的频率变化进行的。观测来自电离区的 OH 辐射时，上述机制意味着辐射将会是线偏振的[10]，因为氢原子的运动表现为沿径向向外，而 OH 分子的旋转轴则倾向于垂直质子方向的平面内。

已知 OH 分子的存在就势必产生 OH^- 分子离子也存在的假定。OH 分子的电子亲和能比氧原子的电子亲和能大，这使得两个我们感兴趣的反应成为可能。第一个反应类似于形成 OH 分子的反应，只是再形成 H_2O 分子。第二个反应是电荷转移过程，将会产生一个氢原子和一个激发态的 OH 分子。除去离子化和其他一些消除 OH 分子的过程外，很明显，还有另外一些通过离子、原子和分子间碰撞来形成 OH 的方式，这些也是必须加以考虑的。

最后，上述机制为我们提供了一些关于其他分子形成方面的诱人前景。具有高的电子亲和能的原子似乎更有可能与质子发生类似的反应。同样地，这些分子的转动能级将会受到激发。氢原子、碳原子、氧原子、硅原子和硫原子具有形成负离子的能力。对于每一种原子，这种预结合过程是否都会发生还不清楚。因为氮原子无

every case. Since nitrogen does not form a stable negative ion, NH may not be observed. Nevertheless, similar reactions may take place between N^+ and O^- or C^- to give NO and CN molecules.

The formation of H_2 from H^- and H^+ ions may require higher relative velocities, but the cross-section for H^- production from H is four orders of magnitude less than for O^- formation. Such a process may not be observable on this count alone, without invoking the question of the frequency range in which signals may be expected.

In summary, the association mechanism appears to offer some prospect of success in accounting for the anomalous intensity ratios; the emitted radiation may well be linearly polarized if a magnetic field is present; some suggestions can be made as to kinds of molecules that might be formed. More theoretical and experimental work on reactions between negative and positive ions appears to be necessary to establish their importance.

I thank Dr. B. J. Robinson and his colleagues of C.S.I.R.O. Radiophysics Laboratory for their advice and for making available the results of their investigations before publication.

(**208**, 1195-1196; 1965)

References:

1. Gardner, F. F., Robinson, B. J., Bolton, J. G., and van Damme, K. J., *Phys. Rev. Letters*, **13**, 3 (1964).
2. Robinson, B. J., Gardner, F. F., van Damme, K. J., and Bolton, J. G., *Nature*, **202**, 989 (1964).
3. Radford, H. E., *Phys. Rev. Letters*, **18**, 534 (1964).
4. McGee, R. X., Robinson, B. J., Gardner, F. F., and Bolton, J. G., *Nature* (preceding communication).
5. Herzberg, G., *Molecular Spectra and Molecular Structure; Spectra of Diatomic Molecules* (D. Van Nostrand Co., Inc., 1959).
6. Garvin, D., Broida, H. P., and Kostkowski, H. J., *J. Chem. Phys.*, **32**, 880 (1960).
7. King, I. R., *J. Chem. Phys.*, **37**, 74 (1962).
8. Miller, W. J., and Calcote, H. F., *J. Chem. Phys.*, **41**, 4001 (1964).
9. Weaver, H., Williams, D. R. W., Dieter, N. H., and Lum, W. T., *Nature*, **208**, 29 (1965).
10. Weinreb, S., Meeks, M. L., Carter, J. C., Barrett, A. H., and Rogers, A. E. E., *Nature*, **208**, 440 (1965).

法形成稳定的负离子，所以可能无法观测到 NH。但是类似的反应可以在 N^+ 与 O^- 或 C^- 之间发生，分别形成 NO 和 CN 分子。

H^- 与 H^+ 离子结合形成 H_2 可能需要很大的相对速度，但是 H 产生 H^- 的反应截面要比产生 O^- 的反应截面少 4 个数量级。在不知道所产生的谱线可能的频率范围的情况下，这种过程是无法观测到的。

总而言之，结合机制为解释异常的强度比值现象提供了某些可能；如果磁场存在，发射辐射可能会被充分线偏振化；这一机制还可能用于形成其他的分子种类。有必要对正、负离子之间的反应做更多的理论和实验研究，以确定其重要性。

我要感谢鲁滨逊博士及其在澳大利亚联邦科学与工业研究组织放射物理实验室的同事们提出的建议，并感谢他们在发表之前就向我提供了他们的研究结果。

（王耀杨 翻译；沈志侠 审稿）

Biochemistry and Mental Function*

S. S. Kety

Editor's Note

In 1951, American neuroscientist Seymour Kety became the first scientific director of the National Institute of Mental Health, Bethesda, and here he reflects on the Institute's work. Alongside Carl Schmidt, Kety had devised a method to measure circulation and metabolism in the brains of animals and people in states of normal and altered consciousness. These elegant studies showed that metabolism varied between affective states and brain regions. Deeply interested in the biological roots of mental illness, he also describes various neurochemical theories of schizophrenia, and emphasizes the need for a rigorous, heuristic approach to the study of mental health.

IF we are ever to understand and rationally to meliorate the disturbed processes which underlie mental illness, it will be by investigation of the clinical problems themselves and examination of the mental, social, neural and biological elements which comprise behaviour. It is all of these which the Americans call "psychiatric research", and in Great Britain, the Mental Health Research Fund has added much to its vigour for more than a decade.

Although they are not alone in their importance to psychiatry[1], the biological sciences have a significance which is not attenuated by community with the social and psychological sciences, nor is their power less real by having been only partially demonstrated. It is the area, tentative as yet, between biology and human psychology that I have chosen to dwell on, and I shall do so largely in terms of the work of my associates and myself in the Laboratory of Clinical Science at the National Institutes of Health, Bethesda, without any pretension that this will constitute an adequate review of a growing field.

The time is not yet at hand, if, in fact, it will ever be reached, when one can speak meaningfully of the biochemistry of mental state. There are, however, a few areas where one can see the beginnings of correlations and significant interrelationships and these include consciousness, intellectual function and affect.

My interest in consciousness goes back to the Science and Philosophy Club at the Central High School in Philadelphia, a club which bore the brave motto "*Felix qui potuit rerum cognoscere causas*", and in which a great teacher, Edwin Landis, introduced us to Berkeley,

---

* Substance of the Third Mental Health Research Fund (38, Wigmore Street, London, W.1) Lecture delivered on February 26.

生物化学与心理功能*

凯蒂

编者按

1951 年，美国神经科学家西莫尔·凯蒂成为贝塞斯达市国家心理健康研究所的第一任科学主任，在本文中他对研究所的工作进行了仔细思考。凯蒂与卡尔·施密特一起设计出一种方法，用来测量在正常意识状态和意识改变状态下动物与人的脑循环及代谢。这些研究巧妙地展现出在不同情感状态下不同脑区域中代谢情况的差异。怀着对精神疾病的生物学病因的极大兴趣，他也提出了几种精神分裂症的神经化学理论，并且强调心理健康的研究需要采用一种严谨的、探索性的方法。

如果我们想要理解并合理地改善那些导致精神疾病的心理失常过程，就必定要研究它们本身的临床问题，并对构成其表现的心理、社会、神经和生物学要素进行检查。美国人将以上过程称为“精神病学研究”，而在英国，心理健康研究基金十多年来为这一研究增添了许多活力。

对于精神病学来说，虽然它们的重要性不是唯一的[1]，但生命科学的重要性不会因为社会科学与心理科学的参与而减弱，也不会因为只得到了部分阐明而降低其真实性。我选择目前还处于试验性阶段、介于生物学与人类心理学之间的领域来进行论述，这在很大程度上将依据我的同事们和我自己在贝塞斯达市国立卫生研究院临床科学实验室所做的工作，毫不夸张地说，这将构成这个正在发展的领域的全面性综述。

时间尚未来到，假如这一时刻确实会来临的话，也是在人们能够对心理状态的生物化学进行有意义的谈论时。不过，人们逐渐能够在包括意识、智力功能和情感等一些领域中看到某些相关性和显著的相互作用。

我对意识产生兴趣，要追溯到费城中心中学科学与哲学俱乐部，这个俱乐部支持那句勇气十足的格言，即“幸福属于能够理解事物起因的人”；在俱乐部里，一位了不起的教师埃德温·兰迪斯为我们介绍了伯克利、马赫和爱丁顿，还将我们引

---

* 发表于 2 月 26 日，第三届英国心理健康研究基金会（伦敦市威格莫尔街道 38 号）报告的内容。

Mach, Eddington, and the fathomless problem of the nature of consciousness. Many years later I was introduced to the cerebral circulation by Carl Schmidt, through his definitive work in the rhesus monkey, and began to feel how much might be learned from measurements in man, whose brain, with its subjective wealth, and whose diseases could not be replicated in animals. Making use of some fundamental principles of inert gas exchange, the Fick principle, and a little calculus, which there is no time to discuss in any detail, we were eventually able to make what still appear to be satisfactory measurements of blood flow, oxygen and glucose consumption in the conscious human brain under a variety of physiological and pathological conditions. In Table 1 are presented some normal values representing, in fact, the average of the first investigations of healthy volunteers of about twenty-five years of age[2]. Measurement of glucose consumption followed later, confirming the thesis that the major substrate for oxidative energy in the brain is glucose, the utilization of which represented an almost stoichiometric equivalent of the oxygen consumed. From these measurements it was possible to compute the rate of energy utilization by the human brain which turned out to be close to 20 W. In comparison with the enormous expenditure of energy which modern computers require, this represents a remarkable degree of efficiency and miniaturization.

Table 1. Over-all Blood Flow and Energy Metabolism of the Normal Human Brain

Blood flow ml./100 g/min	54
Oxygen consumption ml./100 g/min	3.3
Respiratory quotient (CO_2/O_2)	0.99
Glucose consumption mg/100 g/min	4.9

We were anxious to examine states markedly different from the normal in functional level and chose states of altered consciousness (Table 2). It was quite apparent that there was a rough correlation between level of consciousness and over-all oxygen and energy utilization by the brain[3]. In anaesthesia, for example, where the cerebral oxygen consumption was reduced by 40 percent, there appeared to be support *in vivo* to the earlier *in vitro* investigations of Quastel[4], who had shown that anaestheties interfere with the oxygen consumption of brain slices. But all these data merely tell us that the oxygen consumption and energy-level of the brain are reduced in states of depressed consciousness; they do not explain the coupling between function and metabolism which is one of the most interesting topics of present concern. One could argue that the primary effect in any of these conditions was on the metabolic "power supply" of the brain necessary for the maintenance of consciousness. An alternative hypothesis, however, would be that the primary site of interference was in the interaction between neurons at the synapses, which once inhibited, depressed both the functional activity and the energy requirements of the system. This interesting problem of the coupling between function and metabolism must await clarification by the work of those like McIlwain, Rodnight, Larrabee and Chance, among others.

入了关于意识本质这个难理解的问题中。许多年后，卡尔·施密特通过他在恒河猴身上所做的权威性的工作，为我介绍了脑循环。我开始感觉到，由于人类的脑具有它的主观性资源，所以人类的脑和脑的疾病在动物身上是不能重复的，我们对人类进行测量，从中可能学到很多。利用惰性气体交换的一些基本原理、菲克原理以及少量微积分（这里无暇进行细节的讨论），我们最终能够对处于清醒状态的人脑在多种生理和病理条件下的血流量以及氧与葡萄糖的消耗量进行似乎还算满意的测量。表 1 中列出的是一些正常值，实际上是对一批大约 25 岁的健康志愿者进行初次研究的平均值 [2]。之后对葡萄糖消耗量进行测量，结果证实了脑内氧化产能的主要底物是葡萄糖，对葡萄糖的利用代表了几乎化学计量相等的耗氧量。通过这些测量，有可能计算出接近 20 瓦的人脑能量利用率。与现代计算机所需的巨大能量消耗相比，这表现了非常高效和小型化的特点。

表 1．正常人脑的总血流量和能量代谢

血流量 毫升 /100 克 / 分钟	54
耗氧量 毫升 /100 克 / 分钟	3.3
呼吸商（CO_2/O_2）	0.99
葡萄糖消耗量 毫克 /100 克 / 分钟	4.9

我们期望对那些在功能水平上与正常状态具有显著差别的状态进行检查，并选择了一些意识改变的状态（表 2）。非常明显的是，在意识水平和人脑的总氧气与能量利用之间存在着一种粗略的相关性 [3]。例如，在麻醉时，脑的耗氧量会减少 40%，体内实验结果似乎支持夸斯特尔早期进行的体外研究 [4]，他曾经指出，麻醉会影响脑切片的耗氧量。但是所有这些数据只能告诉我们，在意识处于受抑制状态时，脑的耗氧量与能量水平会下降；他们并没有解释功能与代谢之间的联结关系，这是目前关注的最有趣的话题之一。有人可能会认为在上述任何条件下，主要是对维持意识所必需的脑的代谢“能量供应器”产生影响。然而，另一种假设认为影响的主要部位是在突触处神经元之间的交互作用，这种交互作用一旦受到抑制，系统的功能活性和能量需求都会降低。这个关于功能与代谢之间的联结作用的有趣的问题还必须等待麦基尔韦恩、罗德奈特、拉腊比和钱斯以及其他人的研究工作来阐明。

Table 2. Cerebral Oxygen Consumption in States of Depressed Consciousness
(Expressed as Percentage of the Value in Healthy Young Men)

Senile psychosis	82
Diabetic acidosis	82
Insulin hypoglycaemia	79
Surgical anaesthesia	64
Insulin coma	58
Diabetic coma	52

There are states of altered consciousness, however, in which such a neat correlation with total cerebral metabolism and energy does not exist (Table 3). Normal sleep is one such state; the poetic description of the wakening brain by Sir Charles Sherrington in "Man on His Nature" is well known:

"Suppose we choose the hour of deep sleep. Then only in some sparse and out of the way places are nodes flashing and trains of light-points running … the great knotted headpiece of the whole sleeping system lies for the most part dark. … Should we continue to watch the scheme we should observe after a time an impressive change which suddenly accrues. In the great head end ... spring up myriads of twinkling stationary lights and myriads of trains of moving lights of many different directions. … the great topmost sheet of the mass, that where hardly a light had twinkled or moved, becomes now a sparkling field of rhythmic flashing points with trains of travelling sparks hurrying hither and thither. The brain is waking and with it the mind is returning."

Table 3. Cerebral Oxygen Consumption in Various Mental States
(Expressed as Percentage of the Value in Normal Control States)

Normal sleep	97
Schizophrenia	100
LSD psychosis	101
Mental arithmetic	102

Not only did our results[5] force the rejection of a simple cerebral ischaemic theory for sleep which dated back to Alcmaeon; they challenged as well the generally accepted "Sherringtonian" notion which equated sleep with neuronal inactivity. More recent neurophysiological findings are more consonant with what we learned about the nature of sleep. Evarts[6], in very elegant investigations of the activity of individual neurons which he has observed through microelectrodes chronically implanted in the cortex of unanaesthetized cats, has found no net decrease in cortical neuronal activity during natural sleep. He has, on the other hand, demonstrated characteristic alterations in the activity of individual neurones or groups of neurones, some showing inhibition when the animal sleeps, but others coming into greater activity at that time.

The results in schizophrenia[7], during LSD psychosis[8] or in mental arithmetic[9] all reinforce the concept that the brain, unlike the heart or the liver or kidney, is an organ

表 2．意识处于受抑制状态时脑的耗氧量
（以相对于健康年轻人数值的百分比表示）

老年性精神病	82
糖尿病性酸中毒	82
胰岛素低血糖	79
外科麻醉	64
胰岛素昏迷	58
糖尿病昏迷	52

然而，有些改变的意识状态，总脑代谢与能量之间不存在这样的净相关性（表 3）。正常睡眠就是这样一种状态。查尔斯 · 谢灵顿爵士在《关于人类的本性》一书中对于觉醒状态的大脑所做出的富于诗意的描述是广为人知的：

“假设我们选取深度睡眠的时刻。那么，只在某些零星、偏远的位置，才会有节点闪烁着，以及带有亮点的队列在延续着……整个睡眠系统中最复杂的中枢位于最黑暗的角落里。……继续观望这一图景，过一段时间后，我应该能观察到突然产生的令人印象深刻的变化。在那伟大的首端……无数闪烁着的、静止的亮点和无数向不同方向运动的亮点组成的队列陡然跃起。……在那总体的最高层，曾经罕有光亮闪烁或者移动的地方，现在变成了一片闪亮的场所，到处是有节奏的闪烁光点与匆忙移动的发光队列。大脑醒来了，意识恢复了。”

表 3．各种精神状态下脑的耗氧量
（以相对于正常对照状态时数值的百分比表示）

正常睡眠	97
精神分裂症	100
LSD 精神异常	101
心算	102

我们的结果[5]不仅使我们拒绝接受关于睡眠的简单的脑缺血性理论（这个理论要回溯至阿尔克迈翁），而且向已被普遍认可的“谢灵顿的”将睡眠等同于神经元处于静止状态的观点提出了挑战。最近神经生理学的研究结果与我们关于睡眠本质的认识相一致。埃瓦茨[6]对单个神经元的活动进行了非常巧妙的研究，他将微电极长期植入未经麻醉的猫的脑皮层进行观测，发现在自然睡眠期间，皮层的神经元活动没有净减少。另一方面，他还论证了单个神经元或神经元群活动的特征性改变，在动物睡眠时有些表现为抑制状态，而当时另外一些则更活跃。

精神分裂症[7]、LSD 精神异常[8]或者心算[9]时的结果都强化了这样一个概念，

for computation and communication. In such functions there is no necessary correlation between the energy utilized and the efficiency of the process or the quality of the output. To differentiate these alterations of consciousness in terms of the cerebral oxygen consumption would be like trying to correlate the nature of a radio programme with the power used.

Some of our more recent investigations have attempted to examine the energy utilization of many structures within the living brain. The first approach to measurement of oxygen consumption is in defining the local perfusion rates. Using basic principles similar to those of the nitrous oxide method, we have related the quantity of an inert diffusible substance taken up by a small tissue region to its perfusion[10]. If the tracer is radioactive, one can measure its uptake during a standard time interval in the various structures of the brain by autoradiography. In the autoradiogram, density is related to the concentration of tracer which in turn can be related to the blood flow during the physiological state just prior to the abrupt killing of the animal. Under most physiological conditions there is reason for believing that the blood flow is determined by the oxygen consumption, so that in a rough way the autoradiographic density gives information on the differential energy utilization in various structures of the brain. Such investigations have revealed a remarkable differentiation of cortical blood flow in the unanaesthetized brain with the primary sensory areas showing far greater activity[11]. This differentiation does not appear to be present in the brain of the foetus or the neonate. Anaesthesia obscures this differentiation, reducing the areas of greater cortical oxygen consumption to a relatively homogeneous average value, while there is evidence that sensory stimulation results in a recognizable increase in blood flow and, presumably, oxygen consumption along the appropriate sensory pathways[12].

The maturation of intellectual function and its maldevelopment depends on many processes in addition to oxygen consumption. In 1949, when Sokoloff first became associated with us, we undertook an investigation of cerebral blood flow and oxygen consumption in patients with hyperthyroidism. This resulted in the quite surprising finding that although the total oxygen consumption of such patients was markedly elevated, there was no significant increase in the oxygen consumption of the brain[13]. These results demonstrated that the effects of thyroid hormone were not uniformly applied to the metabolism of all cells in the body. A finding such as this requires an explanation and Sokoloff set about to find one. Using radioactive thyroxine he learned that the hormone crossed the blood-brain barrier and was available to the cells of the brain. He knew also that the brain was peculiar, in that its oxidative processes were almost entirely confined to a single substrate, glucose, and that, although Richter, Waelsch and others had demonstrated an active protein synthesis in the mature brain, that process was still considerably slower in brain than in liver and could scarcely account for a significant fraction of the cerebral oxygen consumption. These considerations led him to the hypothesis that thyroxine neither stimulated oxidative metabolism directly not uncoupled it from phosphorylation (which were the prevailing concepts) but acted on some specialized process such as protein synthesis.

即脑与心脏、肝脏或肾脏不同，它是一个负责计算和交流的器官。在实现这些功能时，能量的利用与过程的效率或输出质量之间不一定有相关性。要根据脑的耗氧量来区别这些意识改变，就如同试图在广播节目的性质与其所用的能量之间建立关联一样。

我们最近的一些研究尝试检查活脑内多种结构的能量利用。第一种测量耗氧量的方法是定义局部灌注率。应用与一氧化二氮方法类似的基本原理，我们把一小块组织区域吸收的某种惰性扩散物质的量与其灌注联系起来[10]。如果示踪物具有放射性，就可以通过放射自显影法测量脑的不同结构在标准时间间隔内的吸收量。在放射自显影图中，密度与示踪物浓度有关，依次地，浓度与动物在被突然杀死前所处的生理状态期间的血流量有关。在绝大多数生理条件下，我们有理由相信血流量是由耗氧量决定的，因此放射自显影图像密度大致提供了脑的各种结构中能量利用差别的信息。这些研究已经揭示了未麻醉的脑中皮层血流量具有显著的差异，同时其初级感觉区的活性要大得多[11]。这种差异似乎并不存在于胎儿或新生儿的脑中。麻醉通过降低具有较大皮层耗氧量的区域的耗氧量至相对均匀的平均值来淡化这种差异，不过有证据表明，感觉刺激会导致可识别的血流量增加，由此推测，相应感觉传导通路的耗氧量也增加[12]。

除耗氧量外，智力功能的成熟与发育障碍还取决于很多过程。1949 年索科洛夫与我们首次合作，进行一项针对甲亢患者的脑血流量与耗氧量的研究。该研究得出了令人非常惊讶的发现：尽管这些患者总的耗氧量显著地升高了，但是脑的耗氧量没有显著增加[13]。这些结果证明，甲状腺激素的作用并非对生物体内所有细胞的新陈代谢都一样适用。诸如这样的发现需要一个解释，索科洛夫便开始寻找原因。通过使用放射性甲状腺素，他认识到激素可以穿过血–脑屏障从而为脑细胞所利用。他还发现，脑是非常特殊的，因为脑中的氧化过程几乎只局限于葡萄糖这一种底物。尽管里克特、韦尔施和其他一些人曾证明过在成熟的脑中有一种活性蛋白质的合成，但是与在肝脏中相比，该过程在脑中还是要慢很多，而且它几乎不能对脑耗氧量的主要部分给出解释。基于上述考虑，他做出了如下假设，即甲状腺素既不直接刺激氧化代谢也不参与磷酸化作用的解耦联（这是普遍流行的看法），而是作用于一些特殊的过程，如蛋白质合成。

In 1954 he came to the National Institute of Mental Health and began a highly productive collaboration with Kaufman. In 1959 they were able to report that 1-thyroxine, administered to normal animals *in vivo* or added directly to the incubation medium *in vitro*, stimulated the rate of amino-acid incorporation into protein in cellfree, rat liver homogenates. This stimulation of protein synthesis *in vitro* occurred in the absence of changes in oxygen consumption or oxidative phosphorylation. They further suggested that the characteristic effects of thyroxine on energy metabolism were secondary to the stimulation of reactions which required energy such as protein biosynthesis[14].

The mitochondria are clearly involved in this process since it is these structures alone rather than the microsomes or the cell sap which differentiate hyperthyroid rats from euthyroid controls in the ability to stimulate amino-acid incorporation into protein[15]. Thyroxine in the presence of mitochondria and an oxidizable substrate apparently produces a soluble factor that can be isolated and which will in itself stimulate protein synthesis. The evidence indicates that this factor stimulates the transfer of *s*RNA-bound amino-acids into microsomal protein[16,17]. Much remains to be done in identifying the factor and further defining its action on the microsome and the precise step in protein synthesis at which it occurs. The demonstration of a stimulation of protein synthesis by thyroxine, however, clearly defined as it is by *in vitro* investigations and confirmed *in vivo*, appears to be the fundamental mechanism of action of this hormone and explains much of its physiological effects.

Recently, Sokoloff, in collaboration with Klee[18], has reexamined the effects of this hormone on the brain. Although thyroxine does not stimulate protein synthesis in mature brain, explaining its failure to increase cerebral oxygen consumption in adult man, it does so significantly in neonatal brain, and again it is the mitochondria which differentiate the two.

These findings help to explain the well-known clinical effects of the thyroid hormone on the development of the brain and of intellectual function in infants compared with its relatively minor effects on these functions in the adult. They corroborate and offer a mechanism for Eayrs's finding of the requirement for thyroxine in the dendritic proliferation of immature cerebral cortex. Thus, this work forms a crucial link between the absence of thyroid hormone and the retarded cerebral development in cretinism.

In 1956, soon after the Laboratory of Clinical Science, National Institute of Mental Health, was organized, some of us became interested in the cluster of thought disorders which is called schizophrenia, and gave attention to the hypothesis which attempted to explain many of the mental symptoms of schizophrenia on the basis of an abnormal degradation of circulating epinephrine to abnormal oxidation products such as adrenochrome or adrenolutin[19]. That hypothesis seemed especially plausible because it took cognizance of the evidence for genetic factors as well as the importance of stressful life experiences in the pathogenesis of the mental disorder. The difficulty in testing the hypothesis lay in the lack of knowledge concerning the normal metabolism of epinephrine,

1954 年，他来到国家心理健康研究所，与考夫曼开始了一个卓有成效的合作。1959 年，他们报道称：将 1– 甲状腺素直接给予正常动物进行体内实验，或者体外直接添加至培养基内，它均能提高无细胞系的大鼠肝脏匀浆中氨基酸合成蛋白质的速率。这种刺激蛋白质体外合成的作用发生在耗氧量或氧化磷酸化未变化的情况下。他们进一步提出，甲状腺素对能量代谢的特征性作用次于对需要能量的反应的刺激作用，如蛋白质生物合成[14]。

很明显，这一过程涉及线粒体，只有它能够将甲状腺机能亢进的大鼠与甲状腺机能正常的对照大鼠在刺激氨基酸合成蛋白质方面区分开[15]，而不是微粒体或者细胞液。在线粒体和某种可氧化的底物存在时，甲状腺素明显地产生出一种可以分离出来的可溶性因子，这种因子本身刺激蛋白质合成。有证据表明，这种因子刺激 *s*RNA 结合的氨基酸转化为微粒体蛋白质[16,17]。我们仍然需要做很多工作来鉴别该因子，并进一步阐明它对微粒体的作用以及它出现于蛋白质合成过程中的确切步骤。然而，甲状腺素对蛋白质合成的刺激作用似乎是这种激素的基本作用机制，并解释了该激素的多种生理作用，这一论证是通过体外实验明确阐释的并在体内实验中得到确认。

最近，索科洛夫与克莱[18]合作重新考察了这种激素对脑的影响。尽管甲状腺素不促进成熟脑中的蛋白质合成这一事实解释了它不能增加成人脑的耗氧量，但是它在新生儿大脑中有非常显著的影响。线粒体依然可以用来区分这两种情况。

这些发现有助于解释甲状腺激素对婴儿脑与智力功能的发育这一众所周知的临床作用，相比之下，它对成人的这些功能的作用相对较小。他们证实了埃尔斯关于甲状腺素是未成熟的脑皮层树突增殖所必需的这一发现，并提出了一种作用机制。因此，这一工作表明呆小症患者的甲状腺激素缺乏与脑发育迟滞之间存在重要的关联。

1956 年，国家心理健康研究所临床科学实验室组建后不久，我们中的一些人开始对思维障碍症候群即精神分裂症产生了兴趣，并注意了试图根据循环肾上腺素异常降解为异常氧化产物（如肾上腺素红或肾上腺黄素）来解释精神分裂症所具有的多种精神症状的假说[19]。这种假说看起来似乎很有道理，因为它既认识到遗传因素的证据，又认识到充满压力的生活经历对于精神障碍发病机理的重要性。检验这一假说的困难在于我们缺乏关于肾上腺素正常代谢的知识，更不要说在精神分裂症中可能出现的异常情况。在 1956 年，人们能够对给予的约为 5%的肾上腺素作出解释，

let alone its possible abnormality in schizophrenia. In 1956 one could account for some 5 percent of administered epinephrine which was excreted unchanged in the urine, while the remaining 95 percent was disposed of by unknown mechanisms.

Isotopic techniques, which had been so valuable in the tracing of other metabolic pathways, were not readily applied to this problem because the pharmacological potency of epinephrine prevented the administration of enough of the hormone labelled with carbon-14 which was then available to permit characterization of its products. It was apparent that to use isotopic techniques to advantage for studies of the metabolism of epinephrine, especially in man, would require an isotopically labelled epinephrine of unheard-of specific activity. We were finally successful in having a few millicuries of 7-^{3}H-epinephrine synthesized. The tritium label made possible the high specific activities required, while its position at C7 met our expectation that the label would be retained through the various possible metabolic degradations.

In 1957, Armstrong, McMillan and Shaw identified the first major metabolite of epinephrine (vanillylmandelic acid, VMA, or 3-methoxy-4-hydroxymandelic acid) in the urine of a patient with phaeochromocytoma and in normal urine[20].

A few years before, Julius Axelrod had joined the Laboratory, bringing with him great interest and competence in the catecholamines. Although the metabolism of adrenaline to VMA was generally regarded as involving first deamination by monoamine oxidase and then *O*-methylation, Axelrod, on the basis of pharmacological and biochemical evidence, postulated the existence of an alternative pathway with *O*-methylation as the first step followed by deamination. He then proceeded to demonstrate in the urine the existence of that hypothetical compound which he designated "*O*-methylepinephrine" or "metanephrine", a second major metabolite of epinephrine[21]. He described and characterized the enzyme responsible for this conversion (catechol-*O*-methyltrans-ferase) and the requirement of *S*-adenosylmethionine as the methyl donor[22]. He suggested that *O*-methylation rather than deamination was the principal enzymatic process involved in the inactivation of circulating epinephrine and later went on to show that norepinephrine was metabolized through completely analogous pathways by the same enzymes[23]. Fig. 1 shows the present state of knowledge of the metabolism of these two catecholamines with a number of additional minor metabolites which Axelrod *et al.* have identified. Together all these metabolic products account for some 98 percent of administered epinephrine or norepinephrine and, presumably, a similar accountability would hold for these substances when they are released into the circulation under physiological conditions.

这部分随尿液原样排出，而其余的 95%通过未知机制发生代谢。

同位素技术在其他代谢途径的示踪研究中具有极大价值，但尚不适用于这一问题，因为肾上腺素的药理作用强度不允许给予足量的 C–14 标记的激素，而给予足量的 C–14 标记的激素使获得产物的特征成为可能。很显然，若要利用同位素技术研究肾上腺素代谢，尤其是在人体内，就需要用前所未闻比活度的同位素标记肾上腺素。我们最终成功地合成了几个毫居里的 7–^{3}H– 肾上腺素。用氚标记使得所需的高比活度成为可能，而它所处的 C7 位置满足我们的期望，即在各种可能的代谢降解过程中标记将被保留下来。

1957 年，阿姆斯特朗、麦克米伦和肖在一位嗜铬细胞瘤患者的尿液和正常人尿液中首次鉴别出肾上腺素的主要代谢产物（香草扁桃酸、VMA 或 3– 甲氧基 –4– 羟基扁桃酸）[20]。

几年前，尤利乌斯 · 阿克塞尔罗德加入了实验室，带来了其对儿茶酚胺浓厚的研究兴趣和很强的研究能力。尽管人们通常认为从肾上腺素到 VMA 的代谢过程首先涉及单胺氧化酶的脱氨基作用，随后进行氧位甲基化作用，但是根据药理学和生物化学方面的证据，阿克塞尔罗德认为可能存在另外一种途径，即氧位甲基化作用为第一步，随后才是脱氨基作用。接着，他开始证明在尿液中存在这种假设的化合物，他将其称之为“氧位甲基化肾上腺素”或“甲氧基肾上腺素”，它是肾上腺素的第二种主要代谢产物[21]。他描述了负责这一转化过程的酶及其特征（儿茶酚氧位甲基转移酶），而且需要 *S*– 腺苷甲硫氨酸作为甲基供体[22]。他提出，在涉及循环肾上腺素失活的主要酶促过程中，涉及的是氧位甲基化作用而非脱氨基作用，后来他又进一步表明，去甲肾上腺素是借助同一种酶通过完全类似的途径产生代谢变化的[23]。图 1 显示出目前我们对这两种儿茶酚胺代谢过程的认识情况，其中一些是由阿克塞尔罗德等人鉴别的一些额外的次要代谢产物。所有的这些代谢产物可以解释给予的肾上腺素或去甲肾上腺素中约 98%的部分，据推测，当这些物质在各种生理条件下释放到循环中，可以得到相似程度的解释。

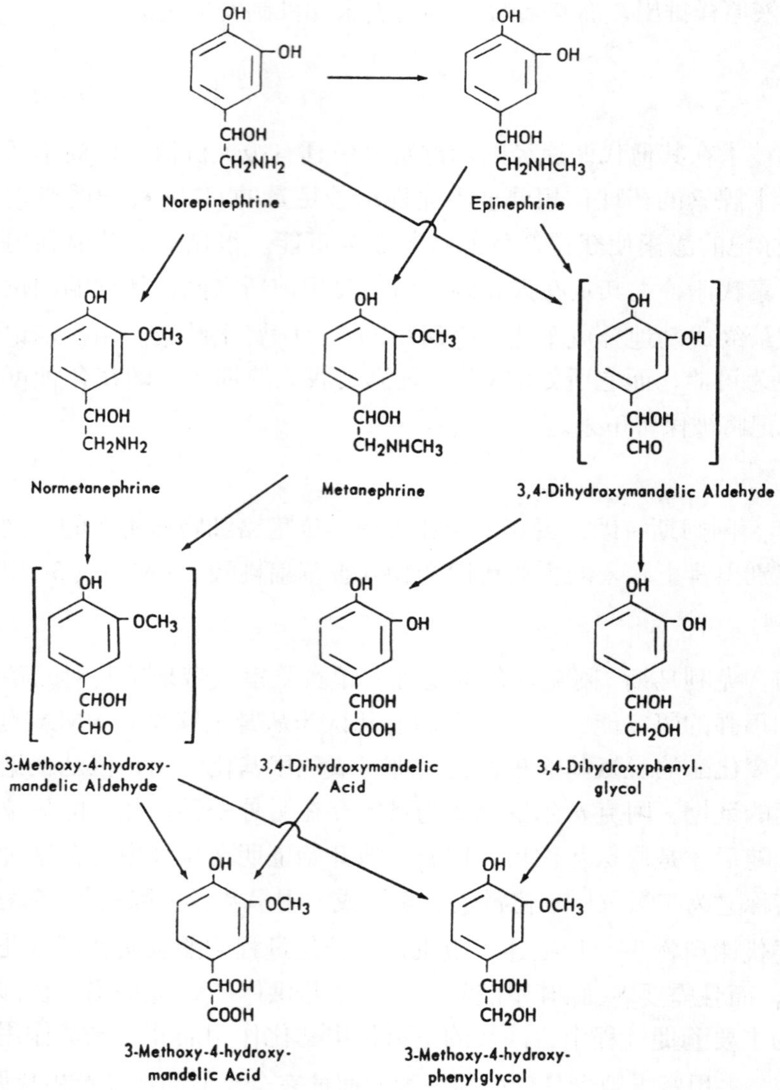

Fig. 1. Present knowledge of the metabolism of epinephrine and norepinephrine (after Axelrod and Kopin)

With the background of information on the normal degradation of the hormone which was thus provided, it was then possible to examine the metabolism of epinephrine in schizophrenic patients and normal volunteers using the tritium-labelled substance[24,25]. We were unable to find any evidence for a significant abnormality in the metabolism of intravenously administered epinephrine among the schizophrenics either qualitatively or quantitatively, the four normal metabolites and the unchanged hormone accounting for 98 percent of the tritium in the urine in both groups of subjects.

The synthesis of tritiated epinephrine which was stimulated by that hypothesis but, most important, the work of Axelrod *et al.* have, however, had important implications for

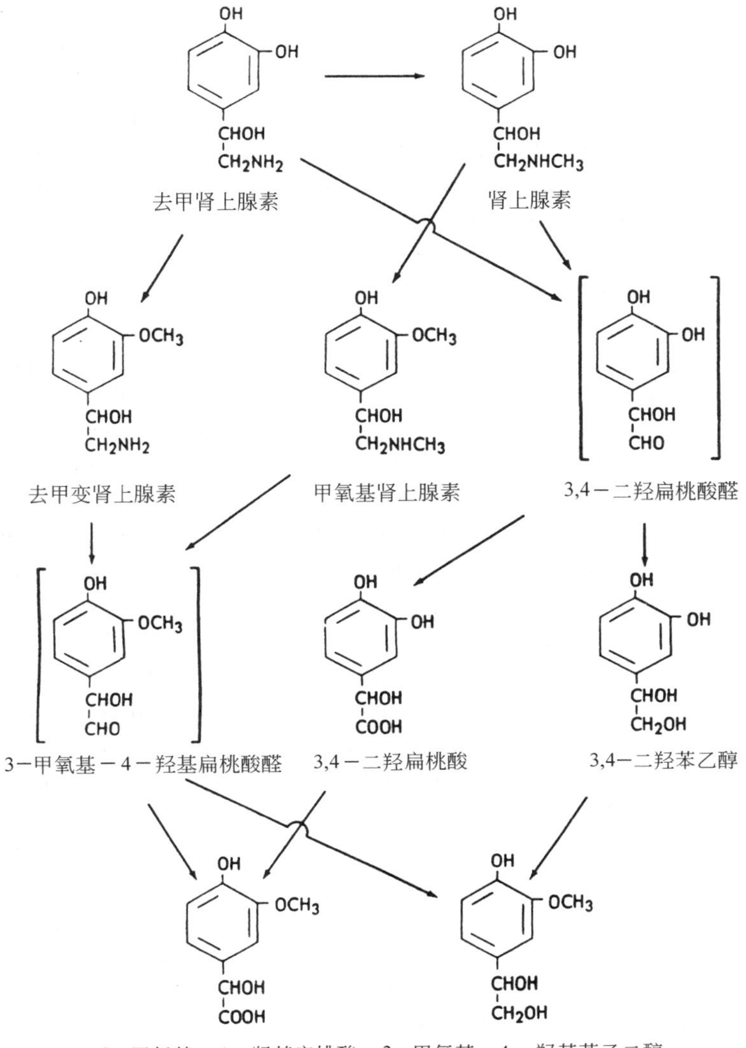

图 1．目前认识的肾上腺素和去甲肾上腺素代谢过程（继阿克塞尔罗德和科平之后）

基于提供的关于激素正常降解的背景信息，我们就有可能利用氚–标记物检查肾上腺素在精神分裂症患者和正常志愿者体内的代谢过程[24,25]。对于精神分裂症患者，我们未能发现静脉给予肾上腺素后代谢过程发生显著异常的任何定性或定量证据；在两组对象中，四种正常的代谢产物和未发生改变的激素可以解释尿液中氚含量为98%这一现象。

这个假设促进了氚标记的肾上腺素的合成，但是，最重要的是阿克塞尔罗德等人的工作对精神病学已经产生了重要的意义。肾上腺素代谢产物的鉴定以及在尿液

psychiatry. The identification of the metabolites of epinephrine and the development of methods for their estimation in urine make it possible to obtain information on the secretion of this hormone in a variety of physiological and pathological states and in response to drugs. Investigations by Axelrod and Kopin, among others, with norepinephrine were a logically related step, and in the past few years the storage and release of norepinephrine at the sympathetic nerve endings and the factors which control these processes have become one of the most exciting fields of pharmacology[26]. The insights which such investigations have given us into the possible actions of drugs which affect mood will be discussed later.

Thirteen years ago Osmond and Smythies, in conjunction with Harley-Mason[27], advanced the interesting hypothesis that there was an accumulation of an abnormal methylated compound with hallucinogenic properties in schizophrenia. They were led to this possibility by the fact that the potent psychotomimetic drug, mescaline, was almost identical with trimethylated dopamine. In the same communication Harley-Mason pointed out that the dimethyl derivative (3,4-dimethoxyphenyl-ethylamine), which had interesting behavioural effects, could possibly be formed by transmethylation *in vivo*. In 1961, Pollin, Cardon and I[28] tested this hypothesis by observing the mental effects of methionine given orally to a small number of chronic schizophrenic patients who had been maintained on a monoamine oxidase inhibitor. We reasoned that under those conditions it was conceivable that the levels of *S*-adenosylmethionine, which Cantoni[29] had shown to be an important methyl donor, could be increased and the biological transmethylation of amines facilitated. In some of the patients there was a temporary but quite obvious exacerbation of psychotic symptoms associated with methionine administration. These observations have now been confirmed by several other groups[30-32]; in addition, Brune and Himwich found similar effects with betaine, another methyl donor[30].

Further work by investigators in our laboratory has tended to support some of this reasoning. The absence of information regarding tissue levels of *S*-adenosylmethionine led Baldessarini and Kopin[33] to devise an ingenious assay of high specificity. By means of this they found a considerable elevation of *S*-adenosylmethionine in brain and liver of rats following methionine feeding. Axelrod[34] demonstrated the presence in normal mammalian tissue of an enzyme capable of methylating normal metabolites, that is, tryptamine and serotonin, to their dimethyl derivatives in the presence of *S*-adenosylmethionine. Dimethyltryptamine has been shown to be a potent psychotomimetic agent[35].

In 1962, Friedhoff and Van Winkle[36] detected a substance which behaved like 3,4-dimeth oxyphenylethylamine in the urine of a substantial fraction of schizophrenic patients and which appeared to be absent from normal urine. That finding, which has had substantial confirmation by Bourdillon and Ridges[37], lends further support to the hypothesis of Osmond, Smythies and Harley-Mason, especially since it was that compound to which Harley-Mason had directed attention ten years previously.

中其含量的测定方法的发展，使得获取肾上腺素在各种生理状态、病理状态以及在药物作用下的分泌信息成为可能。由阿克塞尔罗德、科平和其他一些人利用去甲肾上腺素展开的研究在逻辑上是有关联的步骤，并且在过去的几年中，去甲肾上腺素在交感神经末梢的储存和释放以及控制这些过程的因素已成为药理学中最令人兴奋的研究领域之一[26]。这些研究使我们了解影响情绪的药物的可能效应，这些观点将在后面加以讨论。

13 年前，奥斯蒙德、斯迈西斯与哈利–梅森[27]合作提出了一个有趣的假说，即在精神分裂症患者体内存在具有致幻作用的异常甲基化化合物的积累。强效的拟精神病药墨斯卡灵与三甲基化的多巴胺几乎一样的事实使他们开始考虑这一可能性。在同一篇通讯中，哈利–梅森指出，具有有效的行为学作用的二甲基衍生物（3,4–二甲氧基苯乙胺）有可能在体内通过转甲基作用形成。1961 年，波林、卡登和我[28]给少量使用单胺氧化酶抑制剂维持治疗的慢性精神分裂症患者口服甲硫氨酸，通过观察甲硫氨酸产生的心理效应对这一假说进行检验。我们推测，在那样的条件下，可以想象 *S*–腺苷甲硫氨酸（坎托尼[29]指出，它是一种重要的甲基供体）的水平会升高并且胺的生物转甲基作用得到增强。有些患者出现了短暂的但是非常明显的与甲硫氨酸使用相关的精神病症状的恶化。其他一些研究组已经证实了这些观测结果[30-32]；此外，布龙和希姆威奇发现另外一种甲基供体甜菜碱具有类似的作用[30]。

我们实验室的研究人员的进一步工作倾向于支持其中的一些推测。由于缺乏组织中有关 *S*–腺苷甲硫氨酸水平的信息，巴尔代萨里尼和科平[33]设计出一种精巧的具有高度特异性的检测方法。通过这种方法他们发现，在喂食了甲硫氨酸之后，大鼠的脑和肝脏中的 *S*–腺苷甲硫氨酸含量明显增加。阿克塞尔罗德[34]证明了在正常哺乳动物的组织中存在着一种酶，这种酶在有 *S*–腺苷甲硫氨酸存在时能够使正常的代谢产物（即色胺和 5–羟色胺）发生甲基化作用从而形成其二甲基衍生物。二甲基色胺已经被证明是一种强效的拟精神病药物[35]。

1962 年，弗里德霍夫和范温克尔[36]在很大一部分精神分裂症患者的尿液中检测到一种表现类似于 3,4–二甲氧基苯乙胺的物质，该物质似乎不存在于正常人的尿液中。该发现得到了鲍迪伦和布里奇斯[37]的确认，这为奥斯蒙德、斯迈西斯和哈利–梅森的假说提供了进一步的支持，尤其是因为哈利–梅森早在 10 年前就特别关注该化合物了。

Our observations of the effect of methionine in schizophrenic patients, as well as the findings of Friedhoff and Van Winkle, are open to a number of alternative explanations which have not been ruled out. Nevertheless, the hypothesis that the accumulation of one or more methylated compounds plays a significant part in some forms of schizophrenia remains a plausible and parsimonious explanation of a number of different and independent observations and seems worthy of further evaluation.

The possible interrelationships between the biogenic amines and affective states have become a subject of lively interest and productive investigations in the relatively few years which have elapsed since the pioneering studies of Gaddum and Vogt in Great Britain, Erspamer in Italy, Rapport and Woolley in the United States. Interest centred at first on serotonin after remarkable demonstration by Shore *et al.*[38] of a depletion of that amine from the brain during reserpine-induced depression and its elevation following the antidepressant monoamine oxidase inhibitors. As evidence accumulated, however, it was learned that these drugs also affected noradrenaline- and dopamine-levels in the brain and that the catecholamine precursor, dopa, promptly and effectively reversed the depressant actions of reserpine in animals, suggesting to some an equally important role for catecholamines in the action of these drugs and possibly in affective states. It has been difficult to explain, however, the action of two effective antidepressant drugs in terms of the central biogenic amines. These agents, amphetamine and imipramine, are not especially active as monoamine oxidase inhibitors and have not been shown to elevate the levels of norepinephrine or serotonin in the brain.

Recently, Kopin was able to demonstrate, in the isolated, perfused heart, a differential metabolism of tritiated noradrenaline released under different circumstances[39]. When the catecholamine was liberated in a manner which did not provoke its characteristic effects on the heart, that is, by reserpine, it appeared largely as deaminated products in the perfusate. On the other hand, when its release was accompanied by cardiac stimulation as with stimulation of the cardiac sympathetic nerves or by tyramine, *O*-methylated products appeared in the perfusate. These observations have suggested the generalization that catechol-*O*-methyl transferase is the enzyme normally involved in the degradation of norepinephrine which is released physiologically and perhaps its *O*-methylated metabolites are indicative of adrenergic activation, at least in the periphery.

The release and metabolism of noradrenaline in the brain, however, remained quite a mystery, since the blood-brain barrier prevented the uptake by the brain of radioactive norepinephrine and the amount of label which could be applied through synthesis from tagged tyrosine was hardly enough for fractionation. In 1964, Glowinski, who had applied Feldberg's technique to injection into the lateral ventricles of rats, joined Axelrod and Kopin and succeeded in developing what appears to be a valid technique for labelling, at a high specific activity, the norepinephrine stores within the brain by injecting the tritiated form intraventricularly[40]. the label distributes itself quite rapidly in a pattern similar to that of endogenous norepinephrine and shows the same intracellular localization. Furthermore, it follows a curve of disappearance from the brain similar to that of ^{14}C-norepinephrine endogenously produced from ^{14}C-tyrosine.

我们观测到的甲硫氨酸在精神分裂症患者体内的作用结果，以及弗里德霍夫与范温克尔的发现都存在大量仍未被排除掉的其他解释的可能性。不过，一种或多种甲基化的化合物的积累在某些形式的精神分裂症中起着重要作用的假说，对于大量不同的、独立的观测结果来说，仍然是一种似有道理且又过于简单的解释，并且看来好像值得进一步评价。

由于英国的加德姆和沃格特、意大利的厄斯帕莫以及美国的拉波特和伍利的开创性研究，在随后的几年里，生物胺与情感状态之间可能的相互关系已成为一个引人注目的、成果颇丰的研究课题。在肖尔等人[38]对利血平诱导的抑郁期间脑内胺的耗竭以及在使用抗抑郁药单胺氧化酶抑制剂之后胺含量升高做出了出色的论证后，研究兴趣最初集中于5–羟色胺。然而，随着证据的积累，我们认识到这些药物也会影响脑内去甲肾上腺素和多巴胺的水平，并且儿茶酚胺前体多巴会快速而有效地逆转利血平在动物体内的抑制作用，表明儿茶酚胺在这些药物的作用中和可能在情感状态中起着某些同等重要的作用。但是，始终难以从主要的生物胺的角度来解释两种有效的抗抑郁药物的作用机制。安非他明和丙咪嗪这些药剂作为单胺氧化酶抑制剂不是特别有效，也还未曾表现出能够提高脑内去甲肾上腺素或5–羟色胺的水平。

最近，科平能够论证分离的、灌注后心脏在不同条件下释放的氚标记的去甲肾上腺素的代谢[39]。当儿茶酚胺以不引发其对心脏的特征性作用的方式释放时，即通过利血平的方式，那么它作为脱氨基产物就会在灌注液中大量出现。另一方面，当儿茶酚胺的释放同时伴随着心刺激（如同心交感神经产生的刺激）或者酪胺，那么灌注液中就会出现氧位甲基化的产物。这些观测结果提示了一般性的结论，即去甲肾上腺素的降解过程一般都要涉及儿茶酚氧位甲基转移酶，它是生理性释放的，也许它的氧位甲基化的代谢产物标志着肾上腺素的活性，至少在外周如此。

然而，去甲肾上腺素在脑内的释放和代谢仍然是个谜，因为血–脑屏障阻止了脑对放射性去甲肾上腺素的吸收，并且通过由标记的酪氨酸合成的标记物的量几乎不能满足分馏法。1964年，格洛温斯基（他曾经应用费尔德伯格的技术对大鼠的侧脑室进行注射）参与到阿克塞尔罗德与科平的合作中来，并成功地开发出一种看来很有效的、可获得高比活度的标记技术，通过心室内注射氚标记物使得去甲肾上腺素存储在脑内[40]。标记物以一种与内源性去甲肾上腺素类似的形式非常快速地扩散，并且显示出相同的细胞内定位。此外，它遵循着与由^{14}C–酪氨酸内源性生成的^{14}C–去甲肾上腺素类似的从脑内消失的曲线。

With convincing evidence that they were studying the metabolism of endogenous norepinephrine in the brain, they examined the effects of a number of psychoactive drugs. Reserpine caused a rapid depletion and the predominant formation of deaminated products as it did in the heart. On the other hand, monoamine oxidase inhibitors, amphetamine and imipramine, all of which are antidepressant or euphoriant drugs, were followed by an increase in *O*-methylated norepinephrine products in the brain[41]. If one may generalize from Kopin's findings in the heart and infer physiological activity from an increase in norepinephrine *O*-methylation, these findings are compatible with the thesis that the drugs which induce depression or elevation of mood do so by depressing of facilitating the release of physiologically active norepinephrine in the brain or altering its availability at effector sites.

Such a hypothesis as well as the possibility that normal and abnormal changes in mood are dependent on alterations of catecholamines in the brain remain to be validated. The possibility of labelling norepinephrine in the brain has overcome a major obstacle in the way of elucidating its physiological role there.

Another recent development in this laboratory has some clear-cut implications, this time for cardiology. Despite the expectation that monoamine oxidase inhibitors should elevate the levels of the sympathetic neurotransmitter, these agents are found to have hypotensive and other sympatholytic effects which, though undesirable in psychiatry, have been found useful in the treatment of hypertensive disease and angina pectoris. An explanation of this paradoxical effect has been advanced by Kopin *et al.* [42], who presented evidence for the normal synthesis and accumulation of octopamine, the β-hydroxylated derivative of tyramine, in the region of the sympathetic nerve endings, its enhancement by monoamine oxidase inhibitors and its release by sympathetic stimulation. Their hypothesis that this relatively inactive amine may replace norepinephrine and act as a false neurochemical transmitter appears capable of explaining the partial sympathetic blockade observed after chronic inhibition of monoamine oxidase.

Much of what I have outlined is illustrative of an important generalization from the history of science, a principle which, though taken for granted by most scientists, nevertheless requires reinforcement today. The most practical way to attack a major medical problem or to bridge a great hiatus is not usually head-on, but by strengthening and extending the foundations on both sides and narrowing the gap which lies between. This is best accomplished when the scientists themselves choose their logical next steps, which each will do from his knowledge of the state of the field, the feasibility of an approach, the likelihood and significance of its being successful.

Nearly a hundred years ago in England, Thudichum, whom many regard as the father of modern neurochemistry, advanced a hypothesis that many forms of insanity were the result of toxic substances produced within the brain by faulty metabolism. But, more important, he went on to suggest that these processes, then quite obscure, would be obvious when we understood the biochemistry of the brain to its utmost detail[43]. It was

根据他们研究脑内源性去甲肾上腺素代谢令人信服的证据，他们研究了多种精神药物的作用。利血平导致快速耗竭，并主要形成就像其在心脏代谢一样的脱氨基产物。另一方面，单胺氧化酶抑制剂安非他明和丙咪嗪都是抗抑郁药物或称安乐药，会引起脑内氧位甲基化的去甲肾上腺素产物的增加[41]。如果人们能从科平在心脏中的发现归纳出结论，并从去甲肾上腺素的氧位甲基化作用增加推断其生理活性的话，那么这些发现就与下面的论点相吻合，即导致情绪抑郁或高涨的药物是通过抑制促进脑内有生理活性的去甲肾上腺素的释放，或者通过改变其在效应物部位的利用度来发挥效应。

情绪的正常和异常变化取决于脑内儿茶酚胺的变化这样一种假说和可能性尚有待于证实。对脑内去甲肾上腺素进行标记的实现，克服了在阐明它的生理作用方面的主要障碍。

该实验室另一项新近的进展在心脏病学领域具有某些明确的影响。尽管预期单胺氧化酶抑制剂会提高交感神经神经递质的水平，却发现这些药物具有降血压和其他一些抗交感神经的作用，尽管这些作用并不是精神病治疗法所需要的，但已经发现其对高血压和心绞痛的治疗确实是有用的。科平等人[42]对这种自相矛盾的作用提出了一个解释，他们提供了章鱼胺（酪氨β–羟基化的衍生物）在交感神经末梢区域的正常合成与积累、单胺氧化酶抑制剂使其增加、交感神经刺激使其释放的证据。他们的假说认为，这种相对无活性的胺会取代去甲肾上腺素并作为假性神经化学递质，该假说似乎可以解释单胺氧化酶在长期抑制之后所观察到的局部交感神经阻滞。

我所描述的大部分内容都是对科学历史重要的概括性的说明，原理尽管已经为大多数科学家所承认，但在今天仍需要强化。解决一个主要医学难题或者桥接巨大裂缝时，最实用的方法并不是通常的正面冲锋，而是在两个方面加强和扩展基础并且缩短横亘其间的裂隙。当科学家自己选择他们逻辑的前进步骤，从他对所研究领域的认识、方法的可行性以及获得成功的可能性和重要性出发，就可以最完美地达到成功。

在大约100年前的英格兰，被很多人看作现代神经化学之父的图迪休姆提出了一个假说，认为很多种形式的精神错乱是由于代谢缺陷使得脑内产生有毒物质而造成。但他进一步提出，更为重要的是，当我们最大可能详细地理解脑内的生物化学反应时，这些过程（当时还所知甚少）将是显而易见的[43]。他在此后的10年中致

in the latter area that he spent the next ten years in what was to become the classical isolation, description and characterization of the chemical constituents of the brain.

It is not difficult to predict what would have resulted had Thudichum spent those years and the funds made available to him by the Privy Council in a premature search for the toxins of insanity. With the tools, techniques and knowledge available to him at that time, it is extremely unlikely that he would have found any of those hypothetical substances; it is equally unlikely that he would have made his fundamental contributions to our present knowledge of the biochemistry of the brain.

(**208**, 1252-1257; 1965)

Seymour S. Kety: Laboratory of Clinical Science, National Institute of Mental Health, National Institutes of Health, Bethesda, Maryland.

References:

1. Kety, S. S., *Science*, **132**, 1861 (1960).
2. Kety, S. S., and Schmidt, C. F., *J. Clin. Invest.*, **27**, 476 (1948).
3. Kety, S. S., in *Metabolism of the Nervous System*, edit. by Richter, D., 221 (Pergamon Press, London, 1957).
4. Quastel, J. H., *Anesthes. Analg.*, **31**, 151 (1952).
5. Mangold, R., Sokoloff, L., Conner, E., Kleinerman, J., Therman, P. G., and Kety, S. S., *J. Clin, Invest.*, **34**, 1092 (1955).
6. Evarts, E. V., Bental, E., Bihari, B., and Huttlenlocher, P. R., *Science*, **135**, 726 (1962).
7. Kety, S. S., Woodford, R. B., Harmel, M. H., Freyhan, F. A., Appel, K. E., and Schmidt, C. F., *Amer. J. Psychiat.*, **104**, 765 (1948).
8. Sokoloff, L., Perlin, S., Kornetsky, C., and Kety, S. S., *Ann. N. Y. Acad. Sci.*, **66**, 468 (1957).
9. Sokoloff, L., Mangold, R., Wechsler, R. L., Kennedy, C., and Kety, S. S., *J. Clin. Invest.*, **34**, 1101 (1955).
10. Kety, S. S., in *Methods in Medical Research*, edit. by Bruner, H. D., **8**, 228 (Year Book Publishers, Chicago, 1960).
11. Landau, W. M., Freygang, W. H., Rowland, L. P., Sokoloff, L., and Kety, S. S., *Trans. Amer. Neurol. Assoc.*, **80**, 125 (1955).
12. Sokoloff, L., in *Regional Neurochemistry*, edit. by Kety, S. S., and Elkes, J., 107 (Pergamon Press, Oxford,1961).
13. Sokoloff, L., Wechsler, R. L., Mangold, R., Balls, K., and Kety, S. S., *J, Clin. Invest.*, **32**, 202 (1953).
14. Sokoloff, L., and Kaufman, S., *Science*, **129**, 569 (1959).
15. Sokoloff, L., and Kaufman, S., *J. Biol. Chem.*, **236**, 795 (1961).
16. Sokoloff, L., Kaufman, S., Campbell, P. L., Francis, C. M., and Gelboin, H. V., *J. Biol. Chem.*, **238**, 1432 (1963).
17. Sokoloff, L.: The action of thyroid hormones on protein synthesis, as studied in isolated preparations and in the whole rat. *Proc. Second Intern. Congr. Endocrinol.*, London, Aug. 17, 1964 (Elsevier Publishing Co., Amsterdam; in the press).
18. Klee, C. B., and Sokoloff, L., *J. Neurochem.*, **11**, 709 (1964).
19. Hoffer, A., Osmond, H., and Smythies, J., *J. Ment. Sci.*, **100**, 29 (1954).
20. Armstrong, M. D., McMillan, A., and Shaw, K. N. F., *Biochim. Biophys. Acta*, **25**, 422 (1957).
21. Axelrod, J., *Science*, **126**, 400 (1957).
22. Axelrod, J., and Tomchick, R., *J. Biol. Chem.*, **233**, 702 (1958).
23. Axelrod, J., *Physiol. Rev.*, **39**, 751 (1959).
24. La Brosse, E. H., Axelrod, J., and Kety, S. S., *Science*, **128**, 593 (1958).
25. La Brosse, E. H., Mann, J. D., and Kety, S. S., *J. Psychiat. Res.*, **1**, 68 (1961).
26. Kopin, I. J., *Pharmacol. Rev.*, **16**, 179 (1964).
27. Osmond, H., and Smythies, J., *J. Ment. Sci.*, **98**, 309 (1952).
28. Pollin, W., Cardon, P. V., and Kety, S. S., *Science*, **133**, 104 (1961).
29. Cantonl, G. L., *J. Biol. Chem.*, **204**, 403 (1953).
30. Brune, G. G., and Himwich, H. E., in *Recent Advances in Biological Psychiatry*, **5**, 144 (Plenum Press, New York, 1963).
31. Alexander, F., Curtis, G. C., Sprince, H., and Crosley, A. P., *J. Nerv. Ment. Dis.*, **137**, 135 (1963).
32. Park, L. C., Baldessarini, R. J., and Kety, S. S., *Arch. Gen. Psychiat.*, **12**, 346 (1965).

力于后一问题，他的研究成为脑内化学组分经典的分离、描述和鉴定。

不难预料图迪休姆在那些年的努力所取得的成果以及他因为对精神错乱毒素的早期研究而获得枢密院的资助。采用当时所具备的设备、技术和知识，他发现那些假设的物质中的任何一种几乎都是不可能的；他同样不大可能对我们现代的脑生物化学知识做出根本性的贡献。

（王耀杨 翻译；李素霞 审稿）

33. Baldessarini, R. J., and Kopin, I. J., *Anal. Biochem.*, **6**, 289 (1963).

34. Axelrod, J., *Science*, **134**, 343 (1961).

35. Szara, S., *Fed. Proc.*, **20**, 855 (1961).

36. Friedhoff, A. J., and Van Winkle, E., *J. Nerv. Ment. Dis.*, **135**, 550 (1962).

37. Bourdillon, R. E., and Ridges, A. P., in *Amine Metabolism in Schizophrenia*, edit. by Himwich, H. E., Smythies, J. R., and Kety, S. S. (to be published).

38. Shore, P. A., Pletscher, A., Tomich, E. G., Carlsson, A., Kuntzman, R., and Brodie, B. B., *Ann, N. Y. Acad. Sci.*, **66**, 609 (1957).

39. Kopin, I. J., and Gordon, E., *J. Pharmacol.*, **140**, 207 (1963).

40. Glowinski, J., Kopin, I. J., and Axelrod, J., *J. Neurochem.*, **12**, 25 (1965).

41. Glowinski, J., and Axelrod, J., *J. Pharmacol.* (in the press).

42. Kopin, I. J., Fischer, J. E., Musacchio, J. M., Horst, W. D., and Weise, V. K., *J. Pharmacol.*, **147**, 186 (1965).

43. Thudichum, J. L. W., *A Treatise on the Chemical Constitution of the Brain*, 13 (Baillière, Tindall and Cox, London, 1884).

Malaria and the Opening-Up of Central Africa

R.Weatherall

Editor's Note

In the nineteenth century, the British government was much occupied with the exploration of tropical Africa, partly because of the government's decision to do what it could to suppress the slave trade. This paper, based on a book by Michael Gelfand, who had taken up the post of professor at the University of Salisbury in Southern Rhodesia (now Harare in Zimbabwe), describes how those efforts were confounded by malaria until the development of powerful insecticides in the early twentieth century, such as DDT. But the author's conclusion that "in Central Africa the conquest of malaria is now almost complete" will be regarded now as premature.

IN his inaugural address to the University College of Rhodesia and Nyasaland, Prof. Michael Gelfand took the opportunity to review the part which malaria played in delaying the opening-up of Central Africa to European traders and settlers[1]. His original paper is illustrated with reproductions of some fine contemporary pictures which add to the interest of the text.

The earliest in the field were the Portuguese, who were setting up trading posts along the west coast of Africa as early as 1443. Somewhat later they were establishing footholds along the east coast too, but the "Angel of Death" effectively blocked their penetration into the interior. When quinine became available, the Portuguese took to it more readily than the British and put it to more effective use. Its introduction, although spread over a longer period of time, "had an impact on medicine similar to that of antibiotics today".

The legend that cinchona bark was introduced to Europe by the Countess of Chinchon, wife of the Viceroy of Peru, has been convincingly disproved. What is clear is that Jesuit missionaries were in contact with Indians who were aware of the medical properties of cinchona bark, at Loxa, in Brazil, and in Peru, about the beginning of the seventeenth century. Its first recorded importation into Europe was made by Barnabe de Cobo, after exploring parts of Mexico and Peru in 1632. News of it soon spread from Spain to Italy and the Netherlands, and it was introduced to England by James Thomson of Antwerp in 1650.

In many places its acceptance by doctors was very varied, in part perhaps on religious grounds, but in England, resort to its use was stimulated by some serious epidemics of ague, so that the weekly publication *Mercurius Politicus* could report that, by 1658, the bark was on sale by several London chemists. Its fame was heightened by Robert Talbot, who among many others treated King Charles II and the Dauphin Charles of France. He

疟疾和中部非洲的开放

韦瑟罗尔

编者按

19 世纪，英国政府忙于非洲热带地区的探险，这部分是由于政府废止奴隶贸易的决定。本文是根据南罗得西亚索尔兹伯里（现津巴布韦的哈拉雷）大学教授迈克尔·盖尔芬德的著作编写成的。它描述了 20 世纪初期在开发出强效杀虫剂（如 DTT）前，疟疾是如何给那些进行艰难尝试的人们带来困惑的。但是许多科学家认为，作者得出的“在中部非洲现在基本完成攻克疟疾”的结论还为时过早。

迈克尔·盖尔芬德教授在罗得西亚和尼亚萨兰大学的就职演说中，利用这个机会评述了在中部非洲向欧洲商人和移民开放问题上疟疾所起到的延缓作用[1]。他在原始文章中插入了一些精美的、同时代的复制图片，这增加了人们对文章的兴趣。

最早来到中非的是葡萄牙人，他们早在 1443 年就在非洲西海岸建立了贸易站。随后又在东海岸有了立脚点，但“死神”有效地抑制了他们向内地的扩展。当药物奎宁出现后，葡萄牙人比英国人更容易获得它并将其更加有效地利用。尽管该药的广泛使用经历了较长时间，但它的引进“对医学的影响类似于今天的抗生素”。

已经令人信服地证实秘鲁的钦琼伯爵夫人将金鸡纳树皮引入欧洲这个传说是虚构的。现在清楚的是，大约 17 世纪初期在巴西的洛查和秘鲁的耶稣会传教士与了解金鸡纳树皮药学特性的印第安人已经有往来。1632 年巴纳比·德科沃勘探了墨西哥和秘鲁部分地区后，记录下了该药物首次进入欧洲。这则消息很快从西班牙传到意大利和荷兰，1650 年来自安特卫普的詹姆斯·汤姆森将该药引入英国。

不同地方的医生对该药物的接受程度是不一样的，部分可能是由于宗教原因，但是英国在经历几次严重的疟疾大流行后刺激了该药的使用，因此《英共和联邦政治信息公报》周刊报道，直至 1658 年该药已经在伦敦多家药房销售。罗伯特·塔尔博特用此药治好了查尔斯 II 世国王和法国查尔斯皇太子的病，提高了该药的声誉。

made a fortune out of its secret use. Sydenham was convinced of its efficacy as a medicine, and administered the powdered bark mixed with red wine. As early as 1659 Willis found that the bark relieved acute attacks of ague, although relapses were common; and it was not until 1768 that James Lind observed that, in cases of fever, the drug was most effective if given early in large doses.

In 1745, Claude Touissant de Cagarage attempted to produce an extract of quinine, as did Bernadino Antonio Gomes, of Lisbon, in 1810. Ten years later, Pierre Joseph Pelletier and Joseph Caventou were the first to isolate two of the four alkaloids in the substance. This discovery so stimulated the demand for cinchona bark that exploitation of the forests of Peru, Ecuador and Bolivia was carried to such an extent that fears arose about their exhaustion; the English and the Dutch took up its cultivation, and by 1862 the Dutch had almost established a monopoly in its supply, mainly based on Java.

In comparison with the Portuguese, the British were slow in making attempts to trade with or settle in Central Africa. One of the earliest schemes for settlement was made by William Bolts; it was sponsored by Maria Theresa of Austria. The expedition set out from Leghorn in 1776. It consisted of 152 Europeans, who set up stations along the Masoomo River, in Delagoa Bay, but malaria soon made its presence felt; local Africans rose against the enfeebled party, which was later attacked by the Portuguese, and within three years the entire scheme had collapsed.

These experiences might be taken as representative of a series of disasters which were to follow. About that time some people thought that the Niger joined up with the Nile, others that it had a confluence with the Gambia River. To explore the Niger, the British African Association sent out a Major Houghton, but he, after travelling through the kingdom of Bambouk, was robbed of his possessions and later died. His task was taken over by a Dr. Mungo Park, who left England with two servants in 1795. He reached the Niger in 1796, followed it for 300 miles, and then, emaciated with fever, returned home.

In 1803 Mungo Park led a fresh expedition. This time he asked for a mosquito net and two pairs of trousers for each man. The party left England in 1805; and, after having to contend with malaria, dysentery, incessant rain, swollen rivers and mud, they reached the Niger. There they built a schooner, and sailed down the Niger past Timbuktu, after which the boat capsized and all were drowned. Of the 44 Europeans in the expedition, 35 died of malaria.

An expedition financed by the Navy and led by Captain James Kingston Tuckey set out from England in 1816. The party entered the mouth of the Congo, and some members worked their way up the River as far as Soondy Nsanga, 280 miles from Cape Padron, where, stricken by disease, they had to abandon all hope of progressing farther. Of the 44 Europeans in the party, 18 died of malaria. Dr. McKerrow, a member of the team, gave a good description of the symptoms of malaria. He noticed that the men most seriously affected were those who had visited African villages or slept in the open. As a medicine

他因该药的用途尚不为人所知而大发其财。西德纳姆非常确信其药效并将树皮粉末和红酒混合进行使用。早在1659年威利斯就发现金鸡纳树皮能够缓解急性疟疾的发作，尽管常有复发；直到1768年詹姆斯·林德才发现发热患者早期大量服用该药效果最好。

1745年，克劳德·图森·德卡加拉热尝试制备奎宁粗提物，1810年里斯本的伯纳迪诺·安东尼奥·戈梅斯对此又进行了尝试。10年后，皮埃尔·约瑟夫·佩尔蒂埃和约瑟夫·卡文图从该物质中首次分离出了4种生物碱中的2种。这个发现极大地刺激了对金鸡纳树皮的需求，导致秘鲁、厄瓜多尔和玻利维亚的森林被大量采伐，以致人们开始担心其会因如此采伐而灭绝。于是英国人和荷兰人开始种植金鸡纳树，到1862年荷兰人几乎已经垄断了其供应，主要在爪哇地区。

与葡萄牙人相比，英国人尝试在中部非洲进行贸易或移民要慢一些。最早的移民计划之一由威廉·伯尔茨提出，并由奥地利的玛丽亚·特蕾西亚赞助。探险是1776年从意大利里窝那开始的。此次探险共包含152名欧洲人，他们在德拉瓜湾沿着马苏莫河建立站点，但是疟疾很快就体现出了其危害性。当地的非洲人起来反抗这个乏力的团队,随后又受到葡萄牙人的袭击,但是3年内整个计划还是以失败而告终。

这些经历可能被认为是随后要发生的一系列灾难的代表。那时候有些人认为尼日尔河与尼罗河是连接的，另一些人认为它和冈比亚河相汇合。为了开发尼日尔河，英国非洲协会派出霍顿少校，但是他在穿过邦布王国后遭到抢劫，不久就死亡了。芒戈·帕克医生接管了他的工作，他于1795年带着两名仆人离开英国并于1796年到达尼日尔河，沿河走了300英里后开始发热，最后虚弱地返回了家乡。

1803年芒戈·帕克开始了新的探险。这一次他为每个人准备了一个蚊帐和两条裤子。这个团队于1805年离开英国，在经过和疟疾、痢疾、连夜雨、暴涨的河流和淤泥斗争之后到达了尼日尔河。他们在那里建了一艘帆船并沿着尼日尔河向下经过廷巴克图，后来船倾覆了，所有人都被淹死了。在探险的44名欧洲人中有35人死于疟疾。

1816年一支由海军资助并由詹姆斯·金斯顿·塔基船长带领的探险队从英国出发。这个团队进入刚果河口后，一些成员沿河向上游航行远至松迪恩桑加——一个离帕德隆角280英里的地方，他们在此地遭遇了疾病的袭击从而不得不放弃继续前进的所有希望。团队的44人中有18人死于疟疾。该团队的麦克罗医生详细地描述了疟疾的症状。他注意到最严重的患者是那些到访过非洲农村或露宿过野外的人。

he made some use of cinchona bark, but only as a last resort, and the results were unpromising.

Another expedition, sponsored by the Admiralty, left England in 1822, with the view of exploring the east coast of Africa, Madagascar and parts of Arabia. A small detachment attempted to make its way up the Zambesi, reaching as far as Senna. Of the three Europeans in the group, one had already died, and the other two died on the journey back to their base.

The failure of the Congo expedition, sent out in 1816, intensified the desire to solve the problem of the Niger. In 1822 Hugh Clapperton with two companions set out to cross the desert from Tripoli. They discovered Lake Chad; then Oudney, one of the group, died, leaving Clapperton to struggle as far as Sokoto by way of Kano, whence he was able to return alive.

Clapperton made another attempt in 1825, with five Europeans in the party. From the Bight of Benin, one of the group reached Yaourie before being murdered by his followers. The remainder went on to Jannah, where they were all ill with fever; but against formidable odds, Clapperton reached Katunga, crossed the Niger, and moved on to Kano. Weakened with dysentery and malaria he died at Sokoto, so that, of the Europeans, four died.

At about the same time, a further expedition set out to reach the Niger by way of Tripoli and Timbuktu. It was led by Major Alexander Gordon, who was the first known European to reach Timbuktu, but he was murdered by Arabs soon afterwards. In 1827, a Frenchman, René Caillié, starting from Freetown, reached the Niger and became the second European to see Timbuktu; he succeeded in returning to France alive.

The riddle of the Niger still remained unresolved. To solve it, Richard Lander, who had been a member of Clapperton's expedition, and his brother, John, offered their services to the British Government. They left Portsmouth in 1830, followed Clapperton's route as far as Bussa, and set sail down the Niger with four Negroes as a crew. They reached Eboe, near the Atlantic, but were then captured by Ibu traders and held by different people until finally released, when they found their way to the Atlantic along one of the subsidiary channels of the Niger delta. A boat picked them up and took them to Rio de Janeiro before they could return to England. They had been advised to take two to five grains of quinine every six hours.

Interest in the Niger rose still higher. A company at Liverpool financed an expedition which was led by Richard Lander and had the use of three small steamboats. Special attention was paid to the physique and fitness of the crews. But before the ships reached the Niger, fever began to take its toll. Moving up to Eboe, two of the boats were surrounded by dense vegetation and swamps on either side, and the men were exposed to relentless rain and "torrents of sandflies and mosquitoes".

他使用了一些金鸡纳树皮作为药物，但那只是最后一根救命稻草，而且效果并不理想。

1822 年另一支由海军部赞助的探险队离开英国，目的是开发非洲东海岸、马达加斯加和部分阿拉伯半岛。一部分人试图沿赞比西河而上，直达赛纳河。团队的 3 名欧洲人中，有 1 人先死了，其余 2 人死在返回基地的路上。

始于 1816 年的刚果探险的失败强化了人们解决尼日尔河问题的愿望。1822 年，休·克拉珀顿和两个同伴从的黎波里出发穿越沙漠。他们发现了乍得湖，后来一个队员奥德莱死了，剩下克拉珀顿及另一同伴艰难地经过卡诺到达索科托，并在那里活着返回了家乡。

1825 年，克拉珀顿进行了另一次尝试，团队中有 5 名欧洲人。从贝宁湾开始，到达亚乌雷后一名成员被同伴处死。其余的人继续前进并到了坚奈，在那里所有人都患上了发热的疾病，但是经过痛苦的磨难后，克拉珀顿到达了卡通加并穿过尼日尔河最后转移到卡诺。他由于罹患痢疾和疟疾而身体虚弱，在索科托去世，因此 5 名欧洲人中 4 人死了。

几乎是在同一时间，另一支探险队出发了，经的黎波里和廷巴克图到达尼日尔河。此次探险由亚历山大·戈登少校带领，他是第一个已知的到达廷巴克图的欧洲人，但不久之后就被阿拉伯人谋杀了。1827 年，法国人勒内·卡耶从弗里敦出发到达尼日尔河，并成为第二个看到廷巴克图的欧洲人，他后来成功地回到了法国。

尼日尔河之谜仍然未得到解决。为了揭开其神秘面纱，曾是克拉珀顿探险队成员的理查德·兰德及其弟弟约翰开始为英国政府服务。1830 年他们离开朴次茅斯，沿着克拉珀顿曾航行过的路线远至布萨，和 4 名黑人船员沿着尼日尔河向下航行。他们到达了邻近大西洋的埃博，但是被奴隶贩卖者俘获并在不同的人手中周转，直到他们发现了通向大西洋的尼日尔河三角洲的一条支流后才最终逃脱。他们搭乘一条船并被载至里约热内卢，直到返回英格兰。他们曾被建议每 6 小时服用 2~5 粒奎宁。

人们对尼日尔河更感兴趣了。利物浦的一个公司资助了由理查德·兰德带领并使用 3 艘小型蒸汽船的探险活动。这次探险特别注重了船员的体格和体质。但是船还没有到达尼日尔河，发热就已经开始了。向埃博行进过程中，其中的 2 艘船都有一侧陷入茂密的植被和沼泽中，船员们受到持续的暴雨、“无穷的白蛉和蚊子”的折磨。

Further up stream, one of the boats, the *Quorra*, ran aground and remained stuck fast from November until the following March. At the end of March, MacGregor Laird penetrated up stream as far as Fundah, but got no further, and what had been the supply ship, the *Alburkah*, reached Raba and then turned round. At the end of two years, of the total European complement of the three ships, numbering 82, 64 were dead.

By this time the British Navy was active along the west coast of Africa, attempting to suppress the slave trade. Some indication of the health risks to which the crews were exposed is conveyed by the fact that in 1834, of 792 men serving in seven British ships, 204 died. Nevertheless, in 1841 the British Government and members of the public jointly financed the Great Niger Expedition. Three special ships were built, with the *Wilberforce* joining them later. Each boat had a special system of ventilation: during the night as few men as possible were to remain on deck, and when up river, all the white crew had to sleep below. Special clothing was provided, and dry clothing was to be readily available. The men selected were all robust and in the prime of life.

The ships left Woolwich in 1841, and in August, entered the Niger. On September 4 a virulent attack of fever struck the crew of the *Albert*; soon after, the *Soudan* was sent down stream with all the sick. In October the plan to reach Raba was given up. Sickness and deaths continued so that the British Government decided to recall the expedition. Of a total of 145 Europeans, 42 died—almost all of them of malaria.

In his book on this expedition, M'Williams, surgeon of the *Albert*, reported that the practice of blood-letting, which had been the procedure of first choice for almost all the earlier expeditions, was of no value whatsoever, while quinine given at a late stage and in large doses was of some benefit; but he missed the point, which his own records would have shown, that quinine was more effective if given early. He gave details of eight autopsies in each of which he found the gall bladder distended with bile, "the colour and consistence of tar". The colon was generally empty except for "dark pultaceous matter viscid and tenacious".

By this time it was obvious that Africans were much less susceptible to malaria than Europeans, although these too became more resistant if they lived in the country for long periods. This realization, along with a better appreciation of the value of quinine, marked the turning-point in the opening-up of Central Africa. Quinine had been put to medicinal use in the Navy by Sir William Burnett, although it was not given a fair trial. But Alexander Bryson, who was later to become Director General of the Naval Medical Service, recommended that it should be used as a prophylactic and administered to all members of crews on going ashore and on their return, as well as to those who remained on board in swampy places.

With considerations like these in mind, a new vessel, the *Pleiad*, set sail from Plymouth in 1854, under the command of Mr. Beecroft—later succeeded by Dr. William Blaikie. With 12 Europeans and 53 coloured men on board, it entered the mouth of the Niger

再向上游行进中，其中一艘船“柯拉号”搁浅了，从 11 月到次年 3 月一直停留在那里。3 月末，麦格雷戈·莱尔德逆游而上直达丰达，但是没能走得更远，而供给船“阿尔布加号”到达了拉巴后就返回了。在 2 年探险结束时，3 艘船上 82 名欧洲船员中共有 64 人死亡。

到这个时候英国海军已活跃在非洲的西海岸，试图镇压那里的奴隶交易。1834 年，服务于 7 艘英国船只上的 792 人中有 204 人死亡，这一事实表明了船员所面临的健康风险。尽管这样，1841 年英国政府和市民共同资助了“伟大的尼日尔河探险”。人们建造了 3 艘专门的船，随后“威尔伯福斯”号也参与进来。每艘船上都装有特殊的通气系统，在夜间尽可能少地让人留在甲板上，向上游行驶时所有的白人船员都必须睡在船舱里面。同时船员配备了特别的衣物，而且可以随时得到干衣物。挑选的船员都非常强壮而且正值壮年。

1841 年这些船离开伍力奇，8 月到达尼日尔河。9 月 4 号“艾伯特号”上的船员遭受致命的发热袭击，不久，“苏丹号”载着所有患者沿下游返回。10 月，探险队放弃了抵达拉巴的计划。疾病和死亡还在继续，因此英国政府决定终止这次探险。在总共 145 名欧洲人中，42 人死亡，几乎全部死于疟疾。

“艾伯特号”上的外科医生威廉姆斯在其描述这次探险的书中写道：在几乎所有的早前探险活动中，放血疗法被认为是治疗此病的第一选择，但没有任何效果，而晚期大剂量服用奎宁则有一些效果。但是他忽略了他的记录中本来可以找到的关键点，即如果早期服用奎宁效果会更好。他详细描述了 8 例患者的尸检情况，其中每个患者的胆囊由于胆汁而膨胀，“胆汁类似于柏油的颜色和稠度”；除了“黑色柔软的黏稠物质”外，结肠通常是空的。

到现在很明显的是欧洲人比非洲人更容易患疟疾，尽管有些欧洲人在当地居住长时间后也能变得更有耐受性。意识到这个问题以及正确评价奎宁的价值是中部非洲开放过程中的转折点。虽然奎宁还没有受到公正的评判，但威廉·伯内特先生已将其应用到海军的医疗服务中。后来成为海军医疗服务主管的亚历山大·布赖森建议将奎宁作为预防性药物，并给所有上岸和返回的船员以及沼泽地区的船员服用。

考虑到以上几点，一艘新船“昴星团号”于 1854 年从普利茅斯出发，船长是比克罗夫特先生，后期换成了威廉·布莱基医生。船上共有 12 名欧洲人和 53 名有色

and travelled as far as Tshomo; scurvy broke out among the crew, yet although the Europeans were subject to great fatigue and went ashore in unhealthy places, while some of them slept on deck, none of them died. They took three to four grains of quinine every morning, and sometimes in the afternoon.

At this stage David Livingstone came into the picture. It was through reading M'Williams's account of the Niger expedition that he devised his famous pill, consisting of quinine and purgatives. That was in 1850. With it he first treated an English party and members of his own family. His procedure was to give doses large and early; by means of it he was able to cross Africa from coast to coast. His confidence in the pill was so great that he severed connexion with the London Missionary Society, so that he could operate on a wider scale.

By then a national hero, Livingstone had no difficulty in persuading the Foreign Office to sponsor an expedition to ascend the Zambesi as far as Chobe and plant a mission somewhere near the Batoka plateau. When the party reached Africa the members took two grains of quinine every day. Livingstone doubted if that was enough, but he felt that he could stave off serious attacks of fever by extra doses. Altogether, at first things went fairly well in spite of personal dissensions, and in spite of the fact that with a good deal of malaria about, some individuals became more seriously affected. Livingstone also believed in the therapeutic value of physical exertion.

In April 1859, he discovered the Shire Highlands, and in September, Lake Nyasa. Soon afterwards he heard of the fate of the Helmore-Price expedition to Linyanti—an "unhealthy place". There was no medically trained person in the group, and out of nine Europeans, six lost their lives.

Further experience of malaria, to which Europeans made a varying response, induced Livingstone to abandon the prophylactic use of quinine for a time. He ran into difficulties over the U.M.C.A. Mission at Magomero, and a series of disasters followed, including the death of Bishop Mackenzie, who lost his supply of quinine when a boat capsized. Worse was to follow: Livingstone's wife died of malaria; the Mission at Magomero, which had been moved to Chibisa, had to be closed down, and he was recalled to England.

The two doctors, John Kirk and Charles Meller, now with extensive experience of malaria, realized that the disease was not so simple as Livingstone had imagined. They identified the dysenteric kind called "blackwater fever". Meller distinguished the asthenic and hepatic forms, and experience convinced him of the prophylactic value of quinine, with doses of up to five grains taken daily.

The next steps in the conquest of malaria are more widely known. In 1880, Laveran, a French Army doctor, discovered the cyst-like bodies of the protozoon in the red corpuscles of human blood. This observation was only slowly taken up, but it was confirmed by Marchiafava in 1884; and in 1889, the tertian, quartan and malignant types of the disease were distinguished. Following the discoveries of Manson and Theobald Smith, that insects

人种，船进入了尼日尔河口并一直航行到乔莫。船员中暴发了坏血病，但是尽管这些欧洲人极度疲劳而且在危险的地方登岸，尽管有些人睡在甲板上，但没有一个人死亡。他们每天早上服用 3~4 粒奎宁，有时候下午也服用。

这一时期戴维 · 利文斯通进入了人们的视线。通过阅读威廉姆斯尼日尔河探险的报道后，1850 年他发明了包含奎宁和泻药的著名药片。他首次用该药治疗了一个英国团队及其自己的家人。他的方法是早期大剂量给药，借助于这种方法他能够跨越非洲，从东海岸到达西海岸。他对此药非常有信心，以至于与伦敦传道会建立联系以便更大范围地推广该药。

利文斯通此时已是国家英雄，他成功说服外交部资助一次新的探险，这次航行沿着赞比西河直到乔贝，并在巴托卡高原附近留下了一个代表团。当这个团队到达非洲时每个成员每天服用两粒奎宁。利文斯通不能肯定这个剂量是否足够，但他觉得能用额外的剂量来抵御严重的发热袭击。尽管存在个人纷争，或有些人严重感染疟疾的事实，但事情起初进展得非常顺利。利文斯通也相信体能的治疗价值。

他在 1859 年 4 月和 9 月分别发现希雷高原和尼亚萨湖。不久他听说了赫尔莫–普赖斯到利尼扬蒂沼泽地区——一个“危险的地区”——探险的命运。他们的团队中没有经过医学训练的人，导致 9 名欧洲人中 6 人死亡。

欧洲人对疟疾的更多经历产生了不同的反应促使利文斯通一度放弃将奎宁作为预防性药物使用。他在麦高麦罗的“中非大学传教会”任务中遇到了困难，随后出现了一系列灾难，包括毕肖普 · 麦肯齐因一艘船倾覆得不到奎宁而去世，随后出现了更糟糕的事情：利文斯通的妻子死于疟疾。这样已经转移到奇比萨的麦高麦罗任务不得不终止，而利文斯通也被召回英国。

那时对疟疾有丰富经验的两名医生约翰 · 柯克和查尔斯 · 梅勒意识到，这个疾病并非如利文斯通想象的那样简单。他们发现了一种称为“黑尿热”的痢疾样疾病。梅勒将其区分为虚弱型和肝型，而且经验告诉他日均服用 5 粒奎宁预防效果最好。

攻克疟疾的下一阶段更广为人知。1880 年，法国军医拉韦朗在人类血液的红细胞中发现了疟原虫。这个发现逐渐被人接受并于 1884 年得到了马尔基亚法瓦的证实。1889 年相继发现了该疾病的 3 种类型：间日疟，三日疟和恶性疟。随后，曼森和西奥博尔德 · 史密斯发现昆虫能够作为疾病的载体。英国军医罗斯根据曼森的建议开

can act as vectors of disease, on Manson's suggestion, Ross, a British Army doctor, started work in India, and in 1897 found the oocyst in the outer wall of a mosquito's stomach. He worked out the life-cycle of the avian type of the plasmodium in the following year.

Up to 1914, quinine was the only drug known to be effective against *Plasmodium falciparum*, *P. vivax* and *P. malariae*, but not against the gametocytes. The outbreak of the First World War stimulated the search for other preventatives, particularly in Germany where supplies of quinine might be cut off. An observation by Guttmann and Ehrlich, in 1891, that methylene blue had some action against the plasmodium served as a starting-point for Schulemann, who after a series of trials synthesized plasmoquin in 1925, the first artificial anti-malarial. The discovery of atebrin soon followed. This proved to be a valuable drug for prophylactic use in the Second World War. Still more potent drugs, chloroquine and amodiaquine, were isolated shortly afterwards. These two are excellent, having a complete prophylactic action against almost all forms of malaria, while producing no side-effects. Two further anti-malarials to be discovered were proguanil and pyrimethamine ("Daraprim"), the latter being particularly long-lasting. It was discovered by George Hitching of the Burroughs Wellcome Laboratories.

The conquest of malaria has also been greatly assisted through the use of insecticides, such as pyrethrum, Paris green, benzene hexachloride (BHC) and DDT. In the case of some of these there was long delay between their first discovery and exploitation. BHC, for example, was isolated by Faraday in 1825, yet its insecticidal properties were only discovered in the United States in 1933; and a German chemist, Zeidler, synthesized DDT in 1874, yet its properties as an insecticide were first noticed by Paul Müller in the Geigy Laboratories, in Basle, in 1939. The Second World war did a great deal to stimulate the production and exploitation of these compounds. As an example of insecticidal potency, one might mention BHC, which six months after application on mud walls is capable of killing 80 percent of *Anopheles gambiae*.

Taken together, all these developments have completely transformed the situation in relation to the conquest of malaria. In Nyasaland, for example, as late as 1897, the death rate among European settlers averaged between 9 and 10 percent, mainly from fever, in a young population. In Northern Rhodesia, during 1907-08, the death rate from malaria and blackwater fever combined was 30.4 per 1,000; in 1925, even before the aforementioned developments, it had fallen to 2.8.

Such results can be compared with those associated with the construction of the Kariba Dam, which was started in 1956 and completed by 1960. Not once was work held up or even interrupted because of disease. This huge undertaking involved the importation of enormous numbers of African workers from many parts of the country and the employment of many Europeans who had not previously built up any immunity through exposure to malaria. For health and comfort, the living quarters were placed on high ground. All workers were informed about the dangers of heat stroke, and employers were encouraged to allow their workers a period for acclimatization. A survey of the locality

始在印度工作，于 1897 年在蚊子的胃外壁发现了卵囊。次年，他发现了禽疟原虫的生活周期。

直到 1914 年，奎宁一直是已知的有效治疗恶性疟原虫、间日疟原虫和三日疟原虫的唯一药物，但对配子体的治疗效果不好。第一次世界大战的爆发刺激了对其他预防性药物的开发，尤其是在奎宁供应被切断的德国。1891 年，古特曼和埃尔利希发现亚甲基蓝有抗疟原虫的作用，这成为舒勒曼实验的起点。1925 年，舒勒曼经过一系列试验合成了扑疟喹，该药是第一个人工合成的抗疟药。随后发现了阿的平。第二次世界大战证实该药是非常好的预防性药物。不久以后人们分离出了更强效的药物氯喹和阿莫地喹。这两种药效果非常好，对所有类型的疟原虫都有预防作用而且无副作用。宝来威康实验室的乔治·希青发现了另外两种抗疟药：氯胍和乙胺嘧啶（“达拉匹林”），后者药效尤其持久。

杀虫剂的使用为攻克疟疾做出了一定的贡献，比如除虫菊杀虫剂、巴黎绿、六氯环己烷（六六六）和 DDT。就这些杀虫剂而言，其首次发现和利用之间还有一段间隔。比如 1825 年法拉第分离出六六六，而 1933 年在美国才发现其杀虫特性。1874 年德国化学家蔡德勒合成了 DDT，而在 1939 年巴塞尔嘉基实验室的保罗·米勒首次发现其杀虫特性。第二次世界大战在很大程度上刺激了这些化合物的生产和开发。对于杀虫剂效价的实例，人们可能会想到六六六，该药喷洒到泥墙上 6 个月后能够杀死 80% 的冈比亚按蚊。

总体来说，所有的这些发展已经完全改变了人们攻克疟疾的形势。比如在尼亚萨兰，迟至 1897 年，欧洲青年群体移居者的平均死亡率在 9%~10% 之间，病因主要是发热。在北罗得西亚，1907 年 ~ 1908 年间由疟疾和黑尿热引起的人口死亡率是 30.4‰；但到 1925 年，即使在上述提到的发展出现之前，死亡率就降到了 2.8‰。

这样的结果可以与修建的卡里巴坝有关的结果相比较。该大坝始建于 1956 年，竣工于 1960 年。工程从没有因为疾病而延迟甚至受到干扰过。这个大型工程招募了大量来自非洲各个地区的工人以及许多之前未暴露于疟疾环境中而形成任何免疫力的欧洲人。为了健康和舒适，住房建于高地上。所有工人都被告知了发热疾病的危险，并且提倡雇主们允许工人们有一段环境适应期。对该地区的调查显示原住民和当地

showed a spleen rate of 80 percent, and a parasite rate of more than 30 percent among the original, local community. All the interior walls of dwellings were sprayed with BHC, and this procedure was repeated three times a year.

As a preliminary measure, an attack was made against mosquito breeding-places through spraying with "High Spread Malariol" (Shell). Survey counts showed that the operation was effective, so that there was no need to repeat it later. All workers were required to take the prophylactic drug with which they were provided—at first, 0.4 g of camoquin weekly for the Europeans, and 100 mg of mepacrin for the Africans. Later, daraprim was substituted at the rate of 25 mg each per week.

All windows of the European houses were screened, and this helped to keep away millions of other insects as well as mosquitoes. As a consequence, there was not one death from malaria among Europeans living on the site during the first two years. There were two deaths, however, of men living in temporary camps outside the recognized limits, and nearly all the European cases of fever gave a history of irregular prophylaxis, or fishing or hunting at night beyond the controlled area.

These results show that apart from human factors, in Central Africa the conquest of malaria is now almost complete. They also show that in Africa it is a mistake to think of medicine in terms of individual territories.

(**208**, 1267-1269; 1965)

Reference:
1. Gelfand, M., *Rivers of Death* (Supplement to *The Central African Journal of Medicine*, **11**, No. 8; August, 1965).

人群中脾肿率是 80%，寄生虫感染率超过 30%。住宅的所有内墙壁都喷洒六六六，每年三次。

他们采取了初步的措施，在蚊子滋生的场所喷洒了“高度扩散性的疟蚊杀”（谢尔）。调查数据显示该措施效果非常好，因此以后不必重复。要求所有工人按照他们提供的药量服用预防性药物——最初是欧洲人每周服用 0.4 克卡莫喹，非洲人每周服用 100 毫克米帕林。后来，全部替换成每周服用 25 毫克乙胺嘧啶。

欧洲人住宅的所有窗户都被封闭，这有助于阻挡成数百万的其他昆虫和蚊子。结果在最初的两年内在他们所居住的地方，没有一个欧洲人因为疟疾而死亡。但是，居住于认可范围之外临时住所的人中，有两例死亡；而且几乎所有发热的欧洲人都曾不规律服用预防性药物或者在控制区域之外夜间垂钓或打猎。

这些结果显示除了人为因素，在中部非洲攻克疟疾现在基本完成。这也表明在非洲从单个区域角度考虑医学问题是错误的。

（毛晨晖 翻译；金侠 审稿）

Characterization of Glucose-6-Phosphate Dehydrogenase among Chinese

P. W. K. Wong *et al.*

Editor's Note

Glucose-6-phosphate dehydrogenase (G-6-PD) deficiency is an inherited condition that can cause a particular type of anaemia. This common enzyme defect is found across the globe, and here Paul Wong and colleagues identify three variants of G-6-PD deficiency found in Chinese people. The variants differ in their pattern on an eletrophoretic gel, and in the way they cause anaemia—one patient only developed anaemia after ingesting toxic drugs. Other "triggers" of G-6-PD-related anaemia have since been identified, and it is now known that certain infections, medicines and foods can sometimes cause this anaemia in G-6-PD-deficient people.

VARIATIONS in the physico-chemical characteristics of glucose-6-phosphate dehydrogenase (G-6-PD) have been described both in individuals with normal[1-4] and deficient[5-11] enzyme activity. Recently, Kirkman, McCurdy and Naiman[12] have reported on the characteristics in three unrelated Chinese males with G-6-PD deficiency. They found that the G-6-PD migrated slightly faster than normal G-6-PD but the migration was not quite as fast as that of (A-) G-6-PD observed in Negroes. The enzyme had slightly more thermolability, a bimodal *p*H optimum curve similar to that of the Mediterranean variant, abnormally low *Kms* for G-6-P and TPN and relatively greater utilization of G-6-P analogues.

This communication reports on the character of G-6-PD in a group of normal and deficient Chinese subjects. For these investigations, blood was collected in ACD (formula *A*, U.S.P.) solution. G-6-PD activity was determined by the method of Glock and McHean as modified by Zinkham[13]. Purification of erythrocyte G-6-PD was performed according to the method of Kirkman *et al.*[8]. Starch-gel electrophoresis was performed as described by Shows *et al.*[10].

Starch-gel electrophoresis was performed on haemolysate of 38 normal males and 29 normal females of Chinese origin. Of this group, 36 were Cantonese, 21 were Fukianese, and one each came from Shanghai, Chieking, Shangtung, Hupei and Hunan. The remaining five subjects came from the Chinese mainland, but their place of origin is unknown. All 67 were found to show the single band normally seen in Caucasians.

Detailed investigations were carried out in four normal and four G-6-PD-deficient Chinese

中国人体内的葡萄糖–6–磷酸脱氢酶的特征

黄保罗（音译）等

编者按

葡萄糖–6–磷酸脱氢酶 (G–6–PD) 缺陷是一种遗传疾病，能引起某种特定类型的贫血病。这种常见的酶缺陷在全球广泛存在，本文中黄保罗及其同事们鉴定了在中国人体内发现的 G–6–PD 缺陷的三种变异。这些变异的凝胶电泳模式和导致贫血的方式都不同——一个病人只有在摄入毒性药剂后才会发展为贫血。目前已经鉴别出其他一些能够“引发”与 G–6–PD 有关的贫血因素。并且现在已知某些感染、药品和食品有时能引发 G–6–PD 缺陷人群出现这种贫血。

在酶活性正常 [1-4] 的个体和缺乏 [5-11] 的个体中葡萄糖 –6– 磷酸脱氢酶（G–6–PD）的物理化学性质都存在差异。最近，柯克曼、麦柯迪和奈曼 [12] 报道了三位彼此无关且 G–6–PD 缺陷的中国男性的特征。发现他们的 G–6–PD 比正常的 G–6–PD 迁移得快一些，但是没有黑人体内观察到的 A 型 G–6–PD 迁移得那么快。该酶的热不稳定性略有提高，具有与地中海型变异类似的双峰状最适 pH 曲线，G–6–P（葡萄糖 –6– 磷酸）和 TPN（三磷酸吡啶核苷酸）的米氏常数都异常低，而对 G–6–P 类似物的利用率相对较高。

这篇通讯文章报道了一组酶正常和缺陷的中国人体内的 G–6–PD 的特征。在这些研究中，血液保存在酸性柠檬酸盐葡萄糖（根据《美国药典》中的 *A* 配方）溶液中。用格洛克和麦克希恩提出并经辛克罕 [13] 改进的方法测定 G–6–PD 的活性。依据柯克曼等人 [8] 提出的方法提纯红细胞中的 G–6–PD。用肖 [10] 等人描述的方法进行淀粉凝胶电泳。

对 38 位正常中国男性和 29 位正常中国女性的溶血液进行淀粉凝胶电泳。这些受试者中，36 个是广东人，21 个是福建人，另有 5 人来自上海、山东、湖北和湖南等地，其余 5 位受试者也来自中国大陆但籍贯未知。所有 67 名受试者的电泳结果都只出现了高加索人中常见的单一条带。

另外，对来自中国香港的 4 位正常的和 4 位 G–6–PD 缺陷的受试者进行了仔

subjects from Hong Kong. Patient 1 is a healthy 2-year-old male who has a heamoglobin level of 14-15g percent. The deficiency of G-6-PD was detected only following a haemolytic episode after the use of drugs. Patients 2, 3 and 4 have the typical clinical picture of congenital non-spherocytic haemolytic disease, with persistent reticulocytosis and a haemoglobin level of 6-8 g percent.

Erythrocyte G-6-PD (expressed as units/100 ml. red blood cell) was decreased in all four deficient subjects, ranging from 0 to 15 units as compared with an average value of 228 units in Chinese controls and 210 units in Caucasian controls. Leucocyte G-6-PD (expressed as μM TPN reduced/h/10^6 white blood cell) was also decreased. In patients 1 and 2 the values were 0.35 and 0.61 as compared with 1.05 in Chinese controls and 1.02 in Caucasian controls. Starch-gel electrophoresis performed on purified enzyme showed patients 1, 2 and 3 having a single band which migrated 100 percent (corresponding to that normally seen in Caucasians), while patient 4 showed a single band at 106 percent (corresponding to that usually seen in Pamaquin-sensitive Negro males (Fig. 1)). In all four patients the *Km* for G-6-P was reduced to half the normal values seen in both Chinese and Caucasian controls, but the *Km* for TPN was only slightly reduced in patient 4 and not reduced in the other three. Investigations of *p*H optima were carried out twice on purified enzyme from each patient. Patients 1, 2 and 3 showed a single peak at *p*H 8, while patient 4 showed a bimodal distribution (Fig. 2). Relative thermostability studies were carried out at 41°C and there was no significant difference between the patients and controls. Finally, substrate specificity was tested with G-6-P analogues. There was a slight but definite increase of activity using both galactose-6-phosphate and 2-desoxy-glucose-6-phosphate as substrates. The increase was more marked in patient 4.

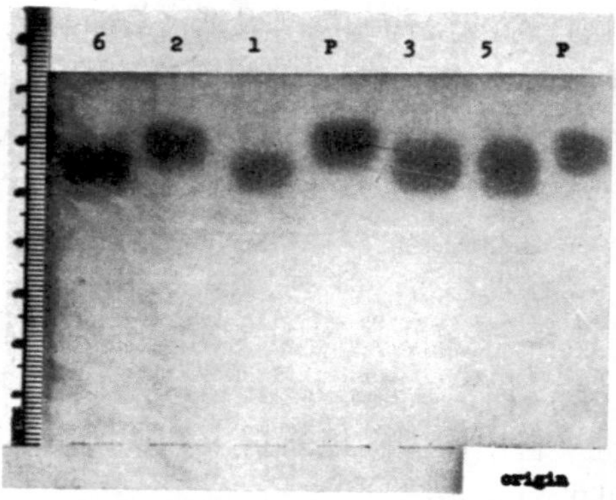

Fig. 1. Vertical starch-gel electrophoresis patterns of red blood cells G-6-PD. Slots 6, 3 and 5 contain preparations from Caucasians. Slots *P* contain preparations from pamaquin-sensitive Negroes. Slot 1 contains preparation from patient No. 3 and slot 2 contains preparation from patient No. 4

细的研究。患者 1 是个健康的 2 岁男孩，其血红蛋白水平为 14 克 /100 毫升 ~15 克 /100 毫升，只是在对他用药后的溶血期才检测到 G–6–PD 缺乏。患者 2、3 和 4 都有先天性非球形红细胞溶血病的典型临床症状，他们患有持续的网状细胞增多症，其血红蛋白水平为 6 克 /100 毫升 ~8 克 /100 毫升。

在所有 4 名酶缺陷的受试者中，红细胞 G–6–PD（以每 100 毫升红细胞中的酶活力单位数表示）都减少了，其值在 0~15 个酶活力单位之间，与之相比，作为对照的中国人的平均含量为 228 单位，作为对照的高加索人的平均值为 210 单位。白细胞 G–6–PD（以每 10^6 个白细胞每小时能使 TPN 降低多少微摩尔来表示）也减少了。在患者 1 和患者 2 中，得到的值分别是 0.35 和 0.61，与之相比，作为对照的中国人的值是 1.05，作为对照的高加索人的值是 1.02。对提纯后的酶进行淀粉凝胶电泳，结果显示，来自患者 1、2 和 3 的酶只有迁移率 100% 的单一条带（和高加索人的正常可见结果一致），而来自患者 4 的酶则只显示出迁移率 106% 的单一条带（和对扑疟喹啉敏感的黑人男性中的常见结果一致（图 1）。在全部 4 位患者中，G–6–P 的米氏常数都降低至对照中国人和对照高加索人中的正常值的一半，但是只在患者 4 中 TPN 的米氏常数略有降低，而在另外 3 位患者中并没有降低。对来自每一位患者的纯化出的酶进行两次最适 pH 的测定。来自患者 1、2 和 3 的纯化出的酶显示出位于 pH 8 单峰，而来自患者 4 的纯化出的酶则显示出双峰式分布（图 2）。相关热稳定性研究在 41℃ 条件下进行，患者组和对照组之间没有显著差异。最后，用 G–6–P 类似物检验底物特异性。在使用半乳糖 –6– 磷酸和 2– 脱氧 – 葡萄糖 –6– 磷酸作为底物时，酶活性都有轻微但明确的升高。对于患者 4，升高得更为明显。

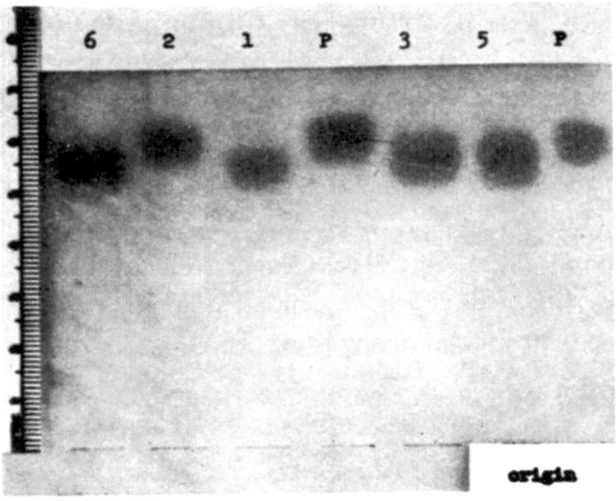

图 1. 红细胞中 G–6–PD 的垂直淀粉凝胶电泳图。6 号、3 号和 5 号上样孔中加入了来自高加索人种受试者的样品，上样孔 *P* 中加入了来自对扑疟喹啉敏感的黑人的样品。1 号上样孔中加入了来自患者 3 的样品，2 号上样孔中加入了来自患者 4 的样品。

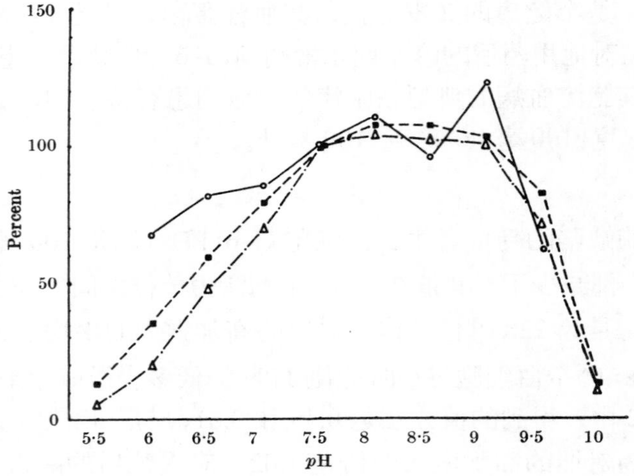

Fig. 2. *p*H Optimum curves for Chinese patients and a Caucasian control. Activity is expressed as percentage of that at *p*H 7.5. ■, Caucasian control; △, patient No. 3; ○, patient No. 4

These results indicate that several variants of G-6-PD exist among Chinese. One variant (patient 4) shows a persistent non-spherocytic haemolytic anaemia associated with G-6-PD deficiency. This variant is characterized by a fast band on electrophoresis, a decrease of *Km* for both G-6-P and TPN, and a bimodal *p*H optimum curve. This corresponds closely to the patients described by Kirkman, McCurdy and Naiman[12]. Another variant (patients 2 and 3) shows a non-spherocytic haemolytic anaemia with a normal electrophoretic pattern and a single *p*H optimum peak at *p*H 8.0. A third variant (patient 1) shows a G-6-PD deficiency without spontaneous haemolytic anaemia, where the haemolytic process can be induced by toxic drug ingestion. Other variants are likely to be found as individuals with normal and deficient enzyme activity are studied more extensively from various parts of China and South-East Asia.

This work was supported by grants from the Chicago Community Trust, the Kettering Foundation and the U.S. Public Health Service (*T*1-*HD*-00036 and *T*1-*AM*-05186).

(**208**, 1323-1324; 1965)

Paul. W. K. Wong, Ling-Yu Shih and David Yi-Yung Hsia: Genetic Clinic, Children's Memorial Hospital, Department of Paediatrics, Northwestern University Medical School, Chicago, Illinois.

Y. C. Tsao: Department of Paediatrics, University of Hong Kong.

References:

1. Boyer, S. H., Porter, I. H., and Weilbacher, R. G., *Proc. U.S. Nat. Acad. Sci.*, **48**, 1868 (1962).

2. Porter, I. H., *et al.*, *Lancet*, i, 895 (1964).

3. Nance, W. E., and Uchida, I., *Amer. J. Human Genet.*, **16**, 380 (1964).

4. Long, W. K., Kirkman, H. N., and Sutton, H. E., *J. Lab. Clin. Med.*, **65**, 81 (1965).

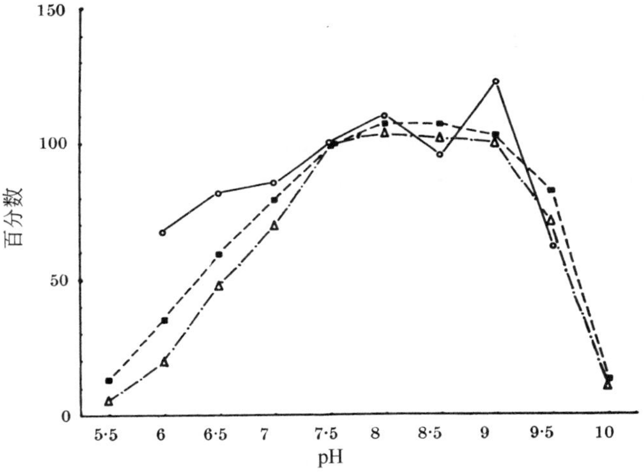

图 2. 来自中国患者和 1 个作为对照的高加索人的酶的最适 pH 曲线。酶活性用占 pH 7.5 时酶活性的百分数来表示。■ 代表作为对照的高加索人；△代表患者 3；○代表患者 4。

这些结果表明在中国人体内存在多种 G–6–PD 变异。其中一种 G–6–PD 变异（患者 4）表现出与 G–6–PD 缺陷相关的持续性非球形细胞溶血性贫血。这种变异的特征是在电泳中出现快速迁移的条带，G–6–P 和 TPN 的米氏常数都降低，而且最适 pH 曲线具有双峰。这与柯克曼、麦柯迪和奈曼 [12] 所描述的患者的情况颇为吻合。另一种变异（患者 2 和 3）也表现出非球形细胞溶血性贫血，具有正常的电泳模式和位于 pH 8.0 处的最适 pH 单峰。第三种变异（患者 1）则表现出 G–6–PD 缺陷，但并没出现自发性溶血性贫血，不过在摄入有毒药剂会诱发溶血过程。对中国和东南亚各地区酶活性正常和缺乏的个体进行广泛研究，有可能还会发现其他的变异。

这项工作受到了芝加哥社区信用社、凯特林基金会和美国公共卫生署（*T*1-*HD*-00036 和 *T*1-*AM*-05186）的资助。

（王耀杨 翻译；崔巍 审稿）

5. Kirkman, H. N., Riley, H. D., and Crowell, B. B., *Proc. U.S. Nat. Acad. Sci.*, **46**, 938 (1960).

6. Marks, P. A., Banks, J., and Gross, R. T., *Nature*, **194**, 454 (1962).

7. Kirkman, H. N., Schettini, F., and Pickard, B. M., *J. Lab. Clin. Med.*, **63**, 726 (1964).

8. Kirkman, H. N., *et al., J. Lab. Clin. Med.*, **63**, 715 (1964).

9. Ramot, B., *et al., J. Lab. Clin. Med.*, **64**, 895 (1964).

10. Shows, jun., T. B., Tashian, R. E., Brewer, G. J., and Deru, R. J., *Science*, **145**, 1056 (1964).

11. Grossman, A., *et al., Paediatrics* (in the press).

12. Kirkman, H. N., McCurdy, P. R., and Naiman, J. L., *Cold Spring Harbor. Symp. Quant. Biol.*, **29**, 391 (1964).

13. Zinkham, W. H., *Paediatrics*, **23**, 18 (1959).

Thymus and the Production of Antibody-Plaque-Forming Cells

J. F. A. P. Miller *et al.*

Editor's Note

From the eighteenth century onwards, physicians recognised that a person infected by a bacterial or viral disease would thereafter be immune (or partially immune) to further infections of the same kind. By the beginning of the twentieth century, the cause of this immunity was found to be the production of antibodies against proteins carried by the bacteria or viruses responsible for the infection. The mechanism by which antibodies are produced was, however, obscure. Much interest centred on the role of the thymus gland, which is intimately connected with blood circulation, but its functions were not understood until the mid-1960s. One difficulty was that the removal of the thymus gland from experimental animals reduced their capacity to resist infection for a period of several months. This paper identified the cause of this delay. J. F. A. P. Miller, the first author of this paper, migrated to Australia soon after its publication and eventually became director of the Walter and Eliza Hall Institute in Melbourne, Victoria.

ALTHOUGH the thymus itself does not play an active part in immune responses[1], its presence is essential for the normal development of immunological faculties. Neonatal thymectomy in many species considerably impairs the capacity of an animal to produce some types of immune responses[2]. Thymectomy in adult life has no immediate effect but, after a period of 6-9 months, reduces the capacity to react to a newly encountered antigen[3]. The possible mechanisms by which the thymus exerts its influence on the immunological system have been discussed elsewhere[4], and it has been concluded that the immunological defects encountered after thymectomy are primary and not secondary to infection or autoimmunity[5]. Evidence is presented here to show that thymectomy practically inhibits the development of the capacity to produce antibody-plaque-forming cells following the injection of sheep erythrocytes. This impairment is evident in clinically healthy suckling baby mice thymectomized at birth.

Mice of the inbred strain *CBA*, F_1 hybrids from crosses between *T*6 and *Ak* mice, and non-inbred Swiss (*SWS*) mice were thymectomized on the day of birth. A sham operation involving thoracotomy, but not removal of the thymus, was performed in litter-mates. The mice were given an intraperitoneal injection of 0.15 ml. of a 5 percent suspension of sheep erythrocytes in saline on the 10th day of life and killed at intervals of 2 days-3 weeks after injection. Cell suspensions were prepared from their spleens and assayed for the number of antibody-plaque-forming cells by plating out the suspension in agar gel containing sheep erythrocytes according to the technique described by Jerne *et al.*[6]. Routine histological investigations were performed on the thymus area in all thymectomized

胸腺与抗体空斑形成细胞的产生

米勒等

编者按

从18世纪开始，医生们就认识到，得过细菌性或者病毒性疾病的人此后再遭遇相同感染时会产生免疫（或部分免疫）。到了20世纪初期，人们发现这种免疫的原因是能够对引起感染的细菌或病毒携带的蛋白产生抗体。但是抗体产生的机制尚不清楚。大家的注意力集中在了与血液循环密切相关的胸腺的作用上，但直到20世纪60年代中期人们才认识到胸腺的功能。研究中遇到的一个难题是，实验动物在切除胸腺几个月后其抗感染能力才会下降。这篇文章确定了免疫力延迟的原因。本文的第一作者米勒在文章发表后不久便移民到澳大利亚，后来成为位于维多利亚州首府墨尔本的沃尔特–伊丽莎·霍尔研究所的主任。

尽管在免疫应答中，胸腺本身并不直接发挥作用[1]，但它的存在对免疫机能的正常发展是必要的。切除许多种系新生动物的胸腺，会极大程度地损害该动物产生某些类型的免疫应答能力[2]。在成年期切除胸腺并不立即产生影响，但是6~9个月后，对遭遇到的新抗原的免疫能力降低[3]。胸腺作用于免疫系统的可能机制在其他文章中已经讨论过了[4]，得出的结论是：胸腺切除后出现的免疫缺陷是原发性的，而不是由感染或自身免疫继发性的[5]。该证据表明，对切除胸腺的个体注射绵羊红细胞，实际上抑制了机体产生抗体空斑形成细胞的能力。对于刚出生就切除了胸腺的健康乳鼠，这种损伤是很明显的。

近交系 *CBA* 小鼠、*T6* 和 *Ak* 小鼠杂交的子一代（F_1）小鼠以及非近交系瑞士（*SWS*）小鼠在出生当日进行胸腺切除术。对同窝出生的小鼠进行开胸但不切除胸腺的假手术。向10日龄小鼠的腹腔内注射0.15毫升含5%绵羊红细胞的生理盐水，在注射后间隔2天~3周处死这些小鼠。根据杰尼等人[6]描述的技术制备动物脾脏的细胞悬液，并将其涂布于含有绵羊红细胞的琼脂凝胶，用来检测抗体空斑形成细胞的数量。对所有胸腺切除小鼠的胸腺区域进行常规组织学检查，以确认胸腺切除是否完全。

mice to ensure that thymectomy had been complete. Mice with thymus remnants were discarded from the experiments.

The spleens of normal or operated mice aged between 1 week and 4 months and not challenged with sheep erythrocytes gave usually less than 1 antibody-plaque-forming cell per million spleen cells. The results obtained in immunized mice are shown in Figs. 1, 2 and 3 and analysed statistically in Table 1. In sham-thymectomized mice, the number of antibody-plaque-forming cells rose sharply from 2 to 3 days after immunization to reach a peak level at 4, 5 or 6 days, depending on the strain. Thereafter, the number fell rapidly to reach a low, yet significant, level at about 10 days after immunization. By contrast, neonatally thymectomized mice produced very few antibody-plaque-forming cells, the assays being made at intervals from 2 days to 3 weeks after challenge. The difference between the mean peak levels of the thymectomized and control group was highly statistically significant for the three strains of mice used (Table1).

Table 1. Antibody Plaque Formation by Spleens and Thymuses of Normal, Sham-operated and Thymectomized Mice

Strain	Treatment given	Cells plated	No. of mice	Age at immunization	Age at death	Antibody-plaque-forming cells per 10^6 cells	
						(Peak) level ± *S.E.*	*P* values
(Ak×T6)F$_1$	Sham-thymectomy at birth	Spleen	8	10 days	14 days	204±27	< 0.001
	Thymectomy at birth	Spleen	10	10 days	14 days	5±2	
CBA	Sham-thymectomy at birth	Spleen	5	10 days	16 days	106±6	< 0.001
	Thymectomy at birth	Spleen	5	10 days	16 days	4±2	
SWS	Sham-thymectomy at birth	Spleen	6	10 days	15 days	276±53	< 0.001
	Thymectomy at birth	Spleen	8	10 days	15 days	15±2	
SWS	None	Spleen	6	56 days*	61 days*	945±82	Not significant
	Thymectomy at 42 days*	Spleen	6	56 days*	61 days*	901±65	
	None	Thymus	6	56 days*	61 days*	6±1	

* Average age.

有胸腺残留的小鼠从实验中剔除。

对于 1 周龄至 4 月龄之间的正常小鼠或切除胸腺的小鼠，如果没有用绵羊红细胞进行免疫处理，其脾脏中每百万个脾细胞通常只产生不足一个抗体空斑形成细胞。经过免疫处理的小鼠获得的结果见图 1、图 2 和图 3，对结果的统计分析见表 1。进行了假胸腺切除手术的小鼠，免疫后 2~3 天抗体空斑形成细胞的数量迅速增加，不同品系的小鼠分别于第 4 天、第 5 天或第 6 天达到峰值。之后，细胞数量急剧下降，大约在免疫后第 10 天降到一个比较低但仍然显著的水平。与此对比，在免疫后间隔 2 天到 3 周的时间内，对切除了胸腺的新生小鼠进行检测，其只产生了很少量的抗体空斑形成细胞。所使用的 3 种品系的小鼠，胸腺切除组与对照组平均峰值上的差别在统计学上极为显著（表 1）。

表1. 正常小鼠进行假胸腺切除术和胸腺切除术后小鼠脾脏与胸腺的抗体空斑形成

品系	给予的处理	涂布的细胞	小鼠数量	免疫时的年龄	死亡时年龄	抗体空斑形成细胞数量/10^6细胞	
						(峰位)均值±标准误差	*P*值
$(Ak \times T6)F_1$	出生日假切除胸腺	脾脏	8	10日	14日	204±27	<0.001
	出生日切除胸腺	脾脏	10	10日	14日	5±2	
CBA	出生日假切除胸腺	脾脏	5	10日	16日	106±6	<0.001
	出生日切除胸腺	脾脏	5	10日	16日	4±2	
SWS	出生日假切除胸腺	脾脏	6	10日	15日	276±53	<0.001
	出生日切除胸腺	脾脏	8	10日	15日	15±2	
SWS	无	脾脏	6	56日*	61日*	945±82	无显著性
	第42日*切除胸腺	脾脏	6	56日*	61日*	901±65	
	无	胸腺	6	56日*	61日*	6±1	

* 平均年龄。

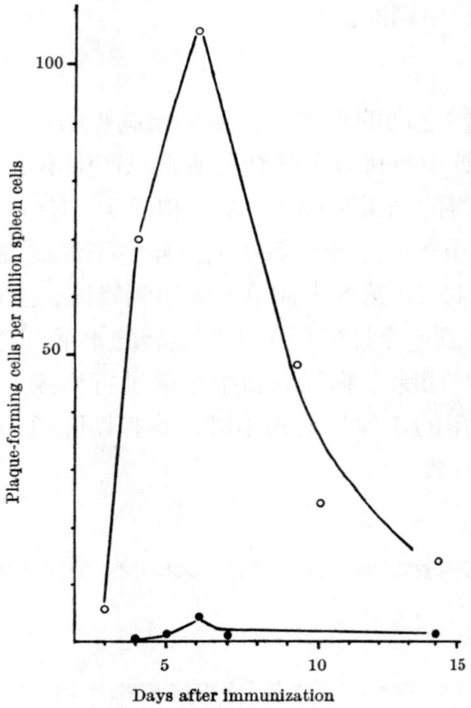

Fig. 1. Number of antibody-plaque-forming cells in spleens of *CBA* mice at various intervals after immunization with sheep erythrocytes given at 10 days of age. Each point represents the average value of assays on 2-5 mice. ○, Mice sham-thymectomized at birth; ●, mice thymectomized at birth

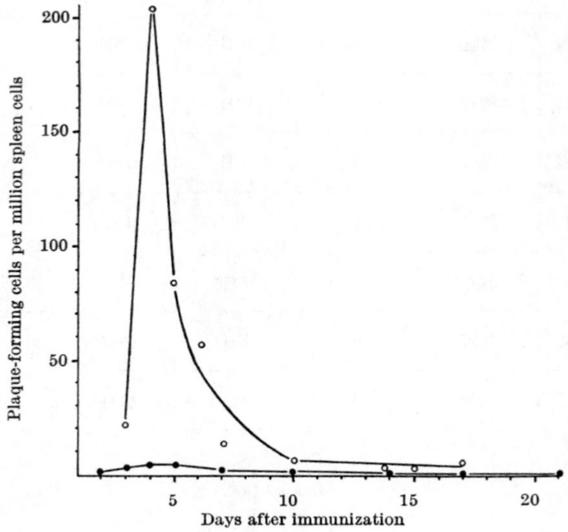

Fig. 2. Number of antibody-plaque-forming cells in spleens of $(Ak \times T6)$ F_1 mice at various intervals after immunization with sheep erythrocytes given at 10 days of age. Each point represents the average value of assays on 2-10 mice. ○, Mice sham-thymectomized at birth; ●, mice thymectomized at birth

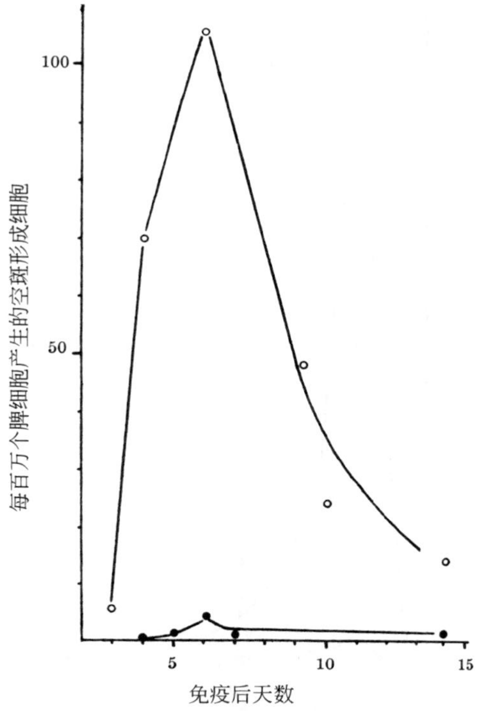

图 1. 10 日龄 *CBA* 小鼠用绵羊红细胞免疫后，脾脏产生的抗体空斑形成细胞数量随时间变化图。每一点代表对 2~5 只小鼠测定的平均值。○代表在出生当日进行假胸腺切除手术的小鼠，●代表在出生当日进行胸腺切除手术的小鼠。

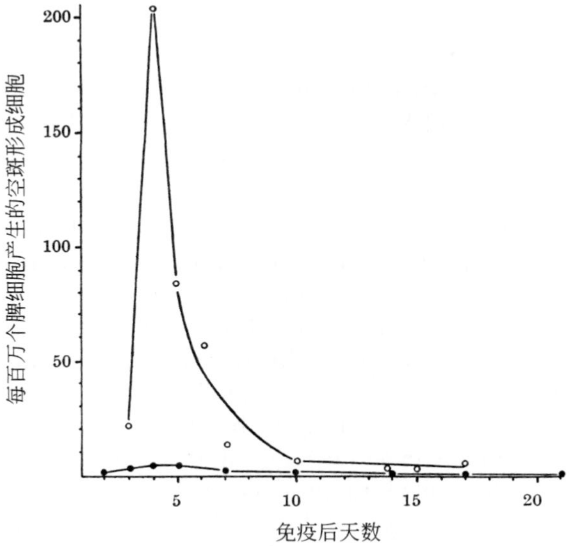

图 2. *Ak* 和 *T6* 小鼠杂交的子一代 10 日龄小鼠用绵羊红细胞免疫后，脾脏产生的抗体空斑形成细胞数量随时间变化图。每一点代表对 2~10 只小鼠测定的平均值。○代表在出生当日进行假胸腺切除手术的小鼠，●代表在出生当日进行胸腺切除手术的小鼠。

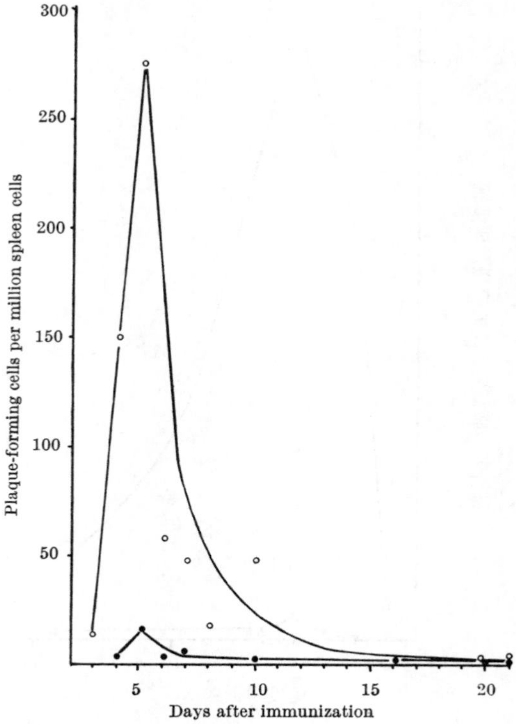

Fig. 3. Number of antibody-plaque-forming cells in spleens of *SWS* mice at various intervals after immunization with sheep erythrocytes given at 10 days of age. Each point represents the average value of assays on 2-8 mice. ○ , Mice sham-thymectomized at birth; ● , mice thymectomized at birth

Thymectomy of 6-weeks-old *SWS* mice did not interfere with their capacity to produce antibody-plaque-forming cells when immunized at about 9 weeks of age (Table 1). In contrast to the spleens of normal *SWS* mice immunized with sheep erythrocytes, very few antibody-plaque-forming cells were present in the thymuses of the same mice (Table 1).

The results demonstrate that, in the absence of the thymus from birth, the capacity to produce antibody-plaque-forming cells in response to an injection of sheep erythrocytes has failed to develop. Very few antibody-plaque-forming cells appeared in the spleens during the first 3 weeks after immunization of neonatally thymectomized mice of two inbred strains and one non-inbred stock. This deficiency is presumably a primary effect of neonatal thymectomy and not secondary to infection or ill-health: it was evident in very early life in suckling baby mice the growth rate of which was identical to that of litter-mate controls. In a similar experiment it has been reported that colony-bred mice thymectomized at birth also failed to produce normal numbers of antibody-plaque-forming cells when challenged at 4 weeks of age[7]. Thymectomy in adult mice, by contrast, had no immediate effect on the response to sheep erythrocytes although a delayed effect was observed as reported elsewhere[3]. The amount of antibody produced per plaque-forming cells was judged to be within normal limits in the thymectomized mice as estimated by the size of the plaques in our experiments and in those of Takeya *et al.*[7].

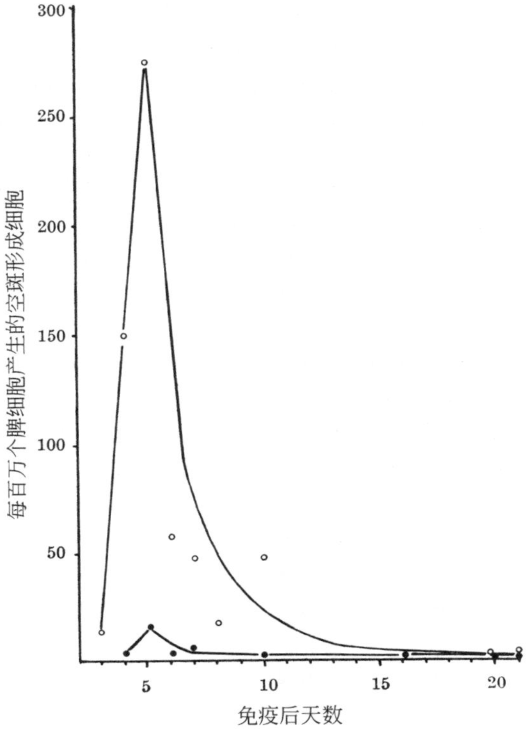

图 3. 10 日龄 *SWS* 小鼠用绵羊红细胞免疫后，脾脏产生的抗体空斑形成细胞数量随时间变化图。每一点代表对 2~8 只小鼠测定的平均值。○代表在出生当日进行假胸腺切除手术的小鼠，●代表在出生当日进行了胸腺切除手术的小鼠。

SWS 小鼠在 6 周龄时切除胸腺，在约 9 周龄时进行免疫，其产生抗体空斑形成细胞的能力并不会受到影响（表 1）。与用绵羊红细胞免疫的正常 *SWS* 小鼠的脾脏相比，相同小鼠的胸腺中只有极少量的抗体空斑形成细胞（表 1）。

研究结果表明，如果出生后就切除胸腺，则不能发展出应答绵羊红细胞而产生抗体空斑形成细胞的能力。切除胸腺的 2 种近交系新生小鼠和 1 种非近交系新生小鼠，在免疫后前 3 周其脾脏中极少有抗体空斑形成细胞产生。这种缺陷可能是新生动物胸腺切除的原发效应，而不是因感染或者健康状况欠佳的继发效应，这在乳鼠生命初期是很明显的，因为切除胸腺的小鼠的生长速度与同窝出生的对照小鼠是相同的。已有类似的实验报道显示：群体繁殖的小鼠若出生时即切除胸腺，在 4 周龄时进行免疫，它们也不能产生正常数量的抗体空斑形成细胞 [7]。与此形成对照的是，小鼠成年后切除胸腺并不立即影响其对绵羊红细胞的应答，但另有报道称观察到了延迟效应 [3]。在我们的实验以及竹谷等人 [7] 的实验中，对于胸腺被切除的小鼠，根据空斑大小估算的每个抗体空斑形成细胞产生抗体的量是在正常范围内的。

It can be seen that the thymus itself produced only very few antibody-plaque-forming cells (Table1) after immunization of adult mice. This observation has also been made in other strains of mice[8]. By contrast, specific antibody-plaque-forming cells have been demonstrated in the thymus of rabbits 5 days after a single systemic injection of 5 μg of somatic polysaccharide of *Salmonella enteritidis*[9]. Since significant numbers of plaque-forming cells have been detected in the peripheral blood in these rabbits[10], and since radical alterations in the structure of the thymus have been reported after administration of endotoxin[11], it is conceivable that circulating antibody-forming cells may have penetrated into the thymus of rabbits immunized with somatic polysaccharide.

In conclusion, it seems that the thymus itself fails to produce significant numbers of antibody-producing cells in response to an antigenic stimulus, but its presence from birth is essential to ensure that such cells will develop in the periphery. Whether the initial development of these cells takes place within the thymus and their final maturation occurs after emigration from the organ cannot be decided on the basis of present evidence. Experiments using thymus tissue enclosed in cell-impenetrable chambers in neonatally thymectomized mice have suggested that a humoral thymus factor plays a part in the maturation of potentially immunologically competent cells[12].

The investigations were supported by grants to the Chester Beatty Research Institute (Institute of Cancer Research, Royal Cancer Hospital) from the Medical Research Council and the British Empire Cancer Campaign for Research, from the Tobacco Manufacturers Standing Committee, and Public Health Service grant *CA*-03188-08 from the National Cancer Institute, U.S. Public Health Service.

Note added in proof. Since this paper was submitted, similar results obtained by Friedman have been published[13].

(**208**, 1332-1334; 1965)

J. F. A. P. Miller, P. M. de Burgh and G. A. Grant : Chester Beatty Research Institute, Institute of Cancer Research, Royal Cancer Hospital, Fulham Road, London, S. W. 3.

References:

1. Fagraeus, A., *Acta Med. Scand.*, **130**, Suppl. 204, 3 (1948). Bjorneboe, M., Gormsen, H., and Lundquist, T., *J. Immunol.*, **55**, 121 (1947). Harris, S., and Harris, T. N., *J. Exp. Med.*, **100**, 269 (1954).
2. Miller, J. F. A. P., *Lancet*, ii, 748 (1961); *Proc. Roy. Soc.*, B, **156**, 415 (1962). Archer, O. K., Pierce, J. C., Papermaster, B. W., and Good, R. A., *Nature*, **195**, 191 (1962). Jankovic, B. D., Waksman, B. H., and Arnason, B. G., *J. Exp. Med.*, **116**, 159 (1962). Sherman, J. D., Adner, M. M., and Dameshek, W., *Blood*, **23**, 375 (1964).
3. Taylor, R. B., *Nature* (following communication). Metcalf, D., *Nature* (following communication). Miller, J. F. A. P., *Nature* (following communication).
4. Miller, J. F. A. P., *Science*, **144**, 1544 (1964); *Brit. Med. Bull.*, **21**, 111 (1965).
5. McIntire, K. R., Sell, S., and Miller, J. F. A. P., *Nature*, **204**, 151 (1964). Miller, J. F. A. P., and Howard, J. G., *J. Reticuloendothelial Soc.*, **1**, 369 (1964).
6. Jerne, N. K., Nordin, A. A., and Henry, C., in *Cell-Bound Antibodies*, edit. by Amos, B., and Koprowski, H., 109 (Wistar Institute Press, Philadelphia, 1963).
7. Takeya, K., Mori, R., and Nomoto, K., *Proc. Jap. Acad.*, **40**, 572 (1964).
8. Friedman, H., *Proc. Soc. Exp. Biol.*, **117**, 526 (1964).

可以看到，成年小鼠在进行免疫后，胸腺本身只产生很少的抗体空斑形成细胞(表 1)。在其他品系的小鼠身上也观察到了这种现象[8]。与此不同的是，用 5 微克肠炎沙门氏菌的菌体多糖对兔子进行单次体内注射，5 天后在兔子胸腺中会出现特异性的抗体空斑形成细胞[9]。因为在这些兔子的外周血中检测到数量显著的抗体空斑形成细胞[10]，且有报道称注射内毒素后胸腺的结构会发生根本改变[11]，因此可以认为，在菌体多糖免疫后的兔子体内，循环的抗体空斑形成细胞可能是渗透到胸腺中的。

总之，看来胸腺本身并不能产生数量显著的抗体形成细胞以应答抗原刺激，但出生后胸腺的存在对于确保外周区域中产生抗体形成细胞是必需的。基于目前的证据，还不能确定这些细胞是否最初在胸腺发育但从胸腺迁移出去之后才最终成熟。有实验将胸腺组织包裹于细胞不能透过的小室中，然后将其植入切除胸腺的新生小鼠体内，结果说明，胸腺体液因子对具有潜在免疫活性的细胞的成熟有一定的作用[12]。

这项研究由医学研究理事会和大英帝国癌症运动组织提供给切斯特·贝蒂研究所（皇家肿瘤医院肿瘤研究所）的基金支持，同时也受到来自烟草制造商常设委员会提供的基金以及美国公共卫生署国家癌症研究所的公共卫生署基金 *CA*-03188-08 的支持。

附加说明 自本文提交后，弗里德曼所得到的类似结果已经发表[13]。

（吴彦 翻译；金侠 审稿）

9. Landy, M., Sanderson, R. P., Bernstein, M. T., and Lerner, E. M., *Science*, **147**, 1591 (1965).

10. Landy, M., Sanderson, R. P., Bernstein, M. T., and Jackson, A. L., *Nature*, **204**, 1320 (1964).

11. Rowlands, D. T., Claman, H. N., and Kind, P. D., *Amer. J. Path.*, **46**, 165 (1965).

12. Osoba, D., and Miller, J. F. A. P., *Nature*, **199**, 653 (1963); *J. Exp. Med.*, **119**, 177 (1964). Osoba, D., *J. Exp. Med.*, **122**, 633 (1965).

13. Friedman, H., *Proc. Soc. Exp. Biol.*, **118**, 1176 (1965).

Decay of Immunological Responsiveness after Thymectomy in Adult Life

R. B. Taylor

Editor's Note

When neonatal mice have their thymus glands removed, lymphoid tissues fail to develop properly and the immune system becomes severely compromised. But in the early 1960s the role of the adult thymus was debated. In the first of three back-to-back papers addressing this issue, R. B. Taylor of the UK Medical Research Council's centre at Mill Hill describes the effects of removing the adult thymus in mice. At first there is little change, but months later a rapid decline in immunological response is seen. Taylor concludes that the adult thymus continues to exert a stimulatory influence on the production of competent cells, but that a low rate of production may still occur after the thymus is removed.

THE remarkable effects of neonatal thymectomy are by now well documented[1]. Primary among these is a failure of the lymphoid tissues to develop properly, which is marked particularly by a deficiency of small lymphocytes. Other features, probably resulting from this, include a defective capacity to perform all kinds of immune responses, and a progressive wasting disease ending in early death.

By contrast, only minimal effects have been found to follow from thymectomy in adult life. In mice, the operation had no effect on growth rate, breeding behaviour, longevity or susceptibility to common infections[2], although blood lymphocyte counts and lymphoid organ weights were somewhat depressed[3]. A wasting disease has been reported in guinea-pigs thymectomized at 150-160 g body-weight[4]. No significant depression of antibody response has been detected after thymectomy of adult rabbits[5,6]. These results have led to the assumptions that once the lymphoid tissues have been formed, the thymus ceases to perform in its developmental role, and that the function of lymphopoiesis is then taken over by the other lymphoid tissues[7]. Yet no distinct morphological change has been described in the thymus on the attainment of immunological maturity, and it continues its high rate of cell production even in adult life. Indeed, it is still necessary for the recovery of immunological responsiveness after this has been depressed by irradiation[8], and thus it must be able to resume its lymphopoietic function, if only in response to a stimulus such as might be provided by destruction of lymphoid tissues. Even without, this stimulus, however, the thymus must play some part in normal turnover of lymphoid cells, since thymectomy in adult life largely prevents recovery from immunological paralysis[9,10]. It therefore seemed probable that the lymphoid tissues might not be able to maintain themselves indefinitely in the absence of the thymus, and that if mice were left for a sufficiently long time after thymectomy in adult life they should eventually show a decline in their primary immune responsiveness.

成年期胸腺切除后免疫应答能力的下降

泰勒

编者按

当新生小鼠的胸腺被移除后，淋巴组织不能正常发育，免疫系统受到严重损害。但是在20世纪60年代早期，成体胸腺的作用尚处于争论之中。在关于这个研究连续发表的三篇论文中的第一篇中，英国医学研究理事会中心（位于米尔山）的泰勒描述了小鼠成年期胸腺移除后的效应。起先，只有一点点变化，但是数月后，其免疫应答迅速下降。泰勒推断成体胸腺会持续地对免疫活性细胞的生成施加影响；但是当移除胸腺后，免疫活性细胞仍以低速率生成。

目前已经详细论述了新生动物胸腺切除的显著影响[1]。其中最主要的影响是淋巴组织不能正常发育，其显著特征是缺乏小淋巴细胞。其他症状可能都是由此引发的，包括各种免疫应答能力的缺陷以及因慢性消耗性疾病而夭折。

与此不同的是，研究发现在成年期切除胸腺后所带来的影响微乎其微。对小鼠进行胸腺切除手术后，尽管血液中淋巴细胞数量和淋巴器官的重量有所降低[3]，但生长速度、繁殖行为、寿命或对普通感染的易感性都没有受到影响[2]。有报道称体重为150 克~160 克的豚鼠在胸腺被切除后会得一种消耗性疾病[4]。成年家兔在切除胸腺后检测到抗体反应没有明显降低[5,6]。根据以上结果产生了这样一种猜想，即一旦淋巴组织形成，胸腺就停止执行它在发育过程中的功能，其他淋巴组织取代其生成淋巴细胞的功能[7]。目前还没有关于胸腺达到免疫成熟后发生明显形态学变化的报道，而且甚至在成年期，胸腺仍然高速率地生成细胞。实际上，辐射引起免疫能力下降[8]后，胸腺对于免疫应答能力的恢复依然是必不可少的，因此只要对类似免疫组织破坏这样的刺激做出应答，那它必须恢复生成淋巴细胞的功能。然而，即使没有这样的刺激，胸腺对于淋巴细胞的正常周转必然也起着某些作用，因为成年期切除胸腺在很大程度上阻碍了机体从免疫麻痹状态的恢复[9,10]。因此，看来在胸腺不存在的情况下淋巴组织也许不能无限期地自我维持，而且如果小鼠在成年期切除胸腺后存活足够长时间，它们最终将出现初次免疫应答能力下降。

In the first experiment the immune responsiveness of *CBA* mice was assessed by the ability of their lymphoid cells to cause a graft-versus-host (GVH) reaction after transfer to young (*C57BL*×*CBA*) F_1 hybrid mice. The strength of the GVH response was estimated by the degree of spleen enlargement in the hosts. The 4-point assay procedure outlined by Simonsen[11] and developed by Michie[12] was then used to relate the spleen enlargement response to the dose of lymphoid cells, so that a quantitative comparison could be made of the immune potency of cell suspensions made from thymectomized and control mice. *CBA* female mice were thymectomized (or sham-operated) at 2-3 months of age. Groups of 8-16 mice were tested by GVH assay at intervals up to one year after thymectomy. In each assay the pooled lymph node (cervical, axillary, brachial, inguinal and mesenteric) and spleen cells of one "test" mouse were compared for immune potency against those from one "control" mouse. At the intervals 4, 9, 25 and 29 weeks the thymectomized mice were compared with sham-operated controls of the same age. By 52 weeks the potency of these controls might be expected to have declined somewhat through age alone[13]; therefore both thymectomized and sham-operated mice were compared with untreated controls aged 4-6 months. To obtain a measure of the overall responsiveness of the whole "test" animal as a percentage of the control, each value for the relative potency of a cell suspension was multiplied by the fraction: total number of lymphoid cells obtained from the "test" mouse/total number of lymphoid cells obtained from the "control" mouse.

The results of the assays are shown in Fig. 1. The responsiveness of the thymectomized mice remained level with controls for about 25 weeks, then dropped fairly sharply, and thereafter remained about 15 percent of normal. This fall in responsiveness was due mainly to a fall in the immune potency of the cell suspensions, but also to a fall in the numbers of cells recovered. The responsiveness of sham-operated mice fell only slightly, and at 52 weeks after operation was still about 75 percent of the 4-6-month-old controls.

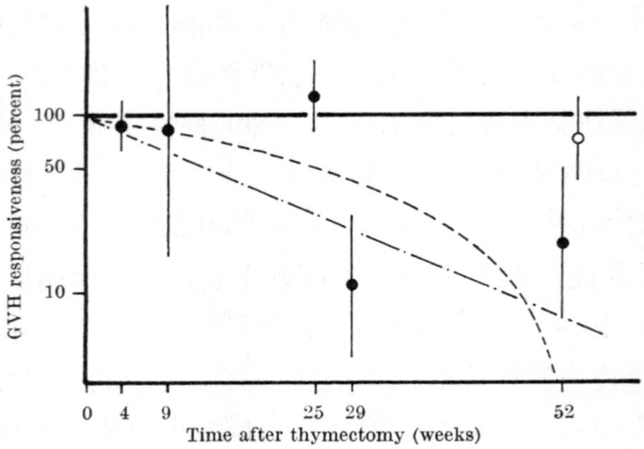

Fig. 1. Results of GVH assays. Each point represents the mean and standard deviation of the responsiveness of thymectomized relative to control mice (computed on log-transformed data). ●, Thymectomized versus sham-operated controls of the same age (4-29 weeks groups) or versus 4-6 month untreated mice (52-week group); ○, sham-operated (14 months old) versus 4-6 month untreated mice. $P<0.01$ for difference between 25 and 29 week groups; $P<0.001$ for difference between thymectomized and sham-operated groups at 52 weeks. Hypothetical linear (– – –) and exponential (– · –) decay curves are shown

在第一个实验中，将 *CBA* 小鼠的淋巴细胞转移到年幼的（*C57BL*×*CBA*）F_1 杂交小鼠体内后，通过引起移植物抗宿主（GVH）反应的能力来评定 *CBA* 小鼠的免疫应答能力。GVH 反应的强度通过宿主脾脏增大的程度来衡量。由西蒙森[11]提出、并经米基[12]改进的 4 点测定法被用来分析脾脏增大与淋巴细胞量之间的关系，由此能够定量比较从胸腺切除小鼠与对照小鼠制备的细胞悬液的免疫效力。*CBA* 雌性小鼠在 2~3 月龄进行胸腺切除（或假手术操作）。8~16 只小鼠一组，在胸腺切除后 1 年内，每隔一段时间用 GVH 分析法进行检测。在每次分析中，比较“测试组”小鼠与“对照组”小鼠的淋巴结（颈部的、腋下的、臂的、腹股沟的和肠系膜的）和脾细胞的免疫效力。在 4 周、9 周、25 周和 29 周时将胸腺切除小鼠与同龄的假手术对照组小鼠进行比较。到 52 周时，对照组小鼠的免疫效力可能单纯因年龄因素会稍有下降[13]，因此胸腺切除组小鼠和假手术对照组小鼠都与 4~6 月龄未经处理的对照组小鼠进行比较。为获得所有“测试”动物整体的应答能力相对于对照动物的百分比，每一组细胞悬液相对免疫效力的值都要乘以如下分数：从“测试组”小鼠获得的淋巴细胞总量 / 从“对照组”小鼠获得的淋巴细胞总量。

分析结果如图 1 所示，在大约 25 周内胸腺切除小鼠的免疫应答能力保持在与对照组小鼠一样的水平上，之后应答能力则急剧下降，然后会维持在对照组的 15%左右。这一免疫应答能力的降低主要是由于细胞悬液免疫效力的降低，但也与恢复的细胞数量下降有关。假手术组小鼠的应答能力只是稍微降低，在手术后 52 周时应答能力仍然是 4~6 月龄对照组小鼠的 75%左右。

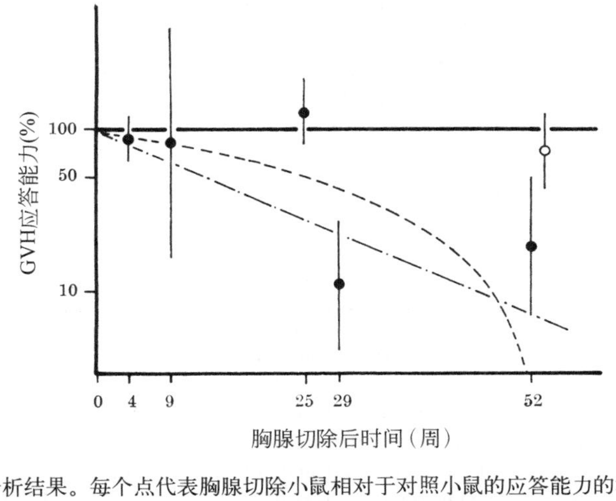

图 1. GVH 分析结果。每个点代表胸腺切除小鼠相对于对照小鼠的应答能力的均值和标准差（数据进行对数变换后再计算）。●代表胸腺切除组与同龄（4~29 周组实验）的假手术对照组或与 4~6 月龄未处理小鼠（52 周组实验）的比较；○代表假手术组（14 月龄）与 4~6 月龄未处理小鼠的比较。25 周组与 29 周组之间有差别 $P<0.01$；52 周时胸腺切除组与假手术组有差别 $P<0.001$。（– – –）显示假设的线性衰减曲线，（– · –）显示假设的指数衰减曲线。

In another experiment immune responsiveness was tested by the ability to produce circulating antibody to bovine serum albumin (BSA). The results have been collated from four experiments which were set up with other primary objects in mind. *CBA* mice of both sexes were thymectomized or sham-operated either at 4 weeks or at 10-14 weeks of age. They were challenged at intervals thereafter by subcutaneous injection of BSA in Freund's adjuvant, and the serum antibody titres estimated 20 and 40 days later by a modification[14] of Farr's antigen-binding-capacity method[15]. Since the absolute titres varied from one experiment to another, the titres from thymectomized mice have been presented as a percentage of the controls in each group (Fig. 2). The decay of responsiveness was less obvious than it was in the GVH experiment, but cell-transfer experiments indicate that a small difference in anti-BSA titre can reflect a larger difference in the number of competent cells[16]. However, the general pattern was similar in that the decline did not reach its most rapid phase for a considerable time after thymectomy. (The apparent initial fall which can be seen in the mice thymectomized at 4 weeks old reflects an increase in the responsiveness of controls, due to normal growth processes, rather than a decrease in the thymectomized mice.) This rapid phase can be seen at about 10 weeks after thymectomy in the mice thymectomized at 4 weeks old. In those thymectomized at 10-14 weeks old the time varied: in one experiment the responsiveness was still normal at 16 weeks, but in another it had already reached its lower level by 12 weeks after thymectomy (indicated by asterisk) and showed no further fall at 32 weeks. An effect of thymectomy was also seen in the general condition of the mice. While not amounting to a serious wasting disease, it appeared as a distinct ruffled condition of the fur, most obvious on the underside, and was associated with a slight loss of weight.

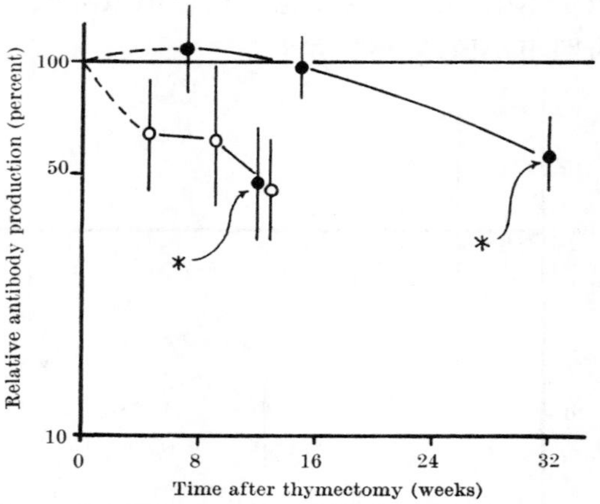

Fig. 2. Results of antibody titrations. Each point represents the mean antibody titre in thymectomized mice as a percentage of that in controls, with standard deviation (computed on log-transformed data). Results from 20 and 40 day bleedings have been combined. Symbols represent four separate experiments: ○, thymectomized at 4 weeks old; ●, thymectomized at 10-14 weeks old. * See text

It may be concluded that even in the adult the thymus has a part to play in the maintenance of the numbers of competent cells in the body. If the effect of thymectomy

在另一个实验中，用牛血清白蛋白（BSA）产生循环抗体的能力来衡量免疫应答能力。结果由原计划用于其他目的的四个实验整理而来。对两种性别的 *CBA* 小鼠在 4 周龄或 10~14 周龄时切除胸腺或进行假手术处理。之后每隔一段时间皮下注射混悬于弗氏佐剂的 BSA，20 天和 40 天后用改良 [14] 的法尔氏抗原结合能力法 [15] 测定血清抗体的滴度。由于各组实验间绝对滴度的变化太大，因此我们把每组中胸腺切除小鼠的滴度表示成相对于对照组小鼠的百分比（图 2）。应答能力的下降不如在 GVH 实验中那么明显，但是细胞转移实验显示抗 BSA 滴度的微小变化能够反映出免疫活性细胞数量更大的变化 [16]。但是，基本的模式是类似的，在胸腺切除后相当长时间内应答能力的衰减并没有达到其最快速阶段。（4 周龄切除胸腺的小鼠初期应答能力明显降低是因为对照组小鼠由于在正常生长过程中应答能力的增加，而不是因为胸腺切除小鼠的应答能力降低。）4 周龄切除胸腺的小鼠会在胸腺切除约 10 周后进入快速衰减阶段。而那些 10~14 周龄切除胸腺小鼠的应答能力明显衰减的时间则是不一致的：在一次实验中，应答能力直到 16 周还是正常的，但在另一次实验中胸腺切除后 12 周应答能力就降到较低水平（星号所示），直到 32 周才没有再降低。从小鼠的总体情况也可以看到胸腺切除的影响。尽管小鼠没有发生严重的消耗性疾病，但皮肤明显褶皱，特别是下侧皮肤褶皱最明显，这与体重稍微降低有关。

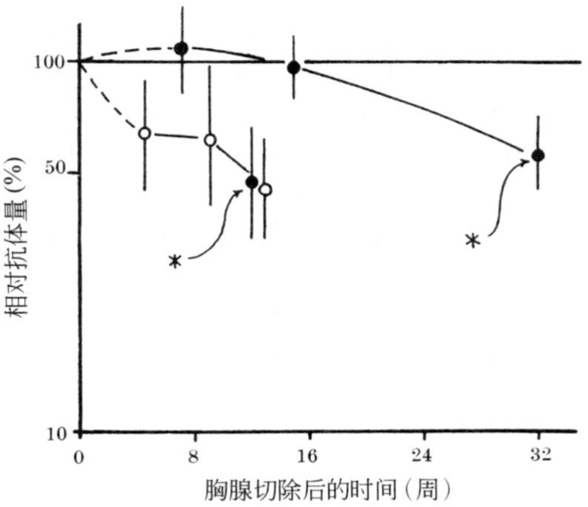

图 2. 抗体滴定的结果。每个点代表胸腺切除小鼠滴度的均值（以占对照组小鼠滴度的百分比来表示）和标准差（数据进行对数转换后再计算）。20 天和 40 天取血的结果已经合并。符号代表了 4 个独立的实验：○代表 4 周龄时切除胸腺；●代表 10~14 周龄时切除胸腺。
* 见正文内容

我们可以得出以下结论：甚至在成体内，胸腺对于维持机体内活性细胞的数量也起着一定的作用。如果胸腺切除能够完全断绝新的活性细胞的供给，那

was to cut off entirely the supply of new competent cells, then the ensuing decay of responsiveness should reflect the rate of loss of the competent cells originally present. According to two simple hypotheses their numbers might be expected to decay in linear fashion of they had a definite life-span, or exponentially if their life depended on chance events—such as encounter with antigens. Support for the latter possibility may be drawn from investigations of irradiated human patients[17] in whom certain of the circulating lymphocytes were distinguishable by the presence of acentric chromosome fragments, which could be seen after stimulation of mitosis *in vitro* with phytohaemagglutinin. During division these fragments fail to become attached to the mitotic spindle, and thus are not transmitted to the daughter cells. The half-time between irradiation and either division or death of the cells was 366 days.

In the present experiments, however, the decay curve of immune responsiveness after thymectomy did not readily fit with either expectation (Fig. 1). In particular, although the responsiveness fell to a sub-normal level, it appeared to attain equilibrium by about 7 months after thymectomy, and showed no further decline towards the levels seen after neonatal thymectomy or irradiation. The same was shown by at least one of the BSA experiments (Fig. 2, asterisk). This suggests either that there is a distinct population of cells with a very long life, or that the production of competent cells can continue at a sub-normal rate in the absence of the thymus. In view of the much more severe and permanent depression of responsiveness which can be obtained after neonatal thymectomy, or adult thymectomy followed by irradiation, this latter process would presumable take place only in mature, unirradiated lymphoid tissue.

Although the early part of the curve approximates the linear, rather than the exponential mode of decay, it might still be consistent with an exponential loss of cells if these were being replaced by differentiation from some other cell type. This could be an intermediate form which had already undergone the thymus-dependent phase in its maturation. The eventual exhaustion of such cells could then account for the more rapid fall between 25 and 29 weeks. In conclusion, it is suggested that the thymus continues in adult life to exert a stimulatory influence on the production of competent cells, but that a low rate of production may still occur after thymectomy. It will be of interest to see if this residual responsiveness differs qualitatively from the major fraction, which decays more rapidly after thymectomy.

(**208**, 1334-1335; 1965)

R. B. Taylor: Division of Experimental Biology, National Institute for Medical Research, Mill Hill, London, N. W. 7.

References:

1. Good, R. A., and Gabrielsen, A. E., edit. by, *The Thymus in Immunobiology* (Harper and Row, New York, 1964).

2. Miller, J. F. A. P., *Adv. Cancer Res.*, 6, 291 (1961).

3. Metcalf, D., *Brit. J. Haematol.*, 6, 324 (1960).

么随后发生的应答能力下降应该反映了最初存在的活性细胞的损失速度。根据两种简单的假说，如果这些细胞有一定的寿命，那么可以预料它们的数量会以线性形式减少，而如果它们的寿命取决于类似遭遇抗原这样的偶发事件，那么其数量会以指数形式减少。对后一种可能性的支持来源于对受辐射的人类患者的研究[17]，这些患者体内的某些循环淋巴细胞因存在无着丝点染色体碎片而容易辨识，在体外用植物凝血素刺激诱发有丝分裂后可以看到这些碎片。在分裂过程中，这些碎片不能附着在有丝分裂纺锤体上，因而不能转入子细胞。细胞从受到辐射到分裂或死亡的半衰期是 366 天。

然而，在该实验中，胸腺切除后免疫应答能力的衰减曲线并不能与任何一种预期很好地吻合（图 1)。特别是，尽管应答能力降到了低于正常的水平，但似乎在胸腺切除约 7 个月后又达到了平衡，并不继续下降到出生即切除胸腺或受辐射中出现的水平。BSA 实验中至少有一次也显示了相同情况（图 2 中星号所示)。这表明，要么存在一群非常长寿的细胞，要么在胸腺不存在的情况下活性细胞能以低于正常水平的速率继续产生。考虑到在出生即切除胸腺或成年切除胸腺后受辐射的情况中观察到更为严重和持久的应答能力下降，后一种情况大概只在成年期未受辐射的淋巴组织中发生。

尽管曲线的开始部分是近似线性而非指数模式的衰减，但如果这些细胞被某些其他细胞类型的分化替换它仍可能符合细胞指数下降。这可能是在其成熟过程中已经经历过胸腺依赖性阶段的一种中间态形式。这些细胞的最终耗竭可以解释在 25~29 周时更为急剧的下降。总之，可以认为成体胸腺会持续地对免疫活性细胞的生成施加影响，但是切除胸腺后，免疫活性细胞仍以低速率生成。比较一下这些残留的应答能力和胸腺切除后更加迅速下降的主要应答能力在性质上是否不同应该是很有趣的。

（吴彦 翻译；陈新文 陈继征 审稿）

4. Comsa, C., *Acta Endocr. (Kbh.)*, **26**, 261 (1957).
5. Harris, T. N., Rhoads, J., and Stokes, J., *J. Immunol.*, **58**, 27 (1948).
6. Maclean, L. D., Zak, S. J., Varco, R. L., and Good, R. A., *Transpl. Bull.*, **4**, 21 (1957).
7. Leading article, *Brit. Med. J.*, ii, 840 (1962).
8. Miller, J. F. A. P., *Nature*, **195**, 1318 (1962).
9. Claman, H. N., and Talmage, D. W., *Science*, **141**, 1193 (1963).
10. Taylor, R. B., *Immunology*, 7, 595 (1964).
11. Simonsen, M., *Prog. Allergy*, **6**, 349 (1962).
12. Michie, D. (personal communication).
13. Makinodan, T., and Peterson, W. J., *Proc. U.S. Nat. Acad, Sci.*, **48**, 234 (1962).
14. Mitchison, N. A., *Proc. Roy. Soc.*, B, **161**, 275 (1964).
15. Farr, R. S., *J. Infect. Dis.*, **109**, 239 (1958).
16. Taylor, R. B. (unpublished observations).
17. Norman, A., Sasaki, M. S., Ottoman, R. E., and Fingerhut, A. H., *Science*, **147**, 745 (1965).

Delayed Effect of Thymectomy in Adult Life on Immunological Competence

D. Metcalf

Editor's Note

In the early 1960s a flurry of research papers attempted to elucidate the function of the adult thymus. It was well known that neonatal thymectomy (thymus removal) triggers rapid atrophy of the lymphoid organs, and Australian physiologist Donald Metcalf had previously shown that adult thymectomy essentially slowed this process. Here Metcalf shows that the effects of adult mouse thymectomy are apparent in around half the animals at about 18 months, suggesting that the adult thymus has a continuing influence on the immunological response. His is the second of three *Nature* papers, published back-to-back, to arrive at similar conclusions. Today it is accepted that the thymus plays a functional, albeit diminished role, in adulthood.

NEONATAL thymectomy leads to the rapid development of lymphoid organ atrophy and well-characterized immunological deficiencies[1-3], but thymectomy performed in adult life leads only to the slow development of a moderate degree of lymphoid atrophy[4] with no loss of immunological competence when the animals are tested immediately after operation[5,6]. However, adult thymectomy combined with whole-body irradiation does lead to immunological deficiencies of the same general nature as those following neonatal thymectomy[7]. Recent investigations have shown that continuous repopulation of normal haemopoietic organs occurs in normal life[8,9]. This suggests that whole-body irradiation by causing cell damage and repopulation in haemopoietic organs may merely accelerate a process which occurs continually throughout life, albeit at a much slower rate. These considerations prompted a re-examination of the long-term effects of adult thymectomy on immunological competence.

Six-week-old mice of the long-lived $(AKR \times C57BL)F_1$ strain were thymectomized or sham-operated and challenged 1 week, 11 months or 18 months after operation with intraperitoneal sheep red cells.

Haemagglutinin titres in mice challenged immediately after thymectomy did not differ from those in control mice (Table 1). However, in mice tested 11 months after thymectomy, some lower titres were found, particularly in the early (19*S*) phase of the response (Fig. 1). In mice tested 18 months after operation, approximately half the thymectomized mice produced no detectable haemagglutinins (Table 1), the remainder producing titres within the control range. The titres in the thymectomized mice challenged 18 months after operation corresponded almost exactly with those observed by Miller[7] in young adult mice subjected to thymectomy and 350-r. whole-body irradiation. The spleen is the major

成体胸腺切除对免疫功能的延迟性影响

梅特卡夫

编者按

在 20 世纪 60 年代早期，一系列研究论文试图阐明成体胸腺的功能。众所周知，新生动物胸腺切除（胸腺移除）能引起淋巴器官迅速萎缩，并且澳大利亚生理学家唐纳德·梅特卡夫先前曾指出，成体胸腺切除本质上会减慢淋巴器官萎缩的过程。在本文中，梅特卡夫指出：大约一半的成年小鼠在摘除胸腺后 18 个月出现了明显的淋巴器官萎缩现象,这意味着成体胸腺对免疫反应具有持续的影响。本文是连续在《自然》杂志上发表的能得出类似结论的三篇文章中的第二篇。现在，人们认为胸腺在成年期发挥功能性作用，尽管其作用减小。

新生动物胸腺切除将导致淋巴器官的快速萎缩和明显的免疫缺陷[1-3]，但是当胸腺切除后立即检测动物则会发现成体胸腺切除只引起缓慢的淋巴样中度萎缩[4]，而免疫功能并没有丧失[5,6]。但是，将成体胸腺切除并进行全身辐射，那么成体也会出现像新生动物胸腺切除后那样的免疫缺陷[7]。最近的研究显示，正常个体中常规的造血器官可以持续再生[8,9]。这就提示我们，全身辐射造成造血器官的细胞损伤和再生，可能仅仅是加快了个体中持续发生着的某个过程，虽然是以很慢的速度进行的。这些考虑促使我们重新研究成体胸腺切除对免疫功能的长期影响。

将 6 周龄的长寿命的（$AKR \times C57BL)F_1$ 系小鼠进行胸腺切除术或假手术。手术 1 周、11 个月或 18 个月后，用腹腔注射的绵羊红细胞进行刺激。

胸腺切除后立即进行刺激的小鼠的血凝素滴度与对照组小鼠的血凝素滴度没有区别（表 1）。但是，胸腺切除 11 个月后再对小鼠进行检测就会发现血凝素滴度有所降低，特别是在反应的早期（19*S*）（图 1）。而在手术 18 个月后进行检测时发现，胸腺切除的小鼠约有一半不能产生可检测的血凝反应（表 1），其余小鼠的血凝素滴度则在对照组范围之内。胸腺切除 18 个月后接受刺激的小鼠的血凝素滴度，几乎与米勒[7]在实验中发现的进行了胸腺切除并接受 350 伦琴全身辐射的年轻成年小鼠的

source of haemagglutinin-production (Metcalf, unpublished results) and in the immunized thymectomized mice challenged 18 months after operation, a general disorganization of the structure of the spleen lymphoid nodules was observed with an obvious decrease in the numbers of germinal centres and small lymphocytes and a diminished number of pyroninophilic mitotic cells.

Table 1. Primary Haemagglutinin Response of *(AKR×C57BL)F*$_1$ Mice to Sheep Red Blood Cells

Type of mouse	No. of animals	Haemagglutinin titres (log_2)											
		0	1	2	3	4	5	6	7	8	9	10	11
Normal 2 months old. No antigen	14	12		1			1						
Normal 18-20 months old. No antigen	18	18											
Thymectomy + antigen. 1 week after operation	13									5	7	1	
Sham-thymectomy+antigen. 1 week after operation	14									5	6	3	
Thymectomy + antigen. 11 months after operation	23			1		3	2	6	10	1			
Sham-thymectomy + antigen. 11 months after operation	31							1	13	13	3		1
Thymectomy + antigen. 18 months after operation	13	6	1				2			2	2		
Sham-thymectomy + antigen. 18 months after operation	48				4	4	4	7	11	12	3	2	1

Immunizing does: 0.2 ml. of 20 percent R.B.C. i.p. Sera titrated on day 10 following immunization.

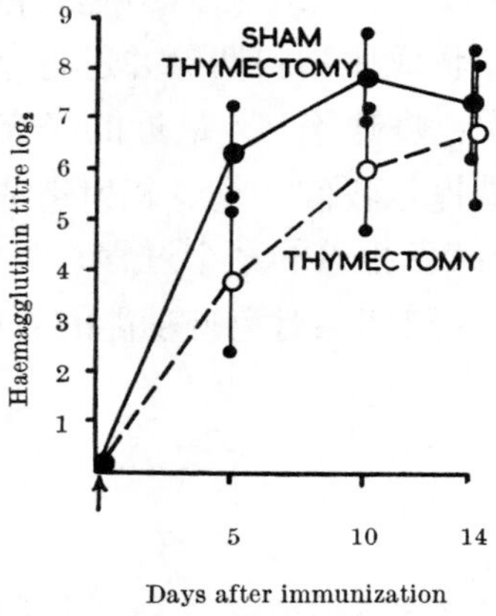

Fig. 1. Haemagglutinin titres in *(AKR×C57BL) F*$_1$ mice tested 11 months after thymectomy or sham-operation at six weeks of age. No. of mice: thymectomy 23, sham-thymectomy 31. Bars represent standard deviations

The observations recorded here suggest that simple thymectomy performed on adult mice does lead to demonstrable immunological deficiencies in at least some mice, provided sufficient time is allowed to elapse before the animals are tested. The present results are only preliminary and need confirmation with other mouse strains and other antigens. The irregular nature of the loss of immunological competence in individual mice following thymectomy, suggests a deletion or loss of responsiveness in some mice of clones of cells

血凝素滴度完全符合。脾脏是产生血凝反应的主要来源（梅特卡夫未发表的实验结果），而在胸腺切除 18 个月后被刺激的免疫小鼠中，可以观察到脾脏淋巴小结结构普遍被破坏了，同时还伴随生发中心与小淋巴细胞数量的明显下降以及嗜派洛宁有丝分裂细胞的减少。

表 1. $(AKR \times C57BL)F_1$ 小鼠对绵羊红细胞的初次血凝反应

小鼠类型	动物数量	血凝素滴度（$\log_2$）											
		0	1	2	3	4	5	6	7	8	9	10	11
正常 2 月龄，无抗原	14	12		1			1						
正常 18~20 月龄，无抗原	18	18											
胸腺切除 + 手术 1 周后抗原刺激	13									5	7	1	
假胸腺切除 + 手术 1 周后抗原刺激	14									5	6	3	
胸腺切除 + 手术 11 个月后抗原刺激	23			1		3	2	6	10	1			
假胸腺切除 + 手术 11 个月后抗原刺激	31							1	13	13	3		1
胸腺切除 + 手术 18 个月后抗原刺激	13	6	1				2			2	2		
假胸腺切除 + 手术 18 个月后抗原刺激	48				4	4	4	7	11	12	3	2	1

免疫剂量：腹腔注射 0.2 毫升 20% 的红细胞。免疫 10 天后对血清进行滴定检测。

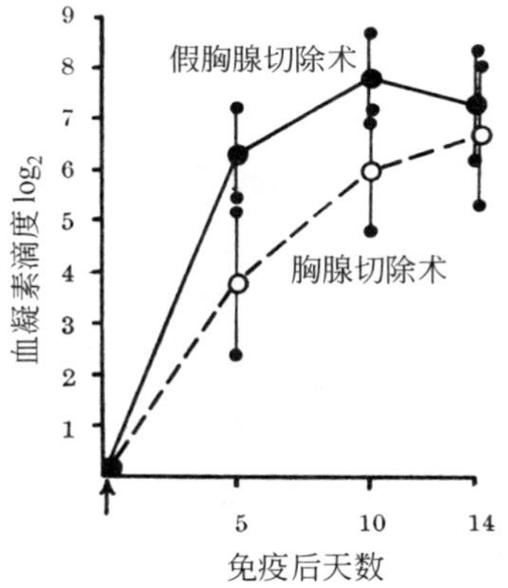

图 1. 6 周龄（$AKR \times C57BL$）F_1 系小鼠进行胸腺切除术或假胸腺切除术 11 个月后检测的血凝素滴度。受试小鼠数量：进行胸腺切除术的有 23 只，进行假胸腺切除术的有 31 只。图中竖线代表标准差。

本文中记录的观测结果表明，如果在经过足够长的时间后才进行检测，那么即便是只对成体小鼠胸腺进行切除，也至少有一些小鼠出现了明显的免疫缺陷。本文的结果只是初步的，还需要利用其他种系的小鼠和其他的抗原加以验证。这种胸腺切除后个体小鼠免疫功能的丧失是无规律的，这表明某些种系的小鼠中对所用抗原有应答能力的细胞克隆缺失或丧失了其应答功能。这种丧失明显是随机发生的，并

capable of responding to the antigen used, this loss apparently being on a random basis and time dependent.

The present result re-emphasize that the thymus has a continuing influence on immunological responsiveness throughout adult life, but do not indicate the processes involved. The thymus is known to produce the humoral factor L.S.F. throughout life[10] and a humoral influence of the thymus has been shown to be necessary for the full responsiveness of competent cells following antigenic stimulation[11,12]. Since there is continuous spleen and lymph node cell repopulation throughout life, the thymus could also serve as a production site for immunologically competent cells, continually reseeding the peripheral organs.

This work was supported by the Carden Fellowship Fund of the Anti-Cancer Council of Victoria.

(**208**, 1336; 1965)

Donald. Metcalf: Cancer Research Laboratory, Walter and Eliza Hall Institute, Post Office Royal Melbourne Hospital, Victoria, Australia.

References:

1. Miller, J. F. A. P., *Lancet*, ii, 748 (1961).
2. Miller, J. F. A. P., *Science*, **144**, 1544 (1964).
3. Martinez, C., Kersey, J., Papermaster, B. W., and Good, R. A., *Proc. Soc. Exp. Biol.*, **109**, 193 (1962).
4. Metcalf, D., *Brit. J. Haematol.*, **6**, 324 (1960).
5. Fichtelius, K. E., Laurell, G., and Philipsson, L., *Acta Pathol. Microbiol. Scand.*, **51**, 81 (1961).
6. MacLean, L. D., Zak, S. J., Varco, R. L., and Good, R. A., *Transpl. Bull.*, **4**, 21 (1957).
7. Miller, J. F. A. P., *Nature*, **195**, 1318 (1962). Miller, J. F. A. P., Doak, S. M. A., and Cross, A. M., *Proc. Soc. Exp. Biol.*, **112**, 785 (1963).
8. Harris, J. E., Barnes, D. W. H., Ford, C. E., and Evans, E. P., *Nature*, **201**, 884 (1964).
9. Metcalf, D., and Wakonig-Vaartaja, R., *Proc. Soc. Exp. Biol.*, **115**, 731 (1964). Metcalf, D., and Wakonig-Vaartaja, R., *Lancet*, i, 1012 (1964).
10. Metcalf, D., *Brit. J. Cancer*, **10**, 442 (1956).
11. Osoba, D., and Miller, J. F. A. P., *Nature*, **199**, 653 (1963).
12. Levey, R. H., Trainin, N., and Law, L. W., *J. Nat. Cancer Inst.*, **31**, 199 (1963).

且具有时间依赖性。

本文结果再次强调，胸腺对于整个成年期免疫应答的影响是持续性的，但是无法指出其中涉及的过程。人们已经知道，胸腺能终生性地产生一种叫做肝抑制因子的体液因子[10]。而且对于抗原刺激后活性细胞完整应答来说，胸腺的体液影响是必需的[11,12]。既然脾脏和淋巴结细胞在持续地、终生性地再生着，那么胸腺也可能就是担负着免疫活性细胞的生成，并发挥持续地供应外周器官的作用。

此项工作由维多利亚州抗癌协会卡登研究基金支持。

（李响 翻译；陈新文 陈继征 审稿）

Effect of Thymectomy in Adult Mice on Immunological Responsiveness

J. F. A. P. Miller

Editor's Note

Here the French-born biologist Jacques Miller provides further evidence for the continuing immunological function of the thymus in later life. His adult mouse thymectomy experiments point to a delayed immunological decline that is evident after 6 months, suggesting that the adult thymus helps maintain a pool of immunologically competent cells. Removing the thymus, he explains, has no immediate effect because the pool can buffer the blow. But when the pool itself becomes depleted, owing to the limited life span of its cells, the immunological defects become apparent. This is the last of three papers, published back-to-back, to arrive at the same conclusion. It is now known that the thymus builds up its stock of infection-fighting T-lymphocytes early in life, and has a less active role in adulthood.

THYMECTOMY in adult animals has been associated with a lowering of the population of lymphocytes in blood, thoracic duct lymph, lymph nodes and spleen[1,2]. However, no significant defects in the capacity for rejecting allogeneic skin homografts[2] or for producing serum antibodies[2,3] have been observed in animals thymectomized in adult life and challenged within 1-2 months after thymectomy. This is in marked contrast to the severe immunological defects which occur following neonatal thymectomy[4]. These observations have suggested that, during early life, the thymus is essential for the complete and normal development of some immunological faculties. Evidence that the function of the thymus in initiating immunogenesis is not necessarily restricted to early life has, however, been produced. Adult mice thymectomized and afterwards exposed to total body irradiation have shown severe deficiencies in immunological functions[2,5] indicating that the thymus in the adult is still essential to re-establish immune mechanisms when the immunological apparatus has been damaged or destroyed. It has been shown, furthermore, that thymectomy in adult immunologically tolerant mice prevented the reappearance of reactivity with respect to that antigen[6]. The thymus in the adult would thus appear to be essential for the correction of specific immunological defects. The work described here gives further evidence for a continuing immunological function of the thymus through adult life.

In one experiment inbred *CBA* mice and $(Ak \times T6)$ F_1 mice were thymectomized at 2-3 months of age and challenged at various intervals up to 2 years after thymectomy with 0.3ml. of a 5 percent suspension of sheep erythrocytes in saline. 4-6 days after challenge, the mice were killed and their spleens removed to assay the number of antibody-plaque-forming cells per million spleen cells, according to the technique described by Jerne *et al.*[7].

成年小鼠胸腺切除对免疫应答的影响

米勒

编者按

在本文中法裔生物学家雅克·米勒对于胸腺在成熟期继续发挥免疫功能提供了进一步的证据。在他的成年小鼠胸腺切除实验中，小鼠在6个月后免疫能力明显下降，这表明成年胸腺帮助维持一些免疫活性细胞。他解释说，移除胸腺后没有立即产生效应，是因为这些免疫活性细胞能够减缓这一影响。但是由于免疫活性细胞寿命有限，当其耗尽后，免疫缺陷就变得明显。这是三篇连续发表的论文中的最后一篇，得出了与其他两篇相同的结论。我们现在知道胸腺在发育早期积聚抗感染T淋巴细胞，而在成年期其活性减弱。

成年动物胸腺切除与血液、胸导管淋巴、淋巴结和脾脏中的淋巴细胞数量的降低有关[1,2]。然而，成体在切除胸腺后1~2个月内进行刺激，并没有观察到其排斥同种异源皮肤移植能力[2]或血清抗体产生能力[2,3]的明显缺陷。这与新生动物胸腺切除后出现的严重免疫缺陷形成了鲜明的对比[4]。这些观察结果提示，在发育的早期，胸腺对于一些免疫功能完全地、正常地发育是必不可少的。然而，已有证据表明胸腺启动免疫发生的功能并不只局限于发育的早期。成年小鼠胸腺切除后接受全身辐射会发生严重的免疫功能缺失[2,5]，这说明，当免疫器官被损伤或受到破坏时，成体中的胸腺对于免疫机能的重建仍然是必需的。此外，有实验表明，对免疫耐受的成年小鼠进行胸腺切除会使其无法再对相应抗原做出反应[6]。所以，看起来成体的胸腺对于特异的免疫缺陷的修复是很重要的。本文所述的工作将进一步为胸腺在整个成体阶段具有持续的免疫功能提供证据。

在一组实验中，对2~3月龄的近交系*CBA*小鼠和（*Ak*×*T6*）F_1小鼠进行了胸腺切除手术，在胸腺切除后2年内的不同时间，用0.3毫升溶于生理盐水的5%绵羊红细胞悬液刺激。刺激后4~6天，处死小鼠取出脾脏，根据杰尼等所述的方法[7]检测每百万个脾细胞中抗体空斑形成细胞的数量。还取出淋巴结、一小部分脾脏和胸腺

Lymph nodes, a small part of the spleen and the thymus area were also removed and kept for histological examination. The results of the plaque assays are shown in Table 1. There was no difference in the capacity of thymectomized and sham-thymectomized mice to produce antibody-plaque-forming cells when injected with sheep erythrocytes 2 months after the operation. However, thymectomized mice challenged 9 or more months after operation produced less antibody-plaque-forming cells than controls.

Table 1. Effect of Thymectomy in Adult Life on the Production of Antibody-plaque-forming Cells in the Spleen

Strain	Treatment at 2-3 months	Age (months) at immunization	No. of mice	No. of mice* showing following No. of antibody-plaque-forming cells per 1,000,000 spleen cells:				
				0-100	101-300	301-500	501-800	801-1,200
*(Ak×T6)F*1	Sham-thymectomy	4	5					5
	Thymectomy	4	6					6
	Sham-thymectomy	9	6					6
	Thymectomy	9	8			6	2	
CBA	Sham-thymectomy	4	4					4
	Thymectomy	4	4					4
	Sham-thymectomy	18	5			1	4	
	Thymectomy	18	7	1	4	1	1	
	Sham-thymectomy	24	3			2	1	
	Thymectomy	24	3	3				

* Killed at time of peak titre after immunization.

In another experiment, *C3Hf/Bi* mice were thymectomized or sham-operated at 2-4 months of age and killed from 4 to 60 weeks later. Cell suspensions were prepared from the spleens and mesenteric lymph nodes and 5-6 million cells in 0.05 ml. buffered Ringer phosphate solution were injected intravenously into new-born $(C3Hf\times C57BL)F_1$ mice. Half of each litter (about 3-4 mice) received the cells and the other half received only the buffered solution. The capacity of the cell suspensions from a given donor to produce a graft-versus-host (GVH) reaction was determined by Simonsen's method of spleen assay[8]. The relative spleen weight (mg spleen/10 g bodyweight) of the injected baby mice was determined at 10 days of age. Spleen indices were calculated by dividing the average relative spleen weights of the cell-injected mice by the relative spleen weights of the litter-mate controls. The average spleen index of 36 control mice was 1.00 ± 0.13 and animals with indices $\geqslant 1.5$ were considered to show definite evidence of a GVH reaction. The results shown in Table 2 indicate that lymphoid cells from thymectomized mice are as effective as cells from control mice in producing a GVH reaction when collected up to 6 months after thymectomy. After a period of 6-9 months, cells from only 4 of 14 thymectomized mice were effective. Cells from 3 of 8 sham-thymectomized mice aged more than 1 year were ineffective in producing a GVH reaction possibly as a result of the decline of immunological capacity which occurs with advancing age[9]. In the thymectomized group, cells from only 2 of 16 mice killed 9-14 months after thymectomy produced signs of GVH reaction.

区以进行组织学检查。空斑的检测结果见表 1。对于进行胸腺切除手术和假胸腺切除手术的小鼠，在术后 2 个月时注射绵羊红细胞后产生抗体空斑形成细胞的能力并没有区别。但是，在术后 9 个月或更长时间后接受刺激，那么胸腺切除小鼠比对照组小鼠产生的抗体空斑形成细胞的数量要少。

表 1. 成体胸腺切除对脾脏中抗体空斑形成细胞数量的影响

种系	2~3 个月时的处理方式	免疫时的年龄（月）	小鼠数量	每 1,000,000 个脾细胞中产生下列数量的抗体空斑形成细胞的小鼠数量 *				
				0~100	101~300	301~500	501~800	801~1,200
$(Ak\times T6)F_1$	假胸腺切除	4	5					5
	胸腺切除	4	6					6
	假胸腺切除	9	6					6
	胸腺切除	9	8			6	2	
CBA	假胸腺切除	4	4					4
	胸腺切除	4	4					4
	假胸腺切除	18	5			1	4	
	胸腺切除	18	7	1	4	1	1	
	假胸腺切除	24	3			2	1	
	胸腺切除	24	3	3				

* 免疫后出现滴度峰值时处死。

在另一组实验中，对 2~4 月龄的 *C3Hf/Bi* 小鼠进行胸腺切除手术或假手术，在术后 4~60 周时处死。制备脾脏和肠系膜淋巴结细胞悬浮液，并将 0.05 毫升含 500万~600 万个细胞的林格磷酸盐缓冲液通过静脉注射到新生的（$C3Hf\times C57BL$）F_1 小鼠中。对每窝小鼠中的一半（约 3~4 只）注射细胞悬液，另外一半只注射缓冲液。按照西蒙森的脾细胞分析方法 [8] 测定来自特定供体的细胞悬浮液产生移植物抗宿主（GVH）反应的能力。在接受注射的新生小鼠 10 日龄时，测量其脾脏的相对重量（每 10 克体重所对应的以毫克为单位的脾脏重量）。脾脏指数的计算方法是用注射了细胞悬液的小鼠的相对脾脏重量的平均值除以同窝对照组小鼠的相对脾脏重量。36 只对照组小鼠的脾脏指数的平均值是 1.00 ± 0.13，脾脏指数 $\geqslant1.5$ 的动物被认为是显示 GVH 反应发生的确凿证据。表 2 中给出的结果表明，胸腺切除后 6 个月内收集的来自胸腺切除小鼠的淋巴细胞与来自对照组小鼠的淋巴细胞在产生 GVH 反应的效率上是没有差别的。手术后 6~9 个月，14 只胸腺切除小鼠中只有 4 只的细胞能有效地产生 GVH 反应。超过 1 岁龄的 8 只假胸腺切除的小鼠中有 3 只的细胞不能有效地产生 GVH 反应，这可能是由于随着年龄增长免疫功能发生下降造成的 [9]。在胸腺切除组中，胸腺切除后 9~14 个月时处死的 16 只小鼠中只有 2 只的细胞能产生 GVH 反应。

Table 2. Effect of Thymectomy in Adult Life on the Capacity of Lymphoid Cells to produce Graft-versus-Host Reactions

Treatment at 2-4 months	No. of mice with lymphoid cells capable of producing GVH reactions* at following periods (weeks) after operation		
	4-25	26-40	41-60
Sham-thymectomy	8/8	7/8	5/8
Thymectomy	12/13	4/14	2/16

*Expressed as fraction of mice with cells producing, in new-born recipients, an average spleen index $\geqslant 1.5$.

Histological examination of the spleen and lymph nodes of old thymectomized animals revealed a striking depletion of cells in the periarteriolar lymphocytic sheaths and primary lymphoid follicles.

It is now well established that some small lymphocytes are long-lived cells[10] capable of initiating graft-versus-host reactions and possibly other types of immunological reactions[11]. The results presented here demonstrate that thymectomy of adult mice is associated with a decline in immunological capacity which becomes significant after a period of 6-9 months. They suggest that the thymus continues to function during adult life in order to maintain an adequate pool of immunologically competent cells. Thymectomy in the adult, unlike thymectomy in the new-born, has no immediate effect on immunological capacity, presumably because an adequate pool of competent cells has already been constructed. Only when the pool becomes depleted, owing to the limited life span of its cells, do immunological defects with respect to newly encountered antigens become evident.

This work was supported by grants to the Chester Beatty Reasearch Institute (Institute of Cancer Research, Royal Cancer Hospital) from the Medical Research Council and the British Empire Cancer Campaign for Research, from the Tobacco Manufacturers Standing Committee, and from the National Cancer Institute, U.S. Public Health Service (grant *CA*-03188-08).

(**208**, 1337-1338; 1965)

J. F. A. P. Miller: Chester Beatty Research Institute, Institute of Cancer Research, Royal Cancer Hospital, Fulham Road, London, S.W.3.

References:

1. Metcalf, D., *Brit. J. Haematol.*, **6**, 324 (1960). Bierring, F., *Ciba Found. Symp. on Haemopoicsis: Cell Production and its Regulation*, edit. by Wolstenholme, G. E. W., and O'Connor, M., 185 (Churchill, London, 1960).
2. Miller, J. F. A. P., Doak, S. M. A., and Cross, A. M., *Proc. Soc. Exp. Biol.*, **112**, 785 (1963).
3. Harris, T. N., Rhoads, J., and Stokes, J. A., *J. Immunol.*, **58**, 27 (1948). MacLean, L. D., Zak, S. J., Varco, R. L., and Good, R. A., *Transplant. Bull.*, **4**, 21 (1957). Fichtelius, K. E., Laurell, G., and Philipsson, L., *Acta Path. Microbiol. Scand.*, **51**, 81 (1961).
4. Miller, J. F. A. P., *Lancet*, ii, 748 (1961). *Proc. Roy. Soc.*, B, **156**, 415 (1962). Good, R. A., Dalmasso, A. P., Martinez, C., Archer, O. K., Pierce, J. C., and Papermaster, B. W., *J. Exp. Med.*, **116**, 773 (1962).
5. Miller, J. F. A. P., *Nature*, **195**, 1318 (1962). Globerson, A., Fiore-Donati, L., and Feldman, M., *Exp. Cell. Res.*, **28**, 455 (1962).
6. Claman, H. N., and Talmage, D. W., *Science*, **141**, 1193 (1963). Taylor, R. B., *Immunology*, 7, 595 (1964).

表 2. 成体胸腺切除对淋巴细胞产生移植物抗宿主反应能力的影响

2~4 个月时的处理方式	术后不同阶段（周）淋巴细胞能够产生 GVH 反应 * 的小鼠数量		
	4~25	26~40	41~60
假胸腺切除	8/8	7/8	5/8
胸腺切除	12/13	4/14	2/16

* 用平均脾脏指数 ≥1.5 的小鼠与新生受体的比例来表示。

对老龄的胸腺切除小鼠的脾脏和淋巴结进行组织学检测，结果显示在动脉周围淋巴鞘和初级淋巴滤泡中的细胞有明显的衰竭。

现在可以肯定的是，一些小淋巴细胞是长寿细胞 [10]，它们可以引发移植物抗宿主反应，而且还可能引发其他类型的免疫反应 [11]。本文给出的结果表明，成年小鼠的胸腺切除与免疫能力的下降有关，这种免疫能力的下降在胸腺切除 6~9 个月后十分明显。这些结果表明胸腺在成年期会继续发挥作用，以维持有足够的免疫活性细胞。成体胸腺切除并不像新生动物胸腺切除那样很快地影响到免疫功能，这可能是因为成体中已经储备了充足的免疫活性细胞。只有当这些储备的细胞由于本身寿命的限制而消耗殆尽的时候，机体对新出现抗原的免疫缺陷才会显现出来。

此项工作受到提供给切斯特 · 贝蒂研究所（皇家肿瘤医院肿瘤研究所）的基金的支持，这些基金来自于医学研究理事会和大英帝国癌症运动组织、烟草制造商常设委员会以及美国公共卫生署国家癌症研究所（基金 *CA*-03188-08）。

（李响 翻译；陈新文 陈继征 审稿）

7. Jerne, N. K., Nordin, A. A., and Henry, C., in *Cell-Bound Antibodies*, edit. by Amos, B., and Koprowski, H., 109 (Wistar Institute Press, Philadelphia, 1963).
8. Simonsen, M., *Prog. Allergy*, **6**, 349 (1962).
9. Makinodan, T., and Peterson, W. J., *Proc. U.S. Nat. Acad. Sci.*, **48**, 234 (1962).
10. Little, J. R., Brecher, G., Bradley, T. R., and Rose, S., *Blood*, **19**, 236 (1962).
11. Gowans, J. L., McGregor, D. D., Cowen, D. M., and Ford, C., *Nature*, **196**, 651 (1962).

Appendix: Index by Subject
附录：学科分类目录

Physics
物理学

Chemistry
化学

Biology
生物学

Astronomy
天文学

Geoscience
地球科学